JOHN RAMSAY'S CATALOGUE OF
BRITISH DIECAST MODEL TOYS

FIFTH EDITION

A Swapmeet Toys and Models Ltd Publication
Fallowfield House, Westminster Drive,
Bury St Edmunds, Suffolk, England, IP33 2EZ

Originator and Editor
John Ramsay

Technical Editor
John King

1st Edition published 1983
2nd Edition published 1986
3rd Edition published 1988
Update published 1989
4th Edition published 1991
Market Price Review published 1993
5th Edition published 1993

ISBN 0 - 9509319 - 6 - 9

Typeset by Swapmeet Toys and Models Ltd, Colchester and printed in Great Britain by Spottiswoode Ballantyne Ltd, Colchester

CONTENTS

INTRODUCTION

With the publication of this, the 5th Edition of the Catalogue, we celebrate ten years of serving the needs of collectors of die-cast models.

The past decade has been a remarkable period of growth and change for collectors, dealers and manufacturers.

It was as recently as 1983 that Jack O'Dell launched the Lledo 'Models of Days Gone' and the 1st Edition proudly listed issues DG1 - DG6, a total (including variations) of twelve models! What a story of growth and success the Lledo history has been.

The 1st Edition also reported in its 'Stop Press' that the Mettoy Company had in October 1983 asked its bankers to call in the receivers. The subsequent rebirth of the 'New Corgi Company' and its eventual take-over by Mattel has ensured that 'Corgi Toys' have gone from strength to strength, their 'Corgi Classics' range being particularly outstanding.

In common with Meccano 'Dinky Toys', Lesney Products had financial troubles in the late seventies which led to the famous 'Matchbox Toys' company being taken over in 1982 by the 'Universal International' toy company of Hong Kong. In 1987 the 'Dinky Toys' trade name was acquired by Universal International and 1988 saw the launch of 'The Dinky Collection', a superb new range of classic models.

In 1989 'E.F.E.' ('Exclusive First Editions') were launched with a highly acclaimed range of constant scale 'OO' gauge Double Decker Buses, Coaches and Commercial Vehicles.

By the end of the eighties, with the notable exception of Lledo, production of die-cast models had left the UK and was established in Macau and China.

In 1992 the 'Matchbox' trade name was acquired by the mighty US toy company 'Tyco' and models were marketed by 'Tyco Toys (UK) Ltd'.

The past ten years have seen a tremendous development in the number, size and character of Toyfairs, with well in excess of one thousand being held in the United Kingdom in 1992. The largest was at the National Exhibition Centre and attracted more than six thousand people through its doors.

Five years ago relatively few toy auctions took place. They were mostly in London with just the odd quarterly provincial sale. How times have changed! Nowadays auctions take place with great regularity up and down the country with several new auction houses involved. The information that the salerooms provide on the prices achieved does help to bring a certain stability to the overall market place. Some of the prices achieved in respect of particularly rare models and sets have been remarkable, for example £4,600 for a Dinky Foden Lorry.

During this period of change successive Catalogues have endeavoured to keep collectors and traders up to date in respect of new issues, new variations and price changes. In addition, in the Spring of 1993 we provided all Catalogue users with a free copy of the 'Model Price Review' which updated the Catalogue listings and gave details of many new variations and auction price results. The updating information was very well received by Catalogue users and as a result the 'Model Price Review' will again be issued in 1994.

This Edition contains several new listings and features such as the separate numerical indexes for both Dinky Toys and Corgi Toys. In addition, in a new section, the Catalogue has responded to many requests by including a listing of 'Britains Motor Vehicles'.

The success of the Catalogue over the past ten years is in no small way due to the splendid level of support and information supplied by collectors and trade alike. Consequently this new 5th Edition represents the combined efforts of many like minded people to provide the best possible Catalogue for the benefit of all.

MARKET PRICE RANGE GRADING SYSTEM

Based on the findings of the Market Surveys undertaken since 1983 virtually all the models have been given a 'Market Price Range'. The price gap between the lower and higher figures indicates the likely price range a collector should expect to pay for the model. Models qualifying for a price at the top end of the range could include:

- Boxed models where both the model and the box are in pristine condition,
- A scarce or unusual colour,
- An unusual component such as special wheels, e.g., spun hubs on some Dinky Toys cars,
- A model with pristine decals where this is unusual, e.g., Dinky Toys Guy Van No.514, 'Lyons Swiss Rolls',
- A model in an unusual or special box,
- A model priced by a trader who disagrees with the price range quoted in the Catalogue (which is only a guide).

PRICES FOR MODELS IN LESS THAN MINT BOXED CONDITION

Many boxed models seen for sale fail to match up to the exacting standards on which the Market Price Range has been based, having slight model or box damage. In these instances models may be priced at 50% to 60% of the Market Price Range shown, and this is particularly relevant when a model is common. Boxed models with considerable damage or unboxed models will be priced at much lower level.

Note: It cannot be over-emphasised that irrespective of the price guidance provided by this Catalogue, collectors should not always expect to see prices asked within the price ranges shown. Traders will ask a price based on their trading requirements and will NOT be governed by any figures shown in this Catalogue, nor could they be reasonably expected to do so.

MODELS NOT GIVEN A 'MARKET PRICE RANGE'

It has not been possible to give every model a price range and these exceptions are as follows:

NPP No Prices Possible

This is shown alongside models never encountered in the survey and about which there is doubt as to their actual issue, even though a model may have been pictured in a catalogue. This particularly applies to Spot-On models and the odd Dinky Toy. Readers will appreciate that unlike postage stamps or coins, no birth records are available in respect of all the die-cast models designed or issued.

NGPP No Grading Possible at Present

Where a model or gift set is particularly rare and no price information whatsoever is possible, no price grading has been shown as the Compiler believes that this is carrying rarity and value assessment into the realms of pure guesswork.

As and when information becomes available concerning these rarities it will be included in the Catalogue.

GSP Gift Set Price

If a model forms part of a Set (and is not available separately) the price range will be shown against the entry in the relevant Gift Set section and will refer to the complete set.

NRP Normal Retail Price

This is shown alongside models which have been recently issued or for models which have yet to attain a real collectable value. One would not expect to see asking prices for models in this grade set higher than a few pounds unless a model happens to be particulary large, e.g. a common gift set containing several models.

NPE No Price Estimate

This coding is shown against models and gift sets which were never encountered in the survey and about which no up to date asking price or auction price information was obtained. The price shown is therefore the Compiler's estimate of what it would cost should the model come into the market. This grading particularly applies to many of the pre-war Dinkies and also to the Spot-On model range.

Consequently because of rarity considerations, expect to see large price fluctuations occur over and above the catalogue estimate, especially at auctions.

SCARCE COLOURS AND VARIATIONS

Many scarce colours and variations have already been given a separate Catalogue listing. Collectors or traders who know of other variations which they believe warrant a separate listing are invited to forward this information to the Editor together with any supporting evidence.

CLASSIFYING THE CONDITION OF MODELS AND BOXES

The condition of a model and its accompanying box does of course have a direct bearing on its value which makes accurate condition grading a matter of key importance.

Unlike other collecting hobbies such as stamps or coins, no one universal grading system is used to classify the condition of models and boxes.

Nevertheless, whilst several versions exist, there are really two main systems of condition classification in the UK as follows:

1. The 'Specific Condition' Grading System

The following example is fairly typical of the types of descriptions and gradings seen on Mail Order lists.

M	Mint
AM	Almost Mint
VSC	Very Slightly Chipped
SC	Slightly Chipped
C	Chipped
VC	Very Chipped

If a model is described as Mint Boxed, the condition of its box is not normally separately described. However, it is expected to be in first class and as near original condition as is possible, bearing in mind the age of the model concerned.

If a box is damaged the flaws are usually separately described. This method has always seemed to work out quite well in practice, for all reputable dealers automatically offer a 'Sale or Return if not satisfied' deal to their clients, which provides the necessary safeguard against the misrepresentation of the model's condition. The Compiler would stress that the foregoing is only an example of a mail order condition grading system and stricter box grading definitions are known to exist.

2. The 'General Condition' Grading System

This method is often used by auctioneers although it is also to be seen used on the occasional mail order list.

(M)	Mint
(E)	Excellent
(G)	Good
(F)	Fair
(P)	Poor

Usually these gradings are separately applied to describe firstly the condition of the model and secondly the condition of the box. From our observations and purely for guidance purposes, we would suggest the following descriptions approximately represent the different grades.

a) Model Condition Gradings

1. MINT (M)
The model must be complete and as fresh, new and original in appearance as when first received from the manufacturers.

2. EXCELLENT (E)
The model is almost in mint condition and is only barred from that classification by having a few slight flaws, e.g., slight paintwork chipping in unimportant areas.

3. GOOD (G)
The model is in a complete and original condition and retains an overall collectable appearance despite having a few chips or rubbed paintwork.

4. FAIR (F)
The model may not be in its original state having, for example, a broken bumper, replacement radiator or windscreen, or it may have signs of metal fatigue. The paintwork may be faded, well chipped, retouched or repainted. There may be signs of rust. Unless the model is rare it is in a barely collectable condition.

5. POOR (P)
The model may be damaged, incomplete, repainted, altered, metal fatigued, or have a rusted baseplate or heavily chipped paintwork, etc. Unless the model is rare it has little real value to a collector other than as a candidate for a complete restoration or use as spares.

b) BOX Condition Gradings

1. MINT (M)
The box must be complete both inside and out and contain all the original packing materials, manufacturer's leaflet and box labels. It should look as fresh, new and original in appearance as when first received from the manufacturers.

2. EXCELLENT (E)
The box is in almost mint condition but is only barred from that classification by just the odd minor blemish, e.g., there may be slight damage to the display labels caused by bad storage. The original shop price label may have been carelessly removed and caused slight damage. The cover of a bubble pack may be cracked or there may be very slight soiling etc.

3. GOOD (G)
The box is complete both inside and out, and retains an overall attractive collectable appearance. Furthermore, despite showing a few signs of wear and tear, it does not appear 'tired'.

4. FAIR (F)
The box will have a 'tired' appearance and show definite signs of wear and tear. It may be incomplete and not contain the original packing materials or leaflets. In addition it may not display all the exterior identification labels or they may be torn or soiled or a box-end flap may be missing or otherwise be slightly damaged. In this condition, unless the model is particularly rare, it will not add much to the model's value.

5. POOR (P)
The box will show considerable signs of wear and tear. It will almost certainly be badly damaged, torn, incomplete or heavily soiled and in this condition, unless it is very rare, is of little value to a collector.

MODEL and BOX
VALUATION GUIDELINES

The research has produced the following comparative price information concerning the values of both unboxed models and separate boxes in the various condition classifications.

The guidelines have been based on the 'General Condition' grading system as described in the previous section. The percentage value ranges are designed to reflect the relatively higher values of the rarer models and boxes.

UNBOXED MODEL CLASSIFICATION	% VALUE OF MINT BOXED MODEL
Mint	50% - 60%
Excellent	40% - 50%
Good	20% - 40%
Fair	10% - 20%
Poor	0% - 10%

BOX CLASSIFICATION	% VALUE OF MINT BOXED MODEL
Mint	40% - 50%
Excellent	30% - 40%
Good	20% - 30%
Fair	10% - 20%
Poor	0% - 10%

Note: The same model may have been issued in two or more types of box (Yesteryears for example). The model in the earlier box is usually (though not always) the more valuable.

Rare Models and Sets
The exceptions to the foregoing guidelines are in respect of rare models or boxes, or models seldom found in first class condition such as some pre-war models. In these situations rarity commands a premium and the asking price or the price realised at auction will almost certainly reflect it.

SELLING MODELS TO THE TRADE

The model value figures produced by the Price Grading system always refer to the likely *asking prices* for models.

They have been prepared solely to give collectors an idea of the amount they might reasonably expect to pay for a particular model.

The figures given are *not* intended to represent the price which will be placed on a model when it is offered for sale to a dealer. This is hardly surprising bearing in mind that the dealer is carrying all the expense of offering his customers a collecting service which costs money to maintain.

Collectors should not therefore be surprised when selling models to the trade to receive offers which may appear somewhat low in comparison with the figures shown in the Catalogue.

Dealers are always keen to replenish their stocks with quality items and will as a result normally make perfectly fair and reasonable offers for models. Indeed, depending on the particular models offered to them, the actual offer made may well at times exceed the levels indicated in the Catalogue which are only *guidelines* and not firm figures.

One last point when selling models to the trade do get quotations from two or three dealers especially if you have rare models to be sold.

HOW TO USE THE CATALOGUE

a) Identifying models from their lettering
All lettering shown in CAPITAL LETTERS indicates the actual lettering on the model itself. It may appear in either the Model Type (vehicle) or Model Features (description) column. Similarly *lettering in Italics* indicates that it is shown on the actual model.

b) Abbreviations
In this the 5th Edition dependence on abbreviations has been greatly reduced but where necessary they are used to include information concisely. The Abbreviations list is near the back of the book.

CATALOGUE OMISSIONS

Accurate birth records do not exist in respect of all the die-cast models issued. Therefore whilst every effort has been made to provide comprehensive information it is inevitable that collectors will have knowledge of models which have not been included. Consequently the Compiler will be pleased to receive details of these models in order that they may be included in future editions. Naturally, supporting evidence regarding authenticity will be required.

This Catalogue has been prepared solely for use as a reference book and guide to the rarity and asking prices of die-cast model toys.

Whilst every care has been taken in compiling the Catalogue, neither the Compiler nor the publishers can accept any responsibility whatsoever for any financial loss which may occur as a result of its use.

CATALOGUE IMPROVEMENTS

BRITAINS MOTOR VEHICLES (1930 - 1960)
- Mike Richardson has written an introductory article to the first listings included in the Catalogue.

CORGI TOYS
- The listings have been carefully revised and updated with dozens of new colour and wheel variations.
- A numerical index has been added to enable much quicker model identification.
- Mettoy 'Castoys' and 'Miniature Numbers' listed for the first time
- Marks and Spencers 'Trophy' models listed for the first time
- Corgi Rockets have been introduced.
- A new 'Trade Display' listing has been included.
- Gift Sets have been arranged in their own extensive section.

CRESCENT TOYS - Many additional items have been included in this listing.

DINKY TOYS
- The model listings have been further enhanced by the addition of many new variations.
- Superb new colour pictures of pre and post-war models have been included.
- A new 'Trade Boxes' section has been introduced.
- A new 'Trade Display' listing has been included.
- A numerical index has been added to enable much quicker model identification.
- Greatly enhanced Gift Sets information has been included, arranged in their own new section.

E.F.E. - Thanks to Ken Benham of the E.F.E. Club the listings have been completely updated.

HORNBY DUBLO - Complete model range included for first time.

LLEDO 'Models Of Days Gone'
- Thanks to Peter Lloyd of RDP Publications the listings have been completely updated.

LONE STAR - Thanks to Robert Newson the Lone Star listings have been totally revised.

MATCHBOX TOYS
- All the Matchbox listings have been revised and updated.
- The Models of Yesteryear have been totally re-listed on a straightforward numerical basis.
- A basic 'Sky-Busters' listing has been introduced.
- All the latest Tyco Matchbox new products range listed plus superb pictures.

MORESTONE and BUDGIE - Several new body and colour variations have been listed.

SHACKLETON TOYS
- Thanks to Mike and Sue Richardson it has been possible to include a listing for the first time.

SPOT-ON MODELS
- The listings have been enhanced by the addition of many new colour variations.
- Accessories and 'Cotswold Village' listings introduced

TAYLOR and BARRETT - Mike Richardson has written an introductory article to this company's products.

TIMPO TOYS - A first listing has been included.

TRI-ANG MINIC SHIPS
- Thanks to Bob Faye of Sevenoaks Models, several new variations have been added including the Hong Kong issues.

ZEBRA TOYS - Thanks to Robert Newson a listing has been included for the first time.

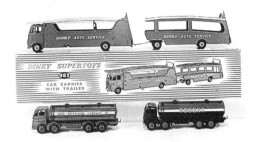

WHEN REPLYING TO ADVERTISEMENTS PLEASE MENTION JOHN RAMSAY'S CATALOGUE

BRITISH DIECAST
MODEL TOYS CATALOGUE

AT LAST! CATALOGUE HOLDERS

ARE NOW AVAILABLE
FOR EACH CATALOGUE EDITION

PROTECT YOUR ASSETS
with one of these strong attractive holders
(Livery: All Black with Gold lettering, approx. size 10″ x 8″).

IDEAL FOR THE BUSY TRADER OR KEEN COLLECTOR

When ordering please advise which edition/editions are required.

Send to: **Swapmeet Publications, Fallowfield House, Westminster Drive, Bury St Edmunds, Suffolk IP33 2EZ**

Terms: U.K. £7.95 Europe £9.95 Rest of World £9.95 (Surface), £17.95 (Airmail).
N.B. All prices include postage and packing
N.B. Australasian Collectors should contact Message Models N.S.W. – see page 77

Payment accepted by Cheque/Eurocheque/Postal Order or International Money
Order made payable to: SWAPMEET PUBLICATIONS.

Credit Cards accepted ☐ Visa ☐ Access ☐ Eurocard ☐ Mastercard

Credit Card Number ☐☐☐☐☐☐☐☐☐☐☐☐☐☐☐☐☐☐

Expiry Date .... Signature ....

Name and Address (in BLOCK CAPITALS please)

....Postcode.......................................

Subject to availability please allow at least 28 days for delivery

TO AVOID DAMAGING YOUR CATALOGUE, DO PLEASE USE A PHOTOCOPY OR LETTER

WHEN REPLYING TO ADVERTISEMENTS PLEASE MENTION JOHN RAMSAY'S CATALOGUE

WHEN REPLYING TO ADVERTISEMENTS PLEASE MENTION JOHN RAMSAY'S CATALOGUE

JONSCOT COLLECTIONS

Buying & Selling Vintage (& Obsolete Modern) Diecast Models in Good to Mint Condition,
Boxed & Unboxed – Dinky, Corgi, Spot On, Lledo, Box, Brooklin etc,
also Hornby O & OO Gauges, Triang & Britain's Soldiers
together with old postcards, cigarette cards & British military cap badges

56A Doddington Road, Wimblington, See me at most Julie & John Webb
March, Cambs PE15 0RD. Toyfairs in Suffolk, Norfolk
Tel: 0354 740788 and Cambridgeshire

J. M. Toys

32 Aston Road, Waterlooville, Hampshire PO7 7XQ

Whitemetal and Obsolete Specialists.
Mail Order. Exports. Credit Cards taken.

Telephone 0705 262446 (Days)   *Fax 0705 252041*

JOHN CLARK – MATCHBOX AND 'YESTERYEAR' SPECIALIST

Locating, Searching, Buying, Swapping – anything connected with Matchbox. World Wide Mail Order Service.

Wanted – Rare, Scarce, Obsolete, Colour Trials and Pre-Production 'Yesteryears', Early Lesney Toys, Moko Toys, TP Series,
Major and King Size Models etc.

Enquiries invited for any Model connected with Matchbox.

Many hundreds of 1st, 2nd, 3rd, 4th and Code 2 'Yesteryears' in stock plus new releases.

Also wanted and for sale – Hornby O Gauge, Hornby Dublo, Trix, Triang and Wrenn Trains, Corgi, Dinky, Budgie and
Morestone Diecast Toys etc.

See me at the major toys shows.

Oak Acres Farm, Park Hall Road, Somersham, Cambs. PE17 3HG. Tel: 0487 840540

– Visitors welcome by appointment –

COLLECTABLE OLD TOYS
BUY – SELL – SWAP
Tatty to Mint Boxed

Dinky, Corgi, Lesney, Spot-On, Minic, Britains, Meccano, Hornby etc. Tin Plate and Diecast.
Specialist in Ford Models.

MAIL ORDER   MAJOR CREDIT CARDS ACCEPTED

Martin Wright
'The man in Red'

Tel (0892) 655893   Mobile (0850) 654286   Fax (0892) 852357

WHEN REPLYING TO ADVERTISEMENTS PLEASE MENTION JOHN RAMSAY'S CATALOGUE

WHEN REPLYING TO ADVERTISEMENTS PLEASE MENTION JOHN RAMSAY'S CATALOGUE

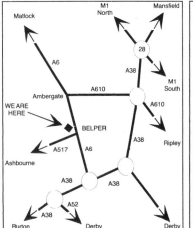

WHEN REPLYING TO ADVERTISEMENTS PLEASE MENTION JOHN RAMSAY'S CATALOGUE

K.H. NORTON

Incorporating Nortons Cash & Carry

1-5 ROMAN STREET, LEICESTER LE3 0BD

TEL: (0533) 549953, FAX: (0533) 471230

WE STOCK THE MOST COMPREHENSIVE RANGE OF DIE-CAST MODELS, PLASTIC KITS & HOBBY ACCESSORIES AVAILABLE TO THE TRADE.

OVER 5,000 LINES AVAILABLE.

PLEASE RING OR FAX FOR TERMS & ACCOUNT DETAILS
CASH & CARRY AND MAIL ORDER SERVICE
FULL TRADE PRICE LIST AVAILABLE

Please ring or write for our die-cast or plastic kit price lists, you will be amazed at our range and prices.

Or visit our cash and carry.

Trade Buyers Only, Minimum Purchase £75

JOHN AYREY

DIE CASTS

BENTLEY HOUSE, 202 MARKET STREET

(off Otley Road)

SHIPLEY, WEST YORKSHIRE BD18 2BY

TEL: (0274) 594119   FAX: (0274) 531505

THE UK's LEADING
WHOLESALE WAREHOUSE

No retail enquiries. Please see your dealer.

10-15% DISCOUNT OFF MOST RANGES
Please send a Business Card or Letterhead stating the price lists you require

MAISTO
—————— 1:18th Scale ——————

JAGUAR XJ220 Silver, Blue & Red

—————— 1:12th Scale ——————

JAGUAR XJ220 Silver and Blue

★ *Always good stocks held* ★

A SUPERB METROBUS COLLECTION

A specially commissioned set of Corgi Metro Bus models of the entire Yorkshire Rider fleet. Each bus in original city or occasion liveries.

No.1 Leeds Bradford Trolley Bus 75th Anniversary.
No. 2 West Yorkshire.
No. 3 Halifax Corporation.
No. 4 Huddersfield Corporation.
No. 5 Leeds Corporation.
No. 6 Bradford Corporation.

No. 7 Huddersfield Tramways.
No. 8 W.Y.P.T.E.
No. 9 Calderdale.
No. 10 Yorkshire Rider second livery "Yorkshire Post". (This is a standard Corgi re-release).
No. 11 Gold Rider.

All these models are available from your normal source or if in difficulty direct from us.

Nos. 1–9 are **£7.95 each.**   No. 10 is **£4.95**

Bradford dark blue and gold Rider to be relased early 1993 — the last in the series.

ARS MODELS

ARS 101 Alfa Romeo Spider convertible
ARS 102 Alfa Romeo Spider open
ARS 103 Alfa Romeo 33 Boxer 16V
ARS 104 Alfa Romeo 22 1.5 TE
ARS 105 Alfa Romeo 155

ARS 106 Alfa Romeo 33 Permanent 4
ARS 107 Alfa Romeo Spider Hard Top
ARS 108 Alfa Romeo Sport Wagon
ARS 108 Alfa Romeo 164 Super V6
(available December)

We are Trade Suppliers for all the following makes:
Matchbox, Solido, Gama, Schabak, NZG, Lledo, Schuco, Corgi, Polistil, Burago, Rio, Ros, Ertl, ARS, Progetto, Detail, Kyosho, Anson, Nascars.

Pentoy Limited
Vicarage House
Priors Marston
Warwickshire CV23 8RT
England

Tel: 0327 61631   Fax: 0327 61040

As the UK's fastest growing model importer, Pentoy has a reputation for stocking a vast range of excellent die-cast models from around the world including Russia, Argentina, Italy, Japan, Australia, France and Holland, alongside well-known British-based manufacturers.

As well as a wide variety of cars, the range includes military vehicles, trucks, motorcycles, construction equipment and utilities.

To compliment this, Pentoy also distributes Jouef, Eggerbahn and Electrotren model trains.

Fast and efficient
World-wide delivery service

CASH AND CARRY WAREHOUSE SUPPLIERS TO THE TRADE ONLY

THE MONTHLY MAGAZINE THAT COVERS ALL ASPECTS OF MODELLING & ASSOCIATED SUBJECTS

- Aircraft
- Railways
- Military
- Cars
- Collectables
- Science Fiction
- Boats
- Engineering

PACKED WITH ADVERTISEMENTS AND INFORMATION

AVAILABLE AT ALL GOOD NEWSAGENTS
Make sure of your copy...
place a regular order with
your Newsagent **NOW!**

BENBROS

The following history and listings of Benbros and Zebra models have been provided by Robert Newson.

Benbros was started in the late 1940s by brothers Jack and Nathan Benenson, at Walthamstow in north-east London. They first called themselves 'Benson Bros' and made diecast toys and lead figures (some of which are marked 'Benson'). The name Benbros was adopted in 1951. One of their best known die-cast toys was a miniature coronation coach (similar to the Moko-Lesney coach) with 'ER' cast on the doors (plain on the Lesney) and 'MADE IN ENGLAND' on the drawbar.

In their range of large die-cast toys were re-issues of various Timpo Toys from whom Benbros had acquired the dies. In the 1960s the Zebra series was introduced, but toy production ceased in 1965 when Benbros was taken over by Unerman Greenman Berger Ltd.

The larger scale Benbros models are diverse, but this list concentrates on their series of miniature models. These were introduced in late 1954 as the 'T.V. Series', packed in individual boxes which resembled a 1950s television set. By 1956 there were 24 models in the series, and soon after this the packaging was changed to red and yellow 'Mighty Midget' boxes. The Mighty Midgets were available up to 1965.

Most models came in a very wide range of colours, so these have not been listed, but full details of colours and other variations are given in the illustrated booklet 'Benbros T.V. Series & Mighty Midgets' by Robert Newson.

Benbros 'T.V. Series' and 'Mighty Midgets'

No.	Model	Description	Price	
1	Horse Drawn Hay Cart	With man and raves. Later models marked 'BENBROS'	£15-20	☐
2	Horse Drawn Log Cart	With man & 'log', 'Made in England' under horse	£15-20	☐
3	AA Motorcycle & Sidecar	With rider and separate windscreen. 'Made in England' under sidecar	£20-30	☐
4	Stage Coach with four horses	'KANSAS STAGE' cast in, separate driver on some, 'BENBROS' on later models	£15-20	☐
5	Horse Drawn Gipsy Caravan	No maker's name on model	£20-25	☐
6	Horse Drawn Milk Cart	Milkman and horse, 2 separate or cast-in churns, 'BENBROS' on later models	£15-20	☐
7	Three-wheeled Electric Milk Trolley	With milkman. 'EXPRESS DAIRY' cast in	£10-15	☐
8	Foden Tractor and Log Trailer	With log (wood dowel)	£15-20	☐
9	Dennis Fire Escape	Separate wheeled escape ladder	£15-20	☐
10	Crawler Bulldozer	with rubber tracks	£10-15	☐
11	Crawler Tractor with Hay Rake	Rubber tracks. Same basic casting as no. 10. No maker's name on model	£10-15	☐
12	Army Scout Car	Separate or cast-in driver	£5-10	☐
13	Austin Champ	Separate or cast-in driver	£10-15	☐
14	Centurion Tank	with rubber tracks	£15-20	☐
15	Vespa Scooter	With rider	£30-35	☐
16	Streamlined Express Loco	('TV Series' only). Runs on four concealed wheels	£15-20	☐
16	Chevrolet Nomad Station Wagon	('Mighty Midget' only). Most models have silver painted flash	£10-15	☐
17	Crawler Tractor with Disc Harrow	Rubber tracks. Same tractor as no. 11. No maker's name on model	£10-15	☐
18	Hudson Tourer	Same chassis as no. 16	£10-15	☐
19	Crawler Tractor and Trailer	Rubber tracks. Same tractor as nos. 11 and 17. No maker's name on model	£10-15	☐
20	Foden 8-wheel Flat Lorry	Early models in two-tone colours	£10-15	☐
21	Foden 8-wheel Open Lorry	Early models in two-tone colours	£10-15	☐
22	ERF Petrol Tanker	Similar to Matchbox 11a. No adverts or with 'Esso' transfer on one side	£15-20	☐
23	AEC Box Van	No transfers. Open rear end	£10-15	☐
23	Bedford Box Van	Without adverts or with 'Dunlop' transfers. Open rear end	£15-20	☐
24	Field Gun	Solid wheels. No maker's name on model. Working firing mechanism	£5-10	☐
25	Spyker	Similar to Charbens no. 2. Both models are marked with the maker's name	£5-10	☐
26	1904 Vauxhall 5 h.p.	No details available	£5-10	☐
27	1906 Rolls-Royce	No details available	£5-10	☐
28	Foden 8-wheel Flat Lorry with Chains	'Chains' are cast with the body	£15-20	☐
29	RAC Motorcycle & Sidecar	With rider and separate windscreen. 'Made in England' under sidecar.	£20-30	☐
30	AEC Army Box Van	Same castings as no. 23 in Military Green paint	£10-15	☐
30	Bedford Army Box Van	Same castings as no. 23 in Military Green paint	£15-20	☐
31	AEC Lorry with Tilt	Cast metal 'canvas' tilt, riveted in place	£10-15	☐
31	Bedford Lorry with Tilt	Cast metal 'canvas' tilt, riveted in place	£15-20	☐
32	AEC Compressor Lorry	No details at present	£10-15	☐
32	Bedford Compressor Lorry	No details at present	£15-20	☐
33	AEC Crane Lorry	No hook cast	£10-15	☐
33	Bedford Crane Lorry	No hook cast	£15-20	☐
34	AA Land Rover	'AA ROAD SERVICE' cast in, open rear end	£15-20	☐
35	Army Land Rover	No lettering on sides, open rear end	£15-20	☐
36	Royal Mail Land Rover	'ROYAL MAIL E-II-R' cast in, open rear end	£15-20	☐
37	Wolseley Six-Eighty Police Car	A little smaller than Morestone/Budgie no. 5	£10-15	☐
38	Daimler Ambulance	Similar to Matchbox no. 14b. Civilian or military paint	£20-25	☐
39	Bedford Milk Float	Similar to Matchbox no. 29a	£10-15	☐
40	American Ford Convertible	Windscreen frame and seats cast with body	£10-15	☐
41	Army Hudson Tourer	No. 18 in Military-Green paint	£15-20	☐
42	Army Motorcycle & Sidecar	With rider and separate windscreen. 'Made in England' under sidecar. 'AA' or 'RAC' cast on sidecar, i.e. this is the same casting as no. 3 or no. 29.	£20-30	☐
43	Bedford Articulated Box Van	Without adverts or with 'Dunlop' transfers, open rear end	£15-20	☐
44	Bedford Articulated Lowside Lorry	First version has hinged tailboard, later fixed	£15-20	☐
45	Bedford Articulated Low Loader	With log (wood dowel)	£15-20	☐
46	Bedford Articulated Petrol Tanker	Without adverts or with 'Esso' transfer on one side	£20-30	☐
47 ?	Bedford Articulated Crane Lorry	No hook cast	£10-15	☐
48	Bedford Articulated Lorry with Chains	'Chains' are cast with the model	£15-20	☐
49	Karrier Bantam Bottle Lorry	Similar to Matchbox 37a. 'Drink Coca-Cola' transfers. No maker's name	£30-40	☐
50 ?	RAC Land Rover	'RAC ROAD SERVICE' cast in, open rear end	£20-30	☐

Benbros 'Zebra Toys'

The following information has been provided by Robert Newson.

Zebra Toys were introduced in the early 1960s and were manufactured along with the existing production of large scale Benbros vehicles. Zebra Toys were packaged in distinctive black and white striped boxes. Most of the models had jewelled headlights and some also had windows and plastic interiors.

The AA and RAC Mini Vans apparently had not been introduced when toy production by Benbros came to an end in 1965. They do not appear on a trade price list dated January 1965 but a small number of these models (probably a trial run) were sold off with the remaining toy stocks and are now in the hands of collectors.

In the following list, numbers in brackets are those shown on Zebra boxes. The other numbers are cast on the models themselves. There seems to be no connection between the two numbering systems! Original retail prices (quoted in shillings and pre-decimal pence) are those given in 1964 and 1965 trade price lists. These models are rare in today's market hence 'NGPP' shown in price range column.

100 (16)	Foden Concrete Mixer	Red cab and chassis, Beige or Yellow barrel, 70 mm. (3s 1d)	NGPP	☐
101 (36)	Scammell Scarab Articulated Van 'BRITISH RAILWAYS'	Maroon cab and trailer, Pale Orange or Mustard-Yellow tilt, 105 mm. (4s 4d)	NGPP	☐
103 (10)	Jaguar 'E'-type	Metallic Light Green, Metallic Light Blue or Metallic Light Brown, 90 mm. (3s 0d)	NGPP	☐
104 (30)	Routemaster Bus	Red, *'Fina Petrol goes a long way'* adverts, 111 mm. (4s 11d)	NGPP	☐
106 (34)	Heinkel Bubble Car	Red or Blue body, 100 mm. (4s 4d)	NGPP	☐
107 (27)	Daimler Ambulance	Cream body, 101 mm. (4s 1d)	NGPP	☐
720	Bedford Cattle Transporter	Red cab and chassis, Light Brown body, 101 mm. (4s 4d)	NGPP	☐
	Lansing Bagnall Rapide 2000	Fork Lift Truck, Red body, 89 mm. (3s 6d)	NGPP	☐
	Field Gun	Dark Green finish, 'BENBROS' cast on model, 102 mm. (2s 0d)	NGPP	☐
	Police Patrol Motorcycle	(Triumph) 'Silver' plated, plastic rider, 'ENT 303' cast, 84 mm. (2s 6d)	NGPP	☐
	Rally Motorcycle	(Triumph) 'Silver' plated, plastic rider, 'ENT 303' cast, 84 mm. (2s 6d)	NGPP	☐
73	Army Despatch Motorcycle	(Triumph) 'Silver' plated, plastic rider, 'ENT 303' cast, 84 mm. (2s 6d)	NGPP	☐
74	Telegraph Boy Motorcycle	(Triumph) 'Silver' plated, plastic rider, 'ENT 303' cast, 84 mm. (2s 6d)	NGPP	☐
	RAC Triumph Motorcycle & Sidecar	Black bike, Blue sidecar, White fairing, plastic rider, 'ENT 303', 84 mm. (3s 5d)	NGPP	☐
76	AA Triumph Motorcycle & Sidecar	Black bike, Yellow sidecar and fairing, plastic rider, 'ENT 303', 84 mm. (3s 5d)	NGPP	☐
760	Austin Mini Van	'AA PATROL SERVICE', Yellow body	NGPP	☐
? (?)	Austin Mini Van	'RAC', Blue body	NGPP	☐

Benbros 'Qualitoys'. We are currently unable to provide a listing of this interesting range from Benbros because of lack of information. The Editor would appreciate any information (however small) on models bearing the 'Qualitoys' mark for inclusion in future editions of the Catalogue.

Collectors Notes

BRITAINS
MOTOR VEHICLES

by Mike Richardson

Most people are aware of the military vehicles made by Britains both before the War and after in 1/32 scale to go with their soldiers, but not so many are acquainted with the contemporary civilian models. Some of these models are only colour variations of the military versions, for example the 59F 'Four-wheeled Lorry with Driver' in the farm series is the same as 1335 'Lorry, Army, Four-wheeled type' but painted in a smart duotone colour scheme instead of khaki. Other models are only available in the civilian type, usually for the good reason that the army could not possibly have a use for a militarised version. A good example of this would be 1656 'John Cobbs Railton Wonder Car' (or 'Railton Mobil Special' as we know it!).

Britains are our oldest toy company which is still in business having been started in 1860 although the first of the famous soldiers did not appear until 1890. This still means over a hundred years continuous toy manufacture, surely a record. The motor lorry models appeared in late 1932 and were based on the Albion army lorries of the time with the familiar 'square' cab design which was to be a hallmark of the Britains lorries until the end of the decade. The range of 4, 6 and 10-wheel farm lorries are still illustrated in the 1940 catalogue. After the War the cab was brought up to date by a change to a more rounded Fordson type, not nearly so attractive.

The military ambulance was also used in civilian versions, a cream 'Corporation' and a blue 'Volunteer Corps' as alternative liveries to the khaki army one. The rarest version of this model is the red and black 'Royal Mail' van which was sold for a short time towards the end of the production run.

There are three civilian cars, a 'Two-seater Coupé' and two 'Sports Model Open Tourers' in the pre-war production. The coup and the open sports car without driver and passenger do not have military equivalents, but when the open sports car has people in it then it is either a 'Mobile Police Car with 2 Officers' (finished in green with black wings), or a 'Staff Car with 2 Officers' as the military offering. The occupants of the car are legless and their lower regions are covered with a tartan rug - how nice for them on cold days! After the War there was a one-piece casting version of the staff car and police car without the separate grilles of the pre-war models and these were rather plain by comparison.

The final group of models consists of the superb record cars 'Bluebird' and 'Railton Special'. These came out in the late 1930s and each is over 6 inches long. The Bluebird was produced in three versions; a) with fully detailed removable chassis, b) without this part, and c) a slightly smaller one (just over 5 inches), without underside detail. The Railton Mobil Special always had the removable chassis and was available painted silver for 1s.6d. or chrome plated for 2s.6d.

After the War two new farm tractor models appeared, a couple of Fordson Majors produced with the active co-operation of the Ford Motor Company. These are excellent models both finished in the correct shade of dark blue and with the name 'Fordson' applied to the front and sides of the radiator. One version has standard wheels but the other (rarer) one had the spiked or 'spud' wheels used on heavy ground.

All these models are to the same scale as the soldiers (1/32), but there is also a similar range in '00' gauge (1/76 scale) to go with model railways. The smaller models date mainly from the post-war era although a sports car and a fastback saloon were seen pre-war. The small scale trucks have a Fordson cab similar to the later large scale farm and army lorries.

The large scale pre-war models are very collectable and prices are consequently very high for rare items in excellent condition and with original lovely boxes. Some few years ago a batch of replicas of the coup were made here in England so exercise care when buying this model. Spare parts are, or have been available for most of these toys to enable repairs to be carried out.

Britains Motor Vehicles   (pre-war issues)

The models were constructed of a lead based alloy and the main body parts were hollow cast. However, parts such as wings and running boards were die-cast individually by hand.

The Market Price Range figures refer to boxed models in excellent condition.

Civilian Vehicles

Ref. No.	Model Type	Model Features and Size	Market Price Range
59 F	Four-wheeled Lorry with Driver	Back and doors open, rubber tyres, 6″	£150-200 ☐
60 F	Six-wheeled Lorry with Driver	Two-tone Blue body, White cab roof, Silver radiator surround, back and doors open, White rubber tyres, 6″	£150-200 ☐
61 F	Ten-wheeled Lorry with Driver	Back and doors open, rubber tyres	£200-250 ☐
90 F	Builders Lorry	As 59 F plus builders name on side. Never seen	NPP ☐
91 F	Builders Lorry	As 60 F plus builders name on side. Never seen	NPP ☐
92 F	Builders Lorry	As 61 F plus builders name on side. Never seen	NPP ☐
1398	Sports Model Open Tourer	Cream body, Black chassis and wheels, White rubber tyres, 4.25″	£750-1000 ☐
1399	Two-Seater Coupé (fitted bumpers)	Cream body, Tan roof, wings and running-boards, Black hubs, White tyres, 4.5″. (Also in other colours)	£1000-1250 ☐
1413	Mobile Police Car with two Officers	2-piece casting, Green body, Black wings, White tyres, 4.75″. (Also in other colours)	£500-600 ☐
1513	Volunteer Corps Ambulance with Driver, Wounded Man and Stretcher	Blue body, 'AMBULANCE', Red/White cross, White tyres	£600-700 ☐
1514	Corporation Type Motor Ambulance with Driver, Wounded Man & Stretcher	Cream body, 'AMBULANCE', Red/White cross, White tyres	£1000-1250 ☐
1552	'ROYAL MAIL' Van with Driver	Post-Office Red body, Black bonnet, 'GR' plus crown design, White tyres	£2000-3000 ☐

Military Vehicles

Ref. No.	Model Type	Model Features and Size	Market Price Range
1333	Lorry, Army, Caterpillar Type with Driver	Military Green finish, rubber tyres, 6″	£150-200 ☐
1335	Lorry, Army, Six-wheeled Type with Driver	Military Green finish, rubber tyres, 6″	£150-200 ☐
1432	Tender, Army, Covered, Ten-wheeled (with Driver)	Military Green finish, White rubber tyres, 6″	£150-200 ☐
1433	Tender, Army, Covered, Ten-wheeled Caterpillar Type (with Driver)	Military Green finish, White rubber tyres, 6″	£150-200 ☐
1448	Car, Staff	Military Green car with 2 Staff Officers, White rubber tyres, 4¼″	£350-450 ☐
1641	Underslung Heavy Duty Lorry (18 wheels) with Driver	Military Green finish, 10½″	£350-450 ☐
1642	Underslung Heavy Duty Lorry (18 wheels) with Driver	with Mounted Searchlight, Military Green finish, 10½″	£350-450 ☐
1643	Underslung Heavy Duty Lorry (18 wheels) with Driver	with Mounted Anti-Aircraft Gun (small)	£350-450 ☐
1643	Underslung Heavy Duty Lorry (18 wheels) with Driver	with Mounted Anti-Aircraft Gun (large)	£600-800 ☐
?	Underslung Heavy Duty Lorry (18 wheels) with Driver	with Mounted Barrage Balloon Winch	£900-1100 ☐

Record Cars (1:43 scale)

Ref. No.	Model Type	Model Features and Size	Market Price Range
1936	Bluebird Record Car, Napier Campbell	Malcolm Campbell's car, lift-off body, detailed engine, White tyres	£150-175 ☐
1939	Napier Railton	John Cobb's car, '350.20 mph World Land Speed Record'	£250-300 ☐

'Lilliput' Series (1:76 scale)

Ref. No.	Model Type	Model Features and Size	Market Price Range
LV 601	Roadster	Various colours	£60-70 ☐
LV 602	Limousine	Various colours	£60-70 ☐
LV 603	Flat Semi-Trailer	Various colours. Green	£25-35 ☐
		Blue	£35-45 ☐

'Motor and Road' Series

Ref. No.	Model Type	Model Features and Size	Market Price Range
1313	Volunteer Corps 'AMBULANCE'	Finished in Blue, with wounded man and stretcher	£300-400 ☐
2024	Light Goods Van with Driver	Various colours, 'BRITAINS LTD' logo	£400-500 ☐

Britains Motor Vehicles (post-war issues)

Ref. No.	Model Type	Model Features and Size	Market Price Range	

'Farm' Series

59 F	Farm Tipping Lorry	with Driver. Light Green or Blue	£150-250	☐
127 F	Fordson 'MAJOR' Tractor	with Driver and spade-end wheels	£200-250	☐
128 F	Fordson 'MAJOR' Tractor	with Driver and rubber-tyred wheels	£175-225	☐

'Clockwork' Series

| 2041 | Clockwork Unit | disguised as a 2-wheeled trailer. 'Will last 1½ minutes when fully wound and capable of driving any other vehicle 20-30 feet' | £45-55 | ☐ |
| 2045 | Clockwork Van | Finished in various colours with 'BRITAINS LTD' logo | £500-700 | ☐ |

Military issues, 'The British Commonwealth of Nations' Series

1334	Four-wheeled Tipper Lorry	with Driver	£150-200	☐
1335	Six-wheeled Army Lorry	with Driver	£150-200	☐
1433	Covered Army Truck	Caterpillar Type with Driver	£150-200	☐
1448	Staff Car	with General and Driver	£350-450	☐
1512	Army 'AMBULANCE'	with wounded man and stretcher	£150-200	☐
1791	Motor Cycle Dispatch Rider	Sold unboxed	£25-35	☐
1877	Beetle Lorry and Driver		£65-75	☐

Post-war 'Lilliput' Series (1:76 scale)

LV 601	Open Sports Car	2.25″ long	£60-70	☐
LV 602	Saloon Car	2.25″ long	£60-70	☐
LV 603	Articulated Lorry	4″ long	£60-70	☐
LV 604	Fordson Tractor with Driver	1.5″ long	£35-45	☐
LV 605	Milk Float and Horse	with Milkman. 2.25″ long	£45-55	☐
LV 606	Tumbrel Cart and Horse	with Hay Racks and Carter. 2.75″ long	£35-45	☐
LV 607	Austin 3-ton Covered Military Truck		£35-45	☐
LV 608	Austin 3-ton Farm Truck		£35-45	☐
LV 609	Austin Military Champ		£65-75	☐
LV 610	Centurion Tank		£35-45	☐
LV 611	Self-propelled 25pdr. Gun		£25-35	☐
LV 612	Humber 1½ ton Military Truck		£35-45	☐
LV 613	Humber 1½ ton Military Truck	Covered version	£35-45	☐
LV 614	Farm Trailer		£15-25	☐
LV 615	Saracen Armoured Vehicle		£15-25	☐
LV 616	1½ ton Truck		£35-45	☐

The Editor would like to express his appreciation to Mike Richardson for the introductory article and to Steven Nagle and Norman Joplin for assistance with the model listings and price information.

CHAD VALLEY

DIECAST CLOCKWORK VEHICLES

The Chad Valley company (makers of board games and wooden toys) produced tinplate toy vehicles from 1932 incorporating the year in the registration number on the number plates. Their first 'Wee-Kin' diecast toy vehicles were produced around 1949 and had 'CV 1949' as the registration number. They were fitted with a key-wound clockwork motor and were designed more as toys than models having generic titles like 'Open Lorry' or 'Fire Engine'. The cars issued between 1951 and 1954 as Rootes Group promotionals are much better attempts at models and were sold at Rootes Group garages as well as normal toy shops. The tractors produced from 1952 are particularly fine and well detailed models.

The years shown below indicate the periods in which Chad Valley offered them for sale though not all the toys were available for the whole of the period and some were still in the shops well after production ceased in 1956.

Ref. No.	Year(s)	Model Type	Model Features and Size	Market Price Range	
220	1949-53	Razor Edge Saloon	Various colours, number plates 'CV 1949', approximate scale 1:43	£90-120	☐
221	1949-53	Traffic Control Car	Casting as 9220 plus loudspeaker, 'CV 1949', approximate scale 1:43	£90-120	☐
222	1949-53	Police Car	Casting as 9220 plus loudspeaker and 'POLICE' sign, 'CV 1949', scale 1:43	£90-120	☐
223	1949-53	Track Racer	'CV 1949' on number plates, no other details	£90-120	☐
224	1949-53	Double Decker Bus	Red body, number plates 'CV 1949', Approximate scale 1:76	£150-200	☐
225	1949-53	Open Lorry	Various colours, 'CV 1949' on number plates	£100-130	☐
226	1949-53	Low-Loader	Green/Red body, 'CV 1949' on number plates, 3 Cream-coloured packing cases	£100-130	☐
227	1949-53	Timber Wagon	'CV 1949', body has round bosses to fit milk churns or other 'loads'	£100-130	☐
228	1949-53	Cable Layer	Red cab, Green body, silver trim, number plates 'CV 1949'	£100-130	☐
229	1949-53	Breakdown Lorry	Number plates 'CV 1949', no other details	£100-130	☐
230	1949-53	Milk Float	Number plates 'CV 1949', load of eight milk churns	£125-150	☐
231	1949-53	Fire Engine	Red body, number plates 'CV 1949'	£100-130	☐
232	1949-53	Tower Repair Wagon	Number plates 'CV 1949', no other details	£100-130	☐
233	1949-53	Milk Tanker	Blue body and logo, White tank, number plates 'CV 1949'	£100-130	☐
234	1949-53	Petrol Tanker	Number plates 'CV 1949', no other details	£100-130	☐
236	1949-53	The Hillman Minx	Grey or Metallic Dark Blue body, Rootes Group promotional, 1:43 scale	£90-120	☐
237	1949-53	The Humber Super Snipe	Metallic Dark Green body, Rootes Group promotional, 1:43 scale	£90-120	☐
238	1949-53	The Sunbeam-Talbot	Light Blue or Metallic Dark Green, Rootes Group promotional, 1:43 scale. Base has the wording 'A Rootes Group Product' plus usual Chad Valley marks	£90-120	☐
239	1949-53	Dust Cart	Body has tinplate sliding side panels, number plates 'CV 1949'	£100-130	☐
240	1949-53	The Commer Avenger Coach	Blue or Red body marked 'A Rootes Group Product', 1:76 scale, promotional	£100-150	☐
242	1949-53	The Commer Hands	(Articulated 6-wheel) 'A Rootes Group Product', Red body with 'Commer Hands' sticker, promotional	£100-150	☐
507	1951-54	The Humber Hawk	Metallic Dark Blue, Metallic Dark Green, or mid-Green body, Rootes Group promotional, 1:43 scale	£90-120	☐

Chad Valley non-clockwork issues   Few of these are seen in collectable condition hence NGPP

no ref.	1950-55	Massey Ferguson Tractor		NGPP	☐
no ref.	1950-55	Ford Tractor		NGPP	☐
no ref.	1950-55	Hillman Minx Saloon		NGPP	☐
no ref.	1950-55	Humber Super Snipe		NGPP	☐
no ref.	1950-55	Guy Truck		NGPP	☐
no ref.	1950-55	Sunbeam Racer		NGPP	☐
no ref.	1950-55	Humber Hawk		NGPP	☐
no ref.	1950-55	Rolls-Royce Razor Edge	Razor Edge Saloon	NGPP	☐
no ref.	1950-55	Routemaster London Bus		NGPP	☐
no ref.	1950-55	Commer Avenger Coach		NGPP	☐
no ref.	1950-55	Guy Truck	'LYONS ICE CREAM'	NGPP	☐
no ref.	1950-55	Sunbeam Saloon		NGPP	☐
no ref.	1950-55	Guy Milk Lorry		NGPP	☐
no ref.	1950-55	Guy Cable Lorry		NGPP	☐
no ref.	1950-55	Guy Petrol Tanker	'REGENT'	NGPP	☐
no ref.	1950-55	Guy 'FIRE' Engine		NGPP	☐
no ref.	1950-55	Guy Container Lorry		NGPP	☐
no ref.	1950-55	Guy Refuse Lorry		NGPP	☐

Chad Valley model Tractors

no ref.	1952	Fordson Major E27N	Dark Blue body, Orange wheels, rubber tyres (2 types of tread on rear) working steering, towbar with pin, clockwork wound by starting handle. Scale 1:16. Illustrated box or plain box with small label	£150-200	☐
no ref.	1954	Fordson Major DDN	Mid-Blue body, Orange wheels, rubber tyres, working steering, lifting bonnet, towbar/pin, hydraulic lift at rear (detachable centre arm) clockwork wound through rear wheel hub. Scale 1:16. Illustrated box or plain box with small label	£150-200	☐
		Static version:	As previous model but without clockwork operation. Illustrated box or plain box plus small label. The word 'working' is deleted from all sides of box	£150-200	☐
		Chrome version:	Static (non-clockwork) version in Chrome plate, with or without wooden plinth. Thought to be a ploughing trophy or Ford presentation model	£250-400	☐
no ref.	1955	Ford Dexta	Mid-Blue body, Orange wheels, radiator panels and 'Fordson Dexta' decal, not steerable, rubber tyres, hook, scale 1:16. Illustrated box	£400-600	☐

5th EDITION
'BRITISH DIECAST MODEL TOYS CATALOGUE'
USERS SURVEY

ether you are a collector or trader we would greatly value your views on this new Edition and would
you to kindly complete and return this questionnaire.

hope to publish the results of this survey and for the three most helpful and constructive replies we
ive we shall be giving a years free subscription to the collecting magazine or newspaper of their
ice. If necessary do please use a separate sheet for your replies.

What do you MOST like about the Catalogue?

....

....

What do you LEAST like about the Catalogue?

....

....

Is the Catalogue now too big?
Would you like to see it split up into 2 volumes, i) Pre 1970 issues ii) Post 1970 issues?

....

....

Do you own model listings, Catalogues or pictures of models not currently listed?

....

....

What other books on toy collecting would you like to see published?

....

....

ME & ADDRESS (BLOCK CAPITALS PLEASE) ....

....

....

lly return the form to:- Swapmeet Toys & Models Ltd, PO Box 21, Bury St Edmunds, Suffolk, England. IP33 2ED.

WINNERS OF THE 4th EDITION 'NEW INFORMATION' COMPETITION

winners were as follows: Mrs S. Clark of Farnham for supplying Matchbox data; Ken Appleyard
)ckendon for supplying Corgi data; Dr Beugels of the Netherlands for supplying Dinky data.
the winners received a one year subscription to the collecting magazine of their choice. Grateful
nks to all those who have contributed new information.

Ref. No.	Year(s)	Model Type	Chad Valley - continued	Market Price Range	
no ref.	1955	Ferguson	Green body, Red wheels, *'Ferguson'* decal on sides, working steering, hook, scale 1:16. Illustrated box inscribed *'Ferguson'*. Promotional	£500-700	☐
		Colour variation:	Grey body, Grey wheels, hydraulic lift at rear	£600-800	☐
no ref.	1955	Fordson Major E27N	Red and Yellow with driver, clockwork, scale 1:43, boxed. Made under licence by Raybro & Sturdy Products S.A. Johannesburg, South Africa (model marked 'Chad Valley GB').	£50-100	☐

The introduction to the Chad Valley section was written by Sue Richardson who also provided the basic listing.
Additional listing information came from the Cecil Gibson archives.
The Editor would like to express appreciation to John G. Butler of Berkhamsted, Herts. for his assistance with the Chad Valley Tractors information.

CHARBENS TOYS

The name 'Charbens' was derived by combining the first part of the names of Charles and Benjamin Reid. The toys were manufactured at their 219 Hornsey Road premises in North London. The listings have been taken from the firm's 1960 Trade Catalogue.

'Old Crocks' Miniature series

OC.1	1960-	Darracq, 1904, 2-seater open car	£10-25	☐
OC.2	1960-	Spyker, 1904, 4-seater open car	£10-25	☐
OC.3	1960-	'Old Bill' Bus, 1914, Double-decker open-top	£10-25	☐
OC.4	1960-	Ford, 1907, Ford Model 'T' car	£10-25	☐
OC.5	1960-	Vauxhall, 1907, 2-seater open car	£10-25	☐
OC.6	1960-	De Dion Bouton, 1906, open 2-seater.....	£10-25	☐
OC.7	1960-	Panhard, 1898, 2-seater, tiller steering	£10-25	☐
OC.8	1960-	Rolls-Royce Silver Ghost, 1906, 4-seater open car	£10-25	☐
OC.9	1960-	Standard 6hp, 1903, 4-seater open car	£10-25	☐
OC.10	1960-	Wolseley, 1902, 4-seater open car	£10-25	☐
OC.11	1960-	Packard Runabout, 1908, open 2-seater	£10-25	☐
OC.12	1960-	Vauxhall Hansom Cab, 1905, with steering wheel on roof!	£10-25	☐
OC.13	1960-	Straker Steam Lorry	£10-25	☐
OC.14	1960-	Stephenson's Rocket (locomotive)	£10-25	☐
OC.15	1960-	Rocket Trailer, Tender for OC.14.............	£10-25	☐
OC.16	1960-	Albion 1909, 2-seater open truck	£10-25	☐
OC.17	1960-	Rover, 1912, 2-seater open sports car	£10-25	☐
OC.18	1960-	Mercedes-Benz, 1911, open 2-seater	£10-25	☐
M.19	1960-	Horse Transport, A 1930s Horse-Box.......	£10-25	☐
OC.20	1960-	Lanchester, 1910, 4-seater sports tourer.....	£10-25	☐
OC.21	1960-	Morris Cowley, 1922, 2-seater open car.....	£10-25	☐
OC.22	1960-	Daimler, 1900, rather tall 2-seater...........	£10-25	☐
OC.23	1960-	Autocar, 1904, open 3-wheeler	£10-25	☐
OC.24	1960-	Grenville Steam Car, 3 wheels, boiler	£10-25	☐
OC.25	1960-	Napier, 1905, famous 2-seater racer.........	£10-25	☐
OC.26	1960-	Fire Engine, 'Dennis'-like Fire Escape......	£10-25	☐
OC.27	1960-	Breakdown Crane Lorry, articulated	£10-25	☐
OC.28	1960-	Mercer Runabout, open 2-seater sports.....	£10-25	☐

Military models

M.30	1960-	Mobile Searchlight, Searchlight on 4-wheel trailer	£10-25	☐
M.31	1960-	Mobile Twin Bofor Gun, on trailer	£10-25	☐
M.32	1960-	Mobile Radar, Radar dish on trailer	£10-25	☐
M.33	1960-	Mobile Field Gun, Large gun on trailer	£10-25	☐
M.34	1960-	Mobile Rocket Gun, Salvo device on trailer.	£10-25	☐
M.35	1960-	Mobile Tank, Armoured car with flag.......	£10-25	☐

Miniature Truck series

6	1960-	Tractor	NGPP	☐
8	1960-	Tipping Truck....................................	NGPP	☐
9	1960-	Coach	NGPP	☐
10	1960-	'ROYAL MAIL' Van..............................	NGPP	☐
11	1960-	Ambulance	NGPP	☐
12	1960-	'CARTER PATERSON' Van, Green body, White/Red logo, Black wheels, 3½"	NGPP	☐
13	1960-	'POLICE' Van	NGPP	☐

14	1960-	'POST OFFICE' Van	NGPP	☐
15	1960-	Fire Escape......................................	NGPP	☐
L.40	1960-	Articulated Tanker, Also listed as a 'Road Tanker'....................................	£10-25	☐
L.41	1960-	Articulated Lorry................................	£10-25	☐
L.41	1960-	Tipping Semi-Trailer............................	£10-25	☐
L.42	1960-	Six-wheeled Lorry...............................	£10-25	☐
L.43	1960-	Six-wheeled Tanker.............................	£10-25	☐

Note: 'CHARBENS' and 'COPYRIGHT' are marked on underside of models. The models are interesting and very difficult to find in good condition. Additional information on any Charbens products would be welcomed.

'Die-Cast Wheel Toys'

The models listed below are rarely seen in mint and boxed condition so there can be little helpful price guidance. Doubtless many of the models are scarce and asking prices would reflect this.

1	1960-	Tree Wagon, with 2 horses, 1 man	NGPP	☐
2	1960-	Horse Roller, and man............................	NGPP	☐
3	1960-	Grass Cutter, with horse and man	NGPP	☐
4	1960-	Farm Haycart, with horse & 2 racks..........	NGPP	☐
5	1960-	Farm Wagon, with horse & 2 racks...........	NGPP	☐
6	1960-	Farm Tractor, and man...........................	NGPP	☐
7	1960-	Bakers Van, with horse and man	NGPP	☐
8	1960-	Tip Lorry	NGPP	☐
9	1960-	Motor Coach	NGPP	☐
10	1960-	Royal Mail Van	NGPP	☐
11	1960-	Ambulance	NGPP	☐
12	1960-	Carter Paterson Van	NGPP	☐
13	1960-	Police Van	NGPP	☐
14	1960-	Post Office Van	NGPP	☐
15	1960-	Fire Engine Set, with 3 firemen................	NGPP	☐
16	1960-	Covered Wagon, with 4 horses & driver....	NGPP	☐
17	1960-	Tree Wagon, with tractor & driver	NGPP	☐
18	1960-	Grass Cutter, with tractor & 2 drivers.......	NGPP	☐
19	1960-	Reaper & Tractor, with 2 drivers	NGPP	☐
20	1960-	Crane & Loose Jib................................	NGPP	☐
21	1960-	Muir-Hill Dumper, with driver	NGPP	☐
22	1960-	Travelling Zoo Set................................	NGPP	☐
26	1960-	Armoured Car	NGPP	☐
27	1960-	Large Tractor	NGPP	☐
28	1960-	Steam Roller	NGPP	☐
29	1960-	Mincing Machine	NGPP	☐
31	1960-	Cable Wagon, with trailer	NGPP	☐
32	1960-	Alfa-Romeo Racing Car..........................	NGPP	☐
33	1960-	Bristol Cooper Racing Car.......................	NGPP	☐
34	1960-	Ferrari Racing Car	NGPP	☐
35	1960-	Tree Wagon, with horse	NGPP	☐
36	1960-	Horse Transport Box.............................	NGPP	☐
37	1960-	Rocket Gun on Lorry, with trailer	NGPP	☐
38	1960-	Savings Bank, with gun to fire coin into bank	NGPP	☐

CORGI TOYS

INTRODUCTION

Corgi Toys were launched in 1956 by the Mettoy Company which had itself been founded in Northampton by Phillip Ullmann in 1953. The 'Mettoy' name was derived from the first three letters of 'Metal' plus 'toy' - the company's main product range being composed of lithographed metal toys. In 1948 Mettoy produced their first cast metal toys and called them 'Castoys'. The Castoy models contained a clockwork motor and when the first Corgi models were introduced they also contained a mechanism. This plus the introduction of windows gave Corgi a competitive edge against their great rivals Dinky Toys and helped Mettoy to successfully launch Corgi Toys onto the market place.

For almost 40 years Corgi Toys have produced a superb range of diecast products to delight collectors the world over. Nowadays Corgi forms part of the US company Mattel and the models are made in the Far East.

Each year the company promotes the 'Worlds Biggest Little Motor Show' at the British Motor Industries Heritage Trust Museum at Gaydon, near Warwick, England. This event covers three days and includes a Trade Day and a large Toyfair plus the Corgi Collectors Club annual convention and dinner. In addition to hosting that event the Gaydon Museum also houses the superb permanent Corgi Toy Collection.

Corgi Toys Identification

Corgi Toys were often referred to as 'the ones with windows', as they were the first manufacturer to produce models with that refinement. Some of their first models also had a mechanical motor. Spring suspension was introduced from 1959 and in 1960 the first die-cast model to have an opening bonnet. The first models were based on real cars of the period. Similarly, with the launch of the 'Corgi Major Toys' in 1959, models of real commercial vehicles were available and competed with the Dinky 'Supertoys' range.

In the 1960s Corgi produced many successful film and TV-related models. Probably the best remembered was the 'James Bond' Aston Martin which sold in huge quantities in the autumn of 1965. Indeed, such was the popularity of the model that a version was still available in 1992!

Corgi introduced many new features in the 1960s such as: jewelled headlights, opening bonnet revealing detailed engine, opening boot revealing spare, self-centring steering, ruby rear lights, etc. One particularly attractive model was the Midland Red Motorway Express Coach. The detailed interior even incorporated a toilet! Needless to say good examples of this model

Model Number and Name All Corgi models have *'CORGI TOYS'* on the underside and virtually all models have the name of the model there as well. Unlike Dinky Toys the model numbers are not shown on all models making them difficult to identify at times. However, models without numbers may be found in the catalogue by looking for them in their own thematic section, e.g: Saloon Car, Novelty, etc.

Windows All Corgi models have windows.

Construction Materials All models are comprised at least in part of a die-cast alloy.

are highly sought after by bus collectors. Similarly the 'Chipperfields Circus' collection of models were beautifully produced and are highly prized today.

Innovations were frequent and imaginative in the 1960s. 'Golden Jacks' for instance, a built-in jacking system which enabled models to have 'Take-Off' wheels. And 'Trans-O-Lites' whereby light rays were captured and fed through prisms to illuminate the headlights. 'WhizzWheels' and the slightly larger scale of 1:42 were introduced in the 1970s.

A market strategy unique to Corgi was the launching a replica model car simultaneously with the real car. To date simultaneous launches have occurred with Austin Metro, Ford Escort, Triumph Acclaim, Ford Sierra and the MG Maestro 1600, which is a unique record. Corgi were the first die-cast manufacturers to introduce the dimensions of light, sound and movement into their models by using the micro-chip in their 'Corgitronic' range. The models 'come alive', for example by just pushing down on the rear axle or, in the case of the Road Repair Unit, by pressing the workman to activate the pneumatic drill sound. Others (like the Sonic Corgi Truck) can be operated from a remote control handset.

Mechanical Some early Corgi Toys were produced in either the normal form or with a friction type flywheel motor. Exceptions were the sports cars and trucks which could not be converted to take the flywheel. The mechanisms were not robust and were phased out in 1959.

Boxes July 1956 - Blue box, January 1959 - Yellow/Blue box (Two-tone cars were first to use them) December 1966 - Window box (2 square window ends) May 1973 - Angled window box (one square window end, coloured lines around box) 1980 - Yellow window box, 1987 New style Corgi logo box.

Mettoy Diecast Toys - The 'Castoys' series

Castoys were produced by the Mettoy Company between 1948 and 1958 and were instigated by a request from Marks and Spencers for a robust, long lasting toy. The models were made of zinc alloy and advertised as 'Heavy Cast Metal Toys'. They had windows, a clockwork motor and brake plus black rubber tyres on cast hubs. They were packaged in attractive Yellow/Red boxes which displayed a picture of the model inside. Of the original issues only two models, no. 840, the 'Eight Wheel Lorry' and 970 'Delivery Van' remained in production after 1951. The later issues of the Delivery Van with their various attractive body designs are now rare and sought after items.

The following listing contains all the information available at present. The Editor would welcome any additional information on body colours and variations.

Ref. No.	Year(s)	Model Type	Model Features and Size	Market Price Range	
810	1948-51	Limousine	No models seen though body colour shown as Red in 1948 catalogue........................	NPP	☐
820	1948-51	Streamline Bus..........................	Metallic Blue and Gold body with Silver raised roof section and base, Red door with Brown plastic male passenger. Destination board shows 'PRIVATE' and registration 'MTY 718'	£200-300	☐
			Metallic Brown and Pink body with Silver raised roof section and radiator, with Green female passenger..	£200-300	☐
830	1948-51	Vanwall Racing Car	No models seen. Shown as Green with Black tyres in catalogue, RN '18'	£100-200	☐
840	1948-58	8 Wheel Lorry	Metallic Blue cab with Grey rear body, Silver radiator and hubs........................	£100-200	☐
850	1948-51	Fire Engine	Red body, Silver ladder and crank........................	£100-200	☐
			Red body, Silver extending ladder, no crank........................	£100-200	☐
860	1948-51	Tractor..	No models seen but shown in 1951 catalogue with Yellow body plus Red engine cover with Silver hubs and Black tyres, steering wheel and brake........................	£100-200	☐
870	1948-51	Delivery Van.............................	No models seen but shown in 1948 catalogue with plain Dark Blue body.................	£100-150	☐
	1952-55	'EXPRESS DELIVERY' Van...	Yellow body with Red logo and design on sides	£150-200	☐
	1955-58	'POST OFFICE TELEPHONES'	Green body with White logo and Royal crest in Gold, plus Silver two part extending ladder on the roof........................	£200-300	☐
	1955-58	'ROYAL MAIL'	Red body, Silver trim, Yellow logo and Royal crest	£200-300	☐
	1956-58	'B.O.A.C.'	Blue body Silver trim, White 'Fly By B.O.A.C.' on roof........................	£200-300	☐

The 'Miniature Numbers' series

The range of models produced between 1951 an 1954 was based on just two vehicle types - the Standard Vanguard and the Rolls Royce. Models were issued in small and large sizes and featured a clockwork motor plus brake, adjustable steering and rubber tyred wheels. The were packaged in attractive window boxes. The basic Standard Vanguard model was also issued as a Taxi, a Fire Chief's Car and a Police Car. The following listing has been taken from the 1951 Mettoy Catalogue and the Editor would welcome any additional information.

Ref. No.	Year(s)	Model Type	Model Features and Size	Market Price Range	
502	1951	Standard Vanguard Saloon	Shown with Green body in catalogue (2 7/8 inches long)..	NGPP	☐
505	1951	Rolls-Royce Saloon	Shown with Red body in catalogue (3 inches long)	NGPP	☐
510	1951	Standard Vanguard Police Car	Black with White 'POLICE' logo on doors; roof siren and bell............................	NGPP	☐
511	1951	Standard Vanguard Taxi...........	Shown in 1951 catalogue with Yellow body and Red roof rack	NGPP	☐
512	1951	Standard Vanguard Fire Chief..	Red, White 'FIRE CHIEF' on doors; single Silver ladder on roof........................	NGPP	☐
602	1951	Standard Vanguard Saloon	Blue body shown in catalogue (large scale version of 502, 4¼ inches long).................	NGPP	☐
603	1951	Standard Vanguard Saloon	As 602 but with automatic 'to and fro' bump feature	NGPP	☐
605	1951	Rolls-Royce Saloon	Yellow body shown in catalogue (large scale version of 505, 4½ inches long)............	NGPP	☐
606	1951	Rolls-Royce Saloon	As 605 but with automatic 'to and fro' bump feature	NGPP	☐

Ref. No.	Year(s)	Model Type	Model Features and Size	Market Price Range	
C100	1985	'PORSCHE' 956	Yellow/Black body, racing number '7', 'CASTROL', 115 mm.	£7-10	☐
C100/2	1986		Yellow body, racing number '7', 'TAKA-Q'	£7-10	☐
C100/3	1988		Black body, racing number '1', 'BLAUPUNKT'	£7-10	☐
C101	1985	Porsche 956	Red/White body, racing number '14', 'CANON'	£7-10	☐
C101/2	1985	Porsche 956	White body, 'Clipper' logo plus 4 Red stripes on bonnet & tail, 'ADMIRAL ENERGY GROUP Ltd' logo	£15-20	☐
C102	1985	Opel Manta 400	Red body, racing number '43', 'SHELL', 105 mm.	£7-10	☐
	1988		Black body, racing number '18', 'SHELL'	£7-10	☐
C102	1985		Yellow body, racing number '12', 'BRITISH TELECOM'	£7-10	☐
C102/4	1990	'VAUXHALL OPEL' Manta	White body, racing number '6', 'MOBIL' on bonnet	NRP	☐
C103	1985	Opel Manta 400	White body, racing number '15', 'CASTROL'.	£7-10	☐
C104	1985	Toyota Corolla 1600	White/Red body, Yellow racing number '16', 'LAING'.	£7-10	☐
	1986		White/Red body, racing number '2', 'TOTAL'.	£7-10	☐
C105	1985	Toyota Corolla 1600	Red body, Yellow design, racing number '8', 'DUNLOP'	£7-10	☐
	1986		Red body, Yellow design, racing number '5', 'TOTAL'	£7-10	☐
C106	1985	Saab 9000 Turbo	White body, Red/Yellow design, racing number '3'.	£7-10	☐
C106/1	1987		Red body, White design 'FLY VIRGIN'.	£7-10	☐
C106/3	1988		Black body, racing number '7', 'MOBIL'.	£7-10	☐
C106/9	1990	Saab Turbo	White/Maroon body, racing number '4', 'FEDERAL EXPRESS'.	NRP	☐
C107	1985	Saab 9000	Red body, Yellow design, racing number '41', 'BRITAX'.	£7-10	☐
C108	1985	Chevrolet Z-28	Red body, Yellow design, racing number '52', 'WEBER', 115 mm.	£7-10	☐
C109	1985	Chevrolet Z-28	White body, Black/Yellow bands, Red racing number '84', 115 mm.	£7-10	☐
C110	1985	BMW 635	White body with Union Jacks and racing number '6'.	£7-10	☐
C110/1	1986		Red body, racing number '25', 'FERODO'.	£7-10	☐
C110/2	1987		White body, racing number '2', 'MOTUL'.	£7-10	☐
C110/3	1988		White body, racing number '46', 'WARSTEINER'.	£7-10	☐
C111	1985	BMW 635	White/Blue body, racing number '18', 'BRITAX'.	£7-10	☐
	1986		White body, racing number '8', 'PIRELLI'.	£7-10	☐
C113	1987	Saab 9000	Red body, C7PM (Swedish).	£7-10	☐
C139/2	1987	Porsche 911	Orange body, racing number '24', 'JAGERMEISTER'.	£7-10	☐
C139/4	1988		Red/Blue body, racing number '91', 'DENVER'.	£7-10	☐
150	1957-61	Vanwall Racing Car	(Blue box) Light or Mid-Green body, Yellow seat, large 'VANWALL', Blue tinted screen, RN '3'.	£40-50	☐
			Mid-Green body, Silver seat, 'VANWALL' logo, clear screen, RN '1'.	£40-50	☐
			Mid-Green body, Yellow seat, small 'VANWALL' logo, clear screen, RN '1'.	£40-50	☐
		Black/Yellow box:	Red body, Yellow seat, large 'VANWALL' logo, Blue tinted screen, RN '1'.	£40-50	☐
			Red body, Silver seat, small 'VANWALL' logo, clear screen, RN '1'.	£40-50	☐
150 S	1961-65	Vanwall Racing Car	Light or Mid-Red body, Silver seats/driver, clear screen, RN '25', shaped wheels.	£40-50	☐
150	1972-74	Surtees TS9 Formula 1	Metallic Purple or Metallic Blue body, 'BROOKE BOND OXO' logo, 8-spoke WhizzWheels	£20-25	☐
			Metallic Turquoise body with cast 8-stud WhizzWheels	£15-20	☐
		Gift Set model:	Blue/Yellow body with 'DUCKHAMS', (in GS 29 only)	GSP	☐
C150/4	1990	Chevrolet Camaro	Blue body, Orange/Black design, racing number '77'.	NRP	☐
151	1958-60	Lotus XI Racing Car	(Blue box) Silver body (Red seats) Red body (Cream seats) Dull Turquoise (Red seats) all with Blue tinted screen, RN '1'.	£45-50	☐
151 S	1961-63	Lotus XI Racing Car	(Black/Yellow box) Silver body (Maroon seats, RN '7') Dull Blue body (Maroon seats, RN '1', clear screen	£40-45	☐
151 A	1961-63	Lotus XI	Blue body, Red/White design, Silver nose, Red seats, shaped wheels, clear screen, driver, RN '1'.	£40-45	☐
			Lemon body, racing number '3', driver, spring suspension.	£35-45	☐
C151	1974-76	'YARDLEY' Mclaren M19A	White body, RN '55', White drivers helmet, 8-spoke WhizzWheels	£20-25	☐
			White body, RN '55', White drivers helmet, 8-stud WhizzWheels	£15-20	☐
			Same but Blue stripe on White drivers helmet, 8-stud WhizzWheels, (GS30 only).	GSP	☐
152	1958-61	BRM Racing Car	(Blue box) Green body, Yellow or Silver seat, Blue screen, cast wheels, RN '17'.	£45-50	☐
		Black/Yellow box:	Green body, Silver seat, clear screen, cast spoke wheels, RN '3' or '7'.	£40-45	☐
152 S	1961-65	BRM Racing Car	Turquoise body, cast or shaped wheels, RN '1', suspension.	£40-45	☐
C152	1974-76	Ferrari 312 B2	Red body, 'Ferrari/Shell' logo, RN '5', White driver, Orange/Blue helmet, 8-spoke or 8-stud cast wheels	£15-20	☐
153	1960-62	Bluebird Record Car	Blue body, UK & US flags on nose, metal wheels, 127 mm.	£60-70	☐
153 A	1961-65	Bluebird Record Car	Blue body, UK & US flags on nose, plastic wheels, 127 mm.	£45-55	☐
			Blue body with two Union Jacks on nose, Black plastic wheels.	£60-70	☐
153	1972-74	Team Surtees TS 9B	Red body, RN '26', Blue or Blue/White driver (Rob Walker) 8-spoke wheels	£15-20	☐
			Red body, 'NORRIS' logo, (GS30 only).	GSP	☐
154	1963-72	Ferrari Formula 1	Red/Silver body, racing number '36', driver, windscreen, 91 mm.	£25-30	☐
C154	1974-78	'JOHN PLAYER SPECIAL' Lotus	Black body, Gold trim, racing number '1' or '4', drivers Emerson Fittipaldi or Ronnie Petersen.		
			1: 'JPS' logo, Black/Red helmet, 8-stud wheels, 'Fittipaldi' on box	£15-20	☐
			2: 'JPS' logo, Black or Blue helmet, 'Petersen' on box	£15-20	☐
			3: 'JPS TEXACO' logo, Red helmet	£15-20	☐
			4: 'JPS TEXACO' logo, Black helmet, 12-spoke wheels, (GS32 only).	GSP	☐
			5: 'JPS SHELL' logo, Black/Red helmet, (GS30 only).	GSP	☐
		Marks & Spencers issue:	No 'Corgi' on base, 'TEXACO' logo, Orange (?) helmet	GSP	☐

Ref. No.	Year(s)	Model Type	Corgi Toys - continued	Market Price Range	
155	1965-68	Lotus Climax Racing Car	Green/Yellow body, racing number '1' or '4', suspension, driver, 90 mm.	£25-30	☐
C155	1974-76	'SHADOW' F1 Racing Car	Black body, 'UOP' logo, RN '17', driver (Jackie Collins) White/Maroon helmet	£15-20	☐
156	1967-69	Cooper-Maserati Racing Car	Blue body, racing number '7', windscreen, White driver, 90 mm.	£30-35	☐
C156	1974-76	Graham Hill's Shadow	White/Red body, racing number '12', driver, 'EMBASSY RACING', 132 mm.	£20-25	☐
158	1969-72	Lotus Climax Racing Car	Red/White, racing number '8', suspension, driver, windscreen, 90 mm.	£25-30	☐
C158	1975-77	Elf Tyrrell Ford F1	Blue body, racing number '1', 'ELF', Jackie Stewart driving, 110 mm.	£15-20	☐
159	1969-72	Cooper-Maserati	Yellow/White, racing number '3', driver-controlled steering, 90 mm.	£25-30	☐
C159	1974-76	Indianapolis Racing Car	Red body, racing number '20', Patrick Eagle driving, 130 mm.	£20-25	☐
C160	1975-78	'HESKETH' 308 F1	White body, 'HESKETH' logo, White driver, Black helmet, 4-spoke or 8-stud wheels	£15-20	☐
		Marks & Spencers issue:	White body, no 'CORGI' on some, White driver, Orange helmet	GSP	☐
			Yellow body, 'CORGI TEAM' logo, Orange driver (James Hunt) Black helmet, Blue belts, (GS26 only)	GSP	☐
161	1972-75	Santa Pod 'COMMUTER'	Red/Silver 'Dragster' body, racing number '2', WhizzWheels, 123 mm.	£20-25	☐
161	1977	'ELF-TYRRELL' Project 34	Blue body, 'ELF' logo, Red or Blue helmet, 8-stud wheels, RN '4'.	£15-20	☐
162		Tyrell P34	Blue/White body, 'FIRST NATIONAL BANK' logo, White driver, Red or Orange helmet	£15-20	☐
		Marks & Spencers issue:	As previous model but no 'Corgi' on base, 8-stud wheels	GSP	☐
162	1971-72	'QUARTERMASTER' Dragster	Green and White body, aerofoil, driver, plastic wheels, 146 mm.	£20-25	☐
C163	1971-76	Santa Pod Dragster	White/Blue lift-off body, 'GLOWORM', driver, plastic wheels, 113 mm.	£20-25	☐
164	1972-75	Ison Bros 'WILD HONEY'	Yellow/Red 'Dragster' body, 'JAGUAR', WhizzWheels, 171 mm.	£20-25	☐
165	1974-76	Adams Brothers Dragster..........	Orange/Yellow body, 4 x V-8 engines, WhizzWheels.	£20-25	☐
166	1971-74	Ford Mustang.........................	'ORGAN GRINDER', Yellow/Green body, racing number '39', driver	£20-25	☐
C167	1973-74	U.S.A. Racing Buggy	White/Red body, racing number '8', driver, US flag, 95 mm.	£20-25	☐
C169	1974-76	Starfighter Jet Dragster	Blue/Silver/Red body, 'FIRESTONE', 155 mm.	£20-25	☐
C170	1974-76	John Woolfe's 208 Dragster	Blue/Yellow body, 'RADIO LUXEMBOURG', racing driver, 146 mm.	£20-25	☐
190	1974-76	'JOHN PLAYER' Lotus...........	1:18 scale, Black/Gold, RN '1', driver, removable wheels, tools, 270 mm.	£30-35	☐
191	1974-77	'TEXACO MARLBORO' Mclaren	1:18 scale, White/Red, RN '5', removable wheels, tools, 245 mm.	£30-35	☐
C201	1979-82	Mini 1000 'TEAM CORGI'.....	Metallic Silver body, racing number '8', various adverts, 85 mm.	£10-15	☐
			Dark Blue body, ? racing number	NGPP	☐
203	1971-72	De Tomaso Mangusta	Metallic Dark Green, Gold stripes, racing number '1'	£20-25	☐
227	1962-63	Mini Cooper Rally	Blue/White body with flags and rally number '3' or '7', 73 mm.	£150-175	☐
			As previous model but with rally number '1'.	£175-225	☐
			Pale Lemon body, White roof and bonnet, with flags and RN '7'	£100-125	☐
			Pale Lemon body and bonnet, with flags and RN '1'	£175-225	☐
256	1971-74	VW 'EAST AFRICAN RALLY'	Red body, rally number '18', steering on roof, rhinoceros, 91 mm.	£100-140	☐
271	1969-70	Ghia Mangusta De Tomaso.....	Blue/White body, Gold stripes, aerial, detailed engine	£20-30	☐
C281	1982-	'DATAPOST' Metro	Blue/White body, racing number '77', various adverts, 94 mm.	£10-15	☐
282	1971-74	Mini Cooper Rally	White/Black, rally number '177', special lights, WhizzWheels, 73 mm.	£45-55	☐
C291	1982	Mercedes Benz 240 Rally Car ...	Muddy Cream body, rally number '5', roof rack, spare wheel.	£10-15	☐
C299	1987	Sierra Rally	Black body, racing number '7', various adverts, 'TEXACO'.	£5-8	☐
C300	1979-82	Ferrari 'DAYTONA'	Green, multicoloured flash, racing number '5', opening doors, 120 mm.	£10-15	☐
C301	1979-82	Lotus Elite Racing Car	Yellow/Red body, racing number '7', 'FERODO', 120 mm.	£10-15	☐
302	1969	Hillman Hunter Rally	Blue body, White roof, Matt-Black bonnet, RN '75', equipment, kangaroo	£70-80	☐
C302	1979-82	VW Polo	Metallic Brown/Red body, racing number '4', various adverts, 97 mm.	£10-15	☐
303	1970-72	Roger Clark's Capri	White/Black body, racing number '73', decal sheet, WhizzWheels, 102 mm.	£25-35	☐
303 S	1961-65	Mercedes-Benz 300 SL open	White or Blue body, RN '3', Yellow seats/tonneau, shaped spun wheels, driver.........	£40-50	☐
			Cream or Blue body, RN '9', shaped spun wheels, driver	£40-50	☐
			Chrome body, RN '7', Beige or Brown seats/tonneau, Red stripe on bonnet, Grey driver	£75-85	☐
C303	1980-	Porsche 924 Racer	Orange body, racing number '2', 'PIRELLI', 118 mm.	£10-15	☐
304 S	1961-65	Mercedes-Benz 300 SL Hardtop	Chrome finish, Red roof and bonnet stripe, smooth/shaped spun wheels, RN '3'.	£40-45	☐
305	1972-73	Mini Marcos GT 850	White/Red body, Blue/White stripes, racing number '7', 86 mm.	£20-25	☐
C306	1980-	Fiat X1/9S	Blue with Red/Yellow bands, racing number '3' or '6', 110 mm.	£10-15	☐
307	1981-	Renault Turbo	Yellow/Red body, racing number '8', 'CIBIE', other adverts, 100 mm.	£7-10	☐
C308	1972-76	Mini Cooper S	Yellow body, RN '177', rally plaques, roof-rack, 2 spare wheels, WhizzWheels	£30-35	☐
C308	1982-	BMW M1	Yellow body, racing number '25', 'GOODYEAR', detailed engine, 129 mm.	£7-10	☐
			Gold body. Only 144 thought to exist.	£40-50	☐
309	1962-65	Aston Martin DB4	Turquoise/White body, Yellow interior, flags on bonnet, RN '1', '3' or '7'.	£60-70	☐
C309	1982-	VW 'TURBO'............................	White/Brown body, racing number '14', various adverts, 97 mm.	£7-10	☐
C310	1982-	'PORSCHE' 924 Turbo.............	Black/Gold, opening doors and hatchback, 'GOODYEAR', 124 mm.	£7-10	☐
312	1964-68	'E' type Jaguar	Plated Gold or Silver, racing number '2', driver, suspension, spoked wheels	£55-65	☐
C312	1983-	Ford Capri 'S'	White, racing number '6', hinged parcel shelf, various adverts, 97 mm.	£7-10	☐
314	1965-71	Ferrari Berlinetta 250 LM.......	Red body, racing number '4', wire wheels, suspension, 95 mm.	£25-35	☐
315	1964-66	Simca 1000 Sports	Plated Silver, Red interior, RN '8', Red/White/Blue racing stripes.	£35-40	☐
			Metallic Blue body, racing number '8', Red/White/Blue stripes	£100-120	☐
316	1971-73	Ford GT 70	Green/Black body, White interior, racing number '32', flag design	£25-30	☐
317	1964	'MONTE CARLO 1964' Mini Cooper S	Red/White, Yellow interior, racing number '37', roof spotlight, suspension	£60-70	☐
318	1965	'MONTE CARLO 1965' Mini Cooper S	Red/White, 'AJB 44 B', racing number '52', suspension, no roof spotlight	£60-70	☐
318	1965-67	Lotus Elan S2 Open Top	Metallic Blue, racing number '8', driver, opening bonnet, tilt seats, 'I'VE GOT A TIGER IN MY TANK' logo on boot lid	£60-70	☐
		Gift Set variants:	White/Black (GS40) Yellow/Green (GS 37)		

Ref. No.	Year(s)	Model Type	Corgi Toys - continued	Market Price Range	
C318	1983-	'MOTUL' Jaguar XJS..............	Black/Red/White body, racing number '4', *'JAGUAR'*, 118 mm.	£7-10	☐
	1985	Export issue:.........	Green body, racing number '12' and *'DEUTCHSLAND'* logo	NGPP	☐
C318	1985		British Racing Green body with White band, racing number '12'	£7-10	☐
319	1967-68	Lotus Elan Hard Top..............	Blue/White or Green/Yellow lift-off body, racing number '3', 90 mm.	£50-60	☐
C319	1974-75	Lamborghini Miura..................	Silver/Purple/Yellow body, racing number '7', WhizzWheels, 95 mm.	£15-20	☐
321	1965	'MONTE CARLO 1965' Mini Cooper S	Red body, White roof with spotlight, RN '52'	£160-190	☐
321	1966	'MONTE CARLO 1966' Mini Cooper S	Red body, White roof with RN '2' and *'TIMO MAKINEN'* and *'PAUL EASTER'* signatures, no spotlight. Box flashed with '1966' sticker	£200-250	☐
322	1965-66	'Monte Carlo' Rover 2000	Metallic Maroon/White body, RN'136', rally plaques, 95 mm.	£100-120	☐
	1967		White body, Black roof, racing number '21', 'Rally Finish' label on box	£100-120	☐
323	1965-66	'MONTE CARLO 1965' Citroën DS19	Blue/White, rally plaques & number '75', suspension, 97 mm.	£100-120	☐
C323	1974-78	Ferrari Daytona 365 GTB/4	White/Red/Blue body, racing number '81', opening doors, 122 mm.	£10-15	☐
324	1966-69	Marcos Volvo 1800 GT............	White (2 Green stripes) or Blue (2 White stripes) RN '7'	£40-45	☐
324	1974	Ferrari Daytona Le Mans........	Yellow body, racing number '33', *'A.BAMFORD'*, 122 mm.	£10-15	☐
325	1966-69	Ford Mustang Competition	White body with double Red stripe (Blue interior). Shaped spun wheels, detailed cast wheels, wire wheels or cast 'alloy' wheels	£40-50	☐
			White body, double Red stripes, Gold 'alloy' wheels	£60-70	☐
		Note:...............	A sheet of four racing numbers (no.'4') enclosed with each model.		
328	1966-67	'MONTE CARLO 1966' Hillman Imp......................	Metallic Dark Blue/White, 'FRW 306 C', rally plaques & number '107'	£75-85	☐
329	1973-76	Ford Mustang..........................	Green/White body, racing number '69', opening doors, suspension, 113 mm.	£25-30	☐
330	1967-69	Porsche Carrera 6	White/Red with racing number '1' or '20', suspension, 97 mm.	£25-30	☐
			White body, Dark Blue panels, Yellow engine cover, RN '60'	£75-85	☐
331	1974-76	'TEXACO' Ford Capri GT	White/Black body, racing number '5'. 102 mm.	£15-20	☐
333	1966	'SUN/RAC' Mini Cooper S......	Red/White body, RN '21' and *'SUN RAC INTERNATIONAL RALLY'* decals. 222 box with White label '1966 RAC INTERNATIONAL RALLY' etc. in Blue	£150-200	☐
337	1967-69	Chevrolet Stock Car................	Yellow body, racing number '13', suspension, 95 mm.	£25-30	☐
339	1967-72	'MONTE CARLO 1967' Mini Cooper S	Red body, roof rack, RN '177', shaped spun wheels, Austin grille	£120-140	☐
			As previous model but with cast detailed wheels	£140-160	☒
			Red body, cast detailed wheels, Morris grille	£130-150	☐
		Box types:................	1st issue with correct 'flashed' 321 box, 2nd issue 'picture' box, 3rd issue later 'picture' box. (Special leaflet enclosed with each model).		
340	1967-68	'MONTE CARLO 1967' Sunbeam Imp......................	Metallic Blue, RN '77', shaped spun wheels, correct 'flashed' 328 box	£50-60	☐
			Metallic Dark Blue, cast detailed wheels, pictorial 340 box	£80-90	☐
C340	1981	Rover 'TRIPLEX'	White/Red/Blue, racing number '1', hinged parcel shelf, 140 mm.	£7-10	☐
C341	1981-	Chevrolet Caprice....................	Red/White body, racing number '43', *'STP'*, 150 mm.	£7-10	☐
344	1969-73	Ferrari Dino Sports.................	Yellow (number '23') or Red (number '30') WhizzWheels, 104 mm.	£30-35	☐
345	1969	MGC GT Competition Model..	Yellow body, Black bonnet (with bulge) opening doors & tailgate, 90 mm. 'MGB GT' on box overprinted 'NEW MGC'. Self-adhesive numbers enclosed	£50-70	☐
		Gift Set version:	Orange body. (Car Transporter Gift Set 48)	GSP	☐
348	1968-69	Mustang 'Pop Art' Stock Car...	Blue with Red/Orange 'Flower-Power' labels, racing number '20'	£60-70	☐
C350	1985	Toyota Celica Supra...............	Red/White body, racing number '14', *'HUGHES'*, racing tyres. 112 mm.	£7-10	☐
C351	1985	Ford Sierra Pace Car.............	White body, Green/Yellow tampo-print design, warning lights, flags	£7-10	☐
C353	1987	BMW 325i Rally......................	White body, Green logo *'CASTROL'*	£7-10	☐
354	1986	BMW 325	White body, racing number '33', *'FAVRAUD'* logo	£7-10	☐
370	1982	Ford Cobra Mustang	White/Black/Red/Blue, *'MUSTANG'*, with or without tailgate stripe, 135 mm.	£7-10	☐
371	1970-73	Porsche Carrera 6	White/Red, racing number '60', plated Blue engine cover, WhizzWheels, 97 mm.	£15-20	☐
376	1970-72	Chevrolet Corvette Stock Car...	Silver body, racing number '13', *'GO-GO-GO'*, WhizzWheels, 95 mm.	£15-20	☐
C380	1983-	'BASF' BMW M1	Red/White, racing number '80', aerofoil, opening engine cover, 129 mm.	£7-10	☐
C381	1983-	'ELF' Renault Turbo	Red/White/Blue, racing number '5', *'FACOM'*, 100 mm.	£7-10	☐
			Blue/White, racing number '13', *'ELF'*	£7-10	☐
383	1977-78	Volkswagen 1200 Rally............	Blue body, rally number '5', chequered roof and sides	£10-15	☐
384	1978	Volkswagen 1200 Rally Car......	Blue body, rally number '5', chequered stripes	£15-20	☐
385	1970-76	Porsche 917.............................	Metallic Blue or Red body, racing number '3', WhizzWheels, 108 mm.	£15-20	☐
386	1987	Mercedes 2.3/16	White body, Black racing number '17', *'SERVIS'*	£5-8	☐
386/4	1988		As previous model but racing number '17', *'BURLINGTON AIR EXPRESS'*	£5-8	☐
394	1973-76	Datsun 240 Z...........................	Red body, rally number '11', *'EAST AFRICAN SAFARI'*, 97 mm.	£15-20	☐
396		Datsun 240 Z...........................	Red/White body, rally number '46', *'JOHN MORTON'*, WhizzWheels	£20-25	☐
397	1974-78	Porsche-Audi 917-10................	White or Orange, racing number '6', *'CORGI'*, racing driver, 120 mm.	£10-15	☐
399	1985	Peugeot 205	Silver body, racing number '205', multi-coloured tampo-print design	£7-10	☐
399/5	1988	Peugeot 205 T16......................	Yellow body, racing number '2', *'VATENEN'*	£7-10	☐
402	1985	BMW M1	Red/White body, racing number '101', *'CASTROL'*	£7-10	☐
403	1985	Ford Escort	White body, racing number '84', multicoloured print, *'TOTAL'*	£7-10	☐
404	1985	Rover 3500	Red body, racing number '13', *'DAILY MIRROR'*	£7-10	☐
	1986		Red body, racing number '1', *'TEXACO'*	£7-10	☐
420	1984	'BMW M1'	Blue/White body, racing number '11', *'LIGIER'S'*	£7-10	☐
	1985		White body, racing number '17', *'ESSO'*	£7-10	☐
422	1984	'RENAULT 5' TBA................	Blue body, racing number '25', *'BOSCH'* and *'ELF'*.	£7-10	☐
	1985		Dark Blue body, multicoloured print, racing number '18'	£7-10	☐
423	1984	'BROOKLYN' Ford Escort......	Blue/White body, Red seats, racing number '69', *'SHELL'*	£7-10	☐

Ref. No.	Year(s)	Model Type	Corgi Toys - continued	Market Price Range	
424	1984	'FORD MUSTANG'	Black body, Yellow/Red print, racing number '77', 'ESSO'...	£7-10	☐
426	1984	'HEPOLITE' Rover	Yellow/Red, racing number '4', 'FERODO'..	£7-10	☐
	1988		Yellow/Red body, 'DAILY EXPRESS'..	£7-10	☐
435/2	1987	Volvo 760 Turbo	White body, Blue/Yellow print, 'GILLANDERS'..	£7-10	☐
C440	1988	'PORSCHE 944' Rally	White body, Red design...	£7-10	☐
C440/6	1990	Porsche 944 Rally....................	White body, Pink/Blue design, 'PIRELLI', rally number '44'..............................	£4-7	☐
C447	1983	'RENEGADE' 4x4 Jeep...........	Yellow body, racing number '5'. (As 448 but without hood). In GS 36	GSP	☐
C448	1983	'RENEGADE' 4x4 Jeep...........	Yellow body, Red hood, racing number '5'	£7-10	☐
611		Ford Escort	Red body, racing number '77', 'DATAPOST'	NGPP	☐
602	1984	BL Mini 1000	Metallic Dark Blue, racing number '8'...	£20-25	☐
60317	1992	F1 Racing Car.........................	Green/White body, 'FUJI FILM' logo, Boots promotional (35,000)..........................	NGPP	☐

Trophy Models (Marks & Spencers special issues)

The models were specially produced to be sold by Marks & Spencers in 1961. The set consisted of five vacuum plated 'gold' models taken from the existing Corgi product range, each mounted on a detachable black moulded base with a gold name label. The models were packaged in white boxes with red/grey design plus 'St.Michael Trophy Models' in red. They did not sell well at the time of issue but are keenly sought after by present day collectors.

Ref. No.	Year(s)	Model Type	Model Features and Size	Market Price Range	
150 S	1961	Vanwall Racing Car	Gold plated body, Red wheels and radiator grille	£100-200	☐
152	1961	BRM Racing Car	Gold plated body, Red wheels and radiator grille	£100-200	☐
300	1961	Austin-Healey Sports Car........	Gold plated body, plastic windscreen, Red wheels and radiator grille......................	£100-200	☐
301	1961	Triumph TR2 Sports Car.........	Gold plated body, plastic windscreen, Red wheels and radiator grille......................	£100-200	☐
302	1961	MG 'MGA' Sports Car.............	Gold plated body, plastic windscreen, Red wheels and radiator grille......................	£100-200	☐

Marks & Spencers issues

In 1978 a series of special sets and single models were produced for sale through selected M & S stores. They were packed in attractive non-standard boxes and had unique liveries. They were not issued in great quantities.

Single models

8800	1978	Custom Van.............................	No details available...	£25-35	☐
8801	1978	Spindrift Helicopter.................	Black body with Yellow chassis, floats and rotor blades	£25-35	☐
8802	1978	Massey Ferguson Tractor.........	Red/Black body with White arms and Red shovel	£40-50	☐
8803	1978	Buick 'FIRE CHIEF' Car........	Red body with 'City Fire Department' logo on bonnet..	£50-75	☐

Small sets

8000	1978	F1 Racing Set..........................	Includes 162 'ELF' Tyrrell (Dark Blue) and 160 Hesketh F1 (White)........................	£75-100	☐
8001	1978	Wings Flying Team	Includes 301 Lotus Elite (Green) and Nipper aircraft (White) on Grey trailer............	£100-150	☐
8002	1978	Motorway Police Patrol	C429 'POLICE' Jaguar (Green) and Blue Fiat X1-9	£60-80	☐
8003	1978	Spindrift Power Boat Team	301 Ferrari Daytona (Yellow) and Yellow power boat on trailer	£60-80	☐

Medium sets

8100	1978	Racing Team	C421 Land Rover (White with 'FORMULA' logo) 338 Rover, and 301 Lotus on trailer	£100-150	☐
8101	1978	Wings Flying School	C421 Land Rover (Grey with 'WINGS' logo) Grey helicopter and Nipper aircraft on Grey trailer..	£100-150	☐
8102	1978	Motorway Breakdown..............	C429 'POLICE' Jaguar, 293 Renault 5 (Yellow) plus Berliet Wrecker with 'RESCUE BREAKDOWN SERVICES'...	£100-150	☐

Large sets

8400	1978	Grand Prix Racing	Includes 160 Hesketh (White) 162 'ELF' Tyrrell (Dark Blue) Fiat X1-9 (Blue) and Land Rover (White with 'FORMULA 1 RACING TEAM' logo)............................	£250-350	☐
8401	1978	Wings Flying Club	Includes Land Rover, Helicopter, Tipsy Nipper aircraft on trailer plus Lotus Elite	£200-250	☐
8402	1978	Motorway Rescue....................	Includes 'POLICE' Jaguar, Berliet Wrecker, Renault 5 and Fiat X1-9......................	£200-250	☐
8403	1978	Spindrift Power Boat Team	Includes Ferrari Daytona (Yellow) Yellow power boat on trailer, Yellow/Black helicopter, plus M.F. Tractor and 'RESCUE' dinghy	£200-250	☐

Corgi Toys - Saloons, Estates and Sports Cars

Ref. No.	Year(s)	Model Type	Model Features and Size	Market Price Range	
200	1956-61	Ford Consul	Cream, Medium Tan or Dark Tan body, no suspension, 90 mm.	£70-85	☐
			Brownish-Grey body or Light Greyish-Brown	£100-120	☐
			Two-tone Green, Green/Cream or Silver/Cream	£80-95	☐
			Brownish-Grey	£100-120	☐
			Green/Light Grey	£80-100	☐
			Green/Pale Grey	£60-85	☐
200 M	1956-59	Ford Consul	Blue body, flywheel motor, 90 mm.	£70-90	☐
			Dark Green, flywheel motor, 90 mm.	£75-95	☐
C200	1976-78	BLMC Mini 1000	Blue/Silver body with Red and White arrow, 85 mm.	£20-25	☐
201	1956-63	Austin Cambridge	Pale Blue, Turquoise or Mid-Grey body, no suspension, 90 mm.	£70-85	☐
			Light Grey body	£120-140	☐
			Green/Cream, Metallic Green/Silver, or two-tone Green	£80-95	☐
201 M	1956-59	Austin Cambridge	Cream, Red, Orange, Slate Grey or Medium Grey body with motor, 90 mm.	£70-95	☐
202	1956-60	Morris Cowley	Bright Green or Grey body, no suspension, 91 mm.	£70-85	☐
			Blue body, no suspension, 91 mm.	£110-125	☐
			Grey/Blue or Blue/Cream body	£80-95	☐
202 M	1956-59	Morris Cowley	Pale Green or Medium Green body, flywheel motor, 91 mm.	£70-90	☐
			Dark Green, flywheel motor	£90-120	☐
202	1970-72	Renault R16	Blue/Silver body, no suspension, 91 mm.	£15-20	☐
203	1956-60	Vauxhall Velox	Red, Cream or Yellow body, no suspension, 91 mm.	£70-85	☐
			Yellow/Red body	£70-90	☐
203 M	1956-59	Vauxhall Velox	Red or Yellow body, flywheel motor, 91 mm.	£70-90	☐
			Orange body, flywheel motor	£175-225	☐
203	1971-72	De Tomaso Mangusta	Green/Gold body, WhizzWheels, 99 mm.	£15-20	☐
204	1956-60	Rover 90	Pale Grey, Dark Grey, or Metallic Green body, no suspension, 97 mm.	£70-85	☐
			Off-White or Maroon/Grey body	£80-95	☐
			Metallic Cerise/Pale Grey body	£80-100	☐
			Metallic Rose/Pink body	£100-125	☐
204 M	1956-59	Rover 90	Metallic Green, Dark Green, Bright Green or Grey body, flywheel motor, 97 mm.	£70-95	☐
204	1972-74	Morris Mini-Minor	Dark Blue or Orange body with WhizzWheels, 73 mm.	£25-35	☐
205	1956-61	Riley Pathfinder	Red or Blue body, no suspension, 97 mm.	£80-90	☐
205 M	1956-59	Riley Pathfinder	Red or Mid-Blue body, flywheel motor, 97 mm.	£80-90	☐
			Dark Blue body, flywheel motor	£65-85	☐
206	1956-60	Hillman Husky Estate	Tan or Greyish Light-Brown body, no suspension, 86 mm.	£50-75	☐
			Blue/Silver body, 86 mm.	£80-95	☐
206 M	1956-59	Hillman Husky Estate	Cream, Dark Blue or Grey body, flywheel motor, 86 mm.	£80-90	☐
207	1957-62	Standard Vanguard III	White/Red, Green/Red or Grey/Red body, 95 mm.	£70-85	☐
207 M	1957-59	Standard Vanguard III	Yellow or Green/Red body, flywheel motor, 95 mm.	£60-80	☐
208	1957-60	Jaguar 2.4 litre	White body, no suspension, 95 mm.	£70-90	☐
208 M	1957-59	Jaguar 2.4 litre	Dark Blue body, flywheel motor, 95 mm.	£70-90	☐
208 S	1960-62	Jaguar 2.4 litre	Lemon body, with spring suspension, smooth spun wheels, 95 mm.	£50-60	☐
			Pale Lemon body, shaped spun wheels	£140-160	☐
210	1957-60	Citroën DS19	Yellow body, Red roof, Grey baseplate, 97 mm.	£50-60	☐
			Yellow body, Red roof, Silver baseplate with detailed drive shaft	£120-140	☐
			Metallic Green body, Black roof	£50-60	☐
210 S	1960-65	Citroën DS19	Red body, Grey baseplate, spring suspension, 97 mm.	£40-45	☐
211	1958-60	Studebaker Golden Hawk	Blue/Gold body, no suspension, smooth spun wheels, 104 mm.	£70-90	☐
211 M	1958-59	Studebaker Golden Hawk	White/Gold body, flywheel motor, no suspension, smooth spun wheels	£60-70	☐
211 S	1960-65	Studebaker Golden Hawk	Gold ('plated') body, White flash, suspension, shaped spun hubs	£60-70	☐
			Gold (painted) body, shaped spun hubs	£100-140	☐
214	1959-62	Ford Thunderbird Hardtop	Green/Cream body, cast wheels, White-wall tyres, no suspension, 102 mm.	£55-65	☐
214 M	1959	Ford Thunderbird Hardtop	Green/White or Pink/Black body, flywheel motor, no suspension	£100-140	☐
214 S	1962-65	Ford Thunderbird Hardtop	Metallic Grey/Red body, Lemon interior, with suspension	£60-70	☐
215	1959-62	Thunderbird Open Sports	White with Blue interior, left-hand drive, no suspension, 102 mm.	£60-70	☐
215 S	1962-65	Thunderbird Open Sports	Red body with Yellow interior and driver, with spring suspension	£55-65	☐
216	1959-62	Austin A40	Two-tone Blue or Red/Black body, no suspension, 86 mm.	£65-75	☐
216 M	1959	Austin A40	Red/Black body, flywheel motor, no suspension	£150-175	☐
217	1960-63	Fiat 1800 Saloon	Two-tone Blue, Blue with Yellow interior, Pale Yellow/Brown, Light Tan	£35-45	☐
218	1960-62	Aston Martin DB4	Brick Red or Primrose Yellow, opening bonnet, suspension, 95 mm.	£50-60	☐
219	1959-62	Plymouth Suburban Sports	Cream/Brown or TT Brown body, seats, steering wheel, 104 mm.	£50-60	☐
			Pink body with Light Brown roof	£50-60	☐
220	1960-62	Chevrolet Impala	Pink (Yellow interior) or Blue (Red or Yellow interior) smooth/shaped spun hubs	£35-40	☐
222	1959-60	Renault Floride	Dark Red or Metallic Pale Green body, smooth spun hubs, 91 mm.	£35-45	☐
			Maroon body, Lemon interior, shaped spun hubs	£40-50	☐
			Metallic Blue body, Red interior, shaped spun hubs	£50-60	☐
224	1961-66	Bentley Continental	Seats, opening boot with removable spare, steering, special lights, 108 mm.	£45-65	☐
			Cream/Metallic Apple Green, Pale Green/White, TT Green, Gold, or Black/Silver	£40-50	☐
225	1961-66	Austin 7 (Mini) Saloon	Red body, windows, suspension, seats, steering wheel, 73 mm.	£175-225	☐
			Primrose-Yellow body, Red interior, suspension, smooth/shaped spun wheels	£30-35	☐
226	1960-71	Morris Mini Minor	Light Blue or Red body, suspension, smooth/shaped spun wheels	£30-35	☐
			Metallic Maroon body, suspension, detailed cast wheels, 73 mm.	£30-35	☐

Ref. No.	Year(s)	Model Type	Corgi Toys - continued	Market Price Range	
228	1962-66	Volvo P-1800	Light Brown body, (Red interior) or Dark Red (Lemon interior) shaped spun hubs ..	**£40-45**	☐
			Pink or Dark Pink body	**£55-65**	☐
229	1961-66	Chevrolet Corvair......................	Blue or Gold body, smooth or shaped spun wheels, 97 mm....................................	**£40-50**	☐
230	1962-64	Mercedes-Benz 220 SE Coupé...	Maroon (Lemon interior) or Cream (Red interior) shaped spun hubs, spare wheel in boot	**£35-45**	☐
			Black body, Lemon interior, shaped spun wheels, spare wheel in boot	**£80-100**	☐
231	1961-65	Triumph Herald.........................	Blue/White or White/Gold body with Red seats, spring suspension, 90 mm.	**£40-50**	☐
232	1961-65	Fiat 2100.................................	Two-tone Mauve body, Venetian blinds, suspension, special lights, 95 mm.	**£35-50**	☐
233	1962-72	Heinkel Trojan	Red, Orange, or Lilac body, 3 smooth spun hubs or detailed cast wheels	**£35-40**	☐
			Metallic Blue body, smooth spun wheels	**£50-60**	☐
234	1961-64	Ford Consul Classic	Cream/Pink or Gold, opening bonnet, detailed engine, suspension, 95 mm.	**£45-55**	☐
235	1962-66	Oldsmobile Super 88	Black/White or Metallic Steel Blue/White, suspension, 108 mm.	**£35-40**	☐
			Light Blue/White body	**£45-50**	☐
236	1964-69	Motor School Austin A60.........	Light Blue, 2 figures, steering control on roof, 'L' plates, 'Highway Code' leaflet	**£40-50**	☐
238	1962-67	Jaguar Mk.10...........................	Opening bonnet & boot, luggage, battery operated lights.		
			Pale Blue, Light Blue, Metallic Steel Blue, Emerald Green or Metallic Cerise Red	**£50-60**	☐
			Metallic Deep Blue or Metallic Bright Kingfisher Blue body	**£70-80**	☐
	1966-66		Silver body	**£125-150**	☐
239	1963-68	Volkswagen 1500 Karmann Ghia	Cream (Red interior) or Red (Yellow interior) spare wheel/suitcase in boot	**£35-40**	☐
			Gold body, Red or Yellow interior, spare wheel/suitcase in boot	**£35-40**	☐
240	1963-65	Fiat 600 Jolly	Light Blue body, detachable roof, suspension, figures, 79 mm.	**£55-65**	☐
			Dark Metallic Blue body	**£65-75**	☐
241	1963-69	Chrysler Ghia L64	Shaped spun or detailed cast wheels, Corgi dog on rear shelf, 108 mm.		
			Metallic Blue/White, Metallic Green, Metallic Copper, Metallic Yellow or Metallic Silver Blue	**£40-50**	☐
242	1965-66	Fiat 600 Jolly	Yellow body, driver, passenger, suspension, no canopy, 79 mm.	**£40-50**	☐
245	1964-68	Buick Riviera	Metallic Gold, 'Trans-O-Lites', spoked wheels, towing 'grab', 108 mm.	**£35-40**	☐
			Metallic Light Blue body, towing hook..	**£35-40**	☐
			Metallic Greenish-Blue body, cast wheels	**£45-50**	☐
246	1965-68	Chrysler Imperial......................	Red body, Pale Blue interior, detailed cast wheels, 2 figures, golf trolley	**£45-50**	☐
			Dark Red body, Pale Blue interior, shaped spun wheels	**£55-60**	☐
			Metallic Bluish-Green body, Pale Green interior, cast wheels	**£100-125**	☐
			Metallic Greenish-Blue body, Pale Blue interior, cast wheels	**£100-125**	☐
247	1964-69	Mercedes-Benz Pullman	Metallic Maroon body, windscreen wipers, instruction sheet, 121 mm.	**£35-45**	☐
248	1965-67	Chevrolet Impala	Brown body, Cream roof/interior, Chrome side stripe, shaped spun wheels	**£40-45**	☐
249	1965-68	Morris Mini-Cooper	Black/Red body, wickerwork panels, spun or cast wheels, 73 mm.	**£60-70**	☐
251	1963-66	Hillman Imp	Blue body, opening window, suspension, 83 mm.	**£40-45**	☐
			Metallic Bronze body	**£60-70**	☐
			Light Blue body with 'JENSON'S' logo. Dutch promotional	**£300-400**	☐
252	1963-66	Rover 2000	Metallic Blue or Metallic Maroon body, suspension, special lights, 95 mm.	**£40-50**	☐
253	1964-68	Mercedes-Benz 220 SE Coupé...	Metallic Cerise, Metallic Maroon or Metallic Blue, luggage, spare wheel	**£40-45**	☐
255	1964-68	Motor School A60.....................	Dark Blue body, left-hand drive, 5 language leaflet, (USA issue of 236)	**£125-150**	☐
C257	1985	Mercedes-Benz 500 SEC...........	White body, 'Magic Top' (fold-away roof)	**£7-10**	☐
C258	1985	Toyota Celica Supra..................	Brown body, Black base, opening doors and tailgate, 125 mm.	**£7-10**	☐
			Blue body	**£7-10**	☐
			Blue and Cream body with Red line	**£7-10**	☐
259	1966-69	Citroën 'Le Dandy'	Metallic Dark Maroon body with Yellow interior..	**£50-60**	☐
			Metallic Blue body, White roof and boot	**£60-70**	☐
260	1969	Renault 16 TS	Metallic Maroon, opening bonnet & hatchback, adjustable seats, 91 mm.	**£25-35**	☐
262	1967-69	Lincoln Continental...................	Opening doors/bonnet/boot, battery 'colour TV', special lights, 149 mm.		
			Metallic Gold/Black body...	**£50-60**	☐
			Light Blue/Beige body	**£110-130**	☐
263	1966-69	Marlin Rambler Sports	Red/Black (or Blue/Black in No.10 GS) suspension, tow-hook, 102 mm.	**£35-40**	☐
264	1966-69	Oldsmobile Toronado...............	Metallic Medium or Dark Blue body, smooth or cast spoked wheels, 108 mm.	**£45-65**	☐
273	1970	Rolls-Royce Silver Shadow	Metallic Silver/Blue, Golden Jacks, Take-Off wheels, spare, 120 mm.	**£30-40**	☐
			Greenish-Blue/Metallic Grey body	**£50-60**	☐
273	1982-83	Honda Ballade 'BSM'	Driving School car with Yellow body and Red side stripes	**£25-35**	☐
274	1970-72	Bentley T Series........................	Pink body, opening doors & bonnet, special lights, WhizzWheels, 120 mm.	**£40-50**	☐
275	1968-70	Rover 2000 TC	Metallic Lime Green body, Golden Jacks, spare on boot (opening cover) 95 mm.	**£40-50**	☐
			White body	**£80-90**	☐
			Metallic Green, Maroon or Purple body.	**£35-45**	☐
C275	1981-	Mini Metro...............................	Blue or Red body, Yellow interior, opening doors & hatchback, 94 mm.	**£10-15**	☐
		Royal Wedding Mini Metro......	As previous model but Mauve body with Silver 'Charles & Diana' crest	**£10-15**	☐
276	1968-70	Oldsmobile Toronado...............	Metallic Blue, Gold or Gold body, Golden Jacks, cast Take-Off wheels, 108 mm.	**£20-30**	☐
C276	1982-	Triumph Acclaim.......................	Metallic Blue body, steering control, 120 mm.	**£7-10**	☐
C277	1982-	Triumph Acclaim 'BSM'	Driving School car with Yellow/Red body, steering control, 118 mm.	**£7-10**	☐
C279	1979-	Rolls-Royce Corniche...............	Metallic Dark Red body, opening doors/bonnet/boot, tilt seats, 114 mm.	**£10-15**	☐
	1985		Metallic Blue, Bright Red, Off-White/Cream, Cream or Silver/Grey body	**£10-15**	☐
	1987		Silver/Black body with chrome trim	**£10-15**	☐
C279/3	1990	Rolls-Royce	Gold body with White seats..	**£5-8**	☐
			Royal Blue body with White seats...	**£5-8**	☐
			Light and Dark Brown body	**£5-8**	☐
C280	1970-78	Rolls-Royce Silver Shadow	Opening doors/bonnet/boot, special lights, WhizzWheels, 120 mm.		
			Metallic Blue/Silver (1st issue) Metallic Mid-Blue or Gold body...............................	**£25-35**	☐
281	1971-73	Rover 2000 TC	Metallic Maroon or Mauve body, clear roof, WhizzWheels, 95 mm.	**£25-35**	☐
283	1971-74	DAF 'City' Car	Red/Black body, White interior, opening doors/bonnet, WhizzWheels.......................	**£20-25**	☐

35

Ref. No.	Year(s)	Model Type	Corgi Toys - continued	Market Price Range	
C284	1970-76	Citroën SM	Metallic Gold or Metallic Mauve, opening doors, WhizzWheels, 112 mm.	£20-25	☐
C285	1975-81	Mercedes-Benz 240 D	Silver, Blue or Copper/Beige, (all Metallic) WhizzWheels, 127 mm.	£10-15	☐
C286	1975-79	Jaguar XJC V-12	Blue/Black, Red/Black, Red, Blue, Orange, (all Metallic) WhizzWheels	£10-15	☐
C287	1975-78	Citroën Dyane	Metallic Yellow/Black or Metallic Green/Black, duck decal, WhizzWheels	£10-15	☐
C288	1975-79	Minissima	Green and Cream body, opening doors & bonnet, 63 mm.	£10-15	☐
C289	1977-81	Volkswagen Polo	Metallic Green body, opening doors and hatchback, 97 mm.	£10-15	☐
C289	1977-81	Volkswagen Polo 'PTT'	As previous model but Yellow body. German issue	£20-25	☐
291	1977-78	AMC Pacer	Metallic Maroon body, opening doors & hatchback, 118 mm.	£10-15	☐
C293	1977	Renault 5 TS	Metallic Yellow/Black trim or Metallic Orange/Black trim, 97 mm.	£10-15	☐
		French issue:	As previous model but Blue body with 'SOS MEDICINS'.	£60-70	☐
C294	1980	Renault 5 TS Alpine	Black body with White stripe, opening doors and hatchback, 97 mm.	£8-12	☐
C299	1982	Ford Sierra 2.3 Ghia	Metallic Light Brown/Black stripe, Dark Brown or Grey interior, Brown or Dark Grey base. Issued in a special two-tone Blue 'Ford' box.	£60-70	☐
			As previous model but Metallic Light Brown, Metallic Blue, Red or Yellow body, packed in White/Red 'Ford' box or normal Black/Yellow/Red box	£10-15	☐
	1985		Metallic Silver or Yellow body	£10-15	☐
	1985		Red body, White broken ground	£10-15	☐
C299/4	1990	Ford Sierra	Pink body, *MR TOMKINSON'S CARPETS* logo	£7-10	☐
300	1956-63	Austin Healey 100-4	Red (Cream seats) Cream (Red seats) Blue (Red seats) windscreen, 86 mm.	£60-80	☐
300	1970-72	Corvette Stingray	Lacquered-finish Bright Green or Dark Red body, Golden Jacks, luggage	£25-35	☐
301	1956-59	Triumph TR2	Cream (Red seats) or Green (Cream seats) windscreen, 86 mm.	£70-85	☐
301	1970-73	Iso Grifo 7 litre	Metallic Blue body, matt Black bonnet, WhizzWheels, 102 mm.	£20-30	☐
302	1957-64	MG 'MGA'	Red (Cream seats) smooth spun wheels, 90 mm.	£50-60	☐
			Red body, shaped spun wheels	£70-80	☐
			Metallic Light or Mid-Green body (Cream or Yellow seats) smooth or shaped spun wheels	£50-60	☐
303	1958-60	Mercedes-Benz 300 SL open	White body, White or Blue seats/tonneau, smooth/shaped spun wheels	£35-45	☐
			Blue body, White or Yellow seats/tonneau, smooth/shaped spun wheels	£35-45	☐
304	1959-61	Mercedes-Benz 300 SL Hardtop	Yellow/Red body, smooth spun wheels, no suspension	£60-70	☐
304	1971-73	Chevrolet Camaro	Dark Blue body, White bonnet band & detachable roof, special lights	£30-40	☐
305	1960-62	Triumph TR3	Metallic Green body, Red seats, no suspension, smooth spun wheels, 86 mm.	£65-85	☐
305S	1962-64	Triumph TR3	Light Green or Cream body, spring suspension, shaped spun wheels, 86 mm.	£80-110	☐
306	1971-73	Morris Marina 1.8 Coupé	Metallic Red (White seats) or Metallic Lime Green, WhizzWheels, 98 mm.	£30-40	☐
307	1962-64	Jaguar 'E' type	Red or Metallic Grey body with Red removable hard-top, 95 mm.	£65-75	☐
			Plum body, Red hard-top	£70-90	☐
310	1963-68	Chevrolet Stingray	Metallic Deep Pink, Yellow interior, shaped wheels, 90 mm.	£35-40	☐
			Silver body, wire wheels	£35-40	☐
310	1984	Porsche 924 Turbo	Black body (Gold design, Red seats) or Red body with Porsche badge	£10-15	☐
311	1970-72	Ford Capri V6	Crimson (Black bonnet or Fluorescent Orange/Black, WhizzWheels, 102 mm.	£30-40	☐
312	1971-73	Marcos Mantis	Metallic Plum body with opening doors, spoked wheels, 110 mm.	£25-35	☐
313	1970-73	Ford Cortina GXL	Metallic Light Blue or Bronze, 'vinyl' roof, Graham Hill figure, 102 mm.	£40-50	☐
C314	1976-79	Fiat X1-9	Metallic Lime Green/Black or Silver/Black body, suspension, hook, 110 mm.	£15-25	☐
C314	1982-	Supercat Jaguar XJS-HE	Black body, Red or Tan interior, opening doors, 118 mm.	£10-15	☐
C315	1976-78	Lotus Elite	Red or Yellow with White seats, opening doors, suspension, 120 mm.	£20-30	☐
316	1963-66	NSU Sport Prinz	Metallic Red (with Yellow seats) or Maroon body, suspension, 86 mm.	£30-40	☐
318	1981	Jaguar XJS	Blue/Cream body with Red line	£10-15	☐
	1988		Pale Blue body, Beige seats	£7-10	☐
318/8	1990	Jaguar XJS	Blue body with White seats	£7-10	☐
318	1965-68	Lotus Elan	Blue or Green/Yellow body, opening bonnet, tilting seats, suspension	£50-60	☐
319	1967-68	Lotus Elan S2 Hardtop	Dark Green/Yellow top, or Blue/White top	£50-60	☐
			Red body, White top	£60-70	☐
			Red body, Red top	£60-80	☐
319	1978-82	Jaguar XJS	Metallic Plum/Black body, opening doors, suspension, 128 mm.	£15-20	☐
320	1965-67	Ford Mustang Fastback 2 + 2	Opening doors, suspension, Corgi dog, half-open window, 95 mm.		☐
			Silver (Red interior) or Metallic Deep Blue (White interior) detailed cast wheels	£40-50	☐
			Metallic Deep Blue or Light Green body, spoked wheels	£40-50	☐
			Metallic Lilac body, spoked wheels	£70-80	☐
321	1978-82	Porsche 924 Saloon	Red body ('Porsche') or Metallic Green body with hook, 118 mm.	£15-20	☐
			Metallic Light Brown body, Red interior	£60-70	☐
325	1981-	Chevrolet Caprice	Metallic Light Green and Dark Green body, White-wall tyres, 150 mm.	£10-15	☐
			Metallic Silver over Dark Blue (US market)	£70-80	☐
327	1967-69	MGB GT	Red body with suitcase in opening boot, spoked wheels, tilting seats, 90 mm.	£60-70	☐
329	1980-	Opel Senator	Dark Blue, Bronze or Silver body, opening doors, 142 mm.	£10-15	☐
Q330/1	1989	Mini 30th Anniversary	Pearlescent Cherry Red, Austin-Rover mail-order model (17,500)	£8-10	☐
(Q24/1)	1989	Mini 30th Anniversary	Q330/1 Mini specially packaged with 'MINI' book	£45-55	☐
C330/10	1990	Mini 'AFTER EIGHT'	Dark Blue with Gold stripe, French export model (5,000)	£10-15	☐
332	1967-69	Lancia Fulvia Sports	Metallic Green, Metallic Blue, Yellow/Black or Red, suspension, tilt seats.	£25-35	☐
334	1968-70	Mini Cooper 'Magnifique'	Pearlescent Dark Blue or Green, jewelled lights, sunshine roof, 73 mm.	£35-45	☐
C334	1981-	Ford Escort 1.3 GL	Yellow, Red or Blue body, opening doors, suspension, 112 mm.	£10-15	☐
335	1968-69	Jaguar 4.2 litre 'E' type	Deep Red body, opening doors/bonnet/hatch, spoked wheels	£60-70	☐
			Metallic Blue body	£40-50	☐
338	1968-71	Chevrolet SS 350 Camaro	Golden Jacks & Take-Off wheels, sliding headlight cover, removable hardtop, Metallic Gold/Black or Metallic Yellow body, 102 mm.	£35-45	☐
C338	1980-	Rover 3500	Metallic Blue, Red/Black or Orange/Brown body, suspension	£10-15	☐
341	1968-70	Mini Marcos GT 850	Metallic Crimson (Cream seats) or Metallic Maroon body, Golden Jacks, 86 mm.	£30-40	☐
342	1970-72	Lamborghini P400 Miura	Red/Black or Lemon Yellow, Black bull figure, WhizzWheels, spare wheel	£25-35	☐
343	1969-73	Pontiac Firebird	Metallic Silver/Black, Red seats, Gold/Red Take-Off wheels, Golden Jacks	£25-35	☐

36

Ref. No.	Year(s)	Model Type	Corgi Toys - continued	Market Price Range	
343	1980-	Ford Capri 3 litre	Yellow or Silver body, Black designs, opening doors/hatchback, 124 mm.................	**£10-15**	☐
C345	1981-	Honda Prelude	Metallic Lt. or Dk.Blue, Cream/Green or Metallic Yellow body, sunshine roof.........	**£10-15**	☐
C346	1982-84	Citroën 2cv Charleston.............	Yellow/Black or Burgundy/Black body, opening bonnet, chrome trim.......................	**£10-15**	☐
347	1969-74	Chevrolet Astro Experimental...	Metallic Dark Blue or Green body, Gold/Red wheels, driver & passenger	**£30-40**	☐
			As previous model but with WhizzWheels...	**£25-35**	☐
C352	1986	BMW 325	White with Black logo. Swiss export model	NGPP	☐
353/1	1986	BMW 325	Red body, Black trim, opening features	NRP	☐
353/9	1990	BMW 325i	Black body with Red seats...	NRP	☐
C370	1982	Ford Cobra Mustang	White body, Red interior, Blue/Red design..	**£10-15**	☐
372	1970-72	Lancia Fulvia...........................	Red/Black body, opening doors/bonnet, suspension, WhizzWheels, 91 mm.	**£25-35**	☐
C373	1981-	Peugeot 505	Red body, Silver or Black lining, opening doors, suspension, 127 mm.	**£10-15**	☐
C374	1970-73	Jaguar 'E' type 4.2 ltr 242.......	Red or Yellow body, WhizzWheels, 108 mm.	**£30-40**	☐
C374	1973	Jaguar 'E' type 5.3 litre	Yellow or Metallic Yellow body. 'New' on box label	**£30-40**	☐
375	1970-73	Toyota 2000 GT	Translucent 'candy' Blue or Purple body, aerial, WhizzWheels, 102 mm.	**£25-35**	☐
377	1970-73	Marcos 3 litre	Yellow/Black, White/Grey or Metallic Blue body, WhizzWheels, 91 mm.	**£25-35**	☐
378	1970-72	MGC GT	Red/Black body, opening doors and hatchback, WhizzWheels, 90 mm.	**£35-45**	☐
			Orange body, (this version in Gift Set 20)	GSP	☐
C378	1982-	Ferrari 308 GTS	Red body, pop-up headlights, opening engine cover, 115 mm.	**£10-15**	☐
380	1970-72	Alfa Romeo P33	White body, Gold roll bar, Red seats, WhizzWheels, 95 mm.	**£25-35**	☐
381	1970-74	VW Beach Buggy	Metallic Red/White, Orange/White or Red/White, 2 skis, WhizzWheels	**£15-25**	☐
382	1970-73	Porsche Targa 911S	Metallic Blue/Black or Metallic Green body, WhizzWheels, 95 mm.	**£25-30**	☐
			Metallic Silver-Blue body, only seen in Gift Set 20	GSP	☐
C382	1981-	Lotus Elite 2.2	Blue body, 'Elite 2.2', opening doors, number plates, 120 mm.	**£10-15**	☐
383	1970-71	Volkswagen 1200	Red or Orange body with Green 'Flower Power' base and flower labels.	**£50-60**	☐
383	1970-73	VW 1200 'ADAC'	Yellow/Black body, 'ADAC' logo (Continental equivalent of 'AA')	**£60-70**	☐
383	1970-76	Volkswagen 1200	Orange or Red body, no labels.	**£25-35**	☐
384	1970-73	Adams Brothers Probe	Metallic Maroon (Blue interior) or Metallic Gold body, WhizzWheels, 97 mm.	**£25-35**	☐
384	1983-84	Renault 11 GTL	Cream/Brown body with Red seats, opening doors & boot, 110 mm.	**£10-15**	☐
385	1984	Mercedes 190 E	Silver/Black body, White seats, number plates, chrome trim.	**£10-15**	☐
	1985		All-Silver body	**£10-15**	☐
386	1971-74	Bertone Barchetta.....................	Yellow/Black 'RUNABOUT', aerofoil, WhizzWheels, 83 mm.	**£25-35**	☐
386/8	1990	Mercedes 2.3/16	Red body with Beige seats..	NRP	☐
387	1970-73	Chevrolet Corvette Stingray	'Candy' finish Blue/Black or Red/Black, retractable headlights, WhizzWheels............	**£25-35**	☐
388	1970-74	Mercedes-Benz C111	Orange/Black body, WhizzWheels, 104 mm.	**£25-35**	☐
389	1971-74	Reliant Bond 'BUG' 700 ES	Lime Green/White or Orange/White, hinged centre, 67 mm.	**£25-35**	☐
392	1973-74	Bertone Shake Buggy	Yellow/Green or Pink/Green, detailed engine, flag, 89 mm.	**£25-35**	☐
C393	1972-79	Mercedes Benz 350 SL	White (Black line) or Metallic Blue (Silver line) spoked wheels, 102 mm.	**£35-45**	☐
			Metallic Green or Dark Blue body.	**£15-20**	☐
394	1973-76	Datsun 240 Z...........................	Red/Black body, non-rally version, 102 mm.	**£20-25**	☐
C400	1974-77	Volkswagen 1200	Metallic Blue or Metallic Red, 'CORGI MOTOR SCHOOL' or		
			'CORGI FAHR SCHULE', with roof steering wheel	**£30-35**	☐
C401	1975-77	Volkswagen 1200	Same as C400 but supplied with 24 'bollards' for miniature driving practice	**£35-40**	☐
424	1961-65	Ford Zephyr Estate	Two-tone Blue, suspension, luggage, smooth shaped spun wheels, 97 mm.	**£45-55**	☐
435	1986	Volvo 760 Turbo	Dark Blue or Silver body.	**£4-8**	☐
C435/12	1990	Volvo 760 Turbo	Green body with White seats.	**£4-8**	☐
440	1966-67	Ford Cortina Estate	Blue/Brown, opening tailgate, suspension, 2 figures, golf equipment, 95 mm.	**£80-110**	☐
C440	1988	Porsche 944 Saloon	Red body.	NRP	☐
445		Plymouth Suburban Sports Station Wagon	Pale Blue body, Red roof, Silver stripe	**£40-50**	☐
C453	1984	Ford Escort RS 1600 i	White body, Red seats, Black design, 79 mm.	**£10-15**	☐
485	1966-69	Mini Countryman	Sea-Green body, 2 surfboards on roof-rack, male figure, special leaflet, 79 mm.	**£65-80**	☐
491	1967-69	Ford Cortina Estate	Metallic Dark Grey, Brown 'wood' panels, shaped spun wheels............................	**£40-45**	☐
			As previous model but with cast detailed wheels	**£50-60**	☐
			Red or Metallic Blue body, Brown 'wood' panels, shaped spun wheels	**£40-50**	☐
600	1984	Ford Escort	All Red or Red/Black or Red/White body, opening doors, 110 mm.	**£10-15**	☐
601	1984	Fiat N-9	Red or Silver/Red body, opening doors, 110 mm.	**£10-15**	☐
602	1984	BL Mini 1000	Yellow body, with or without 'CITY', opening doors, 85 mm.	**£10-15**	☐
602	1984	BL Mini 1000	Chrome plated model, wooden plinth, in black 'Austin-Rover' box, 'Austin-Rover Mini 25th Celebration Donington Park - August 1984'	**£70-80**	☐
603	1984	Volkswagen Polo	Green/White or White body, opening doors, 90 mm.	**£10-15**	☐
604	1984	Renault 5	Dark Blue or Black or Yellow body, with or without 'Le Car TL', 95 mm.	**£10-15**	☐
605	1984	Austin Mini Metro	Blue body, with or without 'TURBO', 90 mm.	**£10-15**	☐
C675/14	1990	BMW 635	Red/Black body, White-wall tyres	NRP	☐
C1009	1984	MG Maestro	Yellow body, White flash, 'AA SERVICE'	**£10-15**	☐

MAJOR PACK

1126	1961-65	Racing Car Transporter	Metallic Dark Blue body with 'ECURIE ECOSSE' in Yellow lettering	**£150-200**	☐
		later version:..................	with logo in Orange lettering	**£90-110**	☐
			with logo and raised ridges in Light Blue	**£90-110**	☐
		colour variant:..............	Metallic Light Blue body with 'ECURIE ECOSSE' in Red lettering	**£90-110**	☐

Corgi Toys - 'Cars Of The '50s' series

Ref. No.	Year(s)	Model Type	Model Features and Size	Market Price Range	
C801	1982	1957 Ford Thunderbird............	White/Tan, Cream/Orange or Cream/Black, White-wall tyres, suspension	**£8-12**	☐
C802	1982	Mercedes 300 SL	Burgundy or Silver body, opening doors, suspension, 126 mm.	**£8-12**	☐
			Red body, no suspension	**£8-12**	☐
C803	1983	1952 Jaguar XK120 Sports	Red body/Black hood, suspension, spoked wheels, opening bonnet & boot................	**£8-12**	☐
C803/1	1983	1952 Jaguar XK120 Rally	Cream body, rally number '56'	**£8-12**	☐
			White body, rally number '56'	**£8-12**	☐
C804	1983	Jaguar 'Coupé des Alpes'.........	Cream body, Grey/Black tonneau, rally plate & number '56' or '414'......................	**£8-12**	☐
			As previous model but with rear wheel 'spats'.	**£15-20**	☐
C805	1983	'56 Mercedes 300SC Cabriolet ..	Black body, Tan hood, suspension, opening bonnet & boot............................	**£8-12**	☐
	1984		Maroon body	**£8-12**	☐
	1986		Beige body and hood	**£8-12**	☐
	1987		Blue body, Black hood, export model	**£8-12**	☐
C806	1983	'56 Mercedes 300SL Roadster...	Black body, Grey/Black folded hood, suspension, opening bonnet & boot...............	**£8-12**	☐
	1986		Black/Green body, Beige seats	**£8-12**	☐
	1986		Red body, Cream interior, export model	**£8-12**	☐
C810	1983	1957 Ford Thunderbird............	White body, tinted windows, White-wall tyres, suspension, spare wheel................	**£8-12**	☐
	1984		Pink body	**£8-12**	☐
	1987		Red body	**£8-12**	☐
			Cream body, Orange roof	**£8-12**	☐
			Black body, White flash, Red/White interior	NGPP	☐
C811	1984	1954 Mercedes SL	Silver body, suspension, opening doors and bonnet, 127 mm.	**£8-12**	☐
	1986		Red body	**£8-12**	☐
	1987		Grey body, export model	**£8-12**	☐
C812	1985	1953 MG TF	Green body, Tan seats, opening bonnet, luggage rack, spare wheel....................	**£8-12**	☐
C813	1985	1955 MG TF	Red body, Black hood, opening bonnet, luggage rack, spare wheel...................	**£8-12**	☐
	1987		Cream body, Red mudguards, export model	**£8-12**	☐
C814	1985	1952 Rolls-Royce Silver Dawn..	Red/Black body, Brown seats, opening bonnet and boot............................	**£8-12**	☐
	1986		White/Beige body	**£8-12**	☐
	1986		Silver/Black body, export model	**£8-12**	☐
C815	1985	1954 Bentley 'R' type	Black or Cream body, Beige hood, opening bonnet and boot, chrome trim	**£8-12**	☐
	1986		Dark Blue and Light Blue body	**£8-12**	☐
	1986		Cream/Brown body, export model	**£8-12**	☐
			White body, Black roof..	**£15-20**	☐
C816	1985	1956 Jaguar XK120...................	Red body, Black tonneau, racing number '56', plastic chassis	**£8-12**	☐
C819	1985	1949 Jaguar XK120...................	White body, Black hood, racing number '7', plastic chassis	**£8-12**	☐
C825	1985	1957 Chevrolet Bel Air.............	Red body, White roof and flash, White-wall tyres....................................	**£8-12**	☐
	1987		Black body, White roof and flash, export model	**£8-12**	☐
C869	1986	MG TF Racing Car	Royal Blue body, Beige seats, racing number '113', spare wheel, roll-bar	**£8-12**	☐
C870	1986	Jaguar XK120..........................	Green body, Yellow seats, racing number '6', export model	**£8-12**	☐

Corgi Toys - Twin Packs ('Little and Large')

These packs combine standard models with similar 'Junior' models. The models listed are known to have been featured and the compiler would welcome any further information.

1352 Renault 5 Turbo (307) Metro (C275)
1354 Texaco Lotus (C154) Junior 53
1355 Talbot Matra Rancho (457)
1356 Fiat XI/9 (306) Ford Escort (334)
1357 Golden Eagle Jeep (C441)
1359 Ford Escort (334) Junior 105

1363 Buck Rogers (607)
1364 Space Shuttle 'NASA' (648)
1365 Routemaster Bus 'BTA' (469)
1371 Volkswagen Turbo (309)
1372 Jaguar XJS (319)

1373 Ford Capri (312) Junior 61
1382 Ford Mustang (320)
1389 Ford Sierra (299) Junior 129
1397 BMW M1 'BASF' (380)
1402 Scania Tipper plus Dumper Truck

Corgi Classics - Cars (original issues)

A factory fire ended production in 1969 of this original series of 'Classics' cars. Boxes are of two types: one with separate lid with coloured line-drawings printed on it and containing a separate picture of the model; and type two which has the model attached to a sliding-drawer style base in an outer box with half-flaps (similar printing to 1st type).

Ref. No.	Year(s)	Model Type	Model Features and Size	Market Price Range	
9001	1964-69	1927 3-litre Bentley	British Racing Green, racing number '3', detachable hood, driver, 102 mm.	**£30-40**	☐
9002	1964-68	1927 3-litre Bentley	Red body, civilian driver, no racing number, detachable hood	**£50-60**	☐
9004	1967-69	'WORLD OF WOOSTER' Bentley	As previous model but in Green or Red and with Jeeves and Wooster figures	**£70-90**	☐
9011	1964-68	1915 Model T Ford	Black body, driver, passenger, spoked wheels, brass radiator, 86 mm.	**£30-35**	☐
9012	1965-68	Model T Ford	As previous model but Yellow body	**£30-35**	☐
9013	1964-69	1915 Model T Ford	Blue/Black body, detachable hood, spare wheel, driver cranks, 83 mm.	**£25-35**	☐
9014		1915 'LYONS TEA' Van	Appeared in 1967/68 catalogue but was not issued	NGPP	☐
9021	1964-69	1910 38 hp. Daimler	Red body, driver and 3 passengers, folded hood, detailed chassis, 108 mm.	**£25-35**	☐
9022		1910 38 hp. Daimler	Appeared in the 1966 catalogue but not issued	NGPP	☐
9031	1965-68	1910 Renault 12/16	Lavender/Black body with carriage lamps, spoked wheels, 102 mm.	**£25-35**	☐
9032	1965-69	1910 Renault 12/16	Same as previous model but Primrose Yellow and Black body	**£25-35**	☐
9041	1966-70	1912 Rolls-Royce Silver Ghost	Silver and Black body, carriage lamps, spoked wheels, 118 mm.	**£25-35**	☐
		variant:	Maroon body, Silver roof and bonnet.	NGPP	☐

Corgi Classics Cars (re-introduced issues)

Some of the 'Classics' were re-introduced in 1985 when original tools were discovered. These later models are distinct from the originals as they have 'SPECIAL EDITION' on their baseplates and are packed in Grey/Red boxes which do not contain a picture of the model. The model numbers are different and 13,500 of each colour were made.

C860 (9041) 1985	1912 Rolls-Royce Silver Ghost	Silver, Black or Ruby Red body	**£8-11**	☐
C861 (9002) 1985	1927 3-litre Bentley open top	British Racing Green, Black or Ruby Red body	**£8-11**	☐
C862 (9031) 1985	1910 Renault 12/16	Yellow, Pale Blue, Cream or Brown body	**£8-11**	☐
C863 (9012) 1985	1915 Model T Ford	Black, Red or Blue body	**£8-11**	☐

Corgi Toys - Aircraft

Ref. No.	Year(s)	Model Type	Model Features and Size	Market Price Range	
Note:			Helicopters and Space Vehicles are listed in the Emergency Services, Novelty and Military Sections.		
650	1973-80	'B.O.A.C.' Concorde Airliner	White/Blue with Gold tail design, all-card box	£50-60	☐
			White/Blue with Red/White/Blue tail, display stand	£10-15	☐
651	1973-81	'AIR FRANCE' Concorde	White/Blue with Gold tail design, all-card box	£70-80	☐
			White body, Red/White/Blue tail, display stand	£10-15	☐
652	1973-81	'JAPAN AIRLINES' Concorde	White/Red/Blue/Black, all-card box	£200-250	☐
653	1973-81	'AIR CANADA' Concorde	White/Red/Blue/Black, all-card box	£145-195	☐
1301	1973-77	Piper Cherokee Arrow	Yellow/Black with White wings, or White/Blue, 'N 286 4 A'	£35-45	☐
1302	1973-77	Piper Navajo	Red/White or Yellow/White, 'N 9219 Y'	£35-45	☐
1303	1973-77	Lockheed F104A Starfighter	Silver or Camouflage with Black crosses	£35-45	☐
1304	1973-77	Mig-21 PF	Blue or Silver, number '57', Red stars, retractable undercarriage	£35-45	☐
1305	1973	Grumman F-11a Tiger	Blue 'NAVY', or Silver with U.S. stars	£35-45	☐
1306	1973-77	North American P51-D Mustang	Silver or Camouflage, Black props, U.S. stars, moveable control surfaces	£35-45	☐
1307	1973-77	Saab 35 X Draken	Silver or Camouflage, retractable undercarriage, Swedish Blue/Yellow markings	£35-45	☐
1308	1973-77	BAC (or SEPCAT) Jaguar	Silver or Camouflage, retractable wheels, moveable control surfaces	£35-45	☐
1309	1973-77	'B.O.A.C.' Concorde	Dark Blue/White, retractable wheels	£35-45	☐
1310	1973-77	'AIR FRANCE' 'BOEING 707B'	White/Blue body, Silver wings, retractable wheels	£35-45	☐
1312	1973-77	Boeing 727 'TWA'	White body, Silver wings, retractable wheels	£35-45	☐
1313	1973-77	Japanese Zero-Sen A6M5	Green or Silver with Red circles, retractable wheels	£35-45	☐
1315	1973-77	'PAN-AM' Boeing 747	White body, Silver wings, hinged nose, retractable wheels	£35-45	☐
1315/1		'BRITISH AIRWAYS' Jumbo	Boeing 747, White/Silver, Blue logo, hinged nose, retractable wheels	£35-45	☐
1316	1973-77	McDonnell Douglas F-4c5	Phantom II in Silver or Camouflage with retractable undercarriage	£35-45	☐
1320	1978-80	'BRITISH AIRWAYS' VC-10	White/Silver with Red tail, Blue logo, retractable wheels	£35-45	☐
1325	1978-80	'SWISSAIR' DC-10	White/Silver with Red stripe and tail, retractable wheels	£35-45	☐

Corgi Toys - Small Commercial Vehicles and Vans

Excluding models issued from 1987 as 'Corgi Classics' (see separate listing)

Ref. No.	Year(s)	Model Type	Model Features and Size	Market Price Range	
403	1956-61	Bedford 15 cwt Van	'DAILY EXPRESS' on Dark Blue body, 83 mm.	£75-85	☐
			As previous model but Deep Blue body	£100-120	☐
403 M	1956-59	Bedford 15 cwt Van	'K.L.G. PLUGS' on Red/Silver body, flywheel motor, 83 mm.	£125-150	☐
404	1956-62	Bedford Dormobile	Cream, Metallic Cerise or Turquoise body, smooth roof, smooth/shaped wheels	£60-70	☐
			Blue or Yellow body with ribbed roof, smooth/shaped wheels	£75-85	☐
			Lemon Yellow body with Blue roof	£100-125	☐
404 M	1956-59	Bedford Dormobile	Red or Blue body, flywheel motor, 83 mm.	£65-75	☐
C405	1982	Ford Transit Milk Float	'LOTTA BOTTLE' on Blue/White body, opening doors, 143 mm.	£10-15	☐
407	1957-61	Smiths Karrier Bantam Mobile Grocery Shop	'HOME SERVICES HYGIENIC MOBILE SHOP', Pale Green/Red, 95 mm.	£65-80	☐
408	1957-62	Bedford 15 cwt 'AA'	Yellow/Black body, divided windscreen, smooth wheels, leaflet, Blue box	£75-85	☐
			As previous model but with undivided windscreen	£65-75	☐
			with undivided windscreen and shaped wheels	£55-65	☐
			As previous model but in Blue/Yellow box	£65-75	☐
411	1958-62	Karrier Bantam Van 'LUCOZADE'	Yellow body, Grey plastic shutter, smooth wheels, Blue box	£70-80	☐
			As previous model but with shaped wheels, Blue/Yellow box	£80-90	☐
413	1957-62	Smiths Karrier Bantam Mobile Butchers	White/Blue van, 'FAMILY BUTCHERS', meaty decals, 93 mm. Blue box	£85-100	☐
421	1960-62	Bedford 12 cwt Van	'EVENING STANDARD', Black body, Silver roof, 83 mm.	£80-90	☐
			'EVENING STANDARD', Black lower body, Silver upper body and roof	£100-120	☐
422	1960-62	Bedford 12 cwt Van	'CORGI TOYS', Yellow body, Blue roof, smooth or shaped wheels, 83 mm.	£100-130	☐
		reversed colours:	Blue body, 'CORGI TOYS', Yellow roof, smooth wheels	£300-400	☐
		variation:	Blue lower half with Yellow upper body, 'CORGI TOYS'	£300-400	☐
C424	1977-79	Security Van	Black/Yellow/White body, 'SECURITY', windows with grilles, 100 mm.	£10-15	☐
426	1962-64	Karrier Bantam Van Circus Booking Office	Red/Blue body, 2 circus & office staff. 'Chipperfields Booking Office', 91 mm.	£80-120	☐
C426	1978-81	Chevrolet Booking Office Van	Yellow/Red/Blue body, 'PINDER-JEAN RICHARD', 2 loudspeakers	£25-35	☐
428	1963-66	Karrier Ice-Cream Van 'MR. SOFTEE'	Blue/White body, detailed chassis, salesman swivels. 91 mm.	£75-90	☐
431	1964-66	Volkswagen Pick-Up	Yellow/Red, suspension, 91 mm.	£45-55	☐
433	1962-64	Volkswagen Delivery Van	'VW' logo on side, seats, steering wheel, 91 mm.	£50-60	☐
			'VROOM & DREESMAN', Grey body, shaped spun wheels, Dutch promotional	£250-350	☐
434	1962	Volkswagen Kombi	Metallic two-tone Green body, Red or Yellow 'VW' badge and seats	£45-55	☐
435	1962-63	Karrier Bantam Dairy Produce Van	Blue/White/Yellow body, 'DRIVE SAFELY ON MILK',	£60-70	☐
437	1979-80	Chevrolet Van 'COCA-COLA'	Red body, White logo, tinted roof windows, crates	NGPP	☐
441	1963-67	Volkswagen Van 'TOBLERONE'	Blue body with Trans-o-lite headlamps, 'CHOCOLATE TOBLERONE', 91 mm.	£65-75	☐
443	1963-65	Plymouth Suburban US Mail	Blue/White body, 'ADDRESS YOUR MAIL CAREFULLY', 104 mm.	£50-65	☐
447	1964-67	Ford Thames Van 'WALLS ICE CREAM'	Pale Blue/Cream van with salesman and boy, 90 mm.	£120-150	☐
450	1964-67	Austin Mini Van	Green body, opening doors and bonnet, 79 mm.	£50-60	☐
			Olive-Green body (slightly paler shade than previous model)	NGPP	☐
			Green body with White '2001' logo, (promotional)	NGPP	☐
452	1956-63	Commer Dropside Lorry	Red/Fawn/Silver body, hinged tailboard, 120 mm.	£65-75	☐
453	1956-60	Commer Refrigerated Van 'WALL'S ICE CREAM'	Light or Dark Blue cab, Cream body, 'MORE THAN A TREAT - A FOOD'	£100-125	☐
454	1957-62	Commer Platform Lorry	Yellow/Silver or Metallic Blue/Silver, 120 mm.	£70-80	☐
455	1957-61	Karrier Bantam 2 ton	Blue cab, Red platform, 102 mm.	£70-80	☐
	1955-57	variant:	Early METTOY issue: Red body with 'CWS SOFT DRINKS' logo on rear	£100-125	☐
456	1960-63	E.R.F 44G Dropside Lorry	Yellow/Metallic Blue, smooth/shaped wheels, 120 mm.	£60-70	☐
457	1957-62	E.R.F 44G Platform Lorry	Two-tone Blue or Yellow/Blue body, 120 mm.	£60-70	☐
459	1958-60	E.R.F 44G Van	Yellow/Red, 'MOORHOUSES LEMON CHEESE', 117 mm.	£150-175	☐
462	1970	Commer Van 'CO-OP'	White/Blue promotional model, 90 mm.	£70-80	☐
462	1971	Commer Van 'HAMMONDS'	Green/Blue/White promotional model, 90 mm.	£90-100	☐
465	1963-66	Commer Pick-Up Truck	Red/Orange or Green/Grey, Red interior, Trans-O-Lites, 90 mm.	£25-35	☐
466		Commer Milk Float	White cab, chassis and load; Blue rear roof and sides	£35-45	☐
471	1965-66	Karrier Bantam Snack Bar	Blue/White, 'JOE'S DINER' with figure and opening hatch, 95 mm.	£70-85	☐
			Blue/White, 'PATATES FRITES'. Belgian issue	£130-160	☐
474	1965-67	'WALLS' Ice Cream Van	Musical version of model 447, without figures, 90 mm.	£80-100	☐
479	1968-71	Commer Mobile Camera Van	Blue/White body, 'SAMUELSON FILM COMPANY LTD', camera/operator	£80-90	☐
484	1967-71	Dodge Livestock Transporter	Beige/Green body, 'KEW FARGO', 5 figures, 140 mm.	£30-40	☐

Ford Escort 55 Vans

Type 1: Black plastic rear bumper (fitted to models before 1986)
Type 2: Metal rear bumper (fitted to models from mid-1986 to 1989)
Type 3: New one-piece moulded body (without opening rear doors) from 1989

Assume models to be Type 1 unless shown otherwise. The models feature a metal body with a plastic chassis and wheels. They have amber side & tail lights, opening rear doors (types 1 & 2) and beige (types 1,2,3) or black (2 & 3) interiors. White or brown interiors sometimes appear with type 1.

C496	1983	'ROYAL MAIL'	Red body, Gold design	£7-10	☐
C496/1	1986	'ROYAL MAIL'	Red body, Gold design, (types 2/3)	£7-10	☐
C496/2	1986	'POLICE'	White body, Red stripe, rooflight bar (types 2/3)	£7-10	☐
C496/3	1986	'BRITISH GAS'	Blue/White body, (towbar fitted to Gift Set model) type 2	£7-10	☐
C496/4	1987	'BRITISH AIRWAYS'	Dark Blue/Silver body, Red flash, (type 2)	£7-10	☐
C496/5	1987	'NOTRUF'	Red body, Blue rooflight, (type 2) Swiss export model	£10-15	☐
C496/9	1988	'BRITISH TELECOM'	Yellow body, Black ladder, (types 2/3)	£7-10	☐
C496/15	1988	'HOOVER'	White body, Dark Blue stripe, Red logo, (type 2)	£7-10	☐
C496/16	1988	'B.B.C.'	Grey body, Black/White design, (type 2)	£7-10	☐
C496/17	1988	'FORD'	White body, Blue stripe, (type 2)	£7-10	☐
C496/18	1988	'BRITISH GAS'	Blue/White body, revised logo, (types 2/3)	£7-10	☐
C496/19	1990	'BRITISH TELECOM'	Yellow body, Black ladder, (type 3)	£7-10	☐
C496/20	1989	'UNIGATE'	Red/White body, 'FRESH MILK' logo, (type 3)	£7-10	☐
C496/24	1990	'PTT TELECOM'	Green body, Yellow/Red design, Dutch export model	NRP	☐
C497	1983	'RADIO RENTALS'	White body, Green/White design	£7-10	☐
C498	1983	'BRITISH GAS'	Blue/White body	£7-10	☐
C499	1983	'BRITISH TELECOM'	Yellow body, Black ladder, (Gift Set version has towbar fitted)	£7-10	☐
C503	1984-85	'DUNLOP'	White body, Yellow/Red/Black print, (deleted 1985)	£7-10	☐
C503/7	1984	'TELEVERKET'	Orange body, Black logo, Swedish export model	£10-15	☐
C504	1984	'JOHN LEWIS'	Green with White/Lime Green logo, Limited Edition of 2,500	£10-15	☐
C512	1984	'BOLTON EVENING NEWS'	Yellow body, Black/White logo, Limited Edition of 5,000	£7-10	☐
C514	1984	'CHUBB'	Cambridge Blue body, White label, Limited Edition of 500	£15-20	☐
C514	1984	'DIGBYS TOYSTORE'	Cambridge Blue body, Gold label, Limited Edition of 504	£15-20	☐
C514	1984	'DIGBYS TOYSTORE'	Oxford Blue body, Gold label, Limited Edition of 1,000	£15-20	☐
C515	1984	'NATIONAL EXHIBITION CENTRE'	Red/White/Blue body and logo, Limited Edition of 5,000	£7-10	☐
C532	1985	'R.A.C. Rescue Service'	White/Blue, (1/2). (in Gift Set has towbar & 'Service' print)	£7-10	☐
C534	1985	'PIZZA SERVICE'	White with Red lower body, Red/Black logo	£7-10	☐
C537	1985	'A.A. SERVICE'	Yellow/White, roof lights, (types 1/2) (in Gift Set has towbar)	£7-10	☐
C543	1985	'TELEVERKET'	Blue body, Red 'Tele' logo, Swedish export model	£10-15	☐
C549	1985-86	'HOTPOINT'	Beige/Brown body, deleted 1986	£7-10	☐
C557	1985	'FIRE SALVAGE'	Yellow body, Black logo, Blue rooflight	£10-15	☐
C559	1985	'JAGO AUTOMOTIVE'	Silver body, Red tampo print design, Limited Edition of 1,000	£15-20	☐
C560	1985	'WILTSHIRE FIRE'	Red body, Gold logo, plastic ladder on roof	£10-15	☐
C561	1985	'WAITROSE'	White body, Black/Orange logo, Limited Edition of 1,000	£15-20	☐
C562	1985	'GAMLEYS'	White body, Red/Blue tampo print design, Limited Edition of 2,500	£10-15	☐
C563	1985	'McVITIES'	Blue body, Red/Yellow print, Limited Edition of 2,500	£8-12	☐
C564	1986	'TELEVERKET'	White body, Blue/Orange print, (type 2) Swedish export model	£15-20	☐
C577	1985	'PLESSEY'	White/Blue body, Black tampo print, Limited Edition of 2,500	£15-20	☐
C578	1985	'BEATTIES'	Black with Yellow labels, Limited Edition of 2,500	£7-10	☐
C584	1985	'MANCHESTER Eve. News'	Yellow and Black body, Limited Edition of 2,644	£7-10	☐
C621	1986	'POLICE'	White body, Red stripe, roof light bar	£7-10	☐
C626	1986	'CHUBB FIRE'	Blue body, 'FIRE COVER', Limited Edition of 5,000	£7-10	☐
C632	1986	'KAYS'	White body, mail-order only, (type 2)	£7-10	☐
91610	1992	'AA SERVICE'	Yellow body, White stripe, roof light bar, towbar, (type 3)	NRP	☐
91611	1992	'RAC SERVICE'	White body, Blue stripe, Orange roof light, (type 3)	NRP	☐
91612	1992	'ROYAL MAIL'	Red body, revised logo, (type 3)	NRP	☐
91620	1992	'YORKSHIRE GAS'	Blue/White body, commissioned by John Ayrey, (type 3)	NGPP	☐
91984	1992	'AUTO FEDERATION'	Yellow/Black body, roof light bar, 'NAF' logo, Norwegian export, (type 3)	£9-12	☐

Mercedes 207-D Vans

C516	1985	'BMX SERVICE'	White body, Yellow band, rider design.	£6-9	☐
C535	1985	'ATHLON'	Colours unknown	£6-9	☐
539	1985	'GROUP 4'	White body, Yellow band, 'SECURITY SERVICES'	£6-9	☐
548	1985	'SECURITAS'	Blue body, Black/Gold/Red print. Limited Edition 6,500, export model	£6-9	☐
564	1985	Swiss 'PTT'	Yellow/White body, Red/Black lines	£6-9	☐
568	1996	'B.F.GOODRICH'	Black body, Red/White/Blue print, roof-rack	£6-9	☐
576	1986	'PEPSI'	White/Blue body, Red roof.	£6-9	☐
576/2	1986	'PORSCHE RACING'	White body, Red/Blue print, roof-rack, spares	£6-9	☐
576	1986	'PARCELINE'	Black/Green body, White logo	£6-9	☐
576	1987	'LEKER OG HOBBY'	White body, Red design.	£6-9	☐
576/9	1988	'OVERNITE TNT'	White/Orange body with Black/Red print.	£6-9	☐
576/10	1989	'C.R.SMITH'	White/Blue body, 'DOUBLE GLAZING'	£6-9	☐
588	1987	'CURTIS HOLT'	White body, 'PRO-NGA', Limited Edition of 2,500	£6-9	☐
		'GROUP 4'	White body, 'SECURITY SERVICES', stretcher	£6-9	☐
630	1986	'KAYS'	Produced for Kays as a mail-order model	£6-9	☐
631	1986	'BLUE ARROW'	Kays mail-order model	£6-9	☐

Ford Transit Vans (redesigned issues 1987 onwards)

See also under 'Ambulance, Fire, Police and Rescue Vehicles' section.

656/1	1987	'RAC Rescue Services'	White body, Blue/Red design	£6-9	☐
656/2	1987	'DATAPOST'	Red body, Gold logo, 'ROYAL MAIL'	£6-9	☐
656/3	1987	'AMBULANCE'	White body, Red stripe and cross, roof light bar	£6-9	☐

Ref. No.	Year(s)	Model Type	Corgi Toys - continued	Market Price Range	
656/4	1987	'FORD'	White body, Blue/Red design	£6-9	☐
656/5	1987	'A.A. SERVICE'	Yellow/White body, Black logo	£6-9	☐
656/7	1987	'POSTBIL'	Yellow post van with Red/Black design, Danish export	£9-11	☐
656/8	1987	'POLISSI'	Black body, Red stripe, roof light bar, Finnish export	£9-11	☐
656/9	1987	'POLIS'	Black body, Red stripe, roof light bar, Swedish export	£9-11	☐
656/12	1987	'KTAS'	Orange body, Black logo, Danish export model	£9-11	☐
656/16	1988	'BUNDESPOST'	Yellow body, German export model	£9-11	☐
656/18	1988	'FALCK SERVICE'	White body, Red stripe, roof light bar, Danish export model	£9-11	☐
C656/21	1988	'LYNX'	Black with Red panels, 'EXPRESS DELIVERY NETWORK'	£6-9	☐
C656/22	1988	'POLICE'	White with Red stripe, roof light bar	£6-9	☐
C656/28	1988	'NOTTINGHAM'	White, Yellow stripe, 2 roof lights, 'Nottingham Ambulance Service'	£6-9	☐
Q656/29	1990	'CENTRE PARCS'	White body, 'ELVEDEN FOREST HOLIDAY VILLAGE', Export	£6-8	☐
Q656/30	1990	'CENTRE PARKS'	White body, 'SHERWOOD FOREST HOLIDAY VILLAGE'	NRP	☐
C656/31	1990	'UNICHEM'	White body with Black/Green design	£7-9	☐
Q656/33	1990	'McDOUGALL ROSE'	Blue/Red/Grey, 'SUPPLIERS OF DULUX', 'ICI'	NRP	☐
656	1990	'FIRE SERVICE'	Red body, White stripe	NRP	☐
656	1990	'KAYS'	White body, Kays mail order model	NRP	☐
656	1990	'AMBULANSE'	White/Red body, roof light bar, Norwegian export model	£9-11	☐
656	1990	'AMBULANSSI'	White body, Red stripe and cross, roof light bar, Finnish export model	£9-11	☐
91640	1992	'S.WALES POLICE'	Blue body, Orange stripe, roof light	NRP	☐
91642	1992	'NATIONAL BREAKDOWN'	Orange body, roof light bar, 'FALKEN' logo, Danish	£9-12	☐
91647	1992	'POLITI'	White body, Red/Blue stripe, roof light bar, Danish	£9-11	☐
	1992	'POLIS'	White/Blue/Red, roof light bar, Export	£9-11	☐
91657	1992	'BELGIAN RED CROSS'	White body, Red stripe, two roof lights	NGPP	☐

Corgi Toys - Large Commercial Trucks and Tankers

Excludes models issued from 1987 as 'Corgi Classics' (see separate listing)

Ref. No.	Year(s)	Model Type	Model Features and Size	Market Price Range	

Bedford Trucks

Ref. No.	Year(s)	Model Type	Model Features and Size	Market Price Range	
1100	1958-63	'S' Carrimore Low Loader	Red cab, Blue trailer, drop-down ramps, operable winch, 220 mm.	£65-75	☐
			Yellow cab, Blue trailer	£75-85	☐
1101	1957-63	'S' Carrimore Transporter	Red cab, Blue transporter body, 'CORGI CAR TRANSPORTER'	£65-75	☐
			Blue cab, Yellow transporter body	£75-85	☐
1104	1957-63	'S' type Carrimore Machinery Carrier	Red cab, Silver trailer, detachable rear axle, operable winch, 220 mm.	£65-75	☐
			Blue cab, Silver trailer	£75-85	☐
1104	1974-77	'TK' type Horse Transporter	Green/Orange articulated body, 'NEWMARKET', 4 horses, boy, 256 mm.	£60-75	☐
1105	1962-66	Car Transporter	Red cab, Blue/White trailer, collapsible decks, 'Corgi Car Transporter', 273 mm.	£60-80	☐
1110	1959-64	'S' type 'MOBIL' Tanker	Red/White articulated body, detachable cab, 'MOBILGAS', 191 mm.	£100-125	☐
1129	1962-65	'S' type 'MILK' Tanker	Blue/White articulated body, detachable cab, 191 mm.	£100-125	☐
1131	1963-66	'TK' type Carrimore Machinery Carrier	Blue/Yellow articulated body, detachable cab and rear axle, suspension	£60-70	☐
1132	1963-65	'TK' Carrimore Low Loader	Yellow/Red articulated body, detachable cab and rear axle, suspension, 241 mm.	£100-125	☐
1140	1965-67	Bedford 'TK' Petrol Tanker	Red/Silver/White articulated body, tilting cab, 'MOBILGAS', 191 mm.	£100-125	☐
1141	1965-67	Bedford 'TK' Milk Tanker	Blue/White articulated body, tilting cab, 'MILK', 191 mm.	£100-125	☐
1110	1965-67	'TK' type 'SHELL' Tanker	Blue/White articulated tanker, 'SHELL BENZEEN', Dutch model	£750-1000	☐

Berliet Trucks

Ref. No.	Year(s)	Model Type	Model Features and Size	Market Price Range	
C1105	1977-81	Racehorse Transporter	Brown/White, 'NATIONAL RACING STABLES', 4 horses, 280 mm.	£40-50	☐
C1107	1979-	'UNITED STATES LINES'	Blue/White body, 2 Grey containers, jockey wheel, 290 mm.	£35-45	☐

Ford Trucks   These models feature a tilt cab which uncouples from the trailer section.

Ref. No.	Year(s)	Model Type	Model Features and Size	Market Price Range	
1108	1982	'MICHELIN'	Blue/White body, 2 containers, 243 mm.	£20-25	☐
1109	1979	'MICHELIN'	Blue/Black body, 2 containers, 243 mm.	£20-25	☐
1137	1966-69	'EXPRESS SERVICES'	Blue/Silver/Red body, 'H' series tilt-cab, 235 mm.	£50-60	☐
1138	1966-69	'CORGI CARS' Transporter	Red/Silver cab, two-tone Blue transporter body	£50-60	☐
1157	1976-81	'ESSO' Tanker	White/Red articulated body, 270 mm.	£20-25	☐
1158	1976	'EXXON' Tanker	White/Black body, 270 mm. German issue	£30-35	☐
1159	1976-79	Ford Car Transporter	Blue/White or Green articulated body, 360 mm.	£25-30	☐
1160	1976	'GULF' Tanker	White/Orange articulated body, 270 mm.	£25-30	☐
1161	1979-80	'ARAL' Tanker	Blue/White/Black articulated body, 270 mm. German export model	£25-30	☐
1169	1982	'GUINNESS' Tanker	Cream/Brown/Black articulated body, 270 mm.	£20-25	☐
1170	1982	Ford Car Transporter	Red/White/Yellow articulated body, 360 mm.	£20-25	☐
1191	1985	'FORD QUALITY'	White cab, chassis and tampo print, 2 Blue containers	£15-20	☐
	1985	'BALLANTINES FINEST SCOTCH'	Container holds 6 miniatures! Available duty-free shops (20,000)	£45-55	☐
	1985	'KAYS' Container Truck	Red/White body, Cerise/Black tampo print, Mail-order model (4,000)	£10-15	☐

Ford Cargo Box Vans   These models have mirrors, authentic radiators, 4 headlights and 6 wheels.

1190	1985	'THORNTONS'	Blue/White body, Red logo	£10-15	☐
1190	1985	'EVER READY'	Red body, Black chassis	£10-15	☐
1192	1985	'LUCAS'	Green body, Black chassis, White tampo print	NGPP	☐
1228	1986	'THE NEW LEWIS'S'	White body, (2,500)	£10-15	☐
1249	1986	'WHITES BAZAAR'	Blue body, Red/White tampo print, not generally released	NGPP	☐

Mack Trucks

1100	1971-73	'TRANS-CONTINENTAL'	Orange cab, Black/Orange/Silver trailer, sliding doors, jockey wheel, 257 mm.	£40-50	☐
1106	1971-77	'A.C.L.' Container Truck	Yellow/Black body, 2 Red containers with White logo, 290 mm.	£40-50	☐
1151		'EXXON' Tanker	Red/White body, striped window box	£60-70	☐
1152	1971-75	'ESSO' Tanker	White/Red/Blue articulated body, Gloster Saro Petrol Tanker (detachable)	£40-50	☐

Mercedes-Benz Articulated Container Trucks and Tankers

The models feature 8 wheels, uncoupling trailer, cab streamliner and authentic radiator.

1109	1984	'SEALINK'	Blue cab and trailer, 2 White containers, 220 mm.	£8-12	☐
1129	1983	'CORGI'	Multicoloured body, 207 mm.	£8-12	☐
1129	1984	'ASG'	*'TRANSPORT-SPEDITION'*, export model, 220 mm.	£10-15	☐
1130	1983	'CORGI CHEMCO' Tanker	Yellow/Black/Silver body, 110 mm.	£8-12	☐
1131	1983	'CHRISTIAN SALVESON'	White/Black/Blue refrigerated van body, 207 mm.	£8-12	☐
1139	1984	'HALLS BACON'	White/Blue refrigerated van body, mail-order model, 220 mm.	£8-12	☐
1141	1984	'SHELL' Tanker	Red/Yellow cab, Yellow/Black tank, 170 mm.	£8-12	☐
1144	1983	'ROYAL MAIL'	Red body, Gold print, 'E II R' crest, 207 mm.	£8-12	☐
1145	1984	'YORKIE'	Red/Yellow cab, Blue trailer, 220 mm.	£8-12	☐
	1984	'IDM'	*'INTERNATIONAL DISTRIBUTORS MEET'*, 220 mm. Not generally available	£8-12	☐
	1984	'HOMESPEED'	*'HOME DELIVERIES FROM PICKFORDS'*, 220 mm.	£8-12	☐
1146	1983	'DUNLOP'	Black/White/Red/Yellow body, 207 mm.	£8-12	☐
1166	1984	'ARLA'	Red tampo print on White trailer, export model, 207 mm.	£10-15	☐
1166	1984	'GUINNESS' Tanker	Black/Cream, 170 mm.	£8-12	☐
1167	1984	'DUCKHAMS' Tanker	Yellow/Blue body, 170 mm.	£8-12	☐
1167	1984	'7 UP' Tanker	Green/White body, 170 mm.	£8-12	☐
1167	1984	'CORGI CHEMCO' Tanker	White/Black body	£8-12	☐
1175	1983	'ZANUSSI'	Black/Yellow body, White/Black logo, 207 mm.	£5-10	☐
1175	1984	'RALEIGH'	TT Blue and Yellow, 207 mm.	£5-10	☐
1176	1983	'WEETABIX'	Yellow/Red body, Blue logo, 207 mm.	£5-10	☐
1178	1983	'MAYNARDS'	Red/White/Green body, 207 mm.	£5-10	☐

Model redesigned in 1985 with a new style cab. Length overall is 235 mm.

1112	1985	'MICHELIN'	Yellow body, Blue chassis and tampo print	£5-10	☐
1129	1985	'ASG'	Yellow body, Blue chassis and tampo print	£5-10	☐

Mercedes-Benz Box Vans   feature 6 wheels and authentic radiator design.

1192	1986	'PEPSI'	White body, Red/Blue tampo print, 235 mm.	£5-10	☐
1203	1986	'HERNGLAS'	Two-tone Blue body, export model, (6,500) 235 mm.	£5-10	☐

Mercedes-Benz 'Superhaulers'   Small size trailers fitted to all these:

1111	1982	'SAFEWAY'	Sold only in Safeway supermarkets	NGPP	☐
	1984	'HOARESPEED'	Very rare - only 100 issued	NGPP	☐
	1984	'IDM DISTRIBUTORS'	Virtually unobtainable - only 20 issued (in US)	NGPP	☐
1137	1984	'SOUKS'	Very rare - sold in Saudi Arabian supermarkets	NGPP	☐
1139	1984	'HALLS BACON'	Reverse labels variant	NGPP	☐
1144	1983	'ROYAL MAIL'	Variant with roof aerofoil	NGPP	☐

Scammell Trucks

Scammell Handyman Articulated Trucks   featuring 8 wheels and uncoupling trailer.

1146	1970-73	Carrimore Mk.V Tri-deck	Orange/White/Blue articulated transporter with 3 collapsible decks, 290 mm.	£80-100	☐
1147	1970-72	'FERRYMASTERS'	Yellow/White body, *'INTERNATIONAL HAULIERS'*, 235 mm.	£50-60	☐
1148	1969-72	Carrimore Mk.IV Car	Red/White transporter body with Yellow chucks	£80-100	☐
1151	1970	Co-operative Society	Blue/White body, promotional	£100-120	☐

The Scammell model was updated in 1984 with a new cab and streamliner, and large front bumper. 220 mm.

1176	1984	'WEETABIX'	Yellow body, Red design	£7-10	☐
1177	1984	'NORMANS'	Yellow body, Red tampo print	£7-10	☐
1177	1984	'RALEIGH'	Two-tone Blue and Yellow body	£7-10	☐
1180	1984	Container Truck	White cab & trailer. Shown in catalogue but may not have been issued	£7-10	☐
1186	1984	'McVITIES'	Blue body, Red/Yellow print	£7-10	☐
1188	1984	'ROYAL MAIL'	Red/Black body, Gold design	£7-10	☐
1189	1985	'DUCKHAMS' Tanker	Blue/Yellow main body, Black filler cap area	£7-10	☐

Scammell Articulated Trucks redesigned in 1986 feature big horns on cab roof, sleeping compartment, exhaust pipes and ten wheels. All models are container trucks unless otherwise described.

Ref. No.	Year(s)	Model Type	Description	Market Price Range	
1220	1986	Flat Bed Crate Truck	Red cab and trailer, Black chassis, 4 'EXPORT' crates, standard release	£7-10	☐
1246/7	1986	'YORKIE'	Beige cab, Blue trailer & box	£7-10	☐
1246	1987	'DR PEPPER'	Red/White cab, White trailer, multicoloured 'Iced drinks' design	£7-10	☐
1246	1987	'COCA-COLA' Race Team Transporter	Red/White/Grey, with Corgi Junior 3700 car	NGPP	☐
1246	1987	'COCA-COLA'	Red cab, Red/White trailer, Black chassis	NGPP	☐
1246	1987	'HERSHEYS MILK CHOCOLATE'	Chocolate Brown body, White chassis & logo, Choc bar design	NGPP	☐
1246	1987	'FRANCOIS AVRIL'	Red/White cab/trailer/container, Black logo, French export model	£10-15	☐
1247	1987	'GOODRICH'	Black body, Red/White/Blue tampo print	NGPP	☐

Scammell 'Superhaulers'

Type 1: non-sleeper cabs, 2 axles, small trailer,   Type 2: sleeper cab, 3 axles, large trailer

Ref. No.	Year(s)	Model Type	Description	Market Price Range	
1141	1985	'SHELL' Tanker	No other details available	NGPP	☐
1145	1985	'YORKIE'	Beige cab, Blue trailer (Type 1)	£7-10	☐
	1985		Red/Yellow cab, Red trailer (Type 1)	£7-10	☐
C1246/12	1990	'CORNING'	White with Pale Blue sides, Blue/White logo, (USA export model)	NGPP	☐
91350	1992	'EDDIE STOBART'	White/Black, Yellow logo	£7-10	☐
91510	1992	'FAU SCHWARZ'	Black, US issue	£7-10	☐

NB. Other variations exist and the Editor would welcome additional information.

Scania Trucks

All are Box Vans unless otherwise specified and feature a cab streamliner, 6 wheels and an authentic radiator.

Ref. No.	Year(s)	Model Type	Description	Market Price Range	
1123	1984	'KOHLER' Silo Truck	Red main body and silos, White cab sleeper and filler caps, 145 mm.	£10-15	☐
1132	1984	'SWEDISH POST'	Yellow body, export model	£10-15	☐
1132	1984	'DANZAS'	Yellow/Black body, 138 mm.	£7-10	☐
1133	1983	Giant Tipper	Green/Silver body, 145 mm.	£7-10	☐
1134	1983	'KOHLER' Silo Truck	Red cab and silos	£7-10	☐
?	1983	'LANTMANNEN'	Cream and Green silo truck	£7-10	☐
1146	1983	'CORGI'	White/Blue/Black body, 138 mm.	NGPP	☐
1147	1983	'RYDER TRUCK RENTALS'	Yellow/Black body, 138 mm.	£7-10	☐
1148	1983	'SECURICOR PARCELS'	Blue/White body, 138 mm.	£7-10	☐
1149	1983-	'BRS TRUCK RENTALS'	White/Red/Blue body, 138 mm.	£7-10	☐
1150	1983	'BRITISH SUGAR' Silo Truck	Blue/White body, 'SILVER SPOON', 145 mm.	£7-10	☐
1151	1983	'SPILLERS' Silo Truck	Orange/White body, 'GRADED GRAINS', 145 mm.	£7-10	☐
1182	1984	'HONDA'	Red body, White chassis and cab sleeper, 140 mm.	£7-10	☐
1182	1985	'SUZUKI'	Blue cab and chassis, Yellow box, Red print, 140 mm.	£7-10	☐
1183	1984	'ADIDAS'	White cab and chassis, Blue box, White design, 140 mm.	£7-10	☐
1183	1985	'GLASSENHETER'	Red/White/Blue body, export model, 140 mm.	£10-15	☐
1183	1985	'BROSSARD'	Orange body, export model, 140 mm.	£7-10	☐
1238	1997	'McCAIN OVEN CHIPS'	Red cab with Yellow roof and container, Black/White design	£7-10	☐
1238/2	1987	'CADBURYS FLAKE'	Yellow/White cab, Yellow container, Purple logo	£7-10	☐
1238/3	1988	'SECURICOR EXPRESS'	Blue body, Black chassis, White logo, Yellow/Red design	£7-10	☐
1251	1987	'B.O.C.' Tanker	White body, multicoloured print	£7-10	☐
1251/2	1988	'ROLO' Tanker	Red cab and chassis, Red/White printed design	£7-10	☐
1264/2	1988	'ELF' Tanker	White cab and tank, Orange/Green printed design	£7-10	☐

Seddon Atkinson Trucks

Container trucks and tankers featuring 8 wheels, sleeping compartment, horns and uncoupling trailer.

Seddon Atkinson Cabs: Type 1 - with cab roof horns,   Type 2 - without horns
Tankers: Type 1 - Cylindrical shape (old type)   Type 2 - Base of tank wider than the top (new type)

Ref. No.	Year(s)	Model Type	Description	Market Price Range	
1238	1987	'McCAIN OVEN CHIPS'	(Type 1) Red cab, Yellow roof/container, Black/White design	£7-10	☐
1238		'SILENTNIGHT'	White body, Pink/Blue/Yellow/Grey design	£7-10	☐
1238/2	1987	'CADBURYS FLAKE'	(Type 1) Yellow/White cab, Yellow container, Purple logo	£7-10	☐
1238/3	1988	'SECURICOR EXPRESS'	(Type 1 cab) Blue body, Black chassis, White logo, Yellow/Red design	£7-10	☐
1238/4	1988	'RADIO ROADSHOW'	White body, Red/Blue design	£7-10	☐
C1238/13	1990	'CADBURY'S WISPA'	Blue body, Yellow/Orange design	£7-10	☐
Q1238/14	1990	'PARCEL FORCE'	Post-Office Red body with 'ROYAL MAIL', (18,750 made)	£5-8	☐
1251/1	1987	'B.O.C.' Tanker	(Type 1 tank) White body, multicoloured print	£7-10	☐
1251/2	1988	'ROLO' Tanker	(Type 2 tank) Red cab and chassis, Red/White print	£7-10	☐
1264/1		'BP TANKER'	White body, Type 2 tank, BP offer model	£7-10	☐
1264/2	1988	'ELF' Tanker	White cab and (Type 2) tank, Orange/Green printed design	£7-10	☐
		'DATAPOST'	Red body, Gold logo, (part of Despatch Centre set)	£7-10	☐
		'LYNX'	Black body, Gold logo, (BP offer model)	£7-10	☐

Volvo Trucks and Tankers

Most of these models are container trucks based on the Volvo Globetrotter (GBT) (205 mm.) or the Volvo F12 Truck (190 mm.). They feature eight wheels, uncoupling trailer, chrome trim and opening rear doors on the (plastic) containers. Models from C1221 on have improved sleeping compartments, horns and exhausts.

Ref. No.	Year(s)	Model Type	Description	Price	
1193	1984	Volvo Car Transporter	GBT, Red body and chassis, White upper deck, retractable jacks	£7-10	☐
1194	1985	'LEE COOPER'	F12 Truck with Red body	£7-10	☐
1196	1985	'HOTPOINT'	F12 Truck with White body, Black chassis	£7-10	☐
1197	1985	'AS'	F12 Truck, Yellow cab, Blue trailer	£7-10	☐
	1985	'TOYMASTERS'	Globetrotter, available in 'Toymasters' toyshops	£7-10	☐
1206	1985	'HILLARDS LOW PRICES'	GBT, Red/White body, Black/White design, (2,500)	£7-10	☐
1207	1985	'BRITISH HOME STORES'	GBT with Blue/White body, Blue/Silver pack design with 'BHS' on the front	NGPP	☐
	1986		As previous model but 'WHEEL' pack design without 'BHS'	NGPP	☐
1211	1986	'RILEYS CRISPS'	GBT, Red cab, Orange box trailer, mail-order model	£7-10	☐
1212	1986	'TNT OVERNITE'	GBT, Red/Orange/White body	£7-10	☐
1221	1986	Volvo and Flatbed Trailer	GBT, Red/Yellow cab, Red trailer, 2 'Export' crates, pallet load of drums/sacks	£7-10	☐
1222	1986	Volvo Car Transporter	GBT, Red cab and lower deck, Blue upper deck, ramps	£7-10	☐
1224	1986	'CADBURYS FLAKE'	GBT, Cream cab, trailer and box with Blue logo	£7-10	☐
1225	1987	'BILSPEDITION'	Superhauler, Swedish export model	£7-10	☐
1227	1986	'BEEFEATER'	GBT with White body, 'BY LEISUREKING LTD', (2,000)	NGPP	☐
1231	1986	'McCAIN OVEN CHIPS'	GBT, Red/Yellow body, Black/White printed logo	£7-10	☐
1231/2	1986	'WIMPEY'	GBT, Red and White cab, chassis and trailer	£7-10	☐
1231	1987	'WOOLWORTHS'	GBT, Pale Green/Black body, Red/Black logo	£7-10	☐
1231	1987	'TESCO'	GBT with White/Red body and logo, with horns	£7-10	☐
			As previous model but with cab aerofoil and without horns	NGPP	☐
1231	1987	'B.H.S.'	GBT with Blue cab, White trailer, Red/Blue design	£7-10	☐
1231	1987	'COCA-COLA'	GBT, Red cab and trailer	£7-10	☐
1231	1987	'MMM MARABOU'	GBT, All Black truck plus sweeties, Swedish export models	£10-15	☐
1231	1987	'GATEWAY'	GBT with Yellow/Green cab and container, White logo	£7-10	☐
1231	1988	'FRIZZY PAZZY'	GBT, Red body, Yellow chassis, export model	£7-10	☐
1231	1988	'MARS'	GBT, Black body, Yellow/Red printed logo	£7-10	☐
C1231	1988	'STEIFF'	Yellow/White cab, Red Teddy-Bear design	£7-10	☐
C1231/31	1989	'SAFEWAYS'	All White with Red/White/Yellow design	£7-10	☐
C1231/34	1990	'OPAL FRUITS'	Yellow body, Red/Green design	£7-10	☐
1232	1986	'BOSCH PLATINUM'	GBT, White cab, Blue chassis, Black container	£7-10	☐
1233	1987	'CADBURYS CHOCOLATE'	GBT with White body, Purple choc-bar logo	£7-10	☐
1243	1986	'KAYS'	GBT produced as a mail-order model for Kays	£10-15	☐
1245	1986	'FUJI FILM'	GBT, Red cab, Green container, Red design	£7-10	☐
1246	1986	'CARTERS LEMONADE'	GBT, White/Orange body. Not generally available	£7-10	☐
1246	1987	'GAMINO'	GBT, Yellow and White, Red design, export model	£7-10	☐
1250	1987	'TEXACO' Tanker	Red/Silver cab, Red/Black/Grey tank, simulated delivery hoses	£7-10	☐
1250	1987	'NOROL' Tanker	White body, Black chassis, simulated delivery hoses	£7-10	☐
1250	1987	'NORSKE OLJE' Tanker	White body, Red/Blue design, Norwegian export model	£10-15	☐
1250/3	1987	'POLO' Tanker	Green/White/Black body and printed logo	£7-10	☐
1265/1	1987	'TEXACO' Tanker	Red/Silver cab, Red/Black tank, '1270'	£7-10	☐
C1265/4	1990	'NESTE' Tanker	Green/White/Blue cab & tank design, (Finnish export model)	£10-15	☐
C1265/5	1990	'SHELL' Tanker	Grey/Silver body, Yellow/Red design	£10-15	☐
Q1265/6	1990	'BP PRODUCTS'	White/Green body, Yellow design, (New Zealand export model)	£10-15	☐
98100	1993	'SWIFT SERVICE'	Red cab and container, White 'Swift' logo	£7-10	☐
98101	1993	'AMTRAK'	White cab and container, Red/Blue 'AMTRAK' logo, Black 'Express'	£7-10	☐
98102	1993	'UTC'	Blue and Yellow cab and container, Yellow 'UTC' logo	£7-10	☐
98103	1993	'P & O FERRYMASTERS'	Yellow cab & trailer, White container	£7-10	☐
	1992	'SNICKERS'	Chocolate Brown body	NGPP	☐
	1992	'EDDIE STOBART'	Green body, Yellow logo	£7-10	☐

NB. Other variations exist and the Editor would welcome additional information.

Volvo 'Superhaulers'

1984-86 Type 1 cab - no horns or aerofoil on roof, small trailer
1986-87 Type 2 cab - horns or aerofoil on roof, larger trailer

Ref. No.	Year(s)	Model Type	Description	Price	
1206	1985	'HILLARDS'	Red/White body, certificated issue, (Type 1)	£50-60	☐
1212	1986	'TNT OVERNITE'	GBT, Red/Orange/White body, (Type 2)	£50-60	☐
1221	1986	Flatbed Trailer	Sacks and drums load, (Type 1)	£7-10	☐
1222/2	1988	Car Transporter	Blue body. (BP offer)	£7-10	☐
1231	1987	'COCA-COLA'	Issued in British Home Stores box (Type 2)	£50-60	☐
1231/1	1987	'WEETABIX'	Yellow body (Type 2)	£7-10	☐
1232	1986	'BOSCH'	White cab, Blue chassis (Type 2)	£50-60	☐
1243	1985	'KAYS'	Type 1 Kays mail-order model	£7-10	☐
	1986	'KAYS'	Type 2 Kays mail-order model	£7-10	☐
	1987	'DATAPOST'	Red body, Gold logo, (part of Despatch Centre set G13/01)	GSP	☐

Corgi Toys   -   Agricultural Models

Ref. No.	Year(s)	Model Type	Model Features and Size	Market Price Range	
50	1959-66	Massey Ferguson 65 Tractor.....	Red/Beige body, 79 mm.	**£60-70**	☐
C50	1974-77	Massey Ferguson 50B Tractor ..	Yellow/Black/Red body, windows, 138 mm.	**£20-25**	☐
51	1959-69	Massey Ferguson Tipper Trailer....................	Red/Brown body, 102 mm.	**£15-20**	☐
53	1960-66	Massey Ferguson Tractor with Shovel	Red/Brown tractor, Grey/Blue shovel, 124 mm.	**£50-60**	☐
54	1974	Massey Ferguson Tractor with Shovel	Yellow/Red or White/Red body, 150 mm.	**£30-35**	☐
54	1958-62	Fordson Half-Track Tractor.....	Blue body, Orange rollers and wheels, Black rubber tracks, lights in radiator grille, 91 mm. Plain 'early' box	**£100-130**	☐
			Same model but with Grey rubber tracks, lights at sides of grille, picture box	**£100-130**	☐
55	1961-63	Fordson Major Tractor.............	Blue/Grey/Red body, 83 mm.	**£50-60**	☐
55	1977	David Brown Tractor...............	Black/Red/White body, steering wheel, 105 mm.	**£20-25**	☐
56	1961-63	Four-Furrow Plough	Red/Brown/Yellow body, 90 mm.	**£15-20**	☐
56	1977	Farm Tipper Trailer	Red/Yellow or Red/White body with drop-down tailboard, 130 mm.	**£10-15**	☐
57	1963-65	Massey Ferguson Tractor with Fork	Red/Silver/Cream body, driver, steering wheel, 127 mm.	**£60-75**	☐
58	1965-72	Beast Carrier...........................	Red, Cream and Blue body, 4 calves, 112 mm.	**£20-25**	☐
60	1964-66	Fordson Power Major Tractor..	Blue body, plough lifts, 83 mm.	**£55-65**	☐
61	1964-70	Four-Furrow Plough	Blue/Silver body, 90 mm.	**£5-10**	☐
62	1965-70	Ford Tipper Trailer	Red/Yellow body, 144 mm.	**£10-15**	☐
64	1965-69	Conveyor on Jeep	Red body, Yellow/White conveyor, farmhand figure, 197 mm.	**£40-45**	☐
66	1966-72	Massey Ferguson 165 Tractor...	Red/Blue/White body, engine sound, 76 mm.	**£45-55**	☐
67	1967-72	Ford Super Major Tractor.......	Blue/White/Silver body, 'FORD 5000', 90 mm.	**£55-65**	☐
69	1967-70	Massey Ferguson 165 Tractor and Shovel	Red/Blue body, Silver shovel, figure, 127 mm.	**£55-65**	☐
71	1967-72	Fordson Disc Harrow	Yellow/Red/Silver body, 90 mm.	**£5-10**	☐
72	1971-73	Ford 5000 Tractor and Towbar	As Corgi 67 but with frame, bucket and pipes, 90 mm.	**£55-65**	☐
73	1970-72	Massey Ferguson Tractor and Saw	As Corgi 66 plus Yellow rotating saw. 90 mm.	**£60-70**	☐
74	1969-72	Ford 5000 Tractor and Scoop...	As Corgi 67 plus Yellow/Silver scoop, 90 mm.	**£55-65**	☐
100	1957-61	Dropside Trailer	Yellow/Red/Grey body, 108 mm.	**£10-15**	☐
101	1958-61	Platform Trailer	Yellow/Grey or Blue/Grey body	**£10-15**	☐
102	1957-65	Rice's Pony Trailer	Red or Brown body, Brown pony, 2 drop-down ramps, 86 mm.	**£10-15**	☐
112	1969-72	Rice Beaufort Horse-Box	Blue/White horse-box with mare and foal	**£25-30**	☐

MAJOR PACKS (and large Agricultural Models)

1111	1959-62	M-F Combine Harvester	Red/Yellow body, metal tines, 172 mm.	**£70-80**	☐
1111	1968-72	M-F Combine Harvester	Same as previous model but with plastic tines	**£55-65**	☐
C1112	1977-78	David Brown Tractor and Combine Harvester	Corgi 55 Tractor with Red/White/Black combine harvester, 220 mm.	**£30-35**	☐
1129	1969-72	Rice Beaufort Horsebox	Blue double horsebox body, White roof, 2 horses	**£30-35**	☐

Corgi Toys   -   Emergency Vehicles
(Ambulance, Fire, Police & Rescue Vehicles)

Ref. No.	Year(s)	Model Type	Model Features and Size	Market Price Range	

Please see the 'Classics' section for more emergency vehicles which are listed there.
Emergency vehicles based on Ford Escort and Transit vans may also be found under those headings in the 'Corgi Small Commercials and Vans' section.

Ref. No.	Year(s)	Model Type	Model Features and Size	Market Price Range	
C106/13	1990	Saab 'BRANDWEER'	Red body, White side panels, 'ALARM', (Dutch export model)	**£15-20**	☐
209	1958-61	Riley Police Car......................	Black and Silver body, bell, 'POLICE', 97 mm.	**£65-75**	☐
213	1959-61	Jaguar Fire Service Car	Red body, bell, Grey aerial, roof sign, smooth spun wheels, 95 mm.	**£80-90**	☐
213s	1961-62	Jaguar Fire Service Car	As previous model but with suspension and shaped spun wheels	**£100-120**	☐
223	1959-61	Chevrolet Impala 'State Patrol'	Black body, Silver stripe, 'STATE PATROL', Grey aerial, 108 mm.	**£35-45**	☐
237	1962-66	Oldsmobile Sheriffs Car............	Black body, White or Off-White roof, 'COUNTY SHERIFF', clear or Blue light	**£50-60**	☐
260	1979-81	Buick 'POLICE' Car	Blue/White body, 'CITY OF METROPOLIS', 2 flashing light bars	**£10-15**	☐
284	1982-83	Mercedes-Benz 240 D................	Red body, 'NOTRUF 112', flashing lights, German export model	**£10-15**	☐
293	1980-81	Renault 5 TS	Light Blue/Dark Blue, 'S.O.S. MEDICINS'	**£10-15**	☐
295	1982-83	Renault 5 TS	Red/White 'SAPEURS POMPIERS', warning lights, French export model	**£10-15**	☐
297	1982-86	Ford Escort 'POLICE' Car	Light or Dark Blue, White doors, Blue warning lights	**£10-15**	☐
299	1985	Ford Sierra 'POLIS' Car	Blue/Yellow/Black body, warning lights, Swedish export model	**£10-15**	☐

Ref. No.	Year(s)	Model Type	Corgi Toys - continued	Market Price Range	
299/7	1985	Sierra Ghia 2.3 'POLIS'	White/Black body with White logo, (Sweden)................................	£10-15	☐
C317	1986	Peugeot 'POLITI'	Black/White body, warning lights, Norwegian export model	£10-15	☐
C326	1980-81	Chevrolet Caprice Police Car	Black/White body, 'POLICE', suspension, 150 mm.	£10-15	☐
C332	1980-81	Opel Doctors Car	White/Red body, 'NOTARTZ', opening doors	£10-15	☐
C339	1980	Rover 3500 Police Car	White and Red body, 'POLICE', 140 mm.	£10-15	☐
353	1987	BMW 'NOTARTZ'	Red/White body, 2 Blue warning lights, German export model	£10-15	☐
357	1987	Ford Sierra 'BRANDCHEFF'..	Red body, door badge, warning lights	£5-10	☐
C358/1	1987	Ford Sierra 'POLICE'	White body, Yellow/Black stripe, warning lights unit on roof	£10-15	☐
358	1987	Ford Sierra 'POLITI'	White body, Red/Blue logo, warning lights, export model	£10-15	☐
358	1987	Ford Sierra 'POLICE'	White body, Red logo, warning lights, German export model	£10-15	☐
C358/3	1986	'RIJKSPOLITIE'......................	White body, White/Red bonnet, crest, roof beacon, (Holland)	£10-15	☐
C358/4	1986	'LEGIBIL'	White/Black body, 'LEGE', twin roof beacons, (West Germany)	£10-15	☐
361	1987	Volvo 'POLIS'	White body, Black/Yellow logo, Swedish export model	£10-15	☐
373	1970-76	Volkswagen 1200 Police Car	Black/White/Blue body, 'POLICE', WhizzWheels, 91 mm.	£10-15	☐
373	1987	Peugeot 'POLITI'	Black/White body, warning lights, Norwegian export model	£10-15	☐
383	1970-73	VW 1200 'ADAC'	Yellow/Black body, 'ADAC' logo (Continental equivalent of 'AA')	£60-70	☐
386	1987	Mercedes 'POLIZEI'	Green/White body, 2 Blue warning lights, German export model	£10-15	☐
402	1972-77	Ford Cortina Police Car	White/Red body, 'POLICE', warning lights, opening doors, 102 mm.	£25-35	☐
405	1956-60	Bedford Fire Tender................	Green body, Silver or Black ladder, 'A.F.S.' in Yellow, 83 mm.	£80-90	☐
			With Black ladder	£80-100	☐
405 M	1956-59	Bedford Fire Tender................	Red body, Silver or Black ladder, 'FIRE DEPT' in Yellow or Red, 83 mm.	£90-110	☐
C405	1978-80	Chevrolet Ambulance	White/Orange, opening doors, ambulancemen, 119 mm.	£10-15	☐
C406	1980-81	Mercedes Bonna	White body, Red/Black design, opening doors, stretcher, ambulancemen	£10-15	☐
		'AMBULANCE'................	German issue: Cream body, 'KRANKENWAGEN'	£10-15	☐
			Danish issue: Red/White body, 'FALCK'	£10-15	☐
			Swedish issue: White/Red/Black body, 'SDL 951'	£10-15	☐
C406/2	1990	Mercedes Bonna	White/Red stripes, 'FALCK', (Danish export model)	£5-10	☐
412	1957-60	Bedford 15 cwt Ambulance.......	Cream 'Utilicon' body, 'AMBULANCE', 83 mm.	£60-70	☐
C412	1976	Mercedes 'POLIZEI' Car	Green/White body, Blue roof lamp, German issue	£10-15	☐
414	1976-77	Jaguar XJ12-C........................	White/Blue body, 'COASTGUARD'	£10-15	☐
416	1959-62	R.A.C. Land Rover..................	Blue, metal canopy, 'RADIO RESCUE', smooth wheels, aerial, Blue/Yellow box......	£70-80	☐
			As previous model but with plastic canopy and shaped wheels	£75-85	☐
416s	1962-64	R.A.C. Land Rover..................	Blue body, plastic canopy, 'RADIO RESCUE', aerial, with suspension, 95 mm.	£55-65	☐
416s	1962-64	R.A.C. Land Rover..................	Blue body with plastic tilt, 'RADIO RESCUE', 'RAC' logo on bonnet and doors......	£55-65	☐
C416	1977-79	Buick Police Car....................	Metallic Blue body, 'POLICE', 2 policemen, 150 mm.	£15-20	☐
419	1960-63	Ford Zephyr Motorway Car	White body, 'POLICE', aerial, clear roof light, 97 mm.	£45-55	☐
			As previous model but Off-White body, big or small Blue roof light	£45-55	☐
421	1977-79	'FOREST WARDEN'S' Land Rover......................	Red/White body, roof-rack, spare wheel, opening doors, 135 mm.	£15-20	☐
422	1977-80	Riot Police Wagon	Red/White body, number '6' & 'RIOT POLICE' on doors, water cannon	£15-20	☐
423	1960-62	Bedford Fire Tender................	Red body, Black ladder, 'FIRE DEPT', smooth spun wheels, renumbered 405	£70-80	☐
			With unpainted ladder, shaped spun wheels	£80-100	☐
424	1976-79	'SECURITY' Van....................	Black/Yellow/White body, mesh windows, WhizzWheels	£10-15	☐
C428	1978-79	Renault Police Car	Black/White body, 'POLICE', aerial, warning lights, 97 mm.	£10-15	☐
C429	1978-80	Police Jaguar XJ12-C	White/Red/Blue body, 'POLICE', aerial, warning lights, 127 mm.	£15-20	☐
C430	1978-80	Porsche 924 'Police'	Black/White body, 'POLICE', warning light, 118 mm.	£15-20	☐
C430	1978-80	Porsche 924 'Polizei'	White/Green body, 'POLIZEI', warning light, 118 mm.	£15-20	☐
C435/13	1990	Volvo 'POLIS'	White with Blue panels front & rear, flashing lights bar	£5-10	☐
437	1962-68	Cadillac Superior Ambulance....	White body, Blue roof, battery-operated Red flashing light, 114 mm.	£30-40	☐
			Red body, Cream roof, shaped spun wheels, battery-operated flashing light......	£40-50	☐
C438	1987	Rover Sterling 800..................	White body, Red stripe, 'POLICE', flashing lights bar	£5-10	☐
439	1963-65	Chevrolet Impala 'FIRE CHIEF'	Red body, White stripe, aerial, Orange roof light, firemen, 108 mm.		
			with White painted door labels with 'FIRE DEPT'	£60-70	☐
			with White rectangular label on front doors 'FIRE DEPT'	£50-60	☐
			with round Red label on front doors 'FIRE DEPT'..........................	£50-60	☐
448	1964-69	Police Mini Van	Blue body, 'POLICE', dog and policeman, warning lights, 79 mm.	£75-85	☐
454	1984	Ford Sierra 'POLIZEI'.............	Green/White body, Swiss export model	£10-15	☐
456	1986	Ford Sierra 'POLIZEI'.............	Green/White body, German export model	£10-15	☐
461	1972-74	'Police' Vigilant Range Rover...	White/Blue, warning lights, policemen, 'POLICE' emergency signs	£20-25	☐
			White/Red body, 'LANGZAAM', policemen, emergency signs, Dutch model......	£20-25	☐
463	1964-66	Commer 'AMBULANCE'	Cream or White body, Red interior, Blue tinted windows and roof light, 90 mm.......	£45-55	☐
464	1963-	Commer 15 cwt 'POLICE' Van	Dark Blue, 'COUNTY POLICE', window bars, clear roof light, leaflet	£55-65	☐
	1963-		As previous model but Metallic Light Blue, with Blue roof light	£50-60	☐
			Dark Blue, window bars, Red roof light, 'CITY POLICE', instruction leaflet....	£175-200	☐
			Dark Blue, 'open' windows, Blue roof light, White 'POLICE' cast into sides, instructions	£45-55	☐
			Deep Green body, 'POLICE', export model	£400-500	☐
			Metallic Green body, 'POLIZEI', German issue	£100-150	☐
			Metallic Blue body, 'SECOURS', French issue	£100-150	☐
			Metallic Blue body, window bars, 'RIJKSPOLITIE', Dutch issue	£100-150	☐
477	1966-67	Land Rover Breakdown............	Red/Yellow/Silver, spare wheel on some, hook, WhizzWheels, 114 mm.	£30-35	☐
481	1965-69	Chevrolet Police Car	White/Black body, 'POLICE PATROL', Red roof lights, 2 policemen, 108 mm. ..	£40-50	☐
482	1966-69	Chevrolet Impala 'FIRE CHIEF'	Red over White body, Chrome stripe, bonnet logo, Blue light, Grey aerial		
			with rectangular 'FIRE CHIEF' label on front doors, shaped spun wheels......	£40-50	☐
			with round label on front doors 'FIRE CHIEF', shaped spun wheels	£65-75	☐
			with round label on front doors 'FIRE CHIEF', detailed cast wheels	£55-65	☐

Ref. No.	Year(s)	Model Type	Corgi Toys - continued	Market Price Range	
482	1974-77	Range Rover Ambulance	White/Red/Blue body, 'AMBULANCE', stretcher, 2 ambulancemen	£15-20	☐
483	1979	Belgian Police Range Rover......	White body, Red stripes, warning lights, policemen, emergency signs	£10-15	☐
C484	1978-80	AMC Pacer 'RESCUE'...........	White/Orange/Black body, number '35', special lights, 118 mm.	£5-10	☐
C489	1980	Volkswagen Police Car............	White/Green body, 'POLIZEI', opening doors and hatchback, 97 mm.	£10-15	☐
C490	1967-70	Volkswagen Breakdown	Beige/Red, tool-box, 2 spare wheels, 102 mm.	£35-45	☐
492	1966-69	VW 'POLIZEI' Car.................	Green body, White roof, White 'POLIZEI' on bonnet, No. '18' logo.................	£40-50	☐
492	1966-69	VW European Police Car.........	Dark Green body, White roof & wings, Red 'POLIZEI', Blue lamp, 91 mm.	£40-50	☐
			All-White body, crest on doors, 'POLITIE', Blue lamp, Dutch model..................	£200-250	☐
506	1968-71	Sunbeam Imp 'Panda' Car.........	White body, Black bonnet and roof, Blue roof light..................................	£40-50	☐
			White body, Black roof, 'luminous' door panels, Blue roof light....................	£40-50	☐
			Light Blue body, White roof, 'luminous' door panels, Blue roof light..............	£50-60	☐
509	1970-72	Porsche Targa Police Car.........	White/Red body, 'POLIZEI', siren, warning lights, 95 mm.	£40-50	☐
541	1986	Ford Sierra 'POLICE'...............	Black/White body, Norwegian/Danish export model...............................	£10-15	☐
541	1987	'POLITI'	White with Blue/Yellow side stripes, (Norway).................................	£10-15	☐
541/2	1988	Ford Sierra 'NOTRUF'	Red body, warning lights, German export model..................................	£10-15	☐
542	1987	Bonna 'AMBULANCE'...........	Red/White body, 2 warning lights, Norwegian export model......................	£10-15	☐
576	1988	Mercedes 207 D Van	Red body, White 'POMPIERS', French export model.............................	£10-15	☐
597	1986	Ford Sierra 'POLICE' Car........	White body, Yellow/Black logo, 2 warning lights................................	£5-10	☐
598	1986	Range Rover 'POLICE'	White body, Yellow/Black print, 2 warning lights...............................	£5-10	☐
619	1988	Land Rover	Red/White body, 'SAPEUR POMPIERS', export model..........................	£5-10	☐
621	1986	Ford Escort 'POLICE' Van........	White body, Red/Black side flash, Blue logo..................................	£5-10	☐
656	1987	Ford Transit Van	White/Red body, flashing lights bar, Red Cross, 'AMBULANCE'.................	£5-10	☐
656	1987	Ford Transit Van 'POLICE'.....	Black body, White logo, Finnish export model.................................	£5-10	☐
656	1987	Ford Transit Van 'FALCK'......	White body, 2 Red stripes, warning lights, export model........................	£10-15	☐
656	1987	Ford Transit Van	White/Red, 'AMBULANSE', flashing lights bar, Norwegian export model	£10-15	☐
C656/28	1990	Ford Transit	White/Yellow stripe, 'NOTTINGHAM AMBULANCE SERVICE'.................	NRP	☐
C674/1	1988	'AA' Ford Transit	Breakdown truck with Yellow body, White stripe, Black rear lifting gear	NRP	☐
C674/2	1988	'RAC' Ford Transit...............	Breakdown truck with White body, Red/Blue stripe, Black lifting gear	NRP	☐
C674/3	1988	'POLICE' Ford Transit...........	Breakdown truck with White body, Red stripe, roof lights, Black lifting gear	NRP	☐
C674/4	1988	'BARNINGSKAREN' Transit	Red/Yellow breakdown truck, Black lifting gear, export model...................	£9-11	☐
700	1974-79	Motorway Ambulance	White/Red body, 'ACCIDENT', Red Cross, 98 mm.	£15-20	☐
702	1975-79	Breakdown Truck	Red/Black, single bumper, hook, 'ACCIDENT', 100 mm.	£10-15	☐
703	1976-78	Hi-Speed Fire Engine	Red body, Yellow ladder, warning lights, 115 mm.	£10-15	☐
911	1976-80	Air-Sea Rescue Helicopter	Blue/Yellow body, Black 'flick-spin' rotor, 'N 428', operable winch	£15-20	☐
921	1975-81	Hughes OH-6A Helicopter.......	White/Red, 'POLICE', 'RESCUE', warning lights, 143 mm.	£15-20	☐
921/1	1979-80		White/Blue, 'POLIZEI', 'flick-spin' rotor, operable winch, German issue.........	£15-20	☐
921/2	1979-80		White/Blue, 'POLITIE', 'flick-spin' rotor, operable winch, Dutch issue..........	£15-20	☐
921/4	1979-80	'ADAC' Helicopter..................	Yellow body, 'D-HFFM', 'flick-spin' rotor, operable winch.....................	£15-20	☐
921/6	1979-80	Swiss Red Cross Helicopter	Red body, Black blades, 'flick-spin' rotor, operable winch.....................	£15-20	☐
924	1977-81	Air-Sea Rescue Helicopter	Orange/Yellow/Black body, 'RESCUE', 150 mm.	£15-20	☐
927	1978-79	Surf Rescue Helicopter	Blue/White body, 'SURF RESCUE', 156 mm.	£15-20	☐
931	1979-80	Jet Ranger Helicopter..............	White/Red body, 'POLICE RESCUE', 'flick-spin' rotor, operable winch	£15-20	☐

MAJOR PACKS (Emergency Vehicles)

Ref. No.	Year(s)	Model Type		Market Price Range	
1103	1976-81	'PATHFINDER AIRPORT CRASH TRUCK'.............	Red/Silver, 'AIRPORT FIRE BRIGADE', operable pump & siren, Orange decal	£35-45	☐
			As previous model but non-working siren, Brick-Red decal........................	£35-45	☐
			Red/Silver, operable pump & siren, 'new YORK AIRPORT' logo................	£35-45	☐
C1118	1981-83	'AIRPORT FIRE SERVICE' ...	Red body, 'EMERGENCY UNIT', operable water pump	£40-50	☐
1120	1984	Dennis Fire Engine..................	Red body, turntable, warning lights, Yellow plastic ladder, crest design	£10-15	☐
1126	1977-81	'SIMON SNORKEL' Dennis Fire Engine	Red/White/Yellow, turntable, ladder, 6 firemen, 265 mm.	£25-30	☐
1127	1964-74	'SIMON SNORKEL' Bedford TK Fire Engine	Red/Yellow/Silver, turntable, ladder, 6 fireman, 252 mm.	£70-80	☐
1140	1982	Ford Transit Wrecker...............	White/Red, '24 Hour Service', operable winch, hook, 131 mm.	£10-15	☐
			As previous model but logo changed to 'RELAY'.............................	£10-15	☐
	1982		Red/Yellow body, 'ABSCHLEPPDEENST', export model......................	£10-15	☐
	1987		Red body, Gold 'FALCK' logo, Danish export model........................	£10-15	☐
	1987		Red body, Yellow side panels, 'VIKING', export model.......................	£10-15	☐
1142	1967-74	'HOLMES WRECKER'	Red/White, Grey or Gold twin booms, ladder, 2 spare wheels 114 mm.	£70-80	☐
C1143	1969	'AMERICAN LA FRANCE'...	Articulated Fire Engine in Red/White/Yellow, shaped spun or detailed cast wheels, 4-part extending ladder, 5 firemen, plain early box..............................	£70-80	☐
			As previous model but in later striped window box	£50-60	☐
1144	1975-78	Berliet Wrecker Recovery.........	Red/White/Gold body, with Gold or Grey hoists, 130 mm.	£50-60	☐
2029	1985	Mack Fire Engine...................	Red body, 4 warning lights, 'HAMMOND FIRE DEPT'	£10-15	☐
91822	1992	'FALKEN' Ford Transit...........	White body, Blue/Gold stripes, Black lifting gear, export model	£9-11	☐

Corgi Toys - Taxis

Ref. No.	Year(s)	Model Type	Model Features and Size	Market Price Range	
221	1960-63	Chevrolet Impala Cab	Yellow body, *'YELLOW TAXIS'*, smooth/shaped spun wheels, 108 mm.	**£50-60**	☐
C327	1980	Chevrolet Caprice Taxi	Yellow body, *'THINK TWA'*, fare table on door, 90 mm.	**£10-15**	☐
388	1987	Mercedes 190 Taxi	White or Beige body, Yellow/Black *'TAXI'* logo, export model	**£5-10**	☐
C411	1976-80	Mercedes Benz 240 D	Orange/Black or Off-White body, *'TAXI'* on roof, 127 mm.	**£10-15**	☐
			Cream and Black body (German issue)	NGPP	☐
418	1960-65	Austin FX4 Taxi	Black body, Orange sign, suspension, smooth or shaped wheels, 97 mm.	**£25-35**	☐
C425	1978	London Taxi	FX4 type taxi with Black body, *'TAXI'*, WhizzWheels, 121 mm.	**£10-15**	☐
425/1	1986	London Taxi	FX4 type taxi with Black body, *'RADIO CAB'*, Yellow design on door	**£5-10**	☐
430	1962-64	Ford Bermuda 'TAXI'	Ford Thunderbird, White body, Yellow and Red canopy, 102 mm.	**£40-50**	☐
			White body, Lime Green and Red canopy	**£40-50**	☐
			White body, Blue and Red canopy	**£30-40**	☐
			White body, Green and Pink canopy	**£30-40**	☐
			Metallic Blue/Red	**£200-250**	☐
434	1985	Mercedes 'TAXI'	Yellow body, Red taxi sign, chrome trim	**£10-15**	☐
450	1983	Peugeot Taxi	Beige with Blue label, *'739:33:33'*, (French issue)	**£10-15**	☐
451		Ford Sierra Taxi	Cream body. (No other details)	NGPP	☐
480	1965-66	Chevrolet Impala Taxi	Dark Yellow and Red body, Chrome stripe, shaped spun wheels, 108 mm.	**£40-45**	☐
			As previous model but with detailed cast wheels	**£50-55**	☐
507	1969	Chrysler Bermuda Taxi	Shown in catalogue but not issued	NGPP	
91812	1992	Taxi	Cream body, *'FINANCIAL TIMES'* logo	NGPP	

Corgitronics and Corgimatics

Ref. No.	Year(s)	Model Type	Model Features and Size	Market Price Range	

These models have 'Battery-operated Micro-Chip Action'.

Ref. No.	Year(s)	Model Type	Model Features and Size	Market Price Range	
C1001	1982	HCB Angus Firestreak	Red/Yellow/White, *'RESCUE'*, electronic siren, on/off switch 165 mm.	**£40-50**	☐
C1002	1981	Sonic Corgi Truck Set	Yellow/White/Black/Red, *'SHELL SUPER OIL'*, *'BP OIL'*, remote control	**£20-25**	☐
C1002	1981	'YORKIE' Truck Set	White/Yellow/Blue/Orange, *'MILK CHOCOLATE YORKIE'*, remote control	**£20-25**	☐
C1003	1981	Ford Road Hog	Black, Yellow/White twirls, 2-tone horn, press-down start, 150 mm.	**£10-15**	☐
C1004	1981	'Beep Beep Bus'	Red, *'BTA WELCOME TO BRITAIN'*, 2-tone horn, press-down start, 123 mm.	**£20-25**	☐
	1983		Red body with *'WELCOME TO HAMLEYS'* logo	**£20-25**	☐
C1005	1982	Police Land Rover	White/Red/Blue, *'POLICE'*, electronic siren, press-down start, 132 mm.	**£10-15**	☐
C1006	1982	'RADIO WEST' Roadshow	*'Your Local Radio 605'*, AM radio, advertised but not issued	NGPP	
C1006	1982	'RADIO LUXEMBOURG'	Red/White, *'RTL 208'*, AM radio, 3 loudspeakers, 123 mm.	**£20-25**	☐
C1007	1982	Road Repair Unit Land Rover & Trailer	Yellow/Red/Silver, *'ROADWORKS'*, press start, road drill & sound	**£10-15**	☐
C1008	1982	Fire Chief's Car	Red/White/Yellow/Silver, *'FIRE DEPARTMENT'*, press-down start, siren	**£10-15**	☐
C1009	1983	MG Maestro 1600	Yellow/Black, press start, working rear lights, 118 mm.	**£15-20**	☐
			Red/Black body	**£202-25**	☐
C1024	1983	'Beep Beep Bus'	Red, *'BTA'*, supplied exclusively to Mothercare shops	**£20-25**	☐

A scarce Corgi Gift Set 40 "The Avengers" comprising John Steeds Vintage Bentley, in red and black, and Emma Peel's Lotus Elan S2 in white. Complete with figures and 3 umbrellas. In original display box, VGC to Mint (minor chips). Sold by Wallis & Wallis, Lewes, Sussex (£350), and picture reproduced by their kind permission.

Corgi car transporter with 6 cars Gift Set (GS41), 1138 'H' Series car transporter carrying 3 Minis, Ford Cortina Estate, Rover 2000 and a Hillman Imp. In original box with instructions. VGC to Mint (minor paint blemishes). Sold by Wallis & Wallis, Lewes, Sussex (£260).

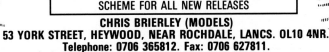

WHEN REPLYING TO ADVERTISEMENTS PLEASE MENTION JOHN RAMSAY'S CATALOGUE

Corgi Toys   -   Military and R.A.F. models

Ref. No.	Year(s)	Model Type	Model Features and Size	Market Price Range
			Unless described otherwise, all models in this listing are finished in Military-Green or Olive-Drab camouflage.	
C290	1977-80	Bell Army Helicopter	Red crosses, Black rotor, 'ARMY' markings, 160 mm.	**£15-20** ☐
350	1958-62	Thunderbird Missile	Red/White guided missile, Air Force Blue loading trolley, 140 mm.	**£100-125** ☐
351	1958-62	R.A.F. Land Rover	Blue/Silver, R.A.F. roundel, spare wheel, windows, 95 mm.	**£40-50** ☐
352	1958-62	R.A.F. Vanguard Staff Car	Blue/Silver Standard Vanguard with R.A.F. roundel, 95 mm.	**£40-50** ☐
353	1959-61	Decca Radar Scanner	Blue/Orange, scanner rotates, 83 mm.	**£25-35** ☐
354	1964-66	Commer Military Ambulance	Red crosses, seats, steering wheel, suspension, Army driver, 90 mm.	**£40-50** ☐
355	1964-65	Commer Van 'MILITARY POLICE'	Battery-operated flashing light, suspension, Army driver, 90 mm.	**£70-80** ☐
356	1964-66	VW Personnel Carrier	*'US PERSONNEL'*, seats, suspension, Army driver, 91 mm.	**£40-60** ☐
357	1964-66	Land Rover Weapons Carrier	suspension, seats, aerial, White star, 95 mm.	**£125-150** ☐
358	1964-68	1961 Oldsmobile Staff Car	Army driver and 3 passengers, White star, suspension, 108 mm.	**£50-60** ☐
359	1964-66	Commer Army 'FIELD KITCHEN'	Driver, attendant, seats, open windows, suspension, 91 mm.	**£80-100** ☐
414	1961-64	Bedford Military Ambulance	Red crosses, windows, 83 mm.	**£50-60** ☐
500	1963-64	US Army Land Rover	Rare version of model 357, 95 mm.	**£200-250** ☐
C900	1974-78	German Tiger Mk.I Tank	Brown/Green, Rubber tracks, fires shells (12 supplied) aerial, '144', 103 mm.	**£15-20** ☐
C901	1974-78	Centurion Mk.I Tank	Rubber tracks, fires shells (12 supplied) aerial, Union Jacks, 121 mm.	**£15-20** ☐
C902	1974-80	American M60 A1 Tank	Rubber tracks, fires shells (12 supplied) 115 mm.	**£15-20** ☐
C903	1974-80	British Chieftain Tank	Fires shells (12 supplied) rubber tracks, 125 mm.	**£15-20** ☐
C904	1974-78	German King-Tiger Tank	Rubber tracks, fires shells (12 supplied) Black crosses, 'B 34', 120 mm.	**£15-20** ☐
C905	1975-76	Russian SU100 Tank Destroyer	Grey, Fires shells (12 supplied) rubber tracks, Red Star, 112mm.	**£15-20** ☐
C906	1975-76	Saladin Armoured Car	Rubber tracks, fires shells (12 supplied) elevating gun, 108 mm.	**£15-20** ☐
C907	1976-80	German Rocket Launcher	Steel Blue/Red, half-track, detachable limber, fires rockets (12) 167 mm.	**£15-20** ☐
C908	1977-80	French AMX Recovery Tank	Crane, lifting dozer blade, equipment, 3 figures, 127 mm.	**£40-50** ☐
C909	1977-80	Tractor Gun & Trailer	Sand-coloured British gun and trailer, fires shells (12 supplied) 280 mm.	**£25-35** ☐
C910		Bell Army Helicopter	Military-Green helicopter with Army markings, Black or Green rotor	**£15-20** ☐
C922	1975-78	Casualty Helicopter	Red/White/Yellow Sikorsky helicopter, number '3', Red crosses	**£15-20** ☐
C923	1975-78	Sikorsky Sky Crane	Military-Green helicopter, Red cross, 'ARMY' marking, 160 mm.	**£15-20** ☐

MAJOR PACKS   -   (and large Military and R.A.F. models)

Ref. No.	Year(s)	Model Type	Model Features and Size	Market Price Range
1106	1959-61	Karrier Decca Radar Van	Cream/Orange, rotating scanner, aerial, 134 mm.	**£80-100** ☐
1108	1958-61	Bristol Bloodhound Guided Missile & Launching Ramp	with lifting mechanism and Yellow/Red/White Guided Missile, RAF markings	**£65-75** ☐
1109	1959-62	Bristol Bloodhound Guided Missile & Loading Trolley	with lifting mechanism and Yellow/Red/White Guided Missile, RAF markings	**£65-75** ☐
1112	1959-62	Corporal Guided Missile on Launching Ramp	with lifting mechanism and White/Red Guided Missile, 330 mm.	**£80-100** ☐
1113	1959-62	Corporal Guided Missile Erector Vehicle	with lifting mechanism and Guided Missile, spare wheel, 292 mm.	**£90-120** ☐
1115	1958-62	Bristol Ferranti Bloodhound	Yellow/Red/White Guided Missile with RAF markings	**£40-50** ☐
1116	1959-62	Bloodhound Launching Ramp	Military-Green launching ramp for 1115. Rotates, has lifting mechanism	**£70-80** ☐
1117	1959-62	Bloodhound Loading Trolley	for use with model 1115. Military-Green, spare wheel, drawbar pivots	**£25-35** ☐
1118	1958-62	International 6x6 Army Truck	Six wheeled truck with windows, 140 mm.	**£90-110** ☐
1124	1959-62	Launching Ramp for Corporal Guided Missile	Military-Green, lifting mechanism, adjustable feet	**£25-35** ☐
1133	1965-66	Troop Transporter	Six wheeled truck, 'US 7811332', hook, 140 mm.	**£125-150** ☐
1134	1965-66	'US ARMY' Fuel Tanker	Articulated tanker with detachable cab, US Army star, 'NO SMOKING', 191 mm.	**£200-250** ☐
1135	1965	Heavy Equipment Transporter	US Army articulated vehicle, driver, detachable rear axle, ramps, 241 mm.	**£200-250** ☐

Corgi Toys - Novelty, Film & TV related models

Ref. No.	Year(s)	Model Type	Model Features and Size	Market Price Range	
104	1965-66	Dolphin 20 Cabin Cruiser	Blue/White boat, Red trailer, helmsman, 136 mm.	£20-25	☐
107	1967-70	Batboat on Trailer	Black, fluorescent Red fin, flame decals, Batman/Robin figures	£60-70	☐
201	1970-72	The Saint's Volvo	White body, White 'Saint' symbol on Red label, WhizzWheels, no driver	£50-60	☐
258	1965-69	The Saint's Volvo	White body, Black, Red or Blue 'Saint', driver, turned hubs	£50-60	☐
C259	1979-	Penguinmobile	White car with 'The Penguin' figure under Red/Yellow parasol, 95 mm.	£25-30	☐
C260	1981-	Superman Police Car	Blue body, 'CITY OF METROPOLIS', 150 mm.	£35-40	☐
261	1965-68	James Bond's Aston Martin DB5	Gold body, retractable gun, ejector seat, rear shield, figures, 97 mm.	£90-110	☐
C261	1979-82	Spiderbuggy	Red/Blue body, 2 figures, 150 mm.	£20-25	☐
C262	1979-82	Captain Marvel's Porsche	White with flames and stars, driver, 120 mm.	£40-45	☐
C263	1979-82	Captain America's Jetmobile.....	Red/White/Blue body, with Blue driver, 155 mm.	£20-25	☐
C264	1979-82	The Incredible Hulk Van	Hulk in cage on Mazda pick-up, 120 mm.	£20-25	☐
C265	1981-82	Supermobile	Red/Blue/Silver body, 3 wheels, pilot, moving 'fists', 148 mm.	£20-25	☐
266	1968-72	Chitty Chitty Bang Bang...........	Silver body with Yellow/White retractable wings, driver & 3 passengers, detailed interior, windscreen, jewelled lights, handbrake, spare, 162 mm.	£140-170	☐
	1992	25th Anniversary model.....	Replica on 'mahogany' display stand. Direct mail pre-release price..................	£70-80	☐
C266	1979-	Spider Bike	Red/Black motorcycle, Red/Black figure, rocket launcher, 115 mm.	£20-25	☐
C267	1966-67	Batmobile...............................	Black car, Red 'Batman' logo on doors, tinted Blue canopy, chrome launchers, Gold trim, rocket firing/tyre slashing mechanisms, spare rockets, Batman badge.		
			1st issue: has Red 'Bat' logo on wheels, picture box...........................	£150-200	☐
			2nd issue: is without 'Bat' logo on wheels, in window box	£80-100	☐
			3rd issue: WhizzWheels version	£50-60	☐
268	1967-70	Green Hornet 'Black Beauty'	Black body with Green interior, Green Hornet logo on roof. Fires Red missiles from front, Red radar scanners from rear. Four of each (and 'Secret Instructions') are included in the box.	£180-200	☐
C268	1978-	Batman's Bat Bike....................	Black/Red motorcycle with Batman figure, rocket launchers, 110 mm.	£30-35	☐
269	1977-81	James Bond's Lotus Esprit........	White body, Red '007' on bonnet, roof periscope, working rockets and hydroplanes. (From the film 'The Spy Who Loved Me').	£55-65	☐
270	1968-76	James Bond's Aston Martin......	Silver body, with ejector seat and passenger, 102 mm.	£130-150	☐
			As previous model but presented in pictorial bubble-pack	£150-200	☐
C271	1978-	James Bond's Aston Martin......	Silver body, with ejector seat and passenger, 130 mm.	£45-55	☐
C272	1982	James Bond's Citroën 2cv	Yellow body, bonnet pops open when front pressed down, 108 mm.	£35-45	☐
			'Gold' plated version with Certificate of Authenticity (25 only)....................	NGPP	☐
277	1968-70	'MONKEES' Monkeemobile	Red body, White roof, Yellow logo, Chrome & Gold trim plus the 4 Monkees	£150-200	☐
C278	1981-	Dan Dare Car..........................	Red/Yellow body, retractable wings, 132 mm.	£20-30	☐
C290	1976-81	Kojak Buick	Bronze body, warning lights, badge, 2 figures, 150 mm.	£30-35	☐
C292	1978-81	Starsky & Hutch Ford Torino ..	Red/White body, 3 figures, 153 mm.	£30-35	☐
	1986		Reissued as an export model in a production run of 20,000	£10-15	☐
C320	1978-81	The Saint's Jaguar XJS	White body, opening doors, Saint logo on bonnet, 128 mm.	£30-35	☐
336	1967-69	James Bond's Toyota 2000 GT	White body, Red aerial/pennant, Grey/Red driver, Blue/Pink figure firing pistol, self-adhesive '007' badge, opening boot, fires missiles (8 supplied)	£150-200	☐
C342	1980-82	'PROFESSIONALS' Ford Capri	Silver/Black body, tinted windows, opening doors, 3 figures, 124 mm.	£35-45	☐
348	1968-69	Ford Mustang 'POP ART'........	Stock Car with Blue body & interior, 5 Red/Yellow psychedelic labels with racing number '20'. Never appeared in catalogues	£50-60	☐
C348	1980-	Vegas Thunderbird	Red body, with Dan Tanner, 124 mm.	£35-45	☐
349	1967	'POP ART' Morris Mini	Red body, Yellow interior, 4 psychedelic labels, 'MOSTEST' logo, Model not generally released or shown in catalogues, few only produced	£700-900	☐
391	1972	James Bond's Mustang Mach I	Red/Black body, Yellow interior, WhizzWheels. Standard boxes had 'JAMES BOND - DIAMONDS ARE FOREVER' stickers..........................	£125-175	☐
391	1972-73	Fire Bug.................................	Orange body, Yellow ladder, 'FIREBUG', 83 mm.	£15-25	☐
426	1962-63	Circus 'BOOKING OFFICE' ...	Karrier Bantam in Chipperfields Circus colours of Red and Blue, with 'BOOK IN ADVANCE' logo and Clown posters	£110-140	☐
C426	1978-82	Circus Booking Office...............	Yellow/Red body, 'JEAN RICHARD PINDER', 122 mm.	£15-20	☐
C423	1978	'ROUGH RIDER'	Chevrolet van with Yellow body, motorcycle side labels	£20-25	☐
C431	1979	'VANATIC'	Chevrolet van with White body, polychromatic side labels	£20-25	☐
C432	1979	'VANTASTIC'	Chevrolet van with Black body, Yellow/Red design	£20-25	☐
C433	1978	'VANISHING POINT'	Chevrolet van shown in 1978 catalogue but not issued	NPP	☐
C434	1978	'CHARLIE'S ANGELS'..........	Chevrolet van with Pink body, Black/Yellow labels	£20-30	☐
C435	1979	'SUPERMAN'	Chevrolet van with Metallic Silver, 'SUPERVAN'	£20-30	☐
C436	1979	'SPIDERMAN'	Chevrolet van with Blue body, 'SPIDERVAN'.	£20-30	☐
C437	1979	'COCA COLA'........................	Chevrolet van with Red body, White design	£20-25	☐
436	1963-65	Citroën 'WILDLIFE SAFARI'	Yellow Citroën ID19, driver & passenger, detailed interior, suspension. 108 mm.	£50-60	☐
472	1964-66	'VOTE FOR CORGI' Land Rover	Corgi 438 in Green/Yellow with 2 loudspeakers & 2 figures in rear	£65-75	☐
475	1964	Citroën Olympic Winter Sport..	White/Yellow Citroën Safari, '1964', roof-rack, skier, skis, 108 mm.	£70-80	☐
475	1965-66	'CORGI SKI CLUB' Citroën ...	Off-White body, Red roof-rack, 4 Yellow skis & 2 poles, bonnet transfer, Brown dashboard/rear seats, Green front seats, 108 mm.	£70-80	☐
			White body, Yellow roof-rack, 4 Red skis & 2 poles, Green dashboard/rear seats, Brown front seats	£70-80	☐

Ref. No.	Year(s)	Model Type	Corgi Toys - continued	Market Price Range
486	1967-69	'KENNEL CLUB' Truck..........	White over Orange Chevrolet Impala with 'Vari-View' dachshund picture plus 4 White dogs .... **£50-60** ☐	
487	1966-69	'CHIPPERFIELDS' Land Rover	438 Land Rover in Red/Blue, *CIRCUS IS HERE*, loudspeakers, Clown.................. **£100-125** ☐	
497	1966-69	The Man From U.N.C.L.E.'s 'Thrush Buster' Chevrolet	Metallic Dark (Purplish) Blue body, 'U.N.C.L.E.' logo, gun sound, 2 figures, has 'Waverley' ring in box which shows Napoleon Solo & Ilya Kuryakin .... **£120-140** ☐ Export version with White body (other details as above)........................... **£300-400** ☐	
499	1968-69	Citroën 1968 Winter Olympics..	White body, Blue roof/tailgate, Silver sled, 2 Red skis & 4 poles, skier, *GRENOBLE* bonnet transfer, 108 mm. .... **£80-100** ☐	
503	1966-72	Giraffe Transporter	Red/Blue body, *CHIPPERFIELDS CIRCUS*, 2 giraffes, 97 mm. .... **£50-75** ☐	
510	1970-72	Citroën Team Managers Car	Red, *Tour De France*, figures, spare wheels, *Paramount*, 108 mm. .... **£45-60** ☐	
511	1970-72	'CHIPPERFIELDS' Circus...... Poodle Truck......................	Chevrolet Pick-Up with Blue/Red body & *PERFORMING POODLES* labels, female trainer, 4 White poodles & platform, 2 Black poodles........... **£250-300** ☐	
513	1970-72	Citroën 'Alpine Rescue' Car	White/Red/Yellow Citroën Safari, roof-rack/dog/sled/male figure, 108 mm. .. **£150-200** ☐	
607	1962-68	Chipperfields Elephant Cage	Brown/Yellow/Blue, *CHIPPERFIELDS CIRCUS*, Grey elephant, 76 mm. .... **£20-30** ☐	
C647	1981	Buck Rogers Starfighter	Yellow/White/Blue, retractable wings, 2 figures, 150 mm. .... **£20-25** ☐	
C648	1980	NASA Space Shuttle	White body, *U.S.A. Satellite*, opening hatch, 156 mm. .... **£20-25** ☐	
C649	1980	James Bond's Space Shuttle	Same as C468 but with *MOONRAKER*.. **£20-25** ☐	
681		Stunt Bike................................	Gold body (with 'Rockets' base) Blue rider, Yellow full-face helmet, No.'8', window-box .... **NGPP** ☐	
700	1974	Motorway Service Ambulance ..	White body, Red details, two Blue roof lights .... **£8-12** ☐	
701	1974	Inter-City Mini-Bus	Orange body, tinted windows, Yellow labels .... **£8-12** ☐	
801	1969-73	Noddy's Car	Yellow/Red car with figures of Noddy, Big-Ears, and Black faced Golly ...... **£750-1000** ☐ Golly with Pink or Light Tan face .... **£200-400** ☐	
802	1970-72	Popeye's Paddle-Wagon	Yellow/White body, Red wings, Blue paddle covers, chrome trim, anchors, moving figures of Popeye, Olive Oyl, Swee'Pea, Bluto and Wimpey............ **£300-350** ☐	
803	1969-72	The Beatles Submarine.............	Yellow/White, psychedelic design, periscope rotates when model is pushed, hatches (Yellow rear, White front open to show John, Paul, George & Ringo, pictorial window box with Green inner lining.................................. **£250-300** ☐ As previous model but with Red hatch covers.. **£200-250** ☐ unusual variant with one Red hatch and one White hatch............................ **£300-400** ☐	
804	1969-73	Noddy's Car	As 801 (with Noddy and Big-Ears) but with Mr. Tubby instead of Golly ...... **£130-160** ☐ Noddy's Car with Noddy only .... **£80-100** ☐	
805	1970	The Hardy Boys Rolls Royce ...	Red/Yellow/Purple/Green car with the 5 Hardy Boys on roof .... **£125-150** ☐	
806	1970-72	Lunar Bug	Red/White/Blue, *Lunar Bug*, windows, drop-down ramps, 127 mm. .... **£80-100** ☐	
807	1971-74	Dougal's Car	Multicoloured, with Brian, Dougal and Dylan, 118 mm. .... **£120-140** ☐	
808	1971-73	Basil Brush's Car.....................	Red/Yellow, hand-painted Basil figure, laugh tapes in box, ('boom', 'boom'). **£80-100** ☐	
809	1973-76	Dick Dastardly's Car................	Multicoloured car plus Dick and Muttley, 128 mm. .... **£80-100** ☐	
811	1972-73	James Bond's Moon Buggy.......	White/Metallic Blue/Yellow, rotating radar dish, James Bond in cockpit ...... **£200-250** ☐	
H 851	1973-74	Magic Roundabout Train	Multicoloured, with Dougal, Mr. Rusty, Basil, Rosalie and Paul, locomotive and two carriages, 311 mm. .... **£150-200** ☐	
H 852	1973-74	Musical Carousel	Multicoloured. Features Dylan plus the children. 200 mm. .... **£500-600** ☐	
853	1973-74	Magic Playground	Contains: H851, H852, 860/1/2 and kids, 820 mm. .... **£350-450** ☐	
H859	1972-74	Mr. McHenry's Trike	Multicoloured. Mr. McHenry and Zebedee, 117 mm. .... **£100-130** ☐	
860-868		Magic Roundabout individual figures:.............	860 Dougal, 861 Florence, 862 Zebedee, 863 Mr Rusty, 864 Brian Snail, 865 Basil, 866 Ermintrude the Cow, 868 Dylan the Rabbit. Each:.................. **£20-40** ☐	
C926	1976	Stromberg Helicopter	Black/Yellow body. (James Bond).. **£25-30** ☐	
C925	1981	Batcopter...............................	Black/Yellow, 'Batman' logo, winch, 143 mm. .... **£25-30** ☐	
C928	1981	Spidercopter............................	Blue/Red body, retractable tongue, 142 mm. .... **£25-30** ☐	
C929	1981	'DAILY PLANET' Jetcopter....	Red/White body, rocket launcher, 156 mm. .... **£15-20** ☐	
C930	1980	Drax Helicopter	White/Yellow, *Drax Airlines*, rocket launcher, 156 mm. .... **£20-25** ☐	

The Exploration Range

Ref. No.	Year(s)	Model Type		Market Price Range
D2022	1980	'SCANOTRON'	Green/Black/Yellow .... **£15-25** ☐	
D2023	1980	'ROCKETRON'	Blue/Yellow, Black tracks .... **£15-25** ☐	
D2024	1980	'LASERTRON'	Orange/Black/Yellow .... **£15-25** ☐	
D2025	1980	'MAGNETRON'........................	Red/Black .... **£15-25** ☐	

The Muppets Show Models

Ref. No.	Year(s)	Model Type		Market Price Range
D2030	1979-82	Kermit's Car	Yellow car with a famous Green frog .... **£30-35** ☐	
D2031	1979-82	Fozzie Bear's Truck..................	Red/Brown/White truck with Fozzie at the wheel .... **£30-35** ☐	
D2032	1979-82	Miss Piggy's Sport Coupé	Pink sports car with the famous porcine beauty driving.............................. **£30-35** ☐	
D2033	1979-82	Animal's Percussionmobile........	An accident involving a Traction-Engine, a Drum-Kit and some sort of . . . . . . 'Animal' .... **£30-35** ☐	

MAJOR PACKS   (Corgi Novelty, Film & TV-related models)

Ref. No.	Year(s)	Model Type		Market Price Range
1119	1960-62	H.D.L. Hovercraft..................	Green/Blue/White body, *SR-N1*, 120 mm. .... **£30-40** ☐	
1121	1960-68	'CHIPPERFIELDS' Crane Truck........................	Red body, Blue logo and wheels, crane jib & hook both operate .... **£100-125** ☐	
1123	1961-63	'CHIPPERFIELDS' Circus Cage........................	Red body, metal cage bars, diecast or Blue plastic end sliding doors with drop-down front flaps, 2 plastic lions .... **£45-55** ☐	
1130	1962-72	'CHIPPERFIELDS' Horse Transporter	Bedford TK truck, Red/Blue, 2 drop-down ramps, Red 'circus' label (front) 'horse-head' design (rear) 6 Grey/Gold horses .... **£100-130** ☐	
1139	1962-72	'CHIPPERFIELDS' Menagerie Transporter	Scammell Handyman Mk.III, Blue/Red cab, Blue trailer with 3 plastic cages, 2 lions, 2 tigers and 2 bears, *MENAGERIE*................................ **£175-225** ☐	
1144	1969-72	'CHIPPERFIELDS' Crane & Cage with Hippo.....	Scammell Handyman Mk.III, Red/Blue body, silver jib & hook. Cab front has *CHIPPERFIELDS* label, *COME TO THE CIRCUS* on sides .... **£200-250** ☐	

54

Ref. No.	Year(s)	Model Type	Corgi Toys - continued	Market Price Range	
C1163	1978-82	Circus Cannon Truck..............	Red and Blue body, 'MARVO' figure, 130 mm.	£30-40	☐
C1164	1980-83	Berliet 'DOLPHINARIUM'	Yellow/Blue cab and trailer, Clear plastic tank, 2 dolphins, girl trainer	£45-55	☐

Corgi Toys - Roadmaking Vehicles and Cranes

Ref. No.	Year(s)	Model Type	Model Features and Size	Market Price Range	
54	1974	Massey Ferguson Shovel..........	Orange/White tractor body, Silver shovel, 'Block Construction', 150 mm.	£35-45	☐
109	1968-69	'PENNYBURN' Trailer............	Blue body, Yellow chassis, 76 mm.	£30-35	☐
403	1974-79	Thwaites Skip Dumper............	Yellow/Green tipping body, driver, WhizzWheels, 83 mm.	£25-35	☐
406	1971-75	Mercedes-Benz Unimog............	Yellow/Green or Yellow/Red body, detachable top, suspension, hook, 91 mm...........	£25-35	☐
409	1971-75	Unimog Dumper	White/Red or Blue/Yellow body, suspension, hook, 104 mm.	£20-30	☐
C409	1981	'ALLIS CHALMERS' Forklift	Yellow body, pallets/load/driver, 112 mm.	£15-20	☐
413	1976-78	Mazda Motorway Maintenance........................	Yellow/Black body, figure, road signs, bollards, decal sheet enclosed......................	£25-35	☐
458	1958-66	E.R.F. Earth Dumper	Red and Yellow body, ('E.R.F.' cast-in) 95 mm.	£40-45	☐
459	1974-78	Raygu Rascal Roller	Yellow/Green body, 'Road Roller', 125 mm.	£20-25	☐
460	1959-60	E.R.F. Cement Tipper............	Yellow/Grey body, (Neville) (E.R.F. cast-in) 95 mm.	£45-55	☐
483	1968-72	Dodge Tipper Truck...............	Yellow/Black or White/Blue body, 'KEW FARGO', spun or cast wheels, 136 mm.	£25-35	☐
494	1967-72	Bedford Tipper......................	Red/Yellow body, rear view mirror, 102 mm.	£35-45	☐
		variant:	Red body, Silver tipper	£65-75	☐

MAJOR PACKS (Corgi Roadmaking Vehicles and Cranes)

Ref. No.	Year(s)	Model Type	Model Features and Size	Market Price Range	
C1101	1976-81	Mobile Crane	Yellow/Blue body, 'Warner & Swasey', 150 mm.	£25-30	☐
1102	1958-62	'EUCLID' TC 12 Tractor........	Pale Lime Green body, Pale Grey tracks, 159 mm. Box has inner lining.	£80-90	☐
			As previous model but with Black tracks	£50-60	☐
C1102	1974-76	'BERLIET' Bottom Dumper	Yellow and Orange body, 'Road Construction', 287 mm...............	£30-35	☐
1103	1960-63	'EUCLID' Crawler Tractor.......	Pale Lime Green body, Pale Grey tracks, 111 mm.	£80-90	☐
			As previous model but with Black tracks	£50-60	☐
1107	1963-66	'EUCLID' with Dozer..............	Yellow/Green body, tracks, driver, 159 mm.	£60-70	☐
1110	1976-80	'JCB' Crawler Loader............	Yellow/White body, Red working bucket, Black tracks, driver.	£15-20	☐
1110	1976-80	J.C.B. Crawler	Yellow and White body, driver, 115 mm.	£15-20	☐
			Light Blue/Orange with Light Blue chassis, driver....................	£15-20	☐
			Yellow body, Light Blue cab, Red bucket....................	£15-20	☐
			Red body, Light Blue cab and bucket....................	£15-20	☐
C1113	1981-86	'HYSTER' Handler..................	Yellow or Black/White main body, 'US Lines', hoist, 212 mm.	£15-20	☐
	1986-87		Yellow or Black/White main body, 'SEALINK', container, export model	£10-15	☐
	1986-87		White/Dark Blue/Yellow, 'MICHELIN', container	£10-15	☐
1119	1983	Mercedes Load Lugger............	Yellow/Red body, 'CORGI'....................	£15-20	☐
1121	1983	Ford Transit Tipper	Orange/Beige body, 'CORGI', (Corgimatic)....................	£15-20	☐
1122	1984	Mercedes Mixer	Orange body, Black stripes	£10-15	☐
1122	1985		Orange body, White revolving drum, Black/Yellow design	£10-15	☐
1128	1963-76	'PRIESTMAN' Cub Shovel......	Red/Yellow body, driver, 165 mm.	£30-35	☐
1128	1984	Mercedes Tipper	Yellow cab, Red tipper, 6 wheels, 'BLOCK' logo	£10-15	☐
1128	1985	Mercedes Tipper	Black body, White logo 'TARMAC'	£10-15	☐
1145	1970-76	Unimog Goose Dumper............	Yellow/Red body, '406', 171 mm.	£30-35	☐
1150	1971	Mercedes 406 Snowplough........	Unimog in Green/Black, 2 Red flags, Orange/Silver plough	£30-35	☐
1152	1983-	'BARRATT' Tipper	Green/White body, tipper section tips, 145 mm.	£5-10	☐
1153	1973-74	'PRIESTMAN' Crane..............	Red/Orange body, 'Higrab', 230 mm...............	£45-55	☐
C1153	1983-84	'WIMPEY' Tipper Truck.........	Green/Silver body, tipping section tips, 145 mm. (Scania)....................	£5-10	☐
C1153	1984		Yellow body	£5-10	☐
C1153	1985	'LAING' Tipper Truck	As previous model but with Yellow body and Black logo	£5-10	☐
1154	1974-76	Priestman Crane Truck	Yellow/Red body, Silver boom, hook, 240 mm.	£45-55	☐
1154	1979	'BLOCK CONSTRUCTION'.......	Orange/Yellow crane, White body, brick pallet load	£25-35	☐
C1155	1975-79	'Skyscraper' Tower Crane	Yellow/Red body, Black tracks, 340 mm.	£35-40	☐
1156	1977-80	Volvo Concrete Mixer............	Yellow/Red body, 'RAPIER'	£20-25	☐
1156	1980		Orange/White body, 'BLOCK CONSTRUCTION'	£15-20	☐

Corgi Truckers

A new series of 1:76 scale models

Ref. No.	Year(s)	Model Type	Model Features and Size	Market Price Range	
C1300/1	1989	MAN Container	Yellow/Blue body, 'YORKIE'	NRP	☐
C1301/1	1989	MAN Tanker 'BP'....................	White body, Yellow/Green design	NRP	☐
C1301/2	1989	MAN Tanker 'MOBIL'	Beige body, Blue/Red logo	NRP	☐
C1302/1	1989	MAN Tipper	All Orange	NRP	☐
C1303/1	1989	Ford Cargo Container............	Yellow body, Orange tilt, 'SCHWEPPES'	NRP	☐
C1302/2	1989	Ford Cargo Container............	White/Green body, '7 UP'	NRP	☐
C1304/1	1989	Ford Cargo Tanker	White/Blue/Yellow, 'DUCKHAMS OILS'	NRP	☐
C1304/2	1989	Ford Cargo Tanker	Yellow/Silver body, 'SHELL'	NRP	☐
C1305/1	1989	Ford Cargo Tipper	Grey/Green/Silver body	NRP	☐
C1305/2	1989	Ford Tipper	Red/Silver body....................	NRP	☐

Corgi Toys - Miscellaneous models

Jeeps, Land Rovers, Pick-ups, Caravans, Motor Cycles, Go-Karts, Trailers, Public Service Vehicles, etc

Ref. No.	Year(s)	Model Type	Model Features and Size	Market Price Range	
C46	1983-	Super Kart	Blue or Orange main body, Red/Silver racing driver	£5-10	☐
100	1957-61	Dropside Trailer	Cream/Red or Yellow body, drawbar, 108 mm.	£10-15	☐
101	1958-61	Platform Trailer	Grey/Yellow body, drawbar and axle swivel, 108 mm.	£10-15	☐
C171	1982-	Street Bike	Red, Silver and Black body, multicoloured swirl	£5-10	☐
C172	1982-	'POLICE' Bike	White/Black/Silver body	£5-10	☐
C173	1982-	Cafe Racer	Silver and Black racing number '26', '750 cc Class'	£5-10	☐
289	1976	VW Polo 'DBP'	Yellow/White, Blue roof beacon, left-hand drive, WhizzWheels, (German issue)	NGPP	☐
383	1970-73	VW 1200 'PTT'	Yellow Swiss Postal livery, (Swiss issue)	£100-150	☐
383	1970-73	VW 1200 'ADAC'	Yellow/White 'ADAC' livery, (German issue)	£100-150	☐
406	1957-63	Land Rover Pick-Up	Yellow body, Black roof, spare wheel on bonnet, smooth spun wheels, Blue box	£45-55	☐
			As previous model but shaped wheels, Blue/Yellow box	£45-50	☐
			Metallic Bright Blue body, Cream roof, smooth wheels, Blue/Yellow box	£45-50	☐
			Yellow body, Red seats, Grey steering wheel, smooth wheels	£80-90	☐
409	1959-63	Forward Control Jeep	Blue body, Red grille, 91 mm.	£25-35	☐
C415	1976-78	Mazda Camper	Red body with drop-down tailboard, White caravan, 140 mm.	£25-30	☐
417	1963-65	Land Rover Breakdown	Red/Yellow, 4 strut bumper, smooth wheels, 'BREAKDOWN SERVICE'	£40-50	☐
417s	1963-65	Land Rover Breakdown	As previous model but solid bumper, shaped wheels, suspension	£35-45	☐
C419	1978-79	Covered Jeep CJ5	Green with White plastic top, 100 mm.	£15-20	☐
420	1962-66	Ford 'Airborne' Caravan	Ford Thames in Blue/Grey, Blue/Green, or Two-tone Green, or Blue	£35-55	☐
			Lilac body	£70-80	☐
C421	1977-79	Land Rover Safari Hardtop	Orange/Black body, roof rack with ladder, spare wheel, 114 mm.	£15-20	☐
		Land Rover Safari Hardtop	A variant of C421 with 'FOREST FIRE WARDEN'	£15-20	☐
431	1964-66	Volkswagen Pick-Up	Yellow/Red, seats, steering wheel, suspension, 91 mm.	£45-55	☐
434	1963-66	Volkswagen Kombi	Two-tone Green, Red or Yellow seats, 91 mm.	£45-55	☐
438	1963-77	Land Rover	Red, Dark Green or Metallic Green body with either Grey, Dark Grey or Cream plastic canopy, spare wheel on bonnet, 95 mm.	£50-60	☐
438	19?-?	Land Rover 'LEPRA'	Metallic Green and Cream, 'LEPRA', promotional	£200-250	☐
C440	1979-	Mazda Custom Pick-Up	Orange/Yellow/Red, US flag, 120 mm.	£10-15	☐
C441	1979-82	'GOLDEN EAGLE' Jeep	Brown/Tan or Gold/White, detachable roof, spare wheel on some, 100 mm.	£10-15	☐
C447	1983	'RENEGADE' Jeep	Yellow with Red hood	£10-15	☐
C448	1985	4 x 4 'RENEGADE' Jeep	Red/White body, roll bar, 100 mm.	£5-10	☐
C457	1981-83	Talbot Matra Rancho	Red/Black or Green/Black, opening doors and boot, tilt seats, 120 mm.	£10-15	☐
C457	1984	Talbot Matra Rancho	Green or White/Blue body, Brown seats, 120 mm.	£5-10	☐
470	1965-72	Forward Control Jeep	Blue/Grey or Mustard Yellow, suspension, left-hand drive, 91 mm.	£30-35	☐
477	1966-67	Land Rover Breakdown	Red/Yellow/Silver, spare wheel on some, hook, WhizzWheels, 114 mm.	£30-35	☐
478	1965-69	Jeep Tower Wagon	Green, Yellow and Silver body, figure, 129 mm.	£20-25	☐
C490	1967-70	Volkswagen Breakdown	Tan/Red, tool-box, 2 spare wheels, 102 mm.	£40-50	☐
C490	1976-79	Touring Caravan	White and Blue body, opening doors, drawbar, 125 mm.	£10-15	☐
C493	1976-78	Mazda B 1600 Pick-Up	Blue body, drop-down tailboard, 120 mm.	£10-15	☐
C495	1983-	4x4 Mazda 'OB TRUCK'	Blue/Black, 'Corgi Cruiser', drop-down tailboard, 121 mm.	£5-10	☐
C495	1985	4x4 Mazda	As previous model but Blue/White body, 'SURF RIDER'	£5-10	☐
C501	1984	Range Rover	Beige and Dark Brown body	£5-10	☐
C507	1987	Range Rover Rally	Navy Blue body, White roof, 'PARIS - DAKAR' logo	£20-30	☐
C522		Range Rover	Red/White/Blue, 'STIMOROL'	NGPP	☐
C567	1984	Range Rover	White body, 'PARIS MATCH', and 'VSD'	£7-10	☐
C619	1986	Land Rover	Dark Beige body, Black ladder, roof-rack, luggage	£5-10	☐
Q619/3	1990	'NORWEB' Land Rover	White with 3 Black side stripes, spare wheel	NRP	☐
681	1971	Stunt Bike	Gold engine, Silver WhizzWheels, Mauve/Yellow rider, Red trolley (19,000 made)	NGPP	☐

MAJOR PACKS   (Miscellaneous Corgi models)

1106	1984	'CORGI' Loadlugger	Yellow body and chassis, Red 'BIG BIN'	£10-15	☐
1114	1984	Mercedes Gritter	Yellow/Black body and plough, ladder	£10-15	☐
1114			Yellow/Black body with Red stripes, 'MOTORWAY MAINTENANCE'	£10-15	☐
1115	1985	Parisienne Refuse Truck	Green body, 'PARIS' logo, export model	£10-15	☐
1116	1979	S & D Refuse Collector	Orange or Red body, 'City Sanitation', 151 mm.	£15-20	☐
1116/2	1988		Blue cab, White tipper, 'BOROUGH COUNCIL'	£5-10	☐
1117	1980	'FAUN' Street-sweeper	Orange/Yellow vehicle with operator	£15-20	☐
			All-Yellow version	£15-20	☐
1119	1960-62	HDL Hovercraft 'SR-N1'	Blue/Grey/White body, Yellow rudders and wheels	£30-35	☐
1150	1974-77	Unimog with Snow Plough	Yellow/Brown body, Silver blade, 2 flags, 155 mm.	£30-35	☐

Corgi Rockets

This model range was issued between 1970 and 1972 to compete against Mattel 'Hot Wheels' and similar products. The models had 'WhizzWheels' and featured a special 'Tune-Up' system which increased the play value and speed of the virtually frictionless wheels. In addition they were very robust, being advertised as 'four times stronger' than most other diecast racers. To begin with seven Corgi Juniors were adapted as Rockets and five of those received a superb vacuum metallised finish.

A range of accessories was also issued in the form of 'Speed Circuits' etc, and each car was issued with a special 'Golden Tune-Up Key' which released the base. The bubble-packed models are difficult to find in top condition and the prices reflect their scarcity.

Ref. No.	Year(s)	Model Type	Model Features and Size	Market Price Range	
D 901	1970-72	Aston-Martin DB-6	Metallic Deep Gold body, Green interior	£30-40	☐
D 902	1970-72	Jaguar XJ-6	Metallic Green body, Cream interior	£30-40	☐
D 903	1970-72	Mercedes-Benz 280 SL	Metallic Orange body, White interior	£30-40	☐
D 904	1970-72	Porsche Carrera 6	Orange-Yellow body, Black number '19'	£30-40	☐
D 905	1970-72	'The Saint's Volvo P1800	White body, Blue/White 'Saint' label on bonnet	£40-50	☐
D 906	1970-72	Jensen Interceptor	Metallic Red body, Yellow interior	£30-40	☐
D 907	1970-72	Cadillac Eldorado	Metallic Copper body, White interior	£30-40	☐
D 908	1970-72	Chevrolet Astro	Metallic Red/Black body	£30-40	☐
D 909	1970-72	Mercedes-Benz C111	Red or Blue body, White interior	£20-30	☐
D 910	1970-72	Beach Buggy	Orange body, Black interior	£20-30	☐
D 911	1970-72	Marcos XP	Gold body, Chrome interior	£20-30	☐
D 913	1970-72	Aston-Martin DBS	Metallic Blue, Yellow interior	£30-40	☐
D 916	1970-72	Carabo Bertone	Metallic Green/Blue, Orange interior	£20-30	☐
D 917	1970-72	Pininfarina Alfa-Romeo	Metallic Purple/White	£20-30	☐
D 918	1970-72	Bitzzarini Manta	Metallic Dark Blue, White interior	£20-30	☐
D 919	1970-72	'Todd Sweeney' Stock Car	Red/Purple, Yellow/Black front, RN '531'	£50-75	☐
D 920	1970-72	'Derek Fiske' Stock Car	White/Red, Silver bonnet, Red logo, RN '304'	£50-75	☐
D 921	1970-72	Morgan Open Sports	Metallic Red body, Black seats	£30-40	☐
D 922	1970-72	Rally Ford Capri	Yellow body, Orange/Black stripe, RN '8'	£30-40	☐
			Green body, Black bonnet, (GS 2 model)	£30-40	☐
D 923	1970-72	'James Bond' Ford Escort	White body, Pale Blue stripes, 'JAMES BOND', White '007' and 'SPECIAL AGENT' logos. (From film 'On Her Majesty's Secret Service')	£150-200	☐
D 924	1970-72	Mercury Cougar XR7	Red body with Black roof, Yellow interior	£30-40	☐
		'James Bond' issue:	Red/Black with Yellow side flash, interior and skis on roof rack. (From film 'On Her Majesty's Secret Service').	£150-200	☐
D 925	1970-72	'James Bond' Ford Capri	White body with Black/White check design, 2 bonnet stripes and RN '6'. (From film 'On Her Majesty's Secret Service')	£150-200	☐
D 926	1970-72	Jaguar 'Control Car'	Metallic Brown body, Red roof blade, Blue/White figures	£75-100	☐
D 927	1970-72	Ford Escort Rally	White body, Red RN '18', 'DAILY MIRROR' labels on doors, '1970 Mexico World Cup Rally Winner'	£75-85	☐
D 928	1970-72	Mercedes 280 SL 'SPECTRE'	Black body with Red 'S.P.E.C.T.R.E.' logo, plus bonnet design	£150-200	☐
D 930	1970-72	Bertone Barchetta	Metallic Green over White body, Red interior	£20-30	☐
D 931	1970-72	'Old MacDonalds Truck'	Yellow cab, Brown rear, Silver engine	£75-100	☐
D 933	1970-72	'Holmes Wrecker'	White cab, Gold/Red rear assembly with Red *AUTO RESCUE*. (Not seen)	NGPP	☐
D 937	1970-72	Mercury Cougar	Metallic Dark Green body, Yellow interior and spoiler	£20-30	☐

Corgi Rockets Gift Sets

D 975	1970	Super Stock Gift Set 1	Contains D 905, D 919, Trailer and 3 figures	NGPP	☐
D 976	1970	Super Stock Gift Set 2	Contains Green/Black D 922, D 920, Trailer and 3 figures	NGPP	☐
D 977	1970	Super Stock Gift Set 3	Contains D 926, D 919, D 920 and 5 figures	NGPP	☐

The listing above has been prepared from a Corgi Rockets 1970 catalogue. The sets themselves have not been seen and further information is required.

D 978		'O.H.M.S.S.' Gift Set	Models of cars in the James Bond film 'On Her Majesty's Secret Service': D 923 and D 925 (as driven in the ice-racing scene) D 924 (as driven by 'Tracey') D 928 (as driven by the Chief of 'S.P.E.C.T.R.E.')	£500-750	☐

Corgi Rockets 'Speedsets' and 'Speed Circuits' Track Layouts

D 2051	1970	Action Speedset	One car, 'Autostart', 12 ft of track	NGPP	☐
D 2052	1970	Super Autobatics Speedset	One car, 'Autostart', 16 ft of track plus 'leaps' etc	NGPP	☐
D 2058	1970	Race-Abatic Speedset	Two cars, 'Autostart', 2 x 16 ft of track plus 'leaps' etc	NGPP	☐
D 2071	1970	Jetspeed Circuit	One car, 'Superbooster', 16 ft of track plus 'leaps' etc	NGPP	☐
D 2074	1970	Triple-Leap Speed Circuit	One car, 19 ft, 6 in. of track plus 'leaps' etc	NGPP	☐
D 2075	1970	Grand Canyon Speed Circuit	One car, 12 ft of track	NGPP	☐
D 2079	1970	World Champion Speedset	Two cars, 2 x 16 ft of track, 2 Boosters	NGPP	☐

Corgi Rockets catalogues

no ref.	1969	8-page booklet	listing the first 7 issues, Green model on cover	£20-25	☐
no ref.	1970	16-page booklet	listing most issues, good pictures of rare models, sets and accessories	£30-35	☐

Corgi Rockets Accessories

D 1931 Superleap, D 1934 Autofinish, D 1935 Connections (3) D 1936 Space Leap, D 1937 Autostart, D 1938 Super Crossover, D 1945 Adaptors (3) D 1963 Track (16ft) D 1970 Super Booster, D 1971 Hairpin Tunnel, D 1976 Quickfire Start, D 1977 Lap Counter, D 1978 Pitstop, D 1979 Spacehanger Bend

Corgi Toys Gift Sets

Ref. No.	Year(s)	Set Name	Contents	Market Price Range	
1	1957-62	Transporter and 4 Cars	1101 Blue/Yellow Bedford Carrimore Transporter plus 201 Austin Cambridge, 208 Jaguar 2.4, 301 Triumph TR2 and 302 MGA, plus 2 Yellow/Black 'Corgi Toys' dummy boxes	£500-600	☐
1	1957-62	Transporter and 4 Cars	1101 Red/Two-tone Blue Transporter, 200 Ford Consul, 201 Austin Cambridge, 204 Rover 90, 205 Riley Pathfinder, 2 Yellow 'Corgi Toys' dummy boxes	£400-500	☐
C1	1983	Ford Sierra Set	Ford Sierra 299 with Blue body and Blue/Cream Caravan	£20-30	☐
C1/2	1985	'London Scene'	469 'LONDON STANDARD', Sierra Police Car and 425/1 Taxi	£15-20	☐
2	1958-66	Land Rover and Pony Trailer Set	438 Land Rover (Green, Beige tin tilt) and 102 Pony Trailer (Red/Black)	£150-175	☐
		colour change:	As previous set but Light Brown Land Rover (Cream plastic tilt) Light Brown/Cream trailer	£70-80	☐
2	1971-73	Unimog Dumper and Shovel	1128 and 1145	£30-35	☐
C2		Fire Set	no details at present	£15-20	☐
3	1959-62	Land Rover with Thunderbird Missile	Contains 350 and 351	£60-70	☐
3	1967-69	Batmobile and Batboat	1st issue: 267 Batmobile plus 107 Batboat, in plain window box with 4 figures	£200-250	☐
3	?	2nd issue:	267 Batmobile and 107 Batboat in pictorial window box, only 2 figures	£100-125	☐
4	1959-62	Bristol Ferranti Bloodhound Guided Missile Set	Contains: 351, 1115, 1116, 1117 (see 'Military Vehicles' section)	£250-350	☐
4	1974-75	Country Farm Set	Models 50, 62 and equipment	£40-50	☐
5	1959-60	Racing Car Set	150 (Red) 151 (Blue) 152 (Green). All have flat spun wheels	£150-200	☐
5	1960-61	Racing Car Set	150 (Red) 151 (Blue) 152 (Green). All have cast spoked wheels	£150-200	☐
5s	1962-63	Racing Car Set	150s (Red) 151a (Blue) 152s (Turquoise). 'Gift Set 5s' stickers on box	£150-200	☐
5	1967-72	Agricultural Set	484 Livestock Transporter and pigs, 438 Land Rover (no hood) 62, 69, accessories 1490 skip & churns, 4 calves, farmhand & dog, 6 sacks	£150-200	☐
6	1959-62	'Rocket Age' Set	Contains: 350, 351, 352, 353, 1106, 1108, 1117 (see 'Military' section)	£600-800	☐
6	1967-69	Cooper Maserati Racing Set	Contains 490 VW Breakdown Truck plus 156 on trailer	£70-90	☐
7	1959-63	Tractor and Trailer Set	Contains 50 and 51	£70-80	☐
7	1968-75	'DAKTARI' Set	438 Land Rover in Green with Black Zebra stripes. 5 figures: Paula, Dr Marsh Tracy with chimp Judy on his lap, a Tiger on the bonnet, and Clarence The Short-Sighted Lion (with spectacles!)	£75-85	☐
8	1959-61	Combine Harvester, Tractor & Trailer Set	Contains 1111, 50 and 51	£150-175	☐
8	1960-74	'Lions Of Longleat' Set	Land Rover, keeper, 3 lions, dens and meals	£70-80	☐
C8/2		Police Set		£15-20	☐
9	1959-62	Corporal Guided Missile Set	Contains: 1112, 1113, 1118 (see 'Military Vehicles' section)	£250-300	☐
9	1968-72	Tractor, Trailer and Shovel Set	Contains 66, 69 and 62	£100-125	☐
9		3 Racing Minis Set	Yellow, White and Blue, numbers/stripes/adverts, special Red 'Hamleys' box	£90-110	☐
10	1968-69	Rambler Marlin and Kayaks	Blue/White 319 with Trailer and 2 Canoes	£100-130	☐
10	1974-78	Centurion Tank and Transporter Set	Contains 901 and 1100 Mack articulated transporter	£70-80	☐
10	1982	Jeep Set	Red 441 plus two motorcycles on trailer	£20-25	☐
11	1960-64	E.R.F. Dropside and Trailer	456 and 101 with cement and planks	£80-100	☐
11	1971-75	London Gift Set	Contains 418 Taxi with 468 'OUTSPAN' and 226 Mini	£75-95	☐
C11	1980	London Gift Set	C425 Taxi with C469 Bus 'B.T.A.' and policeman	£30-35	☐
12	1961-66	Circus Gift Set	1121 Circus Crane Truck and 1123 Circus Cage, plus instructions	£150-175	☐
12	1968-70	Grand Prix Racing Set	155, 156 and 330 with Volkswagen tender, trailer and equipment	£200-250	☐
12	1970-72	Grand Prix Racing Set	158, 159 and 330 (or 371) with Volkswagen tender, trailer and equipment. The artwork on the box and the vac-formed base are different from previous issue	£200-250	☐
C12	1981-	Glider and Trailer Set	345 with Trailer and Glider	£30-40	☐
13	1964-67	Fordson Tractor & Plough Set	Contains 60 and 61	£75-85	☐
13	1969-72	Renault 16 'PARAMOUNT' Film Unit	White/Black body, 'TOUR DE FRANCE' logos, camera/operator, cyclist	£75-85	☐
13	1981-82	Tour De France 'RALEIGH' Team Car	373 Peugeot, White body, Red/Yellow 'RALEIGH' and 'TOTAL' logos, racing cycles and Manager with loudhailer	£50-60	☐
14	1961-65	Tower Wagon Set	409 Jeep, Yellow cradle, lamp standard & electrician	£60-70	☐
14	1969-73	Giant 'DAKTARI' Set	Gift Set 7 items plus 503 and 484 transporters	£200-250	☐
15	1963-64	Silverstone Set	150s, 151a, 152s, 215s, 304s, 309, 417s, 3 buildings, plain box (no picture)	£750-£1000	☐
15	1964-66	Silverstone Set	150s, 154, 152s, 215s, 304s, 309, 417s, 3 buildings, layout shown on box	£750-£1000	☐
15	1968-76	Land Rover & Horsebox Set	Contains 438, 112, mare and foal	£50-60	☐
16	1961-66	'ECURIE ECOSSE' Set	1126 Transporter with 3 racing cars with instruction leaflet.		☐
		i)	Metallic Dark Blue 1126 Transporter (with Orange lettering) 150 Vanwall (Red, no.'25') 151 Lotus Eleven (Blue, number '3') 152 BRM (Turquoise, no.'3').	£200-250	☐
		ii)	Metallic Dark Blue 1126 Transporter (with Yellow lettering) 150s Vanwall, 151a Lotus Eleven (Blue, no. '7') 152s BRM	£300-350	☐
	1965	iii)	Metallic Light Blue 1126 Transporter (with Red lettering) 150s Vanwall, 152s BRM, 154 Ferrari (Red, no.'36')	£200-250	☐
		iv)	Metallic Dark Blue 1126 Transporter (with Light Blue lettering and ridges) 150s Vanwall, 152s BRM, 154 Ferrari	£200-250	☐
17	1963-67	Ferrari Racing Set	Contains 438 Land Rover in Red with Green canopy, plus Red 154 Ferrari F1 on Yellow trailer	£60-75	☐
17	1976-81	Military Set	Contains 904, 906, 920 (see 'Military Vehicles' section)	£40-50	☐
C17	1986	'BRITISH TELECOM' Set	Ford Cargo Box Van, Ford Escort Van and a Compressor	£15-20	☐

Ref. No.	Year(s)	Model Type	Corgi Toys - continued	Market Price Range	
18	1961-63	Ford Tractor and Plough Set....	Contains 55 and 56	£60-70	☐
18	1976-77	Emergency Gift Set	Contains 402, 481, C921 (see 'Emergency Vehicles' section)	£40-50	☐
C18/1	?	3 Mini Racers Set	with 'CHELSEA', 'PARK LANE' and 'PICADILLY' logos...	£20-30	☐
C18/2	?	Mini Special Editions Set	with 'RED HOT', 'RITZ' and 'JET BLACK' logos	£20-30	☐
		Note:.....	C18/1 and C18/2 were sold (in long 'window' boxes) exclusively by Woolworths.		
19	1962-68	'CHIPPERFIELDS' Cage Set...	438 Land Rover (plastic tilt) and 607 Elephant and cage on trailer............................	£150-175	☐
19		'R.N.L.I.' Set	438 Land Rover plus Orange dinghy on trailer with 'Mumbles Lifeboat' logo	£45-65	☐
C19	1972-77	Land Rover & Nipper Aircraft	438 Land Rover (Blue/Orange) Yellow/Red or All-Orange plane '23' on trailer........	£45-55	☐
19	1973-77	'CORGI FLYING CLUB'.......	Blue/Orange Land Rover (438) with aircraft...	£60-70	☐
C19	1979-82	Emergency Gift Set	Contains C339 and C921	£30-40	☐
C19	1980-82	Emergency Gift Set	Contains C339 and C931 in Red/White liveries	£35-45	☐
C19/7	1990	Norwegian 'AMBULANSE' Set..	White Ford Transit Van & Saab 9000 'POLITI'	£30-40	☐
C19/8	1990	Swedish 'AMBULANS' Set	White/Red Ford Transit Van & White/Blue Saab 9000 'POLIS'	£30-40	☐
C19/9	1990	Swedish Breakdown Set	Red/Yellow Ford Transit 'Bjarnings', Black Saab 9000 'BRANDCHEF'	£30-40	☐
20	1961	Golden Guinea Set	Gold-plated 224 Bentley Continental, 234 Ford Consul, 229 Chevrolet Corvair, Catalogue, 2 Accessory Packs..	£150-200	☐
20	1973	Tri-Deck Transporter Set	1st issue contains 1146 Transporter with 210 'Saint's' Volvo, 311 Ford Capri, 343 Pontiac, 372 Lancia, 377 Marcos, and 378 MGC GT (rare Orange version)	£500-600	☐
20		Tri-Deck Transporter Set	late issue with WhizzWheels (sold in Harrods) contains 377 Marcos (Silver Green), 382 Porsche Targa (Silver Blue), 201 Volvo (Orange 'Saint' label), 313 Ford Cortina GXL (Bronze/Black), 334 Mini (Orange), plus retailers pull-out leaflet illustrating Transporter..	£500-600	☐
C20	1978-80	Emergency Gift Set	Contains C429, C482, C921 (see 'Emergency Vehicles' section)	£30-40	☐
C20/2	1986	A.A. Set....................................	Ford Escort and Transit Vans, Ford Transit Breakdown	£15-20	☐
21	1962-66	E.R.F. Dropside and Trailer	456 and 101 with milk churns and self-adhesive accessories	£175-225	☐
21	1969-71	'CHIPPERFIELDS' Circus Set..	Contains 1144 Crane & Cage and 1139 Menagerie Transporter	£750-1000	☐
C21	1980-82	Superman Set............................	Contains 260, 265 and 925..	£85-100	☐
C21/2	1986	R.A.C. Set.................................	Range Rover, Ford Escort Van and Ford Transit Breakdown	£15-20	☐
22	1962-66	Farming Models Set	111, 406, 51, 101, 53, 1487, 1490, accessories & GS18...	£600-700	☐
C22	1980-82	James Bond Set	Contains 269, 271 and 649...	£125-150	☐
C22	1986	'ROYAL MAIL' Set	Ford Cargo & Escort Vans, Austin Mini Metro 'DATAPOST'	£15-20	☐
23	1962-66	'CHIPPERFIELDS'	1st issue: 1121 Crane Truck, 2 x 1123 Animal Cages (2 lions, 2 polar bears) plus Gift Set 19 and 426 Booking Office	£400-500	☐
	1964	2nd issue:.....	as 1st issue but 503 Land Rover replaces 426 Booking Office	£350-450	☐
C23	1980-82	Spiderman Set............................	Contains 261, 266 and 928..	£75-90	☐
24	1963-68	Commer Constructor Set	2 cab/chassis units, 4 interchangeable bodies, milkman, accessories.....................	£90-110	☐
24	1976-	Mercedes and Caravan Set	Contains 285 and 490 with colour change 1980..	£25-35	☐
25	1963-66	BP or Shell Garage Set	Contains Garage with 5 various cars, figures and accessories	£150-200	☐
25	1969-71	Racing Car and Tender Set.......	Contains 159 and Volkswagen Tender...	£80-90	☐
25	1980	Talbot Rancho Set	457 plus two motorcycles on trailer	£15-20	☐
26	1971-75	Beach Buggy Set	381 plus Sailing Boat	£30-40	☐
26	1981-83	Corgi Racing Set	457 Talbot Matra Rancho, 160 Hesketh (Yellow) on 'Corgi Racing Team' trailer	£35-45	☐
27	1963-72	Priestman Shovel on Machinery Carrier	1128 and 1131 (Bedford Machinery Carrier)..	£90-110	☐
C27		Emergency Set	no details	£15-20	☐
28	1963-66	Transporter and 4 Cars.............	1105 Bedford TK Transporter with 222 Renault Floride, 230 Mercedes-Benz, 232 Fiat, 234 Ford Classic, 2 dummy 'Corgi Toys' boxes, instructions. Pictorial box	£400-500	☐
28	1963-66	Mazda Dinghy Set....................	493 Mazda plus dinghy on trailer	£40-45	☐
C28	1987	Post Set....................................	Contains 656/2, Red Sierra (racing number '63')...	£20-25	☐
29	1963-64	Massey Ferguson Tractor and Trailer Set...........	Contains 50, 51, driver..	£65-75	☐
C29	1981	'CORGI' Pony Club.................	Contains 441 Jeep, 112 trailer, girl on pony, 3 jumps, 3 hay bales	£25-35	☐
29	1975-76	Ferrari Racing Set	Contains 323 and 150, 'DUCKHAMS'...	£60-75	☐
30	1973-73	Grand Prix Gift Set	'Kit' versions of 151 Yardley (1501), 154 JPS (1504), 152 Surtees (1502) plus 153 Surtees (1503)? in unique Norris livery. Mail order only....................................	£150-200	☐
C30	1978-80	Circus Gift Set..........................	Land Rover and Trailer	£50-60	☐
31	1965-68	Buick Riviera Boat Set	245 Buick, Red boat trailer, and Dolphin Cabin Cruiser towing water skier	£75-100	☐
C31	1977-80	Safari Land Rover Set..............	C341 Land Rover with animal trailer, Warden and Lion..	£30-40	☐
32	1965-68	Tractor, Shovel and Trailer Set	Contains 54 and 62	£100-125	☐
C32	1976-79	Lotus Racing Set	Black/Gold C301 Lotus Elite, and C154 JPS Lotus on trailer	£50-75	☐
C32	1979-83	Lotus Racing Set	Black/Gold C301 Lotus Elite, and C154 Texaco Lotus on trailer...........................	£50-75	☐
C32	1989-90	3 Model Set	Contains Concorde, Taxi and Routemaster Bus 'STANDARD'	£20-30	☐
33	1965-68	Tractor & Beast Carrier	Contains 55 and 58	£100-125	☐
?	1968-72	Tractor & Beast Carrier	Contains 67 and 58	£70-80	☐
C33	1980	'DLRG' Rescue Set	White/Red 421 Land Rover and boat on trailer	£25-30	☐
34	1977-79	Tractor and Tipping Trailer	Contains 55 and 56	£25-35	☐
35	1965-68	London Gift Set	418 Taxi with 648 'Corgi Toys' and policeman	£80-100	☐
C35	1978-79	'CHOPPER SQUAD' Surf Boat	Contains 927, 419, trailer, rescue boat	£30-40	☐
36	1967-70	Marlin Rambler Set..................	Contains 263 and Boat	£45-65	☐
36	1967-70	Oldsmobile Toronado Set	Contains 276 (Greenish-Blue) Chrome trailer, Yellow/Blue speedboat, 3 figures	£100-120	☐
36	1983	Off-Road Set	447 (Dark Blue/Cream, racing number '5') plus power-boat on trailer......................	£25-35	☐
C36	1976-78	Tarzan Set................................	Includes Light Green 421 Land Rover, paler Green 'zebra' stripes, Tarzan, Jane, Cheetah (chimp) boy, dinghy with hunter, elephant, snake, vines, trailer (same colours as Land Rover) with White cage	£90-120	☐

Ref. No.	Year(s)	Model Type	Corgi Toys - continued	Market Price Range	
37	1966-69	'Lotus Racing Team'	490 VW Breakdown Truck, Red trailer with cars 318, 319, 155, plus 2 sets of racing numbers ('5' and '9') a 1966 illustrated checklist and a pack of cones.........................	£200-250	☐
37	1979-82	Fiat X-19 Set	Fiat X-19 and Boat 'Carlsberg'	£30-40	☐
38	1977-78	Mini Camping Set	Mini with 2 figures, tent, barbecue................................	£35-45	☐
38	1965-67	'1965 Monte Carlo Rally'..........	318 Mini Cooper 'S', 322 Rover 2000, and 326 Citroën DS19. Monte Carlo emblem on each bonnet.........................	£400-500	☐
C38	1980-	Jaguar XJS Set	319 with Powerboat on Trailer	£20-30	☐
40	1967-69	The Avengers Set......................	John Steed & his Bentley, Emma Peel & her Lotus Elan, 3 Black umbrellas	£300-400	☐
C40	1977-80	Batman Gift Set........................	Contains 107, 267, 925...	£120-140	☐
41	1966-68	Ford 'H' Series Transporter and six Cars	1138 Transporter (Red/Two-tone Blue), 252 Rover 2000 (Metallic Plum), 251 Hillman Imp (Metallic Bronze), 440 Ford Cortina Estate (Metallic Blue/Brown 'wood' panels), 204 Morris Mini-Minor (Light Blue), 321 Austin Mini Cooper 'S' (Red, RN '2', '1966 Monte Carlo Rally', with roof signatures), 180 Morris Mini Cooper 'S' (Black/Red, 'wickerwork' panels). (Only sold by mail order)	£300-400	☐
C41	1977-81	Silver Jubilee Set......................	The State Landau with Their Majesties (and a Corgi!)............	£15-20	☐
C42	1979-80	Agricultural Set	Contains C34, C43, Silo/Elevator....................................	£45-55	☐
C43	1979-80	Silo and Conveyor Set..............	Silo and Conveyor 'CORGI HARVESTING COMPANY LTD'	£40-50	☐
C43	1985	'TOYMASTER' Transport Set	Contains C496 'ROYAL MAIL', C515 'BMX' plus Volvo 'TOYMASTER' truck......	£20-25	☐
C44	1978-80	Metropolitan Police Set............	421 Land Rover, 112 Horsebox plus Policeman on horse	£40-50	☐
45	1966	'All Winners' Set	261 James Bond's Aston-Martin, 310 Chevrolet Stingray, 324 Marcos Volvo 1800GT, 325 Ford Mustang Competition, 314 Ferrari Berlinetta. 9,000 sets sold	£300-400	☐
C45	1978-80	Royal Canadian Police Set.......	R.C.M.P. Land Rover (421), Trailer (102) & 'Mountie' on horse	£75-85	☐
46	1966-69	'All Winners' Set	264 Oldsmobile Toronado (Metallic Blue), 307 Jaguar 'E'-type (Chrome finish, RN '2', driver), 314 Ferrari Berlinetta (Red, RN '4'), 337 Chevrolet Stingray (Yellow, RN '13'), 327 MGB GT (Red/Black, suitcase, accessories).............................	£200-250	☐
47	1966-69	Ford Tractor & Conveyor Set...	Contains 67, trailer with conveyor belt, figure, accessories.............................	£75-80	☐
C47	1978-80	Pony Club Set...........................	421 Land Rover & Horsebox in Metallic Bronze, girl on pony figure	£25-30	☐
48	1967-68	Ford 'H' series Transporter and six Cars	1159 Transporter (Orange/Silver/Two-tone Blue) with 252 Rover 2000 (Metallic Maroon), 251 Hillman Imp (Metallic Blue), 440 Ford Cortina Estate, 180 Morris Mini Cooper 'S' (with 'wickerwork' panels), 204 Morris Mini-Minor (Metallic Maroon), 321 Mini Cooper 'S' ('1966 Monte Carlo Rally'), Red/White, RN '2'	£200-250	☐
48	1969	Scammell Transporter and six Cars	1148 Transporter (Red/White) with 327 MGB GT (Orange), 340 Sunbeam Imp (1967 Monte Carlo, Metallic Blue, RN '77'), 201 Saint's Volvo P1800 (White with Orange label), 180 Morris Mini Cooper 'S' (with 'wickerwork' panels), 339 Mini Cooper 'S' ('1967 Monte Carlo Rally', RN '177'), 204 Morris Mini-Minor (Metallic Maroon), plus bag of cones and leaflet	£500-600	☐
		Note:	Gift Sets where 321 'Monte Carlo' Mini Cooper is replaced by 333 'SUN/RAC' Mini Cooper...	£300-350	☐
C48	1978-81	'JEAN RICHARD PINDER' Circus Set............................	Contains C426, C1163, C30, ringmaster, artistes, animals, seating, and cardboard cut-out 'Big-Top' circus tent.............................	£80-90	☐
C48/1	1986	Racing Set................................	C100/2 plus 576/2...	£20-25	☐
C49	1978-80	'CORGI FLYING CLUB' Set	Green/White Jeep (419) with Blue/White Nipper Aircraft.......................	£25-35	☐
C51		'100 Years of the Car' Set........	3 Mercedes: C805 (White) C806 (Black) C811 (Red). (Originally for Germany).......	£20-25	☐
?	1978-80	'The Jaguar Collection' Set	C804 (Cream), C816 (Red), C318 (Mobil Green/White). Sold in 'UNIPART' stores ..	£30-35	☐
C54	1978-80	Swiss Rega Set.........................	Bonna Ambulance and Helicopter.......................................	£30-35	☐
C55	1978-80	Norway Emergency Gift Set	Police Car, Breakdown Truck, Ford Transit Ambulance	£12-18	☐
C56	1978-80	Swedish Set..............................	Ford Sierra 'POLIS', Bonna Ambulance..................................	£12-18	☐
C57	1978-80	Swedish Set..............................	Contains Volvo and Caravan	£12-18	☐
C57	1978-80	Volvo 740 and Caravan	Red Volvo, White/Red/Blue Caravan. Swedish export set	£15-20	☐
C61	1978-80	Swiss Fire Set	1120 Dennis Fire Engine, Sierra 'POLITZEI', Escort Van 'NOTRUF'	£30-35	☐
C62	1986	Swiss Services Set	C554 'PTT', Box Van 'DOMICILE', VW Polo 'PTT'. Export Set..................	£20-25	☐
C63	1986	French Set................................	Bonna Ambulance, Peugeot 505, Renault 5 'POLICE'.............................	£30-35	☐
C63	1986	Emergency Set	Mercedes Ambulance (White body, Blue designs and roof lights, Fire Chief Car ('Sapeurs Pompiers') 'POLICE' Car (White body, Black doors, Blue roof light).........	NGPP	☐
64	1965-69	FC Jeep 150 & Conveyor Belt ..	Jeep (409) Yellow/White Conveyor	£40-45	☐
C65	1978-80	Norway Set...............................	Ford Transit Ambulance plus Helicopter................................	£12-18	☐
C67/1/2/3	1978-80	Cyclists Sets	Sold in France, 2 Cars, 2 Bicycles.................................	£15-20	☐
C70	1978-80	Danish 'FALCK' Set................	Bonna Ambulance and Ford Breakdown Truck	£15-20	☐
C72	1978-80	Norway Set...............................	Contains C542 plus Helicopter 'LN OSH'.............................	£12-18	☐
C73/1	1990	Swedish 'POLIS' Set.................	White/Blue Volvo 740 & Red/White Jet Ranger Helicopter	£12-18	☐
C330/2-5		Mini 30th Anniversary	4 Minis with 'ROSE', 'SKY', 'FLAME' or 'RACING' logos, interior colours vary	£40-50	☐
?		Mini 30th Anniversary	Model of a Mini with Anniversary Book	£35-45	☐
C330/6-9		Four Mini Set...........................	Silver ('CITY'), Blue ('MAYFAIR'), Maroon ('MAYFAIR'), Pale Yellow ('CITY')....	£20-30	☐
1151	1970	Scammell 'Co-op' Set...............	Contains 1147, 466 & 432 in Blue/White livery. Promotional in brown box	£150-200	☐
C1412	?	Swiss Police Set.......................	Range Rover and Helicopter 'POLITZEI'.............................	£18-22	☐
?	1985	Wiltshire Fire Brigade	Dennis Fire Escape plus Escort Van both in red (650)........................	£45-55	☐
?	1985	Race Team Set..........................	'ADMIRAL ENERGY GROUP Ltd' logos on 501 Range Rover (White), Porsche 956 (White) on trailer	£35-45	☐
?	1980	Construction Site Set................	Contains 54 with 440 (Mazda Pick-Up)	£30-35	☐
?	1992	Set of 4 Minis...........................	Black Mini ('Check'), White Mini ('Designer'), Red Mini ('Cooper'), Metallic Blue Mini ('Neon')...........................	£12-14	☐

HOW TO OBTAIN EXPORT MODELS: Please send a stamped addressed envelope to Susan Pownall of the Corgi Collectors Club (address on Corgi Collector page) who will supply a list of UK dealers who stock these models.

Corgi Classics Commercials

This excellent series was introduced in 1985 and features finely engineered models of classic vehicles. Great care has been taken to achieve faithful modelling of the original vehicle using authentic liveries wherever possible.

Variations: Every effort has been made to provide details of the main model variations and their market prices. Occasionally factory errors have led to the fitting of incorrect radiator grilles or wheels or to minor paint variations (i.e. a slightly different shade from the original). These variants have not been listed unless they were produced in sufficient (significant) quantities to warrant inclusion.

Note: A.E.C. Classic Series Buses are listed in the Corgi Buses Section

A.E.C CABOVER BOX VANS

C897/1	1987	'CARTER PATERSON', *'Atora For Xmas'*	£10-15	☐
C897/2	1987	'JOHN KNIGHT', *'Hustler Soap'*	£10-15	☐
897/3	1987	'LMS EXPRESS PARCELS', *'Puck Matches'*	£50-60	☐
897/4	1988	'DUCKHAMS WEARCURE', Silver/White	£9-12	☐
897/5	1988	'AMPLION RADIO', Two-tone Blue....	£9-12	☐
897/6	1988	'WEETABIX', Yellow/White/Red	£9-12	☐
C897/7	1988	'MARS', Brown/Cream/Red	£18-24	☐
897/8	1988	'HIS MASTERS VOICE', Silver/Dark Green	£18-24	☐
D897/9	1988	'INTERNATIONAL', Green/Yellow/Black	£9-12	☐
D897/10	1988	'POTTERS ASTHMA CURE', 'BP' promotional	£10-15	☐
D897/11	1988	'JOHN BARKER', Dark Brown/White	£12-15	☐
D897/12	1989	'ROYAL MAIL', Red/Black	£35-40	☐
D987/13	1989	'GPO TELEPHONES', (see GS D15/1)	GSP	☐
D897/14	1990	'G.W.R.', Dark Brown/White	£15-20	☐
D897/15	1990	'UNITED DAIRIES', see Gift Set D67/1	GSP	☐
97140	1991	'SOUTHERN RAILWAY', *'Express Parcels Service'*	£10-15	☐
97754	1993	'LMS RAILWAY', see Set 97754	GSP	☐

A.E.C. CABOVER TANKERS

C945/1	1987	'FLOWERS BREWERY', Cream/Green	£9-12	☐
C945/2	1987	'GAYMERS CIDER', Dark Blue/Red ..	£9-12	☐
C945/3	1988	'CARLESS CAPEL', Dark Green/Cream	£9-12	☐
C945/4	1988	'DUCKHAMS OILS', Blue/Silver	£9-12	☐
C945/5	1988	'SOMERLITE OIL', Light Blue/White..	£10-14	☐
C945/6	1989	'REDLINE GLICO', Red/Black	£9-12	☐
D945/7	1990	'SHELL', see Gift Set D9/1		☐
C945/10	1988	'BP PETROLEUM', 'BP' promotional ..	£20-25	☐
D945/12	1990	'UNITED DAIRIES', see Gift Set D67/1	GSP	☐
97442	1991	'JOHN SMITHS BREWERY', (Gift Set)	GSP	☐

A.E.C. REGAL HALF-CAB COACHES

97069	1993	'WHITTLES', see Set 97069	GSP	☐
97070	1992	'SILVER SERVICE', see Set 97070	GSP	☐
97075	1992	'SOUTH WALES', see Set 97075	GSP	☐
97180	1991	'GREY-GREEN', Grey/Green	£15-20	☐
97181	1991	'TIMPSONS', Cream/Brown	£22-27	☐
97184	1991	'SHEFFIELD', Off-White/Red	£15-20	☐
97185	1992	'WEST RIDING', Cream/Green	£11-14	☐
97186	1992	'GREY CARS', Grey/Cream/Red	£11-14	☐
97187	1992	'HANSON', Red, Cream flash	£11-14	☐
97189	1991	'OXFORD', Cream/Maroon, Kays LE..	NGPP	☐
97190	1991	'LEDGARD', Blue/Black, GUS LE.......	NGPP	☐
97191	1991	'ROSSLYN MOTORS', Red/Black	£11-14	☐
97193	1992	'CARNEYS', White body, Red roof.....	£11-14	☐
97194	1992	'HARDINGS', Mid-Blue/Dark Blue......	£11-14	☐
97196	1993	'STANLEY FIELD', TT-Green	£11-14	☐
97197	1993	'WESTERN WELSH', White/Red	£11-14	☐
98161	1993	'EASTERN COUNTIES', Cream/Black	£11-14	☐
98162	1993	'WALLACE ARNOLD', Cream/Red	£11-14	☐
	1993	'WHITTLES', Dark Blue, in Set	GSP	☐

A.E.C. MERCURY TRUCKS

97894	1993	'PICKFORDS', Blue/White, Red wheels	NRP	☐

A.E.C. TRUCKS with TRAILERS

97891	1993	'BILLY SMARTS', White/Green	£18-24	☐
97892	1993	'S.HOUSEMAN', Brown/White, *'York'*	£18-24	☐
97893	1993	'J.AYERS', *'Modern Amusements'*	£18-24	☐

BEDFORD 'CA' VANS

D981/1	1989	'PICKFORDS', see Kays Set D74/1	GSP	☐
D981/2	1989	'CAMBRIAN NEWS', White/Black	£6-9	☐
D981/3	1990	'A.A.', Yellow/Black	£6-9	☐
D981/4	1989	'EXPRESS DAIRIES', White/Blue	£6-9	☐
D981/5	1989	'DANDY', see D14/1 Set	GSP	☐
D981/6	1989	'BEANO', see D14/1 Set	GSP	☐
D981/7	1990	'COLLECTOR CLUB 1990', Yellow/Blue	£10-15	☐
D981/9	1990	'EVENING NEWS', Yellow/Black	£6-9	☐
D981/10	1990	'EVENING STANDARD', Silver/Black	£6-9	☐
D981/11	1990	'The STAR', Red body	£6-9	☐
D981/12	1990	'GAS', see GUS Set D54/1	GSP	☐
96900	1991	'MANCHESTER EVENING NEWS', Yellow/Black	£6-9	☐
97740	1991	'The TIMES', see 97740 Set	GSP	☐
98754	1991	'The ADVENTURE', Yellow	£6-9	☐
98965	1992	'EAGLE', see Set 98965	GSP	☐

BEDFORD DORMOBILES

D982/1	1989	Cream/Blue	£6-9	☐
D982/2	1989	Red/Cream	£6-9	☐
D982/3	1990	Cream/Green	£6-9	☐
D982/4	1991	Brown/Cream	£6-9	☐
96920	1991	'POLICE', Dark Blue, beacon	£6-9	☐

BEDFORD 'O' ARTICULATED TRUCKS

97300	1993	'BILLY SMARTS', Grey/Green	NRP	☐

BEDFORD 'OB' BOX VANS

C822/1	1988	'PERSIL', Green/White	£12-16	☐
C822/2	1988	'TATE & LYLE', Blue/White/Red	£13-16	☐
C822/3	1988	'GILLETTE', Green/Black/Red	£13-16	☐
D822/4	1989	'CARTER PATERSON', *'Solidox'* Green body, Green roof	£16-20	☐
		Green body, Red roof	£45-50	☐
D822/5	1989	'MILLERS', (total production 3,200) Cream/Green (Red wings)	£16-20	☐
		Same but Black wings	£20-25	☐
		Same, logo partly hidden	£40-45	☐
D822/6	1990	'SHELL', see Set D17/1	GSP	☐
		Same but 5 rivet base	GSP	☐
D822/7	1989	'CADBURYS', Chocolate/Red	£16-20	☐
D822/8	1989	'MALTESERS', Brown/White/Red	£20-24	☐
D822/9	1989	'ROYAL MAIL', see D7/1 Set	GSP	☐
D822/10	1990	'TERRYS OF YORK', Dark Red	£20-24	☐
D822/11	1990	'L.N.E.R.', Blue/Black	£12-15	☐
		Same but no front body print	NGPP	☐
822/12	1990	'TOYMASTER', Yellow/Red (own shops)	£25-35	☐
D822/13	1990	'BRITISH RAILWAYS', see Set D46/1	GSP	☐
D822/16	1990	'WHITBREAD', see Set D94/1	GSP	☐
97120	1991	'LMS', Crimson/Black	£10-15	☐
97123	1991	'NSPCC', Green/Yellow/Black	£10-15	☐
97125	1993	'GPO Telephones', Olive-Green/Black ...	£10-15	☐
97126	1993	'NATIONAL COAL BOARD', White/Red	£10-15	☐
97781	1993	'TATE & LYLE', see Gift Set 97781 ...	GSP	☐

BEDFORD 'OB' COACHES

Ref. No.	Year(s)	Model Type	Market Price Range	
C949/1	1987	'NORFOLKS', Green, (Pale Yellow stripe) small *Ipswich*	£65-75	☐
		brighter Yellow or Dark Green stripe, large *Ipswich*	£65-75	☐
C949/2	1987	'ROYAL BLUE', Beige/Blue, small *Exeter*	£80-90	☐
		large *Exeter*, Blue door line	£70-80	☐
		no Blue line, lower fleetline	£60-70	☐
C949/3	1987	'ALEXANDER BLUEBIRD', Cream/ Dark Blue	£40-50	☐
C949/4	1987	'GREY CARS', Grey/Cream/Red	£30-35	☐
C949/5	1987	'CROSVILLE', Cream/Green	£30-35	☐
C949/6	1987	'SOUTHDOWN', Green/Cream	£145-175	☐
C949/7	1987	'EASTERN COUNTIES', Cream/Red	£35-40	☐
C949/8	1988	'SOUTH MIDLAND', Red/White	£35-40	☐
C949/9	1988	'PREMIER', Two-tone Blue	£30-40	☐
C949/10	1988	'HIGHLAND', see Set C89	GSP	☐
C949/11	1988	'EAST YORKSHIRE', Cream/Blue	£30-40	☐
D949/12	1989	'CLASSIC CARS', Grey/Maroon	£30-35	☐
D949/13	1989	'HANTS & SUSSEX', Maroon/Red, Dark Cream stripe	£30-35	☐
		with Light Cream stripe	£30-35	☐
Q949/14	1989	'WALLACE ARNOLD', Cream/Red	£30-35	☐
D949/15	1989	'MACBRAYNES', Red/Green/Cream	£30-35	☐
D949/16	1989	'HANTS & DORSET', see D4/1 Set	GSP	☐
D949/17	1990	'GREENSLADES', Cream/Green	£10-15	☐
D949/18	1990	'DEVON GENERAL', Maroon/Cream	£10-15	☐
Q949/19	1990	'SOUTHERN VECTIS', Dark Green	£20-25	☐
D949/20	1990	'RAF AIR PASSENGER COACH', see Set D35/1	GSP	☐
Q949/22	1990	'BOULTONS of SHROPSHIRE', Cream/Maroon	£15-20	☐
D949/23	1990	'HOWARDS TOURS', Cream/Red, Kay's	£20-25	☐
D949/24	1990	'SOUTHERN NATIONAL', Cream/ Green, Kay's	£20-25	☐
D949/25	1990	'EASTERN NATIONAL', Cream, Green base line	£20-25	☐
		Cream, no base line	£20-25	☐
D949/26	1990	'WEST YORKSHIRE', Cream/Red, Grattans	£30-35	☐
D949/27	1990	'BRITISH RAILWAYS', Maroon/Cream, *Melstead*	£20-25	☐
		Maroon/Cream, *Bristol*	£15-20	☐
Q949/28	1990	'YORK FAIR', see Set Q55/1	GSP	☐
D949/29	1990	'BARTONS TRANSPORT', Set D41/1	GSP	☐
Q949/30	1990	'WESTERN NATIONAL', Cream/ Green	£25-30	☐
949/31	1991	'BRITISH RAILWAYS', Maroon/ Cream, (P & K Models)	NGPP	☐
Q949/32	1990	'CORGI ON THE MOVE', Set D82/1	GSP	☐
Q949/33	1990	'STANDERWICK', see Set Q57/1	GSP	☐
97070	1992	'SILVER SERVICE', see 97070	GSP	☐
97075	1992	'SOUTH WALES', Cream/Red	NRP	☐
97078	1993	'CORKILLS COACHES', Green/Black, in Gift Set	GSP	☐
97078	1993	'De VANENBURG', Red/Black, in Set	GSP	☐
97079	1993	'PREMIER', in 70th Anniversary Set	GSP	☐
97100	1991	'ISLE of MAN TOURS', TT-Blue	£12-15	☐
97101	1991	'SCILLY ISLES', Cream/Blue, *Vic's Tours*	£12-15	☐
97103	1991	'SKILLS of NOTTINGHAM', TT-Green, (A.B.Gee)	£14-18	☐
97105	1992	'FELIX', Maroon body, Red trim	£12-15	☐
97106	1992	'BIBBYS', Black body, White roof	£12-15	☐
97107	1992	'MURGATROYD', Cream/Pale Blue	£12-15	☐
97108	1992	'GRANVILLE TOURS', TT-Blue	£15-20	☐
97109	1993	'WHITTAKERS Tours', Cream/Red/ Pale Blue	£12-15	☐
97111	1993	'MEREDITH', White/Yellow, 'Malpas'	£12-15	☐
97113	1993	'WARBURTONS', Black/Pale Grey	£12-15	☐
97698	1993	'Metropolitan Police', in Set 97698	GSP	☐
97741	1991	'J.M.T.', see Set 97741	GSP	☐
97741	1991	'PIONEER', see Set 97741	GSP	☐
97765	1993	'WILES', Pale Blue/White, (in Set)	GSP	☐
98163	1993	'GREY-GREEN', Grey/Green, 'Clacton'	£12-15	☐
98164	1993	'EDINBURGH', Maroon/White	£12-15	☐
no ref.	1992	'SMITH'S COACHES', Cream/Red, (only 3 made)	NGPP	☐

BEDFORD 'OB' PANTECHNICONS

Ref. No.	Year(s)	Model Type	Market Price Range	
C953/1	1987	'PICKFORDS', Dark Blue, *3401*	£40-50	☐
D953/1	1989	'PICKFORDS', no number, Set D74/1	GSP	☐
C953/2	1987	'WARING & GILLOW', Green/White/ Black	£70-80	☐
C953/3	1987	'FRASERS of IPSWICH', Black/ White/Grey	£45-55	☐
C953/4	1987	'STEINWAY & SONS', Green/Black	£30-35	☐
C953/5	1988	'GRIFF FENDER', Blue/Off-White	£15-20	☐
C953/6	1988	'DUCKHAMS', Green/White, *NOL*	£16-21	☐
C953/7	1988	'CAMP HOPSON', Cream body	£35-40	☐
Q953/8	1990	'MICHAEL GERSON', Dark Green/ Black	£40-50	☐
D953/9	1989	'STYLO', Blue/Black/Red	£30-35	☐
D953/10	1989	'WEETABIX', Yellow/Brown	£30-35	☐
D953/11	1990	'SHELL THE WINNER', see Set D17/ 1	GSP	☐
D953/12	1989	'BISHOPS MOVE', Yellow/White	£30-35	☐
		Same but with thicker lettering	£25-30	☐
D953/13	1990	'WYLIE & LOCKHEAD', Black/ White	£25-30	☐
D953/14	1990	'ARTHUR BATTY', Green body	£10-15	☐
Q953/15	1990	'YORK FAIR 1765-1990', see Set Q55/ 1	GSP	☐
D953/16	1990	'LEE BROTHERS', Green/White, Silver wheels	£25-30	☐
		with standard wheels	£15-20	☐
Q953/17	1990	'SLUMBERLAND BEDS', Set Q57/1	GSP	☐
97080	1991	'JOHN JULIAN', Dark Blue/Cream	£10-15	☐
97081	1991	'BREWER & TURNBULL', Blue/ White	£15-20	☐
97082	1991	'PICKFORDS', curved *Pickfords*	£16-22	☐
97083	1991	'BLACKPOOL TOWER CIRCUS', *Charlie Cairoli*	£20-25	☐
97085	1991	'SLUMBERLAND BEDS', Deep Red, normal pack	£10-15	☐
97086	1992	'FREEBORNS', White/Orange/Brown	£12-15	☐
97087	1992	'BARNARDO'S', White/Green	£12-15	☐
97088	1993	'WHITE & Co.', 'Portsmouth'	£12-15	☐
97089	1993	'JOHN MASON', 'Liverpool Philharmonic'	£12-15	☐
97091	1993	'G.H.LUCKING & SONS', Blue/ White	£12-15	☐
97195	1992	HOWELLS & SON, Red/Black/White	£12-15	☐
D82/1	1990	'CORGI ON THE MOVE', Set D82/1	GSP	☐
	1993	'RILEYS', 'Billiard Tables'	£12-15	☐

BURLINGHAM SEAGULL COACHES

Ref. No.	Year(s)	Model Type	Market Price Range	
97067	1993	'WHITTLES', Blue/Red, in Gift Set	GSP	☐
97170	1993	'SEAGULL', Grey/Black, 'Blackpool'	NRP	☐
97171	1993	'N & C', Dark Brown/Red, 'Swansea'	NRP	☐
97173	1993	'RIBBLE', Cream and Red	NRP	☐
97174	1993	'YELLOWAY', Yellow/Orange	NRP	☐
	1993	'STRATFORD BLUE', Cream/Dark Blue	NRP	☐
	1993	'WHITTLES', Dark Blue/Red, in Set	GSP	☐

FIRE APPLIANCES

Ref. No.	Year(s)	Model Type	Market Price Range	
C1143/2	1990	La France Aerial Ladder, see 97320		
97320	1991	La France Aerial Ladder, Bright Red, open cab	£16-22	☐
97321	1992	La France Aerial Ladder, Crimson/ White, closed cab	NRP	☐
97322	1993	La France, closed, *CHICAGO*	NRP	☐
97323	1993	La France, closed, *CARNEGIE*, Blue	NRP	☐
97324	1993	La France, open cab, *ORLANDO*	NRP	☐
97325	1993	La France, closed, *DENVER*, White body	NRP	☐
?	1993	La France, open, *SCOTTDALE*, in Gift Set	GSP	☐
?	1993	La France, closed, *SOUTH RIVER*, in Gift Set	GSP	☐
97352	1993	AEC Ladder Truck, *STOKE-on-TRENT*	NRP	☐
97355	1992	AEC Merryweather Pumper, Red/ Silver, wheeled escape	NRP	☐

Corgi Toys - continued

Ref. No.	Year(s)	Model Type	Market Price Range	
97356	1993	AEC Pump Escape, 'NOTTINGHAM', 'DUNKIRK'.................	£22-25	☐
97357	1993	AEC Pump Escape, 'HERTS'................	£22-25	☐
97358	1993	AEC Pump Escape, 'CLEVELAND'......	£22-25	☐
97385	1993	AEC Ladder Truck, 'CARDIFF'............	£22-25	☐
97386	1993	AEC Ladder Truck, 'BRISTOL'............	£22-25	☐

FODEN TANKERS

Ref. No.	Year(s)	Model Type	Market Price Range	
97781	1993	'TATE & LYLE', see Gift Set 97781	GSP	☐
97950	1993	'GUINNESS', Black/Gold/Red.............	NRP	☐
97951	1993	'Milk Marketing Board', Dark Blue/White	NRP	☐
97952	1993	'HOVIS', White/Black, Red wheels	NRP	☐

FORD FORDSON 8 (Ford Popular) VANS

Ref. No.	Year(s)	Model Type	Market Price Range	
D980/1	1989	'S.A. PEACOCK', Green/Black	£8-10	☐
D980/2	1989	'FULLERS', Grey/Red......................	£8-10	☐
D980/3	1989	'LUTON MOTOR Co', Green/Brown... with lighter Brown wings	£6-9 £6-9	☐
D980/4	1989	'CORGI CLUB 89', Dark Blue/Black....	£10-15	☐
D980/5	1989	'SIGNSMITH', see Grattans Set D23/1	GSP	☐
D980/6	1989	'FRASER COOK Ltd', see Grattans Set D23/1	GSP	☐
D980/7	1989	'LEWIS EAST Ltd', see Grattans Set D23/1	GSP	☐
D980/8	1989	'C. PEARSON', Green/Black	£6-9	☐
D980/9	1989	'COLMANS MUSTARD', Kays Set D72/1	GSP	☐
D980/10	1989	'BOWYERS', see Kays Set D72/1	GSP	☐
D980/11	1989	'PICKFORDS REMOVALS', see Kays Set D74/1	GSP	☐
D980/12	1989	'D. SHELDON', Maroon/Black..............	£6-9	☐
D980/13	1990	'LIMA FURNITURE Ltd', Brown body..............................	£6-9	☐
D980/14	1990	'CAMBRIAN FACTORY Ltd'	£6-9	☐
D980/15	1990	'ABBEYCOLOR', Maroon/Black	£6-9	☐
D980/16	1990	'ROYAL MAIL', Red/Black	£6-9	☐
D980/17	1990	'NATIONAL COAL BOARD', see GUS Set D54/1	GSP	☐
96860	1991	'EASTBOURNE MOTORS', Blue/Grey.............................	£6-9	☐
96862	1991	'ROYAL MAIL', Red/Black	£6-9	☐
96863	1993	'SUNLIGHT SOAP', White/Red	£6-9	☐
96865	1992	'BEEZER', 'Colonel Blink'	£6-9	☐
98109	1991	'ROYAL MAIL', Red/Black	£6-9	☐
98755	1991	'HOTSPUR', 'Willie Wallop'..............	£6-9	☐

FORD MODEL 'T' VANS

Ref. No.	Year(s)	Model Type	Market Price Range	
C865	1986	'LYONS TEA', Blue/White	£8-11	☐
C865/1	1987	'NEEDLERS', Brown/Red, billboards...	£8-11	☐
C865/2	1986	'LYONS TEA', As C865 but Black roof...........................	£100-150	☐
C865/2	1987	'DRUMMER DYES', Yellow/Red, billboards.........................	£8-11	☐
C865/3	1987	'KALAMAZOO', Red, billboards..........	£8-11	☐
C865/4	1987	'PEPSI COLA', White/Blue/Red, billboards.........................	£8-11	☐
C865/5	1987	'TWININGS', Black, Kay's..................	£15-18	☐
D865/6	1988	'AMBULANCE', see Set C88	GSP	☐
D865/7	1989	'KAYS', White/Grey, Kay's..............	£11-14	☐
D865/8	1989	'ROYAL LAUNDRY', see Set C90.......	GSP	☐
	1989	'SUNLIGHT LAUNDRY', see Set C90	GSP	☐
C865/11	1989	'STEIFF', Brown/Black, billboards........	£8-11	☐
D865/12	1989	'A 1 SAUCE', see Set D71/1	GSP	☐
D865/13	1989	'APS MEDICINES', see Set D71/1	GSP	☐
Q865/14	1990	'NAAFI', Blue/Black	£40-50	☐
Q865/15	1990	'JOHN MENZIES', Green/White	£11-14	☐
Q865/17	1990	'WHITBREAD', see Set D94/1	GSP	☐
C873	1986	'ZEBRA GRATE POLISH', Yellow, zebra design	£11-14	☐
C874	1987	'CORGI COLLECTOR CLUB', 2nd Anniversary'......................	£15-20	☐
C875	1986	'SCHOKOLADE GOLD', 'Stollwerck'..	£12-14	☐
C876	1986	'DICKINS & JONES', Green/White/Yellow	£25-30	☐
C877	1986	'ROYAL MAIL', Red/Black	£20-25	☐
C965	1986	'FORDS 75th Anniversary', Blue/White, Yellow windows/logo	£12-15	☐
C965	1986	'FORDS 75th Anniversary', same but White logo	£14-18	☐

Ref. No.	Year(s)	Model Type	Market Price Range	
C966	1986	'FORDS 75th Anniversary', same but White windows/logo..................	£40-50	☐
	1987	'SWAN VESTAS', see Gift Set C69......	GSP	☐
	1987	'THE TIMES', see Gift Set C49	GSP	☐
	1987	'KAY & Co.', see Gift Set C68	GSP	☐
	1987	'T.C. BENNETT', see Set C50	GSP	☐
	1987	'H & C MAILES', see Set C50..............	GSP	☐
	1987	'T.J. POUPART', see Set C50..............	GSP	☐
97464	1992	'CADBURYS', Purple/Cream, Woolworths promotional	NGPP	☐

FORD MODEL 'T' TANKERS

Ref. No.	Year(s)	Model Type	Market Price Range	
C864	1986	'PRATTS MOTOR SPIRIT', Green/Yellow/Red	£8-11	☐
C864/1	1987	'STALEY SALES CORP.', Black/Silver	£10-12	☐
C864/2	1987	'RIMMER BROS Ltd', Green/Black	£10-13	☐
C864/3	1987	'SAN FRANCISCO', Red/Gold, 'Fire'..	£8-11	☐
C864/4	1987	'NATIONAL BENZOLE', Beige body..	£15-18	☐
C872	1986	'DOMINION', TT Blue/Yellow	£9-12	☐
C880	1986	'BP MOTOR SPIRIT', Green/Yellow....	£9-12	☐
C864/6	1988	'OLYMPIC GASOLINE', Green/Yellow, Kay's	£8-11	☐
D864/7	1989	'TEXACO', see Set D71/1	GSP	☐
D864/8	1989	'SOMERLITE', see Set D71/1	GSP	☐

GUY ARAB Double Deck Buses

Ref. No.	Year(s)	Model Type	Market Price Range	
97076/A	1992	'W.ALEXANDER', Red, 'Perth', in Set.............................	GSP	☐
97077/A	1992	'E. LANCASHIRE', Red/Black, in Set..	GSP	☐
97198	1992	'SOUTHDOWN', Green/Cream'...........	£18-22	☐
97199	1992	'BIRKENHEAD', Blue/White.............	£16-20	☐
97201	1993	'BIRMINGHAM', Blue/Cream............	£16-20	☐
97202	1993	'MAIDSTONE', Green/Cream............	£16-20	☐
97203	1993	'LONDON TRANSPORT', 'Dagenham'	£16-20	☐
97204	1993	'COVENTRY', Dark Maroon/Black	£16-20	☐
97205	1993	'BOURNEMOUTH', Yellow/Blue	£16-20	☐
97206	1993	'NORTHERN GENERAL', Red/White.............................	£16-20	☐
	1993	'WALSALL', Mid-Blue/Black	£16-20	☐
	1993	'YORKSHIRE', Red/Black	£16-20	☐

LEYLAND TIGER Coaches

Ref. No.	Year(s)	Model Type	Market Price Range	
97076/B	1992	'W.ALEXANDER', Blue/Black, in Set..	GSP	☐
97077/B	1992	'E. LANCASHIRE', Dark Green, in Set 'ROBINSONS'	GSP	☐
97079/B	1992	'PREMIER', in 70th Anniversary Set	GSP	☐
97192	1992	'RIBBLE', Cream/Red......................	£11-14	☐
97210	1993	'MAYPOLE', Dark Green/Cream.........	£11-14	☐
97211	1993	'BARTONS', Red/Maroon	£11-14	☐
97212	1993	'ELLEN SMITH', White/Red	£11-14	☐
	1993	'PREMIER', Cream/Red, in Set............	GSP	☐

MACK TRUCKS

Ref. No.	Year(s)	Model Type	Market Price Range	
C906/1	1987	'MACK PARTS', Green/Cream............	£10-13	☐
C906/2	1987	'SUNSHINE BISCUITS', Blue/Black	£10-13	☐
C906/3	1987	'WHITE ROCK', Yellow/Black/Red	£10-13	☐
C906/4	1987	'BUFFALO FIRE DEPT', Red/Black	£10-13	☐
C906/5	1987	'PEPSI COLA', Blue/White/Red	£10-13	☐
C906/6	1988	'STANLEY TOOLS', Yellow/Red/White.............................	£10-13	☐
C906/7	1988	'PEERLESS LIGHT', Cream/Maroon/Blue.............................	£10-13	☐
C906/8	1988	'BOVRIL', Cream/Black/Red	£10-13	☐
C906/9	1988	'CARNATION', Red/White	£10-13	☐
C906/10	1988	'GULDENS MUSTARD', Yellow/White/Red.............................	£10-13	☐

MORRIS MINOR 1000 VANS

Ref. No.	Year(s)	Model Type	Market Price Range	
C957/1	1987	'ROYAL MAIL', Red, plastic base........	£20-25	☐
C957/1	1987	same but metal base.......................	£11-14	☐
C957/2	1987	'GAS', Green body, 'Mr Therm'.........	£9-12	☐
C957/3	1987-88	'CORGI Collector Club 3rd Anniversary', 1st type wheels............	£15-20	☐
		with 2nd type wheels..........	£25-30	☐
C957/4	1988	'CASTROL', Green/White..................	£12-16	☐
C957/5	1989	'MICHELIN', Bright Yellow................	£12-16	☐
C957/7	1988	'MACFISHERIES', Blue/White............	£15-20	☐

Ref. No.	Year(s)	Model Type		Price	
C957/8	1989	'GRATTANS', see Grattans Set C91.....	GSP		□
C957/9	1989	'TELEGRAPH & ARGUS', see Grattans Set C91................	GSP		□
C957/10	1989	'MITCHELLS', see Grattans Set C91....	GSP		□
C957/11	1989	'APPLEYARDS', Pale Green................		£6-8	□
D957/12	1989	'D. MORGAN', Blue body		£6-8	□
D957/13	1989	'KIMBERLEY CLARK', Blue, 'HI-DRI'..................		£6-8	□
D957/15	1989	'POLICE' Van, see Set D13/1................	GSP		□
D957/15	1989	'POLICE' Van, see Set D13/1................	GSP		□
D957/16	1989	'FRYS COCOA', see Kays Set D72/1....	GSP		□
D957/17	1989	'RINGTONS TEA', see Kays Set D72/1	GSP		□
D957/18	1989	'ROYAL MAIL', see D7/1 Set..............	GSP		□
D957/19	1989	'PICKFORDS', see D74/1 Set..............	GSP		□
D957/20	1989	'GUERNSEY POST OFFICE', Blue.....		£8-12	□
D957/21	1989	'7 UP', White van		£6-8	□
D957/22	1990	'BISHOPS REMOVALS', (as 96845)			□
D957/23	1991	'A. DUNN & SON', Issued as 96844			□
D957/24	1990	'B.A.T.R.', White/Red (with cert)..........		£75-90	□
D957/25	1990	'ROYAL AIR FORCE', see Set D35/1..	GSP		□
D957/26	1990	'NAMAC 25' (Dutch) White/Red, 'England' on base.............................		£25-30	□
		'China' on base.............................		£15-20	□
D957/27	1990	'GPO TELEPHONES', Yellow/Blue......		NRP	
C958/1	1987	'POST OFFICE TELEPHONES', Olive Green, plastic base.............................		£20-25	□
C958	1987	same but metal base..........................		£18-22	□
D958/2	1989	'GPO TELEPHONES', see D15/1 Set ...	GSP		□
C959	1987	'SMITHS CRISPS', Dark Blue/White, Black interior..............................		£11-14	□
		with Brown interior.................................		£11-14	□
C959/6	1988	'FOYLES FOR BOOKS', Red body		£9-12	□
96840	1991	'BRISTOL WATER', Green body		£6-9	□
96842	1991	'P.O. TELEPHONES', Yellow/Blue.......		£6-9	□
96844	1991	'A.DUNN & SON, Blue, (was D957/23).............................		£6-9	□
96845	1991	'BISHOPS REMOVALS', Yellow, (intended D957/22).............................		£6-9	□
96846	1992	'TIGER', 'Roy of the Rovers'..............		£6-9	□
96847	1993	'COLMANS', Red/Yellow, 'Mustard'		£6-9	□
97740	1991	'The SUNDAY TIMES', see 97740 Set	GSP		□
98104	1993	'ROYAL MAIL', Red/Black		£6-9	□
98756	1991	'The ROVER', Orange van.....................		£6-9	□
	1993	'BIRDS CUSTARD', Yellow/Red/Blue		£6-9	□

MORRIS 'J' VANS

Ref. No.	Year(s)	Model Type		Price	
D983/1	1990	'POST OFFICE TELEPHONES', Olive		£6-9	□
D983/2	1990	'ROYAL MAIL', Red/Black		£6-9	□
D983/4	1990	'Metropolitan Police', see 96883 below			
D983/5	1991	'WALLS ICE CREAM', Cream/Blue		£6-9	□
D983/6	1990	'ELECTRICITY', see GUS Set D54/1...	GSP		□
D983/7	1990	'BEANO', see D47/1 Set.....................	GSP		□
D983/8	1990	'BRITISH RAILWAYS', see Set D46/1.	GSP		□
96880	1991	'PICKFORDS', Dark Blue body		£6-9	□
96882	1991	'ROYAL MAIL', Red/Black		£6-9	□
96883	1990	'Metropolitan Police', (was D983/4).......		£6-9	□
96887	1992	'The TOPPER', '4d Every Friday'..........		£6-9	□
96891	1993	'MORRIS SERVICE', 'BMC' logo........		£6-9	□
98758	1992	'WIZARD', 'The Bumper Boys Paper' ..		£6-9	□
99140	1993	'GPO Telephones', Olive-Green/Black ...		£6-9	□
	1991	'COLLECTOR CLUB '91', Yellow/Blue..............................		NGPP	□
	1993	'BOVRIL', Blue/Black		£6-9	□

1926 RENAULT BOX VANS

Ref. No.	Year(s)	Model Type	Price	
C824		'MARCEL GARDET', Blue body	£8-11	□
C824/3	1988	'THE LIPTON', Dark Blue/Brown	£11-14	□
C902	1985	'ROYAL MAIL', Red/Blue/Gold, with or without cab scuttle.........................	£60-70	□
C917	1986	'COURVOISIER', Green/Gold/Red	£7-9	□
97000	1991	'PERRIER WATER', Green/White	£7-9	□

RENAULT CANVAS BACKED TRUCKS

Ref. No.	Year(s)	Model Type	Price	
C922	1986	'GALERIES LAFAYETTE', White/Green.............................	£8-11	□
C925	1986	'GERVAIS DANONE', Blue/Yellow.....	£8-11	□

RENAULT OPEN TRUCKS

Ref. No.	Year(s)	Model Type	Price	
C823/1	1985	'JULES COLARD', Blue/Gold/White ...	£7-9	□
C824/1	1988	'HERLOIN', Grey/Blue/Red	£8-11	□

RENAULT BEER LORRIES

Ref. No.	Year(s)	Model Type	Price	
D889/1	1989	'STELLA ARTOIS', Red/White/Black ..	£8-11	□

SCAMMELL SCARAB Articulated Vehicles

Ref. No.	Year(s)	Model Type	Price	
97910	1993	'RAIL FREIGHT', Yellow/Black	NRP	□
97911	1993	'BRITISH RAILWAYS', Maroon/Cream...........................	NRP	□

THORNEYCROFT BOX VANS
(without billboards)

Ref. No.	Year(s)	Model Type	Price	
C821	1985	'WAKEFIELD CASTROL', Green/Black...........................	£9-12	□
C821/1	1988	'HEIDELBERGER', Green/Gold/White...........................	£9-12	□
C828	1985	'GAMLEYS', Blue/Red/Silver...............	£20-25	□
C830	1985	'W & R JACOB', Rust/White/Gold......	£45-55	□
C831	1985	'HUNTLEY & PALMERS', Blue/Gold/White...........................	£20-25	□
C832	1985	'CORGI 1st ANNIVERSARY', Blue Corgi Club model		
		1: 'Kingsway, Fforestfach Ind.Est.'	£50-60	□
		2: 'Kingsway Ind.Est., Fforestfach'	£40-50	□
C833	1985	'MACFARLANE LANG', Green/Gold...........................	£7-9	□
C834	1985	'LYONS SWISS ROLLS', Dark Blue...	£65-75	□
C839	1985	'NURDIN & PEACOCK', Blue/Silver, with A4 certificate & plinth	£35-40	□
C840	1985	'ALLENBURYS', Red/White	£25-35	□
C841	1985	'PEEK FREANS', Green/Cream, Orange scuttle.............................	£12-15	□
		without cab scuttle.............................	£60-70	□
C842	1985	'CARTER PATERSON', Green/Red.....	£15-18	□
C843	1985	'EDDERSHAWS', Brown/Gold.............	£15-18	□
C845	1985	'DUCKHAMS OIL', Silver body with spoked wheels.............................	£10-14	□
		with disc wheels.............................	£13-18	□
C846	1985	'IND COOPE', Green/Black/Gold	£15-18	□
C847	1985	'KEILLERS', Cream body	£15-20	□
C848	1985	'NEWS OF THE WORLD', Black/Silver...........................	£14-18	□
C849	1987	'GOODYEAR', Blue/Brown, (for USA)	£35-38	□
C853	1985	'M. A. RAPPORT', Maroon/Cream......	£18-24	□
C854	1985	'LINCOLNSHIRE Ambulance', White..	£15-20	□
C855	1985	'LINCOLNSHIRE FIRE', Red.............	£15-20	□
C856	1985	'LINCOLNSHIRE POLICE', Black	£15-20	□
C859/6	1987	'KAYS', Maroon/Beige, Kay's	£30-40	□
D859/12	1990	'SHELL OIL', see Set D9/1.................	GSP	□
C907	1986	'HP SAUCE', Red/White/Gold..............	£14-18	□
C910	1986	'SMALL & PARKES', Black/White	£14-18	□
C911	1986	'PERSIL', Green/Red, German export ..	£12-15	□
C913	1986	'DEWARS WHISKY', Red/White.........	£10-14	□
C914	1986	'LIPTONS TEA', Blue/Gold/Red	£10-14	□
C915	1986	'OXO', Red/White	£12-15	□
C924	1986	'SAFEWAY', Red/Black	£22-26	□
C926	1986	'DOUBLE DIAMOND', Black/Gold	£18-22	□
C931	1986	'STEPNEY TYRES', Red/Gold............	£25-28	□
C932	1986	'PURITAN SOAP', Yellow/Black.........	£14-17	□
C933	1986	'BUY PUNCH', Red/Black...................	£25-30	□
C968	1986	'RADIO STEINER', Blue, no cab scuttle, Swiss.................................	£32-37	□

Promotional Issues presented to factory visitors and not sold through normal outlets:

		'SWANSEA BANKERS', Beige, no cab scuttle, 20 issued......................................	NGPP	□
		'MARCONI', White/Blue, 20 issued	NGPP	□

THORNEYCROFT BOX VANS
(with billboards)

Ref. No.	Year(s)	Model Type	Price	
C859	1986	'THORLEYS CATTLEFOOD', Yellow/Red.................................	£11-14	□
C859/1	1987	'SCOTTS EMPIRE BREAD', Blue/Red.................................	£11-14	□
C859/2	1987	'CHIVERS JAMS', Green/Cream/Blue..	£11-14	□
C859/3	1987	'ARNOTTS BISCUITS', Australian export model, 8,200 (5,000 with Certs)..	£45-55	□
C859/4	1987	'GOODYEAR', C849 with billboards....	£9-11	□
C859/5	1987	'GRATTANS 75th', Green, no scuttle...	NGPP	□
C859/6	1987	'KAYS', see Gift Set C68	GSP	□

Corgi Toys - continued (left column)

Ref. No.	Year(s)	Model Type		Market Price Range
C859/7	1989	'LEDA SALT', Grey/Black	**£9-11**	☐
C859/8	1988	'VOLVOLUTUM', Green/Brown/ Yellow	**£9-11**	☐
C859/9	1988	'ASDA', Blue/Yellow	**£11-14**	☐
C859/10	1988	'BATCHELORS PEAS', Green/Cream..	**£15-19**	☐
C859/11	1988	'LEA & PERRINS', Orange/Brown	**£12-15**	☐
C859/12	1989	'SHELL OIL & PETROL', see Set D9/1	**GSP**	☐
C859/13	1989	'McDOUGALLS', Brown/Red	**£25-30**	☐
C859/16	1990	'ASDA', '25th Birthday'	**£11-14**	☐
C929	1986	'GAMLEYS', Green/Black/Red	**£20-25**	☐
97754	1993	'LMS RAILWAY', see Set 97754	**GSP**	☐

97150,1,2,3,4,5 1992 'ROYALS' Six souvenir vans in various colours and representing different castles or royal residences. Each has 'Queen's 40th Anniversary' logo. Normal retail price (**£8-12**)

THORNEYCROFT BEER TRUCKS

Ref. No.	Year(s)	Model Type		Market Price Range
C867	1986	'THOMAS WETHERED', Green/Red ..	**£8-11**	☐
C867/1	1987	'CHARLES WELLS', Brown/Cream	**£8-11**	☐
C867/2	1987	'TOOHEYS PILSNER', Red/White......	**£8-11**	☐
		Blue/White version	**£8-11**	☐
C867/3	1987	'SWAN LAGER', Black/Red	**£8-11**	☐
C867/4	1988	'CARLSBERG', Green/White	**£8-11**	☐
C882	1986	'ST. WINIFREDS', Red body	**£8-11**	☐
C883	1988	'TAUNTON CIDER', Green/Red/ Yellow	**£8-11**	☐
C867/5	1990	'CHARRINGTONS', see Set D52/1	**GSP**	☐
C867/6	1990	'GREENE KING', see Set D51/1	**GSP**	☐
97742	1991	'JOHN SMITHS BREWERY', in Set.....	**GSP**	☐

THORNEYCROFT CANVAS BACKED TRUCKS

Ref. No.	Year(s)	Model Type		Market Price Range
C827	1985	'G.W.R.', Brown/Cream, no 'GWR' ..	**£35-40**	☐
		with 'GWR' (Kay's)	**£35-40**	☐
C836	1985	'L.M.S.', Maroon/Cream	**£40-45**	☐
C837	1985	'SOUTHERN RAILWAY', Olive/ Cream	**£35-40**	☐
C838	1985	'L.N.E.R.', Blue/Cream	**£35-40**	☐
C923	1986	'FIELD AMBULANCE', Olive-Green ..	**£12-15**	☐
C923/2	1986	'TROESCH', Green/Brown, Swiss	**£200-300**	☐

THORNEYCROFT OPEN TRUCKS

Ref. No.	Year(s)	Model Type		Market Price Range
C820/1	1985	'EAST ANGLIAN FRUIT Co', Brown	**£5-8**	☐

THORNEYCROFT DOUBLE DECKER BUS

1st type: 4 top-rail supports,
2nd type: 8 top-rail supports.

Ref. No.	Year(s)	Model Type		Market Price Range
C858	1986	'SANDEMANS', Red 1st type	**£14-16**	☐
C858	1986	2nd type body	**£14-16**	☐
C858/1	1987	'NATIONAL MOTOR MUSEUM', Red/White 2nd type	**£14-16**	☐
		Red body, Red cab canopy	**£25-30**	☐
C858/2	1987	'CHARLIE CHAPLIN', Yellow/Red 2nd type	**£14-16**	☐
C858/3	1987	'PALM TOFFEE', Green, 2nd type....	**£14-16**	☐
C858/4	1987	'IDRIS SODA WATER', Black/ Yellow	**£14-16**	☐
C858/5	1987	'The TIMES', Red body	**£14-16**	☐
C858/6	1987	'L. & N.W.R.', Brown/Yellow/White ..	**£14-16**	☐
C858/7	1988	'OAKEYS KNIFE POLISH', Red/ White	**£14-16**	☐
C858/8	1988	Military Bus, Kay's Set C88	**GSP**	☐
C858/9	1988	'BAXTERS', Kay's Set C89	**GSP**	☐
C858/10	1988	'SCHWEPPES', 'BP' & Corgi PRM	**£25-30**	☐
C858/11	1988	'GREAT EASTERN RAILWAY', White/Red	**£25-30**	☐
C884	1986	'BEER IS BEST', Red/White, 1st type..	**£14-16**	☐
C885	1986	'THOMAS TILLING', Yellow/Black, 1st type	**£20-30**	☐
C885	1986	same but 2nd type	**£25-35**	☐
C886	1986	GRANTS MORELLO CHERRY BRANDY, Red, 1st type	**£25-30**	☐
		with reversed advert logos	**£25-30**	☐
C975	1986	'ALLENBURYS PASTILLES', Orange/Rust	**£14-18**	☐
96985	1992	'EAST SURREY', Blue/White/Red	**£12-15**	☐
96986	1993	'BRIGHTON & HOVE', Blue/Red......	**£12-15**	☐
96988	1993	'BEAMISH', Dark Red/White/Black	**£12-15**	☐

CORGI TRAMLINES

A range of Tram models in '00' gauge (1:76 scale) introduced in 1988.

SINGLE DECK TRAMS (open platforms)

Ref. No.	Year(s)	Model Type		Market Price Range
C990/1	1988	'SOUTHAMPTON CORPORATION', Red/White	**£15-20**	☐
C990/2	1988	'SHEFFIELD CORPORATION', Dark Blue/White	**£15-20**	☐
D990/3	1989	'DERBY CORPORATION', Green/ White	**£15-20**	☐
D990/4	1989	'WOLVERHAMPTON', Green/White...	**£20-25**	☐
D990/5	1990	'MAIDSTONE CORPORATION', White/Yellow	**£15-20**	☐

OPEN TOP TRAMS
(Double deck, open platforms, no roof)

Ref. No.	Year(s)	Model Type		Market Price Range
C991/1	1988	'L.C.C.', Red/White/Black	**£15-20**	☐
D991/2	1988	'BLACKPOOL CORPORATION', White/Green, 3 saloon end colours:		
		1: Green ends,	**£10-15**	☐
		2: White ends,	**£10-15**	☐
		3: White AND Green ends	**£15-20**	☐
D991/3	1989	'BATH ELECTRIC', Beige/Blue......	**£15-20**	☐
D991/4	1989	'BOURNEMOUTH', Brown/Yellow	**£20-25**	☐
D991/5	1989	'BURTON & ASHBY', White/Brown ...	**£20-25**	☐
D991/6	1990	'CROYDON', Brown/Cream/Red	**£15-20**	☐
Q991/7	1990	'GARDEN FESTIVAL', Brown/ Cream	**£15-20**	☐
D991/8	1990	'LLANDUDNO', Green/Cream, (also 97242)	**NGPP**	☐
97240	1991	'LOWESTOFT', Dark Brown/Cream	**£10-13**	☐
97241	1991	'SOUTH METROPOLITAN', Dark Green/Cream	**£10-13**	☐
97290	1992	'HULL', Maroon/White	**£12-15**	☐
97291	1992	'SOUTH SHIELDS', Maroon/Cream ...	**£12-15**	☐
98150	1993	'LOWESTOFT', Maroon/Cream..........	**£10-13**	☐
98151	1993	'S. METROPOLITAN', Green/Cream...	**£10-13**	☐

CLOSED TOP TRAMS
(double-decker with roof, open platforms to lower deck)

Ref. No.	Year(s)	Model Type		Market Price Range
C992/1	1988	'LEEDS CITY TRANSPORT', Red/ White	**£15-20**	☐
C992/2	1988	'GLASGOW CORPORATION', Yellow/White	**£15-20**	☐
C992/3	1988	'L.C.C.', Red/White, GUS model..........	**£15-20**	☐
C992/4	1988	'BLACKPOOL', White/Green, Kay's	**NGPP**	☐
C992/5	1988	'BRADFORD', Cream/Blue, Grattans ..	**£32-37**	☐
D992/6	1989	'SOUTHAMPTON', Red/White	**£20-25**	☐
D992/7	1989	'BIRMINGHAM', Cream/Dark Blue	**£20-25**	☐
D992/8	1990	'LONDON TRANSPORT', Red/White	**£20-25**	☐
97260	1991	'BIRKENHEAD', Maroon/White..........	**£10-13**	☐
97261	1991	'SOUTH SHIELDS', Blue/Cream, (also D992/9)	**£10-13**	☐
98152	1993	'GLASGOW', White/Red/Yellow..........	**£10-13**	☐
98153	1993	'LONDON'	**£10-13**	☐
98154	1993	'DOVER', Green/White....................	**£20-25**	☐

FULLY CLOSED DOUBLE DECK TRAMS
(with roof and enclosed platforms)

Ref. No.	Year(s)	Model Type		Market Price Range
D993/1	1989	'PORTSMOUTH', Maroon/White.........	**£15-20**	☐
D993/2	1989	'DOVER', Green/White......................	**£20-25**	☐
D993/3	1991	'COVENTRY', Red/White...................	**£10-13**	☐
97262	1993	'BLACKPOOL', Green/Cream..............	**£10-13**	☐
97285	1992	'LEICESTER', Maroon/Cream	**£10-13**	☐
97286	1992	'SUNDERLAND', Red/White	**£10-13**	☐
97288	1992	'SHEFFIELD', Blue/White	**£10-13**	☐
98154	1993	'DOVER', Green/White......................	**£20-25**	☐

Commemoratives/Promotionals

Ref. No.	Year(s)	Model Type		Market Price Range
D37/1	1990	'PENNY POST', '150th Anniversary', special box	**£15-20**	☐
	1993	'BRITISH TRAM CO.', promotionals for regional newspapers: 'Nottingham', 'Newcastle', 'Leicester', 'Sunderland', 'Sheffield', 'South Shields, 'Hull'............	**NGPP**	☐

N.B. Volkswagen Vans etc., are listed at the end of the Corgi Classic Cars.

Corgi Classics Cars

AUSTIN-HEALEY 3000

D733/1	1990	Hard-Top, Red/White	£6-9	☐
D733/2	1990	Hard Top, see D53/1 Kays Set	GSP	☐
D734/1	1990	Open Soft-Top, Blue body	£6-9	☐
D735/4	1990	Closed Soft-Top, Pacific-Green/Grey	£6-9	☐
96200	1991	Hard Top, Turquoise/White, rack	£6-9	☐
96220	1991	Open Top, Metallic Blue/Cream, rack	£6-9	☐
96240	1991	Open Top, Cream, luggage rack	£6-9	☐
99050	1993	Open Top, Pale Blue	£6-9	☐
99051	1991	Soft Top, Dark Green/Grey, rack	£6-9	☐

FERRARI 250

D739/1	1990	250 GTO Sport, Red, number '151'	£6-9	☐
D740/1	1990	250 GTO Road, see 96320 (below)		
96320	1990	250 GTO Road, Red, no number	£6-9	☐
98124	1993	250 GT Road, Red, no number	£6-9	☐

FORD CORTINA and Lotus Cortina

D708/1	1989	Lotus Cortina, White/Green, (also in Gift Set D53/1)	£6-9	☐
D708/2	1989	Ford Cortina, Maroon body	£6-9	☐
D708/3	1989	Lotus Cortina, Monaco Red	£6-9	☐
D708/4	1989	Ford Cortina, Aqua Blue	£6-9	☐
D708/5	1989	Rally car, see Set D16/1	GSP	☐
D708/6	1990	Police car, White, 'POLICE'	£6-9	☐
D708/7	1990	Ford Cortina, Black body	£6-9	☐
D708/8	1990	Ford Cortina, Spruce-Green body	£6-9	☐
96760	1991	Rally car, Red/Gold, (Sir John Whitmore)	£6-9	☐
96763	1992	Rally car, Red/Black, (Roger Clark)	£6-9	☐
96764	1992	Rally car, Cream/Green, (Jim Clark)	£6-9	☐
98130	1993	Lotus Cortina, White/Green stripe	£6-9	☐

FORD POPULAR Saloon

C701/1	1988	Grey-Blue	£6-9	☐
C701/3	1989	Black	£6-9	☐
C701/5	1989	Fawn	£6-9	☐
D701/6	1989	Rally car, see Gift Set D16/1	GSP	☐
D701/7	1989	Pale Green	£6-9	☐
D701/8	1990	Grey	£6-9	☐
D701/9	1990	Winchester Blue	£6-9	☐
98132	1993	Black	£6-9	☐

FORD ZEPHYR Mk.II Saloon

D710/1	1989	Black body	£6-9	☐
D710/2	1989	Blue body	£6-9	☐
D710/3	1989	Monaco Red	£6-9	☐
D710/4	1989	Regency Grey	£6-9	☐
D710/6	1990	Maroon body	£6-9	☐
D710/7	1990	Pompadour Blue	£6-9	☐
D710/9	1990	see Gift Set D36/1	GSP	☐
D710/10	1990	see Gift Set D36/1	GSP	☐
D710/11	1990	see Gift Set D36/1	GSP	☐
D710/12	1991	Linden Green	NGPP	☐
D35/1	1990	see Gift Set D35/1	GSP	☐
96721	1991	Rally car, White, (Anne Hall)	£6-9	☐

FORD ZODIAC Mk.II Saloon

D709/1	1989	Maroon/Grey	£6-9	☐
D709/2	1989	Two-tone Blue	£6-9	☐
D709/3	1989	Yellow/White	£6-9	☐
D709/4	1989	Red/White	£6-9	☐
D709/6	1990	Black/Blue	£6-9	☐
D709/7	1990	Two-tone Green	£6-9	☐
		Grey/Yellow (very few made)	NGPP	☐
D709/8	1990	Ermine White/Grey	£6-9	☐

JAGUAR 'E'-type

96080	1991	Open Top, Red, Black interior	£6-9	☐
97680	1991	Open Top, see Gift Set 97680	GSP	☐
97700	1991	Soft Top, see Gift Set 97700	GSP	☐
?	1991	Soft Top, Red body, Tan top	£6-9	☐
96042	1991	Soft Top, Cream/Black	£6-9	☐
96043	1991	Open Top, Black, Cream interior	£6-9	☐
96081	1992	Open Top, Primrose, Red interior	£6-9	☐
96082	1992	Soft Top, Silver, (Ken Baker)	£6-9	☐
98120	1993	Soft Top, British Racing Green	£6-9	☐
98121	1993	Open Top, Silver Blue	£6-9	☐

JAGUAR Mk.II Saloon 1959

C700/1	1988	Red body	£6-9	☐
C700/3	1988	Black, CLE of 7,000	£6-9	☐
D700/4	1989	Metallic Golden Sand	£6-9	☐
D700/5	1988	Green body	£6-9	☐
D700/6	1989	Metallic Blue	£6-9	☐
D700/7	1989	Metallic Grey	£6-9	☐
D700/8	1989	Silver-Blue body	£6-9	☐
D700/9	1990	Willow-Green body	£6-9	☐
D700/10	1990	Maroon. Not issued	NPP	☐
D700/11	1990	Rally car, see Kays Set D53/1	GSP	☐
C706/1	1988	Police car, Black, 'POLICE'	£6-9	☐
D706/2	1989	Police car, see Kays Set D75/1	GSP	☐
96680	1991	Rally car, Black, (Stirling Moss)	£6-9	☐
96681	1991	Rally car, Cream, (John Coombes)	£6-9	☐
96682	1991	'Inspector Morse', Maroon, Black roof	£6-9	☐
98131	1993	Silver Blue	£6-9	☐

JAGUAR XK 120

96040	1991	Open Top, White body	£6-9	☐
96041	1991	Open Top, British Racing Green	£6-9	☐
96044	1991	Soft Top, Black, White top	£6-9	☐
96060	1991	Open Top, Black body	£6-9	☐
97700	1991	Open Top, see Gift Set 97700	GSP	☐
	1993	Rally Car, Blue, RN '6'	£6-9	☐
	1993	Rally Car, White, RN '7'	£6-9	☐
	1993	Rally Car, Red, RN '8'	£6-9	☐

MERCEDES-BENZ 300SL ROADSTER

96410	1993	Open Top, Red, Cream seats	£6-9	☐
96411	1993	Open Top, Dark Grey, Red seats	£6-9	☐
96415	1993	Soft Top, Ivory, Black top	£6-9	☐
	1993	Soft Top, Light Grey, Black top	£6-9	☐

96200
AUSTIN HEALEY
Hard Top/Green

99050
AUSTIN HEALEY
Open Top/Blue

98124
FERRARI 250 GT
Hard Top/Red

96081
JAGUAR E TYPE
Open Top/Yellow

98123
PORSHE 356
Open Top/Silver

98131
JAGUAR MK II
Silver Blue

99045
SAAB 96
Maroon

96742
MORRIS MINOR
London to Peking

96682
JAGUAR MK II
Inspector Morse

M.G. 'MGA'

Ref. No.	Year(s)	Model Type	Price	
D730/1	1990	Hard-Top, Silver/Black	£6-9	☐
D730/2	1990	Hard Top, see Kays Set D53/1	GSP	☐
D731/1	1990	Open Soft-Top, British Racing Green	£6-9	☐
D732/1	1990	Closed Soft-Top, Red/Black	£6-9	☐
96140	1991	Hard Top, Red, luggage rack	£6-9	☐
96160	1991	Open Top, Black, luggage rack	£6-9	☐
96180	1991	Soft Top, White/Grey, luggage rack.......	£6-9	☐
97695	1992	White body, Black top, RN '324', in 'Abingdon' Set...................................	£6-9	☐
97695	1992	Red body, Black top, RN '38', in 'Abingdon' Set...................................	£6-9	☐
99046	1993	Hard Top, Silver/Black	£6-9	☐
99048	1993	Closed Soft-Top, Red/Black	£6-9	☐

MINI - COOPER

94140	1992	Red/White, 'Monte Carlo', RN '37'	NRP	☐
94141	1992	Black/White, RN '7'.............................	NRP	☐
97713	1992	see 'The Italian Job' Set 97713	GSP	☐
98136	1993	Almond-Green/White...........................	NRP	☐
98137	1993	with 'wickerwork' panels........................	NRP	☐

MORRIS MINOR 1000 Saloon

C702/1	1988	'B.S.M.', Black, with 'L' plates..............	£6-9	☐
C702/2	1988	Dark Blue...	£6-9	☐
D702/4	1989	'Millionth Minor', Lilac body.................	£6-9	☐
D702/5	1989	Maroon..	£6-9	☐
D702/6	1990	Almond-Green (see 98134).....................	£6-9	☐
D702/7	1990	Ivory body..	£6-9	☐
D702/8	1990	Clipper Blue	£6-9	☐
D702/9	1990	(99137) Sage Green, Not issued.............	NPP	☐
C703/1	1988	'Panda' Car, Blue/White, 'POLICE' separate hubs, thin end of sign attached to roof, no mirror/wiper detail, thick quarterlights	£15-20	☐
		integral (larger) hubs, detailed windscreen, thick end of sign attached to roof, thin quarterlights	£20-25	☐
		NB. Ist issue castings with 2nd type wheels exist.		
96740	1991	Rally car, Cream, (Pat Moss)	£6-9	☐
96741	1992	'Himalayan Rally' car, Dark Blue	£6-9	☐
96742	1993	Rally car, 'London to Peking'	£6-9	☐
98134	1993	Almond Green (reissued D702/6)	£6-9	☐

PORSCHE 356b SPEEDSTER

D741/1	1990	Hard-Top, Red/Black	£6-9	☐
D742/1	1990	Open Soft-Top, White/Black	£6-9	☐
D743/1	1990	Closed Soft-Top, Black, Red seats	£6-9	☐
96360	1991	Open Top, Blue, Black hood	£6-9	☐
98122	1993	Closed Soft-Top, Black body & hood	£6-9	☐
98123	1993	Open Top, Silver, Black hood	£6-9	☐

SAAB 96 Saloon

D711/1	1990	Dark Red..	£6-9	☐
D711/2	1990	Light Blue...	£6-9	☐
D712/1	1990	Rally car, Red, (Erik Carlsson)	£6-9	☐
96662	1991	Rally car, Light Blue, (Pat Moss)...........	£6-9	☐
99045	1993	Maroon..	£6-9	☐

TRIUMPH TR3a Sports Car

D736/1	1990	Hard-Top, Red, Black top.....................	£6-9	☐
D737/1	1990	Open Soft-Top, see 99053 (below)		☐
D738/1	1990	Closed Soft-Top, Yellow/Black..............	£6-9	☐
96300	1991	Closed Soft-Top, Red/Black, rack	£6-9	☐
99052	1993	Hard Top, Red body, Black top.............	£6-9	☐
99053	1990	Open Soft-Top, Pale Blue	£6-9	☐
99054	1993	Closed Soft-Top, Cream, Black top	£6-9	☐

MISCELLANEOUS Corgi Classics Cars

C582/2	1989	Chevrolet Bel Air, Pale Blue, Silver fin ..	£6-9	☐
C582/2	1989	Chevrolet Bel Air, Black/White, Silver fin..	£6-9	☐
96570	1992	Chevrolet Bel Air, Gold, 'Millionth'	£6-9	☐
96570	1992	Chevrolet Bel Air, Pale Blue, White fin..	£6-9	☐
C810/2	1989	Ford Thunderbird, Black	£6-9	☐

VOLKSWAGEN CARAVANETTES and CAMPERS

D984/1	1990	Caravanette, see 96940 (below)		
96940	1992	Caravanette, Red/Grey	£6-9	☐
96941	1991	Caravanette, Grey/White	£6-9	☐
97040	1991	Camper, Green/White, spare wheel	£6-9	☐

VOLKSWAGEN VANS

D985/1	1990	(no livery) Blue, Silver 'VW'	£6-9	☐
96960	1991	'BOSCH AUTO ELECTRICAL', Yellow	£6-9	☐
96961	1992	'LION', White/Red, 'Captain Condor'...	£6-9	☐
98757	1991	'SKIPPER', Cream/Blue	£6-9	☐
98965	1992	'EAGLE', see Gift Set 98965	GSP	☐
	1992	'CORGI', 'Collector Club 92'.................	NGPP	☐

96040
JAGUAR XK 120
Open Top/White

99052
TR3A
Hard Top/Red

99054
TR3A
Soft Top/Cream

96863
FORD POPULAR VAN
Sunlight Soap

96891
MORRIS J VAN
Morris Service

99048
MGA
Soft Top/Red

96415
MERCEDES-BENZ
300 SL ROADSTER
Soft Top/Ivory

99140
MORRIS J VAN
G.P.O.

98120
JAGUAR E TYPE
Soft Top/B.R. Green

98122
PORSCHE 356
Soft Top/Black

96940
V.W. CARAVANETTE
Red/Grey

96847
MORRIS 1000 VAN
Colman's Mustard

Corgi Classics Gift Sets

Note: All Gift Sets include numbered certificates unless indicated by 'no Cert'.

Ref. No.	Year(s)	Set Name	Contents	Market Price Range	
D4/1	1989	'Transport of the Early 50s'	OB Coach & Routemaster Bus, 'HANTS & DORSET' Dark Green/Cream, 4,800	**£40-50**	☐
D7/1	1989	'ROYAL MAIL' Set	Bedford OB Box Van & Morris Minor Van in Post Office Red, 4,600	**£40-50**	☐
D9/1	1989	'SHELL 1910-1940'	Grattans Set, Thorneycroft Box Van 'SHELL OIL', 'SHELL PETROL' & AEC Cabover Tanker 'YOU CAN BE SURE OF SHELL', 4,400	**£20-25**	☐
D13/1	1989	'Police Vans' Set	Two Morris 1000 Vans: a White one with 'DOG SECTION' and a Black version with 'GATESHEAD POLICE INCIDENT VAN', 4,500	**£35-40**	☐
D14/1	1989	'DANDY & BEANO' Set	2 Bedford CA Vans: a Yellow 'DANDY', and a Blue 'BEANO', 4,400	**£40-50**	☐
D15/1	1989	'GPO Telephones' Set	AEC Cabover & Morris Minor Van in Olive-Green GPO livery, 4,400	**£28-33**	☐
D16/1	1989	'RALLYING WITH FORD'	3 Fords: Yellow/White Zodiac (RN '21') Monaco Red Zephyr (RN '29') and a Pale Green Popular (no rally number). 3,400	**£30-35**	☐
D17/1	1989	'SHELL 1950-1960'	Yellow/Red Bedford OB Box Van & White/Yellow OB Pantechnicon, 5,000	**£32-38**	☐
D23/1	1989	Ford Popular Van Set	Purple/Black van 'FRASER COOK Ltd', Black van 'LEWIS EAST Ltd', and a Light Blue/Black van 'SIGNSMITH'. Grattans Mail-Order Set, 5,000	**£30-35**	☐
D35/1	1990	'50th Anniversary of the Battle of Britain' Set	Airforce-Blue Bedford OB Coach & Morris Minor Van, Black Ford Zephyr (some Zephyrs were issued with Zodiac grilles). 13,000	**£23-28**	☐
D36/1	1990	'Racing Zephyrs' Set	Three Ford Zephyrs, 1: White body, Black bonnet, RN '47', 'ENGLAND' 2: Yellow body & wheels, RN '117', 3: Black body & wheels, RN '97', 8,000	**£20-25**	☐
D37/1	1990	'PENNY POST'	Red/Black fully closed Tram, '150th Anniversary', 'Penny Black' design	**£15-20**	☐
D41/1	1990	'BARTONS TRANSPORT'	Red Bedford OB Coach & Red/Cream AEC Double-Decker Bus, 12,000	**£20-25**	☐
D46/1	1990	'Vehicles of the '50s & '60s'	Maroon/Cream OB Box & Morris 'J' vans, 'BRITISH RAILWAYS', 13,000	**£16-20**	☐
D47/1	1990	'BEANO 1990'	'Bash Street Kids' AEC Bus, & 'Minnie the Minx' Morris J Van, 15,000	**£20-25**	☐
C49	1986	'Transport of The 30s' Set	'The TIMES' Thorneycroft Bus and Ford Model T Van, 8,900	**£15-19**	☐
C50	1987	'Transport of The 30s' Set	'London Markets' Set (5,000, no Cert) containing 3 Ford Model T Vans: 'SMITHFIELD', 'COVENT GARDEN' and 'BILLINGSGATE'	**£15-20**	☐
D51/1	1990	'GREENE KING' Set...............	Mid-Green AEC Tanker & Thorneycroft Beer Truck, Kays Mail-order, 4,900	**£18-22**	☐
D52/1	1990	'CHARRINGTONS' Set	Orange/Black AEC Tanker & Thorneycroft Truck, Kays Set, 5,000	**£25-30**	☐
D53/1	1990	4-piece 'Rally' Set	Blue Jaguar Mk.II ('3') White/Grey Ford Cortina (no RN) Red/White Austin-Healey ('66') Blue/Black MGA ('48') Kays Set, 4,500	**£27-32**	☐
D54/1	1990	4-piece 'Utilities' Set	Kay's Set with Bedford CA Van (Green, 'GAS'), Ford Popular Van (Red/Black), Morris J Van, (Blue/Black), Morris Minor Van (Green/Black) 5,000	**£35-40**	☐
Q55/1	1990	'YORK FAIR' Set	Bedford OB Coach with Yellow/Pink/White body and Clown design, and Bedford OB Pantechnicon in Cream/Blue, '225 Years', 5,300	**£40-45**	☐
Q57/1	1990	'The Northern Collection'	Contains Bedford OB Coach 'RIBBLE/STANDERWICK' and Q953/17 OB Pantechnicon 'SLUMBERLAND', 4,900	**£30-35**	☐
C67/1	1991	'Systeme' Rally Set	Export set	**£10-13**	☐
C67/2	1991	'Peugeot' Rally Set	Export set	**£10-13**	☐
D67/1	1990	'UNITED DAIRIES' Set.........	Orange AEC Cabover Van, White AEC Cabover Tanker, 7,500	**£11-15**	☐
C68	1987	'Transport of The 30s' Set	Thorneycroft & Ford T Vans 'KAYS', (Kays Mail-order Set)	**£40-45**	☐
C69	1987	'Transport of The 30s' Set	Mail-Order Set, Thorneycroft & Ford T Vans 'BRYANT & MAY', 10,000	**£15-18**	☐
D71/1	1989	'Ford Model 'T' Set	Kays Mail-Order Set: Blue 'SOMERLITE' & Red 'TEXACO' tankers with Red/Brown 'A1 SAUCE' van & White/Black 'APS MEDICINES' van, 2,500	**£30-35**	☐
D72/1	1989	'Minor & Popular Vans' Set	2 Morris Vans: 'RINGTONS TEA' & 'FRYS COCOA & CHOCOLATE', with 2 Ford Popular Vans: 'COLMANS MUSTARD' and 'BOWYERS WILTSHIRE SAUSAGES'. 3,400 (Kays Mail-Order Set)	**£30-35**	☐
D74/1	1989	'PICKFORDS' Set	OB Pantechnicon, Ford Popular & Morris Minor vans, Kays Set, 3,500	**£70-80**	☐
D75/1	1989	'Police Cars' Set......................	Kays Mail-Order 3-car Set: White Jaguar Mk.II, Blue/White 'PANDA' Morris Minor, and Black Ford Zephyr. 3,100	**£40-45**	☐
D82/1	1990	'CORGI ON THE MOVE'.......	Dark Blue/White Bedford OB Coach and Pantechnicon, (Corgi Club members model, personalised certification)..	**£25-30**	☐
C88	1988	'Military Gift Set'.....................	Thorneycroft Bus '2nd Division', Ford T Van 'Order of St.John', Kays Set, 6,000	**£30-35**	☐
C89	1988	'60 Years of Transport'.............	3 models: Thorneycroft Bus 'BAXTERS' with OB Coach 'HIGHLAND' and, Green/White Tram 'FORD FOR VALUE', Kays Mail-order Set, 3,100	**£140-160**	☐
C90	1988	'Model T Ford Utility' Set	'ROYAL LAUNDRY' & 'SUNLIGHT' vans, Kays Mail-order LE, 8,600	**£12-16**	☐
C91	1989	'Morris Minor Vans' Set	3 vans: Green 'GRATTANS' van with Cream/Brown 'MITCHELLS' and Yellow 'TELEGRAPH & ARGUS', (Grattan's Mail-order LE, 5,000)	**£55-65**	☐
D94/1	1990	'WHITBREAD' Set	Bedford OB Box Van and Ford Model T Van in Brown/Black livery, 5,800	**£15-20**	☐
93715	1992	3-piece Mini Set.......................	Red, Silver and Green Minis sold only by Woolworths	NGPP	☐
96445	1993	'Goldfinger' Set.......................	30th Anniversary of Goldfinger, James Bond Aston Martin	NGPP	☐
96990	1992	AEC Bus Set	Yellow/Dark Blue AEC Double-Decker and AEC Regal coach, both with AEC logos	**£20-25**	☐
96995	1992	'IAN ALLAN' Set	Red AEC Double Deck Bus and Green/White Bedford CA van	**£17-20**	☐
97050	1993	Regent Bus Set	2 open top buses (White/Red and Cream/Blue)	NRP	☐
97051	1993	Invictaway Set	Dark Blue Metrobus, Cream/Green Plaxton	NRP	☐
97061	1991	'COVENTRY' Bus Set............	A.E.C. Double-Decker ('VERNONS') and Bedford OB coach in Maroon	**£20-25**	☐
97063	1991	'YELLOWAYS' Set	Yellow/Orange Bedford OB coach and A.E.C. Regal coach	**£20-25**	☐
97064	1993	'BLACKPOOL' Bus Set............	AEC Routemaster 'Travel Card', Metrobus 'Roller Coaster', Plaxton 'Seagull'	NRP	☐
97065	1993	Stagecoach Set	Routemaster, Metrobus, Plaxton. White/Orange/Red/Blue livery	NRP	☐
97066	1993	'Routemasters in Exile'	Scotland: Kelvin, Clydesdale, Perth, Strathtay	NRP	☐
97067	1993	'Routemasters in Exile'............	Midlands: K & M Gagg, East Midlands, Confidence, United Counties	NRP	☐
97068	1994	'Routemasters in Exile'	North: Burnley/Pendle, Manchester, East Yorkshire, Carlisle	NRP	☐
97069	1993	'WHITTLES' Set	Burlingham Seagull and AEC Regal coaches in Dark Blue/Red livery	NRP	☐
97070	1992	'SILVER SERVICE' Set	AEC Regal and Bedford OB coaches both in Silver and Blue livery	**£27-32**	☐
97071	1992	'DEVON' Bus Set	AEC Double-Decker & AEC Regal coach (Cream/Green)	**£27-32**	☐
97072	1992	'GOSPORT & FAREHAM'	AEC DD & Regal coach in Spruce-Green/Black 'PROVINCIAL' livery	**£27-32**	☐
97074	1994	'Routemasters in Exile'............	South: Southampton, Kentish, Capital, Southend	NRP	☐
97076	1992	'W.ALEXANDER' Bus Set......	Red Guy Arab double decker and Mid-Blue Leyland Tiger	**£30-35**	☐

Ref. No.	Year(s)	Model Type	Corgi Toys - continued	Market Price Range	
97075	1992	'SOUTH WALES' Bus Set	Maroon/Red AEC Regal and Cream/Red OB Coach	£24-29	☐
97077	1992	'EAST LANCASHIRE' Set	Red/Black Guy Arab and Dark Green Leyland Tiger	£28-33	☐
97078	1993	'Corkills - de Vanenburg'	Bedford coaches in Maroon/Black, and Turquoise/Black, 'Hotel Kasteel', (Dutch)	£20-25	☐
97079	1993	'PREMIER' Set	70th Anniversary Set (Tiger and OB)	NRP	☐
97086	1992	'FREEBORNS'	Bedford OB Pantechnicon, Grattans mail-order	£13-16	☐
97106	1992	'BIBBYS'	Bedford OB Coach, 'Ingleton', Kays mail-order	£13-16	☐
97107	1992	'MURGATROYD'	Bedford OB Coach, Grattans mail-order	£13-16	☐
97185	1992	'WEST RIDING'	AEC Regal Coach, Grattans mail-order	£13-16	☐
97200	1991	'BRS' Set	Green/Black Bedford OB Box & Morris 'J' vans. Kays LE 5,000	£15-19	☐
97331	1992	La France Set	Green open backed and Yellow closed Fire Engines	£24-28	☐
97351	1992	AEC Ladder Set	AEC Ladder Truck and Bedford CA Van 'Bristol'	£24-28	☐
97391	1992	AEC Pumper Set	AEC Fire Engine and Bedford CA Van 'Bristol'	£24-28	☐
97680	1991	'30 Years of the 'E' type'	Light Grey open & Red closed 'E' types	£13-16	☐
97681	1991	'Stirling's Choice' Set	Silver Austin-Healey ('7') & Green Jaguar XK120 (open) special box	£15-20	☐
97690	1991	'Ferrari' Set	Light Green ('15'), Dark Blue ('5'), Light Grey ('10'), Kays LE 5,000	£25-30	☐
97695	1992	'Abingdon' Set	Dark Green Morris 'J' van 'BMC', White MGA ('324'), Red MGA ('38')	£18-22	☐
97696	1993	'R.A.C.' Set	Bedford CA van and Mini Cooper	NGPP	☐
97697	1993	Leicestershire & Rutland Police Set	Morris 1000 Van and Jaguar Mk.II, both in White with Black 'Police' logos	NRP	☐
97698	1993	'Metropolitan Police' Set	Bedford OB Coach and Morris 1000 Car	NRP	☐
97700	1991	'Jaguar Through the Years'	Black 'E' type ('110'), White open XK120, Light Blue Mk.II	£17-22	☐
?	1991	'Jaguar XK120' Set	Cream (closed, '65'), White (open, '166'), Green (closed, '64'), GUS 5,000	£17-22	☐
97701	1991	'Racing 'E' types' Set	Grey (Black top, '170'), Red (Black top, '108'), special box, 7,500	£17-22	☐
97702	1992	'Jaguar Collection'	A Maroon Mk.II, a Green XK120 and a Red 'E' type, on wood plinth	£24-29	☐
97706	1993	Jaguar XK120 Set	'First Time Out'. 3 XK120s (Red '8', White '7', Blue '6')	NRP	☐
97708	1993	Tour de France Set...................	Jaguar Mk.II ('82'), Ferrari GTO ('165'), Mini-Cooper ('8')	NRP	☐
97709	1993	Alpine Rally Set	Ford Cortina ('29'), Austin-Healey ('95'), Mini-Cooper ('38')	NRP	☐
97712	1992	'Monte Carlo Mini' Set............	3 Red/White Minis, Rns '37', '52', '177'	£18-22	☐
97713	1992	'The Italian Job'	3 Minis from the film - Red, White, Blue	£18-22	☐
97730	1992	'Austin-Healey' Set.................	3 competition Austin-Healeys, Red ('76'), Green ('18'), Green ('414')	£18-22	☐
97735	1992	'CUMBRIAN' Set....................	Bedford OB Van plus Morris 'J' Van in Red and White..............................	£16-19	☐
97740	1991	'The TIMES' Gift Set...............	Contains Bedford CA Van and Morris Minor Van	£15-18	☐
97741	1991	'ISLAND TRANSPORT'	Two Bedford OB coaches: 'J.M.T.' and 'PIONEER' liveries	£10-15	☐
97742	1991	'JOHN SMITHS BREWERY'	Contains Thorneycroft Beer Truck and A.E.C. Tanker	£15-20	☐
97746	1991	'TOYMASTER' Set..................	Yellow/Red Bedford 'CA' & Blue 'CORGI' Morris 'J' vans, (own shops only)..........	£15-19	☐
97747	1991	'WEBSTERS' Brewery Set.......	Blue/Red AEC Cabover Tanker & Thorneycroft Truck, GUS LE 5,000	£18-22	☐
97749	1991	'BRITISH RAIL' Gift Set	Fordson 8 and Bedford 'CA' van in Maroon/Cream livery, special box	£16-20	☐
97750	1992	'EAST KENT' Set	Bedford OB and AEC Regal coaches in Dark Red livery................................	£24-27	☐
97751	1992	'BASS' Brewery Set	Red/Black Thorneycroft & Blue/Black Ford 'T' Van, (Kays)	£19-22	☐
97752	1992	'RUDDLES' Brewery Set	Bedford OB Box Van and Thorneycroft Beer Truck	£20-25	☐
97753	1992	'TERRYS of YORK' Set...........	Thorneycroft Box Van plus Ford Model 'T' Van	£13-16	☐
97754	1993	'LMS Railway' Set	AEC Cabover and Thorneycroft van in Maroon/Black 'LMS' livery	£19-22	☐
97755	1992	'WHITBREAD' Brewery Set ...	AEC Tanker and Thorneycroft van in Dark Brown/Black	£19-22	☐
97765	1993	'STRATHBLAIR' Set...............	'Wiles' Bedford coach and 'Forbes' Morris 'J' van......................................	£16-20	☐
97781	1993	'TATE & LYLE'	Foden Tanker and Bedford OB Van	NGPP	☐
97891	1992	'BILLY SMARTS'....................	White/Green *Circus'* Truck and Trailer...	£20-25	☐
97892	1993	'S.HOUSEMAN'.......................	Brown/White Truck and Trailer, *'York'*..	£20-25	☐
97893	1993	'J.AYERS'	Red Truck and Trailer, *'Modern Amusements'*..	£20-25	☐
98759	1991	'DANDY' Set	Morris 'J' van and Bedford 'CA' van	£12-15	☐
98960	1992	'BEANO' Set	Morris 1000 van ('Biffo') and Morris 'J' van ('Beryl The Peril')	£18-22	☐
98965	1993	'EAGLE' Set	Volkswagen van and Bedford CA van	£16-20	☐
98970	1992	'X Men' Set	Bedford Van plus Morris 'J' Van	£17-20	☐
98972	1992	'Spiderman' Set	Morris 'J' Van and Morris 1000 Van	£17-20	☐
98973	1992	'Captain America' Set	White/Red VW Van and Two-tone Blue Ford Popular Van............................	£17-20	☐
032/A/ 96041	1991	'The Classic British Sports Car Collection'	8 cars on wooden plinth: 96041, 96060, 96160, 96180, 96220, 96300, 99051, 99053. Originally a Sunday magazine direct-mail offer, then through Corgi Club.................	£35-45	☐
	1993	'Premier Albanian' Set	Leyland Tiger and Bedford OB Coaches with 'PREMIER' logo	NRP	☐
?	1993	La France Pumper Set	'SCOTTDALE' (open, Green) and 'SOUTH RIVER' (closed, Orange).................	£30-35	☐
	1993	'Connoisseur Collection 'E'-type Jaguars..................	One open, one closed, Chrome plated, Black plinth, Black box. CLE of 5,000 direct-mailed..	£48-55	☐

RECOMMENDED ADDITIONAL READING ON CORGI CLASSICS

The Catalogue Editor is indebted to George Hatt the author of 'The Corgi Classics Collectors Guide' for providing much invaluable information. Classics collectors are strongly advised to purchase a copy of George's book for it contains considerable additional information plus colour photographs of rare issues.
Send to: 16 Horse Road, Hilperton, Trowbridge, Wiltshire, BA14 7PE.

Corgi Toys   -   Buses, Minibuses and Coaches

(Excluding models issued as 'CORGI CLASSICS')

Only models thought to have been 100% produced by Corgi have been included in the listings.

1: ROUTEMASTER DOUBLE-DECKER BUSES
  a) Identification
  b) 1st and 2nd casting Routemasters sold through normal retail outlets
  c) Difficult to catalogue Routemasters
  d) Customer exclusive models
  e) Electronic issues

2: A.E.C. REGENT DOUBLE-DECKER BUSES

3: METROBUS Mk.2 DOUBLE-DECKER BUSES

4: PLAXTON PARAMOUNT COACHES

5: FORD TRANSIT MINIBUSES

6: MAJOR MODELS - COACHES

7: MISCELLANEOUS

1a: Routemaster Double-Decker Buses - Identification

1ST CASTING 1964-1975 - MODEL No. 468 ONLY - CLOSED TOP MODEL

Length 114 mm, die-cast body comprised of two separate castings which make up the lower and upper decks. The castings are separated by a white plastic joint. The baseplate is die-cast, painted grey and stamped 'Corgi Toys', 'LONDON TRANSPORT', 'ROUTEMASTER', 'MADE IN ENGLAND' plus the Patent No. 904525. The early issues had turned metal wheels with rubber tyres. These lasted until 1973 when cast metal wheels were introduced with plastic tyres and in 1974/75 WhizzWheels were seen.

Early issues also had jewelled headlights which were replaced in 1973 by the cast-in type painted silver. The decals are of the transfer printed variety and there is a board at the front only. The model has spring suspension, windows, a metal platform handrail and a driver and clippie. The interior seats are white or cream.

2ND CASTING - 1975 ONWARDS - CLOSED TOP AND OPEN TOP MODELS

MODEL Nos: C460, C463, C464, C467, C469, C470, C471, C473, C475, C476, C477, C479, C480, 1004 and all the numbers allocated to the 'Specials'.

Length 123 mm, die-cast body comprised of two separate castings which make up the lower and upper decks. The castings are separated by a cream plastic joint for normal issues and very often by a coloured joint for 'Specials'. Until Model No. 480 was issued as an AEC Renown in 1983 the plastic baseplates were stamped 'CORGI', 'LONDON TRANSPORT', 'ROUTEMASTER' and 'MADE IN ENGLAND'. However 'LONDON TRANSPORT' and 'ROUTEMASTER' were removed from this time onwards.

The logos were originally stick-on labels followed by tampo printing in the mid-eighties. The seats were normally white or cream but other colours are used for the 'Specials' (eg. Red in the 'BRITISH DIE-CAST MODEL TOYS CATALOGUE' Special). The model has silver painted cast-in headlights, spring suspension, windows, a metal platform handrail but apart from the very early issues does not have a driver or clippie.

The wheels are of the WhizzWheel type. The early issues were of a close fitting type e.g. 'BTA', 'SWAN & EDGAR', 'DISNEYLAND'. However by the time the model was issued they had become protruding. The wheel hubs are either chrome (earlier models) or painted with plastic tyres.

1b: Routemaster Buses, 1964-1975, (1st casting)

Ref. No.	Year(s)	Model Name	Body Colour, Fleetname, Route, Other Details	Market Price Range	
468	1964-66	'NATURALLY CORGI'	Red, London Transport, *'CORGI CLASSICS'*	**£60-70**	☐
468	1964	'NATURALLY CORGI'	Green/Cream/Brown, (Australian) 'NEW SOUTH WALES', *'CORGI CLASSICS'*	**£500-750**	☐
468	1967-75	'OUTSPAN ORANGES'	Red, London Transport, 10, (diecast or WhizzWheels)	**£30-40**	☐
468	1968	'GAMAGES'	Red, London Transport, '10'	**£80-100**	☐
468	1969	'CHURCH'S SHOES'	Red, London Transport, '10', Union Jacks	**£80-100**	☐
468	1970	'MADAME TUSSAUDS'	Red, London Transport, '10'	**£80-100**	☐
468	1975	'THE DESIGN CENTRE'	Red, London Transport, '10'	**£50-60**	☐
468	?	'cokerchu'	Red, London Transport, '2½d', PRM	NGPP	☐

70

1b: Routemaster Buses, 1975 onwards, (2nd casting)

Ref. No.	Year(s)	Model Name	Body Colour, Fleetname, Route, Other Details	Market Price Range	
C460	1984	'BOLTON EVENING NEWS'	Maroon, Bolton Transport, '197 LEE LANE'	£10-15	☐
C463	1984	'BRITISH MEAT'	Red/White, London Transport, '279'	£10-15	☐
C464	1984	'BRITISH MOTOR SHOW'	Blue/Red, JOHN MENZIES, 'NEC'	£10-15	☐
C467	1977	'SELFRIDGES'	Red, London Transport, '12'	£20-25	☐
C469	1975-76	'BTA WELCOME TO BRITAIN'	Red, London Transport, '11', driver, clippie	£20-25	☐
C469	1976	'THE DESIGN CENTRE'	Red, London Transport, '11', driver, clippie, 'Visit The Design Centre' in black or red	£125-150	☐
C469	1977	'CADBURYS'	Orange, 'Cadburys Double Decker', on-pack offer, special box	£15-20	☐
C469	1979	'SELFRIDGES'	Red, London Transport, '12'	£15-20	☐
C469	1979	'LEEDS PERMANENT' BUILDING SOCIETY'	Dark Green/Yellow, ADDIS, '22', 'George Schilibeer 1829 - London Transport 1979'	£25-30	☐
C469	1979	'SWAN & EDGAR'	Red, London Transport, '11'	£40-50	☐
C469	1979	'HAMLEYS'	Red, London Transport, '11', (few only)	£20-25	☐
C469	1978-80	'BTA'	Red, London Transport, ('7', '11' or '12')	£15-20	☐
C469	1982	'BLACKPOOL'	Cream/Green, 'Blackpool Illuminations', '21'	£30-40	☐
C469	1983	'GAMLEYS'	Red, 'Toyshop Of The South'	£15-20	☐
C469	1983	'EAGLE STAR'	White/Black, '1 Threadneedle Street'	£15-20	☐
C469	1983	'REDGATES'	Cream/Brown (Red seats) '25'	£50-55	☐
C469	1983	'LONDON TRANSPORT GOLDEN JUBILEE'	Red/White/Silver, 21, '1933-1983', (1,000)	£40-50	☐
C469	1983	'DIECAST and TINPLATE'	Black, 'John Gay - Upchurch', (500)	£10-15	☐
C469	1983	'BLACKPOOL PLEASURE BEACH'	Cream/Green, Blackpool Transport, '23', 'Britain's No.1 Tourist Attraction'	£40-50	☐
		Open-top version:	As previous model but with open top	£50-55	☐
C469	1983	'NORBROOK MOTORS'	Dark Blue (White seats) route '57'	£20-30	☐
		colour change:	As previous model but Red version	£20-35	☐
C469	1983	'JOLLY GIANT'	Yellow/Green, route '459'	£10-15	☐
		colour change:	As previous model but with Red body	£15-20	☐
C469	1983	'GLOUCESTER TRAIN AND TOY SALE'	Black, Yellow/Red labels, route '25'	£10-15	☐
C469	1983	'ARMY AND NAVY'	Red, London Transport, '24'	£10-15	☐
C469	1983	'MANCHESTER UNITED'	Red open top double decker, route '83'	£10-15	☐
C469	1983	'LLANDINDROD FESTIVAL'	Green/White, route '14'	£10-£14	☐
C469	1983	'DION DION'	Dark Blue, 'Saves You More' in Orange	£15-20	☐
		South African issue:	has incorrect label 'Saves You Money'	£20-30	☐
C469	1983	'TROWBRIDGE TOYS AND MODELS'	Two tone Blue, route '5'	£15-20	☐
C469	1983	'THORNTONS'	Brown/Cream, route '14'	£10-15	☐
C469	1983	'MANCHESTER LIONS'	Cream, route '105BN Manchester'	£25-30	☐
C469	1983	'MANCHESTER EVENING NEWS'	Open Top bus, Yellow, '164'	£10-15	☐
C469	1983	'ROUND LONDON'	Open Top bus, Red or Orange	£10-15	☐
C469	1983	'BTA WELCOME'	Open Top bus, Red, '14'	£10-15	☐
C469	1983	'BRITISH TOY'	Red (with White seats) '14'	£10-15	☐
C469	1984	'JOHN WEBB'	Red/Green, 'John Webb'	£10-15	☐
C469	1984	'TWININGS'	Blue/Black, '11'	£10-15	☐
C469	1984	'STRETTON SPRING WATER'	White/Yellow, '2'	£10-15	☐
C469	1984	'READING EXPRESS'	Maroon, GOLDLINE, '11', (700 made)	£10-15	☐
C469	1984	'LIVERPOOL GARDEN FESTIVAL'	Green, Merseyside Transport, '46 Penny Lane'	£10-15	☐
C469	1984	'HAMLEYS'	Red (White seats) London Transport, '6'	£10-15	☐
C469	1984	'THE NEW CORGI COMPANY'	Red, '29th March 1984', 'South Wales - De Cymru, (2,000)	£25-35	☐
C469	1984	'GEMINI DIECAST'	Red/Green, London Country, '24'	£10-15	☐
C469	1984	'BTA'	Red (White seats) London Transport, '24'	£10-15	☐
C469	1984	'MIDLAND BUS MUSEUM'	Blue/Cream, 'BaMMOT', '750 Wythall'	£10-15	☐
C469	1985	'GREAT WESTERN Rly'	Brown/Cream, GWR, '150 Paddington'	£10-15	☐
C469	1985	'ESSEX ORGAN Studios'	Blue, Southend Transport, '18 Foulness'	£15-20	☐
C469	1985	'FAREWELL TO ROE'	Red, West Riding, '24'	£10-15	☐
C469	1985	'HAMLEYS'	Red, London Transport, '6', ('five-man' logo)	£10-15	☐
C469	1985	'HAMLEYS' (Open Top)	Cream/Green, Bath	£10-15	☐
C469	1985	'UNDERWOODS'	Red (White seats) '19 Picadilly'	£10-15	☐
C469	1985	'JUST A SECOND'	Green, Southern Vectis, '1 Newport'	£10-15	☐
C469	1985	'COWES STAMP & MODEL SHOP'	Green, Southern Vectis, '1a Cowes'	£15-20	☐
C469	1985	'OLD SMUGGLER'	Brown/White/Maroon, 'Whisky' fleetname	£15-20	☐
C469	1985	'B.T.A.'	Open-top Bus, route '24'	£10-15	☐
C469	1985	'HARLANDS LABELS'	Red, 'Land of Green Ginger'	£10-15	☐
C469	1985	'FARNHAM MALTINGS'	Red, Alder Valley, '268'	£20-25	☐
C469	1986	'LONDON STANDARD'	Red, 'Great Newspaper'	£5-10	☐
C469	1988	'LONDON STANDARD'	As 1986 issue but 'eyebrows' on destination board	£5-10	☐
C469		'ANDREX'	Light Blue, 'Guide Dogs'	NGPP	☐
C469		'TAYLOR & McKINNA'	Red, London Transport	NGPP	☐
C470	1977	'DISNEYLAND'	Yellow Open Top, Disney characters	£16-20	☐
C471	1977	'SEE MORE LONDON'	Silver, 25, 'The Queens Silver Jubilee London Celebrations 1977'	£16-20	☐
C471	1977	'WOOLWORTHS'	Silver, '25', 'Woolworths Welcome The World' & 'Queens Silver Jubilee 1977'	£20-30	☐
C473	1985	'GAMLEYS'	Red, London Transport, '16'	£10-15	☐

71

Ref. No.	Year(s)	Model Type	Corgi Toys - continued	Market Price Range
C475	1983	'TAKE OFF FROM BRISTOL'	Blue (with White seats) Bristol	£10-15 ☐
C476	1983	'BRITISH TELECOM'	Yellow, routes '14' or '406'	£10-15 ☐
C476		'CULTURE BUS'	Yellow body	NGPP ☐
C476		'WHITE LABEL WHISKY'	Yellow, Northern	NGPP ☐
C477	1983	'THE BUZBY BUS'	Pale or Dark Blue (various shades)	£10-15 ☐
C478	1983	'SUNDECKER'	Open-top White/Orange, 'MARRAKESH'	£10-15 ☐
C479	1983	'LONDON CRUSADER'	Green/White, '14' or '406'	£10-15 ☐
C480	1983	'WHITE LABEL WHISKY'	Blue/Yellow/White. (AEC Renown without 'Routemaster' on base)	£10-15 ☐
C481	1984	'BEA'	Blue/White/Black, route 'BEA'	£10-15 ☐
C482	1984	'LEEDS PERMANENT BUILDING SOCIETY'	Dark Green/Yellow, LEEDS, '22', *George Schilibeer 1829 - London Transport 1979*	£10-15 ☐
C483	1984	'HMV SHOP'	Red/Yellow, 'Fare 30p Knightsbridge'	£10-15 ☐
C485	1984	'ISLE OF WIGHT COUNTY PRESS'	Light Blue, 'CENTENARY 1884-1984', '1 Newport', couple reading paper, (1,500)	£10-15 ☐
			Same model but 'Southern Vectis'	£15-20 ☐
C485	1984	'ML ELECTRICS'	Light Blue, Southern Vectis	£10-15 ☐
C486	1984	'THE CULTURE BUS'	Yellow, 'CULTURE BUS'	£10-15 ☐
			As previous model but open-top version	£15-20 ☐
C488	1984	'THE NEW CORGI COMPANY'	Green, *South Wales - De Cymru*, '29th March 1984'	£10-15 ☐
C488	1984	'BEATTIES'	Red, routes '24' & '25'	£10-15 ☐
C492	1984	'GLOBAL SALES'	Yellow, 'H.A.RAPPORT'	£10-15 ☐
C521	1984	'HAIG WHISKY'	Yellow, '16'	£10-15 ☐
C523	1984	'BRITISH DIE-CAST MODEL TOYS CATALOGUE'	Red body & seats, White roof, Black labels, White letters, 'SWAPMEET TOYS & MODELS Ltd', route 'No 1 EDITION 1934-1984 1st FIFTY YEARS', Numbered CLE of 800. Labels read: *'You Can't Afford To Be Without A British Diecast Model Toys Catalogue*	£10-15 ☐
		Variant:	Same but Gold/White letters on labels, (300)	£20-25 ☐
C524	1984	'STEVENSONS'	Yellow/Black/White	£10-15 ☐
C527	1984	'TIMBERCRAFT CABINETS'	Green/Orange/Black	£25-30 ☐
C529	1984	'1985 CALENDAR BUS'	Black/Orange, 'G.WARD'	£10-15 ☐
C530	1984	'YORKSHIRE POST'	Two tone Green, '41'	£10-15 ☐
C558	1985	'RADIO VICTORY'	Open-top, Portsmouth, Red/White/Blue	£10-15 ☐
C566	1985	'GELCO EXPRESS'	Blue/White/Green	£15-20 ☐
C567	1985	'LINCOLN CITY'	White/Green/Black	£10-15 ☐
C567	1985	'SEE MORE LONDON'	White, tourist advertisements	£10-15 ☐
C570	1985	'BUS COLLECTORS SOCIETY'	Open-top, Blue/Navy, '96 Luton'	£10-15 ☐
C571	1985	'The TIMES'	Maroon	£10-15 ☐
C572	1985	'The TIMES'	Blue with thin labels	£15-20 ☐
			Blue with wide labels	£10-15 ☐
C574	1985	'BLACKPOOL CENTENARY'	Red/White, 'Tramway Centenary'	£10-15 ☐
C580	1985	'GUIDE DOGS'	Blue, 'Barclays', '2'	£10-15 ☐
C583	1985	'MANCHESTER EVENING NEWS'	Yellow/Black, route '4'	£10-15 ☐
C589	1985	'AUTOSPARES'	Red	£10-15 ☐
C590	1985	'MEDIC ALERT'	Open, Mauve/Yellow, 'Sponsored By Lions Clubs'	£10-15 ☐
C591	1985	'MEDIC ALERT'	Closed version of C590	£10-15 ☐
	1985	'ROLAND FRIDAY'	Red, 'Roland Friday Keyboards'	NGPP ☐
C596	1986	'HARRODS'	Red, 'Marble Arch', '30'	£10-15 ☐
C625		'CITYRAMA'	Blue body	NGPP ☐
C627	1986	'MODEL MOTORING'	Brown/White, Edinburgh Corporation, '87 Broughton St'	£10-15 ☐
C628	1986	'POLCO PLUS'	Red, 'Rotary International', Limited Edition	£10-15 ☐
C633	1986	'HOSPITAL RADIO'	Blue, 'Blackpool '86', export model	£15-20 ☐
C638	1986	'WEETABIX'	Yellow, Blue logo, Limited Edition	£10-15 ☐
	1989	'Great Book of CORGI'	Yellow/Blue, '1956-1983'. Originally only available with book	£15-20 ☐
91765	1992	'CROSVILLE'	Yellow/Green body, 'Happy Dragon' logo	£7-10 ☐

Additional variations about which more information is required:
'PRUDENTIAL INSURANCE', 'COBHAM BUS MUSEUM', 'GAMLEYS' (Green version) 'EAGLE STAR' (in Blue/White) 1365 'BTA' plus taxi Set

1c: Routemasters Difficult to Catalogue

Shortly before and after Mettoy ceased trading during the period 1982-84 the following models were all given a 469 number and were issued in rapid succession in many different colour variations. The models were normally issued as a closed-top version but some will also be found as open-tops as well. These (open-tops) were issued in either an orange or yellow livery with often a 'BOURNEMOUTH' fleetname. The Route numbers seen were usually '14' or '24'. Corgi have referred to this period as the 'oddball patch'.

The models are: 'OLD HOLBORN', 'OXO', 'AERO', 'TDK', 'LION BAR', 'BARRATT', 'WORLD AIRWAYS', 'PENTEL', 'BUY BEFORE YOU FLY - DUTY FREE'.

The colours seen: Brown/Cream, Blue/Cream, Green/Yellow, Blue, Green, Black, Cream, White.

Fleetnames were not used on the majority of these issues with the following exceptions:

'TAYSIDE' ('Barratt', 'Oxo', 'Aero')
'TRANSCLYDE' ('World Airways', 'Buy Before You Fly')
'SOUTH YORKS' ('TDK', 'World Airways')
'LONDON TRANSPORT' ('Lion Bar', 'Oxo', 'Aero').

Model No 470 was issued bearing the 'LONDON COUNTRY' fleetname in respect of 'Barratt', 'Pentel', 'Buy Before You Fly', 'TDK', and no doubt others. It is known that at the time of Mettoy going into receivership batches of labels were sold off to the trade which no doubt accounts for many of the different variations to be found. Therefore with this background it is not possible to provide meaningful price and rarity guidance.

1d: Customer Exclusive Models

Ref. No.	Year(s)	Model Name	Body Colour, Fleetname, Route, Other Details	Market Price Range	

Note: These models are listed for the sake of completeness but there is little real opportunity of collectors obtaining them as very few were issued (usually 50 or less).

Ref. No.	Year(s)	Model Name	Body Colour, Fleetname, Route, Other Details	Market Price Range	
C468	1965	'RED ROSE COFFEE'	Brown, 1st casting, Australian	NGPP	☐
C469	1977	'METTOY SALES CONFERENCE'	Red body	NGPP	☐
C469	1977	'M.G.M.W. DINNER'	Red body	NGPP	☐
C469	1977	'QUALITOYS VISIT'	Red body	NGPP	☐
C469	1977	'VEDES VISIT TO SWANSEA'	Red body	NGPP	☐
C469	1977	'MARKS & SPENCER VISIT SWANSEA'	Red body	NGPP	☐
C469	1977	'HAROLD LYCHES VISIT'	Red body	NGPP	☐
C469	1977	'METTOY Welcomes SWISS BUYERS to SWANSEA'	Red body	NGPP	☐
C469	1978	'FINNISH VISIT TO SWANSEA'	Red body	NGPP	☐
C469	1978	'M.G.M.W. DINNER'	Red body	NGPP	☐
C469	1983	'OCTOPUSSY'	(The 'James Bond' film). Red body	NGPP	☐
C469	1983	'MARRIOT HOTELS'	Red, GROSVENOR HOUSE	NGPP	☐
C469	1984	'CHARLIE'S ANGELS'	Open-top, Red, (200 to TV-AM)	NGPP	☐
C469	1984	'CORGI COLLECTORS Visit'	Red, SOUTH WALES - DE CYMRU, SWANSEA June 1984. Only 12 made (for guests at first two-day collectors' meeting with Corgi Management)	NGPP	☐
C469	1984	'REDDITCH'	Midland Red, '14', *'Success in the Heart of England'*	NGPP	☐
C469	1984	'SKYRIDER BUS Collectors Society'	White, SOUTH WALES, '72'	NGPP	☐
C469	1985	'WHATMAN PAPER'	Red, London Transport, (240)	NGPP	☐
C469	1985	'COLT 45 SALES CONFERENCE'	Red or Two-tone Blue, London Transport, '45'	NGPP	☐
C469	1985	'SKYRIDER'	*'International Distributors Meeting'*.	NGPP	☐
C461	1986	'MANNHEIM VISIT 1986'	Red/Yellow, Blue logo	NGPP	☐

1e: Electronic Issues

1004	1981	'CORGITRONICS First In ELECTRONIC DIE-CAST'	Red, London Transport, '11'	£15-20	☐

Other issues will be found combining 'BTA', 'HAMLEYS', 'OXO', etc with the 'CORGITRONICS' logo. See that section for details.

2: A.E.C. Regent Double-Decker Bus (Classic Series)

Issued from 1986 onwards with a changed lower deck plus an A.E.C. radiator design whilst retaining the Routemaster upper deck. Labels will be found on the early issues with tampo-print designs being used in part from 599/2.

Ref. No.	Year(s)	Model Name	Body Colour, Fleetname, Route, Other Details	Market Price Range	
D41/1	1990	'BARTONS'	Red/Cream, (see Gift Set D41/1)	GSP	☐
D47/1	1990	'BEANO'	Red/Yellow, (see Gift Set D47/1)	GSP	☐
C599	1987	'TRUSTEE SAVINGS BANK'	Dark Blue/Cream, 'Nottingham City', 4,200	£25-35	☐
C599/1	1986	'WISK'	Red/Yellow	£20-25	☐
D599/1	1989	'WESTERN'	Red/Yellow, 'Wallaces Sausages'	£10-15	☐
C599/2	1987	'WOODHAMS SCOOTERS'	Dark Blue/Cream, 'EASTBOURNE', 4,900	£35-45	☐
C599/3	1987	'HUNTLEY & PALMERS'	Brown/White, 'LEICESTER CITY', 4,000	£30-35	☐
			As previous model but no White windows	£40-45	☐
C599/4	1988	'GLASGOW'	Green/Brown, 'Crown Wallpapers'	£17-25	☐
C599/5	1988	'RHONDDA'	Red/Yellow, 'Premium Bonds', 3,700	£15-20	☐
C599/6	1989	'MORECAMBE'	Green/Yellow, 'HEYSHAM', 5,000	£14-18	☐
C599/7	1989	'BRADFORD'	Blue body, White bands, 5,000	£14-18	☐
C599/8	1989	'HANTS & DORSET'	Dark Green/Cream, in Gift Set D4/1	GSP	☐
D599/10	1990	'BRIGHTON & HOVE'	Red/Cream body, 'Tamplins Ales', 5,100	£12-15	☐
D599/11	1990	'DUBLIN'	Green/Yellow, 'Irish Independent'	£8-10	☐
D599/12	1990	'BATTLE OF BRITAIN'	RAF Blue, 'Wings for Victory'	£8-10	☐
Q599/13	1990	'HALIFAX'	Green/Red, 59, 'Websters XL', 5,300	£14-18	☐
C634	1986	'MAPLES'	Red, new 'bolt head' wheels	£25-30	☐
C643	1986	'NEWCASTLE ALE'	Yellow/White body	£20-25	☐
96980	1991	'STEVENSONS'	Yellow/Black, 'UTTOXETER'	£8-10	☐
96983	1991	'LIVERPOOL Corp.	Green/White, 'Littlewoods'	£8-10	☐
	1991	'ROCHDALE	Blue/White	£8-10	☐
97001	1993	'P.M.T.'	Red/White, 'Stoke'	£7-10	☐
97002	1993	'SHEFFIELD'	Cream, 'Double Diamond'	£7-10	☐
97003	1993	'West BRIDGEFORD'	Maroon/Cream, 'Say CWS'	NRP	☐
97062	1991	'OXFORD'	Red/Black body	£7-10	☐
	1993	'OXFORD'	No details at present	£7-10	☐
	1993	'CORGI'	Blue/Cream Club model, 'Meridian Way, Leicester'	£10-15	☐
97064	1993	'TRAVEL CARD'	Red/White, in 'Blackpool' Set 97064	GSP	☐
97065	1993	'STAGECOACH'	White, in 'Stagecoach' Set 97065	GSP	☐

3: Metrobus Mk.2 Double-Decker Bus

Ref. No.	Year(s)	Model Name	Body Colour, Fleetname, Route, Other Details	Market Price Range	
C675/1	1988	'WEST MIDLANDS TIMESAVER'	Silver, 'Hasbury'	£20-25	☐
C675/2	1988	'READING TRANSPORT GOLDLINE'	Dark Brown/White, Gold logo	£15-20	☐
C675/3	1988	'W. MIDLANDS TRAVEL'	Purple/Cream	£15-20	☐
C675/4	1988	'BEATTIES'	Red, route '25' ('109' on 1990 re-issue)	£10-15	☐
C675/5	1989	'THE BEE LINE'	Yellow/Black, 'SANDFORDS'	£10-15	☐
C675/6	1989	'YORKSHIRE TRACTION'	White/Red, 'FASTLINK'	£10-15	☐
C675/7	1989	'WEST MIDLANDS'	Dark Green, 'Hitachi'	£10-15	☐
C675/9	1989	'NEWCASTLE BUSWAYS'	Yellow/White/Maroon	£10-15	☐
C675/10	1989	'LONDON TRANSPORT'	Red, '109', map design 'Beatties'	£10-15	☐
Q675/12	1989	'MAIDSTONE'	Dark Green, Yellow/Black design	£10-15	☐
			Mid-Green, (2,300 CLE)	£10-15	☐
Q675/13	1989	'EAST KENT'	Red/Yellow, 'E.K.' emblem	£10-15	☐
Q675/14	1990	'GM BUSES'	Orange/White, 'Driving The Dream'	£10-12	☐
Q675/15	1990	'NATIONAL GARDEN FESTIVAL'	Red/White, 'Gateshead 1990'	£10-12	☐
C676/16	1990	'STRATHCLYDE'	Blue/White, 'BLUEBIRD COACHES'	£10-12	☐
91702	1993	'AIRBUS'	Red, 'Heathrow Airport'	£7-9	☐
91848	1992	'Yorkshire Rider'	2nd version	£7-9	☐
91850	1992	'READING'	Cream, '90th Anniversary', 5000	£7-9	☐
91852	1992	'STEVENSONS'	Yellow, 'For Holidays', 5000	£7-9	☐
91853	1992	'BRADFORD'	White/Yellow, 'British Trolleybus', 5000	£7-9	☐
91854	1992	'HALIFAX'	Green/Orange, 'Yorkshire Rider', 5000	£7-9	☐
91855	1992	'W.YORKS'	Red, 'Yorkshire Rider', 5000	£7-9	☐
91856	1992	'SUNDERLAND'	Yellow/White, 'Busways', 5000	£7-9	☐
91857	1992	'NEWCASTLE'	Yellow/White, 'Fenwick', 5000	£7-9	☐
91858	1993	'LEEDS'	Cream/Green, 'Yorkshire Rider', 5000	£7-9	☐
91859	1993	'WY PTE'	Blue/White, 'Halifax 540', 5000	£7-9	☐
91860	1993	'HUDDERSFIELD TRAMWAYS'	Red/White, 'Private 100', 5000	£7-9	☐

Ref. No.	Year(s)	Model Type	Corgi Toys - continued	Market Price Range	
91861	1993	'TODMORDEN'	Dark Green, '80 Years of Buses', 5000	**£7-9**	☐
91862	1993	'BRADFORD Centenary'	Red, '100 Years Public Service', 5000	**£7-9**	☐
91863	1993	'HUDDERSFIELD'	Blue/White, 'Yorkshire Rider', 5000	**£7-9**	☐
91864	1993	'GREY & GREEN'	Grey/Green/Orange, 'Cowie', LE	**£7-9**	☐
91865	1993	'YORKS RIDER'	White/Green, 'Evening Post'	**£7-9**	☐
97051	1993	'INVICTAWAY'	Dark Blue, in Set 97051	**GSP**	☐
97064	1993	'ROLLER COASTER'	Yellow/Blue, in 'Blackpool' Set 97064	**GSP**	☐
97065	1993	'STAGECOACH'	White, in 'Stagecoach' Set 97065	**GSP**	☐

4: Plaxton Paramount Coaches

Ref. No.	Year(s)	Model Name	Body Colour, Fleetname, Route, Other Details	Market Price Range	
C769	1985	'NATIONAL EXPRESS'	Red/White/Blue, 'RAPIDE'	**£10-15**	☐
C770	1985	'HOLIDAY TOURS'	Red/White/Yellow	**£10-15**	☐
C771	1985	'AIR FRANCE'	Red/Blue/White	**£10-15**	☐
	1985	'SAS.'	White, Blue wheels	**£10-15**	☐
C773	1985	'GREEN LINE'	White/Green, Limited Edition	**£10-15**	☐
C774	1985	'RAILAIR LINK'	White, Yellow/Black design	**£10-15**	☐
		'ALDER VALLEY'	'READING - HEATHROW'	**£10-15**	☐
C775	1985	'CITY LINK'	White, 'OXFORD'	**£10-15**	☐
C776	1985	'SKILLS SCENICRUISERS'	Blue/Orange	**£10-15**	☐
C777	1985	'TAYLORS TRAVEL'	White, multicoloured design	**£10-15**	☐
C791	1985	'SWISS PTT'	Yellow/White/Red/Black, export model	**£15-20**	☐
C792	1986	'GATWICK FLIGHTLINE'	Two-tone Green	**£10-15**	☐
C793/1	1986	'INTASUN EXPRESS'	White/Orange/Pink	**£10-15**	☐
C1223	1986	'PHILIPS'	Blue/White, Limited Edition export model	**£10-15**	☐
C769	1987	'CLUB CANTABRICA	Dark Blue, Red flash & logo	**£10-15**	☐
C769/4	1987	'S.A.S.'	White, 'FLYBUSSEN', export model	**£10-15**	☐
C769/5	1988	'GLOBAL'	White, multicoloured design	**£10-15**	☐
C769/6	1989	'POHJOLAN LIJKENNE'	Brown stripes, (Finland)	**£25-30**	☐
C769/7	1990	'SCOTTISH CITYLINK'	Yellow/Blue	**£10-15**	☐
C769/8	1990	'BLUEBIRD EXPRESS'	Blue/White, 'FALKIRK'	**£10-15**	☐
91908	1992	'S.A.S.'	no details at present	**£8-10**	☐
91909	1992	'FINNAIR'	White, Blue stripe, 5000	**£8-10**	☐
91911	1992	'APPLEBY'	no details at present	**£8-10**	☐
91913	1992	'VOYAGER PLAXTON'	no details at present	**£8-10**	☐
91914	1992	'SPEEDLINK'	'HEATHROW/GATWICK'	**£8-10**	☐
91915	1992	'TELLUS'	Red/White, 'Midland Red'	**£10-12**	☐
91916	1992	'EAST YORKS'	White, 'Diplomat', 5000	**£10-12**	☐
91917	1993	'HIGHWAYMAN'	Yellow body, Green logo	**NRP**	☐
97051	1993	'INVICTAWAY'	Cream/Green, in Set 97051	**GSP**	☐
97064	1993	'SEAGULL'	Blue, in 'Blackpool' Set 97064	**GSP**	☐
97065	1993	'STAGECOACH'	White, in 'Stagecoach' Set 97065	**GSP**	☐

5: Ford Transit Minibus

C676/1	1988	'BLUEBIRD'	Blue/White, 'MIDLAND SCOTTISH'	**£5-10**	☐
C676/2	1988	'SOUTH WALES TRANSPORT'	TT Green body, Red logo	**£5-10**	☐
C676/3	1988	'BADGERLINE'	White/Green/Yellow	**£5-10**	☐
C676/4	1988	'FALCK SYGETRANSPORT'	White, Red stripe, Danish	**£9-11**	☐
C676/5	1988	'ROYAL MAIL'	Red/Yellow, 'POST BUS', promotional	**£5-10**	☐
C676/6	1989	'CHASERIDER'	Red/Yellow, 'MINIBUS', '25'	**£5-10**	☐
C676/7	1989	'BRITISH AIRWAYS'	Grey/Blue body, Red flash	**£5-10**	☐
C676/10	1989	'AMBULANS'	White/Red, roof lights, Swedish export	**£9-11**	☐
C676/11	1989	'POLIS'	White/Yellow, roof lights, Swedish export	**£9-11**	☐
C676/12	1989	'OXFORD'	Green/Yellow, 'CITY NIPPER'	**£5-10**	☐
701	?	'INTER-CITY'	No details available	**£5-10**	☐

6: Major Models - Coaches

1120	1961-62	'MIDLAND RED COACH'	Red/Black, uncast wheels, *Birmingham - London Motorway Express*	**£125-150**	☐
C1168	1983	'GREYHOUND'	Red/White/Blue, *Americruiser*	**£15-20**	☐
C1168	1983	'MOTORWAY EXPRESS'	White/Brown/Yellow/Red, Limited Edition	**£10-15**	☐
C1168	1983	'EURO EXPRESS'	White/Red/Blue, Limited Edition	**£15-20**	☐
C1168	1983	'ROVER BUS'	Blue, *Chesham Toy and Model Fair*, LE	**£10-15**	☐
			As previous model but Cream body	**£20-25**	☐

7: Miscellaneous

508	1968-69	Commer 2500 Minibus	Orange/White/Green body, 'HOLIDAY CAMP' logo	**£45-55**	☐

Corgi Toys - Accessories

CORGI KITS

601	1961-68	Batley 'LEOFRIC' Garage	£15-20	☐
602	1961-66	'AA' and 'RAC' Telephone Boxes	£20-25	☐
603	1961-66	Silverstone Pits	£25-30	☐
604	1961-66	Silverstone Press Box	£25-30	☐
605	1963-67	Silverstone Club House and Timekeepers Box	£25-35	☐
606	1961-66	Lamp Standards (2)	£5-10	☐
607	1963-67	Circus Elephant and Cage	£20-25	☐
608	1963-66	'SHELL' Filling Station Building	£20-25	☐
609	1963-66	'SHELL' Filling Station Forecourt Accessories	£20-25	☐
610	1963-66	Metropolitan Police Box and Public Telephone Kiosk	£20-25	☐
611	1963-66	Motel Chalet	£20-25	☐

SPARE WHEELS (for 'Take-off Wheels' models)
Nos 1341 - 1361 were bubble-packed on card

1341	1970	for 344 Ferrari Dino Sport. Shown in 1969 catalogue but model issued with WhizzWheels	£10-15	☐
1342	1968	for 300 Chevrolet Corvette	£10-15	☐
1351	1968	for 275 Rover 2000 TC	£10-15	☐
1352	1968	for 276 Oldsmobile Toronado for 338 Chevrolet Camaro	£10-15	☐
		for 343 Pontiac Firebird. Shown in 1969 catalogue but not issued with 'Take-off Wheels'	£10-15	☐
1353	1970	for 342 Lamborghini P400 for 302 Hillman Hunter Rally	£10-15	☐
1354	1970	for 273 Rolls Royce Silver Shadow	£10-15	☐
1361	1968	for 341 Mini Marcos GT 850 (This was the first 'Take-Off Wheels' model)	£10-15	☐

SPARE TYRE PACKS

1449	1970-71	New Standard 15 mm.	£10-15	☐
1450	1958-70	Standard 15 mm.	£10-15	☐
1451	1961-70	Utility Vehicles 17 mm.	£10-15	☐
1452	1961-70	Major Models 19 mm.	£10-15	☐
1453	1965-70	Mini Cars 13 mm.	£10-15	☐
1454	1967-70	Tractor wheels (Rear) 33 mm.	£10-15	☐
1455	1967-70	Tractor wheels (Front) 19 mm.	£10-15	☐
1456	1967-70	Racing wheels (Rear) 16 mm.	£10-15	☐
1457	1967-70	Racing wheels (Front) 14 mm.	£10-15	☐
1458	1967-70	Commercial (Large) 24 mm.	£10-15	☐
1459	1967-70	Commercial (Medium) 19 mm.	£10-15	☐

SELF-ADHESIVE ACCESSORIES

1460	1959	'A' Pack (66 items) including Tax Discs, Number Plates, 'GB' & 'Running-In' labels, etc	£10-15	☐
1461	1959	'B' Pack (36 items) including White-wall tyre trim, 'Styla Sportsdiscs', Number Plates	£10-15	☐
1462	1959	'C' Pack (69 items) including Number Plates, Commercial & Road Fund Licences (A,B & C) 20mph & 30mph Speed Limit Plates & Trailer Plates, etc	£10-15	☐
1463	1959	'D' Pack (100 items) including Number, Corps Diplomatique & 'L' Plates, Touring Pennants	£10-15	☐
1464	1961	'E' Pack (86 items) including Assorted Badges, Take-Off Wheels, Trade & Licence Plates	£10-15	☐

CORGI 'CARGOES' (bubble-packed on card)

1485	1960	Lorry Load - Planks	£10-15	☐
1486	1960	Lorry Load - Bricks	£10-15	☐
1487	1960	Lorry Load - Milk Churns	£10-15	☐
1488	1960	Lorry Load - Cement	£10-15	☐
1490	1960	Skip and 3 Churns	£10-15	☐

FIGURES

1501	1963-69	Racing Drivers and Pit Mechanics (6)	£10-15	☐
1502	1963-69	Silverstone Spectators (6)	£10-15	☐
1503	1963-69	Race Track Officials (6)	£10-15	☐
1504	1963-69	Press Officials (6)	£10-15	☐
1505	1963-69	Garage Attendants (6)	£10-15	☐

MISCELLANEOUS

1401	1958-60	Service Ramp (operable)	£15-20	☐
1445	1962	Spare Red bulb for 437 Ambulance	£2-3	☐
1441	1963	Spare Blue bulb for 464 Police Van	£2-3	☐
1443	1967	Red flashing bulb for 437 Ambulance	£2-3	☐
1444	1967	Blue flashing bulb for 464 Police Van	£2-3	☐
1445	1967	Spare bulb for TV screen in 262 Lincoln	£2-3	☐
1446	1970	Spare tyres for 1150 Snowplough	£2-3	☐
1480	1959	Spare nose cone for Corporal Missile	£2-3	☐
1497	1967	James Bond Spares (2 Bandits and lapel badge for 261)	£15-25	☐
1498	1967	James Bond Spares (Pack of missiles for 336 Toyota)	£10-15	☐
1499	1967	Green Hornet Spares (Pack of missiles and scanners for 268)	£10-15	☐
	1960s	Corgi Club Badge. Gold Corgi dog on Red background	£20-25	☐

TWO FROM CORGI

that won't be on the shelf for long

A beautifully finished model of a 1968 Winter Olympics Citroen. Corgi collectors will be really enthusiastic about the working features and lifelike figures.
*opening tailgate *folding rear seats *toboggan and rider *skier with skis and sticks *spring suspension *two tone decoration *exciting bonnet badge.

No. 499 Length 4¼" Retail **$1.75**

CORGI GIFT SET No. 6

Corgi Gift Set No. 6 comprises three models— VW Racing Tender featuring working winch and detailed tool box, Cooper Maserati and Racing Car Trailer.

Gift Set No. 6. Overall length 7¾". Retail **$2.95**

AVAILABLE NOW
—the new 1967/68 full colour Corgi catalogue. It's bigger and better than ever.

'Husky' and 'Corgi Juniors' series   (1965-1975)

'Husky' models were introduced by Mettoy Playcraft in 1965 to compete with the Matchbox 1-75 range. These small-scale models have plenty of detail and action-features and the range includes cars, commercials, military and Film/TV specials.

The models have either a plastic or die-cast chassis together with various types of regular wheels and WhizzWheels. Models could only be obtained from 'Woolworths' stores and were only sold in blister packs.

Production under the 'Husky' trade name ceased in 1969 and the range was reissued in 1970 as 'Corgi Juniors'. To facilitate this change, 'HUSKY' was removed from the baseplates which were then re-engraved 'CORGI JUNIORS'.

The models were mostly fitted with 'WhizzWheels' to enable them to be used on the 'Rocket Track' and to compete against the new Matchbox 'Superfast' range. Corgi Juniors were blister packed on blue/white card for the 'regular' issues and red/white card for the 'specials'. Each pack incorporated a 'Collectors Card' picture of the real vehicle and these could be cut out and pasted into a special collectors album. Whilst 'Husky' and 'Corgi Juniors' in mint condition blister packs are no longer cheap, plenty of low priced unboxed models are available hence this range offers the younger collector plenty of scope.

Ref. No.	Year(s)	Model Type	Model Features and Size	Market Price Range	

Husky models and Corgi Juniors issued 1965-1975

Ref. No.	Year(s)	Model Type	Model Features and Size	Market Price Range	
1-a	1965-67	Jaguar Mk.10	Metallic Royal Blue or Medium Blue, 'Husky' on base, Grey plastic wheels, 65 mm..	£10-15	☐
1-b	1967-69	larger version:	Metallic Dark Blue or Mid or Pale Yellow, 'Husky' on base, metal or Grey plastic wheels	£10-15	☐
1-c	1970-72	Reliant TW9 Pick-Up	Orange body, WhizzWheels, 'Juniors' on base	£8-12	☐
1-d	1973-75	Grand Prix Racer	Metallic Green/White, WhizzWheels, 'Juniors' on base	£5-8	☐
2-a	1965-67	Citroën Safari with Boat	Pale Yellow car with Brown boat, Grey plastic wheels, 'Husky' on base	£10-15	☐
2-b	1967-68	larger casting:	Metallic Gold, Brown or Blue boat, Grey plastic wheels, 'Husky' on base, 70 mm.	£10-15	☐
2-c	1970-73	Corgi Juniors issue:	Blue or Yellow body, metal or Grey plastic wheels	£8-12	☐
3-1	1965-68	Mercedes 220	Pale Blue body, Grey plastic wheels, 'Husky' on base	£10-15	☐
3-2	1965-69	VW 1300 'POLICE' Car	White/Black body, 'Husky' on base	£15-20	☐
	1970-74	Corgi Juniors issue:	As previous model with or without 'Husky' on base	£10-15	☐
3-3	1975	VW 1300 'POLICE' Car	White body, WhizzWheels, 'Juniors' on base	£8-12	☐
4-a	1965-67	Jaguar Mk.10	Red body, 'FIRE' on doors, 'Husky' on base	£15-20	☐
4-b	1967-69	larger casting:	otherwise as previous model, 'Husky' on base, 70 mm.	£15-20	☐
4-c (E4)	1970-75	Zetor 5511 Tractor	Orange/Red body, non-WhizzWheels, 'Juniors' on base	£10-15	☐
5-1	1965-69	Lancia Flamina	Mauve body, opening bonnet, Grey plastic wheels, 'Husky' on base	£10-15	☐
5-2	1968-69	Willys Jeep	Metallic Green with Grey or Yellow windscreen, non-WhizzWheels, 'Husky'	£10-15	☐
	1970-73	Corgi Juniors issue:	Brown or Orange body, non-WhizzWheels, 'Juniors' on base	£8-12	☐
6-1	1965-67	Citroën Safari Ambulance	White body with Red cross, warning lights, 'Husky' on base	£10-15	☐
6-2	1967-69	Ferrari Berlinetta 250GT	Red body, spoked wheels, 'Husky' on base	£10-15	☐
6-3	1970-73	De Tomaso Mangusta	Yellow or Purple body, WhizzWheels, 'Juniors' on base	£8-12	☐
7-1	1965-67	Buick Electra	Orange body, Grey plastic wheels, 'Husky' on base	£10-15	☐
7-2	1968-69	Duple Vista 25 Coach	Green/White or Red/White body, 'Husky' on base	£15-20	☐
	1970-73	Corgi Juniors issues:	Yellow/White, Purple/White or Orange/White	£10-15	☐
7-a	1965-67	Ford Thunderbird Open Top	Pink/Black body, Grey plastic wheels, 'Husky' on base	£10-15	☐
7-b	1966-67	Ford Thunderbird Hard Top	Yellow with Blue removable top, 'Husky' on base	£10-15	☐
8-1	1968-69	Farm Tipper Trailer	Yellow/Red body, 'Husky' on base	£5-7	☐
9-1	1965-68	Buick 'POLICE' Car	Light or Dark Blue body, Red logo, 'Husky' on base	£15-20	☐
9-2	1968-69	Cadillac Eldorado	Blue body with tow hook, 'Husky' on base	£10-15	☐
	1970-72	Corgi Juniors issues:	Metallic Green or White/Black body, 'Juniors' on base	£8-12	☐
10-1a	1965-69	Guy Warrior Coal Truck	Red body, Blue windows, rear corner windows, 'Husky' on base	£20-25	☐
10-1c	1967-69	casting change:	Red body but no rear corner windows, 'Husky' on base	£15-20	☐
10-2	1973-75	Ford GT-70	Orange body, opening hatch, detailed engine, 'Juniors' on base	£9-12	☐
11-1a	1966-67	Forward Control Land Rover	Green/Brown body, Blue windows, rear corner windows, 'Husky' on base	£10-15	☐
11-1b	1967-69	casting change:	Metallic Green/Brown, no rear corner windows, 'Husky' on base	£10-15	☐
11-2	1970-74	Austin Healey LM Sprite	Red body, racing number '50', WhizzWheels, 'Juniors' on base	£15-20	☐
12-1	1965-67	VW Pick-Up Tower Wagon	Yellow/Red with Blue windows, 'Husky' on base	£15-20	☐
12-2	1968-69	Ford Tower Truck	Yellow or White body, Grey plastic wheels, 'Husky' on base	£10-15	☐
12-3	1970-73	Reliant-Ogle Scimitar	White or Metallic Blue, WhizzWheels, 'Juniors' on base	£15-20	☐
13-a	1965-69	Guy Warrior Sand Truck	Yellow/Brown with rear corner windows, 'Husky' on base	£15-20	☐
13-b	1967-68	casting change:	As previous model but without rear corner windows, 'Husky' on base	£10-15	☐
13-b	1968-69	colour variation:	Blue/Brown, with or without rear corner windows	£10-15	☐
13-c	1970-73	Corgi Juniors issues:	Green/Brown or White/Brown, 'Juniors' on base	£8-12	☐
14		Guy Warrior Petrol Tanker			
14-a	1965-67	'SHELL'	Yellow/White body, with rear corner windows, metal wheels, 'Husky' on base	£20-25	☐
14-b	1967-68	'SHELL'	As previous model but without rear corner windows, 'Husky' on base	£15-20	☐
14-c	1968-69	'ESSO'	White body, metal wheels, no rear corner windows, 'Husky' on base	£15-20	☐
14-d	1970-75	Corgi Juniors issue:	As 14-c with metal wheels or WhizzWheels, 'Juniors' on base	£9-12	☐
15-1	1965-67	Volkswagen Pick-Up	Turquoise body with Brown removable canopy, 'Husky' on base	£10-15	☐
15-2a	1967-69	Studebaker TV Car	Yellow or Metallic Blue with Blue windows, 'Husky' on base	£15-20	☐
15-2b	1970-71		Green or Yellow body, WhizzWheels, 'Juniors' on base	£10-15	☐
15-3(E15)	1973-74	Mercedes 'SCHOOL BUS'	Metallic Blue body, WhizzWheels, 'Juniors' on base	£9-12	☐
16-a	1965-67	Dump Truck	Aveling Barford, Yellow or Red body, 'Husky' on base	£8-10	☐

Ref. No.	Year(s)	Model Type	Corgi Toys - continued	Market Price Range	
16-b	1971-75	Land Rover Pick-Up	Metallic Green, tinted windows, WhizzWheels, 'Juniors' on base	£6-9	☐
17-1a	1965-67	Guy Warrior 'MILK' Tanker	White body with rear corner windows, oval tank, 'Husky' on base	£20-25	☐
17-1b	1967-68	casting change:	As previous model but without rear corner windows, 'Husky' on base	£15-20	☐
17-1c	1968-69	casting change:	White or Cream body, square tank, no rear corner windows, 'Husky', 71 mm.	£15-20	☐
17-2(E17)	1970-75	VW 1300 Beetle	Metallic Green with flower designs, WhizzWheels, 'Juniors' on base	£10-15	☐
18-1a	1965-67	Jaguar 'E'-type 2+2	Gold plated or Silver plated body, 'Husky' on base, 75 mm.	£15-20	☐
18-1b	1967-69	Jaguar 'E'-type 2+2	Gold plated in various shades, 'Husky' on base	£15-20	☐
18-2	1973-75	Wigwam Camper Van	Orange or Blue body, WhizzWheels	£12-15	☐
19-1a	1965-69	Commer Walk-Thru Van	Green with Red doors and Grey driver, sliding doors, 'Husky' on base	£10-15	☐
19-1b	1968-69	Commer Walk-Thru Van	All Red body and door, 'Husky' on base	£15-20	☐
19-2	1969-70	Speedboat on Trailer	Red/Cream, 'HUSKY' on hull, Gold trailer	£8-11	☐
19-2	1970-73	Corgi Juniors issues:	Red/Cream, Blue trailer with 'Juniors' on base, WhizzWheels or metal wheels	£5-7	☐
20-1	1965-68	Ford Thames Van	Red body with Yellow ladder & TV aerial, opening rear door, 'Husky' on base	£15-20	☐
20-2a	1968-69	VW 1300	Blue with Black luggage on roof, 'Husky' on base	£10-15	☐
20-2b	1970-71	Corgi Juniors issues:	Brown or Red body, WhizzWheels, 'Juniors' on base	£9-12	☐
21-1a	1965-67	Military Land Rover	Olive body, star on cab roof, rear corner windows, 'Husky' on base	£15-18	☐
21-1b	1967-69	casting change:	As previous model but without rear corner windows, 'Husky' on base	£11-14	☐
21-2	1968-69	Jaguar 'E'-type 2+2	Metallic Maroon body, spoked wheels, 'Husky' on base	£15-20	☐
21-3	1970-74	Mini Cooper 'S' 1300	Metallic Purple body, WhizzWheels, 'Juniors' on base	£10-15	☐
22-1	1965-68	Military Ambulance	Citroën Safari with Olive body, Red cross on roof, Blue warning lights, 'Husky'	£10-15	☐
22-2a	1968-69	Aston Martin DB6	Metallic Gold or Purple body, 'Husky' on base	£15-20	☐
22-2b	1970-71	Corgi Juniors issue:	Metallic Green body, 'Juniors' on base	£10-15	☐
22-3(E22)	1973-75	Formula 1 Racer	Yellow body, racing number '3', Union Jack decals, WhizzWheels	£10-15	☐
23-1	1965-67	US Army Tanker	Guy Warrior, Olive body, star on cab, Blue windows, 'Husky' on base	£15-20	☐
23-2a	1967-69	Loadmaster Shovel	Orange or Yellow with plated parts, 'Husky' on base	£9-12	☐
23-2b	1970-73	Corgi Juniors issue:	Yellow body, 'Juniors' on base	£7-10	☐
24-1	1966-69	Ford Zephyr Estate Car	Blue or Metallic Red body, opening tailgate, 'Husky' on base	£15-20	☐
24-2	1971-74	Aston Martin DBS	Green body, WhizzWheels, 'Juniors' on base	£10-15	☐
25-a	1966-69	S & D Refuse Van	Light Blue or Dark Red body, 'Husky' on base	£10-15	☐
25-b	1970-73	Corgi Juniors issue:	Orange body, 'Juniors' on base	£8-11	☐
26	1966-69	Sunbeam Alpine Hard Top	Metallic Bronze/Blue or Red/Blue, removable hardtop, 'Husky' on base	£20-25	☐
27-1a	1966-69	Bedford TK Lorry	Dark Red or Orange body, 'Husky' on base	£15-20	☐
27-1b	1970-72	Corgi Juniors issue:	Orange body, 'Juniors' on base	£10-15	☐
27-2(E27)	1973-75	Formula 5000 Racing Car	Black body, White driver, WhizzWheels, 'Juniors' on base	£7-10	☐
28-a	1966-69	Ford Breakdown Truck	Blue body, plated parts, hook, 'Husky' on base	£9-12	☐
28-b	1970-71	Corgi Juniors issue:	Blue or Green body, hook, 'Juniors' on base	£7-10	☐
29-1	1966-69	ERF Cement Lorry	Yellow/Red with rotating drum, 'Husky' on base	£15-20	☐
29-2a	1970-71	ERF Fire Engine	Red body, metal wheels or WhizzWheels but no windows, 'Juniors' on base	£15-20	☐
29-2b	1972-75	new casting:	Large cab with Blue windows, WhizzWheels, 'Juniors' on base	£10-15	☐
30-a	1966-69	Studebaker Ambulance	(Wagonaire) White, Red crosses, stretcher, metal wheels, 'Husky' on base	£15-20	☐
30-b	1970-73	Corgi Juniors issues:	White with metal wheels or WhizzWheels, 'Juniors' on base	£10-15	☐
31-1	1966-69	Oldsmobile Starfire Coupé	Metallic Blue or Green body, opening boot, 'Husky' on base	£15-20	☐
31-2(31)	1970-79	Land Rover Breakdown	Purple or Blue body with *'WRECKER'* or *'CRASH TRUCK'* logo, 'Juniors' on base	£5-7	☐
32-1	1966-69	VW Luggage Elevator	White/Yellow or Red/Blue, 'Husky' on base	£15-20	☐
32-2	1970-72	Lotus Europa	Metallic Green body, WhizzWheels, 'Juniors' on base	£12-16	☐
33-1a	1967-69	Farm Trailer	Olive or Turquoise trailer with 4 calves, drop-down tailgate, 'Husky' on base	£5-7	☐
33-1b	1970-72	Corgi Juniors issue:	Orange body, 'Juniors' on base	£4-6	☐
33-2	1970-74	Jaguar 'E'-type 2+2	Yellow or Blue body, WhizzWheels, 'Juniors' on base	£8-11	☐
34-a	1967-69	BM Volvo 400 Tractor	Red/Yellow body, Red or Black smoke stack, 'Husky' on base	£12-15	☐
34-b	1970-72	Corgi Juniors issue:	As previous model but with 'Juniors' on base	£9-12	☐
35-a	1966-69	Ford Camper	Metallic Blue or Yellow with sliding door and detailed interior, 'Husky' on base	£11-15	☐
35-b	1970-73	Corgi Juniors issue:	Green or Red body, WhizzWheels, 'Juniors' on base	£8-11	☐
36	1967-69	Fire Engine	Simon Snorkel, Red body with operating boom, 'Husky' on base	£12-16	☐
37-a	1969	NSU R080	Metallic Blue with opening bonnet and detailed engine, 'Husky' on base	£12-16	☐
37-b	1970-73	Corgi Juniors issues:	Metallic Blue, Purple, Orange or Pink, WhizzWheels, 'Juniors' on base	£8-12	☐
38-a	1968-69	Single Horse Box	Rice's Beaufort, Green with White pony, drop-down tailgate, 'Husky' on base	£8-11	☐
38-b	1970-71	Corgi Juniors issues:	Red or Bronze body, WhizzWheels, 'Juniors' on base	£6-9	☐
39-a	1968-69	Jaguar XJ-6	Yellow body with Red tow hook, 'Husky' on base	£20-25	☐
39-b	1970-73	Corgi Juniors issues:	Yellow body (metal wheels) Silver or Maroon body (WhizzWheels) 'Juniors'	£10-15	☐
40-a	1968-69	Ford Transit Caravan	Green/White or Red/White, detailed interior, 'Husky' on base	£14-17	☐
40-b	1970-72	Corgi Juniors issues:	Blue or Grey (WhizzWheels) or Yellow (metal or WhizzWheels) 'Juniors' on base	£10-14	☐
41	1969	Porsche Carrera	Never seen with 'HUSKY' baseplate	NGPP	☐
	1970-72	Corgi Juniors issues:	White body, metal wheels or WhizzWheels, 'Juniors' on base	£10-15	☐
42-1	1971-72	Euclid Dump Truck	Yellow/Red body, Black plastic wheels or WhizzWheels, 'Juniors' on base	£9-12	☐
42-2	1972-76	Terex Rear Dump Truck	Red/Yellow, Yellow/Red or Blue/Beige, 'Juniors' on base	£7-10	☐
43	1970-75	Farm Tractor with Blade	Massey-Ferguson 3303, Yellow body, 'Juniors' on base	£8-11	☐
44	1970-75	Road Roller	Raygo Rascal 600, Blue/Orange, 'Juniors' on base	£7-10	☐
45	1970-74	Mercedes Benz 280 SL	Silver (metal wheels) Yellow, Metallic Blue or Red with WhizzWheels, 'Juniors' on base	£7-9	☐
46	1970-74	Jensen Interceptor	Metallic Maroon or Green, or Orange body, WhizzWheels, 'Juniors' on base	£8-11	☐
47	1971-75	Scammell Concrete Mixer	Blue/White/Red body	£8-11	☐
48	1970-73	ERF Tipper Truck	Red/Silver or Blue/Yellow, 'Juniors' on base	£8-11	☐
49	1971-73	Pinifarina Modulo	Yellow body with Maroon stripe, 'Juniors' on base	£10-14	☐
50	1971-74	Ferrari 512 S	Maroon/White or Maroon/Silver, racing number '6', WhizzWheels, 'Juniors'	£8-11	☐
51	1971-73	Porsche 917	Gold/Red body, WhizzWheels, 'Juniors' on base	£10-13	☐
52	1971-73	Addams Probe	Metallic Purple, WhizzWheels, 'Juniors' on base	£7-10	☐
54	1972-75	Container Truck	Ford D1000, Red/Orange or Red/Yellow, WhizzWheels	£8-12	☐
55	1971-73	Double Decker Bus	Daimler Fleetline, Red body, 'ESSO UNIFLO', WhizzWheels	£10-15	☐

Ref. No.	Year(s)	Model Type	Corgi Toys - continued	Market Price Range	
56	1971-73	Fire Chief's Car	Ford Capri, Red/White, 'FIRE' or 'FIRE CHIEF' logo, WhizzWheels, 'Juniors'	£8-11	☐
57	1971-73	Cadillac Eldorado	'HOT RODDER', Pink body, exposed engine, WhizzWheels, 'Juniors' on base	£7-10	☐
58 (E58)	1971-75	Beach Buggy	Metallic Red body, WhizzWheels, 'Juniors' on base	£5-7	☐
59	1971-73	'FUTURA'	Orange body, Yellow/Black logo, WhizzWheels, 'Juniors' on base	£5-7	☐
60	1971-73	VW Beetle Hot Rod	Orange body, WhizzWheels, 'Juniors' on base	£6-8	☐
61	1971-75	'SHERIFF's Car	Mercury Cougar XR7 with WhizzWheels & 'Juniors' on base	£7-10	☐
62	1971-73	Volvo P-1800	Red/Black, WhizzWheels, 'Juniors' on base	£9-12	☐
63	1971-74	Ford Escort Rally	Metallic Blue, racing number '6', WhizzWheels, 'Juniors' on base	£9-12	☐
64	1971-73	Morgan Plus 8 .:	Yellow or Red body, WhizzWheels, 'Juniors' on base	£15-20	☐
65	1971-73	Bertone Carebo	Purple body, Amber windows, WhizzWheels, 'Juniors' on base	£8-10	☐
67	1971-73	Ford Capri Dragster	Yellow body, 'HOT PANTS', Union Jack label, WhizzWheels, 'Juniors' on base	£6-9	☐
71	1971-73	US Racing Buggy	Blue body, Stars & Stripes livery, WhizzWheels, 'Juniors' on base	£6-9	☐
72	1971-75	Mercedes-Benz C111	Red body, Blue windows, WhizzWheels, 'Juniors' on base	£6-8	☐
73	1971-73	Alfa-Romeo P33	Blue body, clear windscreen, WhizzWheels, 'Juniors' on base	£7-10	☐
74	1972-75	Bertone Barchetta	Orange with Black stripe, WhizzWheels, 'Juniors' on base	£6-8	☐
75	1972-75	Super Stock Car	Silver with Union Jack design, WhizzWheels, 'Juniors' on base	£5-7	☐
76 (76)	1974-75	Military Jeep	Military Green with White star and driver, WhizzWheels, 'Juniors' on base	£6-9	☐
77	1971-73	Ital Manta	Pink body, clear windows, WhizzWheels, 'Juniors' on base	£7-10	☐
77	1971-75	Marcos	Orange body, Amber windows, WhizzWheels, 'Juniors' on base	£6-8	☐
78	1971-73	Old MacDonald's Lorry	Red cab, Silver bonnet, Brown truck body	£14-18	☐
80-1	1974-75	Porsche Carrera	White body, racing number '4', Red/Blue design	£7-10	☐

Novelty, Film & TV related Specials

Ref. No.	Year(s)	Model Type		Market Price Range	
1001a	1968-69	James Bond Aston Martin DB6	Metallic Grey body, Grey plastic wheels, 'Husky' on base	£100-125	☐
1001b	1970-72	Corgi Juniors issue:	As previous model but WhizzWheels, 'Juniors' on base	£75-100	☐
1002a	1968-69	Batmobile	Black body, Blue canopy, Grey plastic wheels, 'Husky' on base	£100-125	☐
1002b	1970-72	Corgi Juniors issue:	As previous model but WhizzWheels, 'Juniors' on base	£75-100	☐
1003a	1968-69	Batboat on Trailer	Black/Red plus Gold trailer, Grey plastic wheels, 'Husky' on base	£60-70	☐
1003b	1970-72	Corgi Juniors issue:	As previous model but WhizzWheels, 'Juniors' on base	£40-50	☐
1004a	1968-69	Monkeemobile	Red/White, 'MONKEES', exposed engine	£100-125	☐
1004b	1970-72	Corgi Juniors issue:	As previous model but WhizzWheels, 'Juniors' on base	£75-100	☐
1005a	1968-69	'Man From UNCLE' Car	Blue car with 2 figures, metal wheels, 'Husky' on base	£100-125	☐
1005b	1970-71	Corgi Juniors issue:	As previous model but WhizzWheels, 'Juniors' on base	£75-100	☐
1006a	1968-69	Chitty Chitty Bang Bang	Yellow/Orange or Orange/Yellow, spoked wheels, 'Husky' on base	£100-125	☐
1006b	1970-72	Corgi Juniors issue:	As previous model but WhizzWheels, 'Juniors' on base	£75-100	☐
1007	?	'Ironsides' Police Van	'Juniors' on base	NGPP	☐
1011		James Bond Bobsleigh	Yellow body, Green/Orange figure of JB and '007' logo on front, 'Juniors' on base	£175-200	☐
1012		S.P.E.C.T.R.E. Bobsleigh	Red body, Black rider, 'SPECTRE' logo on front, 'Juniors' on base	£175-200	☐

Major Models

Ref. No.	Year(s)	Model Type		Market Price Range	
2001	1968-69	'HUSKY' Multi Garage	A set of four garages, (no cars) 'Husky' on base	£15-20	☐
	1970-75	Corgi Juniors issue:	As previous model but with 'CORGI' logo, 'Juniors' on base	£10-15	☐
2002	1967-69	'HUSKY' Car Transporter	Hoynor Mk.II, White/Blue/Orange, detachable cab, 'Husky' on base	£20-30	☐
	1970-72	Corgi Juniors issue:	As previous model but with 'CORGI' logo, 'Juniors' on base	£15-20	☐
2003a	1968-69	Machinery Low-Loader	Red/Blue/Yellow, detachable cab, drop-down ramp, 'Husky' on base	£20-30	☐
2003b	1970-73	Corgi Juniors issue:	As previous model with metal wheels or WhizzWheels, 'Juniors' on base	£15-20	☐
2004a	1968-69	Removals Delivery Van	Red cab, plated box, 'HUSKY REMOVALS', metal wheels, 'Husky' on base	£30-40	☐
2004b	1970-72	Corgi Juniors issue:	As previous model but 'CORGI REMOVALS', WhizzWheels, 'Juniors' on base	£20-30	☐
2006	1970-79	Mack 'ESSO' Tanker	White body and tank, WhizzWheels, 'Juniors' on base	£8-11	☐

Husky and Corgi Juniors Gift Sets

Ref. No.	Year(s)	Model Type		Market Price Range	
3001	1968-69	4 Garage Set	Contains 23, 27, 29, or 9, 30 or 36	£50-70	☐
3002	1968-69	Batmobile Set	1002 Batmobile and 1003 Batboat on trailer	£100-150	☐
3002	1970	'Club Racing' Set	Juniors set of 8 racing cars inc. Mini Cooper 'S' (Metallic Mauve), Ford Capri, Morgan, etc.	£100-150	☐
3003	1968-69	Car Transporter Set	2002 Husky Car Transporter plus 16, 26, 6-2, 21-2, 22-2, 26	£100-150	☐
3004	1968-69	4 Garage Set	Contains 23-2, 29	£50-75	☐
3004		James Bond 'OHMSS' Set	Contains 1004, 1001, 1011, 1012 plus un-numbered VW Beetle in Red with Black No.'5' on White circle on sides. (From film 'On Her Majesty's Secret Service').	£600-750	☐
3005	1968-69	Holiday Time/Leisure Time	Contains 2-2, 5-2, 7-2, 15-2, 19-2, 20-2, 21-2, 35-1	£125-150	☐
3006	1968-69	Service Station	Contains 14-c, 22-2, 28	£50-75	☐
3007	1968-69	'HUSKY MULTIPARK'	In 1968 catalogue but not issued	NPP	☐
3008	1968-69	Crime Busters Set	Contains 1001, 1002, 1003, 1005	£350-450	☐
	1970	Corgi Juniors issue	As previous set	£300-400	☐
3011		Road Construction Set	Gift Set containing seven models	£100-125	☐

Husky Accessories

Ref. No.	Year(s)	Model Type		Market Price Range	
1561/2	1968-69	Traffic Signs		£20-30	☐
1571	1968-69	Pedestrians		£10-15	☐
1572	1968-69	Workmen		£10-15	☐
1573	1968-69	Garage Personnel		£10-15	☐
1574	1968-69	Public Servants		£10-15	☐

Ref. No.	Year(s)	Model Type	Corgi Toys - continued	Market Price Range	
1580	1968-69	Husky Collector Case...............	storage for 48 models...	**£10-15**	☐
1585	1968-69	Husky Traveller Case	opens to form Service Station (this item never seen)	NPP	☐
2001	1968-69	'HUSKY' Multi Garage...........	A set of four garages, (no cars) 'Husky' on base.............................	**£15-20**	☐
	1970-75	Corgi Juniors issue:............	As previous model but with 'CORGI' logo, 'Juniors' on base	**£10-15**	☐

Husky and Corgi Juniors Catalogues and listings

Ref. No.	Year(s)	Publication	Cover Features and Details	Market Price Range	
HUSKY CATALOGUES					
Mettoy Playcraft (Sales) Ltd 1966					
	1966	Leaflet (single fold)..................	Red, illustrating No.1 Jaguar Mk.10 on cover and Nos.1-29 inside. '1/9 each'...........	**£20-25**	☐
same ref.	1966	Leaflet (Belgian issue)...............	As previous leaflet but Nos.1-32 shown, printed in French.....................	**£20-25**	☐
same ref.	1966	Booklet (10 pages)	Front/rear covers feature a row of garages and cars. Good pictures of 1002 Batmobile and 1001 James Bond's Aston-Martin, plus Nos.1-36................	NGPP	☐
no ref.	1967	Catalogue (24 pages)	Cover features boy with Husky vehicles and sets. Good pictures of all the rare models and Gift Sets plus accessories and models 1-41	**£30-40**	☐
CORGI JUNIORS CATALOGUES					
Mettoy Playcraft 1970					
		Catalogue (16 pages)	Blue cover with 10 models featured. Contains excellent pictures of all the rare early models including GS 3004 James Bond 'O.H.M.S.S.' Set etc.	**£30-40**	☐

Corgi Toys Catalogues   -   (United Kingdom Editions)

Information taken from the Cecil Gibson Archives and this Catalogue compiler's own collection of reference material. Note: 'Concertina' leaflets were issued with models sold in the early Blue boxes.

The Editor would especially like to express his appreciation for the catalogue updating information received from Mr Mark Atkinson of Essex.

Ref. No.	Year(s)	Publication	Cover Features and Details	Market Price Range	
no ref.	1956	Concertina leaflet......................	Blue cover, famous Corgi dog, shows first 14 models, no prices...................	**£15-20**	☐
no ref.	1956	Concertina leaflet......................	Blue cover with Red/Gold Corgi dog. Depicts first 14 models and shows prices of both normal and mechanical models	**£20-25**	☐
50/157/K1	1957	Concertina leaflet......................	Blue cover with Red/Gold Corgi dog. Depicts ten models and lists the mechanical models in red	**£5-10**	☐
40/257/K1	1957	Concertina leaflet......................	Blue cover with Red/Gold Corgi dog. Depicts ten models but does not list mechanical models	**£5-10**	☐
40/257/K2	1957	Concertina leaflet......................	As previous leaflet but with the addition of 208	**£5-10**	☐
50/557/K3	1957	Concertina leaflet......................	As 40/257/K2 plus 100,150,408, 454, 'WOW! CORGI TOYS' logo.........	**£5-10**	☐
100/1057/K3	1957	Concertina leaflet......................	Blue cover showing 100, 150, 207, 208, 302, 405, 408, 453, 455	**£5-10**	☐
50/1057/K4	1958	Concertina leaflet......................	Blue cover, 'WOW! CORGI TOYS' logo. Listings include models 102, 406/7, and first 'MAJOR' toy (1101)	**£15-20**	☐
50/1157/K4	1957	Concertina leaflet......................	Cover shows 102, 210, 406, 407, 412, 1101, 'WOW! CORGI TOYS' logo	**£5-10**	☐
52/258/K5	1958	Concertina leaflet......................	Cover shows GS 1 & 2, 101, 211, 302, 457, 459, 1100, 1401, 1450	**£5-10**	☐
52/258/K6	1958	Concertina leaflet......................	As previous leaflet plus 350, 351...	**£5-10**	☐
300/658/K7	1958	Concertina leaflet......................	Shows GS 3, 151, 209, 458, 'NEW CORGI TOYS' logo & prices..........	**£5-10**	☐
25/257/C1/ UK	1957	Four-fold leaflet........................	'Blue box' 208 Jaguar on cover, 15 model pictures inside	**£75-100**	☐
25/257/C2/ UK	1957	Four-fold leaflet........................	As previous leaflet but with 24 model pictures..............................	**£75-100**	☐
50/1057/C3/ UK	1957	Four-fold leaflet........................	Shows GS 1 Bedford Transporter and 6 cars on Blue/Yellow cover with details of 100, 150, 200-8, 210, 300-2, 403-8, 412, 452-5, 1101	**£25-30**	☐
25/1157/C4/ UK	1957	Four-fold leaflet........................	As previous leaflet plus 101 and 102	**£25-30**	☐
no ref.	1958	Four-fold leaflet........................	As previous leaflet plus 211. No prices, car listing or ref. no.	NGPP	☐
650/858/C8	1958	Catalogue...................................	First 'book' catalogue. Cover depicts boy playing with Bloodhound Missile, many other vehicles..	NGPP	☐
no ref.	1959	Four-fold leaflet........................	Blue cover with 'THE ROCKET AGE WITH CORGI TOYS'. (This leaflet was issued with Rocket Age models)............................	**£15-20**	☐
no ref.	9/1959	Interim leaflet	Lists 152, 50 Tractor, 350 Thunderbird, new TT van & accessories	NGPP	☐
U.K. 9/59	1959	16 page Catalogue	Cover features Massey Ferguson Tractor No 50 and BRM Racer No 152. Agricultural & 'MAJOR' issues (No.1100 etc) are listed........................	**£30-40**	☐
no ref.	1960	Interim leaflet	Depicts M1 Motorway scene	**£5-10**	☐
U.K. 9/60	1960	20 page Catalogue	Cover has motorway bridge scene & Corgi models. This catalogue was the first with listings of 'CHIPPERFIELDS' issues.....................	**£30-40**	☐
U.K. 9/61	1961	24 page Catalogue	Racetrack scene on cover. Listings and pictures include new Sports Cars, Express Coach and Kits	**£20-25**	☐
no ref.	1962	Two-fold Checklist leaflet...........	Front cover depicts Blue/Yellow 'CORGI TOYS' plus seven models and their features. Red/Grey interior plus first check list	**£15-20**	☐

Ref. No.	Year(s)	Model Type	Corgi Toys - continued	Market Price Range	
C/100/62	1963	32 page Catalogue	Cover depicts schoolboy (in red cap and blazer) crossing road with Corgi dog. No catalogue date is shown on front cover	**£75-100**	☐
no ref.	1963	32 page Catalogue	Same cover as C/100/62 but boy's cap and blazer are Blue. The date '1963-64' is shown on front cover	**£15-20**	☐
Playcraft Toys Ltd 1964					
	1964	Two-fold Checklist leaflet.........	Blue/Yellow 'Corgi Toys' design on cover featuring 241 Ghia.................	**£15-20**	☐
Playcraft Toys Ltd 1964					
	1965	40 page Catalogue	Cover logos: 'CORGI TOYS', 'CORGI CLASSICS', '1965'. Contains Classics and first Routemaster in the listings....................	**£15-20**	☐
Mettoy Playcraft (Sales) Ltd 1965					
	1965	Two-fold Checklist leaflet.........	Six model cars from six different nations are featured on the cover	**£5-10**	☐
Playcraft Toys Ltd 1965					
	1966	40 page Catalogue	Cover depicts model 261 James Bond's Aston Martin DB5. Contents give details of special Rallye Monte Carlo issues. 'Price 3d'	**£15-20**	☐
C2038/66	1966	Leaflet	Cover proudly states 'MODEL CAR MAKERS TO JAMES BOND'	**£8-12**	☐
C2039/4/66	1966	Four-fold Checklist leaflet.........	Similar to previous with 'MODEL CAR MAKERS TO JAMES BOND'. The contents feature 1127 Simon Snorkel etc	**£10-15**	☐
C2017/9/66	1967	48 page Catalogue	The cover & contents are dominated by Film & TV related models of 'BATMAN' & 'THE AVENGERS' etc. Also contains details of a model never issued - 498 Mini Countryman	**£15-20**	☐
Mettoy Playcraft (Sales) 1967					
	1967	Three-fold Checklist leaflet........	Cover shows 'NEW' in 5 languages & 1142 Holmes Wrecker. Listings include 1967 Monte Carlo Rally winners	**£15-20**	☐
C/2017/7/67	1967-68	48 page Catalogue	Model 262 Lincoln Continental makes up the covers. 'Price 6d'. 2 models shown but not issued: 9022 Daimler 38 with Hood, & 9014 Model 'T' Van 'Lyons Tea' (eventually issued as Corgi Classic C865 in Feb 1986)........	**£10-15**	☐
C2017/9/68	1968	48 page Catalogue	Cover features 268 'Chitty Chitty Bang Bang'. Listings include 803 'Yellow Submarine' and 'Take-off Wheels' issues........................	**£15-20**	☐
Mettoy Playcraft (Sales) Ltd 1969					
	1969	Seven-fold Checklist leaflet........	'Concorde' model on cover plus 302 Hillman Hunter. Listings include 'Corgi Comics', 'CHIPPERFIELD' and Scammell Transporter Set No.48	**£5-10**	☐
The Mettoy Co Ltd 1970					
	1970	48 page Catalogue	Cover depicts 388 Mercedes Benz C111, first 'WhizzWheels' models listed	**£5-10**	☐
1970 Mettoy Co Ltd					
	1971	Two-fold Checklist leaflet.........	6 WhizzWheels models on the cover, final 'Take-Off Wheels' issues listed	**£5-10**	☐
C2017 Petty 7/71/LOI7b					
	1972	48 page Catalogue	Cover shows 1972 Car models. Excellent 'CORGI COMICS' pictures inside	**£5-10**	☐
C2017 Petty 7/71/LOI7B (2nd)					
	1972	48 page Catalogue	Cars across both covers	**£5-10**	☐
1973 Mettoy Co Ltd					
	1973	40 page Catalogue	F1 Racing Cars featured on the cover. Good Racing/Rally pictures within	**£5-10**	☐
1974 Mettoy Co Ltd					
	1974	40 page Catalogue	'John Player' Lotus on cover, good Military & Aircraft pictures.............	**£5-10**	☐
1975 Mettoy Co Ltd					
	1975	Three-fold leaflet..............	Helicopters, Noddy's Car, etc on the cover. Numbers given 'C' prefix........	**£5-10**	☐
1976 Mettoy Co Ltd					
	1976	Three-fold leaflet..............	First page features 'KOJAK'. Good Roadmaking and Public Services listings	**£5-10**	☐
C2210	1977	48 page Catalogue	Silver Jubilee Coach on cover. Large section listing Corgi 'Juniors'............	**£5-10**	☐
The Mettoy Co Ltd					
	1978	48 page Catalogue	James Bond's Lotus on cover, 'JEAN RICHARD' models within	**£5-10**	☐
C2250	1979	48 page Catalogue	James Bond's Space Shuttle C649 'MOONRAKER' is featured on the cover, and 'SUPERMAN' & 'THE MUPPETS' are listed inside	**£5-10**	☐
C2270	1980	48 page Catalogue	Rover 3500 'POLICE' C339 & C1001 HCB ANGUS are the cover features. Good listings of Emergency vehicles includes foreign 'POLICE' issues	**£5-10**	☐
C2285	1981	32 page Catalogue	'CORGI' container on cover. Listings feature Film/TV models.............	**£5-10**	☐
C2337	1982	32 page Catalogue	Cover features 'Gull-wing' Mercedes (C802), 'Corgitronics' within	**£5-10**	☐
The Mettoy Co PLC					
	1983	36 page Catalogue	Boxed models on cover, new Mercedes & Scania trucks inside...............	**£5-10**	☐
no ref.	1984	32 page Catalogue	'CORGI '84' & boxed models on cover. Large scale '800' series cars listed. This was the last catalogue to display Corgi Dog emblem.	**£3-5**	☐
no ref.	1985	48 page Catalogue	Cover shows new 'CORGI' trade name logo. The new 'CLASSICS' Commercials range is listed.	**£3-5**	☐

Catalogues issued 1986 - 1993. Please send any information, particularly in respect of Corgi Classics. Thank you.

Overseas Editions of Corgi Catalogues

These are known to have been produced for the USA, Belgium, Eire, Kenya/Uganda, Sweden, Holland, Singapore/ Malaya, France, Denmark and Italy.

Usually the catalogues were identical to the UK editions but included a checklist providing details in the language or currency of the country concerned. Unlike UK editions, no Catalogue price was shown on the cover. However, the 1966 French edition was an exception in that it was printed entirely in French. It is not known whether any overseas editions were published after 1967/68.

The market price range of overseas editions is likely to be similar to corresponding UK editions. However, unique items in pristine condition would attract a premium.

Ref. No.	Year(s)	Model Type	Corgi Toys - continued	Market Price Range

OVERSEAS ISSUES RECORDED TO DATE

25/257/C2/ SM	1957	Four-fold Leaflet	Issued in Singapore/Malaya..	NGPP ☐
7/1058/Cb	1957	16-page Catalogue	Issued in Kenya/Uganda/Tanganyika.......................................	NGPP ☐
10/658/C5	1958	Leaflet	Issued in Eire..	NGPP ☐
no ref.	8/1959	16-page Catalogue	Issued in Belgium (printed in French)....................................	NGPP ☐
no ref.	1966	48-page Catalogue	Issued in France, same cover as C2017/9/66, (printed in French)..............	NGPP ☐
C2017/9/68	1966	48-page Catalogue	Issued in France, same cover as C2017/9/68	NGPP ☐

TRADE CATALOGUES

Catalogues for trade purposes have been produced for some years and occasionally are offered for sale to collectors. No information is available on catalogues issued before 1980 but those from the 1980-90 decade tend to be in the £5 to £15 range.

Corgi Toys shop display and 'point-of-sale' items

Ref. No.	Year(s)	Item	Details	Market Price Range
no ref.	1957-59	Display stand, wooden	Ten cream 'corrugated' hardboard shelves, pale blue display background with yellow/blue plastic 'CORGI TOYS' sign screwed to top of display, (30″ x 29″ x 12″) ..	£200-300 ☐
no ref.	1957-59	Display card/sign	Tin/cardboard, yellow/blue with gold 'dog' logo, 'Wow! Corgi Toys - The Ones With Windows'.	£50-60 ☐
no ref.	1957-59	Display card/sign	As previous item but with 'new Corgi Major Toys - The Ones With Windows'	£50-60 ☐
no ref.	1957-59	Counter display unit..................	Cardboard, single model display card, 'new - CORGI TOYS' logo	£50-60 ☐
no ref.	1957-59	Counter display unit..................	Cardboard, 2 tier unit, 'new - CORGI MAJOR TOYS' in yellow/blue design	£200-300 ☐
no ref.	1957-59	Counter display unit..................	Cardboard, 2 tier unit, 'COLLECT CORGI TOYS' and 'new MODELS EVERY MONTH' logos in yellow/blue design	£200-300 ☐
no ref.	1957-59	Counter display unit..................	Cardboard, Renault Floride (222) pictorial display card with '1959 MOTOR SHOW' and 'EARLS COURT' logos..	£75-100 ☐
no ref.	1957-59	Counter display unit..................	Cardboard, Citroën (475) pictorial display card with 'new - THE CITROEN' and 'OLYMPIC WINTER SPORTS' logos..	£75-100 ☐
no ref.	1960-61	Window sticker.........................	'new MODELS EVERY MONTH'	£15-20 ☐
no ref.	1966-69	Window sticker.........................	Window bills advertising new releases	£15-20 ☐
no ref.	1960-69	Oblong sign.............................	Glass or plastic with 'CORGI TOYS' and 'PRECISION DIE-CAST SCALE MODELS' logos plus gold Corgi 'dog' logo in blue/yellow/red design	£75-100 ☐
no ref.	1971-73	Oblong sign.............................	Plastic, with 'CORGI' and 'TESTED BY THE CORGI TECHNOCRATS' logos plus white Corgi 'dog' logo on red square, yellow background plus 3 'Technocrats' faces..	£50-75 ☐
C2001/2	1963-65	Display stand, rotary................	For self-selection, 7 tray unit, large 'CORGI TOYS' header sign	NGPP ☐
C2003	1963-65	Display stand, rotary................	Self-selection, 4 columns, 4 compartments (45″ x 30″) large 'CORGI TOYS' header boards..	NGPP ☐
C2004	1963-65	Display stand, rotary................	Self-selection, 4 column, 72 compartments (72″ x 30″)................................	NGPP ☐
C2005	1963-65	Display stand, rotary................	Self-selection, 2 column, 36 compartments (72″ x 30″)................................	NGPP ☐
C2006	1963-65	Display stand, rotary................	Self-selection, 2 column, 36 compartments (55″ x 30″)................................	NGPP ☐
C2007	1963-65	Display stand, moulded plastic	Large counter display to house up to 50 models, large black header display board with 'NATURALLY CORGI TOYS' on yellow/blue background, and 'JOIN THE CORGI MODEL CLUB' on display front..	£200-300 ☐
C2008	1960s	Display stand, revolving............	Glass fronted large electric display to house 100-120 models with light and dark simulated wood panels with four 'CORGI' logos, (38″ x 24″ x 24″)	£400-600 ☐
C2009	1957-66	Showcase, glass........................	Three glass shelves, three 'CORGI TOYS' logos (black/blue) plus gold Corgi 'dog' logo on red background, (20″ x 15″ x 9″)	£200-300 ☐

NB. The Editor would welcome any further information on Corgi display material.

Acknowledgments

The Editor would like to express appreciation to the following collectors who very kindly took the time and trouble to provide information about new entries and colour variations.

I. Caldwell, Northfields, Birmingham
John C. Robertson, Whiteness, Shetland
Gino Tartaglia, Aylesbury, Bucks
D. Rowe, Newbury, Bucks
D. F. Rogers, Bournemouth, Dorset
Frank Munford, Lincoln, Lincs
R. M. Holton, Hall Green, Birmingham
Ken Appleyard, South Ockendon, (4th Edition 'New Information' winner)
Barney Austin,
Mark Atkinson, Hockley, Essex
Ian Leonard, Bolton, Lancs
C. Bell, RAF Sek Fong, BFPO1
Colin S. Turnnidge, Centerville, Ohio, USA
Pat O'Shea, Norwich, Norfolk

Michael Tate, Henley on Thames, Oxon
Alan Brown, Pensby Wirral, Merseyside
Derwyn Rowlands, Holyhead, Wales
C. Hall, Rugby, Warwickshire
Peter Cook, Loughton, Essex

CORGI - AUCTION RESULTS 1992-93

(C) = Christies, (V) = Vectis, (W) = Wallis & Wallis
All the items listed below were sold in mint condition and were boxed, unless shown as NM (Not Mint).

CARS

200	Ford Consul, Brownish-Grey	£110 (V)
200	Ford Consul, Green/Light Grey	£90 (V)
201	Austin Cambridge, Light Grey	£150 (V)
202	Morris Cowley, Blue body	£130 (V)
203	Vauxhall Velox, Yellow/Red	£90 (V)
203m	Vauxhall Velox, Orange body	£250 (V)
205s	Riley Pathfinder, Dark Blue	£80 (V)
207m	Standard Vanguard III, Yellow	£80 (V)
208	Jaguar 2.4, White body	£100 (V)
210s	Citroën DS19, Red body	£55 (V)
211s	Studebaker Hawk, Gold (paint)	£140 (V)
224	Bentley Continental, Silver/Black	£45 (V)
226	Mini Minor, Metallic Maroon	£38 (V)
227	Mini Cooper Rally, Yellow/White, '1'	£200 (V)
227	Mini Cooper Rally, Blue/White, '7'	£160 (V)
231	Triumph Herald, Blue/White	£45 (V)
233	Heinkel Economy Car, Orange	£32 (V)
236	A60 Driving School Car, Light Blue	£42 (V)
246	Chrysler Imperial, Metallic Dark Green	£130 (V)
255	A60 Driving School, Dark Blue (USA)	£85 (V)
256	VW East African Safari, with Rhino	£65 (V)
259	Citroën 'Le Dandy', Metallic Blue/White	£85 (V)
300	Austin Healey, Red/Cream	£70 (V)
301	Triumph TR2, Cream/Red seats	£80 (V)
301	Triumph TR2, Green/Cream seats	£75 (V)
302	MGA, Metallic Green/Cream seats	£75 (-)
302	Hillman Hunter Rally, kangaroo	£50 (W)
305	Triumph TR3, Met.Lime Green, Red seats	£70 (V)
307	Jaguar 'E' type, Metallic Dark Grey/Red	£70 (V)
309	Aston Martin DB4, Green, No.'3'	£45 (W)
315	Simca 1000 Sports, Metallic Blue, '8'	£110 (V)
319	Lotus Elan S2, Red/White, No.'7'	£65 (V)
321	'Monte Carlo' Mini, roof signatures	£180 (V)
323	'Monte Carlo' Citroën, Blue/White	£55 (W)
324	Marcos 1800GT, Blue/White stripes	£75 (V)
327	MGB GT, Red/Black	£42 (V)
333	'SUN/RAC' Mini, Red/White, '21'	£150 (W)
339	'1967 Monte Carlo' Mini, Red/White	£75 (W)
345	MGC GT, Yellow/Black	£60 (V)
440	Cortina Estate, Blue, golf figures	£60 (W)
485	Mini Countryman, Sea-Green, surfer	£66 (W)
GS 15	Silverstone Gift Set	£1,150 (W)
GS 37	Lotus Racing Team Set	£125 (W)
GS 38	Monte Carlo Rally Set	£570 (V)

COMMERCIAL VEHICLES

403	Bedford, 'Daily Express', Deep Blue	£120 (V)
421	Bedford, 'Standard', Black/Silver	£100 (V)
422	Bedford, 'Corgi Toys', Blue/Yellow roof	£360 (V)
426	Chipperfields Booking Office	£90 (V)
471	Karrier 'Patates Frites' (Belgian)	£180 (V)
503	Chipperfields Giraffe Transporter	£54 (W)
1110	Bedford Tanker, Red, 'Mobilgas'	£95 (W)
1110	Bedford Tanker, 'SHELL BENZEEN', (Dutch)	£1,100 (V)
1139	Chipperfields Scammell Menagerie	£230 (V)

1144	Chipperfields Crane & Hippo	£240 (V)
1150	Scammell 'Co-operative Society'	£290 (V)
GS 1	Bedford Carrimore Set	£640 (V)
GS 21	ERF 456 & 101, milk churns etc	£160 (W)
GS 21	Scammell Menagerie Set	£1,050 (V)
GS 23	Chipperfields Set (1st issue)	£350 (V)
GS 41	Ford Transporter & 6 cars	£325 (W)

AGRICULTURAL MODELS

438	**Land Rover, Met.Green/Cream,'LEPRA'**	£240 (V)
GS 5	Agricultural Set	£190 (W)
GS 22	Farming Models Set	£680 (V)

EMERGENCY SERVICES VEHICLES

405	Bedford Fire Tender, Black ladder	£100 (V)
405m	Bedford Fire Tender, Silver ladder	£120 (V)
464	Commer 'POLICE' Van, Deep Green, (export)	£450 (V)
492	VW 'POLITIE' Car, White, (Dutch)	£230 (V)
1127	Simon Snorkel Fire Engine	£60 (W)

NOVELTY, FILM & TV-RELATED MODELS

258	The Saint's Volvo P1800	£50 (W)
266	Chitty Chittty Bang Bang	£140 (V)
267	Batmobile, 1st type, 'Bat' wheels	£100 (V)
267	Batmobile, 2nd type, plain wheels	£60 (V)
268	Green Hornet 'Black Beauty'	£135 (V)
270	James Bond Aston Martin, Silver	£145 (V)
277	Monkeemobile, Red, 4 Monkees	£90 (W)
336	James Bond's Toyota 2000GT	£107 (V)
349	'Pop Art' Mini 'Mostest'	£860 (V)
447	Walls Ice Cream van, figures	£95 (W)
474	Walls Ice Cream Van (musical)	£75 (V)
475	Citroën 'Corgi Ski Club'	£50 (V)
497	'The Man from UNCLE' Car, Purple	£57 (W)
499	Winter Olympics Citroën Safari	£80 (W)
510	Citroën 'Tour de France' Car	£50 (V)
802	Popeye's Paddlewagon	£205 (W)
803	Beatles' Submarine, Yellow, White front hatch, Yellow rear hatch	£380 (V)
853	Magic Roundabout Playground	£420 (V)
GS 3	Batmobile (1st) and Batboat Set	£245 (W)
GS 8	'The Lions of Longleat' Set	£60 (C)
GS 40	'The Avengers' Set, Bentley, Lotus	£320 (C)
GS 40	'The Avengers' Set, Bentley, Lotus	£230 -
GS 48	'Jean Richard Pinder' Circus Set	NM £50 (W)

AIRCRAFT and MILITARY VEHICLES

356	US Army VW Personnel Carrier	£45 (W)
357	US Army Land Rover Weapons Carrier	£50 (W)
359	US Army Field Kitchen	£80 (W)
652	Concorde, 'JAPAN AIRLINES'	£280 (V)
653	Concorde, 'AIR CANADA'	£180 (V)
GS 6	Rocket Age Gift Set	£800 (V)

No 802 Popeye Paddlewagon, sold by Wallis & Wallis, Lewes, Sussex for £205.
Picture reproduced by their kind permission.

WHEN REPLYING TO ADVERTISEMENTS PLEASE MENTION JOHN RAMSAY'S CATALOGUE

CRESCENT TOYS

The Crescent Toy Company Limited

The company was founded in July 1922 by Henry G. Eagles and Arthur A. Schneider in a workshop 30 feet square at the rear of a private house at 67 De Beauvoir Crescent, Kingsland Road, London N1. They manufactured model soldiers, cowboys, kitchen sets, etc. from lead alloy. These were hollow castings, hand painted, packed one dozen to a box, and sold to wholesalers at six shillings per dozen boxes.

The small firm prospered and eventually opened up a factory in Tottenham. With the second World War came a ban on metal toys and production was changed to munitions. After the War the firm resumed making metal hollow cast toys and in addition marketed the diecast products of a firm called DCMT (Die Casting Machine Tools Ltd). As a consequence early post-war models had 'DCMT' cast into the underside of the body.

In 1948 the firm opened a modern factory on a 4¼ acre site at Cymcarn, a Welsh mining village near Newport, Monmouth (now Gwent) and two years later transferred all production there, maintaining only an office in London. From this time Crescent toys made their own diecast products without 'DCMT' on them. Hence it is possible to find the same models with or without 'DCMT' cast in. Die Casting Machine Tools went their own way and from 1950 produced models under the name of 'Lone Star'.

Crescent Toys will be best remembered for their excellent ranges of military models and farm equipment but probably most of all for their superb reproductions of the racing cars of the 1950s. The following post-war model listings have been extracted from a unique collection of original trade catalogues (1947-80) most kindly provided by Mr.J.D.Schneider, the former Managing Director of Crescent Toys Ltd. All of the original research and actual compiling of the lists was undertaken by Ray Strutt of the 'Collectors Gazette'.

EARLY POST-WAR MODELS

No.	Year	Description	Price	
223	1948	Racing Car, Various colours	£25-35	☐
422	1949	Sports Car, Assorted colours	£30-40	☐
423	1949	Oil Lorry, Various colours	£30-40	☐
424	1949	Truck Lorry, Various colours	£30-40	☐
425	1949	Saloon Car, Assorted colours	£30-40	☐
800	1947-49	Jaguar, Bright colours	£35-45	☐
802	1947-49	Locomotive, Assorted colours	£25-35	☐
803	1947-48	Locomotive, Silver	£25-35	☐
804	1948-49	Police Car, Black	£35-45	☐
1221	1949	Fire Engine, Red body	£40-50	☐
-		Garages, Retailing at 1/-, 1/6, 2/6 and 4/-. Complete with Modern Pumps, Motor Cars and Garage Attendants, 'CRESCENT GARAGES' logo	NGPP	☐
FC 330		Domestic Iron and Stand	£10-15	☐

FARM EQUIPMENT

No.	Year	Description	Price	
1802	1949-60	Tractor and Hayrake, various colours	£65-75	☐
1803	1967-74	Dexta Tractor and Trailer, various colours	£45-55	☐
1804	1950-59	Tractor and Disc Harrow, various colours	£55-65	☐
1805	1950-61	Tractor, Various colours	£55-65	☐
1806	1950-60	Hayrake, various colours	£5-10	☐
1807	1950	Disc Harrow, various colours	£5-10	☐
1808	1950-56	Platform Trailer, various colours	£5-10	☐
1809	1950-56	Ricklift Trailer, various colours	£5-10	☐
1809	1962-80	Dexta Tractor, various colours	£25-35	☐
1810	1950-80	Box Trailer/Farm Trailer, (No.148 1968-74) various colours	£15-20	☐
1811	1950-67	Animal Trailer/Cattle Trailer, (No.148 1968-71) various colours	£10-15	☐
1811	1975-81	Dexta Tractor and Trailer, various colours	£15-20	☐
1813	1950	Timber Wagon (Horse Drawn) various colours	£75-95	☐
1814	1950-60	Plough Trailer, (No.150 1968-71) various colours	£10-15	☐
1815	1950	Hayloader, various colours	£10-15	☐
1816	1950	Roller Harrow, various colours	£5-10	☐
1817	1950-56	Timber Trailer, various colours	£10-15	☐
1818	1954-60	Tipping Farm Wagon, various colours	£10-15	☐
1819	1954-55	Large Farm Wagon, various colours	£25-35	☐

DIECAST ACTION TOYS

No.	Year	Description	Price	
1222	1954-59	Builders & Decorators Truck, (Red handcart) unpainted ladder & bucket, Beige builder figure on Green base	NGPP	☐
1268	1954-59	Mobile Space Rocket, various colours	NGPP	☐
1269	1954-59	Mobile Crane, various colours	£30-40	☐
1272	1954-59	Scammell Scarab & Box Trailer, various colours	£70-80	☐
1274	1954-59	Scammell Scarab & Low Loader, various colours	£70-80	☐
1276	1955-59	Scammell Scarab & Oil Tanker, various colours	£70-80	☐
2700	1956-60	Western Stage Coach, various colours	£70-80	☐
2705	1955	Western Stage Coach, various colours	NGPP	☐
-		Scammell Scarab Set, Mechanical Horse, Box Trailer and Low Loader	NGPP	☐

MILITARY MODELS

(All are in military colours unless described otherwise)

No.	Year	Description	Price	
155	1960-68	'Long Tom' Artillery Gun	£15-20	☐
235	1946	Cannon, operable	NGPP	☐
F 355	1938	Tank and Cannon Set	NGPP	☐
650	1954-59	Military Set, Two No.696 British Tanks, one No.698 Scout Car and one No.699 Russian Tank	NGPP	☐
NN656/ 2	1938-40	Field Gun and Gunner	NGPP	☐
NN692	1938-40	Deep Sea Diver, with equipment	NGPP	☐
NN693	1938-40	Searchlight Unit, with Officer and two Soldiers	NGPP	☐
NN694	1938-40	Rangefinder Unit, with Officer and Soldier	NGPP	☐
F 695	1946	Howitzer, unpainted, with spring and plunger, 'CRESCENT' cast-in	£10-12	☐
696	1954-59	British Tank	£30-40	☐
698	1954-56	Scout Car	£20-30	☐
699	1954-56	Russian Tank	£30-40	☐
NN700	1938-40	Royal Engineers Set, with 2 Soldiers and Telegraph Pole	NGPP	☐
K 703	1938-40	Field Wireless Unit, 2 Soldiers	NGPP	☐
K 704	1938-40	R.A.M.C. Stretcher Party, with 2 Soldiers and Patient	NGPP	☐

1248	1957	Field Gun..	£5-10	☐
1249	1958-79	18-pounder Quick-Firing Gun............	£10-15	☐
1250	1958-80	25-pounder Light Artillery Gun..............	£10-15	☐
1251	1958-80	5.5" Medium Heavy Howitzer	£10-15	☐
1260	1976-79	Supply Truck....................................	£30-40	☐
1263	1962-80	Saladin Armoured Scout Car...............	£20-30	☐
1264	1975-80	Scorpion Tank..................................	£12-16	☐
1265	1977-80	M109 Self-Propelled Gun...................	£12-15	☐
1266	1978-79	Recovery Vehicle..............................	£12-15	☐
1267	1958-63	'Corporal' Rocket and Lorry	£50-60	☐
1270	1958-60	Heavy Rescue Crane..........................	£40-50	☐
1271	1958-60	Long Range Mobile Gun	£20-30	☐
1271	1976-80	Artillery Force.................................	£15-20	☐
2154	1962-74	Saladin Armoured Patrol, (No.1270 1975-80)........	£10-15	☐

HISTORICAL MODELS (in Regal colours)

1300	1975-76	Royal State Coach...................................	£20-30	☐
1301	1977-79	Royal State Coach, (Commemorative box)........	£20-30	☐
1302	1977	Royal State Coach & Figures....................	£20-30	☐
1450	1956-60	Medieval Catapult.................................	£20-30	☐
1953	1954-60	Coronation State Coach...........................	£30-40	☐

Miniature 'WILD WEST' Transport

906	1956	Stage Coach, various colours	£30-40	☐
907	1956	Covered Wagon, various colours	£30-40	☐

GRAND PRIX RACING and SPORTS CARS

1284	1956-60	Mercedes-Benz, all-enveloping Silver body............	£80-100	☐
1285	1956-60	B.R.M. Mk.II, Bright Green.....................	£80-100	☐
1286	1956-60	Ferrari, Orange-Red...............................	£80-100	☐
1287	1956-60	Connaught, Dark Green...........................	£80-100	☐
1288	1956-60	Cooper-Bristol, Light Blue	£80-100	☐
1289	1956-60	Gordini, French Blue.............................	£80-100	☐
1290	1956-60	Maserati, Cherry Red.............................	£80-100	☐
1291	1957-60	Aston-Martin DB3s, White/Light Blue.....	£80-100	☐
1292	1957-60	Jaguar 'D' type, Dark Green	£80-100	☐
1293	1958-60	Vanwall, Dark Green..............................	£80-100	☐
6300	1957	Racing Cars Set, nos.1284 - 1289 as above in display box	NGPP	☐
	1958-60	Same set but 1290 replaces 1284	NGPP	☐

LONG VEHICLES (various colours)

1350	1975-80	Container Truck	£20-25	☐
1351	1975-80	Petrol Tanker.......................................	£20-25	☐
1352	1975-80	Girder Carrying Truck	£20-25	☐
1353	1975-80	Flat Platform Truck	£20-25	☐

'TRUKKERS' (various colours)

1360	1976-81	Cement Mixer	£5-20	☐
1361	1976-81	Covered Truck	£5-20	☐
1362	1976-81	Tipper Truck..	£5-20	☐
1363	1976-81	Recovery Vehicle	£5-20	☐
1364	1976-81	Super Karrier.......................................	£5-20	☐

CRESCENT TOY SHIPS

BATTLESHIPS

		H.M.S. 'King George V'. Grey hollow cast, with main armament only, boxed......................	£15-20	☐
-		Same but additional separately cast secondary armament..................................	£15-20	☐

		H.M.S. 'Vanguard'. Grey/Black/White, solid casting, 'CRESCENT' cast-in......................	£5-7	☐
Q 3	1940	Battleship Set, Battleship plus 4 Sailors	NGPP	☐
S 3	1940	Warships Set, Battleship and Destroyer plus 8 Sailors	NGPP	☐
NN 691		H.M.S. 'Malaya', Grey hollow cast body, with Black funnels, boxed	£15-20	☐

AIRCRAFT CARRIERS

-		H.M.S. 'Victorious', Grey hollow cast body, separate unpainted aircraft, boxed...	£20-25	☐
NN 667		H.M.S. 'Eagle', Grey hollow cast body, separate unpainted aircraft, Union Jack sticker attached to box	£10-15	☐

OTHER WARSHIPS

		'H' or 'I' Class Destroyer. Unpainted solid cast body, 'CRESCENT' cast into bow.......................	£15-20	☐
		'H' or 'I' Class Destroyer. As previous model plus 3 lead figures of naval personnel..............	£20-25	☐
		'V & W' Class Destroyer.		
		Grey hollow cast body	£2-3	☐
A 34		Gunboat. Grey hollow cast body..............	£2-3	☐
234	1946	Submarine. Unpainted body with conning tower and deck gun, 4"........................	£10-15	☐
C 310		'County' Class Cruiser, 'Cumberland', Grey hollow cast....................................	£7-9	☐
K 664		'County' Class Cruiser, Grey hollow cast body..........................	£7-9	☐
K 665		War Transport Ship, Grey hollow cast body, boxed................	£15-20	☐

PASSENGER SHIPS

		'Queen Mary'. Black/White/Red hollow cast body, boxed	£15-20	☐
		'Dunnottar Castle'. Mauve/White/Red, hollow cast body, boxed.......................	£25-30	☐
		'Athlone Castle'. Mauve/White/Red, hollow cast body, boxed.......................	£25-30	☐

'Dunnottar Castle' and 'Athlone Castle' were part of the 'Union Castle' fleet and the models were sold in souvenir boxes, probably on board.

MISCELLANEOUS

		'Tower Bridge'. Solid cast model of the famous landmark, various colours.........................	£5-10	☐

MODEL IDENTIFICATION. Crescent Ships are of rather crude manufacture and have virtually no identifying features. Only the H.M.S. 'Vanguard' and the 'H' or 'I' Class Destroyer are known to have 'CRESCENT' cast in. A few of the early models had a little paper 'Crescent' half-moon label.
Ship models were packed in cream cardboard boxes of varying quality.

CRESCENT AIRCRAFT

O 2	1940	Spitfire Set. 2 Spitfires with 2 Pilots and 2 Mechanics	£50-75	☐
Q 2	1940	Spitfire Set. As previous set but with a different reference number....................	£50-75	☐
U 2	1940	Aircraft Set. 5 Aircraft plus 3 Pilots and 6 Groundcrew	£75-100	☐
FC 38	1946	Aeroplane, Spitfire................................	£5-10	☐
FC 89	1946	Aeroplane, Mosquito..............................	£5-10	☐
FC 90	1946	Aeroplane, Lightning, 3" x 2" with U.S. markings...	£5-10	☐
FC 179	1946	Khaki Bomber......................................	£5-10	☐
FC 372	1946	Aeroplane, Lightning, 4.75" x 3" with U.S. markings...	£5-10	☐
FC 663	1946	North Sea Patrol, Aeroplane and two men including Pilot................................	£20-25	☐

Acknowledgements.

Thanks are due to the following contributors for additional information on Crescent toys:
Jack Barker, Blackpool, Lancs.   Brian Smart, Chelmsford, Essex.   Ray Pearson, Northwich, Cheshire

DINKY TOYS

INTRODUCTION

This edition sees the introduction of a numerical index system which will enable Catalogue users to quickly find and identify models.

The listings have been made more 'user friendly' by the amalgamation of the formerly separate 'Commercial and Utility Vehicles' and 'Vans' sections into a new consolidated single section. In addition all the Gift Sets have been presented in one numerical list.

As in the 4th Edition we have again published photographs of rare models sold at auction, thus providing a valuable source of additional reference material. The Editor would like to express his appreciation to the auction houses for their support.

During the past two years many new model, colour and wheel variations have been recorded and all have been included in this edition.

Dinky Toys remain as collectable as ever.

HISTORY OF DINKY TOYS

In 1931 Meccano Ltd introduced a series of railway station and trackside accessories to accompany their famous 'HORNBY' train sets. These 'Modelled Miniatures' were in sets numbered 1 - 22 and included railwaymen, station staff, passengers and trains. Set number 22 was comprised of six vehicles which were representative rather than replicas of actual vehicles. It was first advertised in the Meccano Magazine of December 1933.

At about this time 'Tootsie Toys' of America were introducing model vehicles into the United Kingdom and they were proving to be very popular. Consequently Meccano Ltd decided to widen their range of products and issue a comprehensive series of models to include vehicles, ships and aircraft. 'Modelled Miniatures' therefore became 'Meccano Dinky Toys' and set number 22 the first set of 'Dinky Cars'. The first 'Dinky Toys' advertisement appeared in the April 1934 edition of the Meccano Magazine. The first Dinky car produced after the change of name was 23a in April 1934. It was probably based on an early MG but was again generally representative rather than an accurate model. Set 22 cost 4/- and consisted of: 22a Sports Car, 22b Sports Coupé, 22c Motor Truck, 22d Delivery Van, 22e Tractor and 22f Tank and is today highly sought after.

The range of models produced grew quickly so that the Meccano Magazine of December 1935 was claiming that there were 200 varieties to choose from! Although the phrase 'Dinky Toys' became a household name, the actual range was of course far greater and was not limited to cars; it even included dolls house furniture. Indeed, by the time the famous Binns Road factory in Liverpool finally closed its doors in November 1979 over 1000 different designs had been produced. Pre-war models are rare today and fetch high prices, which reflects how difficult it is to find a model in really good condition. This is because so many 1930s models were made from an unstable alloy which has tended to crystallize and disintegrate. Fortunately the post-war models do not suffer from the same problem and much of today's collecting interest is centred around the delightful models produced in the fifties and sixties with Gift Sets being particularly sought after.

In 1987 the Dinky trade name was bought by Matchbox who were at the time part of the Universal International Co. of Hong Kong. They introduced the 'Dinky Collection' in 1988 with some very fine models in a constant scale of 1:43. On the 7th May 1992 it was announced in the 'New York Times' that 'Tyco Toys Inc.' had acquired by merger the 'Universal Matchbox Group' and with it the famous 'Dinky Toys' brand name.

Model Identification

Common Features. There are several features common to various groups of models and to avoid unnecessary repetition in the 'Features' column they are shown below. Exceptions to these general indications are noted in the listings.

'Dinky Toys', 'Meccano Ltd', or 'Meccano Dinky Toys'.
These wordings are to be found cast or stamped on the base-plate or chassis or in the case of early models without a base they are cast into the model itself. Some very early models have 'HORNBY SERIES' cast-in (notably those in the 22 series).

Wheel hubs. Solid one-piece wheel/tyre castings were fitted to the 'Modelled Miniatures' and first pre-war 'Dinky Toys'. They had 'Hornby' or 'Meccano' cast onto their rims and were covered in a thin colour wash or silver-plated. This casting was soon replaced with more realistic cast hubs (having a smooth convex face) fitted with white (sometimes coloured) rubber tyres. Pre-war hubs may be black, coloured or sometimes silver-plated. Post-war hubs were of the 'ridged' type having a discernible ridge simulating a nave-plate or hub cap and were usually fitted with black rubber tyres. They were only painted, never silver-plated.

Supertoy hubs and tyres. When Supertoys were introduced in 1947 the ridged type of hub was used on the Fodens with black 'herringbone pattern' tyres, and on the Guys with smooth black tyres. Fodens graduated to the use of 'fine radial-tread' tyres first in black, later in grey, then to black again but with a more chunky 'block' tread. Supertoys later acquired plastic hubs and plastic tyres.

Wheel materials. Lead was used originally for a short time, the majority of models from the mid-1930s to the early 1960s having diecast mazak hubs. Small models like motor-cycles or the 35b Racer were fitted with solid one-piece wheel/tyre moulding (white or black rubber pre-war, black post-war). In 1958/9 spun aluminium hubs were introduced and some models (such as 131, 178, 179, 180, 181, 182 and 290 Bus) appeared fitted with either type. Plastic hubs replaced the diecast versions on racing cars numbered 230-235 while the Austin A30 and Fiat 600 were given solid one-piece wheel/tyre plastic injection mouldings.

Speedwheels were introduced in the 1970s and some model can be found fitted with metal wheels or Speedwheels. The former are more collectable.

Model Number and Name. It has been assumed that all post-war models have either the model number or name or both marked on the base-plate or chassis. Pre-war models usually had neither (though the 38 and 39 series are exceptions having the model name on their base-plates).

Windscreen. Assumed to be of plastic unless otherwise described, for example celluloid windscreen, tinplate windscreen, open or solid windscreen, open windscreen, solid windscreen.

Base-plate and Chassis. Assumed to be of tinplate or metal construction unless otherwise described (for example plastic chassis).

Construction Materials. All models assumed to be constructed at least in part of a diecast alloy. Some pre-war models were made of a lead alloy like the 22 and 28 series plus the few odd models such as 23 a Racing Car and 23m Thunderbolt Speed Car. The Blaw-Knox Bulldozer was one of the very few produced (right at the end of its production) in plastic.

Windows. The first Dinky to be fitted with plastic window glazing was the Austin A105 Saloon. Some models in production at the time were fitted with glazing later on and may therefore be found with or without windows.

Hooks were not fitted to the first Supertoys Foden models (1947). Small hooks were fitted in early 1948, the usual (larger) hook appearing in mid-1948.

Axles were all 'crimped' pre-war and on these series of models post-war: 23, 25, 29, 30, 34, 35, 36, 37, 38, 39, 40 and 280. Otherwise models had rivet-ended axles until the advent of Speedwheels. Early Guy models had tinplate clips to retain the front axles.

Size of models is usually shown in millimetres and refers to the longest overall measurement (usually the length). In the case of pre-war models slight inaccuracies may occur from expansion of the casting as it ages in the course of time.

The Scale of Dinky Toys was originally 1/43 (with a few exceptions). Supertoys Foden and Guy vehicles (introduced in 1947) were in a scale of 1/48 while military models issued from 1953 were smaller at 1/60. Most aircraft models before 1965 were around 1/200 and ships 1/1800. In the late 1960s and early 1970s the 1/36 scale was introduced.

Dinky Numbering System. The dual/triple reference numbers used on some Dinky Toys and Supertoys (for example 409/521/921 Bedford Articulated Lorry) refers to the basic model type and casting and not to model colours. The renumbering by Meccano was an administration process to re-catalogue production of existing lines and introduce new models. New colours on existing castings which arise at about the time of renumbering are therefore coincidental with it rather than a consequence of it.

PRE-WAR MODELS IDENTIFICATION FEATURES TO LOOK FOR:

1: Wheel hubs generally smooth, not ridged
2: Axles were crimped, not rivetted
3: Base-plates often bare metal (unpainted)
4: Criss-cross chassis (see diagrams)
5: Wing-mounted spare wheel on cars
6: Smooth white (occasionally coloured) tyres
7: Slots in chassis for tinplate figures (36 series)
8: Tinplate radiator grilles
9: Stairs on 29 series Bus absent post-war
10: Thinner axles used pre-war

CLASSIFYING THE EARLY MODEL TYPES

In addition to the details given in the earlier sections, the age and category of a particular model is determined by features such as:—
 i) The type of chassis or Base Plate.
 ii) The type of Radiator Shell and Bumper.
 iii) Body features such as the front of a Lorry, Van or Bus.

Diagrams of all of these features are included in each relevant section.

Dinky Toys Cars

Model Identification - continued

Dinky Toys Cars chassis types 1934-1950

| 1934-1936 'Criss-Cross' Chassis | 1936-1940 Open Chassis | 1946-1947 Plain Chassis | 1948-1950 Moulded Chassis |

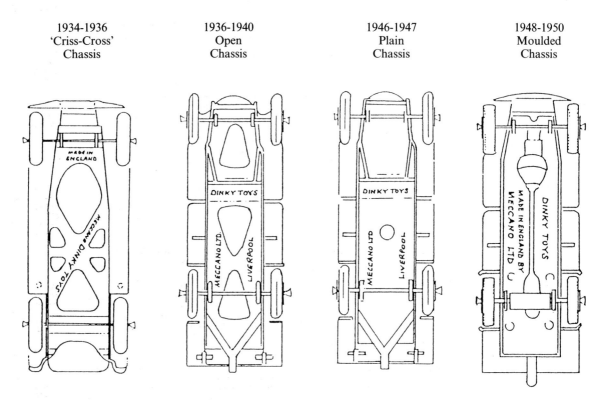

N.B. The diagrams for the Open, Plain and Moulded chassis include the tow bars as seen on the 25 Series lorries. The cars did not have tow bars.

NOTES:

Two paint schemes exist for two-colour issues on models 170, 171 and 172:
1: Lower colour covers wing tops and doors up to windows (generally known as 'Highline') and
2: Lower colour extends only up to ridge on wings/doors ('Lowline').

For other models derived from cars see these sections:
Fire, Police and Ambulance vehicles, Military vehicles, Gift Sets,
Buses, Taxis and Trams, Dinky Action Kits, 'Mini-Dinky' models,
Dinky Toys issued by Airfix Products, Novelty, Space and Film/TV-related models, 'Dinky Dublo' models

Ref. No.	Year(s)	Model Type	Model Features and Size	Market Price Range	
22a	1933-35	Open top Sports Car	'Modelled Miniature' with 'HORNBY SERIES' cast into lead body, solid metal wheel/tyre castings (thinly painted in metallic blue, purple, green, yellow or red, or not painted at all) lead windscreen surround, tinplate radiator (grille may be same colour as body, or overpainted with the colour of the mudguards), 82 mm.		
			Blue body, Yellow seats and mudguards..	£400-500	☐
			Blue body, Red seats and mudguards..	£400-500	☐
			Cream body, Red seats and mudguards...	£400-500	☐
			Cream body, Green seats and mudguards..	£400-500	☐
			Cream body, Blue seats and mudguards..	£400-500	☐
			Red body, Cream seats and mudguards..	£150-250	☐
			Yellow body, Green seats and mudguards...	£400-500	☐
			Orange-Brown body, Cream seats and mudguards................................	£150-200	☐
22b	1933-35	Closed top Sports Coupé	'Modelled Miniature' with 'HORNBY SERIES' cast into lead body, solid metal wheel/tyre castings (coloured or plain, as 22a) tinplate radiator (painted in main body colour) 82 mm.		
			Cream body, Red roof and mudguards..	£400-500	☐
			Red body, Blue roof and mudguards..	£400-500	☐
			Red body, Cream roof and mudguards..	£400-500	☐
			Yellow body, Green roof and mudguards..	£400-500	☐
22g	1935-41	Streamline Tourer......................	Model has cast steering wheel and windscreen, smooth diecast hubs which may be painted as body colour or a contrasting colour, 85 mm.		
			Body colours: Green, Red, Blue, Cream or Black...............................	£150-200	☐
22h	1935-41	Streamlined Saloon....................	Red, Blue or Cream saloon version of 22g (no steering wheel) 85 mm.	£150-200	☐
23	1934-35	Racing Car................................	1st casting. Lead body, no racing number or driver, coloured tyres on some, 4 exhausts, 94 mm.		
		variations:.............	Cream body with either Blue, Cream, Green, Orange or Red top flash	£95-125	☐
23a	1935-41	23 re-issued:.........	1st casting. Diecast body, no driver, no racing number, Black or White tyres, 4 exhausts, 94 mm.		
		variations:............	White body and wheels, Blue top flash and circle on nose..........................	£50-75	☐
			Cream body and wheels, Red top flash and circle on nose...........................	£50-75	☐
			Blue body, White top flash and circle on nose..	£50-75	☐
			Orange body, Green top flash and circle on nose..	£50-75	☐
			Yellow body, Dark Blue top flash and circle on nose	£50-75	☐
			Brown body, Cream top flash...	£50-75	☐
		2nd casting:	With driver plus raised circles for racing numbers, 6 exhausts in fishtail, 94 mm.		
		colour type 1:	With minor colour sidestripes and perhaps coloured tyres,		
		colour type 2:	Broad nose flash, even width top rear flash,		
		colour type 3:	Broad flash at cockpit and pointed ends top flash, plus circle on nose		
		variations:............	(type 3) White body, Blue nose/circle/top flash, number '2'	£50-75	☐
			(type 3) White body, Green nose/circle/top flash, number '6'	£50-75	☐
			(type 3) Orange body, Green nose/circle/top flash, number '4'	£50-75	☐
			(type 1) Cream body, Red stripes, number '9', ('Humbug' version)............	£75-125	☐
			(type 2) Yellow body, Dark Blue top flash, racing number '7'....................	£50-75	☐
			(type 2) Blue body, White top flash, racing number '11'...........................	£50-75	☐
		casting variation:	With driver, raised racing number circle on nearside only, no detailed exhaust,		
			Orange body, Green nose circle, Green racing number '4'	£400-500	☐
23a	1946-50	3rd casting:	With transverse body ribs, no raised circle for racing numbers, and only issued in colour type 3, with or without racing numbers		
			Red body, Silver nose circle, top flash and side circle (Red RN '4')	£30-35	☐
			Silver body, Red nose circle, top flash and side circle (Silver RN '4')	£30-35	☐
		note:.....................	Details of any other 23a colour are welcomed		
23b	1935-41	Hotchkiss Racing Car	Blue body, Dark Blue, Red or White flash & racing number '5', 96 mm.	£50-75	☐
	1935-41		Yellow (Blue flash and RN), Orange (Green flash and RN), or Green (Yellow flash and RN)	£50-75	☐
	1946-48		Red with Silver flash and RN '5', or Silver with Red flash and RN '5'........	£40-50	☐
23c	1936-38	Mercedes Benz Racing Car	Red, Blue, Yellow or Green, plain clipped-in base, various racing numbers, driver cast-in, 92 mm.	£75-95	☐
	1938-40		As previous model but with rivetted baseplate bearing information	£75-95	☐
	1946-50	('Large Open Racing Car')........	Re-issued 23c in Blue or Silver, various racing numbers, 92 mm.	£40-50	☐
23d	1936-38	Auto Union Racing Car............	Red, Blue, Light Blue, Pale Green, Yellow or Silver body, plain clipped-in tinplate base, various racing numbers, driver slotted-in, 100 mm.	£75-95	☐
	1938-41		As previous model but with rivetted baseplate bearing information	£40-50	☐
	1946-50		Re-issued 23d with Silver body, Red racing number '2', no driver	£40-50	☐
23e	1936-38	'Speed Of The Wind' Racing Car............................	Red, Blue, Light Blue, Green, Yellow or Silver body, plain clipped-in tinplate base, driver, various racing numbers, 104 mm.	£75-95	☐
	1938-41		As previous model but with rivetted baseplate bearing information	£40-50	☐
	1946-49		Re-issue of 23e in Red or Silver, rivetted informative baseplate	£30-40	☐
23e (221)	1950-54		Silver (lead or diecast body & wheels, plain base	£30-40	☐
23f (232)	1952-54	Alfa-Romeo Racing Car	Red body, White racing number '8', Red diecast hubs, 100 mm.	£70-85	☐
23g (233)	1952-54	Cooper Bristol Racing Car........	Green body, White racing number '6', Green diecast hubs, 89 mm.	£70-85	☐
23h (234)	1953-54	Ferrari Racing Car	Blue body, Yellow nose, racing number '5' and diecast hubs, 101 mm.	£70-85	☐
23j (235)	1953-54	H.W.M. Racing Car..................	Green body, Yellow racing number '7', Green diecast hubs, 99 mm.	£70-85	☐
23k (230)	1953-54	Talbot-Lago Racing Car	Blue body, Yellow racing number '4', Blue diecast hubs, 103 mm.	£70-85	☐

91

Ref. No.	Year(s)	Model Type	Dinky Toys - continued	Market Price Range
23m	1938-41	'Thunderbolt' Speed Car	Silver body (Black detailing), Union Jacks on tail, boxed, 126 mm.	£70-85 ☐
23n (231)	1953-54	Maserati Racing Car	Red, White flash & racing number '9', Red diecast hubs, 94 mm.	£70-85 ☐
23p	1939-40	Gardner's MG Record Car	Dark Green, White flash and 'MG' logo, Union Jacks, 'MG Magnette' on base, boxed, 104 mm.	£100-125 ☐
	1946-47		Dark Green, Union Jacks, no flash, 'MG Record Car' on base, not boxed	£100-125 ☐
23s	1938-40	Streamlined Racing Car	Light Green (Dark Green detailing), lead or diecast, no flags, 126 mm.	£75-95 ☐
			Light Blue (Dark Blue detailing), lead or diecast, no flags	£75-95 ☐
			Orange body, lead or diecast, no flags	£75-95 ☐
23s (222)	1948-54		Light, Mid or Dark Green, or Dark Blue, Silver flashes, no flags	£30-40 ☐
			Silver body with Red, Green or Blue flashes, no flags	£30-40 ☐
			Red body with Silver or Black flashes, Black base, no flags	NGPP ☐
24b	1934-38	Limousine	Criss-cross chassis, plain or badged radiator, no sidelights, no spare wheel, 3 side windows, 3 'stacked' parallel horizontal bonnet louvres, 98 mm.	
		body/chassis colours:	Maroon/Dark Maroon, Maroon/Grey, Maroon/Black, Blue/Yellow, Dark Blue/Black, Yellow/Brown	£150-250 ☐
	1937-40	casting change:	Same colours but no spare wheel slot, 3 parallel bonnet louvres, open chassis, 'Bentley' grille and bumper	£150-200 ☐
24c	1934-38	Town Sedan	Criss-cross chassis, plain or badged radiator, spare wheel, no sidelights, separate windscreen/steering wheel casting, 97 mm.	
		body/chassis colours:	Green/Black, Green/Yellow, Pale Green/Red, Dark Blue/Dark Blue, Cream/Dark Blue, Cream/Black	£150-200 ☐
	1937-40	casting change:	Same colours but open chassis, no spare wheel slot, narrower boot, shorter door handles	£150-200 ☐
24d	1934-38	Vogue Saloon	Criss-cross chassis, with spare wheel, no sidelights, 97 mm. Blue/Blue, Blue/Black, Blue/Maroon, Cream/Blue, Brown/Green, Pink/Green, Green/Blue, Red/Grey	£150-200 ☐
	1937-40	casting change:	Same colours but open chassis, higher 'domed' roofline	£150-200 ☐
24e	1934-38	Super Streamlined Saloon	Criss-cross chassis, no spare or sidelights, 12 bonnet louvres, 97 mm. Maroon/Black, Red/Dark Red, Red/Black, Green/Red, Green/Blue	£150-200 ☐
	1937-40	casting change:	As previous model but with 13 bonnet louvres	£150-200 ☐
24f	1934-38	Sportsmans Coupé	Criss-cross chassis, with spare wheel, no sidelights, 97 mm. Colours: Blue/Blue, Blue/Black, Yellow/Brown, Cream/Dark Blue, Brown/Buff	£150-200 ☐
	1937-40	casting change:	Open chassis, higher 'domed' roofline, no spare wheel	£150-200 ☐
24g	1934-38	Sports Tourer 4 Seater	Criss-cross chassis, spare wheel hub cast-in, no sidelights, open tinplate windscreen, separate dashboard/steering wheel casting, 100 mm. Yellow/Black, Yellow/Blue, Blue/Brown, Cream/Green, Cream/Brown, Black/Cream, Blue/Maroon	£150-200 ☐
	1937-40	casting change:	Open chassis, filled-in windscreen, cast impression of spare	£150-200 ☐
24h	1934-38	Sports Tourer 2 Seater	Criss-cross chassis, spare wheel hub cast-in, no sidelights, open tinplate windscreen, separate dashboard/steering wheel casting, 98 mm. Red/Red, Green/Green, Yellow/Green, Yellow/Blue, Yellow/Black, Black/Cream, Cream/Green	£150-200 ☐
	1937-40	casting change:	Open chassis, filled-in windscreen, cast impression of spare	£150-200 ☐
24kz	1939-40	Peugeot Car	Red or Blue, tinplate front bumper, rubber tyres for UK, French issue	NGPP ☐

NOTE: The rarest of the 24 Series have coloured tyres matching the body colour and a higher value can be expected.

Ref. No.	Year(s)	Model Type	Dinky Toys - continued	Market Price Range
25j	1947-48	Jeep	Red or Green body, Red wheels and tail-lights, 68 mm.	£75-95 ☐
			Aqua Blue or Sky Blue body, Yellow wheels, Red tail-lights	£100-150 ☐
25y (405)	1952-54	Jeep	Green or Red body with hook, spare wheel on side. 83 mm.	£65-75 ☐
27d (340)	1950-54	Land Rover	Green or Orange body, tinplate windscreen frame, driver, 90 mm.	£50-60 ☐
	1952-53	Gift Set model:	Dark Brown body. Only in Gift Set No.2, Commercial Vehicles Set	GSP ☐
27f (344)	1950-54	Estate Car	Pale Brown body with Dark Brown panels, rear axle pillars, 105 mm.	£60-70 ☐
27m (341)	1950-54	Land-Rover Trailer	Orange body (Beige wheels), Green body (Green wheels), Dark Blue (Blue wheels)....	£20-30 ☐
30a (32)	1935-40	Chrysler 'Airflow' Saloon..........	No chassis, separate bumper units, lead versions exist, 103 mm. Turquoise, Maroon, Cream, Green, Blue, Red, (wheels may be any colour)...............	£200-250 ☐
	1946-48		As previous model but Blue, Cream or Green body (wheels usually Black).................	£125-150 ☐
30b	1935-50	Rolls Royce	Open chassis, no sidelights, authentic radiator, 101 mm. Colours:	
	1935-40		Cream/Black, Blue/Black, Dark Blue/Black, Fawn/Black	£150-200 ☐
			Yellow/Brown, Red/Red, Grey/Grey, Green/Green	£175-250 ☐
	1946-50		Plain (closed) chassis, Navy Blue/Black or Greyish-Brown/Black	£70-85 ☐
30c	1935-50	Daimler...................................	Open chassis, no sidelights, authentic radiator, 98 mm. Colours:	
	1935-40		Cream/Black, Blue/Black, Dark Blue/Black, Yellow/Black, Fawn/Black.....................	£150-200 ☐
			Turquoise/Black, Fawn/Black	£175-250 ☐
			Pink/Maroon, Red/Red	£175-250 ☐
	1946-50		Plain (closed) chassis, Dark Green/Black, Cream/Black, Greyish-Brown/Black, Grey/Black, Light Green/Black	£70-85 ☐
			Medium Green body with Pale Green hubs	£80-120 ☐
30d	1935-50	Vauxhall...................................	Open chassis, no sidelights, spare wheel, 'square' radiator, 98 mm.	
	1935-38		Green/Black, Blue/Black, Grey/Black, Yellow/Black, Brown/Black...........................	£150-200 ☐
			Green/Green, Grey/Grey, Yellow/Brown, Cream/Brown	£175-250 ☐
	1938-40	radiator change:	As previous model but with 'shield' radiator, Black chassis	£150-200 ☐
			With 'shield' radiator and coloured chassis	£175-250 ☐
	1946-50		Plain (closed) chassis, no spare wheel, 'shield' radiator, Green/Black, Brown/Black, Maroon/Black, Yellow/Black, Grey/Black, Olive-Green/Black, Blue/Black	£70-85 ☐

Ref. No.	Year(s)	Model Type	Dinky Toys - continued	Market Price Range	
32 (30a)	1934-35	Chrysler 'Airflow' Saloon.........	Maroon (lead) body, no chassis, separate bumper units, 103 mm...............................	**£200-250**	☐
			Maroon (diecast) body, no chassis, separate bumper units, 103 mm.....................	**£200-250**	☐
35a	1936-40	Saloon Car................................	some versions may have spare wheel cover in darker shade of main colour		
			Blue, Maroon, Grey, Yellow, Red, Turquoise, Black or White solid rubber wheels, 51 mm..	**£90-120**	☐
	1946-48		Grey or Blue body (spare wheel cover not enhanced), Black rubber wheels only	**£70-85**	☐
35az	1939-40	Fiat 2-seater Saloon..................	Red, Blue or Green, White rubber wheels, 'Simca 5' cast inside. French issue............	NGPP	☐
35b	1936-39	Racer...	Red, Silver, Yellow or Blue body, with or without driver, Black or White solid rubber wheels, 57 mm...	**£50-70**	☐
35b (200)	1939-40		Silver body, Red grille, Brown driver, solid Black rubber wheels only	**£50-70**	☐
			Silver body, Red grille, Silver driver, solid Black rubber wheels only	**£50-70**	☐
35c	1936-40	MG Sports Car.........................	Red, Green, Blue or Maroon, Silver detailing, Black or White solid rubber wheels, 52 mm...	**£90-120**	☐
	1946-48		Red or Green body, Silver on radiator only, Black rubber wheels only	**£70-100**	☐
35d	1938-40	Austin 7 Car (open tourer)	Wire windscreen frame, Black or White rubber wheels, Silver radiator & steering wheel, 50 mm., Blue, Green, Grey, Maroon or Yellow, (Yellow may have Orange spare wheel cover)..	**£90-120**	☐
	1946-48		Blue, Fawn, Grey or Yellow body, Silver on radiator only, Black rubber wheels only..	**£50-70**	☐
36a	1937-41	Armstrong-Siddeley Limousine with Driver and Footman.............	Detailed chassis with slots, tinplate figures, sidelights, 97 mm. Red/Dark Red, Grey/Dark Grey, Maroon/Dark Maroon..	**£400-500**	☐
36a	1946-50	Armstrong-Siddeley	(no slots or figures), Mid-Blue/Black, Grey/Black, Maroon/Black, Sky Blue/Black, Powder Blue/Black, Saxe-Blue/Black, Olive-Green/Black	**£70-100**	☐
36b	1937-41	Bentley 2 seat Sports Coupé with Driver and Footman	Detailed chassis with slots, tinplate figures, sidelights, 94 mm. Cream/Black, Yellow/Maroon, Grey/Grey..	**£400-500**	☐
36b	1946-50	Bentley (no slots/figures)	Green/Black, Blue/Black, Grey/Black, Fawn/Black, Light Fawn/Black.......................	**£70-100**	☐
36c	1937-41	Humber Vogue Saloon with Driver and Footman ..... with Driver & Footman.........	Detailed chassis with slots, tinplate figures, sidelights, 91 mm. Green/Dark Green, Blue/Dark Blue, all Royal Blue	**£400-500**	☐
36c	1946-50	Humber Vogue	Brown/Black, Blue/Black, Grey/Black, Maroon/Black, (no slots/figures)	**£70-100**	☐
36d	1937-41	Rover Streamlined Saloon with Driver and Footman	Detailed chassis with slots, tinplate figures, sidelights, 94 mm. Green/Dark Green, Red/Dark Red	**£400-500**	☐
36d	1946-50	Rover (no slots/figures)	Dark, Mid or Bright Blue/Black, Light or Mid-Green/Black	**£70-100**	☐
			Green body with Light Green hubs...	**£100-125**	☐
36e	1937-41	British Salmson 2 seater Sports with Driver	Detailed chassis, cast driver, sidelights, 93 mm. (spare wheel on some, 96 mm.) Royal Blue/Black, Black/Red, Grey/Dark Grey, (hole in seat for driver)....................	**£400-500**	☐
36e	1946-50	British Salmson 2 seater Sports	(no hole), Red/Black, Light or Mid-Green/Black, Fawn/Black, Mid-Blue/Black, Sky-Blue/Black or Saxe-Blue/Black	**£70-80**	☐
36f	1937-41	British Salmson 4 seater Sports with Driver	Detailed chassis, cast driver, sidelights, cast-in spare wheel, 96 mm. Red/Dark Red, Green/Dark Green, (hole in seat for driver)	**£400-500**	☐
36f	1946-50	British Salmson 4 seater Sports	Light or Mid-Green/Black, Brown/Black, Grey/Black, Fawn/Black, (no hole)	**£70-100**	☐
			Brownish-Grey/Black or Light Grey/Black	**£70-100**	☐
38a	1940-41	Frazer Nash BMW Sports Car	Red (Maroon seats), Dark Blue (Fawn seats), lacquered metal base, 82 mm.	**£150-175**	☐
	1946-50		Light or Dark Blue (Fawn or Grey seats), Black base	**£70-100**	☐
			Grey (Fawn or Blue seats), or Grey (Red seats & wheels), Black base	**£70-100**	☐
			Light Grey (Blue seats, Black wheels)	**£70-100**	☐
38a (100)	1950-55		Same as previous models but made for export only (renumbered in 1954)	NGPP	☐
38b	1940-41	Sunbeam Talbot Sports.............	Red (Maroon tonneau), Red or Black wheels, lacquered metal base, 92 mm.	**£150-175**	☐
	1946-49		Red/Maroon or Maroon/Grey, Black baseplate	**£70-100**	☐
			Light Green/Green, Brown/Blue, Black baseplate	**£70-100**	☐
			Light Grey (Grey or Dark Blue tonneau), Black wheels, Black baseplate	**£70-100**	☐
			Dark Grey (Grey or Light Blue tonneau), Black wheels, Black baseplate	**£70-100**	☐
			Yellow/Fawn or Yellow/Green, Black baseplate	**£150-200**	☐
			Dark Blue body, Light Grey tonneau, Black wheels and baseplate	**£70-100**	☐
			Light Blue body, Dark Grey tonneau, Black wheels and baseplate	**£70-100**	☐
			Brown body, Blue tonneau	**£70-100**	☐
38b (101)	1950-55		As previous models but made for export only (renumbered in 1954)	NGPP	☐
38c	1946-50	Lagonda Sports Coupé.............	Green (Black seats), or Green/Dark (Green seats), Black baseplate	**£70-100**	☐
			Grey (Fawn seats), or Grey (Maroon seats)	**£70-100**	☐
			Maroon (Dark Blue seats), Black baseplate, 102 mm.	**£70-100**	☐
			Light Grey (Grey seats), or Mid-Grey (Grey seats)	**£70-100**	☐
38c (102)	1950-55		As previous models but made for export only (renumbered in 1954)	NGPP	☐
38d	1940-41	Alvis Sports Tourer	Green body, Black seats & wheels, lacquered metal baseplate, 95 mm.	**£150-175**	☐
	1946-50		Green/Dark Green, Green/Brown, Black painted base	**£70-100**	☐
			Green body, Black seats and wheels, Black painted base	**£70-100**	☐
			Green body, Black seats, Green wheels, Black painted base	**£70-100**	☐
			Maroon/Grey, Maroon/Red, Light Blue/Dark Blue, Black base	**£100-150**	☐
			Blue/Grey, Grey/Blue, Black painted base	**£70-100**	☐
38d (103)	1950-55		As previous models but made for export only (renumbered in 1954)	NGPP	☐

Ref. No.	Year(s)	Model Type	Dinky Toys - continued	Market Price Range
38e	1940 ?	Triumph Dolomite..................	Planned and catalogued but not issued.	NPP ☐
38e	1946-50	Armstrong Siddeley Coupé	Grey/Blue, Light Grey/Blue, Black painted baseplate, 96 mm.	£70-100 ☐
			Light Grey/Green, or Grey/Dark Green	£70-100 ☐
			Bright Green/Grey, Red/Maroon, Cream/Blue, Black painted baseplate...........	£70-100 ☐
38e (104)	1950-55	.	As previous models but made for export only (renumbered in 1954)	NGPP ☐
38f	1940-41	Jaguar (SS100) Sports Car	Khaki/Blue, Blue/Grey, Light Blue/Grey, Grey/Blue, Grey/Black, Red/Maroon, Fawn/Black, 2 windscreens, lacquered baseplate, 80 mm.	£150-175 ☐
	1946-50		Light or Dark Blue body, Grey seats, Black painted baseplate.................................	£70-100 ☐
			Brown body, Blue seats, Black painted baseplate	£70-100 ☐
38f (105)	1950-55		As previous models but made for export only (renumbered in 1954)	NGPP ☐
39a	1939-41	Packard Super 8 Tourer	Light Green, Grey, Black, Yellow, Blue, lacquered baseplate, 107 mm.	£150-175 ☐
	1946-50		Brown, Green or Olive-Green body, Black painted baseplate	£70-100 ☐
39b	1939-41	Oldsmobile 6 Sedan..................	Black, Maroon, Light or Mid-Grey or Green, lacquered baseplate, 100 mm.	£150-175 ☐
	1946-50		Grey, Brown, Cream, Blue, Green or Fawn body, Black painted base	£70-100 ☐
39bu	1950-52	Oldsmobile Sedan (US issue)	Cream with Dark Blue wings or two-tone Blue, Black painted baseplate	£700-900 ☐
39c	1939-41	Lincoln Zephyr Coupé	Grey, Yellow Red or Green body, lacquered baseplate, 106 mm.	£150-175 ☐
	1946-50		Grey, Brown, Maroon or Red body, Black painted baseplate	£70-100 ☐
39cu	1950-52	US issue:	Red with Maroon wings or Cream with Brown wings, Black painted baseplate.........	£700-900 ☐
39cu	1950-52	US issue:	Tan and Brown	£1000-1250 ☐
39d	1939-41	Buick Viceroy Saloon...............	Grey, Green, Maroon, Cream or Blue, lacquered baseplate, 103 mm.	£150-175 ☐
	1946-50		Light or Dark Green, Maroon, Fawn, Blue, Beige or Grey body, Black base	£70-100 ☐
			Mustard body, Black painted baseplate	£150-200 ☐
39e	1939-41	Chrysler Royal..........................	Yellow, Green, Blue or Grey body, lacquered baseplate, 106 mm.	£150-175 ☐
	1946-50		Light Blue, Mid-Blue, Dark Blue, Light Green, Mid-Green, Dark Green or Dark Grey body, Black wheels and baseplate	£70-100 ☐
			As previous models but with Silvered baseplate..	£250-350 ☐
			Cream body, Green hubs, Black painted baseplate	£100-150 ☐
39eu	1950-52	Chrysler Royal (US issue).........	Yellow with Red wings or two-tone Green body, Black painted baseplate	£700-900 ☐
39f	1939-41	Studebaker State Commander...	Yellow, Green or Grey body, lacquered baseplate, 103 mm.	£150-175 ☐
	1946-50		Mid-Blue, Green, Olive, Maroon or Yellow body, Black baseplate..........................	£70-100 ☐
			Grey or Light Grey body, Black wheels	£70-100 ☐
			Dark Maroon body, Black wheels	£70-100 ☐
			Very Dark Blue body, Black wheels	£70-100 ☐
			Tan body, Black wheels	£120-150 ☐
40a (158)	1947-55	Riley Saloon	Dark Blue, Light Blue, Dark Grey, Light Grey, Light Green, Mid Green or Dark Green, large or small print on Black painted baseplate, 93 mm.	£80-110 ☐
40b	1948-49	Triumph 1800 (Renown)	Light Blue, Fawn, Grey, rear axle pillars, Black baseplate, 91 mm.	£80-110 ☐
			Black body, rear axle held by pillars, Black baseplate	£2000-3000 ☐
40b (151)	1949-55		Mid Blue, Dark Blue, Beige, Grey or Tan, rear axle held by baseplate.....................	£80-90 ☐
40d (152)	1949-54	Austin (A40) Devon	Light Blue, Mid Blue, Dark Blue, Light Green (Cream hubs), Dark Green, Red, Maroon, Tan, large or small print on Black base ...	£80-110 ☐
			Dull Green, Fawn wheels	£80-110 ☐
			Greyish-Green, Beige wheels	£80-110 ☐
40e	1948-50	Standard Vanguard	Tan body, 'open' rear wheel arches, small print on base, 91 mm.	£80-110 ☐
	1950-52		Tan or Light Blue, 'closed' rear wheel arches, small print on base	£80-110 ☐
40e (153)	1952-54		Light Blue, Dark Blue, Fawn, Cream or Tan, 'ridged' boot lid, large base print............	£80-110 ☐
40f (154)	1951-54	Hillman Minx	Light Green, Dark Green, Light Tan or Dark Tan body, large base print, 88 mm.	£80-90 ☐
40g (159)	1950-54	Morris Oxford	Dark Green or Very Dark Green, large or small base print, 93 mm..........................	£80-110 ☐
			Fawn, Light Tan or Grey body, large or small print on base	£80-110 ☐
			Mid-Blue body (similar shade to the 481 'Ovaltine' Bedford CA Van).....................	£1500-2000 ☐
40j (161)	1949-53	Austin (A40) Somerset	Light Blue, Mid Blue or Red body, 89 mm..	£80-110 ☐
101	1957-60	Sunbeam Alpine (touring)........	Pink body, Tan seats, Cream diecast hubs, Grey driver, 94 mm.	£145-175 ☐
			Turquoise body, Blue seats, Light Blue diecast hubs, Grey driver	£145-175 ☐
			Turquoise body, Blue seats, spun aluminium hubs, Grey driver	£150-200 ☐
102	1957-60	MG Midget (touring finish)	Orange body, Red seats and diecast hubs, Grey driver, 83 mm.	£175-225 ☐
			Light Green body, Tan seats, Cream diecast hubs, Grey driver	£175-225 ☐
103	1957-60	Austin Healey 100 (touring).....'.	Red body, Grey seats, diecast hubs and driver, 85 mm.	£145-175 ☐
			Cream body, Red seats and diecast hubs, Grey driver	£145-175 ☐
104	1957-60	Aston Martin DB3S (touring)...	Pale Blue body, Blue seats, Dark Blue cast hubs, Grey driver, 87 mm.	£145-175 ☐
			Pink body, Red seats and diecast hubs, Grey driver...	£145-175 ☐
105	1957-60	Triumph TR2 (touring finish) ...	Grey body, Red seats and diecast hubs, 84 mm.	£90-120 ☐
			Primrose-Yellow body, Green seats and diecast hubs, Grey driver	£120-150 ☐
	1959-60		As previous models but with spun aluminium hubs	£145-175 ☐
106 (140a)	1954-58	Austin A90 Atlantic	Light Blue body, Cream seats, Cream wheels, 95 mm.	£125-150 ☐
			Light Blue body, Red seats, Red wheels	£100-125 ☐
			Light Blue body, Dark Blue seats, Cream wheels	£110-140 ☐
			Black body, Red seats & wheels, White tyres	£100-125 ☐
			Red body	NGPP ☐
107	1955-59	Sunbeam Alpine (competition finish)	Light Blue, Tan or Cream seats, Cream wheels, '26', racing driver, 94 mm.	£75-85 ☐
			Cerise body, Grey seats, Cream wheels, RN '34', racing driver	£60-70 ☐
108	1955-59	MG Midget (competition).........	Red body, Tan seats, Red wheels, RN '24', racing driver, 83 mm.	£100-125 ☐
			White body, Maroon seats, Red wheels, RN '28', racing driver	£100-125 ☐

Ref. No.	Year(s)	Model Type	Dinky Toys - continued	Market Price Range	
109	1955-59	Austin Healey 100 (competition finish)	Cream body, Red seats and hubs, racing driver & number '23', 85 mm.	£75-85	☐
			Yellow body, Blue seats and hubs, racing driver & number '21'	£75-85	☐
110	1956-59	Aston Martin DB3S (competition finish)	Grey body, Blue seats and hubs, racing driver & number '20', 87 mm.	£75-85	☐
			Green body, Red seats and hubs, racing driver and number '22'	£75-85	☐
110	1966-67	Aston Martin DB5	Metallic Red, Cream or Black seats, '110' on base, spoked wheels, 111 mm.	£75-85	☐
	1967-71		Metallic Red, Cream or Black seats, plain base, spoked wheels	£75-85	☐
111	1956-59	Triumph TR2 Sports Car (competition finish)	Pink body, Blue seats and hubs, racing driver & number '29', 84 mm.	£75-85	☐
			Turquoise body, Red seats and hubs, racing driver & number '25'	£75-85	☐
112	1961-66	Austin Healey Sprite II	Red body, suspension & fingertip steering, spun hubs, 78 mm.	£65-75	☐
		South African issues:	Turquoise, Light Blue or Dark Blue body	£500-750	☐
113	1962-69	MG 'MGB'	Cream body, Red seats, Grey plastic driver, 85 mm.	£70-80	☐
		South African issue:	Mid-Blue body (Red interior), or Red body	£500-750	☐
114	1963-71	Triumph Spitfire	Sports car with lady driver (plastic), in Blue, spun hubs, 87 mm.		
	1963-66		Metallic Silver-Grey body (Red seats), or Red body (Cream seats)	£65-80	☐
	1966-70		Metallic Gold body with Red seats and 'Tiger In Tank' on bootlid	£70-80	☐
	1966-70		Metallic Gold body, without bootlid logo	£60-70	☐
	1970-71		Metallic Purple body	£100-125	☐
115	1965-69	Plymouth Fury Sports	White open body, suspension & steering, driver & passenger, 122 mm.	£70-80	☐
116	1966-71	Volvo P 1800 S	Red or Dark Metallic Red, Silver or Gold wheels, suspension, 105 mm.	£45-55	☐
120	1962-67	Jaguar 'E' type	Red, detachable Black hardtop/optional Cream folded soft-top, 92 mm.	£60-70	☐
			Metallic Blue & White body	£60-70	☐
			Metallic Light Blue & Black body, Cream seats	£850-1350	☐
122	1977-80	Volvo 265 DL Estate	Metallic Blue, Cream or Orange body, suspension, plastic wheels, 141 mm.	£15-20	☐
123	1977-80	Princess 2200 HL	Bronze, White, White/Black, White/Blue, suspension, plastic wheels, 128 mm.	£15-20	☐
124	1977-79	Rolls-Royce Phantom V	Metallic Light Blue, boot opens - bonnet does not (see 152), 141 mm.	£20-25	☐
127	1964-66	Rolls-Royce Silver Cloud Mk3	Metallic Blue or Metallic Green, suspension & steering, 125 mm.	£60-70	☐
	1966-69		Metallic Gold	£60-70	☐
	1969-72		Metallic Red	£60-70	☐
128	1964-67	Mercedes-Benz 600	Metallic Red body, suspension & steering, 3 figures/luggage, 147 mm.	£30-35	☐
	1967-75		As previous model but with Black roof, driver only	£25-30	☐
	1975-79		Metallic Blue body, driver, suspension & fingertip steering, 147 mm.	£25-30	☐
129	?-?	MG Midget (U.S. issue)	White body, Maroon seats, Red hubs, no driver or racing number (see 108)	£400-500	☐
			Red body, Tan seats, Red hubs, no driver or racing number (see 108)	£400-500	☐
129	1965-72	Volkswagen 1300 Sedan	Metallic Blue body, spun hubs, suspension & fingertip steering, 100 mm.	£30-40	☐
	1972-76		Metallic Blue body, plastic Speedwheels	£30-40	☐
130	1964-66	Ford Consul Corsair	Red or Metallic Red body, suspension & steering, spun hubs, 106 mm.	£40-60	☐
	1966-69		Light Blue, suspension & fingertip steering, spun hubs	£40-60	☐
131	1956-61	Cadillac Eldorado	Pink (Grey seats), Yellow (Red seats), driver, diecast hubs, 118 mm.	£90-100	☐
	1962-63		As previous models but with spun aluminium hubs	£100-120	☐
131	1968-70	Jaguar 'E' type 2 + 2	White body, suspension, tilting seats, cast spoked wheels, 112 mm.	£70-80	☐
	1970-75		Bronze body, cast spoked wheels or plastic wheels	£70-80	☐
	1975-76		Metallic Purple, Speedwheels	£40-50	☐
	1976-77		Bronze body, Speedwheels	£40-50	☐
	1977-77		Metallic Red body, Speedwheels	£40-50	☐
132	1955-61	Packard Convertible	Light Green/Red, or Light Brown/Red, driver, 112 mm.	£80-110	☐
132	1967-74	Ford 40 RV	Silver, Metallic Blue, Metallic Red, Red/Yellow, spoked wheels, 96 mm.	£25-35	☐
133	1955-60	Cunningham C5R	White (Tan seats), or Off-White (Blue seats), Blue driver, 99 mm.	£70-80	☐
			As previous models but with spun aluminium hubs	£70-80	☐
133	1964-66	Ford Cortina	Metallic Gold/White, suspension, spun hubs, jewelled headlamps, 101 mm.	£40-50	☐
	1966-68		Pale Yellow body, spun hubs.	£40-50	☐
134	1964-68	Triumph Vitesse	Metallic Blue or Metallic Green, suspension, spun hubs, 85 mm.	£60-70	☐
135	1963-69	Triumph 2000 Saloon	Red interior, Grey base, spun hubs, wipers, luggage, 105 mm.		
		normal colours:	Metallic Green with White roof or Metallic Blue with White roof	£55-65	☐
		Gift Set 118 colour:	White body, Blue roof	GSP	☐
		promotional colours:	Black body, Cactus-Green roof	£900-1300	☐
			Black body, White roof	£900-1300	☐
			Blue Grey body, Black roof	£900-1300	☐
			Light Green body, Lilac roof	£900-1300	☐
			Brown body, Light Green roof	£900-1300	☐
			British Racing Green, White roof	£900-1300	☐
			White body, Light Green roof, Blue interior	£900-1300	☐
			Cherry Red body, White roof, Blue interior	£900-1300	☐
			White body, Black roof, Blue interior	£1500-2000	☐
			Greyish-Green body, Cactus-Green roof	£900-1300	☐
136	1964-65	Vauxhall Viva	White body, suspension & fingertip steering, 93 mm.	£30-35	☐
	1965-68		Deep Metallic Blue body	£30-35	☐
	1969-73		Pale Metallic Blue body	£30-35	☐
137	1963-66	Plymouth Fury Convertible	Grey/Cream, Green/Cream, Pink/Cream, Blue/Cream, Two-tone Green, Metallic Light Green/Metallic Dark Green, 122 mm.	£60-80	☐
			Dark Blue/White, detachable hard-top, spun aluminium hubs	£70-80	☐
			Blackish-Green, Pale Green top, Red interior, spun hubs	£80-100	☐

Ref. No.	Year(s)	Model Type	Dinky Toys - continued	Market Price Range	
138	1963-66	Hillman Imp	Metallic Green body, luggage, spun hubs, cast headlamps, 85 mm.	£30-40	☐
	1966-68		Metallic Red body, luggage, spun hubs, jewelled headlamps	£30-40	☐
	1968-73		Metallic Blue body, luggage, spun hubs, jewelled headlamps	£30-40	☐
139	1963-64	Ford Cortina	Pale Blue body, suspension & steering, cast headlamps, 101 mm.	£45-55	☐
	1964-65		Metallic Blue body	£45-55	☐
139a (170)	1949-54	Ford Fordor Sedan	Yellow, Red, Green or Tan body, (all with matching wheels), 102 mm.	£70-90	☐
			Brown body, Red wheels	£70-90	☐
			Red body, Maroon wheels	NGPP	☐
139am	1950-54	US Army Staff Car	(170m) Ford Fordor in Olive drab with White stars on roof and doors	£175-250	☐
139b (171)	1950-54	Hudson Commodore	Dark Blue body, Stone roof & wheels, 111 mm.	£80-100	☐
			Dark Blue body, Fawn roof and wheels	£80-100	☐
			Cream body, Maroon roof & wheels	£80-100	☐
			Royal Blue body, Stone roof and wheels	£100-125	☐
140a (106)	1951-54	Austin A90 Atlantic	Blue body, Dark Blue seats, 95 mm.	£90-110	☐
			Dark Blue body, Red seats	£90-110	☐
			Pink body, Cream seats and wheels	£90-110	☐
140b (156)	1951-54	Rover 75 Saloon	Maroon (Maroon wheels), or Cream (Cream wheels), 101 mm.	£70-90	☐
140	1963-69	Morris 1100	Light Blue or Dark Blue body, suspension & suspension, spun hubs, front number plate may have surrounding casting or not, 87 mm.	£30-40	☐
		South African issue:	White body, Blue roof	£500-750	☐
141	1963-67	Vauxhall Victor Estate Car	Yellow or Maroon body, suspension & steering, spun hubs, 92 mm.	£30-40	☐
		South African issue:	Pink body with Blue interior	£500-750	☐
142	1962-68	Jaguar Mk 10	Metallic Blue or Light Blue, suspension, spun aluminium hubs, 107 mm.	£40-50	☐
		South African issue:	Green body with White roof	£500-750	☐
143	1962-67	Ford Capri	Turquoise body, White roof, suspension, luggage, spun hubs, 90 mm.	£50-60	☐
144	1963-67	Volkswagen 1500	Off-White or Bronze body, suspension, luggage, spun hubs, 93 mm.	£30-40	☐
			Metallic Green body	£400-600	☐
145	1962-67	Singer Vogue	Metallic Light Green body, suspension & steering, spun hubs, 93 mm.	£40-50	☐
			Yellow body, Red interior, spun hubs.	£2000-2500	☐
146	1963-67	Daimler 2.5 litre V8	Metallic Pale Green body, suspension & steering, spun hubs, 95 mm.	£50-60	☐
147	1962-69	Cadillac 62	Metallic Green or Blue body, suspension & steering, spun hubs, 113 mm.	£50-60	☐
148	1962-62	Ford Fairlane	(Non-metallic), Pale Green, closed windows, spun hubs, 111 mm.	£50-60	☐
	1962-65		(Non-metallic), Pale Green, open windows, spun hubs.	£50-60	☐
	1965-67		Light or Dark Metallic Green, open windows, spun hubs.	£50-90	☐
		South African issue:	Bright Blue body, open windows	£500-750	☐
		South African issue:	Greyish-Lilac, spun hubs, no base number, English/Afrikaans box	£800-1000	☐
149	1971-75	Citroën Dyane	Bronze body, Black roof, suspension, Speedwheels, 91 mm.	£25-30	☐
	1971-75		Light Grey body, Dark Grey or Black roof, suspension, Speedwheels	£25-30	☐
150	1959-64	Rolls-Royce Silver Wraith	Two-tone Grey body, suspension, spun hubs, Chrome parts, 117 mm.	£40-50	☐
151 (40b)	1954-59	Triumph 1800 (Renown)	Light Blue, Light Blue wheels, rear axle held in baseplate, 91 mm.	£80-100	☐
			Light Blue, Dark Blue wheels	£80-100	☐
			Pale Brown (Green wheels), or Grey (Blue wheels)	£80-100	☐
151	1965-69	Vauxhall Victor 101	Yellow, Metallic Red or Lime Green, suspension, spun hubs, 105 mm.	£35-45	☐
152 (40d)	1954-56	Austin (A40) Devon	Red (Red wheels), Dark Blue or Dark Green body, 86 mm.	£80-100	☐
			Greyish-Green or Greenish-Grey (same colour or Brown wheels)	£80-100	☐
	1956-60		Deep Yellow lower body, Blue upper body, Dark Blue wheels	£150-175	☐
			Pink lower body, Lime Green upper body, Light Cream wheels	£150-175	☐
152	1965-67	Rolls Royce Phantom V	Dark Blue body, chauffeur and 2 passengers, spun hubs, 141 mm.	£35-50	☐
	1967-77	design change:	Dark Blue or Black body with Chauffeur but no passengers	£25-30	☐
153 (40e)	1954-59	Standard Vanguard	Blue, Brown, Tan, Cream or Fawn, ridged boot, large print on base	£80-110	☐
			White (White wheels), ridged boot lid, large print on base	£80-110	☐
			Maroon (Brown wheels), ridged boot lid, large print on base	£2000-3000	☐
	1959-59		As previous models but having enlarged boot lid lamp casting	£80-110	☐
153	1967-71	Aston Martin DB6	Metallic Blue body, suspension, steering, 111 mm.	£40-45	☐
			Metallic Green body	£60-70	☐
154 (40f)	1954-56	Hillman Minx	Brown (Cream wheels), 87 mm.	£80-90	☐
			Tan body, (Blue wheels)	£80-90	☐
			Light Green (Light Green wheels)	£80-90	☐
	1956-59		Blue lower body, Pink upper body, Dark Blue wheels	£125-150	☐
	1956-59		Bright Green lower body, Cream upper body	£125-150	☐
	1956-59		Olive-Green lower body, Cream upper body	£125-175	☐
			Green lower body, Pinkish-Cream upper body	£125-150	☐
154	1966-69	Ford Taunus 17M	Yellow & White body, suspension, steering, tilt seats, windows, 110 mm.	£25-35	☐
155	1961-66	Ford Anglia 105E	Turquoise or Green body, suspension, windows, spun hubs, 81 mm.	£60-70	☐
		South African issue:	Deep Cream body, Red interior	£500-750	☐
156 (140b)	1954-56	Rover 75	Ivory body, Ivory or Light Blue hubs, 101 mm.	£80-110	☐
			Red (Red wheels), or Maroon (Red wheels)	£80-110	☐
	1956-59		Dark Green lower, Light Green upper body, Light Green wheels	£90-120	☐
	1956-59		Ivory lower, Light Blue upper body, Ivory wheels	£100-125	☐
	1956-59		Ivory lower, Dark Blue upper body, Ivory wheels	£100-125	☐
	1956-59		Ivory lower, Mid-Blue upper body, Beige wheels	£175-200	☐
156	1968-71	Saab 96	Metallic Red or Metallic Blue body, suspension, spun hubs, 98 mm.	£50-75	☐

Ref. No.	Year(s)	Model Type	Dinky Toys - continued	Market Price Range	
157	1954-57	Jaguar XK120............................	Greyish-Green (Fawn wheels), or Red (Red wheels), 97 mm.	£90-110	☐
			Yellow (Yellow wheels), or White (Fawn wheels)	£200-250	☐
	1957-59		Turquoise lower body, Cerise upper body, Cerise wheels................................	£175-225	☐
	1957-59		Yellow lower body, Grey upper body, Grey wheels...	£175-225	☐
	1959-62		Red or Greyish-Green body, spun aluminium hubs	£90-110	☐
157	1968-73	BMW 2000 Tilux.......................	Blue/White, suspension, special lights, spun hubs, 121 mm.	£30-40	☐
			Metallic Blue with Gold upper half, pictorial box lining	£90-120	☐
158 (40a)	1954-60	Riley Saloon	Cream body, Green wheels, large print on base, 93 mm.	£80-100	☐
			Light Green body, Mid-Green wheels, large print on base	£80-100	☐
158	1967-70	Rolls-Royce Silver Shadow	Metallic Red, suspension, spun hubs, 125 mm.	£30-40	☐
	1970-73		Metallic Blue, suspension, opening doors/bonnet/boot..................................	£20-25	☐
159 (40g)	1954-56	Morris Oxford	Grey body with Grey hubs, 93 mm.	£80-110	☐
			Dark Green body (Dark Green hubs), or Light Green body	£80-110	☐
	1956-59		Cream lower body, Green upper body, Green wheels......................................	£150-175	☐
	1956-59		Dark Pink lower body, Cream upper body, Beige wheels.................................	£150-175	☐
159	1967-70	Ford Cortina Mk.II..................	White body, suspension, tilting seats, spun aluminium hubs, 105 mm.	£40-50	☐
160	1958-62	Austin A30................................	Turquoise or Tan body, smooth or treaded solid grey plastic wheels, 77 mm.	£80-110	☐
160	1967-74	Mercedes-Benz 250 SE	Metallic Blue body, suspension, steering, working stop-lights, 117 mm.	£25-35	☐
161 (40j)	1953-56	Austin (A40) Somerset	Light Blue body, Mid-Blue wheels, 89 mm.	£80-110	☐
			Mid-Blue body, Light Blue wheels	£80-110	☐
			Dark Red body, Dark Red wheels	£80-110	☐
	1956-59		Red lower body, Yellow roof, Red wheels	£150-175	☐
	1956-59		Black lower body, Cream roof, Cream wheels...	£150-175	☐
161	1965-69	Ford Mustang Fastback...........	White (Red seats), 'MUSTANG' decal, suspension, steering, 111 mm.	£40-50	☐
	1969-73		Yellow body, Blue seats, cast-in logo replaces decal.....................................	£30-40	☐
			Orange body (without decal), Speedwheels...	£25-35	☐
162	1956-60	Ford Zephyr (Mk I)	Cream and Dark Green body, Cream wheels, 96 mm.	£65-80	☐
			Two-tone Blue body, Light Blue wheels..	£65-80	☐
			Cream and Light (Lime), Green body	£65-80	☐
162	1966-70	Triumph 1300	Metallic Blue, suspension, fingertip steering, spun aluminium hubs, 93 mm...	£35-50	☐
163	1956-60	Bristol 450 Coupé	British Racing Green body, Light Green wheels, RN '27', 98 mm.	£40-65	☐
163	1966-71	Volkswagen 1600 TL................	Red or Dark Metallic Red, suspension, cast detailed hubs, 102 mm.	£30-40	☐
			Metallic Blue body, Speedwheels..	£30-40	☐
164	1957-60	Vauxhall Cresta	Red lower body, Cream upper body, Cream wheels, 96 mm.	£70-80	☐
	1957-60		Green lower body, Grey upper body, Grey wheels..	£70-80	☐
164	1967-71	Ford Zodiac Mk.IV..................	Silver body, suspension, steering, 4 opening doors, 114 mm.	£30-40	☐
			Pale Metallic Blue body, suspension & fingertip steering	£30-40	☐
			Metallic Bronze body, suspension & fingertip steering	£120-150	☐
165	1959-60	Humber Hawk..........................	Maroon/Cream or Green/Black, no front number plate casting, 102 mm.	£60-70	☐
	1959-63		Maroon/Cream or Green/Black, with front number plate casting	£60-70	☐
165	1969-76	Ford Capri	Metallic Green, Blue or Purple, Speedwheels, suspension, 102 mm.	£30-40	☐
166	1958-63	Sunbeam Rapier	Orange lower body, Cream upper body, Cream wheels, 89 mm.	£70-80	☐
			Mid-Blue lower body, Turquoise upper body, Mid-Blue wheels	£60-70	☐
166	1967-70	Renault R16	Metallic Blue, suspension & fingertip steering, spun hubs, 99 mm.	£20-35	☐
167	1958-63	A.C. Aceca Sports Coupé	Grey body, Red roof, Red wheels, 89 mm.	£70-80	☐
			Cream body, Reddish-Maroon roof, Silver cast hubs...................................	£200-250	☐
			Cream body, Brown roof, Cream wheels or spun aluminium hubs.................	£70-80	☐
			Pale Yellow body, Maroon roof, spun aluminium hubs	£80-90	☐
			All Cream body, spun aluminium hubs	£125-175	☐
168	1959-63	Singer Gazelle Saloon..............	Brown lower, Pale Yellow upper body, spun aluminium hubs, 92 mm.	£70-80	☐
			Dark Green lower, Grey upper body, spun aluminium hubs	£60-70	☐
168	1968-70	Ford Escort	Pale Blue or White, cast detailed hubs, 97 mm.	£30-40	☐
	1970-74		Metallic Red body, spun aluminium hubs	£30-40	☐
	1974-75		Metallic Blue body, Speedwheels..	£30-40	☐
169	1958-63	Studebaker Golden Hawk	Green/Cerise body, Cream wheels or spun hubs, White tyres, 106 mm.	£70-80	☐
			Tan/Red body, Cream wheels or spun hubs, White tyres................................	£40-65	☐
169	1967-69	Ford Corsair 2000 E	Silver body, Black textured roof, suspension & steering, 108 mm.	£45-55	☐
170 (139a)	1954-56	Ford Fordor	Single colours: Tan (Red wheels), or Green, Yellow or Red, 102 mm.	£70-90	☐
	1956-58		('Highline'), Red lower body, Cream upper body...	£150-200	☐
	1956-58		('Highline'), Blue lower body, Pink upper body	£150-200	☐
	1958-59		('Lowline'), Red lower body, Cream upper body	£150-200	☐
	1958-59		('Lowline'), Blue lower body, Pink upper body	£150-200	☐
170m	1954-54	Ford US Army Staff Car	(139am) Military Green, US issue, renumbered 675	£175-250	☐
170	1964-70	Lincoln Continental..................	Metallic Orange with White roof, or Blue with White roof, 127 mm.............	£60-80	☐
170	1979	Granada Ghia...........................	Never issued		
171 (139b)	1954-56	Hudson Commodore Sedan	Dark Blue body, Fawn or Stone roof, Fawn wheels, 111 mm.	£80-100	☐
			Cream body, Maroon roof	£80-100	☐
	1956-58		('Highline'), Turquoise lower body with Red upper body, Red wheels...........	£150-200	☐
			('Highline'), Grey lower body with Blue upper body, Blue wheels.................	£150-200	☐
	1958-59		('Lowline'), Turquoise lower body with Red upper body, Red wheels............	£200-250	☐
			('Lowline'), Grey lower body with Blue upper body, Blue wheels	£200-250	☐
171	1965-68	Austin 1800..............................	Pale Blue or Metallic Blue, suspension, steering, spun hubs, 101 mm..........	£40-50	☐

Ref. No.	Year(s)	Model Type	Dinky Toys - continued	Market Price Range	
172	1954-56	Studebaker Land Cruiser	Light Green (Green wheels), or Blue (Fawn wheels), 107 mm.	£70-80	☐
	1956-58		('Highline'), Cream lower body, Maroon upper body, Cream wheels	£100-120	☐
			('Highline'), Cream lower body, Tan upper body, Cream wheels	£100-120	☐
	1958-59		('Lowline'), Cream lower body, Maroon upper body, Cream wheels	£100-120	☐
			('Lowline'), Cream lower body, Tan upper body, Cream wheels	£100-120	☐
172	1965-69	Fiat 2300 Station Wagon	Blue, TT Blue or White/Blue, suspension, steering, spun hubs, 108 mm.	£30-40	☐
173	1958-60	Nash Rambler Station Wagon ..	Turquoise/Maroon, number on baseplate, 101 mm.	£40-50	☐
			Pink/Blue, number on baseplate	£40-50	☐
	1960-62		Turquoise/Maroon, without number on baseplate	£40-50	☐
			Pink/Blue, without number on baseplate	£40-50	☐
173	1969-73	Pontiac Parisienne	Metallic Maroon or Blue, retractable aerials, Speedwheels, 132 mm.	£35-45	☐
174	1958-63	Hudson Hornet......................	Red/Cream body, Grey wheels or spun aluminium hubs, 111 mm.	£70-85	☐
			Yellow/Grey body, Grey wheels or spun aluminium hubs	£70-85	☐
174	1969-73	Ford Mercury Cougar..............	Red body, cast or Speedwheels, retractable aerial, 122 mm.	£25-30	☐
			Blue or Metallic Dark Blue body, cast or Speedwheels	£25-30	☐
175	1958-61	Hillman Minx	Grey body, Blue roof and boot, Blue wheels or spun hubs, 88 mm.	£75-85	☐
			Tan body, Green roof and boot, Cream wheels or spun hubs	£75-85	☐
175	1969-73	Cadillac Eldorado.....................	Metallic Purple/Black or Metallic Blue/Black, Speedwheels, 133 mm.	£30-45	☐
176	1958-63	Austin A105 Saloon	First Dinky Toys car to have windows. Body sides have a contrasting side flash. Treaded tyres may be Black or White. 102 mm.		
	1958-59		Cream body, Dark Blue side flash, Cream wheels	£80-90	☐
			Grey body, Red side flash, Red wheels	£80-90	☐
	1959-63		Cream body, Dark Blue roof and side flash, Cream wheels or spun hubs	£120-150	☐
			Grey body, Red roof and side flash, Red wheels or spun hubs	£120-150	☐
176	1969-74	N.S.U. Ro80...........................	Metallic Red body, spun hubs, luminous seats, working lights, 114 mm.	£30-40	☐
			Blue body	£30-40	☐
177	1961-66	Opel Kapitan	Blue body, suspension, fingertip steering, spun hubs, 100 mm.	£30-45	☐
		South African issue:	Dark Blue body	£500-750	☐
		South African issue:	Pale Yellow body, Red interior	£500-750	☐
178	1959-63	Plymouth Plaza........................	Light Blue body, Dark Blue roof and side stripe, spun hubs, 108 mm.	£60-70	☐
			Pink body, Green roof and side stripe, spun hubs	£60-70	☐
			Blue body with White roof and side stripe, suspension, spun hubs.	£125-145	☐
178	1975-79	Mini Clubman	Bronze or Red body, opening doors, jewelled headlights on some, 82 mm.	£20-30	☐
179	1958-63	Studebaker President	Pale Blue body, Blue stripe, Cream wheels or spun hubs, 108 mm.	£70-80	☐
			Yellow body, Blue stripe, Cream wheels or spun hubs	£70-80	☐
179	1971-75	Opel Commodore	Metallic Blue body, Black roof, suspension, Speedwheels, 107 mm.	£20-30	☐
180	1958-63	Packard Clipper	Fawn/Pink body, Cream wheels or spun hubs, White tyres, 108 mm.	£70-80	☐
			Orange/Grey body, Cream wheels or spun hubs, White tyres	£70-80	☐
			All Green body, White tyres	£70-80	☐
180	1979-80	Rover 3500	White body, plastic chassis & wheels, 131 mm. Made in Italy by Polistil	£15-20	☐
180	1979-80	Volvo Estate Car	Orange body. Made in Italy by Polistil	£15-20	☐
181	1956-70	Volkswagen Saloon	Grey, Air Force Blue or Lime Green, Blue or Green wheels, 90 mm.	£40-70	☐
			Light Blue, spun aluminium hubs	£40-70	☐
		South African issues:......	Cream, Light Green or Light Blue	£500-750	☐
182	1958-66	Porsche 356a Coupé	Light Blue, Cream, Red or Cerise, Cream wheels or spun hubs, 87 mm.	£60-70	☐
			Deep Pink and Gold	£150-175	☐
		South African issue:	Plum body, spun aluminium hubs	£500-750	☐
183	1958-60	Fiat 600...............................	Red body, smooth or treaded solid Grey plastic wheels, 71 mm.	£55-65	☐
			Light Green body, smooth or treaded solid Grey plastic wheels	£50-60	☐
183	1966-72	Morris Mini Minor Saloon	Blue/Black roof, Blue/Red, Red/Black, White/Black, spun hubs, 75 mm.	£40-50	☐
			Metallic Red body and roof, Speedwheels	NGPP	☐
		South African issue:	Red body and roof.	£500-750	☐
184	1961-65	Volvo 122 S	Red body, suspension, windows, plastic wheels, 97 mm.	£60-70	☐
			As previous model but with White body.	£200-250	☐
		South African issue:	Greyish Lilac with White interior	£500-650	☐
		South African issue:	Greyish Green with White interior	£500-650	☐
185	1961-63	Alfa Romeo 1900	Red or Yellow body, suspension & steering, spun hubs, 102 mm.	£40-50	☐
186	1961-67	Mercedes-Benz 220 SE	Light Blue or RAF Blue, suspension, steering, spun hubs, 102 mm.	£30-40	☐
		South African issue:	Greyish Light Blue with Cream interior	£500-750	☐
187	1959-64	VW Karmann Ghia Coupé	Green/Cream, Red/Black or Yellow/Green, suspension, 96 mm.	£40-60	☐
187	1968-77	De Tomaso Mangusta 5000	Red and White body with racing number '7', 102 mm.	£20-25	☐
188	1968-74	Jensen FF	Yellow or Green body, suspension, steering, special lights, 121 mm.	£30-45	☐
189	1959-64	Triumph Herald Saloon	Green/White, spun aluminium hubs, 86 mm.	£50-60	☐
			Blue/White, spun aluminium hubs	£45-60	☐
		special issues:	Blue/White, Magenta, Dark Blue or Lilac	£1000-2000	☐
		special issue:	Red lower, White upper body, plain printed box with Red spot	£2000-2500	☐
		special issue:	Greyish-Green, Pale Whitish-Green roof, plain box with correct colour spot	£1500-2000	☐
		special issue:	Pinkish-Brown body with Pale Grey roof	£750-1000	☐
		special issue:	Dark Grey body and roof, Pale Grey bonnet and boot	£1500-2000	☐
189	1969-76	Lamborghini Marzal	Green/White, Yellow/White or Red/White, cast detailed hubs, 137 mm.	£20-25	☐
	1976-78		Metallic Blue/White or Dark Metallic Green/White, Speedwheels	£20-25	☐
190	1970-74	Monteverdi 375 L....................	Metallic Red body with opening doors, Speedwheels, 116 mm.	£20-25	☐
191	1959-64	Dodge Royal Sedan..................	Cream body with Brown flash, spun hubs, 111 mm.	£50-75	☐
			Cream body with Blue flash, spun hubs	£50-75	☐
			Light Green body with Black flash, spun hubs	£50-75	☐

Ref. No.	Year(s)	Model Type	Dinky Toys - continued	Market Price Range	
192	1959-64	De Soto Fireflite	Grey/Red, spun aluminium hubs, 114 mm.	£75-85	☐
			Sea Green/Fawn, spun aluminium hubs	£75-85	☐
192	1970-80	Range Rover	Bronze, various colours of interior, cast detailed or Speedwheels	£15-20	☐
			Black or Yellow body, Speedwheels	£15-20	☐
193	1961-69	Rambler Cross-Country	Yellow/White body, suspension, steering, roof-rack, spun hubs, 102 mm.	£40-45	☐
		South African issue:	Cream/Mauve, All Mauve, or Lime-Green body	£500-750	☐
		South African issue:	Pale Lilac body, Black roof	£600-800	☐
		South African issue:	Light Greyish-Green body, Black roof	£600-800	☐
194	1961-67	Bentley 'S' Coupé	Grey (Red or Maroon seats), or Gold (Cream seats), suspension, 113 mm.	£55-75	☐
		South African issue:	Avocado Green body, Dark Red seats	£600-800	☐
		South African issue:	Cream body, Red interior	£500-750	☐
195	1960-66	Jaguar 3.4 Mk.II.	Maroon, Cream or Grey body, suspension, fingertip steering, 95 mm.	£60-80	☐
		South African issue:	Pale Bluish-Grey body, White interior	£600-800	☐
196	1963-70	Holden Special Sedan	Bronze/White or Turquoise/White, suspension & steering, 108 mm.	£35-50	☐
		South African issue:	White body, Turquoise roof	£500-750	☐
197	1961-71	Morris Mini Traveller	White body with 'wood' trim, Red or Yellow interior, 72 mm.	£40-50	☐
			Dark Green body with 'wood' trim	£400-600	☐
			Lime Green body	£200-300	☐
			Fluorescent Green body	£120-130	☐
198	1962-69	Rolls-Royce Phantom V	Metallic Green and Cream body, Blue chauffeur, spun hubs, 125 mm.	£55-65	☐
			Cream upper body, Grey lower body with Blue chauffeur, spun hubs	£55-65	☐
		South African issue:	Dark Grey over Metallic Cream body, Red interior	£500-750	☐
199	1961-71	Austin 7 Countryman	Blue body with 'wood' trim, suspension & steering, windows, 72 mm.	£40-50	☐
	1970-71		Fluorescent Pinkish-Orange	£120-130	☐
200 (35b)	1954-57	Midget Racer	Silver body, Red grille, Brown driver, solid Black rubber wheels, 57 mm.	£25-35	☐
200	1971-80	Matra 630 Le Mans	Blue body, racing number '5', '9' or '36', Speedwheels	£15-20	☐
201	1979-80	Plymouth Stock Car	Blue body, racing number '34', wide plastic wheels, 135 mm.	£15-20	☐
202	1971-75	Fiat Abarth 2000	Fluorescent Red/White body, opening doors, Speedwheels, 91 mm.	£15-20	☐
203	1979-80	Customised Range Rover	Black body, plastic chassis, wide wheels, 115 mm.	£15-20	☐
			Yellow body, plastic chassis, wide wheels, 115 mm.	£30-40	☐
204	1971-74	Ferrari 312 P	Metallic Red body & opening doors, Speedwheels, RN '60', 99 mm.	£20-25	☐
			Metallic Red body, White opening doors, Speedwheels, RN '60'	£20-25	☐
205 (230)	1962-64	Talbot Lago Racing Car	Blue, Red or Yellow plastic hubs, RN '4', bubble-packed (230 on base)	£70-85	☐
205	1968-73	Lotus Cortina Rally	White/Red, RN '7', suspension & FS, screw or rivet in base, 105 mm.	£40-60	☐
206 (231)	1962-64	Maserati	Red/White, Red or Yellow plastic hubs, bubble-packed, (231 on base)	£200-300	☐
206	1978-80	Customised Corvette	Red/Yellow or White/Black, plastic chassis and wide wheels, 113 mm.	£15-20	☐
207 (232)	1962-64	Alfa Romeo	Red body, Red plastic hubs, bubble-packed, (232 on base), 100 mm.	£70-85	☐
207	1977-80	Triumph TR7 Rally	White/Red/Blue, RN '8', plastic chassis & wheels, 'Leyland', 98 mm.	£15-20	☐
208 (233)	1962-64	Cooper Bristol Racing Car	Dark Green, Red plastic wheel hubs, bubble-packed, (233 on base), 89 mm.	£200-300	☐
	variant:		As previous model but with Green metal hubs	£150-200	☐
208	1971-75	VW Porsche 914	Yellow body, cast detailed wheel hubs, 89 mm.	£25-30	☐
	1976-80		Metallic Blue/Black body, Speedwheels	£25-30	☐
209 (234)	1962-64	Ferrari Racing Car	Blue, Yellow triangle, Yellow plastic hubs, bubble-packed, (234 on base)	£200-300	☐
210 (239)	1962-65	Vanwall	Green, Yellow plastic hubs, bubble-packed, (239 on base), 95 mm.	£200-300	☐
210	1971-73	Alfa Romeo 33	Red body with Black doors and racing number '36'	£25-30	☐
211	1976-76	Triumph TR7	Metallic Blue-Green body, opening doors, plastic wheels, 98 mm.	£20-25	☐
		promotional issue:	White body, British Leyland promotional	£25-30	☐
	1976-78		Red or Yellow body, Pale Grey bumpers & interior	£25-30	☐
	1978-80		Red or Yellow body, Black bumpers & interior	£25-30	☐
212	1965-70	Ford Cortina Rally	White with Black bonnet, 'Castrol', RN '8', suspension, 102 mm.	£45-60	☐
213	1970-73	Ford Capri Rally	Metallic Red body, Black bonnet, spotlights, wing mirrors, 102 mm.	£40-50	☐
	1973-75		Bronze body, Black bonnet, spotlights, wing mirrors, Speedwheels	£40-50	☐
214	1966-69	Hillman Imp Rally	Blue body with racing number '35', suspension & steering, 86 mm.	£35-55	☐
215	1965-66	Ford GT Racing Car	White body with racing number '7', spun hubs, 96 mm.	£20-30	☐
	1966-70		White body with racing number '7', Silver spoked wheels	£20-30	☐
	1970-74		Green body, Silver or Gold spoked wheels	£20-30	☐
			Yellow or Metallic Blue, removable bonnet, Silver or Gold spoked wheels	£20-30	☐
216	1967-69	Dino Ferrari	Red body, Silver or Gold spoked wheels, 98 mm.	£20-30	☐
	1969-75		Metallic Blue/Black, Silver or Gold spoked wheels or Speedwheels	£20-30	☐
217	1968-70	Alfa Romeo Scarabeo OSI	Red body, Silver spoked wheels, 132 mm.	£15-20	☐
	1969-74		Red, Orange or Green body, Speedwheels	£15-20	☐
218	1969-73	Lotus Europa	Yellow body, Blue panels/roof, chequered flags, Gold engine, 96 mm.	£25-30	☐
	1973-75		Yellow/Black body or Metallic Blue body, Silver engine, Speedwheels	£25-30	☐
219	1977-79	Leyland Jaguar XJ-5.3 Coupé	White body, 'Leyland' decal, 137 mm.	£10-15	☐
219	1978-79	'Big Cat' Jaguar	White/Red, Black 'Big Cat' decal. (This model was not boxed)	£10-15	☐
220 (23a)	1954-56	Small Open Racing Car	Silver (Red wheels), or Red (Silver wheels), RN '4', 94 mm.	£25-30	☐
220	1970-73	Ferrari P5	Red body with opening doors, 96 mm.	£20-25	☐
	1973-75		Red body with opening doors, Speedwheels	£20-25	☐
221 (23e)	1954-56	'Speed Of The Wind' Racing Car	Silver diecast body with plain baseplate, 104 mm.	£30-40	☐
221	1969-76	Corvette Stingray	Metallic Bronze body, Silver or Gold spoked wheels, 113 mm.	£20-30	☐
	1976-78		Red or White body, Black bonnet, opening doors, Speedwheels	£10-15	☐
222 (23s)	1954-56	Streamlined Racing Car	Silver body with Red, Blue or Green trim, 126 mm.	£30-40	☐
222	1978-80	Hesketh 308 E	Dark Blue or Bronze, RN '2', cast-detailed or Speedwheels, 132 mm.	£15-20	☐
		promotional issue:	As previous model but in 'OLYMPUS CAMERAS' box, (Swiss)	£50-75	☐

Ref. No.	Year(s)	Model Type	Dinky Toys - continued	Market Price Range	
223	1970-75	McLaren M8A Can-Am...........	White body, Metallic Blue engine cover, cast detailed wheels, 94 mm.	£20-25	☐
	1976-78		Metallic Green body, Black engine cover, Speedwheels..	£20-25	☐
224	1970-74	Mercedes-Benz C111	White or Metallic Dark Red, cast wheels or Speedwheels, 102 mm.	£20-25	☐
225	1971-76	Lotus F1 Racing Car	Metallic Red body with racing number '7', 127 mm.	£15-20	☐
	1976-77		Lime-Green or Metallic Blue body with racing number '7'	£15-20	☐
226	1972-75	Ferrari 312 B2	Red body with racing number '5', 121 mm.	£15-20	☐
	1976-80		Bronze or Gold body, Black or White rear wing, racing number '5'.	£15-20	☐
227	1975-77	Beach Buggy	Yellow/Grey, Yellow/White, Green/Grey or Pink/Black body, 105 mm.	£15-20	☐
228	1970-72	Super Sprinter	Blue/Silver or Blue/Orange body, suspension, Speedwheels, 115 mm.	£15-20	☐
230 (23k)	1954-60	Talbot Lago Racing Car	Blue body, Yellow racing number '4', Blue diecast hubs, 103 mm.	£70-85	☐
	1960-62		Blue body, Yellow racing number '4', spun aluminium hubs	£70-85	☐
	1962-64		Blue body, RN '4', Red or Yellow plastic hubs, (boxed, see 205).	£70-85	☐
231 (23n)	1954-60	Maserati Racing Car	Red body, White flash and RN '9', Red diecast hubs, 94 mm.	£70-85	☐
	1960-62		Red body, White flash and racing number '9', spun aluminium hubs	£70-85	☐
	1962-64		Red body & plastic hubs, White flash & RN '9', (boxed, see 206)	£70-85	☐
	1962-64		Red, Yellow plastic hubs, White flash & RN '9', (boxed, see 206)	£70-95	☐
232 (23f)	1954-60	Alfa Romeo Racing Car	Red body, White racing number '8', Red diecast hubs, 100 mm.	£70-85	☐
	1960-62		Red body, White racing number '8', spun aluminium hubs	£70-85	☐
	1962-64		Red body, White RN '8', Red plastic hubs, (boxed, see 207).	£70-85	☐
233 (23g)	1954-60	Cooper Bristol Racing Car.......	Green body, White flash and RN '6', Green diecast hubs, 89 mm.	£70-85	☐
	1960-62		Green body, White flash and racing number '6', spun aluminium hubs	£70-85	☐
	1962-64		Green body & plastic hubs, White flash and RN '6', (boxed, see 208)	£70-85	☐
234 (23h)	1954-60	Ferrari Racing Car	Blue body, Yellow nose, diecast hubs & RN '5', 101 mm.	£70-85	☐
	1960-62		Blue body, Yellow nose and racing number '5', spun aluminium hubs	£70-90	☐
	1962-62		Blue body, Yellow triangle on nose, RN '5', spun hubs, boxed	£100-125	☐
	1962-64		Blue, Yellow triangle on nose, Yellow plastic hubs, (boxed, see 209)	£100-125	☐
235 (23j)	1954-60	H.W.M. Racing Car	Light Green body, Yellow RN '7', Green diecast hubs, 99 mm.	£70-85	☐
236	1956-59	Connaught Racing Car	Pale Green body, Mid-Green wheels, RN '32', White driver, 96 mm.	£60-70	☐
237	1957-60	Mercedes Benz Racing Car	White body, Red wheels or spun hubs & RN '30', Blue driver, 98 mm.	£50-60	☐
	1960-62		Cream body, Red wheels or spun hubs, RN '30', Blue driver	£50-60	☐
	1962-64		Cream body, plastic hubs, RN '30', Tan driver	£50-60	☐
238	1957-60	Jaguar 'D' type	Turquoise body, White driver, RN '4', Blue diecast wheels, 87 mm.	£50-70	☐
	1960-62		Turquoise body, White driver, RN '4', spun aluminium hubs	£50-70	☐
	1962-65		Turquoise body, White or Yellow driver, RN '4', Blue plastic hubs.........................	£50-70	☐
239	1958-60	Vanwall Racing Car	Green body, Green wheels, White driver, racing number '35', 95 mm.	£70-85	☐
	1960-62		Green body, White driver, RN '35', spun aluminium hubs	£70-85	☐
	1962-65		Green body, White or Tan driver, RN '35', Yellow plastic hubs	£70-85	☐
	1962-65		Green body, Yellow driver, RN '35', Yellow plastic hubs	£70-85	☐
240	1963-70	Cooper Racing Car	Blue/White, RN '20', spun aluminium hubs, 80 mm.	£30-35	☐
241	1963-70	Lotus Racing Car	Green body with racing number '36', suspension, spun hubs, 80 mm.	£30-35	☐
242	1963-71	Ferrari Racing Car	Red body, RN '36', suspension, opening engine cover, spun hubs, 84 mm.	£30-35	☐
243	1963-71	B.R.M. Racing Car	Green, Yellow opening engine cover, RN '7', suspension, spun hubs, 82 mm.	£30-35	☐
	1963-71		Metallic Green, Yellow opening engine cover, racing number '7'	£30-35	☐
260	1971-72	VW 'Deutsche Bundespost'	Yellow body (129 casting), German export model, 100 mm.	NGPP	☐
262	1959-60	Volkswagen 'PTT' Car	Yellow/Black (181 casting, fixed doors), 'PTT' logo, cast hubs, Swiss export model, 90 mm.	£500-750	☐
	1960-62		Yellow/Black (181 casting, fixed doors), 'PTT' logo, spun aluminium hubs, Swiss export model, 90 mm.	£500-750	☐
	1962-66		Yellow/Black, (181 casting, fixed doors), 'PTT' logo, plastic hubs, Swiss export	£500-750	☐
	1966-72	129 casting:.........	Yellow/Black, opening doors, plastic hubs, 100 mm., Swiss export	£40-50	☐
	1972-76		Yellow/Black, opening doors, Speedwheels, Swiss export	£40-50	☐
340 (27d)	1954-66	Land Rover	Green or Orange body & diecast hubs, Tan driver, spare wheel, 92 mm.	£50-60	☐
	1966-69		Green or Orange body, Blue plastic driver and hubs, spare wheel.	£50-60	☐
	1969-71		Red body, Blue plastic driver & hubs, spare wheel	£40-50	☐
			Red body, Blue plastic driver, Green plastic hubs	£70-80	☐
341 (27m)	1954-66	Land-Rover Trailer	Orange body (Red wheels), or Green body (Green wheels)	£20-30	☐
342	1966-72	Austin Mini-Moke....................	Metallic Green, Grey canopy with 1 or 2 windows, bubble-packed or boxed, 73 mm.	£25-40	☐
	1972-75		Metallic Greenish-Blue, 1 canopy window, Speedwheels, bubble-packed or boxed, 76 mm.	£25-30	☐
344 (27f)	1954-61	Estate Car..............................	Brown/Fawn body, rear axle pillars, 104 mm.	£60-70	☐
344	1970-72	Land Rover Pick-Up	Metallic Blue or Metallic Red body, bubble-packed, 108 mm.	£15-20	☐
	1973-78		Metallic Blue or Metallic Red body, Speedwheels, bubble-packed...........................	£15-20	☐
370	1969-76	Dragster	Yellow/Red, driver, 'FIREBALL', 'INCH-PINCHER', starter unit, 113 mm.	£30-35	☐
405 (25y)	1954-64	Universal Jeep	Red or Green body, diecast hubs, tinplate windscreen frame, 83 mm.	£30-40	☐
	1964-67		Orange body, plastic hubs, tinplate windscreen frame	£30-40	☐
448	1963-68	Chevrolet El Camino Pick-Up with Trailers	Turquoise/White/Red Pick-up & 2 trailers, 'Acme Trailer Hire', 256 mm.	£150-230	☐
449	1961-69	Chevrolet El Camino Pick-up ...	Green/White, suspension, fingertip steering, windows, 111 mm.	£55-65	☐
			Red/Yellow, suspension, fingertip steering, windows, 111 mm.	£55-65	☐
		South African issue:..........	All-Turquoise body.	£500-750	☐
		South African issue:..........	Cream over Chocolate Brown lower body	£500-750	☐
		South African issue:..........	Turquoise over Cream lower body	£500-750	☐
475	1964-66	Model 'T' Ford.......................	Blue body, Yellow panels and wheels, driver/female passenger, 79 mm.	£40-50	☐
476	1967-69	Morris Oxford (Bullnose).........	Yellow body, Blue chassis, Fawn hood, driver, 92 mm.	£40-50	☐
516	1965-66	Mercedes Benz 230 SL	Metallic Red, Cream roof, windows, 85 mm. (French issue)...................................	£65-85	☐
675 (170m)	1954-?	Ford US Army Staff Car	Military Green, US issue	£175-250	☐

Dinky Cars made by Meccano, Paris, France and sold in Britain

Ref. No.	Year(s)	Model Type	Description	Price	
518	1962-65	Renault 4L	Brown body, suspension, steering, windows, 85 mm. (French issue)	**£65-85**	☐
524	1965-67	Panhard 24c	Dark Metallic Grey body, (French issue)	**£65-85**	☐
530	1965-66	Citroën DS19	Light Green body, Light Grey roof. (French issue)	**£65-85**	☐
535	1962-65	2cv Citroën	Blue body, suspension, steering, windows, 88 mm. (French issue)	**£65-85**	☐
550	1962-65	Chrysler Saratoga	Pink/White body, windows, suspension, steering, 129 mm. (French issue)	**£65-75**	☐
553	1962-65	Peugeot 404	Green or White, suspension, steering, windows, 102 mm. (French issue)	**£65-75**	☐
555	1962-65	Ford Thunderbird Convertible	White, driver, windscreen, suspension, steering, 121 mm. (French issue)	**£65-75**	☐

Dinky Toys Cars made in Hong Kong

Ref. No.	Year(s)	Model Type	Description	Price	
57/001	1965-67	Buick Riviera	Blue body with White roof and interior, opening bonnet and tailgate	**£80-100**	☐
57/002	1965-67	Chevrolet Corvair Monza	Red body, Black roof, opening bonnet and rear engine cover, 107 mm.	**£100-125**	☐
57/003	1965-67	Chevrolet Impala	Yellow body with White roof, opening bonnet and tailgate	**£60-70**	☐
		US/Canadian issue:	Yellow body with Yellow roof	**£100-125**	☐
57/004	1965-67	Oldsmobile Dynamic '88'	Blue body. This model replaced Dodge Polara shown in the catalogue	**£100-125**	☐
57/005	1965-67	Ford Thunderbird	Blue body with White roof	**£100-125**	☐
57/006	1965-67	Nash Rambler Classic	Green body with Silver roof trim, opening bonnet, tailgate and windows	**£80-100**	☐
180	1979-80	Rover 3500	White body with opening doors, plastic wheels, 131 mm.	**£10-15**	☐
219	1978-79	'Big Cat' Jaguar	White/Red, Black 'Big Cat' decal. (This model was not boxed)	**£15-25**	☐

Dinky 1:25 Scale Models

Ref. No.	Year(s)	Model Type	Description	Price	
2162	1973-76	Ford Capri	Metallic Blue, Black roof, suspension, windows, number plates, 175 mm.	**£65-75**	☐
2214	1974-76	Ford Capri Rally Car	Red, Black roof & bonnet, RN '12', suspension, windows, 175 mm.	**£65-75**	☐
2253	1974-76	Ford Capri Police Car	White/Orange, 'POLICE', Blue light, suspension, windows, 175 mm.	**£65-75**	☐

MATCHBOX (Matchbox Miniatures) Dinky Toys

Matchbox bought the Dinky Toys trademark in early 1987. Prior to the launch of 'The Dinky Collection' in 1988, the following Matchbox miniatures were released in blister packs which carried the 'Dinky Toys' logo:

MB17 VW Golf, MB44 Citroën Cv15, MB51 Firebird SE, MB60 Toyota Supra, MB69 '84 Corvette, MB74 Fiat Abarth. The models have 'Matchbox' bases.

Matchbox Dinky - 'The Collection'

Manufactured by Matchbox International Ltd in Macau

Ref. No.	Year(s)	Model Type	Description	Price	
DY 1	1988	1967 Jaguar 'E' type (soft-top)	British Racing Green, 'J 916', White-wall tyres	**£12-15**	☐
DY 1 B	1991		Yellow body, Black hood	**£8-12**	☐
	1992	pewter model:	Unpainted pewter model on wooden plinth	**£30-35**	☐
DY 2	1989	1957 Chevrolet Bel Air	Red body, White roof, Silver stripe, 'ASA 174', White-wall tyres	**NRP**	☐
			Dark Red variant reported but not seen (Australian issue)	**NGPP**	☐
DY 3	1989	1965 MGB GT	Blue body, Black roof, 'PGY 323C'	**£10-14**	☐
	1992		Orange body, Black roof	**£7-10**	☐
DY 4	1989	1950 Ford E83W 10 cwt Van	'HEINZ 57 VARIETIES', Yellow body, Black roof, '618 APH'	**£10-14**	☐
	1990		'RADIO TIMES', Green body, Gold logo 'Journal of the BBC'	**£8-10**	☐
DY 5	1989	1949 Ford V8 Pilot	Black body, Silver trim, 'HOY 712'	**£12-15**	☐
DY 5 B	1992		Silver body	**£12-15**	☐
DY 5 C	1993		Tan body	**£12-15**	☐
DY 6	1989	1951 Volkswagen Saloon	Light Blue body, Grey roof, '111A-46003'	**£12-15**	☐
DY 6 B	1991		Black body with Grey roof	**£12-15**	☐
DY 6 C	1992		Red body with Grey roof	**£8-12**	☐
DY 7	1989	1959 Cadillac Coupé De Ville	Metallic Deep Red body, White roof	**£8-12**	☐
DY 7 B	1991		Pink body	**£7-10**	☐
DY 8	1989	1948 Commer 8 cwt Van	'SHARPS TOFFEES', Red body	**£10-14**	☐
DY 8 B	1991		'HIS MASTERS VOICE', Dark Blue body	**£8-12**	☐
	1991	Code 2 model:	'MOTORFAIR '91', sold by Matchbox at that event	**£30-35**	☐
DY 9	1989	1949 Land Rover	Green body, Cream canopy, 'EOP 999'	**£8-12**	☐
DY 9 B	1991	'AA' Land Rover	Yellow/Black body, 'AA' emblem	**£7-10**	☐
DY 10	1989	Mercedes Konferenz Coach	Cream/Dark Blue, 'REISEBURO RUOFF', 'STUTTGART', special box, (1:50)	**£18-22**	☐
DY 11	1990	Tucker Torpedo	Metallic Red body, Silver trim, White-wall tyres	**£8-12**	☐
DY 12	1990	1955 Mercedes 300 SL	Off-White body, Silver trim	**£8-12**	☐

Ref. No.	Year(s)	Model Type	Dinky Toys - continued	Market Price Range	
DY 12 B	1992		Black body, Silver trim	**£7-10**	☐
DY 13	1990	Bentley Continental	Metallic Light Blue, Silver trim	**£10-14**	☐
DY 13 B	1992		Dark Blue, Silver trim	**£7-10**	☐
DY 14	1990	Delahaye 145	Dark Metallic Blue body	**£8-12**	☐
DY 14B	1992		Dark Red body	**£7-10**	☐
DY 15	1989	1953 Austin A40 Van	*'BROOKE BOND TEA'*, Bright Red, (Brooke Bond promotional in plain box)	**£7-10**	☐
DY 15	1990	1953 Austin A40 Van	*'BROOKE BOND TEA'*, Bright Red, (standard issue, normal box)	**£7-10**	☐
DY 15 B	1991		*'DINKY TOYS'*, Cream/Yellow body	**£8-12**	☐
DY 16	1990	1967 Ford Mustang Fastback ...	Metallic Green body	**£8-12**	☐
DY 17	1990	1939 Triumph Dolomite...........	Red body & hubs, Black hood, opening dicky-seat, special box	**£8-12**	☐
DY 18	1988	1967 Jaguar 'E' type (open)	Red body	**£7-10**	☐
DY 19	1990	1973 MGB GT V8	Maroon body, Brown seats, spoked wheels	**£7-10**	☐
DY 20	1991	1955 Triumph TR4....................	White body, Black seats, Silver trim..	**£7-10**	☐
DY 21	1991	1964 Mini Cooper S	Off-White body, Black roof, Silver trim	**£7-10**	☐
	1991	Code 2 model:........	'CLASSIC CAR SHOW 1991', sold by Matchbox at that event	**£40-50**	☐
DY 22	1991	1952 Citroën 15cv...................	Black body, Silver trim	**£8-12**	☐
DY 22 B	1992		Off-White body, Silver trim	**£7-10**	☐
DY 23	1991	Chevrolet Corvette	Red body, White side panel	**£8-12**	☐
DY 23 B	1993		Bronze body, Cream side panel	**£7-10**	☐
DY 24	1991	1973 Ferrari 246 Dino...............	Red body	**£7-10**	☐
DY 25	1991	1958 Porsche 356a	Silver body	**£7-10**	☐
DY 26	1991	Studebaker Hawk	Gold body, White side flash, Silver trim	**£7-10**	☐
DY 27	1991	Chevrolet Bel Air Open Top.....	Light Blue body, White and Blue seats	**£7-10**	☐
			Light Blue body, White and Brown seats	**£60-80**	☐
DY 28	1992	1969 Triumph Stag...................	White body	**£12-15**	☐
	1992	Code 2 model:	'Classic Car Show 1992', sold by Matchbox at that event	**£20-30**	☐
DY 29	1992	1953 Buick Skylark..................	Light Blue body	**£7-10**	☐
DY 30	1992	Austin Healey 100	British Racing Green body	**£7-10**	☐
DY 31	1993	1955 Ford Thunderbird.............	Red body	**£7-10**	☐
DY 32	1993	1957 Citroën 2cv......................	Grey body	**£7-10**	☐
	1991	Sports Cars Set 1.....................	Three models on wooden plinth, colours unique to set: DY 25, (Red body), DY 12 (Silver body), DY 24 (Metallic Blue body)	**£25-30**	☐
	1992	Sports Cars Set 2.....................	Three models on wooden plinth, colours unique to set: DY 20, (Red body), DY 18 (Cream body), DY 30 (Metallic Light Blue)	**£20-25**	☐
DY 921	1992	Jaguar	Cast in pewter, unpainted, special box	**£25-30**	☐
		other pewter issues:	three other models were proposed for the 'pewter' series but were not issued.............	**NPP**	☐

'Mini-Dinky' models

These were issued in 1968 and were made in Hong Kong and Holland. Each model was sold with a free red plastic garage. All the cars and commercial vehicles (the latter never seen), have special features. The models listed are illustrated in the 1968 US issued 3-page fold-out leaflet which advertised them as 'Swinging Value' at 59 cents and 69 cents. The Market Price Range is £30-40 each. (NS = not seen).

10 Ford Corsair, Yellow
11 Jaguar 'E' type, Red
12 Corvette Stingray, Blue
13 Ferrari 250 LM, Red
14 Chevrolet Chevy II, Yellow
15 Rolls-Royce Silver Shadow, Blue
16 Ford Mustang, White
17 Aston Martin DB6, Silver
18 Mercedes Benz 230 SL, Silver/Black
19 MGB, Blue
20 Cadillac Coupé De Ville, Silver
21 Fiat 2300 Station Wagon, Blue
22 Oldsmobile Toronado, Pale Blue
23 Rover 2000, Blue
24 Ferrari Superfast, Red

25 Ford Zephyr 6, Silver
26 Mercedes 250 SE, White
27 Buick Riviera, Blue
28 Ferrari F 1, Red, '7'
29 Ford F 1, White
30 Volvo 1800s, Blue
31 Volkswagen 1600TC, Blue
32 Vauxhall Cresta, Silver
33 Jaguar, Red
61 Lotus Racing Car, Green, '4'
94 International Bulldozer, Yellow, NS
95 International Skid Shovel, Yellow, NS
96 Payloader Shovel, White, NS
97 Euclid R40, Yellow, NS
98 Michigan Scraper, Yellow, NS
99 Caterpillar Grader, Orange, NS

Models 94-99 Construction Vehicles are illustrated in a US issued 'Mini-Dinky' fold-out launch leaflet '1'.

Case .... 'Mini-Dinky' 12-Car Collector Case, with models .... **£400-600** ☐

Dinky Toys - Commercial Vehicles and Vans
Identification of casting types

LORRIES (25 series):

Type 1 - (9134-36), 'open' chassis (usually black), tinplate radiator, no headlamps, no front bumper, 'smooth' cast hubs (various colours) with white tyres. 105 mm.

Type 2 - (1936-40), 'open' chassis (usually black), diecast radiator with headlamps but no front bumper, 'smooth' cast hubs (various colours) ,with white tyres. 105 mm.

Type 3 - (1946-47), 'closed' chassis (only in black), diecast radiator with headlamps but no front bumper,'smooth' or 'ridged' wheel hubs (only in black) ,with black tyres. 105 mm.

Type 4 - (1947-50), detailed chassis (only in black), diecast radiator with headlamps and with bumper, 'ridged' wheel hubs (only in black), with black tyres. 110 mm.

Dinky Toys 25 series Lorry types 1934-1950

1st type 1934-1936 Tinplate radiator without headlights No bumpers Open chassis	2nd type 1936-1940 Diecast radiator with headlights No bumpers Open chassis	3rd type 1946-1947 Diecast radiator with headlights No bumpers Plain (closed) chassis	4th type 1947-1950 Diecast radiator with headlights and front bumper Moulded chassis
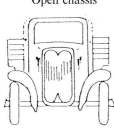		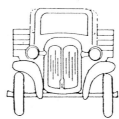	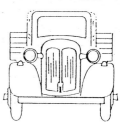

Dinky Toys 25 series chassis types 1934-1950

1934-1936 Open Chassis	1936-1940 Open Chassis	1946-1947 Plain Chassis	1947-50 Moulded Chassis
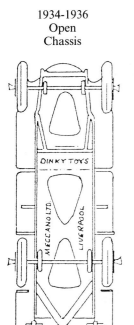	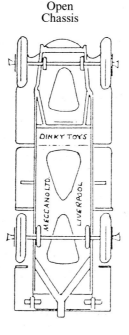	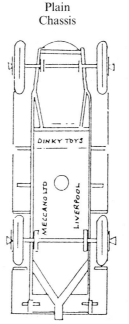	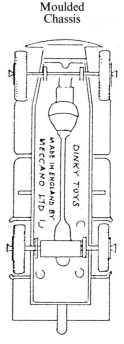

Dinky Toys - Commercial Vehicles and Vans
Identification of Casting Types (continued)

Dinky Toys Heavy Commercials cab types 1947-1964

1947-1952
Foden 'DG' (1st type) cab
Exposed radiator
Colour flashes on sides

1952-1964
Foden 'FG' (2nd type) cab
Radiator behind grille
No colour flashes on sides

1947-1956
Guy 1st type cab
Exposed radiator
No gusset at either
side of number plate

1956-1958
Guy 2nd type cab
Exposed radiator
With gusset at each
side of number plate

1958-1964
Guy 'Warrior' cab
Radiator behind grille
Restyled front with
sidelights in wings

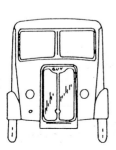 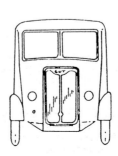 

Identification of Casting Types

Dinky Toys 28 and 280 series Van castings 1933-1954

Type 1 - **(1933-35)**, two-piece lead body with *'HORNBY SERIES'* (early issues) or *'DINKY TOYS'* cast-in under cab roof, tinplate radiator, no headlamps, thinly-painted coloured solid wheel/tyre castings (some silver plated), 84 mm. Note that coloured wheels tend to attract a premium to the price of the model.

Type 2 - **(1935-39)**, one-piece diecast body, cast-in shield-shaped radiator, rear wheel spats, cast 'smooth' wheel hubs with rubber tyres (usually white), 81 mm. All carried advertising.

Type 3 - **(1939-41)**, one-piece diecast body with rear wheel spats, cast 'smooth' wheel hubs (various colours) with black tyres, open rear windows, 83 mm. All carried advertising.

Type 3 - **(1947-54)**, one-piece diecast body with rear wheel spats, cast 'ridged' wheel hubs (usually black) with black tyres, filled-in rear windows, 83 mm. No advertising. Most of post-war Type 3 have a cast boss under the roof to take the loudspeakers on 34c.

1st type	2nd type	3rd type
1933-1935	1935-1939	1939-41, 1947-54
2-piece lead casting	Single diecasting	Single diecasting
Metal wheels/tyres	Metal hubs with	Metal hubs with
Tinplate radiator	white rubber tyres	rubber tyres
without headlights	Cast-in radiator	Cast-in radiator and
No bumpers	No bumpers	front bumper

 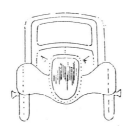 

FORD TRANSIT VANS CASTINGS:

Type 1 - **(1966-74)**, has sliding driver's door, opening hinged side door, and twin rear doors.
Type 2 - **(1974-78)**, non-sliding driver's door, one side-hinged door, one top-hinged rear door.
Type 3 - **(1978-80)**, as Type 2 but with a slightly longer bonnet (18 mm.)

For other models derived from commercial vehicles see these sections:
Fire, Police and Ambulance vehicles, Military vehicles, Farm and Garden, Buses, Taxis and Trams, Dinky Action Kits, Dinky Toys issued by Airfix Products, Novelty, Space and Film/TV-related models, 'Dinky Dublo' models, Road-making Equipment, Gift Sets.

Dinky Toys
Commercial Vehicles and Vans

Ref. No.	Year(s)	Model Type	Model Features and Size	Market Price Range	
14a (400)	1948-54	B.E.V. Truck	Mid-Blue body with Blue wheels, Fawn driver, hook, 85 mm.	£30-35	☐
			Grey body (with Blue, Grey or Red wheels), Fawn driver, hook	£30-35	☐
14c (401)	1949-54	Coventry Climax Fork Lift	Orange, Brown or Dark Red body, Green forks, Fawn driver, 108 mm.	£25-30	☐
14z	1938-40	Three-wheel Delivery Van	'Triporteur' with Green, Red, Grey, Blue or Yellow body, Black hubs, White tyres, driver is always a different colour from van, French model	NGPP	☐
22c	1933-35	Motor Truck	2-piece lead body, tinplate radiator, 'HORNBY SERIES' cast-in, 90 mm. Blue cab (Red truck body), or Red cab (Green, Blue or Cream truck body)	£300-500	☐
22c	1935-40	Motor Truck	Red, Green or Blue (diecast one-piece), body, open rear window, 84 mm.	£100-125	☐
	1946-50		Red, Green or Brown body, rear window filled-in	£60-70	☐
22d	1933-34	Delivery Van	Lead body, tinplate radiator, 'HORNBY SERIES' cast-in, 84 mm. Orange/Blue body or Blue/Yellow body, no advertising, Type 1	£400-500	☐
	1934-34		As previous models but with 'DINKY TOYS' cast-in	£400-500	☐
22d (28n)	1934-35	Delivery Van 'MECCANO'	Yellow body (lead), 'Meccano Engineering For Boys' in Red & Black, Type 1, 84 mm. 22d till April 1935, renumbered 28n	£500-600	☐
25a	1934-36	Wagon	Maroon, Green, Red or Blue body, Black chassis, Type 1	£100-125	☐
	1936-40		Maroon, Green, Red or Blue body, Black chassis, Type 2	£100-125	☐
	1936-40		Blue body with Orange chassis, Type 2	£150-200	☐
	1946-47		Grey, Green, Red, Orange or Blue body, Black chassis, Type 3	£60-70	☐
	1947-50		Grey, Green, Light Blue, Orange, Cream or Red body, Black chassis, Type 4	£60-70	☐
25b	1934-36	Covered Wagon	Blue body, Cream tilt, Black chassis, Type 1	£150-200	☐
	1936-40		Green body, Green, Cream or Yellow tilt, Black chassis, Type 2	£100-150	☐
			Cream/Yellow or Fawn/Cream, Black chassis, Type 2	£100-150	☐
			Orange body, Cream tilt, Green chassis, Type 2	£150-200	☐
	1936-40	Covered Wagon 'CARTER PATERSON'	Green body, Green tilt, Black chassis, Type 2, 'Express Carriers London'	£400-500	☐
		'MECCANO'	Green body, Cream tilt, Black chassis, Type 2, 'Engineering For Boys'	£250-300	☐
		'HORNBY TRAINS'	Fawn body, Cream tilt, Black chassis, Gold lettering, Type 2	£250-300	☐
	1946-47	Covered Wagon	Green/Green, Grey/Light or Dark Grey, Blue/Grey, Black chassis, Type 3	£70-100	☐
	1947-50		Green/Green, Grey/Grey, Cream/Red, Yellow/Blue, Black chassis, Type 4	£70-100	☐
25c	1934-36	Flat Truck	Dark Blue body, Black chassis, Type 1	£150-200	☐
	1936-40		Green or Stone body, Black chassis, Type 2	£100-125	☐
	1946-47		Green, Blue or Grey body, Black chassis, Type 3	£60-70	☐
	1947-48		Green, Blue, Orange or Stone body, Type 4	£60-70	☐
25d	1934-35	Petrol Tank Wagon	Same chassis casting as other 25 series lorries but with hook removed.		
		(plain)	Red body, no advertising, Black chassis, Type 1	£200-250	☐
		'SHELL BP'	Red body, Black chassis, Type 1	£250-300	☐
		'ESSO'	Green body, Black chassis, Type 1	£250-300	☐
		'POWER'	Green body, Black chassis, Type 1	£250-300	☐
		'PRATTS'	Green body, Black chassis, Type 1	£250-300	☐
	1936-46	'PETROL'	Red body, Black chassis, Black or White lettering, Type 2	£150-200	☐
		'SHELL BP'	Red body, Black chassis, Type 2	£250-300	☐
		'MOBILOIL'	Red body, Black chassis, Type 2	£250-300	☐
		'TEXACO'	Red body, Black chassis, Type 2	£250-300	☐
		'PETROL'	Green body, Black chassis, Type 2	£250-300	☐
		'ESSO'	Green body, Black chassis, Black or Blue wheels, Gold lettering, Type 2	£250-300	☐
		'POWER'	Green body, Black chassis, Type 2	£250-300	☐
		'CASTROL'	Green body, Black chassis, Black or Blue wheels, Red lettering, Type 2	£250-300	☐
		'REDLINE GLICO'	Blue body, Black chassis, Red panel, Gold lettering, Type 2	£250-300	☐
		'POOL'	Grey body, Black chassis, Black wheels, Black lettering, Type 2	£250-300	☐
	1946-47	'POOL'	Grey body, Black chassis, Black wheels, Type 2	£225-275	☐
	1946-47	'PETROL'	Red, Orange or Green body, Black chassis, Type 3	£100-150	☐
	1948-50	'PETROL'	Red, Orange, Light Green or Mid-Green body, Black chassis, Type 4	£70-100	☐
	1948 ?	'PETROL'	Yellow body, Black chassis, Type 4	£200-300	☐
25e	1934-35	Tipping Wagon	Maroon/Yellow body, Black chassis, Type 1	£150-200	☐
	1936-40		Maroon/Yellow, Brown/Turquoise or Fawn/Fawn body, Black chassis, Type 2	£100-125	☐
	1946-47		Grey, Stone, Green or Yellow body, Black chassis, Type 3	£80-120	☐
	1947-50		Grey, Stone or Brown body, Black chassis, Type 4	£60-70	☐
	1948-50		Blue/Pink body, Black chassis, Type 4	£60-70	☐
25f	1934-35	Market Gardeners Lorry	Green body, Black chassis, Type 1	£150-200	☐
	1936-40		Green or Yellow body, Black chassis, Type 2	£100-125	☐
			Green body, Yellow chassis, Type 2	£150-200	☐
	1946-47		Green or Yellow body, Black chassis, Type 3	£100-120	☐
	1947-50		Green, Yellow, Red or Orange body, Type 4	£70-100	☐

Ref. No.	Year(s)	Model Type	Dinky Toys - continued	Market Price Range
25g	1935-40	Trailer	Dark Blue or Green body with cast-in hook, tinplate drawbar, 69 mm........................	£20-25
	1946-47		Green, Stone, Pale Blue or Orange body, cast-in hook, tinplate drawbar	£15-20
	1947-48		Green, Stone, Pale Blue or Orange body, cast-in hook, wire drawbar........................	£15-20
	1948-49		Green, Stone, Pale Blue or Orange body, tinplate hook, wire drawbar	£15-20
25g (429)	1950-54		Green or Red body with tinplate hook and wire drawbar	£15-20
25m (410)	1948-54	Bedford Tipper Truck	Green cab and body, Green wheels, crank-handle operates tipper, 100 mm.................	£100-130
			Green cab and truck body, Black wheels	£80-90
			Orange cab and truck body, Green wheels	£100-130
			Orange cab and truck body, Black wheels	£80-90
			Cream cab and truck body, Red wheels	£300-400
			Yellow cab, Royal Blue truck body, Yellow wheels	£250-350
			Red cab, Cream truck body, Red wheels	£80-90
25r (420)	1948-54	Forward Control Lorry............	Red, Green, Grey, Cream, Light Blue or Orange body, Black wheels, 107 mm.	£60-70
			Cream body, Blue wheels, 107 mm.	£90-120
25s	1937-40	Six-wheeled Wagon	Brown body, no tilt, holes in seat (but no figures), 101 mm......................................	£75-95
	1946-48		Brown (various shades), Green or Dark Blue body, Grey or Light Blue tilt, with or without holes for figures (but no figures)	£60-75
25t	1946-47	Flat Truck & Trailer	(25c Flat Truck (Type 3), and matching 25g Trailer), Green, Blue, Orange or Stone..	£140-160
	1947-50		(25c Flat Truck (Type 4), and matching 25g Trailer), Green or Orange......................	£120-140
25v (252)	1948-54	Bedford Refuse Wagon	Fawn body, Green opening hatches and rear door, 106 mm.....................................	£80-90
25w (411)	1949-54	Bedford Truck	Green cab and truck body, Green wheels, 100 mm..	£80-90
			Dark Green cab, Light Green truck body, Light Green wheels	NGPP
25x (430)	1949-54	Commer Breakdown Lorry	'DINKY SERVICE', operable crane, 123 mm.	
			Dark Grey cab with Ocean Blue back, (packed in Orange box)	£100-120
			Dark Grey cab with Royal Blue back, (in Orange box)...	£100-120
			Dark Brown cab with Mid or Dark Green back, (in Orange box)	£100-120
			Mid Tan cab with Mid or Dark Green back, (in striped box)..	£100-120

28 series DELIVERY VANS

Note that coloured wheels on 1st type vans tend to attract a price premium.

28a		'HORNBY TRAINS'	Yellow body, 'Hornby Trains British & Guaranteed' in Gold	
	1934-35		Type 1, 84 mm.	£500-600
	1935-36		Type 2, 81 mm.	£250-350
28a		'GOLDEN SHRED'	Cream body, 'Golden Shred Marmalade' on right hand side, 'Silver Shred Marmalade' on left hand side	
	1936-39		Type 2, 81 mm.	£250-350
	1939-41		Type 3, 83 mm.	£200-300
28b		'PICKFORDS'	Dark Blue, 'Pickfords Removals & Storage, Over 100 Branches' in Gold	
	1934-35		Type 1, 84 mm.	£500-600
	1935-35		Type 2, 81 mm.	£300-400
28b		'SECCOTINE'	Blue body, 'Seccotine Sticks Everything' in Gold	
	1935-39		Type 2, 81 mm.	£300-400
	1939-41		Type 3, 83 mm.	£200-300
28c		'MANCHESTER GUARDIAN'	'The Manchester Guardian' in Gold	
	1934-35		Black/Red body, Type 1, 84 mm.	£500-600
	1935-39		Red body, Type 2, 81 mm.	£300-400
	1939-41		Red body, Type 3, 83 mm.	£200-300
28d		'OXO'	Blue body, 'Beef In Brief' and 'Beef At Its Best' in Gold	
	1934-35		Type 1, 84 mm.	£500-600
	1935-39		Type 2, 81 mm.	£300-400
	1939-41		Type 3, 83 mm.	£200-300
28e		'ENSIGN LUKOS'...........	Orange body, 'Ensign Cameras' and 'Ensign Lukos Films' in Gold	
	1934-35		Type 1, 84 mm.	£500-600
28e		'FIRESTONE'	'Firestone Tyres' in Gold	
	1934-35		White body, Type 1, 84 mm.	£500-600
	1935-39		Blue or White body, Type 2, 81 mm.	£300-400
	1939-41		Blue or White body, Type 3, 83 mm.	£200-300
28f		'PALETHORPES'	Pale Grey-Blue body, Pink sausage decal, 'Palethorpes Royal Cambridge' on van sides, 'Palethorpes Model Factory' on rear	
	1934-35		Type 1, 84 mm.	£500-700
	1935-38		Type 2, 81 mm.	£400-500
28f		'VIROL'	Yellow body, 'Give Your Child A Virol Constitution' in Black	
	1938-39		Type 2, 81 mm.	£250-350
	1939-41		Type 3, 83 mm.	£200-300
28g		'KODAK'...........................	Yellow body, 'Use Kodak Film To Be Sure' in Red	
	1934-35		Type 1, 84 mm.	£500-600
	1935-39		Type 2, 81 mm.	£300-400
	1939-41		Type 3, 83 mm.	£200-300
28h		'SHARPS TOFFEES'........	'Sharps Toffee, Maidstone' in Gold	
	1934-35		Black/Red body, Type 1, 84 mm.	£500-600
	1935-35		Red body, Type 2, 81 mm.	£400-500
28h		'DUNLOP'........................	Red body, 'Dunlop Tyres' in Gold	
	1935-39		Type 2, 81 mm.	£300-400
	1939-41		Type 3, 83 mm.	£200-300
28k		'MARSH & BAXTER'.....	Dark Green body, 'Marshs Sausages' and pig logo in Gold	
	1934-35		Type 1, 84 mm.	£500-600
	1935-39		Type 2, 81 mm.	£300-400
	1939-41		Type 3, 83 mm.	£200-300

Ref. No.	Year(s)	Model Type	Dinky Toys - continued	Market Price Range	
28L		'CRAWFORDS'	Red body, 'Crawfords Biscuits' in Gold		
	1934-35		Type 1, 84 mm.	£500-600	☐
28m		'CASTROL'	Green body, 'Wakefield Castrol Motor Oil' in Red		
	1934-35		Type 1, 84 mm.	£500-600	☐
	1935-39		Type 2, 81 mm.	£300-400	☐
	1939-41		Type 3, 83 mm.	£200-300	☐
28n		'MECCANO'	Yellow body, 'Meccano Engineering For Boys' in Red & Black		
	1934-35		Type 1, 84 mm. Was 22d	£500-600	☐
	1935-35		Type 2, 81 mm.	£300-400	☐
28n		'ATCO'............................	Green body, 'Atco Lawn Mowers Sales and Service' in Gold/Red		
	1935-39		Type 2, 81 mm.	£300-400	☐
	1939-41		Type 3, 83 mm.	£200-300	☐
28p		'CRAWFORDS'	Red body, 'Crawfords Biscuits' in Gold		
	1935-39		Type 2, 81 mm.	£300-400	☐
	1939-41		Type 3, 83 mm.	£200-300	☐
28r		'SWAN'	Black body, 'Swan Pens' and logo in Gold		
	1936-39		Type 2, 81 mm.	£300-400	☐
	1939-41		Type 3, 83 mm.	£200-300	☐
28s		'FRYS'	Brown or Cream body, 'Frys Chocolate' in Gold		
	1936-39		Type 2, 81 mm.	£300-400	☐
	1939-41		Type 3, 83 mm.	£200-300	☐
28t		'OVALTINE'	Red body, 'Drink Ovaltine For Health' in Gold/Black		
	1936-39		Type 2, 81 mm.	£300-400	☐
	1939-41		Type 3, 83 mm.	£200-300	☐
28w		'OSRAM'	Yellow body, 'Osram Lamps - a G.E.C. Product' in Gold/Black		
	1936-39		Type 2, 81 mm.	£300-400	☐
	1939-41		Type 3, 83 mm.	£200-300	☐
28x		'HOVIS'	White body, 'Hovis For Tea' in Gold/Black		
	1936-39		Type 2, 81 mm.	£300-400	☐
	1939-41		Type 3, 83 mm.	£200-300	☐
28y		'EXIDE'	Red body, 'Exide Batteries' and 'Drydex Batteries' in Gold/Black		
	1936-39		Type 2, 81 mm.	£300-400	☐
	1939-41		Type 3, 83 mm.	£200-300	☐

Further issues in this series were numbered 280a -   280f

Ref. No.	Year(s)	Model Type	Dinky Toys - continued	Market Price Range	
30e	1935-40	Breakdown Crane Lorry	Red, Yellow, Green, Brown or Grey body, Black wings, rear window, 92 mm.	£70-80	☐
			Blue body, Dark Blue wings, rear window	£100-120	☐
	1946-46		Red or Grey body, Black wings, rear window	£60-70	☐
	1947-48		Red, Grey or Green body and wings, no rear window	£40-50	☐
30j (412)	1950-54	Austin Wagon..................	Mid-Blue body with hook, Light Blue wheels, 104 mm.	£100-120	☐
			Light, Medium or Dark Maroon body, Maroon or Red wheels	£100-150	☐
			Brown body, Tan wheels	£400-500	☐
			Dark Blue body, Light Blue wheels	NGPP	☐
			Red body, Red wheels	NGPP	☐
30m (414)	1950-54	Rear Tipping Wagon..................	Maroon or Orange cab, Pale Green rear, 'Dodge' on baseplate, 100 mm.	£60-70	☐
			Blue or Dark Blue cab, Grey rear	£60-70	☐
30n (343)	1950-54	Farm Produce Wagon	Green/Yellow, Yellow/Green or Blue/Red body, hook, 104 mm.	£60-70	☐
30p	1950-54	Petrol Tanker....................	Based on a Studebaker vehicle, 112 mm.		
30p	1950-51	'PETROL'	Red or Green body, cast in aluminium	£70-80	☐
	1951-52	'PETROL'	Red or Green body, cast in mazak	£70-80	☐
30p (440)	1952-54	'MOBILGAS'....................	Red body and wheels	£100-120	☐
30pa (441)	1952-54	'CASTROL'	Green body and wheels, some cast in aluminium, most in mazak	£100-120	☐
30pb (442)	1952-54	'ESSO'	Red body and wheels, 'MOTOR OIL - ESSO - PETROL'.	£100-120	☐
30r (422)	1951-54	Fordson Thames Flat Truck	Red or Green body with hook, 112 mm.	£60-70	☐
30s (413)	1950-54	Austin Covered Wagon	Maroon body, Cream cover, Cream wheels, 104 mm.	£100-150	☐
			Dark Blue body, Light Blue cover, Light Blue wheels	£400-500	☐
			Mid-Blue body, Light Blue cover, Light Blue wheels	£100-150	☐
			Red body, Tan cover, Red wheels	£400-500	☐
30v (491)	1949-54	Electric Dairy Van 'N.C.B.'	Cream body, Red chassis, hubs and logo, 85 mm.	£75-90	☐
			Grey body, Blue chassis, hubs and logo.	£75-90	☐
30v (490)	1949-54	'EXPRESS DAIRY'	Cream body, Red chassis, hubs and logo	£75-90	☐
			Grey body, Blue chassis, hubs and logo.	£75-90	☐
30w (421)	1952-54	Electric Articulated Vehicle......	Maroon body, 'British Railways', hook, trailer uncouples, 135 mm.	£60-70	☐
31	1935-35	Holland Coachcraft Van	Red, Green, Blue or Orange, 'Registered Design', lead body, 88 mm.	£300-350	☐
	1935-36		Diecast body.	£250-300	☐
31a (450)	1951-54	Trojan 15 cwt Van 'ESSO'	Red body and wheels, 85 mm.	£110-125	☐
31b (451)	1952-54	'DUNLOP'........................	Red body and wheels, 'The Worlds Master Tyre'	£110-125	☐
31c (452)	1953-54	'CHIVERS'	Green body and wheels, 'CHIVERS JELLIES' and design	£110-125	☐
31d (453)	1953-54	'OXO'	Dark or Mid-Blue body, Blue wheels, 'Beefy OXO'. (Not boxed)	£200-250	☐
33a	1935-36	Mechanical Horse....................	Red, Green, Blue or Yellow body, 2.5 mm. trailer step, 65 mm.	£150-175	☐
	1936-40		As previous model but trailer step is 9.5 mm. long.	£125-150	☐
	1946-)		As previous model but also in Brown, Grey or Khaki	£125-150	☐
33b	1935-40	Flat Truck Trailer	Red, Green, Blue or Yellow body, no sides, 61 mm.	£45-55	☐
33c	1935-40	Open Truck Trailer	Red, Green, Blue or Yellow body, with sides, 61 mm.	£45-55	☐
33d	1935-40	Box Van Trailer....................	Green tinplate body on cast chassis, no advertising, 70 mm.	£100-125	☐
		'HORNBY TRAINS'	Dark Blue body, 'Hornby Trains British and Guaranteed' in Gold	£125-175	☐
		'HORNBY TRAINS'	Green body, 'Hornby Trains British and Guaranteed' in Gold	£125-175	☐
		'MECCANO'	Green body, 'Meccano Engineering For Boys' in Red and Black	£125-175	☐

Ref. No.	Year(s)	Model Type	Dinky Toys - continued	Market Price Range	
33e	1935-40	Dust Wagon Trailer	Blue or Yellow 33c (Open Trailer) with Blue tinplate top, 61 mm.	£45-55	☐
			Grey or Green 33c (Open Trailer) with Green or Blue tinplate top	£45-55	☐
	1946-47		Grey or Red body with Blue tinplate top	£35-45	☐
33f	1935-40	Petrol Tank Trailer....................	Green (33b) chassis/Red tank, or Red chassis/Green tank, no logo, 61 mm.	£45-55	☐
		'ESSO'	Green chassis/Red tank with 'ESSO' in Gold...	£45-55	☐
		'CASTROL'	Red chassis/Green tank, 'Wakefield Castrol'	£45-55	☐
33r	1935-40	Railway Mechanical Horse and Trailer Van	33a Mechanical Horse & 33d Box Van Trailer in railway liveries. 112 mm. These were also available separately as 33ra and 33rd (see below).		
33r		'L.N.E.R.'	Blue and Black, 'L.N.E.R. Express Parcels Traffic'	£125-175	☐
33r		'L.M.S.'	Maroon and Black, 'L.M.S. Express Parcels Traffic'...	£125-175	☐
33r		'G.W.R.'	Brown and Cream, 'G.W.R. Express Cartage Services'	£125-175	☐
33r		'S.R.'...............................	Green (Cream cab roof) and Black, 'Southern Railway'	£125-175	☐
33ra	1935-40	Mechanical Horse 'L.N.E.R.'	Blue and Black, 'L.N.E.R. 901', 65 mm.	£50-75	☐
33ra		'L.M.S.'	Maroon and Black, 'L.M.S. 2246'.	£50-75	☐
33ra		'G.W.R.'	Brown and Cream, 'G.W.R. 2742'	£50-75	☐
33ra		'S.R.'...............................	Green (Cream roof) and Black, '3016 M'	£50-75	☐
33rd		Railway Trailer 'L.N.E.R.'	Blue and Black, 'L.N.E.R. Express Parcels Traffic'	£60-80	☐
33rd		'L.M.S.'	Maroon and Black, 'L.M.S. Express Parcels Traffic'...	£60-80	☐
33rd		'G.W.R.'	Brown and Cream, 'G.W.R. Express Cartage Services'	£60-80	☐
33rd		'S.R.'...............................	Green and Black, 'Southern Railway'	£60-80	☐
33w (415)	1947-54	Mechanical Horse and Open Wagon........................	Grey, Fawn, Dark or Mid-Green, Red, Brown, Blue or Yellow cab, with Maroon, Brown, Light or Mid-Green or Cream trailer, 102 mm. overall.	£65-75	☐
34a	1935-40	'ROYAL AIR MAIL SERVICE'	Blue car body with Silver lettering and Gold crest, 83 mm.	£200-250	☐
34b	1938-47	'ROYAL MAIL' Van..............	Red body, Black bonnet/wings/roof/wheels, open rear windows, 83 mm.	£100-150	☐
	1948-51		Red body, Black bonnet/wings/roof/wheels, filled-in rear windows	£80-100	☐
	1952-52		Red body/roof/wheels, Black bonnet/front wings, filled-in rear windows	£100-125	☐
34c (392)	1948-54	Loudspeaker Van	Fawn or Blue body (280 casting) Black loudspeakers, 81 mm.	£60-70	☐
			Blue or Green body (280 casting) Silver loudspeakers.	£60-70	☐
60y	1938-40	Thompson Aircraft Tender	Red body with 'Shell Aviation Services' in Gold, Black or White solid rubber wheels, 84 mm.	£250-350	☐
151b (25s)	1937-40	6-wheel Covered Wagon...........	Gloss Green body, tinplate canopy, seat holes, spare wheel, 99 mm...........................	£60-70	☐
151b (620)	1947-54	6-wheel Covered Wagon...........	Matt-Green or Greenish-Brown body, (export only from 1950)	£60-70	☐
252 (25v)	1954-60	Bedford Refuse Wagon	Fawn body with Green tinplate shutters, no windows, 107 mm.	£80-90	☐
	1960-62		Fawn body with Green tinplate shutters, with windows	£80-90	☐
	1962-63		Lime-Green body with Black tinplate shutters, with windows	£200-300	☐
	1963-63		Orange/Grey body with Green plastic shutters, windows, diecast wheels or Red plastic wheels, Silver radiator.	£150-200	☐
			As previous model with Black radiator	£200-300	☐
260	1955-61	'ROYAL MAIL' Van..............	(Morris 'J') Red body, Black roof, Gold 'E II R' crest, 78 mm.	£80-100	☐
261	1955-61	Telephone Service Van	(Morris 'Z') Olive-Green/Black, 'POST OFFICE TELEPHONES', ladder, 73 mm.	£80-110	☐
273	1965-70	Mini Minor Van 'R.A.C.'	Blue body, White roof, Black base, 'ROAD SERVICES', 78 mm.......................................	£80-90	☐
			As previous model but with Silver baseplate and redesigned rear doors.	£65-75	☐
274	1964-73	Mini Minor Van 'A.A.'	Yellow body, White roof, 'PATROL SERVICE', original 'entwined' logo	£80-90	☐
			Yellow body, Yellow roof, 'PATROL SERVICE', original 'entwined' logo	£80-90	☐
			Yellow body, White roof, 'AA SERVICE', modern 'simple' logo	£60-70	☐
			Yellow body, Yellow roof, 'AA SERVICE', modern 'simple' logo	£60-70	☐
274	1970-70	'JOSEPH MASON PAINTS'....	(Mini Minor Van). Promotional in special Red box with advert card. Maroon body, roof sign, 'PAINTS' labels, spun wheels. 650 issued	£250-300	☐
275	1964-66	Brinks Armoured Car..............	Grey/Blue, 'Brinks Security Since 1859', 2 figures, 2 crates, plastic wheels	£90-110	☐
	1966-70		Same as previous model but no driver or crates, US packaging	£40-50	☐
			Grey body White roof, Blue base, metal wheels, assembled in USA	NGPP	☐
		Mexican issue:............	Blue body with Grey doors and Red/White/Blue crests, plastic wheels	£1000-1500	☐
280	1948-54	Delivery Van...........................	Red or Blue body, Type 3, filled-in rear windows, no advertising, 83 mm.	£50-60	☐
280	1966-68	Mobile 'MIDLAND BANK'....	White/Silver, Blue stripe, Gold crest, opening doors, figure, 124 mm.	£70-80	☐

280 series DELIVERY VANS

Delivery Vans numbered 280a - 280f (plus those shown as 280 ?) are an extension of the 28 series.

280a		'VIYELLA'	Blue body, 'Viyella for the Nursery' in White & Black		
	1937-39		Type 2, 81 mm..	£250-350	☐
	1939-41		Type 3, 83 mm..	£175-225	☐
280b		'LYONS'	Dark Blue body, 'Lyons Tea Always the Best' in Red & White		
	1937-39		Type 2, 81mm...	£250-350	☐
280b		'HARTLEYS'	Cream body, 'Hartleys is Real Jam' in Red/Green		
	1939-39		Type 2, 81 mm..	£250-350	☐
	1939-40		Type 3, 83 mm..	£175-225	☐
280c		'SHREDDED WHEAT'....	Cream body, Red stripe, 'Welwyn Garden City, Herts' in Black		
	1937-39		Type 2, 81 mm..	£250-350	☐
	1939-40		Type 3, 83 mm..	£175-225	☐
280d	1937-38	'BISTO'	Yellow body, 'Ah! Bisto' with logo, Type 2, 81 mm...	£250-350	☐
280d		'BISTO'	Yellow body, wording altered to 'Bisto' with logo		
	1938-39		Type 2, 81 mm..	£250-350	☐
	1939-40		Type 3, 83 mm..	£175-225	☐

Ref. No.	Year(s)	Model Type	Dinky Toys - continued	Market Price Range	
280e	1937-39	'ECKO'	Dark Green body, *'ECKO Radio'* in Gold, Type 2, 81 mm.	£250-350	☐
280e		'EVENING POST'	Cream body, *'Yorkshire Evening Post - The Original Buff*		
	1938-39		*Type 2, 81 mm.*	£300-350	☐
	1939-39		Type 3, 83 mm.	£200-250	☐
280f		'MACKINTOSHS'	Red body, *'Mackintosh's Toffee'* in Gold		
	1937-39		Type 2, 81 mm.	£250-350	☐
	1939-40		Type 3, 83 mm.	£175-225	☐
280 ?	1939 ?	'BENTALLS'	Green/Yellow, *'Bentalls Kingston on Thames'*, promotional, Type 2	NGPP	☐
280 ?	1939 ?	'BONNETERIE'	Dark Red, *'Maison de Bonneterie, Leverancier'*, promotional, Type 2	£1000-1250	☐
280 ?	1939 ?	'LIVERPOOL ECHO'	Promotional, Type 2, no other details available	NGPP	☐
343 (30n)	1954-64	Farm Produce Wagon	Green cab with Yellow rear, or Yellow cab with Green rear, 104 mm.	£60-70	☐
			Red cab with Blue rear	£100-125	☐
			Late issues with plastic hubs and no bonnet louvres	£70-80	☐

'CONVOY' Series (380-387).   Budget-priced models, having the same cab but with different rear body types.

380	1977-79	Skip Truck.........................	Yellow and Orange body, 112 mm.	£10-15	☐
381	1977-80	Farm Wagon	Yellow and Brown body, 110 mm.	£10-15	☐
382	1978-80	Dumper Truck	Red and Grey body, 118 mm.	£10-15	☐
383	1978-80	'N.C.L.' Truck	Yellow body, *'NATIONAL CARRIERS Ltd'*, 110 mm.	£10-15	☐
384	1977-79	Fire Rescue Wagon..........	Red body, White fire escape, 126 mm.	£10-15	☐
385	1977-79	Royal Mail Truck	Red body, 110 mm.	£10-15	☐
386	1979	Truck................................	Red body, *'AVIS'*. Catalogued but not issued	NGPP	☐
387	1979	Truck................................	Red and Blue body, *'PICKFORDS'*. Catalogued but not issued	NGPP	☐
390	1978	Customised Transit Van..........	White body, aquatic labels with diver and shark	NGPP	☐
392 (34c)	1954-?	Loudspeaker Van	Fawn or Blue body (280 casting), Black loudspeakers, 81 mm.	£60-70	☐
			Blue or Green body (280 casting), Silver loudspeakers	£60-70	☐
400 (14a)	1954-60	B.E.V. Truck	Dark Blue or Mid-Blue (Blue wheels), or Grey with Blue, Grey or Red wheels	£30-35	☐
401 (14c)	1954-64	Coventry Climax Fork Lift.......	Orange body, Green forks, Tan driver, 108 mm.	£25-30	☐
			Red body, Green forks	£300-400	☐
402	1966-69	Bedford TK Lorry..............	Red and White body, *'COCA-COLA'*, six trays of crates, 121 mm.	£125-150	☐
404	1967-79	Climax Fork Lift	Red/Yellow or Orange/Yellow body, *'CG4 Conveyancer'*, 97 mm.	£20-25	☐
406	1963-66	Commer Articulated Truck.......	Yellow/Grey, Blue plastic hubs, Supertoy, (424 without accessories), 175 mm.	£80-100	☐
407		Ford Transit Van			
	1966-69	'KENWOOD'	Blue/White, *'KENWOOD'*, Promotional, 122 mm. Type I	£50-60	☐
	1970-71	'TELEFUSION'.................	White body, *'Colour TV, Telefusion'*. A promotional never issued	NGPP	☐
	1970-75	'HERTZ'	Yellow body, *'Hertz Truck Rentals'*, Promotional, 122 mm. Type I	£50-60	☐
	1970-73	'AVIS'	Red body, *'Avis Truck Rentals'*. Kit only but not issued	NGPP	☐
408 (922)	1956-63	Big Bedford Lorry	Maroon cab, Fawn truck body, Fawn or Cream wheels, 146 mm.	£90-110	☐
			Blue cab, Yellow truck body, Yellow or Cream wheels	£200-300	☐
			Pink cab, Cream truck body, Cream wheels	£1500-2000	☐
			Blue cab, Orange truck body, Pale Yellow or Cream wheels	£250-350	☐
409 (921)	1956-63	Bedford Articulated Lorry	Yellowish-Orange body, Black wings, Black wheels, 'Dinky Toys' on base.	£80-100	☐
410 (25m)	1955-62	Bedford Tipper Truck	Red cab, Cream truck body, Red wheels, crank operates tipper, 97 mm.	£80-90	☐
			Yellow cab, Blue truck body, Yellow wheels	£90-110	☐
410		Bedford CF Van			
	1972-72	'SIMPSONS'	Red/Black, *'Simpsons'* and logos, Canadian promotional, 90 mm.	£35-45	☐
	1974	'DANISH POST'	Yellow body, *'Danish Post'* emblem, Danish promotional, 90 mm.	£35-45	☐
	1974-75	'JOHN MENZIES'	Dark Blue body with *'John Menzies'* logo, promotional, 90 mm.	£25-30	☐
	1974-74	'BELACO'.........................	Brown/Black, *'Belaco Brake and Clutch Parts'*, promotional, 90 mm.	£35-45	☐
	1975-76	'M.J. HIRE'	White body, *'M.J. Hire Service'*, promotional, 90 mm.	£25-30	☐
	1975-77	'MODELLERS WORLD'	White body, *'Modellers World'*, 90 mm. This is a Code 2 model	£25-30	☐
	1975-75	'MARLEY TILES'	Red body with *'Marley Building'* logo, 90 mm.	£25-30	☐
	1979	'COLLECTOR GAZETTE'	White body, *'Collectors Gazette'* logo, 90 mm. A Code 2 model	£25-30	☐
	1972-74	'ROYAL MAIL'.................	Red body with *'ROYAL MAIL'* and 'E II R' crest, 90 mm.	£15-20	☐
	1974-80	'ROYAL MAIL'.................	As previous model but with raised rectangle on roof	£15-20	☐
411 (25w)	1954-60	Bedford Truck	All-Green body and wheels, 104 mm.	£80-90	☐
412 (30j)	1954-60	Austin Wagon...........................	Powder Blue body, Cream or Dark Blue wheels, 104 mm.	£350-450	☐
			Lemon Yellow body, Green or Blue wheels	£350-450	☐
412	1974-80	Bedford CF Van 'AA'.............	Yellow body, *'AA SERVICE'*, headboard, plastic wheels, 90 mm.	£15-20	☐
413 (30s)	1954-60	Austin Covered Wagon	Maroon body, Cream cover, Cream wheels, 104 mm.	£100-150	☐
			Dark Blue body, Light Blue cover, Light Blue wheels	£400-500	☐
			Mid-Blue body, Light Blue cover, Light Blue wheels	£100-150	☐
			Red body, Tan cover, Red wheels	£400-500	☐
			Blue body, Cream cover, Lemon-Yellow wheels	£275-325	☐
			Red body, Grey cover, Grey wheels	£275-325	☐
414 (30m)	1954-61	'Dodge' Rear Tipping Wagon...	Red or Orange cab (with bonnet louvres), Green tipper body, 99 mm.	£60-70	☐
	1961-64		Red or Orange cab (no bonnet louvres), Green tipper body, 99 mm.	£60-70	☐
	1961-64		Blue cab, Grey tipper body.	£60-70	☐
			Royal Blue cab, Grey tipper and wheels	£125-150	☐
415 (33w)	1954-59	Mechanical Horse and Wagon..	(Models 33a + 33d), Blue horse/Cream trailer or Red horse/Brown trailer	£125-175	☐
416	1975-78	Ford Transit Van 'FORD'	Yellow body, *'1,000,000 TRANSITS'*, Type 2, promotional, 129 mm.	NGPP	☐
416	1975-78	'MOTORWAY'	Yellow body, *'Motorway Services'*, special lights, Type 2, 129 mm.	£25-35	☐
417	1978-79	'MOTORWAY'	As previous model but Type 3 casting	£20-30	☐

Ref. No.	Year(s)	Model Type	Dinky Toys - continued	Market Price Range	
417 (931)	1956-59	Leyland Comet Lorry with stake body	Blue cab/chassis, Yellow stake body, 'Dinky Toys' on base, 142 mm.	£90-110	☐
			Yellow cab/chassis, Green stake body	£90-110	☐
			Red cab/chassis, Yellow stake body, Yellow wheels	£90-110	☐
418 (932)	1956-59	Leyland Comet with Hinged Tailboard	Green cab, Orange truck body, Cream or Green wheels, DTB, 144 mm.	£90-110	☐
			Dark Blue cab, Mid-Blue truck body, Blue, Cream or Red wheels	£100-150	☐
419 (933)	1956-59	Leyland Comet Cement Lorry	Yellow body, 'Portland Blue-Circle Cement', DTB, 144 mm.	£100-125	☐
420 (25r)	1954-61	Forward Control Lorry	(Leyland) Red, Grey, Orange, Green or Blue body, hook, 107 mm.	£60-70	☐
421 (30w)	1955-59	Electric Articulated Vehicle	(Hindle-Smart), Maroon body, 'British Railways', hook, 135 mm.	£60-70	☐
422 (30r)	1954-60	Thames Flat Truck	Dark Green or Red body, windows, hook, 112 mm.	£60-70	☐
			Bright Green body and wheels	£100-130	☐
424	1963-66	Commer Convertible Articulated Vehicle	Yellow/Grey, 406 plus trailer canopy & 'stake' body fittings, 175 mm.	£130-150	☐
425	1964-69	Bedford TK Coal Wagon	Red body, 'HALL & Co.', windows, 6 coal bags, scales, 121 mm.	£100-125	☐
428 (951)	1955-64	Large Trailer	Grey body with hook, Red wheels, Black front axle mount, Supertoy, 111 mm.	£20-25	☐
	1967-71		Red body with hook, Silver wheels, Silver front axle mount, DTB	£20-25	☐
429 (25g)	1954-64	Trailer	Dark Green or Red, hook, axle pivot is part of main casting, 69 mm.	£20-25	☐
430 (25x)	1954-64	Commer Breakdown Truck	'DINKY SERVICE' logo, operable crane, 123 mm.		☐
			Light or Mid-Tan cab, Green back, (in striped box)	£100-120	☐
			Cream cab, Pale Blue back, Red wheels, (in Yellow box)	£400-500	☐
			Dark Stone cab, Ocean Blue back, Red wheels, (in Yellow box)	£600-700	☐
			Red cab, Pale Grey back, Blue or Red metal wheels, (Yellow box)	£600-700	☐
			Red cab, Pale Grey back, Blue or Red plastic wheels, (Yellow box)	£600-700	☐
431 (911)	1956-57	Guy 4 ton Lorry	Red 2nd type cab/chassis, Grey body, Red wheels, unpainted hook, DTB	£350-450	☐
			Dark Blue 2nd type cab/chassis, Light Blue body & wheels	£200-300	☐
431	1958-60	Guy Warrior 4 ton Lorry	Beige cab (no windows), Dark Green truck body, painted hook, 136 mm.	£350-450	☐
	1960-64		Beige cab (with windows), Dark Green truck body, painted hook	£350-450	☐
432 (912)	1956-57	Guy Flat Truck	Pale Blue 2nd type cab/chassis/hook, Red flatbed, Pale Blue wheels, DTB	£200-300	☐
	1956-57		Red 2nd type cab/chassis/hook, Pale Blue flatbed and wheels, DTB	£400-500	☐
432	1958-60	Guy Warrior Flat Truck	Green cab (no windows), Red flatbed, Red wheels 136 mm.	£300-400	☐
	1960-64		Green cab (with windows), Red flatbed, Red wheels	£300-400	☐
432	1976-79	Foden Tipping Lorry	White cab, Red chassis, Yellow rear body, 175 mm.	£30-35	☐
433 (913)	1956-57	Guy Flat Truck with Tailboard	Dark Green 2nd type cab/chassis/hook, Mid-Green flatbed and wheels, DTB	£200-300	☐
			Deep Blue 2nd type cab/chassis/hook, Orange body, Light Blue wheels, DTB	£200-300	☐
434	1964-66	Bedford TK Crash Truck	White body with Green flash, 'TOP RANK Motorway Services', 124 mm.	£55-65	☐
	1966-70		Red or Metallic Red cab Pale Grey back, 'AUTO SERVICES'	£55-65	☐
435	1964-66	Bedford TK Tipper	Grey cab with Red rear body, 121 mm.	£35-40	☐
	1966-68		Yellow cab with Yellow or Black roof, Silver rear body	£35-40	☐
	1968-71		White cab and roof, Silver and Blue rear body	£35-40	☐
438	1970-77	Ford D800 Tipper Truck	Red and Black body with opening doors, Yellow tipper, 132 mm.	£25-30	☐
			Red cab with opening doors, Blue tipper, Yellow wheels and tailgate	£25-30	☐
		promotional issue:	White cab, Blue back, Silver chassis, with cardboard load 'POLCARB'. Packed in plain White box with folded leaflet	£200-250	☐
439	1970-76	Ford D800 Snow Plough Tipper	Blue body, Red rear, Yellow plough blade, 194 mm.	£40-50	☐
	1976-78		Blue body, Pale Blue rear, Yellow plough blade, 194 mm.	£40-50	☐
440	1977-78	Ford D800 Tipper Truck	Red body (438 with non-opening doors), Yellow rear, 132 mm.	£30-35	☐
440 (30p)	1954-58	Petrol Tanker 'MOBILGAS'	Red body, 'MOBILGAS' in White letters with Blue borders, 112 mm.	£100-120	☐
	1958-61		Red body, 'MOBILGAS' in Blue letters on White background, 112 mm.	£100-120	☐
441 (30pa)	1954-60	Petrol Tanker 'CASTROL'	Green body, 112 mm.	£100-120	☐
442 (30pb)	1954-60	Petrol Tanker 'ESSO'	Red body, 'ESSO MOTOR OIL - PETROL', 112 mm.	£100-120	☐
442	1973-79	Land Rover Breakdown Crane	White and Red body, 'Motorway Rescue', operable winch, 121 mm.	£15-20	☐
	1974-		White/Red or All-Red body, 'FALCK', export model for Denmark	£15-20	☐
443	1957-58	Petrol Tanker 'NATIONAL'	Yellow body, 'NATIONAL BENZOLE MIXTURE', 112 mm.	£120-140	☐
448	1963-68	Chevrolet El Camino Pick-Up with Trailers	Turquoise/White/Red Pick-up & 2 trailers, 'Acme Trailer Hire', 256 mm.	£150-230	☐
449	1961-69	Chevrolet El Camino Pick-up	Green/White, suspension, fingertip steering, windows, 111 mm.	£150-230	☐
			Red/Yellow, suspension, fingertip steering, windows, 111 mm.	£55-65	☐
		South African issue:	All-Turquoise body	£500-750	☐
		South African issue:	Cream over Chocolate Brown lower body	£500-750	☐
			Turquoise over Cream lower body	£500-750	☐
449	1977-79	Johnston Road Sweeper	Yellow or Lime-Green body, (non-opening doors), 142 mm.	£30-35	☐
			All Yellow body, promotional with 'JOHNSTON' stickers, normal box	£40-50	☐
			All Yellow body, promotional with 'JOHNSTON' stickers, special box	£70-80	☐
450 (31a)	1954-57	Trojan Van 'ESSO'	Red body, White stripe, 'Esso' logo, 85 mm.	£100-125	☐
450	1965-70	Bedford TK Van 'CASTROL'	Green/White body, 'CASTROL - The Masterpiece In Oils', 143 mm.	£100-125	☐
451 (31b)	1954-57	Trojan Van 'DUNLOP'	Red body with 'Dunlop The Worlds Master Tyre', 85 mm.	£100-125	☐
451	1971-77	Johnston Road Sweeper	Orange cab (449 with opening doors), Metallic Green tank, 142 mm.	£30-35	☐
	1971-77		Metallic Green cab (449 with opening doors), Orange tank, 142 mm.	£30-35	☐
452 (31c)	1954-57	Trojan Van 'CHIVERS'	Green body with 'Chivers Jellies' and design, 85 mm.	£80-100	☐
453 (31d)	1954-54	Trojan Van 'OXO'	Blue body and hubs, White 'Beefy OXO', Silver trim, (not boxed)	£250-300	☐

Ref. No.	Year(s)	Model Type	Dinky Toys - continued	Market Price Range
454	1957-59	Trojan Van 'CYDRAX'...........	Light Green body with *'Drink Cydrax'* and design, 85 mm..	£90-110 ☐
455	1957-60	Trojan Van 'BROOKE BOND'	Red body, *'Brooke Bond Tea'* and design, 85 mm..	£90-110 ☐
		promotional issue:	As previous issue with White label on roof. The Red logo states: *'Since 1924 more than 5,700 Trojan 'Little Red Vans' supplied. Replaced on a long life basis'.* A similar label is attached to its (normal) box...	£400-600 ☐
465	1959-59	Morris 10 cwt Van 'CAPSTAN'..........................	Light Blue and Dark Blue body with cigarette design *'Have A Capstan'*...................	£150-180 ☐
470	1954-56	Austin A40 Van 'SHELL-BP' ...	Red and Green body with *'SHELL'* and *'BP'* decals, 89 mm.	£80-100 ☐
471	1955-60	Austin A40 Van 'NESTLES' ...	Red body, Yellow wheel hubs, *'Nestles'* logo, 89 mm.	£80-100 ☐
472	1956-60	Austin A40 Van 'RALEIGH' ...	Dark Green body with *'Raleigh Cycles'* decals, 89 mm.	£80-100 ☐
480	1954-56	Bedford CA Van 'KODAK'	Yellow body, *'Kodak Cameras and Films'* in Red and Black, 83 mm.	£80-100 ☐
481	1955-60	Bedford Van 'OVALTINE'.......	Blue body with *'Ovaltine'* on Cream panel, 83 mm.	£70-90 ☐
482	1956-60	Bedford Van 'DINKY TOYS'..	Cream and Light Orange body, *'Dinky Toys'* logo in Red, 83 mm.	£100-125 ☐
490 (30v)	1954-60	Electric Dairy Van.....................	*'EXPRESS DAIRY'*, Cream body with Red chassis, hubs and logo, 85 mm.	£65-75 ☐
			'EXPRESS DAIRY', Grey body with Blue chassis, hubs and logo	£65-75 ☐
491 (30v)	1954-60	Electric Dairy Van.....................	*'N.C.B.'*, Cream body with Red chassis, hubs and logo, export model...................	£65-75 ☐
			'N.C.B.', Grey body, Blue chassis, hubs and logo, export model	£65-75 ☐
491	1960	Electric Dairy Van.....................	*'JOB'S DAIRY'*, Cream/Red. 1176 made for promotional purposes.	£90-110 ☐
492 (34c)	1954-57	Loudspeaker Van.....................	Blue body, Silver loudspeakers, (280 casting, Type 3), 83 mm.	£60-70 ☐
492	1964-64	Election Mini Van.....................	White body, Red loudspeakers, *'Vote for Somebody'*, figure, 78 mm.	£60-70 ☐
501	1947-48	Foden Diesel 8-Wheel Wagon...	1st type cab (Foden DG) with flash, spare wheel, hook on some, no tank slits in chassis, no chainpost bosses, Black 'herringbone' tyres, Supertoy, 185 mm.	
			Pale Grey cab & body, Red flash & wheels, Black chassis, no hook	£600-700 ☐
			Dark Blue cab & body, Silver flash, Blue wheels, Black chassis, no hook	£600-700 ☐
			Brown cab & body, Silver flash, Brown wheels, Black chassis, no hook	£250-350 ☐
			Red cab & body, Silver flash, Red wheels, Black chassis, no hook	£2500-3000 ☐
			Grey cab & body, Red flash, chassis & wheels, small unpainted hook on some	£400-500 ☐
501	1948-52	Foden Diesel 8-Wheel Wagon...	Hook & tank-slits in chassis (introduced 1948), Black 'radial' tyres	
			Dark Blue cab/chassis, Light Blue flash/body/wheels, small unpainted hook	£1000-1200 ☐
			Red cab/chassis/wheels, Silver flash, Fawn body, unpainted hook, slits on some	£400-500 ☐
501 (901)	1952-54	Foden Diesel 8-Wheel Wagon...	2nd cab (Foden FG) no flash, large painted hook, Supertoy hubs, 188 mm.	
			Dark Blue cab/chassis, Light Blue body and wheels, Grey tyres..............................	£600-700 ☐
			Red cab/chassis, Fawn body, Red wheels, Grey tyres	£250-350 ☐
502	1947-48	Foden Flat Truck	1st type cab (Foden DG) with flash, spare wheel, hook on some, no tank slits in chassis, no chainpost bosses, Black 'herringbone' tyres, Supertoy, 185 mm.	
			Green cab & body, Silver flash, Black chassis, Green wheels, no hook	£350-450 ☐
			Pale Blue cab & body, Dark Blue flash/chassis/wheels, no hook	£650-750 ☐
502	1948-52	Foden Flat Truck	Hook & tank-slits in chassis introduced in 1948, Black 'radial' tyres	
			Blue cab/chassis, Red flash & body, Light Blue wheels, slits on some	£700-800 ☐
			Dull Orange cab/chassis, Green flash & body, Green wheels, slits on some	£600-700 ☐
502	1952-52	Foden Flat Truck	2nd cab (Foden FG) no flash, large painted hook, Supertoy hubs, 188 mm.	
			Blue cab/chassis, Red body, Pale Blue wheels, chainpost bosses	£2000-2500 ☐
502 (902)	1952-54	Foden Flat Truck	Dull Orange cab/chassis, Green body & wheels, chainpost bosses..........................	£350-450 ☐
			Yellow cab/chassis, Green body & wheels, Black or Grey tyres, bosses	£600-700 ☐
503	1947-48	Foden Flat Truck with Tailboard...................	1st type cab (Foden DG) with flash, spare wheel, hook on some, no tank slits in chassis, no chainpost bosses, Black 'herringbone' tyres, Supertoy, 185 mm.	
			Red cab & flatbed, Black flash & chassis, Red wheels, no hook	£650-750 ☐
			Pale Grey cab & flatbed, Blue flash & chassis, Blue wheels, no hook	£700-800 ☐
503	1948-52	Foden Flat Truck with Tailboard...................	Hook & tank-slits in chassis introduced in 1948, Black 'radial' tyres	
			Dark Green cab/chassis, Light Green flash/flatbed/wheels, small hook	£600-700 ☐
			Deep Blue cab/chassis, Dull Orange flatbed, Light Blue wheels, hook, slits	£600-700 ☐
503	1952-52	Foden Flat Truck with Tailboard...................	2nd cab (Foden FG) no flash, large painted hook, Supertoy hubs, 188 mm.	
			Dark Green cab/chassis, Light Green flatbed & wheels, Grey tyres, bosses	£1500-2000 ☐
503 (903)	1952-56		Dark Green cab/chassis, Orange flatbed, Light Blue wheels, chainpost bosses	£250-350 ☐
503	1952-53		Dull Orange cab/chassis, Yellow flatbed & wheels, Grey tyres, bosses	£1700-2000 ☐
503 (903)	1953-54		Dark Blue cab/chassis, Yellow body, Light Blue wheels, chainpost bosses.................	£600-700 ☐
504	1948-52	Foden 14 ton Tanker	1st type cab (Foden DG) with flash, spare wheel, tinplate tank, hook, no advertising, Black 'fine radial tread' tyres, Supertoy, 185 mm.	
			Dark Blue cab/chassis, Silver flash, Light Blue tank & wheels...............................	£250-350 ☐
			Dark Blue cab/chassis, Light Blue flash, tank and wheels	£250-350 ☐
504	1948-52		Red cab/chassis, Silver flash, Fawn tank, Red wheels	£450-550 ☐
504	1952-57	Foden 14 ton Tanker	2nd cab (Foden FG) no flash, large painted hook, Supertoy hubs, 188 mm.	
504	1952-52		Dark Blue cab/chassis, Light Blue tank and wheels, Grey tyres. In correct 2nd type picture box	£2000-3000 ☐
504	1952-53		Red cab/chassis, Fawn tank, Red wheels, Grey tyres	£450-550 ☐
504 (941)	1953-54	'MOBILGAS'......................	Red cab/chassis/tank/wheels, Red filler caps (see 941) Grey tyres............'...	£450-550 ☐
505	1952-52	Foden Flat Truck with Chains	1st type cab (Foden DG) with flash, spare wheel, hook, slits in chassis, 'dimpled' chainpost bosses, Black 'fine radial tread' tyres, Supertoy, 185 mm.	
			Green cab/chassis/flatbed, Light Green flash and wheels....................................	£1500-2000 ☐
			Maroon cab/chassis, Silver flash, Maroon flatbed and wheels...............................	£2000-2500 ☐

112

Ref. No.	Year(s)	Model Type	Dinky Toys - continued	Market Price Range	
505	1952-54	Foden Flat Truck with Chains	2nd cab (Foden FG) no flash, large painted hook, Supertoy hubs, 188 mm.		
			Green cab/chassis/flatbed, Light Green wheels, 'dimpled' chainpost bosses	£200-300	☐
			Maroon cab/chassis/flatbed/wheels, 'dimpled' chainpost bosses	£250-350	☐
505 (905)	1954-56		Green cab/chassis/body, Light Green wheels, 'rounded' chainpost bosses	£200-300	☐
			Maroon cab/chassis/body/wheels, 'rounded' chainpost bosses	£250-350	☐
511	1947-48	Guy 4 ton Lorry	1st cab casting, Supertoy, spare wheel, small unpainted hook, 129 mm.		
			Green cab, truck body and wheels, Black chassis and wings	£200-300	☐
			Brown cab, truck body and wheels, Black chassis and wings	£250-350	☐
			Grey cab, truck body and wheels, Red chassis and wings	£200-300	☐
511 (911)	1948-52	Guy 4 ton Lorry	1st cab casting, Supertoy, large painted or unpainted hook, 132 mm.		
			Red cab/chassis/wings/'ridged' wheels, Fawn truck body	£250-350	☐
			Dark Blue cab/chassis/wings, Light Blue truck body & 'ridged' wheels	£200-300	☐
	1952-54		Red cab/chassis/wings/'grooved' wheels, Fawn truck body	£250-350	☐
			Dark Blue cab/chassis/wings, Light Blue truck body & 'grooved' wheels	£200-300	☐
512	1947-48	Guy Flat Truck	1st cab casting, Supertoy, spare wheel, small unpainted hook, 129 mm.		
			Maroon cab, flatbed and wheels, Black chassis and wings	£300-400	☐
			Dark Brown cab, flatbed and wheels, Black chassis and wings	£400-500	☐
			Yellow cab and flatbed, Black chassis and wings, Red wheels	£350-450	☐
			Khaki cab and flatbed, Black chassis and wings, Green wheels	£550-650	☐
			Grey cab and flatbed, Red chassis and wings, Red wheels	£550-650	☐
			Grey cab and flatbed, Black chassis, Black wheels	£500-600	☐
			Red cab and flatbed, Black chassis, Black wheels	£700-800	☐
	1948-48		Brown cab/chassis/wings, Green flatbed, Green 'ridged' wheels	£400-500	☐
512 (912)	1948-54	Guy Flat Truck	1st cab casting, Supertoy, small or large unpainted hook, 129/132 mm.		
			Blue cab/chassis/wings, Red flatbed, Light Blue 'ridged' wheels	£200-300	☐
	1949-54		Orange cab/chassis/wings, Green flatbed, Green 'ridged' wheels	£400-500	☐
	1952-54		Blue cab/chassis/wings, Red flatbed, Light Blue 'grooved' wheels	£200-300	☐
513	1947-48	Guy Flat Truck with Tailboard	1st cab casting, Supertoy, spare wheel, small unpainted hook, 129 mm.		
			Dark Yellow cab/flatbed, Black chassis, wings and wheels	£400-500	☐
			Dark Yellow cab/flatbed, Dark Blue chassis, wings and wheels	£450-550	☐
			Grey cab and flatbed, Black chassis, wings and wheels	£300-400	☐
			Grey cab and flatbed, Dark Blue chassis, wings and wheels	£500-600	☐
513	1948-52	Guy Flat Truck with Tailboard	1st cab, 'ridged' wheels, Supertoy, small or large unpainted hook, 129/132 mm.		
			Dark Green cab/chassis/wings, Green body and wheels, small hook	£200-300	☐
			Deep Blue cab/chassis/wings, Orange body, Light Blue wheels, large hook	£250-350	☐
513 (913)	1952-54	Guy Flat Truck with Tailboard	1st cab, Supertoy, 'grooved' wheels, large unpainted hook, 132 mm.		
			Dark Green cab/chassis/wings, Green body and wheels	£200-300	☐
			Deep Blue cab/chassis/wings, Orange body, Light Blue wheels	£250-350	☐
			Yellow cab/chassis/wings, Green wheels	£1000-1200	☐
514	1950-52	Guy Van 'SLUMBERLAND'	Red 1st type cab/chassis/body and 'ridged' wheels, 2 opening rear doors, 'Slumberland Spring Interior Mattresses', spare wheel, Supertoy, 134 mm.	£250-350	☐
514	1952-52	Guy Van 'LYONS'	Dark Blue 1st type cab/body, Light Blue 'ridged' wheels, 2 opening rear doors, 'Lyons Swiss Rolls', spare wheel, Supertoy, 134 mm.	£800-1000	☐
			Same model but rear axle in cast mounts	£800-1000	☐
514	1952-52	Guy Van 'WEETABIX'	Yellow 1st type cab/body, Yellow 'ridged' wheels, 2 opening rear doors, 'More Than a Breakfast Food', spare wheel, Supertoy, 134 mm.	£1500-2000	☐
514	1952-54	Guy Van 'WEETABIX'	Yellow 1st type cab/body, Yellow 'grooved' wheels, 2 opening rear doors, 'More Than a Breakfast Food', spare wheel, Supertoy, 134 mm.	£1500-2000	☐
514 (917)	1953-54	Guy Van 'SPRATTS'	Red/Cream 1st type cab/body, Red 'grooved' wheels, 2 opening rear doors, 'Bonio Ovals & Dog Cakes', spare wheel, Supertoy, 134 mm.	£300-400	☐
521 (921)	1948-54	Bedford Articulated Lorry	Red body, Black wings, Black wheels, Supertoy, 166 mm.	£150-200	☐
			Yellow body, Black wings, Black wheels, Supertoy	£200-250	☐
			Yellowish-Orange body, Black wings, Red wheels, Supertoy	£80-100	☐
522 (922)	1952-54	Big Bedford Lorry	Maroon cab, Fawn truck body, Fawn wheels, Supertoy, 146 mm.	£90-110	☐
			Blue cab, Yellow truck body, Yellow wheels, Supertoy, 146 mm.	£200-300	☐
531 (931)	1949-54	Leyland Comet Lorry with stake body	Blue cab and chassis, Light Brown stake body, Supertoy, 144 mm.	£300-400	☐
			Blue cab and chassis, Yellow stake body, Supertoy	£90-120	☐
			Red cab and chassis, Light Brown stake body, Supertoy	£200-300	☐
			Red cab and chassis, Yellow stake body, Supertoy	£100-150	☐
532 (932)	1952-54	Leyland Comet Lorry with Hinged Tailboard	Dark Blue cab, Powder Blue truck body, Supertoy	£300-350	☐
			Red cab, Blue truck body, Blue wheels	£500-600	☐
			Dark Blue cab, Mid-Blue truck body; Blue, Cream or Red wheels	£100-150	☐
			Green cab, Red truck body, Cream wheels	£250-300	☐
			Green cab, Orange truck body, Cream or Green wheels	£90-110	☐
533 (933)	1953-54	Leyland Comet Cement Lorry	Yellow body, 'Portland Blue-Circle Cement', Supertoy, 142 mm.	£100-125	☐
551 (951)	1948-54	Trailer	Grey body, Black wheels, hook, Supertoy, 105 mm.	£20-30	☐
			Yellow body, Black wheels, hook, Supertoy	£100-125	☐
			Green body, Black wheels, hook, Supertoy	£100-125	☐
			Red body, Grey front chassis, protruding chromed hubs. Only in GS 339	GSP	☐
561	1962-64	Citroën Delivery Van	Light Blue body, Red/Yellow 'CIBIE' logo, sliding door, 90 mm.	£60-70	☐

Ref. No.	Year(s)	Model Type	Dinky Toys - continued	Market Price Range	
579	1961-63	Simca Glaziers Lorry.................	UK issue: Yellow and Green body, mirror/glass load, *'MIROITIER'*........................	£70-80	☐
			French issue: Grey and Green body, mirror/glass load, *'SAINT GOBAIN'*	£80-90	☐
581 (981)	1953-54	Horsebox	Maroon body (cast in aluminium) *'British Railways'*, 175 mm........................	£70-80	☐
581 (980)	1953-54	US issue:......................	Maroon, *'Hire Service'*, *'Express Horse Van'*, *'Express'*, Blue box with Orange/		
			White labels with picture of US model	£500-700	☐
581	1962-64	Berliet Flat Truck	Red and Grey body, 6 wheels plus spare, hook, 130 mm. French issue......................	£70-80	☐
582 (982)	1953-54	Pullmore Car Transporter........	*'DINKY TOYS DELIVERY SERVICE'*, aluminium trailer, 250 mm.		
			Light Blue cab & trailer, Fawn or Dark Grey decks, no windows, Supertoy..............	£60-70	☐
			Mid-Blue cab and trailer, Fawn decks, no windows, Supertoy	NGPP	☐
			Mid-Blue cab and trailer, Dark Grey decks, Dark Blue print................................	£750-100	☐
620 (151b)	1950-54	6-wheel Covered Wagon...........	Matt-Green or Greenish-Brown body, 'Export only' (to USA)	£60-70	☐
591 (991)	1952-54	A.E.C. Tanker	Red/Yellow, *'SHELL CHEMICALS LIMITED'*, Supertoy, 151 mm.	£140-175	☐
893	1962-64	Unic Pipe Line Transporter	Beige articulated body, spare wheel, 6 pipes, 215 mm. French issue	£90-110	☐
894	1962-64	Unic Boilot Car Transporter.....	Grey body, *'Dinky Toys Service Livraison'*, 325 mm. French issue	£100-120	☐
901 (501)	1954-57	Foden 8-wheel Diesel Wagon....	2nd type cab (Foden FG), Supertoy, spare wheel, large hook, 188 mm.		
			Red cab and chassis, Fawn truck body, Red wheels	£230-350	☐
902 (502)	1954-56	Foden Flat Truck	2nd type cab (Foden FG), Supertoy, spare wheel, large hook, 188 mm.		
			Yellow cab and chassis, Green flatbed body, Green wheels	£600-700	☐
	1954-57		Orange cab and chassis, Green flatbed body, Green wheels...............................	£250-350	☐
	1957-59		Dark Red cab & chassis, Green flatbed, Green wheels		
			(**NB** Red similar to colour of 919 Guy 'GOLDEN SHRED' van).............................	£2000-3000	☐
903 (503)	1954-55	Foden Flat Truck with Tailboard...................	2nd type cab (Foden FG), Supertoy, spare wheel, large hook, 188 mm.		
			Dark Blue cab and chassis, Yellow flatbed, Light Blue wheels	£600-700	☐
	1954-57		Dark Blue cab and chassis, Orange flatbed, Light Blue wheels	£250-350	☐
	1957-60		Pale Blue cab and chassis, Fawn flatbed, Pale Blue wheels.............................	£600-700	☐
905 (505)	1954-56	Foden Flat Truck with Chains..	2nd type cab (Foden FG), Supertoy, spare wheel, large hook, 188 mm.		
			Maroon, chassis and flatbed, Maroon wheels, rounded chainpost bosses	£250-350	☐
	1954-58		Green cab, chassis and flatbed, Light Green wheels, rounded post bosses	£200-300	☐
	1956-57		Maroon cab, chassis and flatbed, Maroon wheels, rounded chainpost bosses	£250-350	☐
	1957-64		Red cab and chassis, Grey flatbed, Red wheels, rounded post bosses....................	£250-350	☐
908	1962-66	Mighty Antar and Transformer	Yellow cab, Red/Grey trailer, Supertoy, plastic transformer, 335 mm.....................	£400-500	☐
911 (431)	1954-56	Guy 4 ton Lorry......................	2nd type cab casting, Supertoy, 'grooved' wheels, large hook, 132 mm.		
			Red cab and chassis, Grey truck body, Red wheels..	£300-400	☐
			Dark Blue cab and chassis, Light Blue truck body and wheels........................	£200-300	☐
912 (432)	1954-56	Guy Flat Truck	2nd type cab casting, Supertoy, 'grooved' wheels, large hook, 132 mm.		
			Orange cab and chassis, Green flatbed body and wheels................................	£400-500	☐
			Blue cab and chassis, Red flatbed body, Light Blue wheels	£150-250	☐
913 (433)	1954-54	Guy Flat Truck with Tailboard...................	2nd type cab casting, Supertoy, 'grooved' wheels, large hook, 132 mm.		
			Yellow cab and chassis, Green body, Green wheels	£1000-1200	☐
	1954-56		Dark Green cab and chassis, Green flatbed body and wheels	£200-300	☐
			Deep Blue cab and chassis, Orange flatbed body, Light Blue wheels. Usually in		
			Blue/White striped box with picture of Green lorry	£200-300	☐
			Deep Blue/Orange model in box with correct colours	£1000-1200	☐
914	1965-70	A.E.C. Articulated Lorry	Red cab, Grey trailer, Green tilt *'British Road Services'*, 210 mm......................	£110-130	☐
915	1973-74	A.E.C. with Flat Trailer...........	Orange cab, White trailer, *'Truck Hire Co Liverpool'*, 210 mm.	£45-55	☐
			Orange cab, White trailer, *'Thames Board Mills'*, bubble-packed....................	NGPP	☐
917 (514)	1954-56	Guy Van 'SPRATTS'................	Red/Cream 2nd type cab/body, Red 'grooved' wheels, 2 opening rear doors,		
			'Bonio Ovals & Dog Cakes', spare wheel, Supertoy, 134 mm.	£300-400	☐
917	1968-74	Mercedes Truck and Trailer......	Blue cab/chassis (White roof), Yellow trailers, White tilts, 397 mm...................	£45-55	☐
			Blue cab/chassis (White roof), Yellow trailers, Yellow tilts	£55-65	☐
			Dark Blue cab/chassis, Yellow trailers, Dark Blue tilts	£65-75	☐
		'MUNSTERLAND'	Dark Green cab & trailers, White tilts, Green logo, promotional........................	£100-150	☐
		'HALB UND HALB'	*'MAMPE'* & *'BOSCH'* on Blue cab, Elephant design, promotional....................	£75-100	☐
918	1955-58	Guy Van 'EVER READY'.......	Blue 2nd type cab/body, Red 'grooved' wheels, 2 opening rear doors,		
			'Ever Ready Batteries For Life', spare wheel, Supertoy 134 mm.	£200-300	☐
919	1957-58	Guy Van 'GOLDEN SHRED'	Red 2nd type cab/body, Yellow 'grooved' wheels, 2 opening rear doors,		
			'Robertsons Golden Shred', spare wheel, 134 mm.	£550-650	☐
920	1960-60	Guy Warrior Van 'HEINZ'	Red cab (no windows), Yellow body, 2 opening rear doors, spare wheel,		
			'Heinz 57 Varieties', Tomato Ketchup bottle decal, Supertoy, 137 mm.	£1500-2000	☐
921 (409)	1954-56	Bedford Articulated Vehicle......	Yellowish-Orange body, Black wings, Black wheels, Supertoy (521/921/409).............	£80-100	☐
922 (408)	1954-56	Big Bedford Lorry....................	Maroon cab, Fawn truck body, Fawn wheels, Supertoy (522/922/408)..................	£90-110	☐
			Blue cab, Yellow truck body, Yellow wheels	£200-300	☐
923	1955-58	Big Bedford Van 'HEINZ'.......	Red/Yellow, *'Heinz 57 Varieties'* + Baked Beans can, Supertoy, 146 mm.................	£300-400	☐
923	1958-59	Big Bedford Van 'HEINZ'.......	As previous model but Tomato Ketchup bottle instead of Baked Beans can.............	£1200-1500	☐
925	1965-69	Leyland Dump Truck (with Tilt Cab)	8-wheeled Supertoy with *'SAND BALLAST GRAVEL'* on tailgate, 192 mm.		
			White cab and chassis, Blue cab roof, Orange diecast tipper	£200-250	☐
			As previous model but with tinplate tipper in Orange, Pale Grey or Red..................	£200-250	☐

Ref. No.	Year(s)	Model Type	Dinky Toys - continued	Market Price Range	
930	1960-64	Bedford Pallet-Jekta Van	Orange and Yellow body, *'Dinky Toys'* & *'Meccano'*, Supertoy, 177 mm.	**£200-250**	☐
931 (417)	1954-56	Leyland Comet Lorry with stake body	Blue cab, Brown stake body, Blue or Red wheels, (531/931/417)................................	**£300-400**	☐
			Blue cab, Yellow stake body...	**£90-110**	☐
			Red cab, Yellow stake body, Yellow wheels	**£90-110**	☐
932 (418)	1954-56	Leyland Comet with Hinged Tailboard	Green cab, Orange truck body, Cream or Green wheels, Supertoy, (532/932/418).......	**£90-110**	☐
933 (419)	1954-56	Leyland Comet Cement Lorry ..	Yellow body, *'Portland Blue-Circle Cement'*, Supertoy (533/933/419)...................	**£100-125**	☐
934	1956-64	Leyland Octopus Wagon...........	Yellow cab and chassis, Green truck body, Green band around cab (but without Yellow band above radiator), Supertoy, 194 mm....................	**£175-225**	☐
			As previous model but with Yellow band immediately above radiator......................	**£300-350**	☐
			Dark Blue cab/chassis, Yellow truck body, metal or plastic wheels..........................	**£1500-2000**	☐
935	1964-66	Leyland Octopus Flat Truck with Chains	6 chain-posts, 8 wheels, flatbed held by rivet, Supertoy, 194 mm.		
			Green cab/chassis, Pale Grey flat-bed body, Red wheels......................	**£1000-1200**	☐
			Green cab/chassis, Pale Grey flat-bed body, Grey wheels	**£1200-1400**	☐
			Blue cab/chassis, Yellow cab flash, Pale Grey flatbed and wheels..........................	**£3000-4000**	☐
936	1964-69	Leyland 8-wheel Chassis...........	Red/Silver, *'Another Leyland on Test'*, three '5-ton' weights, 197 mm.	**£70-80**	☐
940	1977-80	Mercedes-Benz Truck	White cab (fixed doors), Pale Grey cover, Red chassis, 200 mm.	**£30-40**	☐
		'HENRY JOHNSON'	Dark Green cab, Pale Grey cover, Green logo, promotional	**£250-300**	☐
941 (504)	1956-56	Foden 14 ton Tanker 'MOBILGAS'......................	Red body & wheels, Black filler caps (see 504), Black or Grey tyres, Supertoy...........	**£400-500**	☐
942	1955-57	Foden 14 ton Tanker 'REGENT'	Dark Blue cab/chassis, Red/White/Blue tank, Black tyres, Supertoy, 188 mm.	**£300-400**	☐
943	1958-64	Leyland Octopus Tanker..........	*'ESSO PETROLEUM'*, Red body & tinplate tank with waterslide transfers, metal wheels, spare wheel, hook, Supertoy, 192 mm..................	**£300-400**	☐
			As previous model but with plastic wheels..	**£300-400**	☐
			With plastic wheels, logos on self-adhesive labels	**£350-450**	☐
944	1963-70	Leyland Octopus Tanker..........	*'SHELL-BP'*, Yellow/White cab & plastic tank, Grey or White chassis, plastic wheels may be Red, Black or Grey (Red rare, add £150).....................	**£175-225**	☐
	1963-64	Leyland Octopus Tanker..........	*'CORN PRODUCTS'*, White body and plastic tank, *'Sweeteners For Industry'* in White on Black labels. Only 500 of these promotionals issued	**£1500-2000**	☐
945	1966-75	A.E.C. Fuel Tanker...................	*'ESSO PETROLEUM'*, White body, *'Tiger in Your Tank'* logo on rear, 266 mm.	**£70-80**	☐
	1975-77		As previous model but without logo at rear, bubble-packed....................................	**£60-70**	☐
	1977-77	'LUCAS OIL' Tanker	Green cab and tank, White design on labels, promotional, bubble-packed	**£70-80**	☐
948	1961-67	Tractor Trailer 'McLEAN'	Red cab, Grey trailer (uncouples), *'McLean Winston'*, Supertoy, 290 mm.	**£180-230**	☐
950	1978-79	Foden S20 Tanker 'BURMAH'..........................	Red cab, Red/White trailer (uncouples), Red or Cream wheels, 266 mm.	**£40-50**	☐
950	1978	Foden Tanker 'SHELL'	Red cab, Red/White trailer (uncouples), Cream wheels, 266 mm.	**£60-70**	☐
951 (428)	1954-56	Trailer	Grey body with hook, Red wheels, (551/951/428), 105 mm.	**£20-25**	☐
			Dark Grey body with hook, Lemon Yellow wheels....................................	**£50-70**	☐
958	1961-66	Guy Warrior Snow Plough	Yellow/Black body and plough blade, spare wheel, Supertoy, 195 mm.	**£150-200**	☐
			Yellow/Black body, Silver plough blade..	**£150-200**	☐
			Silver blade version in box with picture showing Silver blade......................	**£250-300**	☐
966	1960-64	Marrell Multi-Bucket Unit........	Pale Yellow body, Grey skip, Black wheels, 115 mm.	**£100-150**	☐
967	1959-64	BBC TV Control Room	Dark Green, *'BBC Television Service'*, Green windows, Supertoy, 149 mm.	**£100-125**	☐
968	1959-64	BBC TV Roving-Eye Vehicle	Dark Green body, BBC crest, camera, windows, Supertoy, 110 mm.	**£100-125**	☐
969	1959-64	BBC TV Extending Mast	Dark Green body, BBC crest, dish aerial, mast, windows, Supertoy, 195 mm.	**£100-125**	☐
974	1968-75	A.E.C. Hoynor Transporter......	Blue/Yellow/Orange body, *'Silcock & Colling Ltd'*, 322 mm.	**£60-70**	☐
977	1960-64	Servicing Platform Vehicle	Red and Cream body, operable platform, spare wheel, 197 mm.	**£150-200**	☐
978	1964-80	Bedford TK 'Refuse Wagon'	Diecast cab, plastic tipping body, 2 plastic bins, 152 mm.		
			Green cab, Grey tipping body	**£50-60**	☐
			Metallic Green cab, Grey tipping body...............................	**£35-45**	☐
	1978-80	Bedford TK 'Refuse Wagon'	Lime-Green cab, Black or Brown chassis..................................	**£35-40**	☐
			Yellow cab with Brown chassis..	**£35-40**	☐
979	1961-64	Racehorse Transport	Grey/Yellow, 2 horses, *'Newmarket Racehorse Transport Service Ltd'*, Supertoy.......	**£200-250**	☐
980 (581)	1954-60	Horsebox (US issue).................	Maroon body (cast in aluminium), *'Hire Service'*, *'Express Horse Van'*, *'Express'*.		
			In Blue/White striped box with picture of model	**£400-500**	☐
981 (581)	1954-60	Horsebox	Maroon body (cast in aluminium), *'British Railways'*, 175 mm.	**£70-80**	☐
982 (582)	1954-60	Pullmore Car Transporter.........	Pale Blue cab & trailer, Fawn decks, no windows, no additional loading ramp, *'Dinky Toys Delivery Service'*, 250 mm. Blue/White striped box	**£60-70**	☐
	1961-64	1st variation:	Mid-Blue cab (without windows), Pale Blue trailer and decks, supplied with Loading Ramp 794/994. Blue/White striped box	**£70-90**	☐
		2nd variation:..............	Mid-Blue cab (with windows), Pale Blue trailer and decks, supplied with Loading Ramp 794/994. Blue/White striped box................	**£100-120**	☐
		3rd variation:	Mid-Blue cab (without windows) and trailer, Brownish-Grey decks and ramp upper surface. Box is fully covered in blue paper with simple label on one end	**NGPP**	☐
983	1958-63	Car Carrier and Trailer	Red/Grey, *'Dinky Auto Service'*, (Supertoys 984 & 985)...........................	**£150-200**	☐
984	1958-63	Car Carrier	Red/Grey body, *'Dinky Auto Service'*, Supertoy, 240 mm.	**£100-150**	☐
985	1958-63	Trailer for Car Carrier	Red/Grey body, *'Dinky Auto Service'*, Supertoy, 196 mm.	**£50-60**	☐
986	1959-61	Mighty Antar with Propeller.....	Red cab (windows on some), Grey low-loader with Bronze propeller, 295 mm.	**£300-400**	☐
987	1962-69	'ABC TV' Control Room..........	Blue/Grey/Red, *'ABC TELEVISION'*, camera/operator, Supertoy, 149 mm...........	**£120-140**	☐
988	1962-69	TV Transmitter Van 'ABC-TV'..................................	Blue/Grey body, Red stripe, revolving aerial dish, Supertoy, 110 mm.	**£150-200**	☐
989	1963-65	Car Transporter.......................	*'AUTO TRANSPORTERS'*, Yellow/Light Grey/Blue, Supertoy, 240 mm.	**£2000-2500**	☐
991 (591)	1954-55	A.E.C. Tanker	Red/Yellow, 'SHELL CHEMICALS LIMITED', Supertoy, 150 mm........................	**£90-120**	☐
	1955-58		Red/Yellow, 'SHELL CHEMICALS', Supertoy, 150 mm...............................	**£90-120**	☐

115

Dinky Toys - Fire, Police and Ambulance vehicles

NB. Ford Transit casting types are described at the beginning of the Commercial Vehicles section.

Ref. No.	Year(s)	Model Type	Model Features and Size	Market Price Range	
24a	1934-38	Ambulance	Criss-cross chassis, open windows, unbadged radiator, 102 mm.		
			Cream body (Red chassis), Cream body (Grey chassis)	£200-250	☐
			Grey body (Dark Grey chassis), Grey body (Maroon chassis)	£250-300	☐
	1938-40		Criss-cross chassis, open windows, radiator bade, 102 mm. See 30f.		
			Cream body (Red chassis), Cream body (Grey chassis)	£200-250	☐
			Grey body (Dark Grey chassis), Grey body (Maroon chassis)	£250-300	☐
			Black body, Black chassis (thought to be for export only)	£500-750	☐
25h	1936-37	Streamlined Fire Engine	Red body, no chassis, tinplate ladder & bell, White tyres, 101 mm.	£125-150	☐
	1937-40		Red body, tinplate baseplate, ladder & bell, Black or White tyres.	£125-150	☐
25h (250)	1948-54		Red body, tinplate baseplate, ladder & bell, Black tyres.	£70-80	☐
25k	1937-39	Streamline Fire Engine	Red body, tinplate base, 6 firemen, ladder, bell, White tyres, 101 mm.	£250-350	☐
30f	1935-38	Ambulance	Grey body, Red wings & criss-cross chassis, plain radiator, open windows	£150-200	☐
	1938-40		Grey body, Black moulded chassis, radiator badge, open windows	£50-60	☐
	1946-47		Grey body, Black moulded chassis, open windows	£50-60	☐
	1947-48		Cream body, Black moulded chassis, filled-in windows	£50-60	☐
30h (253)	1950-54	Daimler Ambulance	Cream body, Red crosses and wheels, no window glazing, 96 mm.	£50-60	☐
30hm (624)	1950-54	Daimler Military Ambulance	Military-Green body, Red crosses on White backgrounds, (US issue)	£250-350	☐
123	1977	Austin Princess 'POLICE' Car	All-White, Bronze/Blue or White/Blue. (This model has not yet been seen)	NPP	☐
195	1971-78	Fire-Chief's Range Rover	Red, 'Fire Service', Blue roof light, Speedwheels, bubble-packed, 109 mm.	£30-35	☐
243	1978-79	Volvo 'POLICE' Car	White body, plastic chassis, 141 mm. (Made in Italy by Polistil)	£15-20	☐
244	1978-79	Plymouth Fury Police Car	Black/White, 'POLICE', warning lights, plastic chassis & wheels, 135 mm.	£15-20	☐
250 (25h)	1954-62	Fire Engine	Red/Silver body, tinplate ladder and bell, 99 mm.	£75-80	☐
250	1968-71	Police Mini Cooper S	White or Off-White, rubber tyres, boot detail on transfer, 75 mm.	£35-40	☐
	1971-73		As previous model but cast boot detail, no aerial.	£35-40	☐
	1973-75		As previous model but with Speedwheels.	£35-40	☐
251	1970-73	U.S.A. 'POLICE' Car	(Pontiac Parisienne), White/Black, beacon, siren, 2 aerials, driver, 132 mm.	£40-45	☐
252	1971-74	R.C.M.P. Police Car	(Pontiac Parisienne), Blue/White, driver, Blue light, Speedwheels, 132 mm.	£40-45	☐
253 (30h)	1954-58	Daimler Ambulance	Cream body, Red crosses and cast hubs, no window glazing, 96 mm.	£50-60	☐
	1958-60		White body, Red crosses and cast hubs, no window glazing	£60-70	☐
	1960-62		White body, Red crosses and cast hubs, with window glazing	£60-70	☐
	1962-64		White body, Red plastic hubs, with window glazing	£80-100	☐
254	1977-79	Police Range Rover	White body, 'Police', opening doors, aerial on some, Speedwheels, 109 mm.	£20-30	☐
255	1955-61	Mersey Tunnel POLICE Van	(Land Rover), Red body, 'Mersey Tunnel' and 'Police', hook, 77 mm.	£60-70	☐
255	1967-71	Ford Zodiac 'POLICE' Car	White body, driver, suspension, steering, aerial, warning lights, 114 mm.	£45-55	☐
255	1977-79	Police Mini Clubman	Blue/White body, 'POLICE', opening doors & bonnet, plastic wheels, 82 mm.	£25-30	☐
256	1960-64	Humber Hawk 'POLICE' Car	Black, no. plate 'PC 49', driver/policeman, suspension/steering, 102 mm.	£65-75	☐
257	1960-68	Canadian 'FIRE CHIEF' Car	(Nash Rambler), flashing light, suspension, windows, 102 mm.	£40-50	☐
258	1960-61	U.S.A. 'POLICE' Car	(192 DeSoto Fireflite), Black/White body, beacon, windows, 114 mm.	£60-70	☐
258	1961-62	U.S.A. 'POLICE' Car	(191 Dodge Royal Sedan), Black body, aerial, windows, 111 mm.	£60-70	☐
258	1962-66	U.S.A. 'POLICE' Car	(149 Ford Fairlane), Black/White body, Fingertip steering, 111 mm.	£40-50	☐
258	1966-68	U.S.A. 'POLICE' Car	(147 Cadillac 62), Black/White, suspension/steering, 113 mm.	£60-70	☐
259	1961-69	Fire Engine (Bedford Miles)	Red body, 'FIRE BRIGADE' & crest, tinplate ladder & bell, 115 mm.	£60-70	☐
			As previous model but with 'AIRPORT FIRE TENDER' (from 276)	£60-70	☐
261	1967-77	Ford Taunus 'POLIZEI'	White and Green body, (German issue), 110 mm.	£150-200	☐
263	1962-68	Superior Criterion Ambulance	Cream, 'AMBULANCE' on windows, stretcher, no beacon, 127 mm.	£50-60	☐
263	1978-80	E.R.F. Fire Tender	Yellow body, 'Airport Rescue', flashing light, 177 mm.	£40-50	☐
264	1962-66	R.C.M.P. Ford Fairlane	Blue/White body, suspension/steering, beacon, aerial, crest, 111 mm.	£70-80	☐
264	1966-68	R.C.M.P. Cadillac	Blue/White body, suspension/steering, beacon, aerial, crest, 113 mm.	£80-90	☐
264	1978-80	Rover 3500	White/Yellow, 'POLICE', beacon, opening doors and bonnet, 131 mm.	£10-15	☐
266	1976-79	E.R.F. Fire Tender	Red body, 'Fire Service', White wheeled escape ladder, 223 mm.	£40-50	☐
	1979-80		As previous model but with Metallic Red body.	£40-50	☐
	1976-79	Danish issue:	Red body, 'FALCK'.	£60-70	☐
267	1967-71	Superior Cadillac Ambulance	Cream/Red body, 'AMBULANCE' on roof, flashing light, 152 mm.	£40-50	☐
267	1978-79	Paramedic Truck	Red, Yellow cylinders, 2 figures, lapel badge, (TV Series 'Emergency').	£15-20	☐
268	1973-77	Range Rover Ambulance	White, 'AMBULANCE', stretcher, bubble-packed, 109 mm.	£15-20	☐
269	1962-66	Motorway 'POLICE' Car	(Jaguar) White body, suspension/steering, 2 policemen, 95 mm.	£70-80	☐
269	1978-79	Ford Transit 'POLICE' Van	White/Red/Blue, figures/lights/signs/cones, Type 3 casting, 129 mm.	£20-25	☐
270	1969-72	Ford 'POLICE' Panda Car	Turquoise body, White doors, Blue/White roof sign, cast hubs, 97 mm.	£20-25	☐
	1972-77		As previous model but fitted with Speedwheels.	£20-25	☐
271	1975-76	Ford Transit 'FIRE'	Red body, hose/axe/bells/plastic ladder, bubble-packed, Type 2, 129 mm.	£40-50	☐
		Danish issue:	As previous model but with 'FALCK' logo.	£60-70	☐
272	1975-77	'POLICE' Accident Unit	White, radar gun/beacon/aerial/cones/signs, Type 2 casting, 129 mm.	£20-25	☐
274	1978-79	Ford Transit Ambulance	White, 'AMBULANCE', Red crosses, beacon, Type 3 casting, 129 mm.	£20-25	☐
276	1962-69	Airport Fire Tender	Red body, 'AIRPORT FIRE CONTROL', bell, 115 mm.	£50-60	☐
			As previous model but 'FIRE BRIGADE' logo (from 259), no crest.	£50-60	☐
276	£976-78	Ford Transit Ambulance	White body, 'AMBULANCE', Type 2 casting	£30-40	☐

Ref. No.	Year(s)	Model Type	Dinky Toys - continued	Market Price Range	
277	1962-68	Superior Criterion Ambulance ..	Metallic Blue, White roof & tyres, driver, roof light, 127 mm.	£50-60	☐
277	1977-80	'POLICE' Land Rover	Blue body, White tilt, flashing light, 110 mm.	£15-20	☐
278	1964-69	Vauxhall Victor Ambulance......	White, 'AMBULANCE', suspension/steering, stretcher, 91 mm.	£50-60	☐
282	1973-79	Land Rover Fire Appliance	Red, 'Fire Service', metal ladder, bubble-packed, 119 mm.	£20-25	☐
	1974-78	Danish issue:	As previous model but with 'FALCK' logo.	£30-35	☐
285	1969-79	Merryweather Marquis..............	Metallic Dark Red, 'FIRE SERVICE', Blue light, wheeled escape, 177 mm.	£40-50	☐
			As previous model but (non-Metallic), Red body.	£40-50	☐
		Danish issue:	As previous model but Metallic Dark Red body with 'FALCK' logo	£70-80	☐
286	1968-74	Ford Transit 'FIRE'.................	Red, 'Fire Service', hose Type 1 casting, bubble-packed, 122 mm.	£40-50	☐
			As previous model but with Metallic Red body.	£40-50	☐
		Danish issue:..............	As previous model but with 'FALCK ZONEN' logo.	£70-80	☐
287	1967-71	Police Accident Unit................	Cream/Orange, roof sign, aerial, Type 1 casting, 122 mm.	£40-50	☐
	1971-74	design change:.............	White/Red body, radar gun, roof rack, Type 1 casting.	£40-50	☐
288	1971-79	Superior Cadillac......................	White/Red, 'AMBULANCE', stretcher, no flashing light, 152 mm.	£30-35	☐
		Danish issue:	White body with Red mid-section and roof bar, 'FALCK'	£70-85	☐
		Danish issue:	Black body/White roof, Blue interior & roof bar, 'FALCK'	£70-85	☐
555 (955)	1952-54	Fire Engine (Commer)............	Red body with Silver trim and ladder, no windows, 2 bells, 140 mm.	£50-60	☐
624 (30hm)	1954-?	Daimler Military Ambulance	Military-Green body, Red crosses on White backgrounds, (US issue).	£250-350	☐
954	1961-64	Fire Station................................	Red, Yellow and 'brick' plastic, base 252 mm. x 203 mm.	£150-200	☐
955 (555)	1954-60	Fire Engine (Commer).............	Red body & diecast hubs, Silver trim & ladder, no windows, 140 mm.	£50-60	☐
	1960-64		Red body & diecast hubs, Silver trim & ladder, with window glazing	£75-90	☐
	1964-70		Red body & plastic hubs, Silver trim & ladder, with windows, in 'picture' box..........	£90-110	☐
956	1958-60	Turntable Fire Escape Lorry (Bedford cab)	Red body & diecast hubs, no windows, Silver deck & ladder, 200 mm.	£50-60	☐
	1960-64		Red body & diecast hubs, with window glazing	£50-60	☐
	1964-70		Red body & plastic hubs, with window glazing	£60-70	☐
956	1970-74	Turntable Fire Escape Lorry (Berliet cab)........................	Metallic Red body & hubs, windows, 'ECHELLE INCENDIE', Silver platform	£200-250	☐
			Red body & hubs, windows, 'ECHELLE INCENDIE', Black platform.....................	£170-200	☐
	1974-?	Danish issue:..............	Metallic Red body & hubs, windows, 'FALCK'..	NGPP	☐
2253	1974-76	Ford Capri Police Car..............	White/Orange, 'POLICE', Blue light, suspension, 175 mm. (1/25 scale).....................	£55-75	☐

Dinky Toys   -   Farm and Garden models

Ref. No.	Year(s)	Model Type	Model Features and Size	Market Price Range	
22e	1933-40	Farm Tractor...........................	'Modelled Miniature' with 'HORNBY SERIES' cast-in, no hook, 70 mm.		
			Yellow/Dark Blue (lead) body, Red or Yellow (lead) wheels	£200-250	☐
			'DINKY TOYS' cast-in, with hook, Red wheels are lead, diecast or both		
			Green/Yellow, Yellow/Blue, Red/Blue, Red/Red	£125-150	☐
			Cream/Blue, Cream/Red, Blue/Cream	£125-150	☐
			'DINKY TOYS' cast-in, with hook, Yellow wheels are lead, diecast or both		
			Green/Yellow, Yellow/Blue, Red/Blue, Red/Red	£150-175	☐
			Cream/Blue, Cream/Red, Blue/Cream	£150-175	☐
27a (300)	1948-54	Massey-Harris Tractor	Red body, Yellow cast wheels, driver, steering wheel, hook, 89 mm.	£60-70	☐
27ak (310)	1952-54	Tractor and Hay Rake	27a Tractor and 27k Hay Rake, 157 mm.	£80-90	☐
27b (320)	1949-54	Halesowen Harvest Trailer.......	Brown body, Red racks, Yellow metal wheels, 133 mm.	£25-35	☐
27d (340)	1950-54	Land Rover	Green or Orange body, tinplate windscreen frame, driver, 90 mm.	£50-60	☐
	1952-53	Gift Set model:	Dark Brown body. Only in Gift Set No.2, Commercial Vehicles Set.	GSP	☐
27c (321)	1949-54	M.H. Manure Spreader	Red body with drawbar, hook, working shredders, 121 mm.	£25-35	☐
27f (344)	1950-53	Estate Car	Pale Brown body, Brown side panels and hubs	£60-70	☐
27g (342)	1949-54	Moto-Cart................................	Brown and Green body, driver, 3 metal wheels/tyres, body tips, 110 mm.	£25-35	☐
27h (322)	1951-54	Disc Harrow	Red/Yellow body, Silver disc blades, tinplate hook, 86 mm.	£25-35	☐
27j (323)	1953-54	Triple Gang Mower	Red frame, Yellow wheels, cast-in hook, 114 mm.	£25-35	☐
27k (324)	1953-54	Hay Rake	Red frame, Yellow wheels, wire tines, operating lever, 77 mm.	£25-35	☐
27m (341)	1952-54	Land Rover Trailer	Orange or Green body and diecast hubs, drawbar and hook, 79 mm.	£20-25	☐
27n (301)	1953-54	'FIELD MARSHALL' Tractor.......................	Orange body, Silver or Green metal wheels, driver, hook, 76 mm.	£75-90	☐
30n (343)	1950-54	Farm Produce Wagon	Model features stake sides to rear body, Black metal base and hook. 104 mm.		
			Yellow cab and chassis, Green stake body and hubs............................	£60-70	☐
			Green cab and chassis, Yellow stake body and hubs............................	£60-70	☐
			Red cab and chassis, Blue stake body and hubs.................................	£60-70	☐
105a (381)	1948-54	Garden Roller.........................	Green handle and Red roller sides, 67 mm.	£15-25	☐
105b (382)	1948-54	Wheelbarrow	Brown and Red body, single metal wheel, 82 mm.	£15-25	☐
105c (383)	1948-54	4 wheeled Hand Truck	Green/Yellow or Blue/Yellow, 126 mm.	£10-15	☐
105e (384)	1948-54	Grass Cutter...........................	Yellow body, Green metal wheels, Red blades, 73 mm.	£15-20	☐
107a (385)	1948-54	Sack Truck..............................	Blue with two small Black metal wheels, 65 mm.	£10-15	☐
300 (27a)	1954-62	Massey-Harris Tractor	Red body, Yellow cast wheels, 'MASSEY-HARRIS', Tan cast driver, 89 mm.	£60-70	☐
	1962-64		Red, Yellow wheels (cast rear, plastic front, rubber tyres), Tan cast driver..............	£60-70	☐
	1964-66		Red, Yellow wheels (all plastic), cast-in seat, Blue plastic driver	£60-70	☐
300	1966-71	Massey Ferguson Tractor.........	As previous model but name changed to 'MASSEY-FERGUSON'.............................	£60-70	☐

Ref. No.	Year(s)	Model Type	Dinky Toys - continued	Market Price Range	
301 (27n)	1954-61	'FIELD MARSHALL' Tractor	Orange body, Green metal wheels, Tan driver, hook, 76 mm.	£75-90	☐
			Orange body, Yellow or unpainted wheels, Tan driver, hook	NGPP	☐
	1962-66		Orange body, Green wheels (plastic front, cast rear, rubber tyres)	£75-90	☐
	1964-66		Red body, Green plastic hubs, rubber tyres	£80-90	☐
305	1965-67	David Brown 900 Tractor	Red cowl, Grey engine, Yellow cab/wheels, 'David Brown 990', 83 mm.	£80-100	☐
	1967-74		White cowl/cab/wheels, Grey engine, 'David Brown Selectamatic 990'	£50-60	☐
	1974-75		White cowl/cab, Red engine/wheels, '995 David Brown Case, bubble-packed	£50-60	☐
308	1971-72	Leyland 384 Tractor	Metallic Red body, Cream hubs, 'LEYLAND', 86 mm. (Bubble-packed)	£50-75	☐
	1972-77		Blue body, unpainted or Black steering wheel	£40-50	☐
	1977-79		Orange body, unpainted steering wheel	£50-60	☐
310 (27ak)	1954-60	Tractor and Hay Rake	300 Tractor and 324 Hay Rake, 157 mm.	£80-90	☐
319	1961-71	Weeks Tipping Trailer	Red/Yellow body, cast or plastic wheels, 105 mm.	£25-30	☐
320 (27b)	1954-60	Halesowen Harvest Trailer	Red/Brown body, Red racks, drawbar, hook, cast or plastic wheels, 133 mm.	£25-35	☐
			Red body, Yellow racks, drawbar, hook, cast or plastic wheels, 133 mm.	£25-35	☐
321 (27c)	1954-62	M.H. Manure Spreader	Red body, Yellow cast wheels, 'MASSEY-HARRIS', shredders, 121 mm.	£25-35	☐
321	1962-73		Red body, plastic hubs, no logo	£25-35	☐
322 (27h)	1954-67	Disc Harrow	Red/Yellow body, Silver disc blades, tinplate hook, 86 mm.	£25-35	☐
322	1967-73		White/Red body, Silver disc blades, no hook, 79 mm.	£25-35	☐
323	1954-63	Triple Gang Mower	Red frame, Yellow blades, Green wheels, cast-in hook, 114 mm.	£25-35	☐
324 (27k)	1954-64	Hayrake	Red frame, Yellow wheels, wire tines, operating lever, 77 mm.	£20-30	☐
325	1967-73	David Brown Tractor and Disc Harrow....................	305 and 322 in White and Red, 152 mm.	£80-90	☐
			305 and 322 in Yellow and Red, 152 mm.	£120-150	☐
340 (27d)	1954-66	Land Rover	Green body, Brown interior and metal wheels, Tan cast driver, 92 mm.	£50-60	☐
340	1966-69		Orange body, Green interior and plastic hubs, Blue cast or plastic driver	£50-60	☐
	1969-71		Red body and plastic hubs, Yellow interior, Blue plastic driver	£50-60	☐
341 (27m)	1954-73	Land Rover Trailer	Orange, Green or Red, drawbar and hook, cast or plastic hubs, 79 mm.	£20-25	☐
342 (27g)	1954-61	Moto-Cart.............................	Tan and Green body, driver, 3 metal wheels/tyres, body tips, 110 mm.	£25-35	☐
343 (30n)	1954-61	Farm Produce Wagon	Red cab and chassis, Blue stake body and cast hubs, 107 mm.	£70-80	☐
			Green cab and chassis, Yellow stake body and cast hubs, 107 mm.	£70-80	☐
343	1961-64		As previous models but no bonnet louvres, cast or plastic hubs	£80-100	☐
344 (27f)	1950-53	Estate Car................................	Pale Brown body, Brown side panels and hubs	£60-70	☐
381 (105a)	1954-58	Garden Roller........................	Green and Red, 67 mm.	£15-25	☐
381	1977-80	Convoy Farm Truck................	Yellow cab, Brown plastic high-sided truck body, 110 mm.	£15-20	☐
382 (105b)	1954-58	Wheelbarrow	Brown and Red body, single metal wheel, 82 mm.	£15-25	☐
383 (105c)	1954-58	4 wheeled Hand Truck	Green or Blue body, 126 mm.	£10-15	☐
384 (105e)	1954-58	Grass Cutter...........................	Yellow body, Green metal wheels, Red blades, 73 mm.	£15-20	☐
385 (107a)	1954-58	Sack Truck.............................	Blue with 2 small metal wheels, 65 mm.	£10-15	☐
386 (751)	1954-58	Lawn Mower	Green/Red, separate grassbox, 'Dinky Toys' cast-in, 140 mm.	£70-80	☐
399	1969-75	Tractor and Trailer.................	300 combined with 428	NGPP	☐
564 (964)	1952-58	Elevator Loader.....................	Yellow with Blue or Dark Blue hubs, hopper and feed chute	£55-70	☐
751 (386)	1949-54	Lawn Mower	Green/Red, separate grassbox, 'Dinky Supertoys' cast-in, 140 mm.	£70-80	☐

Dinky Toys - Military models

See also Action Kits, Ships, Gift Sets

Ref. No.	Year(s)	Model Type	Model Features and Size	Market Price Range	
22f	1933-34	Army Tank	'Modelled Miniature' with 'HORNBY SERIES' cast-in, 87 mm.		
			Green (lead) body, Orange revolving turret, Red rubber tracks	£200-250	☐
			Green (lead) body, Orange revolving turret, Green rubber tracks	£200-250	☐
	1935-40		Green/Orange (lead) body, 'DINKY TOYS' cast-in, Red or Green tracks	£150-200	☐
			Khaki (lead) body, 'DINKY TOYS' cast-in, Green tracks	£150-200	☐
			Grey drab (lead) body, 'DINKY TOYS' cast-in, Green tracks	£150-200	☐
22s	1938-41	Searchlight Lorry......................	Green body, (22c casting), 84 mm.	£200-300	☐
25wm (640)	1952-54	Bedford Military Truck............	Military-Green body, (made for export to the USA only)	£250-350	☐
27m (341)	1952-54	Land Rover Trailer	Military-Green body, (to fit 25wm)	£250-350	☐
30hm (624)	1950-54	Daimler Military Ambulance ...	Military-Green body, Red crosses on White backgrounds, (US issue)	£150-200	☐
30sm (625)	1952-54	Austin Covered Wagon	Military-Green body, made for export to USA only), 112 mm.	£250-350	☐
37c	1937-40	Signal Dispatch Rider	Green body, Khaki rider, White or Black rubber wheels, 45 mm.	£50-60	☐
139am	1950-54	US Army Staff Car..................	(170m) Ford Fordor in Olive drab with White stars on roof and doors	£175-250	☐
150a (600)	1937-40	Royal Tank Corps Officer........	Khaki uniformed figure with Black beret, and binoculars in hand	£10-15	☐
150b (604)	1938-54	Royal Tank Corps Private	Die-cast figure in Khaki uniform, sitting, 22 mm.	£10-15	☐
150c	1937-40	Royal Tank Corps Private	Die-cast figure in Khaki uniform, standing, 30 mm.	£10-15	☐
150d	1937-40	Royal Tank Corps Driver	Die-cast figure in Khaki uniform, sitting, 25 mm.	£10-15	☐
150e	1937-40	Royal Tank Corps NCO...........	Die-cast figure in Khaki uniform, walking, 30 mm.	£10-15	☐
151a	1937-40	Medium Tank.........................	(Gloss) Green body/base, White markings, chain tracks, aerial, 92 mm.	£100-125	☐
			As previous model but with Black rubber wheels instead of tracks	NGPP	☐
	1947-53		(Matt) Green body, Black base, no markings, made for export only	£100-125	☐

Ref. No.	Year(s)	Model Type	Dinky Toys - continued	Market Price Range	
151b	1937-40	6-wheel Covered Wagon............	Gloss Green body, tinplate canopy, seat holes, spare wheel, 99 mm...............	£70-80	☐
151b (620)	1947-54		Matt-Green or Greenish-Brown body, 'Export only' from 1950.................................	£50-60	☐
151c	1937-48	Cooker Trailer..........................	Gloss Green trailer, wire stand, hole in seat but no figure, 60 mm.....................	£30-40	☐
151d	1937-48	Water Tank Trailer	Gloss Green, 52 mm..	£35-40	☐
152a	1937-40	Light Tank................................	(Gloss) Green body/base, White markings, chain tracks, aerial, 68 mm.	£100-125	☐
			As previous model but with Black rubber wheels instead of tracks	NGPP	☐
	1947-50		(Matt) Green body, Black base, no markings, chain tracks, aerial	£100-125	☐
152a (650)	1950-54		(Matt) Green body, Black base, no markings, made for export only	£100-125	☐
152b	1937-40	Reconnaissance Car..................	(Gloss) Green body/base, six wheels, 89 mm...	£100-125	☐
	1947-50		(Matt) Green or Brownish-Green body, Black base	£100-125	☐
152b (671)	1950-54		(Matt) Green body, Black base, made for export only	£100-125	☐
152c	1937-40	Austin Seven............................	Military-Green body, wire windscreen frame, hole in seat, 50 mm.	£100-125	☐
153a	1946-47	Jeep..	Military-Green, White star on flat bonnet, spare wheel at rear, 69 mm.............	£60-70	☐
	1947-50		Military-Green, White star on 'domed' bonnet	£60-70	☐
153a (672)	1950-54		Military-Green, White star on 'domed' bonnet, made for export only	£60-70	☐
160a	1939-40	Royal Artillery NCO................	Khaki uniform, 28 mm...	£10-15	☐
160b (608)	1939-54	Royal Artillery Gunner	Khaki uniform, seated, hands on knees, 24 mm...	£10-15	☐
160c	1939-40	Royal Artillery Gunlayer	Khaki uniform, seated, hands held out, 24 mm.	£10-15	☐
160d	1939-40	Royal Artillery Gunner	Khaki uniform, standing, 28 mm..	£10-15	☐
161a	1939-40	Searchlight on Lorry	Gloss Green body, 151b casting plus diecast or lead searchlight	£200-250	☐
161b	1939-40	Anti-Aircraft Gun on Trailer	Gloss Green, gun elevates, figure holes, cast drawbar & hook, 115 mm.	£40-50	☐
	1946-50		Matt Green or Brownish-Green	£40-50	☐
161b (690)	1950-54		Matt Green, made for export only	£40-50	☐
162a	1939-40	Light Dragon Tractor	Gloss Green body, holes in seats, chain tracks, 65 mm.	£100-125	☐
			As previous model but Black rubber wheels instead of tracks	NGPP	☐
	1946-55		Matt Green or Brownish-Green body (with or without holes) chain tracks	£60-75	☐
162b	1939-40	Ammunition Trailer	Gloss Green body and baseplate, drawbar and hook, 54 mm.................................	£15-20	☐
	1946-55		Matt Green or Brownish-Green body, Black baseplate	£15-20	☐
162c	1939-40	18 pounder Gun	Gloss Green body, drawbar cast-in, tinplate shield, 78 mm.	£20-25	☐
	1946-55	18 pounder Gun	Matt Green or Brownish-Green body and shield..	£20-25	☐
170m	1954-54	Ford US Army Staff Car	(139am) Military-Green, US issue, renumbered 675	£175-250	☐
281	1973-76	Military Hovercraft	Military-Green body, Gunner, aerial, 'Army', 139 mm.	£20-25	☐
341 (27m)	195?-6?	Land Rover Trailer	Military-Green body with drawbar and hook, 79 mm.	£20-25	☐
600 (150a)	194?-4?	Royal Tank Corps Officer........	US only re-issue	£10-15	☐
601	1974-76	Austin Paramoke......................	Military-Green, Tan hood, spun hubs, parachute, 76 mm.	£40-50	☐
	1976-78		Military-Green, Tan hood, Speedwheels	£30-40	☐
603	1950-68	Army Private (seated)...............	Diecast figure in Khaki uniform, Black beret, seated, 20 mm.	£3-4	☐
	1968-71		Plastic figure in Khaki uniform, Black beret, seated, 20 mm.	£3-4	☐
603a	1950-68	Army Personnel Set..................	Six diecast figures (Khaki uniforms, Black berets, seated)	£20-30	☐
	1968-71		Six plastic figures (Khaki uniforms, Black berets, seated)	£20-30	☐
604 (150b)	1954-60	Royal Tank Corps Private	Die-cast figure in Khaki uniform, sitting, export only (to USA).........................	£10-15	☐
604	1960-72	Army Personnel	Six army driver figures (Khaki uniforms)	£20-30	☐
604	1976-79	Land Rover Bomb Disposal	Military-Green/Orange, 'Explosive Disposal', robot de-fuser, 110 mm.	£35-45	☐
608 (160b)	1954-55	Royal Artillery Gunner	Khaki uniform, seated, hands on knees, 24 mm. (Export only)	£10-15	☐
609	1974-78	105 mm. Howitzer & Crew.......	Military-Green body, three soldiers, bubble-packed, 199 mm.	£20-25	☐
612	1973-79	Commando Jeep	Army-Green or Camouflage, driver, two guns, jerricans, aerial, 108 mm.	£20-25	☐
615	1968-74	US Jeep and 105 mm. Gun	Military-Green body with US Army markings, driver, 108/199 mm.	£25-30	☐
616	1968-78	AEC with Chieftain Tank	AEC articulated Transporter 'ARMY' with 683 Tank, 318 mm...........................	£40-50	☐
617	1967-78	VW KDF and 50 mm. Gun	Grey, German markings, operable anti-tank gun, 115/159 mm.	£30-40	☐
618	1976-79	AEC with Helicopter................	AEC articulated Transporter 'RESCUE', 724 Helicopter and net, 318 mm.	£50-60	☐
619	1976-78	Bren Gun Carrier & AT Gun ...	Khaki, plastic tracks, figures, gun/shells, bubble-packed, 125/159 mm.	£25-35	☐
620 (151b)	1954-55	6-wheel Covered Wagon..........	Matt-Green or Greenish-Brown body, export only (to USA)	NGPP	☐
620	1971-73	Berliet Missile Launcher...........	Military-Green launcher body with White/Red missile, 150 mm.	£80-100	☐
621	1954-60	3 ton Army Wagon	(Bedford 'S') tin tilt, no windows, driver on some, 113 mm.	£50-60	☐
	1960-63		(Bedford 'S') tin tilt, with window glazing, driver on some	£50-60	☐
622	1954-63	10 ton Army Truck	(Foden) Military-Green, driver, tin tilt, 137 mm. Supertoys box	£60-70	☐
622	1954-63	10 ton Army Truck	(Foden) Military-Green, driver, tin tilt, Dinky Toys box	£60-70	☐
622	1975-78	Bren Gun Carrier	Green body, White star, driver, passenger, plastic tracks, 125 mm.	£20-30	☐
623	1954-63	Army Covered Wagon	(Bedford 'QL') Military-Green body with or without driver, 105 mm.	£35-45	☐
624 (30hm)	1954-?	Daimler Military Ambulance	Military-Green, Red crosses on White backgrounds, (US issue)	£250-350	☐
625 (30sm)	1952-54	Austin Covered Wagon	Military-Green body, made for export only (to USA) 112 mm.	£250-350	☐
625	1975-78	Six-pounder Gun	Green anti-tank gun, 159 mm.	£15-20	☐
626	1956-61	Military Ambulance	Military-Green, Red crosses cast-in, driver on some, no windows, 110 mm.	£40-50	☐
	1961-62		Military-Green, Red crosses cast-in, driver on some, with window glazing	£40-50	☐
630	1973-78	Ferret Armoured Car	Military-Green body, plastic wheels, spare wheel, 80 mm.	£15-20	☐
640 (25wm)	1954-?	Bedford Military Truck............	Military-Green body, made for export only (to the USA)	£250-350	☐
641	1954-61	Army 1 ton Cargo Truck	Military-Green, tin tilt, with or without driver, no windows, 79 mm.	£35-40	☐
	1961-62		As previous model but with window glazing, with or without driver	£35-40	☐
642	1957-62	R.A.F. Pressure Refueller.........	RAF Blue, French roundel, with or without driver, 142 mm. Supertoys box	£80-90	☐
	1957-62		RAF Blue, French roundel, with or without driver, Dinky Toys box	£90-110	☐
643	1958-61	Army Water Tanker.................	Military-Green body, no windows, with or without driver, 89 mm.	£30-35	☐
	1961-64		Military-Green body with window glazing, with or without driver	£30-35	☐
650 (152a)	1954-55	Light Tank................................	Matt Green body, Black base, no markings, made for export only (to USA)............	£100-125	☐
651	1954-70	Centurion Tank	Military-Green, metal or plastic rollers, rubber tracks, Supertoy, 149 mm.	£30-40	☐

Ref. No.	Year(s)	Model Type	Dinky Toys - continued	Market Price Range	
654	1973-79	155 mm. Mobile Gun	Military-Green body with star, operable gun, plastic shells, 151 mm............................	£15-20	☐
656	1975-79	88 mm. Gun.............................	German Grey, fires plastic shells, 218 mm...	£15-20	☐
660	1956-61	Tank Transporter	Thorneycroft Mighty Antar, Army Green, no windows, driver on some, 335 mm.......	£60-70	☐
	1961-64		As previous model but with window glazing, with or without driver	£60-70	☐
660a	1978-80	Anti-Aircraft Gun with Crew....	Military-Green, 3 soldiers, 218 mm. (Bubble-packed model).................................	£15-20	☐
661	1957-65	Recovery Tractor......................	Army Green, six wheels, driver, operable crane, 134 mm. Supertoy	£60-70	☐
			As previous model but with plastic wheels, packed in Yellow 'picture' box	£70-80	☐
662	1975-77	88 mm. Gun with Crew	German Grey gun (656 without wheels), 3 Germans, shells, bubble-packed	£15-20	☐
665	1964-75	Honest John Missile Erector	Army Green, Black/White missile, 10 wheels plus spare, 188 mm.	£90-100	☐
666	1959-64	Missile Erector Vehicle and Corporal Missile Launcher....	Military-Green, Black/White missile, operable erector, Supertoy, 240 mm.	£150-200	☐
667	1960-64	Missile Servicing Platform........	Military-Green, windows, spare wheel, platform lifts, 197 mm. (Supertoy)	£100-125	☐
667	1976-78	Armoured Patrol Car	Army Green body, aerial, spare wheel, 80 mm.	£15-20	☐
668	1976-79	Foden Army Truck	Military-Green body, windows, plastic tilt and wheels, 197 mm.	£28-33	☐
669	1956-58	U.S.A. Army Jeep	Military-Green body with White star, (US issue) 83 mm.	£250-350	☐
670	1954-64	Armoured Car	Military-Green body, turret rotates, diecast wheels, 73 mm.	£15-20	☐
	1964-70		Military-Green body, turret rotates, plastic hubs, 73 mm.	£15-20	☐
671 (152b)	1954-55	Reconnaissance Car.................	(Matt) Green body, Black base, made for export only	£100-125	☐
672 (153a)	1954-55	US Army Jeep	Military-Green, White star on 'domed' bonnet, made for export only	£60-70	☐
673	1953-61	Scout Car	Military-Green body, squadron markings, holes for personnel, 68 mm.	£15-20	☐
674	1954-66	Austin Champ	Military-Green body, driver, tinplate windscreen, diecast hubs, 69 mm.	£20-25	☐
674	1966-71		Military-Green body, driver, tinplate windscreen, plastic hubs	£20-25	☐
674	1958-70	'U.N.' Austin Champ	White body, driver, tinplate windscreen. Made for export only	£250-300	☐
675 (170m)	1954-59	Ford US Army Staff Car	Ford Fordor with Olive-drab body, White star, export only (to US)	£200-250	☐
676	1955-62	Armoured Personnel Carrier	Military-Green, squadron markings, 6 wheels, revolving turret, 82 mm.	£25-30	☐
676a	1973-76	Daimler Armoured Car	Army-Green body, Speedwheels, 73 mm. (new version of 670)...........................	£15-20	☐
676a	1973-74	Daimler Armoured Car	French made version with camouflage net ('Made in England' on base)..................	NGPP	☐
677	1957-62	Armoured Command Vehicle....	Military-Green body, 6 wheels, (based on an A.E.C. vehicle) 133 mm.	£60-70	☐
680	1972-78	Ferret Armoured Car	Sand or Army-Green, Speedwheels, spare wheel, bubble-packed, 80 mm.	£10-15	☐
681	1972-78	DUKW Amphibious Vehicle	RAF Blue or Army-Green body, Speedwheels, bubble-packed, 127 mm.	£10-15	☐
682	1972-78	Stalwart Load Carrier	Army-Green body, 6 Speedwheels, bubble-packed, 103 mm.	£10-15	☐
683	1972-79	Chieftain Tank........................	Army-Green body, plastic tracks, fires shells, bubble-packed, 217 mm.	£25-35	☐
686	1957-71	25-pounder Field Gun	Military-Green, cast drawbar, (cast hubs, plastic from 1968) 90 mm.	£10-15	☐
687	1957-67	25-pounder Trailer	Military-Green, cast drawbar, (cast hubs, plastic from 1968) 58 mm.	£10-15	☐
687	1978-79	Convoy Army Truck	Green/Black body, 110 mm.	£10-15	☐
688	1957-61	Field Artillery Tractor	Military-Green, driver on some, no windows, cast hubs, 81 mm.	£25-30	☐
	1961-70		Military-Green, driver on some, with windows, (plastic hubs from 1968)	£25-30	☐
689	1957-66	Medium Artillery Tractor	Military-Green, driver on some, holes, 6 wheels, tin tilt, 140 mm. Supertoy	£25-30	☐
690 (161b)	1954-55	Anti-Aircraft Gun on Trailer	Matt Green, 115 mm., made for export only	£40-50	☐
690	1974-79	Scorpion Tank	Army-Green, camouflage net, working gun, bubble-packed, 120 mm.	£15-20	☐
691	1974-79	Striker Anti-Tank	Army-Green, plastic tracks, aerials, 5 firing rockets, 122 mm.	£15-20	☐
692	1955-62	5.5 Medium Gun	Military-Green body, twin cast drawbar, elevating barrel, 131 mm.	£15-20	☐
692	1974-79	Leopard Tank	Grey with German markings, plastic tracks, bubble-packed, 198 mm.	£30-35	☐
693	1958-67	7.2 inch Howitzer Gun	Military-Green body, cast drawbar, elevating barrel, 130 mm.	£15-20	☐
694	1974-80	Hanomag Tank Destroyer........	Grey, German markings, plastic tracks/wheels, bubble-packed, 171 mm.	£25-30	☐
696	1975-79	Leopard Anti-Aircraft Tank	Grey-Green, German markings, plastic tracks, bubble-packed, 152 mm.	£25-30	☐
699	1975-78	Leopard Recovery Tank	Grey-Green, German markings, dozer blade/jib, aerial, bubble-packed.................	£25-30	☐
815	1962-64	Panhard Armoured Tank	Military-Green with French flag, 104 mm. (French issue)	£75-100	☐
816	1969-71	Berliet Missile Launcher...........	Military-Green body, (French issue)...	£150-200	☐
817	1962-64	AMX 13-ton Tank	Green body with French flag, 107 mm. (French issue)	£75-100	☐
822	1962-64	Half-Track M3	Green body, rubber tracks, 121 mm. (French issue)	£75-100	☐
884	1962-64	Brockway Bridge Truck	Military-Green, 10 wheels, bridge parts, inflatables, 180 mm. French issue...........	£150-200	☐

Dinky Toys - Aircraft

Ref. No.	Year(s)	Model Type	Model Features and Size	Market Price Range	
60a	1934-36	Imperial Airways Liner	(Armstrong-Whitworth Atalanta) cast body, tinplate wings, 4 x 2 PB, Yellow fuselage, Blue wingtips & tail, no markings, 127 mm.	£200-250	☐
	1936-39		'sunray' effect in Gold/Blue, White/Blue or Red/Cream, 'G-ABTI'	£200-250	☐
60a (66a)	1939-41		All-over Silver, 'G-ABTI', 'Imperial Airways Liner' under wing	£200-250	☐
60b	1934-36	De Havilland 'Leopard Moth' ..	Cast fuselage, tinplate wings, single 2-blade propeller, 76 mm.		
			Green/Yellow or Dark Blue/Orange, no markings, open windows	£100-150	☐
	1936-39		All-over Silver or Gold, 'G-ACPT', open windows	£100-150	☐
60b (66b)	1939-41		As previous model but blank side windows, & 'DH Leopard Moth' under wing..........	£200-250	☐
60c	1934-36	Percival 'Gull' Monoplane	Cast fuselage, tinplate wings, large 2-blade propeller, 76 mm.		
			White (Blue wingtips), or Buff (Red wingtips) no markings, open windows................	£100-150	☐
60c (60k)	1936-39		White, Red, Yellow or Light Blue, 'G-ADZO' in Black, open windows	£100-150	☐
60c (66c)	1939-41		As previous model but blank side windows, & 'Percival Gull' under wing	£200-250	☐
60d	1934-36	Low Wing Monoplane	(Vickers Jockey) Cast body, tinplate wings, 2-blade propeller, 76 mm.		
			Red/Cream, Orange/Cream or Gold/Blue, no markings, no pilot............................	£100-150	☐

Ref. No.	Year(s)	Model Type	Dinky Toys - continued	Market Price Range	
60d (66d)	1936-41		Red, Orange or Silver, 'G-AVYP' in Black, pilot's head cast-in	**£100-150**	□
60e	1934-36	General 'Monospar'	Two-piece diecasting, 2 x 2-blade propellers, 80 mm.		
			Gold (Red wingtips), or Silver (Blue wingtips) no markings	**£100-150**	□
60e (66e)	1936-41		Silver or Gold, 'G-ABVP' in Black, 'General Monospar' under wing...........	**£100-150**	□
60f	1934-36	Cierva 'Autogiro'......................	Gold body (49 mm.) Blue rotor/propeller, no pilot	**£120-170**	□
60f (66f)	1936-40		As previous model but with pilot. (Other colours are French model 60z) ...	**£120-170**	□
60g	1935-36	De Havilland 'Comet'	Cast fuselage & wings, enclosed wheels, 2 x 2-blade propellers, 86 mm.		
			Red/Gold, Gold/Red or Silver/Blue, no markings..............................	**£100-150**	□
	1936-41		Red, Silver or Gold, 'G-ACSR', 'DH Comet' under wing	**£100-150**	□
60g	1945-49	Light Racer (DH 'Comet')........	Yellow, Red or Silver, 'G-RACE', 'Light Racer' under wing, 2 x 3 PB........	**£200-250**	□
60h	1936-36	'Singapore' Flying Boat............	Cast fuselage (126 mm.), tinplate wings, 4 x 2-blade propellers		
			Silver with stencilled RAF roundels, no roller or 'gliding' hole	**£150-200**	□
60h (60m)	1936-39		As previous model but with plastic or wooden roller and 'gliding' hole......	**£150-200**	□
60h	1939-40		Silver or Grey with accurate RAF roundel (waterslide transfers)	**£150-200**	□
	1940-41		As previous model with gun seat, cutaway bow, no hole, name under wing ...	**£150-200**	□
60k	1936-41	Percival 'Gull' (Amy Mollison)	Blue/Silver version of 60c, 'G-ADZO' in Blue, special box........................	**£150-200**	□
60k	1936-41	Percival 'Gull' (H. L. Brook)	Blue/Silver version of 60c, 'G-ADZO' in Black, special box......................	**£150-200**	□
60k (60c)	1945-48	Light Tourer (Percival 'Gull') ...	Red, Silver or Dark or Light Green, 'Light Tourer' or 'Percival Gull' under wing, no markings, small or large 2-blade propeller, 76 mm...	**£150-200**	□
60m	1936-40	Four Engined Flying Boat	Red, Light Blue, Light Green, Dark Green, Silver or Yellow, 'civilian' version of 60h with 'G-EUTG', 'G-EVCU', 'G-EXGF' or 'G-EYCE'........	**£135-175**	□
60n	1937-40	Fairey 'Battle' Bomber	Silver or Grey, RAF roundels, 1 x 3 PB, undercarriage, 75 mm.	**£90-120**	□
60n (60s)	1938-41		Silver or Grey, RAF roundels, 1 x 3 PB, without undercarriage	**£90-120**	□
60p	1936-39	Gloucester 'Gladiator'	Silver, stencilled roundels, Red 1 x 2 PB, no name under wing, 38 mm. ...	**£100-140**	□
	1939-41		Silver or Grey, transfer roundels, 'Gloucester Gladiator' under wing	**£100-140**	□
60r	1937-40	Empire Flying Boat.................	Silver, 4 x 3 PB, plastic roller, hole, own box, 156 mm. Liveries: 'CALEDONIA', ('G-ADHM'), 'CANOPUS', ('G-ADHL'), 'CORSAIR', ('G-ADVB'), 'CHALLENGER', ('G-ADVI'), 'CLIO', ('G-AETY'), 'CALYPSO', ('G-AEUA'), 'CENTURION', ('G-ADVE'), 'CAPELLA', ('G-ADUY'), 'CERES', ('G-AETX'), 'CALPURNIA', ('G-AETW'), 'CAMILLA', ('G-AEUB'), 'CORINNA', ('G-AEUC'), 'CAMBRIA', ('G-ADUV'), 'CHEVIOT', ('G-AEUG'), 'CORDELIA', ('G-AEUD')...	**£180-230**	□
60r (60x)	1940-49	Empire Flying Boat.................	As previous models but plastic, wood or brass roller, no hole. 'CALEDONIA', ('G-ADHM'), or 'CAMBRIA', ('G-ADUV')...............	**£180-230**	□
60s (60n)	1938-40	Medium Bomber......................	Camouflaged 60n with undercarriage, single roundel has Yellow ring	**£90-110**	□
60s	1940-41	Fairy 'Battle' Bomber	Camouflaged body, two Blue/Red roundels, no undercarriage, 1 x 3 PB ...	**£110-140**	□
60t	1938-41	Douglas DC3 Air Liner	Silver, 'PH-ALI' 2 x 3 PB, hole, tail wheel on some, own box, 132 mm. ...	**£175-225**	□
60v (62t)	1937-41	Armstrong Whitworth Bomber	Silver body, 'gliding' hole in some, RAF roundels, 2 x 3 Red PB. 116 mm. ...	**£150-200**	□
60w	1938-40	Flying Boat 'Clipper III'	Silver, 'USA NC16736', 4 x 3 PB/SBX, plastic roller, hole, 164 mm.	**£150-200**	□
60w	1945-48	Flying Boat..........................	Silver, Blue or Green, no markings, 4 x 3 PB, brass roller, 164 mm.	**£100-130**	□
60x	1937-41	Atlantic Flying Boat..............	Blue/Cream, 'DAUNTLESS', 'G-AZBP', 4 x 3 PB, name under wing, 156 mm.	**£200-250**	□
			Green/Cream, 'WHIRLWIND', 'G-AZBT'	**£200-250**	□
			Black/White, 'DREADNOUGHT', 'G-AZBT'	**£200-250**	□
62a	1939-40	Vickers-Supermarine 'Spitfire'...	Silver body (short nose) RAF roundels, 1 x 3 PB. 52 mm........................	**£100-130**	□
	1940-41	'Meccano Spitfire Fund'............	Model 62a in special souvenir box. Brass ring through fin allows model to be worn as badge or pendant. Sale proceeds went to the Spitfire Fund.		
			Various single colours or Camouflage (originally 2/6 each.)....................	**£450-500**	□
			Chromium plated version (originally 10/6)....................................	**£1000-1200**	□
62a	1945-49	'Spitfire'	Silver body (long nose, bubble cockpit) RAF roundels, 1 x 3 PB. 54 mm. ...	**£100-130**	□
62b	1939-40	Bristol 'Blenheim' Bomber	Silver body, RAF roundels, Red 2 x 3 PB, name under wing, 78 mm.	**£100-130**	□
62b	1945-49	Medium Bomber....................	Silver body, RAF roundels, Red 2 x 3 PB, name under wing, 78 mm.	**£60-80**	□
62d	1940-41	Bristol 'Blenheim' Bomber	62b with Camouflage/Black/White body, RAF roundels, 2 x 3 PB. 78 mm. ...	**£100-130**	□
62e	1940-41	Vickers-Supermarine 'Spitfire'...	62a with Camouflage/Black/White body, RAF roundels, 1 x 3 PB. 52 mm. ...	**£100-130**	□
62f	1939-40	D.H. Flamingo Airliner............	Not issued	NPP	
62g	1939-41	Boeing 'Flying Fortress'	Silver, 4 x 3 PB, 'gliding' hole, name under wing, own box, 144 mm.	**£140-180**	□
62g	1945-48	Long Range Bomber	Silver body, Red 4 x 3 PB, no hole, not boxed, 144 mm.	**£90-120**	□
62h	1938-40	Hawker Hurricane Fighter	Camouflaged body, RAF roundels, 1 x 2 PB, with or without undercarriage ...	**£100-130**	□
62k	1938-41	The King's Aeroplane	Airspeed 'Envoy', Silver/Red/Blue, 'G-AEXX', 2 x 2 PB, own box, 91 mm. ...	**£175-225**	□
62m	1938-41	Airspeed 'Envoy' Monoplane....	Red ('G-ACVJ'), Silver ('G-ADCB'), Blue ('G-ADAZ'), or Green ('G-AENA') ...	**£120-150**	□
62m	1945-48	Light Transport	Red, Silver or Blue body, 'G-ATMH', 2 x 2 PB, name under wing, 91 mm. ...	**£85-115**	□
62n	1938-41	Junkers 'Ju90' Air Liner	Silver, ('D-AALU', 'D-AIVI', 'D-AURE', or 'D-ADLH') 4 x 3 PB, own box ...	**£200-300**	□
62p	1938-41	'Ensign' Air Liner....................	Silver body, Red 4 x 3 PB, hole, own box, 173 mm. 6 liveries: 'ENSIGN' ('G-ADSR'), 'ELSINORE' ('G-ADST'), 'ECHO' ('G-ADTB'), 'EXPLORER' ('G-ADSV'), 'ETTRICK' ('G-ADSX'), 'ELYSIAN' ('G-ADSZ').	**£150-200**	□
62p	1945-49	Armstrong Whitworth Air Liner	As previous casting but no hole, name under wing, 4 x 3 PB, no box, Silver, Blue, Green or Grey/Green, 'EXPLORER' or 'ECHO' markings..........	**£100-150**	□
62r	1939-41	D.H. 'Albatross' Mail Liner......	Silver, 'G-AEVV', Red 4 x 3 PB, hole, name under wing, own box, 145 mm. ...	**£175-225**	□
62r	1945-49	Four Engined Liner.................	Grey, Light Blue or Silver, no markings, no hole, not boxed, 145 mm.	**£100-130**	□
			Grey, Fawn, Light Blue or Silver, 'G-ATPV', Red 4 x 3 PB, 145 mm.	**£100-130**	□
62s	1939-41	Hawker 'Hurricane' Fighter	Silver body, RAF roundels, with undercarriage, 1 x 2 or 3 PB, 55 mm.	**£90-120**	□
	1945-49		Silver body, RAF roundels, no undercarriage, 1 x 3 PB, 55 mm.	**£60-70**	□
62t	1939-41	Armstrong Whitworth Bomber	('Whitley') Camouflage/Black/White, RAF roundels, 2 x 3 PB, own box	**£160-200**	□
62w (68b)	1939-41	'Frobisher' Class Air Liner	Silver body (casting as 62r), 4 x 3 PB, hole, own box, 3 liveries: 'FROBISHER' ('G-AFDI'), 'FALCON' ('G-AFDJ'), 'FORTUNA' ('G-AFDK')........	**£175-225**	□

Ref. No.	Year(s)	Model Type	Dinky Toys - continued	Market Price Range	
62x (68a)	1939-41	British 40 Seat Airliner..............	Red/Maroon, TT-Green, Yellow/Maroon, TT-Blue, 'G-AZCA', not boxed	£150-190	☐
62y	1939-49	Giant High Speed Monoplane ..	Blue/Brown, TT-Blue or TT-Green, 'D-AZBK', hole, not boxed, 160 mm.	£140-180	☐
	1945-49		Light/Mid-Green, Light/Dark Green, Grey/Green or Silver, no hole or box	£140-180	☐
63	1939-41	Mayo Composite Aircraft	Models 63a and 63b together in special box (see below)........................	£200-300	☐
63a	1939-41	Flying Boat 'MAIA'	Silver body, 'G-ADHK', *Mayo Composite* under wing, own body, 156 mm. ..	£100-150	☐
63b	1939-41	Seaplane 'MERCURY'	Silver, 'G-ADHJ', *Mercury Seaplane* under wing, 'hole' in some, 101 mm. ..	£75-100	☐
63b (700)	1945-49	Seaplane..........................	Silver body, 'G-AVKW', no 'gliding' hole, *Seaplane* under wing	£90-120	☐
66a	1940-41	Heavy Bomber.....................	Camouflaged body, RAF roundels, 4 x 2 PB, no name under wing, 127 mm. ..	£250-300	☐
66b	1940-41	Dive Bomber Fighter...............	Camouflaged body, RAF roundels, 1 x 2 PB, 76 mm.	£150-200	☐
66c	1940-41	Two Seater Fighter.................	Camouflaged body, RAF roundels, 1 x 2 PB, 76 mm.	£150-200	☐
66d	1940-41	Torpedo Dive Bomber............	Camouflaged body, RAF roundels, 1 x 2 PB, 76 mm.	£150-200	☐
66e	1940-41	Medium Bomber....................	Camouflaged body, RAF roundels, 2 x 2 PB, *General Monospar* under wing	£150-200	☐
66f	1940-41	Army Co-operation Autogiro ...	Silver body and blades, Red/White/Blue roundels, (60f casting) 49 mm. ..	£150-200	☐
67a	1940-41	Junkers Ju89 Heavy Bomber.....	Black/Pale Blue body, German markings, no hole, own box, 160 mm. ..	£200-250	☐
68a	1940-41	'Ensign' Air Liner	Camouflaged body, RAF roundels, no 'gliding' hole, 4 x 3 PB, 173 mm. ..	£200-250	☐
68b	1940-41	'Frobisher' Class Air Liner	Light or Dark Camouflage, RAF roundels, 4 x 3 PB, 'hole' in some, 145 mm. ..	£200-250	☐
70a (704)	1946-49	Avro 'York' Airliner	Silver body, 'G-AGJC', Red 4 x 3 PB, 160 mm.	£90-120	☐
70b (730)	1946-49	Tempest II Fighter	Silver body, RAF roundels, Red 4 blade prop with large spinner, 63 mm. ..	£35-45	☐
70c (705)	1947-62	Viking Air Liner	Silver or Grey body, 'G-AGOL', Red 2 x 4 PB, large spinners, 140 mm. ..	£55-65	☐
70d (731)	1946-49	Twin-Engined Fighter	Silver body, no markings, two Red 3-blade propellers, 76 mm.	£25-35	☐
			As previous model but 'N' in *MECCANO* is reversed	NGPP	☐
70e (732)	1946-49	Gloster 'Meteor'	Silver body, RAF roundels (with or without Yellow rings), 67 mm.	£25-35	☐
70f (733)	1947-49	Lockheed 'Shooting Star'	Silver body, US markings on wings (star on port wing only), 61 mm.	£25-35	☐
700 (63b)	1952-54	Seaplane..........................	Silver body with 'G-AVKW' marking....................................	£90-120	☐
			Silver body, 'G-AVKW', no 'gliding' hole, *Seaplane* under wing............	£90-120	☐
700	1979	Spitfire Mark II ('Jubilee')	Plated model on plinth, 1 x 3 PB, *Diamond Jubilee of the RAF*............	£75-95	☐
701	1947-49	Short 'Shetland' Flying Boat	Silver body, 'G-AGVD', Black 4 x 4 PB, first Supertoys aircraft, own box ..	£350-450	☐
702 (999)	1954-55	DH 'Comet' Jet Airliner...........	White/Blue body, Silver wings, 'B.O.A.C.' livery, 183 mm.	£100-130	☐
704 (70a)	1954-59	Avro 'York' Airliner	Silver body, 'G-AGJC', Red 4 x 3 PB, 160 mm.	£90-120	☐
705 (70c)	1954-62	'Viking' Air Liner	Silver body with 'G-AGOL' marking....................................	£45-55	☐
			Silver or Grey body, 'G-AGOL', Red 2 x 4 PB, 140 mm.	£45-55	☐
706	1956-57	Vickers 'Viscount' Airliner	Silver/Blue/White, 'AIR FRANCE', 'F-BGNL', Red 4 x 4 PB, 149 mm. ..	£80-90	☐
708	1957-65	Vickers 'Viscount' Airliner	Silver/White or Metallic Grey/White, 'B.E.A.', 'G-AOJA'	£70-80	☐
710	1965-76	Beechcraft S35 'Bonanza'	Red/White, Bronze/Yellow, or Red/Blue/White body, 1 x 2 PB, 133 mm. ..	£40-50	☐
712	1972-77	US Army T.42A	Military Green (715), Beechcraft plus wing-tip tanks, 2 x 2 PB. 153 mm. ..	£30-40	☐
715	1956-62	Bristol 173 Helicopter............	Turquoise body with Red rotors and stripes, 'G-AUXR', 53 mm.	£25-35	☐
715	1968-76	Beechcraft C55 'Baron'	White/Yellow or Red/Yellow body, Yellow 2 x 2 PB, 150 mm.	£25-35	☐
716	1957-62	Westland Sikorsky S-51..........	Red and Cream helicopter body, 2 x 3-blade rotors 66 mm.	£35-45	☐
717	1970-75	Boeing '737'	White/Blue body, White or Blue engines, 'LUFTHANSA', 152 mm.	£35-45	☐
718	1972-75	Hawker 'Hurricane' Mk IIc	Camouflaged body, RAF roundels, Black 1 x 3 PB, guns, 188 mm.	£35-45	☐
719 (741)	1969-77	Spitfire Mk.II.....................	Camouflaged body, RAF roundels, Black 1 x 3 PB (battery-operated), 173 mm. ..	£35-45	☐
721	1969-80	Junkers Ju87b Stuka..............	Camouflage/Yellow, German markings, 1 x 3 PB, cap-firing bomb, 191 mm. ..	£30-40	☐
722	1970-80	Hawker 'Harrier'	Light Blue/Olive Camouflage, RAF markings, pilot, aerial, 125 mm.	£50-60	☐
723	1970-73	Hawker Siddeley HS 125.........	Yellow/White/Blue or Metallic Blue/White, drop-down door/steps, 133 mm. ..	£25-35	☐
724	1971-79	'Sea King' Helicopter	White/Blue, 5-blade rotors, with 'Apollo' space capsule, 179 mm.	£25-35	☐
725	1972-77	Royal Navy 'Phantom II'.........	Dark Blue body, Black nose, roundels, decals in bubble-pack, 132 mm.	£40-50	☐
726	1972-74	Messerschmitt Bf-109E..........	German desert camouflage, 1 x 3 PB, decals in bubble-pack, 165 mm.	£50-60	☐
	1974-76		German Grey/Green camouflage, Brown 1 x 3 PB, decals in bubble-pack ..	£30-40	☐
728	1972-75	R.A.F. 'Dominie'.................	Blue and camouflage body, roundels, retractable wheels, bubble-pack	£30-35	☐
729	1974-76	Multi-Role Combat Aircraft	Grey/Camouflage, swing-wings, decals in bubble-pack, 164 mm.	£30-40	☐
730	1972-76	US Navy 'Phantom II'	Grey/Red body, 'NAVY', 'USS Saratoga', fires missiles, retractable wheels ..	£40-50	☐
731 (70d)	1954-55	Twin-Engined Fighter	Silver body, no markings, two Red 3-blade propellers, 76 mm.	£25-35	☐
731	1973-76	S.E.P.E.C.A.T. 'Jaguar'...........	Metallic Blue & camouflage body, Orange pilot, opening cockpit, 106 mm. ..	£25-35	☐
732	1974-80	Bell Police Helicopter.............	Orange/Blue/White or Red body, 'POLICE' sign boards & cones, 211 mm. ..	£20-25	☐
733 (70f)	1954-62	Lockheed 'Shooting Star'	Silver body, US markings on wings (star on port wing only), 61 mm.	£25-35	☐
733	1973-76	German 'Phantom II'.............	Grey/Green camouflage body, 'Bundesluftwaffe', (German/Austrian market) ..	£50-60	☐
733	1976-77	US F-4K 'Phantom II'	Brown camouflage, retractable wheels, fires missiles, (US market only)	£50-60	☐
734	1955-62	Supermarine 'Swift'	Grey/Green camouflage body, RAF markings, 51 mm.	£30-40	☐
734	1975-78	P47 'Thunderbolt'................	Metallic Silver/Black body, Red 1 x 4 PB, retractable wheels, 190 mm.	£40-50	☐
735	1956-66	Gloster 'Javelin'...................	Camouflaged 'delta-wing' body, RAF markings. 83 mm.	£35-45	☐
736	1955-63	Hawker 'Hunter'..................	Camouflaged body, 54 mm.	£30-40	☐
736	1973-78	Bundesmarine 'Sea King'.........	Grey/Orange helicopter, German markings, decals in bubble-pack, 179 mm. ..	£25-35	☐
737	1959-68	P.1B 'Lightning' Fighter...........	Silver (metal wheels) or Metallic Grey (Black plastic wheels) 55 mm.	£30-40	☐
738	1960-65	DH 110 'Sea Vixen' Fighter.....	Grey/White body, Black nose, RAF roundels, 80 mm.	£30-40	☐
739	1975-78	A6M5 'Zero Sen'	Green/Black, Japanese markings, decals in bubble-pack, 184 mm.	£30-40	☐
741	1978-80	Spitfire Mk II	Camouflaged body, (non-motorised version of 719), 173 mm.	£40-50	☐
749 (992)	1955-56	RAF Avro 'Vulcan' Bomber.....	Silver body (aluminium), only 500 models were made (for Canadian market) 992 is the catalogue (and box) number, '749' is cast into the model.		
			Two castings exist; one has pointed wingtips, the other more rounded	£2000-3000	☐
997	1962-65	Caravelle SE 210 Airliner.........	Silver/White/Blue, 'AIR FRANCE', metal or plastic wheels, 126 mm.	£250-300	☐
998	1959-64	Bristol 'Britannia'	Silver/White body, Red or Blue lines, 'CANADIAN PACIFIC', 225 mm.	£250-300	☐
	1964-65		Metallic Grey/White body, Red lines, 'CANADIAN PACIFIC', 225 mm.	£250-300	☐
999 (702)	1955-65	DH 'Comet' Jet Airliner............	White/Blue body, Silver wings ('G-ALYX' on some) 'B.O.A.C.', 183 mm. ..	£100-130	☐

DINKY TOYS

Gift Sets

Six special selections of popular Dinky Toys and Dinky Supertoys are available. Particulars are given below.

149 Sports Cars in Racing Finish (illustrated above). Contains five sports cars fitted with racing drivers and racing numbers: Sunbeam Alpine Sports, M.G. Midget Sports, Austin-Healey 100 Sports, Aston Martin DB3S, Triumph TR2 Sports. **15/-**

249 Racing Cars
This set comprises the following five racing cars: Alfa Romeo, Maserati, Cooper-Bristol, Ferrari and H.W.M. **12/6**

299 Post Office Services
Contained in this attractive set are the Royal Mail Van, Telephone Service Van, Telephone Call Box, Postman and Telegraph Messenger. **9/6**

698 Tank Transporter with Tank (illustrated below). This fine set consists of the Tank Transporter and Centurion Tank. **25/-**

699 Military Vehicles (1)
Contains four models: 3-ton Army Wagon, Army 1-ton Cargo Truck, Austin Champ Army Vehicle and Armoured Personnel Carrier. **16/6**

990 Pullmore Car Transporter with four cars. The Pullmore Car Transporter is loaded with the following private cars: Hillman Minx (No. 154), Rover 75, Austin Somerset and Ford Zephyr. **28/11**

All the Gift Sets are boxed in attractive presentation boxes.

Prices include Purchase Tax

MADE IN ENGLAND BY MECCANO LTD., LIVERPOOL

Picture taken from Meccano Magazine September 1958

Dinky Toys — Buses, Taxis and Trams

Ref. No.	Year(s)	Model Type	Model Features and Size	Market Price Range	
27	1934-38	Tram Car	Plastic or metal wheels, 'OVALTINE', 'LIPTONS TEA' or no logo, 77 mm.		
			Red, Orange, Green, Yellow or Blue body, Cream upper windows & roof	£200-250	☐
			Light Blue or Dark Blue body, Cream lower/upper windows & roof	£200-250	☐
29 (29a)	1934-38	Motor Bus	Plastic or metal wheels, no logo, or Silver or Red 'MARMITE', 70 mm.		
			Blue, Green, Maroon, Yellow or Red body, Cream or Silver roof	£200-250	☐
29b	1936-46	Streamline Bus	Green/Cream, Orange/Cream, Red/Cream, Black or White tyres, 88 mm.	£125-175	☐
			Two-tone Blue, TT-Green, Yellow/Orange, Red/Maroon, open rear window	£125-175	☐
	1947-50		Two-tone Green or Grey/Blue body, Black tyres, filled-in rear window	£75-100	☐
29c		Double Decker Bus	The different casting types of 29c & 290 are shown in the diagrams below.		
	1938-40	'DUNLOP TYRES'	Type 1 (A.E.C. radiator, cutaway wings), stairs cast-in, 100 mm.		
			Cream upper body with Red, Blue, Maroon, Green or Orange lower, Grey roof	£225-275	☐
			Cream upper body and roof with Red, Blue, Maroon, Green or Orange lower	£225-275	☐
	1946-47	no advertising	Type 1 (A.E.C. radiator, cutaway wings), without stairs, 100 mm.		
			Red/Grey, Red/Cream, Green/Grey, Green/Cream or Two-tone Green	£80-90	☐
	1948-49	no advertising	Type 3 (Leyland radiator), no stairs casting, 100 mm.		
			Red or Green lower body, Cream upper body and roof	£80-90	☐
			Red lower body, Grey upper body and roof	£80-90	☐
	1949-54	no advertising	Type 2 (A.E.C. radiator, straight wings), no stairs casting, 101 mm.		
			Red or Green lower body, Cream upper body	£80-90	☐
29c (290)	1954-54	'DUNLOP'	As previous model but with 'DUNLOP -The World's Master Tyre'	£80-90	☐
29dz	1939-40	Autobus	Green or White body, metal wheels, (French issue sold in UK)	£80-90	☐
29e	1948-52	Single Deck Bus..................	Blue/Dark Blue, Light Green/Dark Green or Cream/Blue, 113 mm.	£40-50	☐
29f (280)	1950-54	Observation Coach	Grey (Red flashes) or Cream (Red flashes), 112 mm.	£50-60	☐
29g (281)	1951-54	Luxury Coach......................	Maroon body with Cream flashes	£80-100	☐
			Orange body with Cream flashes	£150-200	☐
			Fawn/Orange, Blue/Cream, Cream/Blue, or Cream/Red, 113 mm.	£100-125	☐
29h (282)	1952-54	Duple Roadmaster Coach	Red (Silver flashes) or Blue (Silver flashes), 119 mm.	£75-85	☐
36g		Taxi with Driver	'TAXI' cast into Black roof, driver cast into chassis, 72 mm.		
	1936-46		Cream, Yellow, Grey, Blue or Light Green body, open rear window	£150-200	☐
	1947-50		Green, Light Green, Red, Maroon or Brown body, rear window filled-in	£80-100	☐
40h (254)	1951-54	Austin Taxi (FX3)	'TAXI' cast into roof, driver cast into chassis, 94 mm.		
			Yellow body (Brown chassis), or Dark Blue body (Black chassis)	£90-120	☐
067	1959-64	'Dinky Dublo' version:	Blue/Cream body, driver & 'TAXI' cast-in, Grey plastic wheels, 59 mm.	£40-50	☐
115	1979-79	United Biscuits Taxi..................	Yellow/Blue/Black, casting as 120, promotional, 86 mm.	£30-40	☐
120	1979-80	Happy Cab	White/Yellow/Blue, solid wheels, 'flower-power' stickers, 86 mm..........................	£20-30	☐
241	1977-77	'SILVER JUBILEE TAXI'.......	Silver body and hubs, Union Jack on bootlid, 284 casting, 112 mm.	£45-55	☐
254 (40h)	1954-56	Austin Taxi (FX3)	'TAXI' cast into roof, driver cast into chassis, 94 mm.		
			Yellow body, Black chassis..	£80-90	☐
			Dark Blue (Black chassis, Light Blue hubs)...	£90-120	☐
	1956-59		Green and Yellow body	£80-90	☐
	1959-62		Black body, Grey interior, spun aluminium hubs	£90-110	☐
265	1960-64	Plymouth U.S.A. Taxi..............	Yellow/Red, '25c First 1/5 Mile, 5c Additional', windows, aerial, 108 mm.	£80-90	☐
266	1960-66	Plymouth Canadian Taxi	Yellow/Red body with 'Taxi' and '450 Metro Cab', 108 mm.	£100-150	☐
268	1962-67	Renault Dauphine Mini Cab	Red body with 'Meccano', 'Kenwood', and various other adverts, 92 mm.	£80-90	☐
278	1978-80	Plymouth Yellow Cab	Yellow body, 'Yellow Cab Co', plastic chassis, wheels and aerial, 135 mm.	£15-20	☐
280 (29f)	1954-60	Observation Coach......................	Grey (Red flashes) or Cream (Red flashes), 112 mm.	£50-60	☐
281 (29g)	1954-59	Luxury Coach..........................	Fawn/Orange, Cream/Orange, Maroon/Cream or Blue/Cream, 113 mm.	£80-90	☐
282 (29h)	1954-60	Duple Roadmaster Coach	Red/Silver, Blue/Silver, or Dark Blue/Silver, 119 mm.	£75-85	☐
			Yellow body with Red flashes and hubs..	£200-250	☐
			Green lower body with Cream upper body and hubs	£300-400	☐
			Light Blue body	£75-85	☐
282	1967-69	Austin 1800 Taxi	Blue/White body, Red/White 'TAXI' labels on doors & roof, 101 mm.......................	£65-75	☐

Dinky Toys 29c and 290 series Bus radiator types 1938-1963

1st type 1938-1950
AEC radiator
Cutaway wings

2nd type 1950-1957
AEC radiator
Straight across wings

3rd type 1957-1963
Leyland radiator
Straight across wings

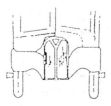

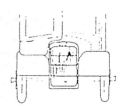

Ref. No.	Year(s)	Model Type	Dinky Toys - continued	Market Price Range	
283	1956-63	B.O.A.C. Coach	Dark Blue/White, *'British Overseas Airways Corporation'*, 120 mm.	£65-75	☐
283	1971-77	Single Deck Bus	Red body with White band, operable doors and bell, *'RED ARROW'*, 167 mm.	£35-40	☐
			As previous model but Metallic Red finish	£40-50	☐
284	1972-79	London Taxi (FX4)	Black (or very Dark Blue) body, driver, Speedwheels, *'TAXI'*, 112 mm.	£30-40	☐
289		**Routemaster Bus issues**	*'London Transport'*, Route *'221'*, *'KINGS CROSS'*, driver/conductor, 121 mm.		
	1964-65	'TERN SHIRTS'	Red body, *'FOR 8am CRISPNESS'*.	£80-95	☐
	1966-69	'SSSCHWEPPES'	Red body, Blue-Green logo on White label	£60-70	☐
	1969-80	'ESSO'	Red body, Red and Blue logo on White label *'ESSO SAFETY-GRIP TYRES'*	£20-25	☐
		'ESSO' variant:	Deep Purple body, *'London Transport'* and *'ESSO SAFETY-GRIP TYRES'* logos, Blue driver and clippie	£400-600	☐
	1968-68	'LONDON STORES'	Red body, Black/Gold logo *'Festival of London Stores'*, pomotional	£100-150	☐
	1970	'INGERSOLL RAND'	Red body, promotional	£75-90	☐
	1974-74	'MECCANO'	Gold body, *'MECCANO - DINKY TOYS'*. (Very few issued to the Press only)	NGPP	☐
	1977-79	'MADAME TUSSAUDS'	Red body with White labels, figures in some, promotional	£65-75	☐
		label change:	As previous model but Dark Blue labels	£60-70	☐
		box change:	Red body, with figures, packed in *'SCHWEPPES'* picture box	£100-120	☐
	1977-77	'WOOLWORTHS'	Silver body, (Silver Jubilee limited issue) figures in some	£20-25	☐
	1977-77	'EVER READY'	Silver body, (New Zealand Silver Jubilee issue) no figures	NGPP	☐
	1979)	'THOLLENBEEK'	Gold body, *'Thollenbeek 1929-79'*, Belgian promotional	£100-125	☐
290 (29c)	1954-59	Double Decker Bus	Type 2 (A.E.C. grille) *'DUNLOP - THE WORLDS MASTER TYRE'*, 103 mm.		
			Green/Cream, Dark Green/Cream or Red/Cream	£80-100	☐
	1959-61		Type 3 (Leyland grille) Green/Cream, Dark Green/Cream or Red/Cream	£80-100	☐
	1961-63		As previous model but with spun aluminium hubs	£80-100	☐
291	1959-61	Double Decker Bus	Type 3 (Leyland grille) Red body, *'EXIDE BATTERIES'* logo, route *'73'*	£80-100	☐
	1961-62		As previous model but with spun aluminium hubs	£80-100	☐
	1962-63		As previous model but with Red plastic hubs	£80-100	☐
291 - 293		**Atlantean City Bus**	A Leyland double-decker bus (123 mm. long) available in several versions:		
291	1974-77	'KENNINGS'	Red body, White engine cover and interior, *'VAN & TRUCK HIRE'*	£30-35	☐
			As previous model but with Pale Blue engine cover and interior	£35-40	☐
			As previous model but seen with 'Yellow Pages' stickers	NGPP	☐
	1977	'LONDON & MANCHESTER ASSURANCE'	White model on plinth. *'Your Best Man For Life'*. (500 issued to agents)	NGPP	☐
292	1962-65	'RIBBLE'	Red and White body with or without *'REGENT'* advertisement	£80-100	☐
			Blue and Cream body with *'CORPORATION TRANSPORT'* fleetname	£80-100	☐
			As previous model but no fleetname or logo	£80-100	☐
293	1963-65	'BP'	Green & Cream body with Yellow logo and smooth roof, *'BP IS THE KEY'*	£80-100	☐
			As previous model but with ribbed roof	£110-130	☐
293	1973-78	Swiss Postal Bus	Yellow body with Cream roof, clear or tinted windows, *'PTT'*, 119 mm.	£20-25	☐
295	1963-69	Atlas Kenebrake Bus	Light Blue/Grey body, suspension, windows, 86 mm.	£35-40	☐
			As previous model but all Blue body	£35-40	☐
295	1973-74	Atlantean Bus 'YELLOW PAGES'	Yellow body, *'Let Your Fingers Do The Walking'*, 123 mm.	£35-40	☐
295	1974-76		As previous model but deeper shade of Yellow	£35-40	☐
296	1972-75	Duple Viceroy 37 Coach	Metallic Blue body, clear or tinted windows, bubble-packed, 119 mm.	£15-20	☐
			As previous model but Yellow and Cream body	£20-25	☐
297	1977-77	Silver Jubilee Bus	Leyland Atlantean (291) Silver/Black body, *'National'*, 123 mm.	£20-25	☐
	1977-77	'WOOLWORTHS'	Silver Jubilee Bus (Leyland Atlantean) Silver body, promotional	£20-25	☐
949	1961-66	Wayne 'SCHOOL BUS'	Deep Yellow body, Red body lines & interior, windows, Supertoy, 195 mm.	£200-275	☐
			As previous model but with Black lines on sides	£200-275	☐
952	1964-71	Vega Major Luxury Coach	Pale Grey with Maroon flash, working indicators, 242 mm. Supertoy	£70-85	☐
			As previous model but White body with Maroon flash	£70-85	☐
953	1963-65	Continental Touring Coach	Blue/White body, *'Dinky Continental Tours'*, windows, 195 mm. Supertoy	£250-325	☐
954	1972-77	Vega Major Luxury Coach	As 952 but without flashing indicators	£60-70	☐
961	1973-77	Vega Major Coach 'PTT'	Orange/Cream body, *'P.T.T.'* and emblem, Swiss model (in normal box)	£125-150	☐
		box variant:	961 in Swiss box (Red/White/Yellow, *'Autocar Postal'*, *'Postauto'*, etc)	£150-200	☐

WHEN REPLYING TO ADVERTISEMENTS PLEASE MENTION JOHN RAMSAY'S CATALOGUE

Dinky Toys - Road-making Equipment and Cranes

Ref. No.	Year(s)	Model Type	Model Features and Size	Market Price Range	
25p (251)	1948-54	Aveling Barford Road Roller....	Mid or Pale Green body with driver and hook, Red wheels, 110 mm.	£30-40	☐
251 (25p)	1954-63	Aveling Barford Road Roller....	Green body with driver and hook, Red wheels, 110 mm.	£30-40	☐
279	1965-71	Aveling Barford Diesel Roller...	Orange body, Grey engine covers, Green wheels, 116 mm.	£25-35	☐
	1971-80		Yellow cab, Black roof, Silver wheels, 116 mm.	£25-35	☐
430	1977-80	Johnson 2 ton Dumper	Orange/Red body with Blue driver, 106 mm.	£20-25	☐
436	1963-69	'ATLAS COPCO' Lorry	Yellow body, compressor, Fingertip steering, opening engine cover, 89 mm.	£30-40	☐
437	1962-70	Muir Hill 2WL Loader.............	Red body with hook, no grille detail, bubble-packed model, 121 mm.	£20-25	☐
	1970-78		Yellow body with hook, with or without grille detail, bubble-packed	£20-25	☐
561 (961)	1949-54	Blaw Knox Bulldozer	Red body, Green or Black rubber tracks, driver, lifting blade, Supertoy. Blue box has Red/White label	£40-50	☐
			As previous model but Dark Blue	£100-150	☐
			Yellow body, Grey blade, Green tracks, Beige driver. Blue box has Orange/White label	NGPP	☐
562 (962)	1948-54	Muir Hill Dump Truck	Yellow body, metal wheels/tyres, hook, 105 mm.	£15-20	☐
563 (963)	1948-54	Blaw Knox Heavy Tractor........	Red, Orange or Blue 561 without the dozer blade, 116 mm. Brown cardboard box has Red/White label	£60-70	☐
564 (964)	1952-54	Elevator Loader......................	See 964 for details		
571 (971)	1949-54	Coles Mobile Crane..................	Yellow and Black, operable crane, Supertoy, 160 mm.	£30-40	☐
752 (973)	1953-54	Goods Yard Crane..................	Yellow operable crane on Blue (or Dark Blue) base (steps in some)	£30-40	☐
924	1972-76	Aveling Barford 'CENTAUR' ..	Red/Yellow body, dump truck, 180 mm.	£30-40	☐
959	1961-68	Foden Dump Truck and Bulldozer	Red/Orange body, model number badge, driver, windows, Supertoy, 165 mm.	£50-60	☐
960	1960-68	Albion Lorry Concrete Mixer ...	Orange/Yellow/Blue body, rotating drum, spare wheel, Supertoy, 130 mm.	£40-50	☐
961 (561)	1954-62	Blaw-Knox Bulldozer	Red or Yellow body, rubber tracks, Tan driver, Supertoy, 138 mm.	£40-50	☐
	1962-64		Blue body, rubber tracks, Tan driver, Supertoy, 143 mm.	£40-50	☐
	1964-?		Orange plastic body with Silver engine detail, Black diecast lifting gear, Green plastic blade and exhaust pipe, Blue driver, Light Green or Olive-Green roller wheels	NGPP	☐
962 (562)	1954-66	Muir Hill Dumper	Yellow body, hook, Supertoy, (rubber tyres from 1962) 105 mm.	£15-20	☐
963 (563)	1954-58	Blaw Knox Heavy Tractor........	961 without blade, Red or Orange body, Green or Black tracks, 116 mm. Packed in Blue/White striped box	£40-50	☐
963	1958-59		As previous model but with Yellow body	£30-40	☐
963	1973-75	Road Grader	Yellow/Red articulated body, Silver blade, bubble-packed, 238 mm.	£20-30	☐
964 (564)	1954-68	Elevator Loader......................	Blue/Yellow chutes or Yellow/Blue chutes	£40-50	☐
965	1955-61	'EUCLID' Dump Truck	Yellow, 'STONE - ORE - EARTH', no windows, operable tipper, 142 mm.	£45-55	☐
	1961-69		As previous model but with window glazing.	£45-55	☐
965	1969-70	'TEREX' Rear Dump Truck	Yellow body (as previous model but 'TEREX' cast under cab) 142 mm.	£75-100	☐
966	1960-64	Marrel Multi-Bucket Unit	(Albion) Yellow body, Grey buckets, windows, Supertoy, 115 mm.	£50-60	☐
967	1973-78	Muir-Hill Loader/Trencher	Yellow/Red or Orange/Black body, with driver, 163 mm.	£25-35	☐
970	1967-71	Jones Fleetmaster Crane	(Bedford TK) Red and Black body, White folding crane, 178 mm.	£50-60	☐
	1971-77		Metallic Red and Black with White folding crane	£60-70	☐
	1971-77		Yellow and Black with White folding crane	£60-70	☐
971 (571)	1954-64	Coles Mobile Crane..................	Yellow/Black body, Yellow crane & diecast wheels & driver, Supertoy, 160 mm.	£30-40	☐
	1964-66		Yellow/Black body, Silver crane, plastic wheels & driver, Supertoy, 160 mm.	£30-40	☐
972	1955-62	Coles 20 ton Lorry-Mounted Crane	Yellow/Orange (no 'Long Vehicle' signs), 2 drivers, Supertoy, 240 mm.	£30-40	☐
	1962-69		Yellow/Orange (with 'Long Vehicle' signs), 2 drivers, Supertoy.	£30-40	☐
	1967-69		Yellow/Black, Blue metal driver in lorry cab only, Yellow plastic wheels, Black tyres, Black/White diagonal stripes around jib, 'COLES CRANE' in Yellow at rear..	£100-150	☐
973 (752)	1954-59	Goods Yard Crane	Yellow operable crane on Blue base.	£30-40	☐
973	1971-75	Eaton 'YALE' Tractor Shovel ..	Red/Yellow articulated body, bubble-packed, 178 mm.	£20-30	☐
975	1963-67	Ruston-Bucyrus Excavator.......	Yellow/Red/Grey plastic body, rubber tracks, operable digger, 190 mm.	£175-250	☐
976	1968-76	'MICHIGAN' Tractor Dozer ...	Yellow/Red body, driver, engine covers, boxed or bubble-packed, 147 mm.	£20-25	☐
977	1973-78	Shovel Dozer	Yellow/Red/Silver, plastic tracks, bubble-packed, 151 mm.	£20-25	☐
980	1972-79	Coles Hydra Truck 150T..........	Lemon Yellow body, triple extension crane, handle at side & rear.	£30-40	☐
			Yellow or Orange body, 2 side handles, no rear handle, 210 mm.	£50-60	☐
		'SPARROWS'......................	Red body, 'SPARROWS CRANE HIRE', (promotional model)	£200-300	☐
984	1974-79	Atlas Digger	Red/Yellow/Black, 'AB 1702', plastic tracks, 247 mm.	£30-40	☐

Dinky Toys - Ships, Boats, Hovercraft

Ref. No.	Year(s)	Model Type	Model Features and Size	Market Price Range	
50a	1934-41	Battle Cruiser 'HMS Hood'	Battleship Grey, (without name cast underneath 1939-41) 146 mm.	£25-30	☐
50b	1934-41	Battleship 'Nelson' Class..........	Battleship Grey, 'HMS Nelson' underneath (no name 1939-41) 117 mm.	£25-30	☐
50b	1934-41	Battleship 'Nelson' Class..........	Battleship Grey, 'HMS Rodney' underneath (no name 1939-41) 117 mm.	£25-30	☐
50c	1934-41	Cruiser 'HMS Effingham'.........	Battleship Grey, (without name cast underneath 1939-41) 100 mm.	£15-20	☐
50d	1934-41	Cruiser 'HMS York'.................	Battleship Grey, (without name cast underneath 1939-41) 98 mm.	£15-20	☐
50e	1934-41	Cruiser 'HMS Delhi'	Battleship Grey, (without name cast underneath 1939-41) 81 mm.	£15-20	☐
50f	1934-41	Destroyer 'Broke' Class............	Battleship Grey, no wording underneath, 57 mm.	£5-10	☐

Ref. No.	Year(s)	Model Type	Dinky Toys - continued	Market Price Range	
50g	1935-41	Submarine 'K' Class	Battleship Grey, wire mast, no wording underneath, 57 mm.	£5-10	☐
50h	1935-41	Destroyer 'Amazon' Class	Battleship Grey, no wording underneath, 52 mm.	£5-10	☐
50x	1935-41	Submarine 'X' Class	Battleship Grey, wire mast, no wording underneath, 61 mm.	£5-10	☐
51b	1934-40	Norddeutscher-Lloyd 'Europa'	Black hull, White superstructure, Brown funnels, name under, 165 mm.	£35-45	☐
51c	1934-40	Italia Line 'Rex'	Black hull, White decks, Red/White/Green funnels, name under, 152 mm.	£35-45	☐
51d	1934-40	CPR 'Empress of Britain'	Canadian Pacific Railway colours of White hull & Cream funnels, 130 mm.	£30-35	☐
51e	1935-40	P & O 'Strathaird'	White hull, Cream funnels, name underneath, 114 mm.	£30-35	☐
51f	1934-40	'Queen of Bermuda'	Furness-Withy Line, Grey/White hull, Red/Black funnels, 99 mm.	£30-35	☐
51g	1934-40	Cunard 'Britannic'	'White-Star' Liner, Black/White/Brown hull, Black/Tan funnels, 121 mm.	£30-35	☐
52	1934-35	Cunard White-Star Liner 'No. 534'	Black/White/Red, '534' cast underneath, boxed, no rollers, 175 mm.	£70-80	☐
			Same model but '534 Queen Mary' cast underneath	£50-60	☐
52 (52b)	1935-35		As previous model with 'Queen Mary' cast underneath, but without '534'	£25-30	☐
52a	1935-41	Cunard White-Star Liner 'Queen Mary'	Black/White/Red, boxed, with plastic rollers, 175 mm.	£25-35	☐
	1946-49		Black/White/Red, boxed, with brass rollers	£45-55	☐
52b (52)	1935-36	Cunard 'Queen Mary'	Black/White/Red, boxed, without rollers, (renumbered from 52)	£20-30	☐
52c	1935-40	'La Normandie'	Black/White, Red/Black funnels, boxed, made in France, 175 mm.	£40-45	☐
52c		Cunard 'Queen Elizabeth'	Announced in 1939 catalogue but never produced	NPP	☐
52m	1936-40	Cunard 'Queen Mary'	Renumbered from 52b, without runners, supplied unboxed	£20-30	☐
53az	1938-39	Battleship 'Dunkerque'	Battleship Grey, with or without plastic rollers, boxed French issue	£30-35	☐
281	1973-76	Military Hovercraft	Military-Green body, Gunner, aerial, 'ARMY', 139 mm.	£20-25	☐
290	1970-76	SRN-6 Hovercraft	Red/White/Yellow, Blue or Black skirt, opening door, radar scanner	£10-15	☐
671	1976-78	Mk.1 Corvette	White/Grey/Brown/Black plastic body, fires missiles, 260 mm.	£10-15	☐
672	1976-77	OSA-2 Missile Boat	Grey/Whit/Black, fires missiles, 206 mm.	£10-15	☐
673	1977-78	Submarine Chaser	Grey/White/Black, fires depth charges, 197 mm.	£10-15	☐
674	1977-78	Coastguard Missile Launch	White/Blue/Red/Yellow, 'Coastguard', fires missiles, 155 mm.	£5-10	☐
675	1973-77	Motor Patrol Boat	Grey hull with Cream/Black/Red, 170 mm.	£5-10	☐
678	1974-77	Air-Sea Rescue Launch	Grey/Black/Yellow, Orange dinghy, pilot/launch, 170 mm.	£10-15	☐
796	1960-62	Healey Sports Boat	Cream (or White) and Green plastic boat, Orange trailer, 2 figures	£20-25	☐

Dinky Toys - Trains

For other Meccano produced railway items, see Dinky-Dublo, Accessories, Hornby-Dublo, and Gift Sets sections.

Ref. No.	Year(s)	Model Type	Model Features and Size	Market Price Range	
16	1936-37	Silver Jubilee Set	Locomotive and 2 interlocking coaches, 'LNER' and '2590' cast-in, open windows, smooth hubs with White tyres, special box, 300 mm.		
			Silver loco and coaches, Grey, Mid-Blue, Red or Orange trim	£175-225	☐
			Silver loco and coaches with Dark Blue trim	£200-250	☐
			Cream loco and coaches with Red trim	£250-275	☐
			Blue loco and coaches with Dark Blue trim	£250-275	☐
			Green loco and coaches with Dark Green trim	£250-275	☐
16	1937-40	Streamlined Train Set	As previous models but with a change of name and box	£150-200	☐
16	1946-52	Streamlined Train Set	Blue/Black loco, 'LNER', Brown/Grey coaches, solid windows, Black tyres	£75-100	☐
16 (798)	1952-54	Streamlined Train Set	As previous model but with tinplate base, with or without 'LNER'	£75-100	☐
16z	1935-40	Articulated Train	TT-Blue, or Cream with Red, Blue or Orange, French issue sold in UK	£200-250	☐
17	1935-40	Passenger Train Set	Black/Maroon loco 17a, Maroon tender 17b, Maroon/Cream coaches 20a/20b	£200-250	☐
			Black/Green loco 17a, Green tender 17b, 2 Green/Cream coaches 20a/20b	£200-250	☐
17a	1934-40	Locomotive	Black/Maroon or Black/Green, diecast cab/boiler, lead chassis, 82 mm.	£150-175	☐
17b	1934-40	Tender	Maroon or Green diecast body, 62 mm.	£40-50	☐
18	1935-40	Tank Goods Train Set	Green/Black loco (21a), and 3 Green/Black open wagons (21b)	£200-250	☐
19	1935-40	Mixed Goods Train	Maroon/Black loco (21a), Green/Red open wagon (21b), Red/Blue 'SHELL' tanker wagon (21d), Yellow/Red/Green lumber wagon (21e)	£350-450	☐
20	1935-40	Tank Passenger Set	Green/Black loco (21a), 2 Brown/Green coaches (20a), Guard's van (20b)	£200-250	☐
20a	1935-40	Coach	Brown/Cream or Green/White roof, diecast body, lead chassis, 81 mm.	£40-60	☐
20b	1935-40	Guard's Van	Brown/Cream or Green/White roof, diecast body, lead chassis, 81 mm.	£40-60	☐
21	1933-35	Modelled Miniatures Train Set	Blue/Red loco (21a), Green open wagon (21b), Green/Blue crane wagon (21c) Red/Blue 'SHELL' tank wagon (21d), Yellow/Red/Green lumber wagon (21e)	£200-250	☐
21a	1932-34	Tank Locomotive	Red/Blue 0-6-0 tank loco, 'HORNBY SERIES' cast into lead body, 82 mm.	£40-60	☐
	1934-41		Maroon/Black or Green/Black, 'DINKY TOYS' cast into lead body, 82 mm.	£40-60	☐
21b	1932-34	Open Wagon	Green/Red, Green/Blue, Green/Black, Maroon/Black, 'HORNBY SERIES', lead	£40-60	☐
	1934-41		Colours as previous model, 'DINKY TOYS' cast into lead body, 58 mm.	£40-60	☐
21c	1932-34	Crane Wagon	Green body, Blue chassis, 'HORNBY SERIES' cast-in, lead, 62 mm.	£40-60	☐
21d	1932-34	Tanker Wagon	Red tank, Blue or Black chassis, 'HORNBY SERIES' cast-in, lead, 58 mm.	£40-60	☐
	1934-41		Red tank, Blue or Black chassis, 'DINKY TOYS' cast-in, lead, 58 mm.	£40-60	☐
21e	1932-34	Lumber Wagon	Brown/Blue, Yellow/Red or Yellow/Black, 'HORNBY SERIES' cast-in, lead	£40-60	☐
	1934-41		Brown/Blue, Yellow/Red or Yellow/Black, 'DINKY TOYS', lead, 58 mm.	£40-60	☐
26	1934-40	G.W.R. Rail Car	Cream roof, Brown, Green, Yellow or Red body, plastic rollers, 106 mm.	£100-125	☐
			Green body with Red roof	£100-125	☐
26z	1937-40	Diesel Road Car	Cream roof, Red, Green, Orange, Yellow or Blue body, 99 mm. (French)	£100-125	☐
784	1972-75	Goods Train Set	Blue engine with Yellow 'G.E.R.', Yellow & Red open wagons	£35-45	☐
798 (16)	1954-59	Express Passenger Train Set	Green/Black loco, BR crest, Cream coaches (Grey roofs), Black hubs/tyres	£100-125	☐
			Green/Black loco, BR crest, Cream coaches/roofs/hubs, Black tyres	£80-100	☐
			Green/Black loco, BR crest, Cream coaches/roofs, Red hubs, White tyres	£100-125	☐

127

Dinky Toys - Novelty, Space, Film & TV-related models

Ref. No.	Year(s)	Model Type	Model Features and Size	Market Price Range	
100	1967-75	Lady Penelope's 'FAB 1'	Pink body, clear or tinted sliding roof (Pink stripes on some), suspension, rockets/harpoons, Lady Penelope & Parker figures (TV series 'Thunderbirds')	£100-150	☐
			As previous model but with Luminous Pink body	£250-300	☐
101	1967-73	Thunderbirds II and IV	Gloss Green body with Yellow legs, plastic Thunderbird IV inside, 143 mm.	£140-170	☐
	1973-73		Metallic Dark Green, Yellow legs, plastic Thunderbird IV inside	£200-250	☐
102	1969-75	Joe's Car	Metallic Green, driver, battery powered, 139 mm. (TV series 'Joe 90')	£85-100	☐
103	1968-75	Spectrum Patrol Car	TV series 'Captain Scarlet', shaped hubs, 'screaming motor', 121 mm.		
			Red body with Yellow base, Yellow or Cream plastic interior	£85-100	☐
			Metallic Red body with White base, Yellow or Cream plastic interior	£65-75	☐
			Gold body with Blue tinted windows, Yellow or Cream plastic interior	£65-75	☐
104	1968-72	Spectrum Pursuit Vehicle	Metallic Blue, 'SPV', separate seat/figure, 160 mm. ('Captain Scarlet')	£80-100	☐
	1973-75		As previous model but seat and figure attached to door	£80-100	☐
105	1968-75	Maximum Security Vehicle	White/Red, Red or Blue inside, 'RADIOACTIVE' crate, ('Captain Scarlet')	£80-100	☐
106	1967-70	'The Prisoner' Mini-Moke	White body, Red/White canopy, 'bicycle' decal on opening bonnet, 73 mm.	£150-175	☐
106	1974-77	Thunderbirds II and IV	Metallic Blue body and metal base, Yellow legs, 153 mm.	£55-65	☐
			Metallic Blue body, White plastic base, Yellow legs, 153 mm.	£40-50	☐
	1977-79		Metallic Blue body, Black plastic base, Red legs, 153 mm.	£40-50	☐
107	1967-68	Stripey the Magic Mini	White/Red/Yellow/Blue stripes, with Candy, Andy & the Bearandas, 75 mm.	£200-250	☐
108	1969-75	Sam's Car	Keyless motor, 111 mm., separate 'WIN' badge, (TV series 'Joe 90'),		
			Silver body, Red or Silver trim, Yellow interior	£55-65	☐
			Gold body, Red or Silver trim, Yellow interior	£80-100	☐
			Pale Blue body, Red or Silver trim, Yellow interior	£100-130	☐
			Metallic Red body, Red or Silver trim, Yellow interior	£45-55	☐
			Wine Red body	£80-100	☐
109	1969-71	Gabriel Model 'T' Ford	Yellow/Black, 'Gabriel', driver, 83 mm. (TV series 'The Secret Service')	£55-65	☐
111	1976-78	Cinderella's Coach	Pink/Gold, plastic figures & horses, 242 mm. ('The Slipper & The Rose')	£20-25	☐
112	1978-80	Purdey's TR7	Yellow body, Black 'P' logo, Speedwheels, 98 mm. ('The New Avengers')	£35-40	☐
			As previous model but with Yellow 'P' in Black logo on bonnet	NGPP	☐
			As previous model but with Silver 'P' logo on bonnet	£30-35	☐
113		John Steed's Jaguar XJC	Met. Dark Blue, Gold pinstripes, plastic 'Steed' inside. Officially not issued	NGPP	☐
115	1979-79	United Biscuits Taxi	Yellow/Blue/Black, casting as 120, promotional, 86 mm.	£30-40	☐
120	1979-80	Happy Cab	White/Yellow/Blue, solid wheels, 'flower-power' stickers, 86 mm.	£20-30	☐
281	1968-70	'PATHE NEWS' Camera Car ..	Black body, Camera and operator, opening doors, (Fiat 2300), 108 mm.	£80-100	☐
350	1970-71	Tiny's Mini Moke	Red body, White/Yellow striped canopy, 73 mm. ('The Enchanted House')	£65-75	☐
351	1971-79	U.F.O. Interceptor	From Gerry Anderson's TV series 'U.F.O', 198 mm., 'S.H.A.D.O.' labels on Light Metallic Green body. Initially packed in card box with pictorial inner mount (prices 10% higher), later bubble-packed.		
			with Black nose, White missile, clear canopy, Red or Orange skids	£30-40	☐
			with Black nose, White missile, Blue canopy, Red or Orange skids	£40-50	☐
			with Red nose, Yellow missile, clear canopy, Red or Orange skids	£30-40	☐
			with Red nose, Yellow missile, Blue canopy, Red or Orange skids	£40-50	☐
352	1971-75	Ed Straker's Car	Gold body, Blue interior, Silver trim, keyless motor, (TV series 'U.F.O.')	£55-65	☐
			Yellow body, Blue interior, Silver trim	£65-75	☐
			Red body, Silver trim	£40-50	☐
353	1971-79	'SHADO 2' Mobile	Military Green body, operable rocket, 145 mm. (TV series 'U.F.O.')	£35-40	☐
			As previous model but later version with Blue body	£45-55	☐
354	1972-77	Pink Panther	Pink car and Panther, flywheel drive, card endflap box, 175 mm.	£15-20	☐
	1977-79	Pink Panther	Similar to previous model but without flywheel, bubble-packed	£10-15	☐
355	1972-75	Lunar Roving Vehicle	Metallic Blue, White astronauts, front/rear steering, 114 mm.	£30-35	☐
357	1977-80	Klingon Battle Cruiser	Metallic Blue, fires 'photon torpedoes', 220 mm. (from 'Star Trek')	£30-35	☐
358	1976-80	'USS Enterprise' ('NCC 1701')	White body, Yellow or White 'photon torpedoes', shuttlecraft, 234 mm.	£30-35	☐
359	1975-79	Eagle Transporter	White/Green body, Red cones/landing gear, 222 mm. (from 'Space 1999')	£30-35	☐
360	1975-79	Eagle Freighter	White, Red cargo hold, 'RADIOACTIVE' drums, 222 mm. (from 'Space 1999')	£30-35	☐
			As previous model but with White cargo hold	£30-35	☐
361	1978-80	Galactic (Zygon) War Chariot ..	Metallic Green or Metallic Blue, White spacemen, rockets, 126 mm.	£25-30	☐
362	1978-79	Trident Star Fighter	Black/Orange, fires rockets, drop-down stairway, 170 mm.	£25-30	☐
363	1979-79	Cosmic Interceptor	Metallic Silver/Blue, 2 pilots, Marks & Spencer model ('St.Michael' box)	NGPP	☐
363	1979-80	Zygon Patroller	Metallic Silver/Blue, 2 pilots, ('368' in some catalogues, '363' on box)	£25-30	☐
364	1979	NASA Space Shuttle	Shown in catalogue but not issued	NPP	
366	1979	Space Shuttle	Shown in catalogue but not issued	NPP	
367	1979-80	Space Battle Cruiser	White/Red body, pilot, plastic weapons, 187 mm.	£50-60	☐
368	1979-79	Cosmic Cruiser	Blue body, Marks & Spencer model (in 'St.Michael' box)	NGPP	☐
368	1979-80	Zygon Marauder	Red/White, 4 spacemen, ('363' in some catalogues, '368' on box)	£30-35	☐
371 (801)	1980	Pocket-size 'USS Enterprise'	Small version of 358, bubble-packed, released after factory closure	£30-35	☐
372 (802)	1980	Pocket-size Klingon Cruiser	Small version of 357, bubble-packed, released after factory closure	£30-35	☐
477	1970-72	Parsley's Car	Green/Black/Yellow, head swivels, 92 mm. ('The Adventures of Parsley')	£80-90	☐
485	1964-67	Santa Special Model T Ford	Red/White body, Santa Claus, Xmas tree/toys/decals, 79 mm.	£80-100	☐
486	1965-69	'Dinky Beats' Morris Oxford	Pink/Green, 'Da gear', 3 beat-group figures, 92 mm.	£80-100	☐
602	1976-77	Armoured Command Car	Military-Green, White star, driver, scanner, 8 plastic wheels, fires sparks	£30-35	☐
801 (371)	1980	Pocket-size 'USS Enterprise'	Small version of 358, bubble-packed, released after factory closure	£30-35	☐
802 (372)	1980	Pocket-size Klingon Cruiser	Small version of 357, bubble-packed, released after factory closure	£30-35	☐

A rare Dinky Toy part set of 28/1 Series Delivery Vans in original Trade Box, with 22c Motor Truck and 22d Delivery Van, as purchased circa 1934. Sold on 20 May, 1993 for £5,500.

Diecast Toy Sales at Christie's South Kensington

'Enthusiasts selling to Enthusiasts'

In 1992 Christie's sold a record number of Dinky, Corgi and other diecast toys for an unprecented total of £300,000 including premium. Of the eight auctions that included diecast toys, The Ashley collection sale was the undoubted highlight; it realised a grand total of £105,530 including the remarkable price of £4,950 paid for a rare black 40b Triumph 1800. 1993 has produced fine material including private collections and rare archive material.

Christie's holds Toy sales on average every five to six weeks, most of which include diecast toys. The finest items are reserved for sales in May and September, with additional sales of special collections widely advertised beforehand.

Whether buying or selling, Christie's offers a comprehensive service to the collector, with detailed and well-presented catalogues giving the condition of each lot. Sales also include a large variety of tinplate cars, other toys and trains. We are always pleased to help buyers with any enquiries about condition of lots, absentee bidding and shipping arrangements.

For further information, please contact Hugo Marsh or Daniel Agnew on (071) 321 3274.

Old Brompton Road, London SW7 3LD
Tel: (071) 581 7611 Fax: (071) 321 3321

CHRISTIE'S

DINKY TOYS

Post and Pre-War Issues

For a list of models and prices realised see the Auction Results page. (6th Nov. 1992).

Picture reproduced by kind permission of Christie's, South Kensington, London.

DINKY TOYS

'The Ashley Collection of Dinky Toys'
For list of models and prices realised see the Auction Results page at the end of chapter.

Picture reproduced by kind permission of Christie's, South Kensington, London.

DINKY TOYS

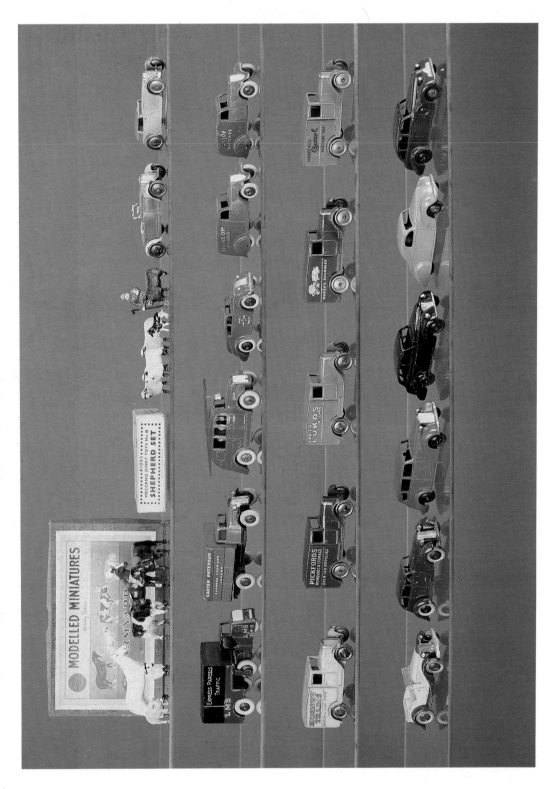

Pre-War Issues — For list of models and prices realised see the Auction Results page. (20th May 1992).

Pictured reproduced by kind permission of Christie's, South Kensington, London.

DINKY TOYS

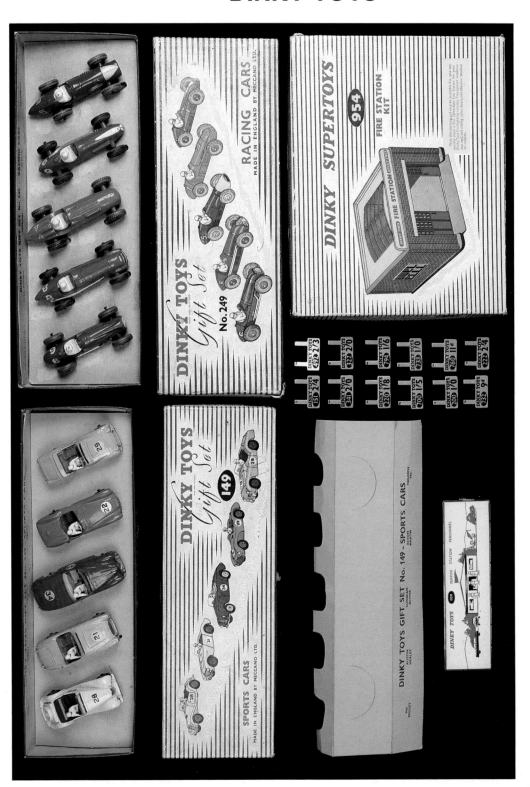

Pre-War Sets:- 149 Sports Car Set (G-E) £1,000
No 4 Racing Cars Set £528 Models (E) Box (Fair).
Bottom left: rare 009 Service Station Personnel Set plus 954 Fire Service Set. Sold as one lot for £440.
In the centre are some original Aluminium 'Dinky Toys', retail price tags — 108 different sold for £352.

Picture reproduced by kind permission of Christie's of South Kensington, London. Models sold at their May 1993 auction.

DINKY TOYS

Trade Boxes like these are listed in the Catalogue for the first time.

Gift Set 399
A scarce set

956 Turntable Fire Escape
Two Berliot 'large cab' versions

Dinky Dublo — made to enhance
'Hornby Dublo' Train layouts

Pre-War Garage No 45
Rare with its box

The models displayed on this page were photographed at the Swapmeet Publications Studio in Bury St Edmunds.

DINKY TOYS

Pre-War Set No 68 Camouflaged Aeroplanes £6,500
French Set No 64 Avions £2,200

Pre-War 28 Series Vans (2nd Type)

L–R: 28d 'Oxo', 28f 'Palethorpes Sausages' £380, 28g 'Kodak' (with fatigue) £180, 'Dunlop' £320, 28m 'Wakefield Castrol Motor Oil' £450, 28n 'Meccano' £380, 28n 'Atco Motor Mowers' £450, 28r 'Swans pens' £320 (F-G), 28w 'Osram Lamps' £450, 28x 'Hovis' (restored) £150, 280c 'Shredded Wheat' £450, 280e 'Ekco' £450, 280 Series promotional 'Maison de Bonneterie, Amsterdam, Den Haag' £900.

Models on this page sold by Phillips West Two, Salem Road, London and picture reproduced by their kind permission.

DINKY TOYS

Post war Export Gift Set
No 3 Private Automobiles
Sold for £2,300 in April 1993

No 189 Triumph Herald Saloon (2750)
March 1993
Note the correct red spot on the box end

No 465 'Capstan' Van (£190)
Mini Minor 1st type Vans — 273 'RAC' (£140), 274 'AA' (£110), 274 'Joseph Mason Paints' (£500)

No 504 Foden Tanker (2nd type cab)
Note the correct box and the 'Hudson Dobson'
U.S. distributor's red label
Sold for £4,800 in June 1993

No 902 Foden Flat Truck
(2nd type cab) in rare colours
Sold in March 1993 for £4,400

Models sold by Vectis Model Auctions at their Guildford Saleroom. The pictures are reproduced by their kind permission.

LONE STAR, TAYLOR & BARRETT, CHARBENS

MG 'TF' & Daimler Conquest Roadster

Darracq 1904 'Genevieve' Film Car

The models shown form part of the David Kerr collection and are shown by his kind permission.
(Swapmeet photos)

Taylor & Barrett No 197 Trolley Bus (small)
Pictured kindly supplied by Mike and Sue Richardson

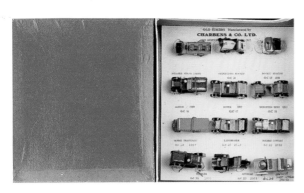

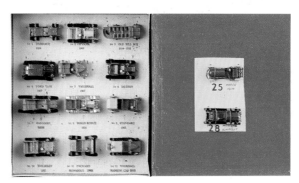

The 'Old Timers' Series
Pictures reproduced by kind permission of Christie's of South Kensington, London.

HORNBY DUBLO

3R 'Ludlow Castle'
Sold May 1993 £450

3R 'Dorchester'
Sold May 1993 £310

3R 'Bristolian Set'
Sold May 1993 £500

3R 'City of Liverpool'
Sold May 1993 £600

Pictures reproduced by kind permission of Vectis Model Auctions, Isle of Wight (see advertisement inside cover page).

HORNBY DUBLO

Rear cover of Christie's, South London, catalogue for the 'Great Hornby Dublo Collection' Sale and reproduced by their kind permission.
For sale results see Auction Prices at end of section.

MOKO TOYS

Models shown form part of the Patrick Talbot collection and are shown by his kind permission
(Swapmeet photos).

MATCHBOX MOKO-LESNEY

Presentation Set No 4
(Swapmeet photo)

Moko Lesney Design
changed to Lesney in 1958

MATCHBOX TOYS

1960's Trade Display stands — highly sought
after today.

Service Station Sets always a popular item

Later types of Gift Sets

MATCHBOX TOYS

Emergency Series

'Stingray'

MC 6 Intercom City Mega Set

1.18 Scale 'Masterclass'

Construction Series

'Matchbox Originals' Series

MC 24 Red Arrows Set

MC 803 Circus

Examples of the current range of Tyco Matchbox products.

MATCHBOX TOYS
'Models of Yesteryear'

Early to late Box types for same model
(Swapmeet photo)

Same model — different boxes
(Swapmeet photo)

Y21-3 Aveling & Porter
Steam Roller 1st Issue

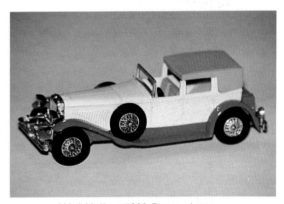

Y4-4 Yellow 1930 Duesenberg
Model 'J' Town Car

'Antiques Roadshow' 1st Issue

'Antiques Roadshow' 2nd Issue

The models pictured on the middle and lower rows form part of the John Clarke collection and are shown by his kind permission
(Swapmeet photos)

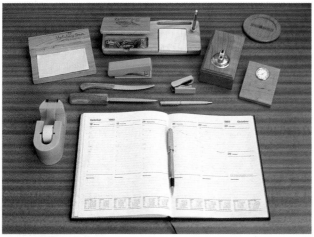

Dinky Toys - Motor Cycles

Ref. No.	Year(s)	Model Type	Model Features and Size	Market Price Range	
			See also Accessories and Gift Sets sections.		
			SWRW = solid White rubber wheels, SBRW = solid Black rubber wheels, (both are of a larger diameter than those used on the small cars).		
14z	1938-40	Three-wheel Delivery Van	'Triporteur' with Green, Red, Grey, Blue or Yellow body, Black hubs, White tyres, rider is always a different colour from van, French model	NGPP	☐
37a	1937-40	Civilian Motor Cyclist	Black cycle, fine paint detail, Blue, Green or Black rider, SWRW, 45 mm	£50-60	☐
	1946-49		Black cycle, crude paint detail, Green or Grey rider, SBRW	£25-30	☐
37a (041)	1950-54		Black cycle, crude paint detail, Green or Grey rider, SBRW, export only	£25-30	☐
37b	1937-40	Police Motor Cyclist	Black motor cycle, Silver detail, Blue rider, solid White rubber wheels	£35-45	☐
	1946-49		Black motorcycle, no detailing, Blue rider, solid Black rubber wheels	£50-60	☐
37b (042)	1950-54		Black motorcycle, no detailing, Blue rider, SBRW, export only	£50-60	☐
37c	1937-39	Signals Despatch Rider	Green motorcycle, Khaki rider, solid White rubber wheels, 45 mm.	£25-35	☐
	1939-41		Green motorcycle, Khaki rider, solid Black rubber wheels, 45 mm.	£25-35	☐
42b	1935-40	Police Motorcycle Patrol	Blue cycle, Green sidecar, Blue figures, detailing, SWRW, 47 mm	£50-60	☐
	1948-50		Blue cycle, Green sidecar, Blue figures, little detailing, SBRW, 47 mm	£25-35	☐
42b (043)	1950-55		Blue/Green, Blue figures, little detailing, SBRW, export only	£25-35	☐
43b	1935-40	R.A.C. Motorcycle Patrol	Black cycle, Blue rider with Red sash, detailing, SWRW, 46 mm.	£50-60	☐
	1946-49		Black cycle, Blue rider, little detailing, solid Black rubber wheels	£25-35	☐
44b	1935-40	A.A. Motorcycle Patrol	Black/Yellow, Brown rider, good detailing, 5 mm.'AA' badge, SWRW, 45 mm.	£50-60	☐
44b (270)	1946-50		Black/Yellow, Tan rider, little detailing, 7 mm.'AA' badge, SBRW, 45 mm.	£25-35	☐
44b (045)	1950-55		AS previous model but made for export only	£25-35	☐
270 (44b)	1959-62		Black/Yellow, Tan rider, 'AA' sign, solid Grey plastic wheels, 46 mm.	£25-35	☐
271	1959-62	T.S. Motorcycle Patrol	Yellow motorcycle combination, Belgian equivalent of the A.A.	£75-85	☐
272	1959-62	A.N.W.B. Motorcycle Patrol	Yellow motorcycle combination, Dutch equivalent of the A.A.	£75-85	☐

'Dinky Dublo' models

061	1958-59	Ford Prefect	Fawn or Grey body, Silver trim, Grey treaded wheels, 59 mm.	£40-50	☐
062	1958-60	Singer Roadster	Orange or Fawn body, Red interior, Silver trim, Grey treaded wheels, 50 mm.	£40-50	☐
063	1958-60	Commer Van	Blue body, Silver trim, Grey treaded wheels, 54 mm.	£35-40	☐
064	1957-62	Austin Lorry	Green body, Silver trim, Black or Grey treaded wheels, 64 mm.	£35-40	☐
065	1957-60	Morris Pick-up	Red body, Silver trim, Grey treaded wheels, 54 mm.	£40-50	☐
066	1959-66	Bedford Flat Truck	Grey body, Silver trim, Grey smooth wheels, with hook, 116 mm	£80-100	☐
			Grey body, Silver trim, Grey treaded wheels, without hook	£40-45	☐
067	1959-64	Austin Taxi	Blue lower body, Cream upper body, 'TAXI' sign, Black or Grey wheels, 59 mm.	£40-50	☐
068	1959-64	'ROYAL MAIL' Van	Morris 1000 van with Red body, 'E II R' crest, Silver trim, 47 mm.	£50-60	☐
069	1959-64	Massey Harris Tractor	Blue body, Silver trim, Grey treaded wheels, hole for driver, 36 mm.	£35-40	☐
070	1959-64	A.E.C. Mercury Tanker	Green cab, Red tank, Black or Grey treaded wheels, 'SHELL-BP', 91 mm.	£75-85	☐
071	1960-64	Volkswagen Delivery Van	Yellow body with Red 'HORNBY DUBLO' logo, Black treaded wheels, 54 mm.	£60-70	☐
072	1959-64	Bedford Articulated Truck	Yellow cab, Red semi-trailer, Black or Grey smooth wheels, 117 mm.	£40-50	☐
073	1960-64	Land Rover/Trailer/Horse	Green car (Grey wheels), Tan or White horse, 105 mm. Trailers:		
			with Bright Green trailer (Green ramp, smooth Grey wheels)	£40-50	☐
			with Green trailer (Brown ramp, treaded Grey wheels)	£100-125	☐
			with Bright Green trailer (Black ramp, treaded Black wheels)	£100-125	☐
076	1960-64	Lansing Bagnall (set)	Maroon tractor & trailer, Blue driver/seat, Black smooth wheels, hooks, 75 mm.	£40-50	☐
078	1960-64	Lansing Bagnall Trailer	Maroon body, hook, wire drawbar	£20-25	☐

Note: All the 'Dublo Dinky' wheels are made of plastic.

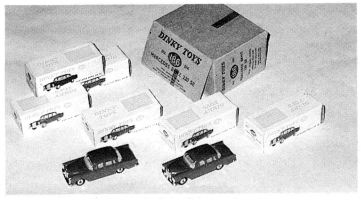

Trade Pack — Sold by Lacy Scott, Bury St Edmunds for £235.
Picture reproduced by their kind permission.

129

Dinky Toys - Caravans

Ref. No.	Year(s)	Model Type	Model Features and Size	Market Price Range	
30g	1936-39	Caravan Trailer	2 wheels, drawbar, body length 81 mm. open roof windows, Colours: Blue/Cream, Red/Cream, Green/Cream, Orange/Cream, Brown/Beige, TT-Green	**£50-60**	☐
	1939-40		As previous models but with filled-in roof windows....................................	**£50-65**	☐
30g	1948-50	Caravan	Orange/Cream body, 'Caravan Club', drawbar, body length 81 mm.	**£45-55**	☐
117	1963-69	Four Berth Caravan	Blue/Cream, clear roof, suspension, detailed interior, 117 mm.	**£25-35**	☐
			Yellow/Cream, clear roof, suspension, detailed interior, 117 mm......................	**£25-35**	☐
188	1961-63	Four Berth Caravan	Green/Cream or Blue/Cream, windows, detailed interior, 132 mm.	**£25-35**	☐
	1963-63		As previous model but larger windows, (this model replaced by 117)	**£25-35**	☐
190	1956-62	Caravan	Orange/Cream, or Blue/Cream, drawbar, metal jockey wheel, 118 mm.	**£25-35**	☐
	1962-64		Orange/Cream, or Blue/Cream, drawbar, plastic jockey wheel, 118 mm..............	**£25-35**	☐

Dinky Action Kits

These Action Kits were issued in the 1970s and have no model numbers on their bases. Paint supplied with the kit is not always the same colour or shade as on the relative model when supplied built and finished.

1001	1971-77	Rolls-Royce Phantom V...........	Various colours (usually Blue), casting as 152	**£20-30**	☐
1002	1971-75	Volvo 1800s Coupé..................	Yellow paint, casting as 116. Doubt exists as to the actual issue	NPP	
1003	1971-75	Volkswagen 1300	Red and White paint supplied, casting as 129..	**£20-30**	☐
1004	1971-77	Ford Escort Police Car	Blue and White paint with 'POLICE' transfers, casting as model 270...................	**£20-30**	☐
1006	1973-77	Ford Escort 'Mexico'	Red paint and 'MEXICO' transfers supplied, casting as model 168	**£20-30**	☐
1007	1971-75	Jensen FF	Various colours of paint (usually Blue), casting as 188	**£20-30**	☐
1008	1973-77	Mercedes-Benz 600	Red, Yellow or Green paint supplied, casting as model 128	**£20-30**	☐
1009	1971-75	Lotus F.1 Racing Car	Green paint and 'Gold leaf' transfers supplied, casting as 225	**£20-30**	☐
1012	1973-75	Ferrari 312-B2	Red paint and 'SHELL' transfers supplied, casting as 226............................	**£20-30**	☐
1013		Matra Sports M530	This item was considered for possible production but was never issued	NPP	
1014	1975-77	Beach Buggy	Blue paint supplied, casting as 227...	**£20-30**	☐
1017	1971-77	Routemaster Bus	Red paint and 'ESSO Safety-Grip Tyres' transfers in kit, casting as 289	**£20-30**	☐
1018	1974-77	Leyland Atlantean Bus.............	Various colours (mostly White), usually 'NATIONAL' transfers, model 295	**£40-50**	☐
1023	1972-77	A.E.C. Single Decker Bus	Green paint and 'GREEN LINE' transfers supplied, casting as 283	**£40-50**	☐
1025	1971-75	Ford Transit Van	Red paint and 'Avis Truck Rental' transfers in kit, casting as 407	**£20-30**	☐
1027	1972-75	Lunar Roving Vehicle	Blue/White paint, casting as model 355	**£20-30**	☐
1029	1971-77	Ford D800 Tipper Truck	Green or Yellow paint supplied, casting as model 438	**£20-30**	☐
1030	1974-77	Land Rover Breakdown Truck	Red or White paint in kit, casting as 442..	**£20-30**	☐
1032	1975-77	Army Land Rover	Military-Green paint and various 'ARMY' transfers in kit, casting as 344	**£20-30**	☐
1033	1971-77	U.S.A. Army Jeep	Military-Green paint and military transfers supplied, casting as 615	**£20-30**	☐
1034	1975-77	Mobile Gun	Military-Green paint in kit, casting as 654	**£20-30**	☐
1035	1975-77	Striker Anti-Tank Vehicle	Military-Green paint and transfer supplied, casting as 691	**£20-30**	☐
1036	1975-77	Leopard Tank	Military-Green paint and transfers supplied, casting as 692	**£20-30**	☐
1037	1974-77	Chieftain Tank	Military-Green paint and transfers, casting as 683	**£20-30**	☐
1038	1975-77	Scorpion Tank	Military-Green paint and transfers, casting as 690	**£20-30**	☐
1039		Leopard Recovery Tank...........	This item was considered for production but was never issued	NPP	
1040	1971-77	Sea King Helicopter	White with Blue or Orange paint plus 'USAF' transfers, casting as 724	**£20-30**	☐
1041	1973-76	Hawker Hurricane Mk.IIc	Camouflage paints and RAF roundels in kit, casting as 718..........................	**£30-35**	☐
1042	1971-77	Spitfire Mk.II	Camouflage paints and RAF roundels in kit, casting as 719..........................	**£25-35**	☐
1043	1974-76	S.E.P.E.C.A.T. Plane...............	Blue and Green paints and transfers supplied, casting as 731	**£20-30**	☐
1044	1972-75	Messerschmitt BF-109e	Brown paint and Luftwaffe transfers in kit, casting as 726	**£20-30**	☐
1045	1975-76	Multi-Role Combat Aircraft	Camouflage paints and transfers supplied, casting as 729	**£20-30**	☐
1050	1975-77	Motor Patrol Boat....................	Black/Blue/White paints/stickers, as model 675...	**£20-30**	☐

WHEN REPLYING TO ADVERTISEMENTS PLEASE MENTION JOHN RAMSAY'S CATALOGUE

A collection of mostly Dinky Toys sold by Bonhams of Chelsea.
Picture reproduced by their kind permission.

WHEN REPLYING TO ADVERTISEMENTS PLEASE MENTION JOHN RAMSAY'S CATALOGUE

'Dinky Toys' issued by Airfix Products Ltd

Issued by Airfix as **'DINKY TOYS'**; made in France to 1/43 scale.
Supplied in the last design of Red/Yellow/Blue 'Dinky Toys' window box with header card.

Ref. No.	Year(s)	Model Type	Model Features and Size	Market Price Range	
500	c1980	Citroën 2cv	Red/Orange body or Green body, 'Duck' motif, open roof	£5-15	☐
500	c1980	Citroën 2cv	Red/Orange body or Green body, 'Duck' motif, closed roof	£5-15	☐
501	c1980	Fiat Strada	Blue or Metallic Bronze body, no decals	£5-15	☐
502	c1980	BMW 530	Purple body with 'flame' decal on doors	£5-15	☐
502	c1980	BMW 530	Metallic Green with Black 'cougar' decal	£5-15	☐
503	c1980	Alfetta GTV	Red or Yellow body with Green 'shamrock' on bonnet	£5-15	☐
504	c1980	Citroën Visa	Red body, no decals	£5-15	☐
505	c1980	Peugeot 504	Blue body with 'flame' decal on doors	£5-15	☐
505	c1980	Peugeot 504	Greenish-Gold with Black 'panther' decal on doors	£5-15	☐
506	c1980	Alfa-Sud	Not seen	NGPP	☐
507	c1980	Renault 14	Not seen	NGPP	☐
508	c1980	Ford Fiesta	Not seen	NGPP	☐

COUGAR Model Toys. Many of the 'Airfix Dinky Toys' appeared erratically in the early 1980s (in France then in the UK), under the name of 'Cougar Model Toys' with these common features:
Plastic base marked *'Dinky Toys made in France'* and the code *'1/43 07 80'*.
Presented in a blister-pack on card with *'Metal Cougar'* and *'Fabrique par Solido'*.
Numbers printed on card are 100 less than numbers moulded on base. (TW = tinted windows)

1301-1401		Citroën 2cv6	Orange-Red body with 'ducks' decal, Grey base/interior/open roof	£10-15	☐
			Green body with 'ducks' decal, Grey base, Orange interior, Tan open roof	£10-15	☐
1302-1402		Citroën Visa	Metallic Jade Green, no decal, White plastic base, Dark Cream interior	£10-15	☐
			Metallic Red body, no decal, Grey plastic base and interior	£10-15	☐
1303-1403		Fiat Ritmo	Metallic Orange body, no decal, Dark Cream plastic base and interior	£10-15	☐
			Metallic Blue body, no decal, Yellow plastic base and interior	£10-15	☐
1304-1404		BMW 530	Metallic Green, 'Cougar' decal, Grey base, Black/Grey interior, Green TW	£10-15	☐
			Metallic Purple, 'flames' decal, Grey base, Black & Grey interior, Yellow TW	£10-15	☐
1305-1405		Alfetta GTV	Red body, 'shamrock' decal, Tan base, Black & Tan interior, Yellow TW	£10-15	☐
			Yellow body, 'shamrock' decal, Tan base, Black & Tan interior, Blue TW	£10-15	☐
1306-1406		Peugeot 504 Berline	Metallic Yellow, 'cougar' decal, Brown base & TW, Black/Brown interior	£10-15	☐
			Metallic Blue body, 'flames' decal, Blue base & interior, clear windows	£10-15	☐

AIRFIX - match-box size miniatures made in Hong Kong.
Although announced in 1980, only a few seem to have appeared in the UK.

101	c1980	'56 Corvette	White body with Red flash, bubble-packed, 68 mm.	£10-15	☐
103	c1980	Chevette Hatchback	Yellow body with 'Turbo' decal, bubble-packed, 68 mm.	£10-15	☐
104	c1980	Honda Accord	Lilac body with Orange flash, bubble-packed, 68 mm.	£10-15	☐
105	c1980	Toyota Celica	Red body, bubble-packed, 68 mm.	£10-15	☐
106	c1980	Datsun 280Z	Brown body, bubble-packed, 68 mm.	£10-15	☐
107	c1980	BMW Turbo	Orange body with Black and Yellow flash, bubble-packed, 68 mm.	£10-15	☐
108	c1980	Alfa Romeo	Purple body with Yellow flash, bubble-packed, 68 mm.	£10-15	☐
110	c1980	Stepside Pick-up	Blue and Brown body, bubble-packed, 68 mm.	£10-15	☐
111	c1980	Camper	Yellow and Two-tone Brown body, 68 mm.	£10-15	☐
113	c1980	Pick-up	Red and Black body, '4 x 4' decal, 68 mm.	£10-15	☐
114	c1980	Firebird	Black body, 68 mm.	£10-15	☐
115	c1980	Camaro	Red body with racing-number 'Z28', 68 mm.	£10-15	☐
116	c1980	'63 Corvette	Metallic Blue body, 68 mm.	£10-15	☐
117	c1980	'71 Corvette	Yellow body with 'Vette' decal, 68 mm.	£10-15	☐
119	c1980	Ford Van	Blue body with Orange flash, 68 mm.	£10-15	☐
120	c1980	Renegade Jeep	Yellow body with Green flash	£10-15	☐
121	c1980	Chevy Blazer	Red body, 68 mm.	£10-15	☐
122	c1980	Sun Van	Orange body with 'Sun Van' decal, 68 mm.	£10-15	☐
123	c1980	Yamaha 250 MX	Blue body with 'Yamaha' decal, 82 mm.	£10-15	☐
124	c1980	Honda MT 250	Orange body with 'Honda' decal, 82 mm.	£10-15	☐
125	c1980	Kawasaki FII 250	Red body with 'Kawasaki' decal, 82 mm.	£10-15	☐
126	c1980	Suzuki TM 400	Yellow and Black body with 'CCI' and 'Suzuki' decals, 82 mm.	£10-15	☐
129	c1980	T-Bird Convertible	Red and White body, 68 mm.	£10-15	☐
130	c1980	Chevy Convertible	Metallic Blue and White body	£10-15	☐

Dinky Toys Gift Sets

Ref. No.	Year(s)	Set Name	Contents	Market Price Range	

Pre-war sets without 'fatigue' and with pristine boxes attract a premium.
See also Accessories and Dinky Toys Trains sections

Ref. No.	Year(s)	Set Name	Contents	Market Price Range	
001 (1)	1954-56	Station Staff ('0' gauge)	1b Guard (flag in right hand), 1c Ticket Collector (right arm extended), 1d Driver, 1e Porter (with oblong bags), 1f Porter (standing)	£90-120	☐
002 (2)	1954-56	Farmyard Animals (6)	2 x 2a horses, 2 x 2b cows, 1 x 2c pig, 1 x 2d sheep, simplified painting	£200-300	☐
003 (3)	1954-56	Passengers ('0' gauge)	3a Woman (with child on left), 3b Businessman (Brown suit and case), 3c Male hiker (no stick), 3d Female hiker (Blue shirt), 3e Newsboy (Grey tray), 3f Woman (Light Red coat, round case)	£90-120	☐
004 (4)	1946-54	Engineering Staff ('0' gauge)	2 x 4b Fitter (all-Blue and all-Brown), 4c Storekeeper (all-Brown), 4d Greaser, 4e Engine-Room attendant	£90-120	☐
005 (5)	1954-56	Train & Hotel Staff ('0' gauge)	5a Conductor, 2 x 5b waiters, 2 x 5c Porter (both Brown or Blue)	£90-120	☐
006 (6)	1954-56	Shepherd Set	6a Shepherd (Green hat), 6b sheepdog (all-Black), 4 x 2b sheep	£150-200	☐
007	1960-67	Petrol Pump Attendants	1 male (White overalls), 1 female (White coat), plastic, 35 mm. tall	£15-20	☐
008	1961-67	Fire Station Personnel	Set of 6 fire-fighters in Blue uniforms plus hose, plastic, 35 mm. tall	£30-40	☐
009	1962-66	Service Station Personnel	Set of 8 plastic figures in various colours and stances, 35 mm. tall	£30-40	☐
010	1962-66	Road Maintenance Personnel	Set of 6 workmen using pick, barrow, shovels, drill etc, plus hut, brazier, barrier, and 4 lamps. Plastic, figures are 35 mm. tall	£60-70	☐
050	1961-68	Railway Staff ('00' gauge)	Set of 12 Blue plastic figures	£50-60	☐
051 (1001)	1954-59	Station Staff ('00' gauge)	Set of 6 Blue figures (re-issue of pre-war Hornby-Dublo Set D1)	£45-55	☐
053 (1003)	1954-59	Passengers ('00' gauge)	Set of 6 Blue figures (re-issue of pre-war Hornby-Dublo Set D2)	£45-55	☐
054	1962-70	Railway Station Personnel	Set of 12 mostly Blue plastic figures	£50-60	☐
1	1932-39	Station Staff (6)	1a Station Master, 1b Guard (flag in left hand), 1c Ticket Collector (with open arms), 1d Driver, 1e Porter (round/oblong bags), 1f Porter (walking)	£150-200	☐
1	1939-41	Station Staff (6)	1a and 1d as above, 1b Guard (flag in right hand), 1c Ticket Collector (right arm extended), 1e Porter (oblong bags), 1f Porter (standing)	£150-200	☐
1 (001)	1946-54	Station Staff (5)	1b Guard (flag in right hand), 1c Ticket Collector (right arm extended), 1d Driver, 1e Porter (with oblong bags), 1f Porter (standing)	£90-120	☐
No.1	1934-9	Railway Accessories Set	'Miniature Luggage and Truck'. A Porter's truck and 4 pieces of luggage (tinplate and cast), items not available separately	NGPP	☐
No.1	1946-48	Commercial Vehicles Set	29c Bus, 25b Wagon, 25d Tanker, 25e Tipper and 25f Market Gardeners Lorry, in mottled Greenish-Brown box, Blue/Beige label showing boy and 6 models	£1250-1750	☐
No.1 (398)	1952-54	Farm Equipment Gift Set	27a Massey-Harris Tractor, 27b Harvest Trailer, 27c Manure Spreader, 27h Disc Harrow, 27k Hay Rake. Blue and White striped box	£400-500	☐
No.1 (699)	1954-55	Military Vehicles Set	621 3-ton Wagon, 641 1-ton Truck, 674 Austin Champ, 676 Armoured Car	£300-400	☐
2	1934-35	Farmyard Animals	2 x 2a horses, 2 x 2b cows, 1 x 2c pig, 1 x 2d sheep, set presented in 'Modelled Miniatures' box	£750-1000	☐
2	1935-40	Farmyard Animals	Six items as previous set but displayed in 'Dinky Toys' box	£500-600	☐
2 (002)	1946-54	Farmyard Animals	Six items as previous set but simplified (less detailed) painting	£200-300	☐
No.2	1934-?	Railway Accessories Set	'Milk Cans and Truck'. A 4-wheel barrow & 6 milk churns, not available separately	NGPP	☐
No.2	1946-48	Private Automobiles Set	39a Packard, 39b Oldsmobile, 39c Lincoln, 39d Buick, 39e Chrysler	£1250-1750	☐
No.2	1952-53	Commercials Vehicles Set	25m Bedford End Tipper, 27d Land Rover (Dark Brown), 30n Farm Produce Wagon, 30p 'Mobilgas' Tanker and 30s Austin Covered Wagon	£2500-3500	☐
3	1932-39	Passengers	3a Woman (with child on right), 3b Businessman (left hand on chest), 3c Male hiker (with stick), 3d Female hiker (White shirt), 3e Newsboy (running), 3f Woman (Red jacket, oblong case)	£150-200	☐
3	1939-41	Passengers	3a Woman (with child on left), 3b Businessman (case in left hand), 3c Male hiker (no stick), 3d Female hiker (White shirt), 3e Newsboy (standing), 3f Woman (Dark Red coat, round case)	£125-175	☐
3 (003)	1946-54	Passengers	3a Woman (with child on left), 3b Businessman (Brown suit and case), 3c Male hiker (no stick), 3d Female hiker (with Blue shirt), 3e Newsboy (Grey tray), 3f Woman (Light Red coat, round case)	£90-120	☐
No.3	1934-?	Railway Accessories Set	'Platform Machines Etc'. A posting box, ticket machine, label machine and two benches, not available separately	NGPP	☐
No.3	1947-52	Private Automobiles Set	30d Vauxhall, 36a Armstrong, 36b Bentley, 38a Frazer-Nash, 39b Oldsmobile	£1250-1750	☐
No.3	1952-54	Passenger Cars Set	27f Estate Car, 30h Daimler Ambulance, 40e Standard Vanguard, 40g Morris Oxford, 40h Austin Taxi, 140b Rover 75	£4000-5000	☐
4	1932-41	Engineering Staff (6)	4a Electrician, 2 x 4b Fitter (Blue/White and Brown/White), 4c Storekeeper (Brown/Black), 4d Greaser, 4e Engine-Room attendant	£150-200	☐
4 (004)	1946-54	Engineering Staff (5)	2 x 4b Fitter (all-Blue and all-Brown), 4c Storekeeper (all-Brown), 4d Greaser, 4e Engine-Room attendant	£90-120	☐
No.4	1934-?	Railway Accessories Set	A combination of No.1 ('Miniature Luggage & Truck'), No.2 ('Milk Cans & Truck'), and No.3 ('Platform Machines Etc'). Individual items from these sets were not available separately	NGPP	☐
No.4 (249)	1953-54	Racing Cars Set	23f Alfa-Romeo, 23g Cooper-Bristol, 23h Ferrari, 23j HWM, 23k Talbot-Lago and 23n Maserati. Blue and White striped box (see 249)	£750-1000	☐
5	1932-39	Train and Hotel Staff	5a Conductor, 2 x 5b waiters, 2 x 5c Porter (1 Red, 1 Green)	£150-200	☐
5	1939-41	Train and Hotel Staff	5a Conductor, 2 x 5b waiters, 2 x 5c Porter (both Brown or Blue)	£125-175	☐
5 (005)	1946-54	Train and Hotel Staff	5a Conductor, 2 x 5b Waiter, 2 x 5c Porter (Brown or Blue) less detail	£90-120	☐
6	1934-36	Shepherd Set	6a Shepherd (Dark Brown smock, hat and leggings, Black boots, lamb under arm), 6b Collie dog (Black/White), 4 x 2b sheep (Beige, 'Hornby Series' cast-in) set presented in 'Modelled Miniatures' box	£500-750	☐
6	1936-40	Shepherd Set	As previous set but in 'Dinky Toys' box	£400-500	☐

133

Ref. No.	Year(s)	Model Type	Dinky Toys - continued	Market Price Range
6 (006)	1946-54	Shepherd Set	6a Shepherd (all Brown below neck, Green hat), 6b Collie dog (all Black), 4 x 2b sheep (without 'Hornby Series')	£150-200 ☐
No.6	1946-48	Commercial Vehicles Set	29c Bus, 29b Streamline Bus, 25h Fire Engine, 30e Breakdown Car, and 30f Ambulance. Mottled Greenish-Blue box with Beige/Blue label	£1200-1800 ☐
12	1938-40	Postal Set	12a GPO Pillar Box, 12b Air Mail Pillar Box, 12c Telephone Call Box, 12d Telegraph Messenger, 12e Postman, 34b Royal Mail Van	£350-450 ☐
15	1937-41	Railway Signals Set	1 x 15a 'Home' and 1 x 15a 'Distant' (single-arm signals) 2 x 15b 'Home/Distant' (double-arm signals), 1 x 15c 'Home' and 1 x 15c 'Distant' (double-arm signals)	£60-80 ☐
22	1933-35	Motor Vehicles Set	22a and 22b Cars, 22c Motor Truck, 22d Delivery Van, 22e Tractor, 22f Tank, Purple box lid with full-size full-colour label, 'Modelled Miniatures'	£2000-3000 ☐
23	1936-40	Racing Cars Set	23c Mercedes-Benz, 23d Auto-Union, 23e 'Speed of the Wind'. Blue box	£500-600 ☐
24	1934-40	Motor Cars Set	24a Ambulance, 24b Limousine, 24c Town Sedan, 24d Vogue Saloon, 24e Super Streamlined Saloon, 24f Sportsman's Coup, 24g Sports Tourer (2 seater), 24h Sports Tourer (4 seater). Blue box lid (with colour label), Purple inner	£5000-7000 ☐
25	1934-37	Commercial Motor Vehicles	25a Wagon, 25b Covered Wagon, 25c Flat Truck, 25d Tank Wagon, 25e Tipper, 25f Market Gardener's Lorry. Mauve 'grained' box lid (colour label)	£2000-3000 ☐
28/1	1934-40	Delivery Vans Set	(1st type) 28a Hornby, 28b Pickfords, 28c Manchester Guardian, 28d Oxo, 28e Ensign Lukos, 28f Palethorpes Sausages	£5000-7000 ☐
28/1		(Revised Vans Set)	28a Hornby, 28b Pickfords, 28c Manchester Guardian, 28e Firestone, 28f Palethorpes, 28n Atco Mowers	£5000-7000 ☐
28/2	1934-40	Delivery Vans Set	(1st type) 28g Kodak, 28h Sharps Toffees, 28k Marsh's, 28L Crawfords Biscuits, 28m Wakefield Castrol, 28n Meccano	£5000-7000 ☐
28/2		(Revised Vans Set)	28d Oxo, 28g Kodak, 28h Dunlop Tyres, 28k Marsh's, 28m Wakefield Castrol, 28h Crawfords	£5000-7000 ☐
28/3	1936-40	Delivery Vans Set	(2nd type) 28r Swan Pens, 28s Frys Chocolate, 28t Ovaltine, 28w Osram Lamps, 28x Hovis, 28y Exide Batteries	£2500-3500 ☐
30	1935-37	Motor Vehicles	30a Chrysler 'Airflow', 30b Rolls-Royce, 30c Daimler, 30d Vauxhall, 30e Breakdown Car (22c 2nd casting), 30f Ambulance	£3000-5000 ☐
30	1937-41	Motor Vehicles	As previous set but 30g Caravan replaces 30f Ambulance	£3000-5000 ☐
33	1935-37	Mechanical Horse and assorted Trailers	33a Mechanical Horse, 33b Flat Truck, 33c Open Wagon, 33d Box Van, 33e Dust Wagon, 33f Petrol Tank with 'WAKEFIELD CASTROL' logo. Blue 'grained' box lid, large colour label	£750-100 ☐
35	1935-40	Small Cars Set	35a Saloon Car, 35b Racer and 35c MG Sports Car	£400-500 ☐
36	1936-40	Motor Cars with Drivers, Passengers and Footmen	36a Armstrong-Siddeley, 36b Bentley, 36c Humber, 36d Rover, 36e British Salmson 2-seater, 36f British Salmson 4-seater, all with figures	£5000-7000 ☐
37a	1937-40	Motor Cycles Set	Six of 37a civilian Motor Cyclists in various colours with hand-painted detail, solid White rubber tyres. Blue box with Green and White pictorial inner	£300-400 ☐
37	1938-40	Motor Cycles Set	Contains 37a (civilian), 37b (Police), 37c (Signals Despatch)	£300-400 ☐
38	1940?	Open Sports Cars Set	Even if this set was planned, the demands of the War would have inhibited its production. 38e Triumph Dolomite would have been in this set if made!	NPP ☐
39	1939-41	USA Saloon Cars Set	39a Packard, 39b Oldsmobile, 39c Lincoln, 39d Buick, 39e Chrysler, 39f Studebaker. Mauve box with full colour label on lid	£1250-1750 ☐
42	1935-40	Police Set	42a Police Box, 42b Motor Cycle Patrol, 42c Point-Duty Policeman (White coat), 42d Point-Duty Policeman (Blue uniform), in Blue box with pictorial inner	£300-400 ☐
43	1935-40	'R.A.C.' Set	43a RAC Box, 43b RAC Motor Cycle Patrol, 43c RAC Guide directing traffic, 43d RAC Guide saluting. In Blue box with pictorial inner part	£350-450 ☐
44	1935-40	'A.A.' Set	44a AA Box, 44b AA Motor Cycle Patrol, 44c AA Guide directing traffic, 44d AA Guide saluting. The box is Blue with a pictorial inner part	£350-450 ☐
46	1937-40	Pavement Set	Dark Grey 'stone' effect (cardboard) pavement pieces in a box	£100-150 ☐
47	1935-40	Road Signs Set	12 road signs, 47e to 47t, (White under base, filled-in triangles)	£125-175 ☐
47 (770)	1946-50	Road Signs Set	12 road signs, 47e to 47t, (Black under base, open triangles)	£90-120 ☐
49	1935-40	Petrol Pumps Set	49a, 49b, 49c, 49d, 49e ('Pratts'). White rubber hoses, Yellow box	£90-120 ☐
49 (780)	1946-50	Petrol Pumps Set	49a, 49b, 49c, 49d, 49e (plain). Yellow plastic hoses, Yellow box	£80-90 ☐
50	1934-42	Ships of the British Navy	50a 'Hood', 50b 'Nelson', 50b 'Rodney', 50c 'Effingham', 50d 'York', 50e 'Delhi', 3 x 50f 'Broke', 50g 'X'-class Submarine, 3 x 50h 'Amazon', 50k 'K'-class Submarine. Blue box with Green/Blue label on lid	£150-200 ☐
51	1934-40	Great Liners Set	51b 'Europa', 51c 'Rex', 51d 'Empress of Britain', 51e 'Strathaird', 51f 'Queen of Bermuda', 51g 'Britannic'	£150-200 ☐
60	1934-39	Aeroplanes Set	60a Imperial Airways, 60b Leopard Moth, 60c Percival Gull, 60d Low-Wing Monoplane, 60e General Monospar, 60f Autogiro. Blue box, colour label	£1000-1500 ☐
60	1939-41	British Aeroplanes Set	As previous set but all planes (except 60f Autogiro) have 'GA-' markings	£900-1200 ☐
60s	1938-40	'Medium Bomber' Set	Two renumbered 62n Fairey 'Battle' Bombers in Stone-colour box	£150-200 ☐
60z	1937-40	'Avions' Set	French Aeroplanes Set with 60az 'Arc-en-Ciel', Hanriot 180t, 61az DeWetoine 500, Breguet Corsair, 60f Cierva Autogiro. Blue box	£900-1200 ☐
61	1937-41	R.A.F. Aeroplanes Set	60h 'Singapore' Flying Boat, 2 x 60n Fairey 'Battle' Bombers, 2 x 60p Gloster 'Gladiator' Biplanes. Contained in Blue box with full colour label on lid	£500-700 ☐
61z	1937-40	'Avions' Set	French Aeroplanes Set with DeWoitine D338, Potez 56, Potez 58, 61az DeWetoine 500d, Farman F360, 60f Cierva Autogiro. Blue box	£900-1200 ☐
62h	1937-41	Hawker Hurricane Trade Box	Six planes, camouflaged topsides, Black undersides, mounted on card base with 'DINKY TOYS No.62h HAWKER HURRICANE SINGLE SEATER FIGHTER'. Green box	£400-600 ☐

134

Ref. No.	Year(s)	Model Type	Dinky Toys - continued	Market Price Range	
62d	1939-41	Bristol Blenheim Bomber Trade Box	Six planes, camouflaged, mounted on card base with 'BRISTOL BLENHEIM BOMBER MARK IV - DINKY TOYS 62d', Green box	£400-600	☐
64	1939-41	Aeroplane Set	60g Light Racer, 62h 'Hurricane' (Camouflaged) 62k 'Kings Aeroplane', 62m Light Transport, 62s 'Hurricane' (Silver) 63b Seaplane 'Mercury'. (In 1940 either 62a 'Spitfire' or 62s were substituted for 62h and 62s)	£500-700	☐
64z	193?-4?	'Avions' Set	French Aeroplanes Set with 61az Dewoitine 'F-ADBF', 64a Amiot 370, 64b Bloch 220 'F-AOHJ', 64c Potez 63, 64d Potez 662 'F-ARAY'. Blue box, Yellow inner	£2000-2500	☐
65	1939-41	Aeroplane Set	60r Flying Boat, 60t 'DC3', 60v 'Whitely' Bomber, 60w 'Clipper III', 62n Junkers, 62p 'Ensign', 62r 'Albatross', 62w 'Frobisher'. Blue box	£900-1200	☐
66	1940-41	Camouflaged Aeroplane Set	66a Heavy Bomber, 66b Dive Bomber Fighter, 66c Fighter, 66d Torpedo, 66e Medium Bomber, 66f Army Autogiro (Silver). Yellow-Brown box	£3000-5000	☐
68	1940-41	Camouflaged Aeroplanes	2 x 60s 'Battle' Bombers, 2 x 62d 'Blenheim', 3 x 62h 'Hurricane' (Camouflage) 3 x 62s 'Hurricane' (Silver), 62t 'Whitely', 68a 'Ensign', 68b 'Frobisher'	£1500-2000	☐
101	1936-40	Dining-Room Furniture	101a Table, 101b Sideboard, 2 x 101c Carver Chair, 4 x 101d Chair	£300-400	☐
102	1936-40	Bedroom Furniture	102a Bed, 102b Wardrobe, 102c Dressing Table, 102d Dressing Chest, 102e Dressing Table Stool, 102f Chair. Brown or Pink. Green box	£300-400	☐
103	1936-40	Kitchen Furniture	103a Refrigerator, 103b Kitchen Cabinet, 103c Electric Cooker, 103d Table, 103e Chair. Light Blue/White or Light Green/Cream	£300-400	☐
104	1936-40	Bathroom Furniture	104a Bath, 104b Bath Mat, 104c Pedestal Basin, 104d Stool, 104e Linen Basket, 104f Toilet. Brown or Pink. Green box	£300-400	☐
118	1965-69	Towaway Glider Set	135 Triumph 2000 (Cream/Blue), Cream/Red trailer, Yellow glider	£150-200	☐
121	1963-66	Goodwood Racing Set	112 Austin-Healey Sprite, 113 MGB, 120 Jaguar, 182 Porsche, 9 figures	£1000-1200	☐
122	1963-65	Touring Gift Set	188 Caravan, 193 Station Wagon, 195 Jaguar, 270 'AA' Patrol, 295 Atlas Kenebrake, 796 Healey Sports Boat on Trailer	£1200-1500	☐
123	1963-65	Mayfair Gift Set	142 Jaguar, 150 Rolls-Royce, 186 Mercedes-Benz, 194 Bentley, 198 Rolls-Royce, 199 Austin Mini Countryman, and 4 figures	£1500-2000	☐
124	1964-66	Holiday Gift Set	952 Vega Luxury Coach, 137 Plymouth, 142 Jaguar, 796 Healey Sports Boat	£400-500	☐
125	1964-66	Fun Ahoy! Set	130 Ford Corsair with driver, 796 Healey Sports Boat with pilot	£100-150	☐
126	1967-68	Motor Show Set	127 Rolls-Royce, 133 Cortina, 151 Vauxhall Victor 101, 171 Austin 1800	£1200-1500	☐
126	1968-69	Motor Show Set	127 Rolls-Royce, 159 Cortina, 151 Vauxhall Victor 101, 171 Austin 1800	£1200-1500	☐
149	1958-61	Sports Cars Set	107 Sunbeam Alpine, 108 MG Midget, 109 Austin-Healey, 110 Aston-Martin, 111 Triumph TR2, all in 'competition finish'. Blue/White striped box	£1000-1200	☐
150	1937-41	Royal Tank Corps Personnel	150a Officer, 2 x 150b Private, 2 x 150c Private, 150e N.C.O.	£200-300	☐
151	1937-41	Medium Tank Set	151a Tank, 151b 6-wheel Wagon, 151c Cooker Trailer, 151d Water Tank Trailer, 150d Royal Tank Corps Driver. Blue box with pictorial inner	£300-400	☐
152	1937-41	Light Tank Set	152a Tank, 152b Reconnaissance Car, 152c Austin 7 Car with 150d Royal Tank Corps Driver. Blue box with pictorial inner	£300-400	☐
156	1939-41	Mechanised Army Set	151a Tank, 151b 6-wheel Wagon, 151c Cooker Trailer, 151d Water Tank Trailer, 152a Tank, 152b Reconnaissance Car, 152c Austin 7 Car with 150d Royal Tank Corps Driver, 161a Lorry with Searchlight, 161b A.A. Gun on Trailer, 162a Light Dragon Tractor, 162b Ammunition Trailer, 162c 18-ponder Gun. Blue box with speckled Beige display inner, with 'Dinky Toys No.156', 'Over 300 Varieties' and '100 per cent British'	£4000-5000	☐
160 (606)	1939-53	Royal Artillery Personnel	160a N.C.O., 2 x 160b Gunner, 160c Gunlayer, 2 x 160d Gunner (standing) Production of this set continued after the War but only for export (to USA)	£150-200	☐
161	1939-41	Mobile Anti-Aircraft Unit	161a Lorry with Searchlight and 161b A.A. Gun on Trailer, in Blue box	£600-800	☐
162	1939-54	18-pounder Field Gun Unit	162a Light Dragon Tractor, 162b Ammunition Trailer, 162c Gun. Blue box	£150-200	☐
201	1965-68	Racing Cars Set	240 Cooper, 241 Lotus, 242 Ferrari, 243 B.R.M.	£600-800	☐
240	1978-80	Dinky Way Set	211 Triumph TR7, 255 Police Mini, 382 Dump Truck, 412 Bedford Van, 20ft of 'roadway', 20 road signs, decal sheet	£50-60	☐
245	1969-73	Superfast Gift Set	131 Jaguar 'E'-type, 153 Aston-Martin DB6, 188 Jensen FF	£100-150	☐
246	1969-73	International Gift Set	187 De Tomaso Mangusta, 215 Ford GT, 216 Ferrari Dino	£100-150	☐
249	1962-63	World Famous Racing Cars	230 Talbot-Lago, 231 Maserati, 232 Alfa-Romeo, 233 Cooper-Bristol, 234 Ferrari, 239 Vanwall. Bubble-packed onto large display card	NGPP	☐
294	1973-77	Police Vehicles Gift Set	250 Mini-Cooper, 254 Range-Rover, 287 Accident Unit. (Replaces Set 297)	£50-60	☐
297	1963-73	Police Vehicles Gift Set	250 Mini-Cooper, 255 Ford Zodiac, 287 Accident Unit. (Replaced by Set 294)	£60-70	☐
298	1963-66	Emergency Services Set	258 Ford Fairlane, 263 Ambulance, 276 Fire Tender, 277 Ambulance, figures	£600-800	☐
299	1957-59	Post Office Services	260 'Royal Mail' Morris Van, 261 'GPO Telephones' Van, 750 Call Box, 011 Messenger, 012 Postman (but no Pillar Box!) Blue and White striped box	£350-450	☐
299	1963-66	Motorway Services Set	434 Bedford Crash Truck, 269 Motorway Police Car, 257 Fire Chief's Car, 276 Airport Fire Tender, 263 (later 277) Criterion Ambulance	£800-1000	☐
299	1978-79	Crash Squad Action Set	244 Plymouth Police Car and 732 Bell Helicopter	£35-45	☐
300	1973-77	London Scene Set	Contains 289 Routemaster Bus 'ESSO' and 284 London Taxi	£30-40	☐
302	1979-?	Emergency Squad Gift Pack	Paramedic Truck and Plymouth Fire Chief Car plus figures of Gage and DeSoto. Advertised but not issued	NPP	☐
303	1978-80	Commando Squad Gift Set	687 Convoy Army Truck, 667 Armoured Car, 732 Army helicopter	£75-100	☐
304	1978-79	Fire Rescue Gift Set	195 Fire Chief Range Rover, 282 Land Rover, 384 Convoy Fire Truck	£60-80	☐
306	1979-?	'Space' Gift Pack	358 'USS Enterprise', 357 Klingon Battle Cruiser, plus Galactic War Chariot. A set advertised but not issued	NPP	☐
307	1979-?	'New Avengers' Gift Pack	Purdey's TR7, John Steed's Special Leyland Jaguar, plus a 'fly-off' assailant! An intended set advertised but not issued	NPP	☐

Ref. No.	Year(s)	Model Type	Dinky Toys - continued	Market Price Range	
309	1978-80	Star Trek Gift Set......	357 Klingon Battle Cruiser and 358 'USS Enterprise'	£80-100	☐
398 (No.1)	1954-64	Farm Equipment Gift Set	300 Massey-Harris Tractor, 320 Harvest Trailer, 321 Manure Spreader,		
			322 Disc Harrow, 324 Hay Rake. Grey box, Red and Yellow overprinting.........	£600-800	☐
399	1969-73	Farm Tractor & Trailer............	300 Massey-Harris Tractor and 428 Large Trailer (Red/Silver)...............	£100-125	☐
399	1977-79	'Convoy' Gift Set	380 Skip Truck, 381 Farm Truck, 382 Dumper Truck. 'Window' box.........	£20-30	☐
606 (160)	1954-55	Royal Artillery Personnel.........	1 x 160a, 2 x 160b, 1 x 160c, 2 x 160d. Export only (to USA).........	£150-200	☐
616	1976-78	AEC Transporter and Tank......	Militarised version of 974 with 683 Chieftain Tank and camouflage net	£65-80	☐
618	1976-79	Transporter and Helicopter......	Militarised versions of 974 and 724 with camouflage netting	£50-60	☐
619	1976-78	Bren-Gun Carrier Set	622 Bren-Gun Carrier and 625 6-pounder Anti-Tank Gun	£20-30	☐
677	1972-75	Task Force Set........................	680 Ferret Armoured Car, 681 D.U.K.W., 682 Stalwart Load Carrier	£50-60	☐
695	1962-66	Howitzer and Tractor...............	689 Medium Artillery Tractor and 693 7.2in. Howitzer	£250-350	☐
697	1957-71	Field Gun Set........................	688 Field Artillery Tractor, 687 Trailer, 686 25-pounder Field Gun	£80-100	☐
698	1957-65	Tank Transporter Set	660 Mighty Antar Tank Transporter and 651 Centurion Tank	£120-150	☐
699 (No.1)	1955-58	Military Vehicles Set	621 3-ton Wagon, 641 1-ton Truck, 674 Austin Champ, 676 Armoured Car......	£250-350	☐
754	1958-62	Pavement Set	Twenty various Grey cardboard pieces representing paving..................	£20-30	☐
766	1959-64	British Road Signs................	Country Set 'A'. Six signs of the times, mostly 55 mm high. Yellow box.........	£100-125	☐
767	1959-64	British Road Signs................	Country Set 'B'. Six signs of the times, mostly 55 mm high. Yellow box.........	£100-125	☐
768	1959-64	British Road Signs................	Town Set 'A'. Six signs of the times, mostly 55 mm high. Yellow box.........	£100-125	☐
769	1959-64	British Road Signs................	Town Set 'B'. Six signs of the times, mostly 55 mm high. Yellow box.........	£100-125	☐
770 (47)	1950-54	Road Signs Set	12 road signs, 47e to 47t, (Black under base, open triangles) US export only ...	£125-175	☐
771	1953-65	International Road Signs	Set of 12 various road signs with Silver posts and bases, in Yellow box	£100-125	☐
772	1959-63	British Road Signs................	(Sets 766, 767, 768 and 769). 24 various road signs in a Red/Yellow box	£200-250	☐
780 (49)	1950-54	Petrol Pumps Set	49a, 49b, 49c, 49d, 49e (plain). Yellow plastic hoses, export only	£90-110	☐
784	1972-74	Dinky Goods Train Set............	Blue loco 'GER', one Red Truck, one Yellow Truck.........	£30-40	☐
851	1961-	Sets of vehicle 'Loads'............	Two each of 846 Oil Drums, 847 Barrels, 849 Packing Cases and 850 Crates............	£30-40	☐
900	1964-70	'Site Building' Gift Set	437 Muir-Hill Loader, 960 Albion Concrete Mixer, 961 Blaw-Knox Bulldozer,		
			962 Muir-Hill Dumper, 965 Euclid Rear Dump Truck. Grey/Red/Yellow box	£600-800	☐
950	1969-70	Car Transporter Set..............	974 AEC Car Transporter with 136 Vauxhall Viva, 138 Hillman Imp,		
			162 Triumph 1300, 168 Ford Escort, 342 Austin Mini-Moke. Not issued	NPP	☐
957	1959-65	Fire Services Gift Set.............	257 Fire Chief's Car, 955 Fire Engine, 956 Turntable Fire Escape	£300-400	☐
990	1956-58	Car Transporter Set..............	Contains 982 Pullmore Car Transporter and these cars:		
			154 Hillman Minx (Light Green/Cream), 156 Rover 75 (Cream/Blue),		
			161 Austin Somerset (Red/Yellow), 162 Ford Zephyr (Green/White)	£1500-2000	☐
1001 (051)	?-1954	Station Staff ('00' gauge)..........	Set of 6 Blue figures (re-issue of pre-war Hornby-Dublo Set D1).........	£45-55	☐
1003 (053)	?-1954	Passengers ('00' gauge)	Set of 6 Blue figures (re-issue of pre-war Hornby-Dublo Set D2).........	£45-55	☐

Dinky Toys   -   Accessories (Pre-War)

See also Gift Sets.

Ref. No.	Year(s)	Accessory	Details	Market Price Range	
1a	1932-41	Station Master	Dark Blue uniform (cap, long coat)	£20-30	☐
1b	1932-39	Guard................................	Dark Blue uniform (cap, jacket), blowing whistle, flag in left hand.........	£20-30	☐
1b	1939-41	Guard................................	Dark Blue uniform (cap, jacket), blowing whistle, flag in right hand.........	£20-30	☐
1c	1932-41	Ticket Collector	Dark Blue uniform (cap, jacket), slightly open arms	£20-30	☐
1d	1932-39	Driver................................	Dark Blue uniform (cap, jacket), holding oil-can	£20-30	☐
1e	1932-39	Porter with Bags....................	Dark Blue uniform, oblong case in right hand, round hat-box in left	£20-30	☐
1e	1939-41	Porter with Bags....................	Dark Blue uniform, oblong case in each hand.........	£20-30	☐
1f	1932-39	Porter...............................	Dark Blue uniform, walking, no luggage	£20-30	☐
1f	1939-41	Porter...............................	Dark Blue uniform, standing, no luggage	£20-30	☐
2a	1932-41	Horses	One Light Brown or Dark Brown horse, one White horse.........	£20-30	☐
2b	1932-41	Cow.................................	3 versions were available; Light Brown, Dark Brown, or Black and White	£10-15	☐
2c	1932-41	Pig..................................	A Pink porker	£10-15	☐
2d	1932-41	Sheep...............................	White sheep with Black hand-painted detail	£10-15	☐
3a	1932-39	Woman and Child	Woman in Green coat, child (in Red) is on woman's right	£20-30	☐
3a	1939-41	Woman and Child	Woman in Green suit with Grey scarf and Red hat, child on woman's left	£20-30	☐
3b	1932-39	Business Man	Dark Blue suit/hat, walking stick in right hand, left hand holds lapels	£20-30	☐
3b	1939-41	Business Man	Grey suit, left hand holds attach case	£20-30	☐
3c	1932-39	Male Hiker	Brown clothing, Khaki rucksack, stick in right hand	£20-30	☐
3c	1939-41	Male Hiker	Brown clothing, Khaki rucksack, no stick	£20-30	☐
3d	1932-41	Female Hiker	Blue skirt, White shirt, stick in right hand	£20-30	☐
3e	1932-39	Newsboy	Brown or Blue clothing, running, papers in right hand and under left arm	£20-30	☐
3e	1939-41	Newsboy	Dark Blue clothing, standing, papers in Cream tray	£20-30	☐
3f	1932-39	Woman	Red jacket, White skirt, coat over left arm, oblong case in right hand	£20-30	☐
3f	1939-41	Woman	Dark Red coat, Black collar, coat over left arm, round case in right hand	£20-30	☐
4a	1932-41	Electrician	Blue overalls, White sleeves, carrying equipment	£10-15	☐
4b	1932-41	Fitter (2 versions)	One in Blue overalls, the other Brown, White sleeves, carrying equipment	£10-15	☐
4c	1932-41	Storekeeper	Brown coat, Black trousers, holding forms in right hand, casting as 1a.........	£10-15	☐
4d	1932-41	Greaser	Brown overalls, holding oil-can in right hand, casting based on 1d.........	£10-15	☐
4e	1932-41	Engine-Room Attendant	Blue overalls, with or without White sleeves	£10-15	☐

Ref. No.	Year(s)	Model Type	Dinky Toys - continued	Market Price Range	
5a	1932-41	Pullman Car Conductor	White jacket, Blue trousers, slightly open arms, casting as 1c	**£20-30**	☐
5b	1932-41	Pullman Car Waiter	White jacket, Blue trousers, two slightly different poses were available	**£20-30**	☐
5c	1932-41	Hotel Porter.............................	Red jacket/Brown trousers, or Green jacket/Blue trousers, casting as 1e	**£20-30**	☐
6a	1932-41	Shepherd	Brown with Dark Brown hat	**£50-75**	☐
6b	1932-41	Sheep-dog	Black and White sheep-dog	**£20-30**	☐
12a	1935-40	G.P.O. Pillar Box 'G.R.'	Red, with or without Red/Yellow 'Post Office' sign on top, White panel, 50 mm.......	**£25-30**	☐
12b	1935-40	Air Mail Pillar Box	Blue body, 'Air Mail', White panel, casting as 12a, 50 mm.	**£35-40**	☐
12c	1936-40	Telephone Box	Cream with Silver windows, or Red with Black window frames, 58 mm.	**£15-20**	☐
12d	1938-40	Telegraph Messenger	Dark Blue body, picked out detail in darker Blue, Brown pouch, 35 mm.	**£15-20**	☐
12e	1938-40	Postman	Dark Blue body, darker Blue detail, Brown post bag and badge, 35 mm...................	**£15-20**	☐
13	1931-40	'HALLS DISTEMPER'	Figures (lead) usually White, Cream (cardboard) panel, Red lettering	**£250-300**	☐
15a	1937-41	Single Arm Signal....................	One Red ('Home') signal, or Yellow ('Distant') signal, 65 mm. high.........................	**£20-30**	☐
15b	1937-41	Double Arm Signal	One Red ('Home') signal and one Yellow ('Distant') signal on single pole	**£20-30**	☐
15c	1937-41	Junction Signal	Two Red ('Home') signals, OR two Yellow ('Distant') signals on single pole............	**£20-30**	☐
42a	1936-40	Police Box	Dark Blue box, 'POLICE' in Silver, 66 mm. high..	**£20-25**	☐
42c	1936-40	Point Duty Policeman	(cast in lead), White coat, Black helmet, 42 mm. tall..	**£20-25**	☐
42d	1936-40	Point Duty Policeman	(cast in lead), Dark Blue uniform, White gauntlets, 40 mm. tall	**£20-25**	☐
43a	1935-40	'R.A.C.' Box	Blue and White (tinplate) call-box with 'R.A.C.' emblem, 51 mm.	**£100-125**	☐
43c	1935-40	'R.A.C.' Guide	(cast in lead), Blue uniform, Red sash, directing traffic, 37 mm. tall.........................	**£20-25**	☐
43d	1935-40	'R.A.C.' Guide (saluting)	(cast in lead), Blue uniform with Red sash, 36 mm. tall	**£20-25**	☐
44a	1935-40	'A.A.' Box	Black/Yellow tinplate box with 'A.A.' badge and 3 signs, 81 mm.............................	**£100-125**	☐
44c	1935-40	'A.A.' Guide	(cast in lead), Tan uniform, Blue sash, directing traffic, 37 mm. tall.........................	**£20-25**	☐
44d	1935-40	'A.A.' Guide (saluting).............	(cast in lead), Tan uniform, Blue sash, 36 mm. tall	**£20-25**	☐
45	1935-40	Garage	Cream/Orange (tinplate) garage, Green opening doors, boxed, 127 x 90 mm............	**£250-350**	☐
46	1937-40	Pavement Set	Dark Grey 'stone' effect (cardboard) pavement pieces in a box	**£100-150**	☐
47a	1935-40	4-face Traffic Lights.................	Black on White post, Yellow beacon, White base, 62 mm. high	**£20-30**	☐
47b	1935-40	3-face Traffic Lights.................	Black on White post, Yellow beacon, White base, 62 mm. high	**£20-30**	☐
47c	1935-40	2-face Traffic Lights.................	Back-to-back lights, Black on White post, Yellow beacon, White base	**£20-30**	☐
47c	1935-40	2-face Traffic Lights.................	Lights at 90 degrees, Black on White post, Yellow beacon, White base	**£20-30**	☐
47d	1935-40	Belisha Beacon	Black on White post, Orange globe, White base, 51 mm. high	**£20-30**	☐
47e	1935-40	'30 MPH' Limit Sign.................	Black on White post, Red top '30', 52 mm. high..	**£20-30**	☐
47f	1935-40	De-restriction Sign...................	Black on White post, diagonal Black bar on White circle, 52 mm. high.....................	**£20-30**	☐
47g	1935-40	'School' Sign	Black on White post, Red top, Black 'beacon' design, 51 mm. high...........................	**£20-30**	☐
47h	1935-40	'Steep Hill' Sign	Black on White post, Red top, Black 'incline' design, 51 mm. high............................	**£20-30**	☐
47k	1935-40	'S-Bend' Sign	Black on White post, Red top, Black 'S-Bend' design, 51 mm. high...........................	**£20-30**	☐
47m	1935-40	'Left-Hand Bend' Sign	Black on White post, Red top, Black 'curve' design, 51 mm. high..............................	**£20-30**	☐
47n	1935-40	'Right-Hand Bend' Sign	Black on White post, Red top, Black 'curve' design, 51 mm. high..............................	**£20-30**	☐
47p	1935-40	'T-Junction' Sign	Black on White post, Red top, Black 'T' design, 51 mm. high....................................	**£20-30**	☐
47q	1935-40	'No Entry' Sign	Black on White post, Red 'bar' design, 48 mm. high...	**£20-30**	☐
47r	1935-40	'Major Road Ahead' Sign	Black on White post, Red top, Black lettering, 54 mm. high	**£20-30**	☐
47s	1935-40	'Crossing. No Gates' Sign	Black on White post, Red top, Black 'loco' design, 51 mm. high	**£20-30**	☐
47t	1935-40	'Roundabout' Sign	Black on White post, Red top, Black 'arrows' design, 51 mm. high	**£20-30**	☐
48	1935-40	Filling/Service Station	Yellow with Blue or Green base, Green, Brown or Yellow roof, tinplate	**£125-175**	☐
49a	1935-53	Bowser Petrol Pump.................	Green pump body, White rubber hose, (Yellow plastic post-war), 46 mm.	**£20-25**	☐
49b	1935-53	Wayne Petrol Pump..................	Pale Blue pump, White rubber hose, (Yellow plastic post-war), 39 mm.	**£20-25**	☐
49c	1935-53	Theo Petrol Pump.....................	Royal Blue pump, White rubber hose, (Yellow plastic post-war), 58 mm.	**£20-25**	☐
49d	1935-53	'SHELL' Petrol Pump...............	Red pump body, White rubber hose, (Yellow plastic post-war), 53 mm......................	**£20-25**	☐
49e	1935-40	'Pratts' Oil Bin......................	Yellow bin body and opening tinplate lid, 'Pratts Motor Oil', 32 mm.		
			49e was only available post-war in Set 49 and without 'Pratts' logo	**£20-30**	☐
101a	1935-40	Dining Table............................	'Wood' effect dining-room table, 64 mm.	*	☐
101b	1935-40	Sideboard.................................	'Wood' effect sideboard with opening doors, tinplate back, 63 mm.	*	☐
101c	1935-40	Carver chair.............................	'Wood' effect chair with armrests, 33 mm. high..	*	☐
101d	1935-40	Dining Chair............................	'Wood' effect chair without armrests, raised 'leather' cushion..................................	*	☐
102a	1935-40	Bed...	Brown or Pink double bed, 74 mm.	*	☐
102b	1935-40	Wardrobe..................................	Brown or Pink wardrobe with opening door, tinplate back, 63 mm.	*	☐
102c	1935-40	Dressing Table..........................	Brown or Pink, opening drawers, tinplate mirror, 51 mm.	*	☐
102d	1935-40	Dressing Chest.........................	Brown or Pink, opening drawer, tinplate back, 40 mm. high	*	☐
102e	1935-40	Dressing Table Stool	Brown or Pink stool, 13 mm. high	*	☐
103a	1935-40	Refrigerator..............................	Light Blue/White or Light Green/Cream, door, tinplate back & food tray	*	☐
103b	1935-40	Kitchen Cabinet........................	Light Blue/White or Light Green/Cream, opening doors/drawer, tin back	*	☐
103c	1935-40	Electric Cooker.........................	Light Blue/White or Light Green/Cream, opening door, tinplate back	*	☐
103d	1935-40	Kitchen Table...........................	Light Blue/White or Light Green/Cream, 34 mm. high	*	☐
103e	1935-40	Kitchen Chair...........................	Light Blue/White or Light Green/Cream, casting as 102f	*	☐
104a	1935-40	Bath	Pink/White or Light Green/White, Gold taps, 69 mm.	*	☐
104b	1935-40	Bath Mat	Mottled Green (rubber) mat, 50 x 37 mm.	*	☐
104c	1935-40	Pedestal Hand Basin.................	Pink/White or Light Green/White, Gold taps, tinplate mirror, 63 mm.	*	☐
104d	1935-40	Bathroom Stool	Pink/White or Light Green/White, 15 mm. high...	*	☐
104e	1935-40	Linen Basket.............................	Pink/White or Light Green/White, hinged lid, 22 mm. high.......................................	*	☐
104f	1935-40	Toilet..	Pink/White or Light Green/White, hinged lid, 34 mm. high.......................................	*	☐

Ref. No.	Year(s)	Model Type	Dinky Toys - continued		Market Price Range
	1935-40	'Dolly Varden' Dolls House......	Not given a reference number, made of 'leather board' (heavy reinforced cardboard), and supplied packed flat. Cream/Brown upper storey, Red brick ground floor, Red roof. 476 x 260 mm. base, 476 mm. high.		NGPP ☐

* Note: It is not really possible to give individual prices for single 'Dolly Varden' items as they are very rarely available in collectable condition. Boxed sets sell for £200-300 for example. See Gifts Sets section for more price information.

Dinky Toys   -   Accessories (Post-War)

Sets of accessories may also be found in the Gift Sets section

Ref. No.	Year(s)	Accessory	Details		Market Price Range
001 (1)	1954-56	Station Staff ('0' gauge)............	1b Guard (flag in right hand), 1c Ticket Collector (right arm extended), 1d Driver, 1e Porter (with oblong bags), 1f Porter (standing).................................		**£90-120** ☐
002 (2)	1954-56	Farmyard Animals (6)................	2 x 2a horses, 2 x 2b cows, 1 x 2c pig, 1 x 2d sheep, simplified painting.....................		**£200-300** ☐
003 (3)	1954-56	Passengers ('0' gauge)................	3a Woman (with child on left), 3b Businessman (Brown suit and case), 3c Male hiker (no stick), 3d Female hiker (Blue shirt), 3e Newsboy (Grey tray), 3f Woman (Light Red coat, round case)		**£90-120** ☐
004 (4)	1946-54	Engineering Staff ('0' gauge)	2 x 4b Fitter (all-Blue and all-Brown), 4c Storekeeper (all-Brown), 4d Greaser, 4e Engine-Room attendant		**£90-120** ☐
005 (5)	1954-56	Train & Hotel Staff ('0' gauge)	5a Conductor, 2 x 5b waiters, 2 x 5c Porter (both Brown or Blue)		**£90-120** ☐
006 (6)	1954-56	Shepherd Set............................	6a Shepherd (Green hat), 6b sheepdog (all-Black), 4 x 2b sheep.......................		**£150-200** ☐
007	1960-67	Petrol Pump Attendants............	1 male (White overalls), 1 female (White coat), plastic, 35 mm. tall		**£15-20** ☐
008	1961-67	Fire Station Personnel	Set of 6 fire-fighters in Blue uniforms plus hose, plastic, 35 mm. tall........................		**£30-40** ☐
009	1962-66	Service Station Personnel	Set of 8 plastic figures in various colours and stances, 35 mm. tall...........................		**£30-40** ☐
010	1962-66	Road Maintenance Personnel....	Set of 6 workmen using pick, barrow, shovels, drill etc, plus hut, brazier, barrier, and 4 lamps. Plastic, figures are 35 mm. tall...		**£60-70** ☐
011 (12d)	1954-56	Telegraph Messenger	Mid-Blue body, detailing in darker Blue, Brown pouch, 35 mm.		**£10-15** ☐
012 (12e)	1954-56	Postman	Mid-Blue body, darker Blue detail, Brown post bag and badge, 35 mm.		**£15-20** ☐
013 (13a)	1954-56	Cook's Man	(An Agent for the Thomas Cook travel company), Dark Blue coat, 40 mm. high.........		**£20-30** ☐
036		Battery	1.5 volt battery for use with models 276 & 277		NGPP ☐
037		Lamp	Red light-bulb for use with model 277		NGPP ☐
038		Lamp	Blue (or Orange) light-bulb for use with model 276		NGPP ☐
039		Lamp	Clear light-bulb for use with model 952		NGPP ☐
081		Spare tyre	White fine tread tyre, 14 mm. in diameter...		NGPP ☐
082		Spare tyre	Black narrow tread tyre, 20 mm. in diameter..		NGPP ☐
083		Spare tyre	Grey tyre, 20 mm. in diameter, (also catalogued as 099)		NGPP ☐
084		Spare tyre	Black 'recessed' tyre, 18 mm. in diameter		NGPP ☐
085		Spare tyre	White tyre, 15 mm. in diameter, (also catalogued as 092 and 14095).......................		NGPP ☐
086		Spare tyre	Black fine tread tyre, 16 mm. in diameter		NGPP ☐
087		Spare tyre	Black big 'tractor' tyre, 35 mm. in dia., (also catalogued as 60687).........................		NGPP ☐
089		Spare tyre	Black 'tractor front tyre', 19 mm. in dia., (also catalogued as 60689)......................		NGPP ☐
090		Spare tyre	Black fine tread tyre, 14 mm. in diameter, (also catalogued as 60790).....................		NGPP ☐
090		Spare tyre	White fine tread tyre, 14 mm. in diameter, (also catalogued as 60791)		NGPP ☐
091		Spare tyre	Black block tread tyre, 13 mm. in diameter, (also catalogued as 60036)..................		NGPP ☐
092		Spare tyre	Black block tread tyre, 15 mm. in diameter, (also catalogued as 14094)..................		NGPP ☐
092		Spare tyre	White block tread tyre, 15 mm. in diameter, (also catalogued as 14095)..................		NGPP ☐
093		Spare tyre	Black medium tractor tyre, 27 mm. in dia., (also catalogued as 13978)		NGPP ☐
094		Spare tyre	Black smooth tyre, 18 mm. in diameter, (also catalogued as 6676).........................		NGPP ☐
095		Spare tyre	Black block tread tyre, 18 mm. in diameter, (also catalogued as 6677)...................		NGPP ☐
096		Spare tyre	Tyre, 19/32″ (15 mm.) in diameter, (also catalogued as 7067).................................		NGPP ☐
097		Spare wheel	Solid rubber wheel, 12 mm. in diameter, (also catalogued as 7383).........................		NGPP ☐
098		Spare wheel	Solid rubber wheel, 12 mm. in diameter, (also catalogued as 10118).......................		NGPP ☐
099		Spare tyre	Black block tread tyre, 20 mm. in diameter, (also catalogued as 10253)..................		NGPP ☐
099		Spare tyre	Grey block tread tyre, 20 mm. in diameter, (also catalogued as 10253)...................		NGPP ☐
1a	1946-54	Station Master	Dark Blue uniform (cap, long coat), (in Set 001 till 1956)		**£20-25** ☐
1b	1946-54	Guard	Dark Blue uniform, blowing whistle, flag in right hand (see Set 001).......................		**£20-25** ☐
1c	1946-54	Ticket Collector	Blue uniform, only right arm is extended (in Set 001 till 1956)...............................		**£20-25** ☐
1e	1946-54	Porter with Bags	Blue uniform, oblong case in each hand (in Set 001 till 1956).................................		**£20-25** ☐
1f	1946-54	Porter	Dark Blue uniform, standing, no luggage (in Set 001 till 1956)		**£20-25** ☐
2a	1946-54	Horses	3 versions; Dark Brown horse (Black tail and mane), Light Brown horse (Light Brown tail and mane), White horse. (2 in Set 002 till 1956).......................................		**£20-25** ☐
2b	1946-54	Cows	3 versions; Light Brown, Dark Brown, or Black and White. (2 in Set 002 till 1956) ...		**£20-25** ☐
2c	1946-54	Pig	Cream body (in Set 002 till 1956)...		**£20-25** ☐
2d	1946-54	Sheep	White body with Black hand-painted detail (in Set 002 till 1956)..........................		**£20-25** ☐
3a	1946-54	Woman and Child	Woman in Green suit & hat (Brown scarf), child on left (see Set 003)		**£20-25** ☐
3b	1946-54	Business Man	Brown suit, left hand holds attach case (in Set 003 till 1956)..................................		**£20-25** ☐
3c	1946-54	Male Hiker	Brown clothing, Khaki rucksack, no stick (in Set 003 till 1956)...............................		**£20-25** ☐
3d	1946-54	Female Hiker	Blue or Dark Blue skirt and shirt, stick in right hand (see Set 003)		**£20-25** ☐
3e	1946-54	Newsboy	Dark Blue clothing, standing, papers in Grey tray (in Set 003 till 1956)..................		**£20-25** ☐
3f	1946-54	Woman	Light Red coat, round case in right hand (in Set 003 till 1956)		**£20-25** ☐

Ref. No.	Year(s)	Model Type	Dinky Toys - continued	Market Price Range
4a	1946-54	Electrician	Blue overalls, White sleeves, carrying equipment (in Set 004 till 1956)	£10-15 ☐
4b	1946-56	Fitters	2 versions; one in Blue, the other Brown, carrying equipment (Set 004)	£10-15 ☐
4c	1946-56	Storekeeper	Brown coat, Black trousers, holding forms in right hand	£10-15 ☐
4d	1946-56	Greaser	Brown overalls, holding oil-can in right hand	£10-15 ☐
4e	1946-56	Engine-Room Attendant	Blue overalls, Blue sleeves	£10-15 ☐
5a	1946-56	Pullman Car Conductor	White jacket, Blue trousers, slightly open arms, casting as 1c	£20-25 ☐
5b	1946-56	Pullman Car Waiter	White jacket, Blue trousers, two slightly different poses were available	£20-25 ☐
5c	1946-56	Hotel Porter	Red jacket/Brown trousers, or Green jacket/Blue trousers, casting as 1e	£20-25 ☐
6a	1946-56	Shepherd	Brown with Green hat	£40-50 ☐
6b	1946-56	Sheep-dog	All-Black sheep-dog	£20-30 ☐
12c (750)	1946-54	Telephone Box	Red call-box with Silver windows, 58 mm. high	£10-15 ☐
12d (011)	1946-54	Telegraph Messenger	Dark Blue body, picked out detail in darker Blue, Brown pouch, 35 mm.	£15-20 ☐
12e (012)	1946-54	Postman	Mid-Blue body, darker Blue detail, Brown post bag and badge, 35 mm.	£15-20 ☐
13a (013)	1952-54	Cook's Man	(An Agent for the Thomas Cook company), Blue coat, 40 mm. high	£20-30 ☐
42a (751)	1954-60	Police Hut	Dark Blue hut, 'POLICE' in Silver, 66 mm. high	£20-30 ☐
502	1961-63	Garage	Blue/Grey plastic garage, opening door, 272 mm. (French issue)	£90-110 ☐
750 (12c)	1954-62	Telephone Box	Red call-box with Silver windows, 58 mm. high	£20-30 ☐
751 (42a)	1954-60	Police Hut	Dark Blue hut, 'POLICE' in Silver, 66 mm. high	£20-30 ☐
752 (973)	1953-54	Goods Yard Crane	Yellow with Blue or Dark Blue, mazak or cast-iron base (100 x 100 mm.)	£40-50 ☐
753	1962-67	Police Crossing	Black/White box on traffic island with policeman directing traffic	£35-45 ☐
754	1958-62	Pavement Set	Grey cardboard paving slabs (20 items in box)	£20-30 ☐
755	1960-64	Lamp Standard (Single)	Grey/Fawn/Orange, plastic single-arm lamp on metal base, 145 mm. high	£10-15 ☐
756	1960-64	Lamp Standard (Double)	Grey/Fawn/Orange, plastic double-arm lamp on metal base, 145 mm. high	£10-15 ☐
760	1954-60	Pillar Box	Red and Black pillar box with 'E II R' cast-in, 42 mm. high	£10-15 ☐
763	1959-64	Posters for Hoarding	Six different coloured poster advertisements (on paper)	£10-15 ☐
764	1959-64	Posters for Hoarding	Six different coloured poster advertisements (on paper)	£10-15 ☐
765	1959-64	Road Hoardings (6 Posters)	Green plastic hoarding, 'David Allen and Sons Ltd', 205 mm.	£10-15 ☐
773	1958-63	4 face Traffic Lights	Black/White, Black base, similar to 47a but without beacon, 62 mm.	£10-15 ☐
777	1958-63	Belisha Beacon	Black/White post on Black base, casting as 47d, 51 mm.	£5-8 ☐
778	1962-66	Road Repair Boards	Green and Red plastic warning signs, 6 different, 30-40 mm.	£10-15 ☐
781	1955-62	'ESSO' Petrol Station	'ESSO' sign, no kiosk, 2 pumps ('ESSO' and 'ESSO EXTRA'), 114 mm.	£50-60 ☐
782	1960-70	'SHELL' Petrol Station	'SHELL' sign, Green/Cream kiosk, 4 Red/Yellow 'SHELL' pumps, 203 mm.	£35-45 ☐
783	1960-70	'BP' Petrol Station	'BP' sign, Green/Cream kiosk, 4 Green/White 'BP' pumps, 203 mm.	£35-45 ☐
785	1960-64	'SERVICE STATION'	Fawn and Red plastic, with 'BP' sign, 335 x 185 mm. (unbuilt kit, boxed)	£125-175 ☐
786	1960-66	Tyre Rack with tyres	Green tyre rack with 21 assorted tyres and 'DUNLOP' on board, 52 mm.	£20-25 ☐
787	1960-64	Lighting Kit	Bulb and wire lighting kit for model buildings	£20-25 ☐
788	1960-68	Spare Bucket for 966	Grey bucket for use with 966 Marrel Multi-Bucket Unit	£5-7 ☐
790	1960-64	Granite Chippings	Plastic bag of imitation granite chippings (50790)	£5-7 ☐
791	1960-64	Imitation Coal	in a plastic bag	£5-7 ☐
792	1960-64	Packing Cases (3)	White/Cream plastic packing cases, 'Hornby Dublo', 38 x 28 x 19 mm.	£5-7 ☐
793	1960-64	Pallets	Orange pallets for 930 Bedford Pallet-Jekta Van and 404 Conveyancer	£5-7 ☐
794 (994)	1954-64	Loading Ramp	Blue loading ramp for use with 582/982 Carrimore Transporter, 233 mm.	£15-20 ☐
846	1961-	Oil Drums	Pack of 6 oil drums. French issue	£5-7 ☐
847	1961-	Barrels	Pack of 6 barrels. French issue	£5-7 ☐
849	1961-	Packing Cases	Pack of 6 packing cases. French issue	£5-7 ☐
850	1961-	Crates of Bottles	Pack of 6 crates. French issue	£5-7 ☐
851	1961-	Sets of vehicle 'Loads'	Two each of 846 Oil Drums, 847 Barrels, 849 Packing Cases and 850 Crates	£20-25 ☐
994 (794)	1954-55	Loading Ramp	Renumbered from 794 to 994 then back to 794 after only a year!	£15-20 ☐
973 (752)	1954-59	Goods Yard Crane	Yellow with Blue or Dark Blue, 1st issues have steps, mazak or cast-iron base	£40-50 ☐

WHEN REPLYING TO ADVERTISEMENTS PLEASE MENTION JOHN RAMSAY'S CATALOGUE

Dinky Toys - Catalogues (U.K. issues)

The compiler of this Catalogue is indebted to Mr David Salisbury of the Vintage Toy & Train Museum, Sidmouth, Devon for providing in-depth information on catalogues and leaflets. In addition, much information has been drawn from the catalogue collection of Dr Cecil Gibson for which due acknowledgment is given.

Pre-War Catalogues, booklets, leaflets and listings

Hornby' Modelled Miniatures' were introduced in 1931 as model railway accessories and the first issues were of Station Staff etc. The first catalogue listings to be published appeared in Hornby Train catalogues, Meccano catalogues and the 'Meccano Magazine'.

Ref. No.	Year(s)	Publication	Cover Features & Details	Market Price Range	
-	1932-33	Hornby 'Book of Trains'..........	First 'Modelled Miniatures' listed as 'Railway Accessories'	£40-50	☐
-	1932	Meccano trade catalogue..........	First 'Modelled Miniatures' listed as 'Railway Accessories'	£40-50	☐
-	1933	'Meccano Magazine'..................	42 Hornby 'Modelled Miniatures' listed in December issue	£20-25	☐
-	1933-34	Hornby 'Book of Trains'..........	Accessories are depicted in full colour...	£40-50	☐
-	1934	Meccano trade catalogue..........	'Modelled Miniatures' briefly renamed 'Meccano Miniatures'	NGPP	☐
-	1934	'Meccano Magazine'..................	February issue contained the last published 'Modelled Miniatures' listing	£30-40	☐
-	1934	'Meccano Magazine'..................	April issue contained the first 'Meccano Dinky Toys' listing	£30-40	☐
-	1934	'Meccano Magazine'..................	The May, June, July, August, September and November issues each reflected increasing number of varieties of 'Dinky Toys'	£15-20	☐
-	1934	'Meccano Magazine'..................	'150 varieties of Dinky Toys' on double pages in October & December issues	£15-20	☐
-	1934-35	Hornby 'Book of Trains'..........	Catalogue shows 150 'Dinky Toys' in full colour on a double page	£50-75	☐
13/834/900	1934-35	Meccano Catalogue	Boat plane and model plus boy on cover, 3 pages of Dinky Toys	NGPP	☐
16/934/100	1934-35	'Hornby Trains/Meccano' Catalogue	Blue cover, full colour design of 'The World', lists 150 models of Dinky Toys............	£70-90	☐
-	1934-35	Meccano Book............................	Cover depicts viaduct over river, complete Dinky Toys range is listed	NGPP	☐
-	1935	Meccano Magazine..................	January to November issues have various Dinky Toys listings	£15-20	☐
-	1935	Meccano Magazine..................	December issue shows 200 varieties of Dinky Toys in Black & White	£15-20	☐
7/835/65	1935-36	Hornby 'Book of Trains'..........	Catalogue features 200 varieties of Dinky Toys in full colour	£40-50	☐
-	1935-36	Hornby/Meccano Catalogue	Has the same cover as the 1934-35 issue...	£70-90	☐
-	1936	Meccano Magazines	The February and August issues featured a road layout and a competition; the May issue introduced the 'Queen Mary' model	£15-20	☐
-	1936-37	Hornby 'Book of Trains'..........	The catalogue features full colour pictures of the Dinky Toys range..........................	£40-50	☐
-	1937	Hornby/Meccano Catalogue	The 1934-35 'World' cover again. Contains 7 pages of listings	£50-70	☐
-	1937	Meccano Magazines	Details given in the monthly listings of the superb new 'Army' range	£15-20	☐
13/638/1150	1938	Hornby/Meccano Catalogue	74 pages with full Dinky Toys listings and numerous Black/White pictures.................	£30-40	☐
13/638/1150/ UK	1938	'Wonder Book of Toys'............	Two boys with Meccano models plus 11 pages with Dinky Toys	NGPP	☐
8/1238/25	1938	'DINKY TOYS' Catalogue.......	Small booklet - cover features boy and 6 models including 29c Bus, 151a Tank, and 63 Mayo Composite Aircraft. Printed in brown on pale-yellow paper	£75-100	☐
-	1938	Meccano Magazine...................	Details of the full range (with pictures] are published each month..........................	£15-20	☐
1/439/10	1939	'DINKY TOYS' leaflet	'New Products' leaflet detailing items such as the Presentation Aeroplane Sets Nos 64 and 65. Black printing on pinkish paper	£20-30	☐
-	1939	MECCANO booklets	with complete Dinky Toys listings:		☐
13/639/1 13/639/	1939	Hornby/Meccano Catalogue	74 pages with full Dinky Toys listings and Black/White pictures..............................	£30-40	☐
11500 UK	1939	'A Wonder Book Of Toys'........	Green and Yellow cover depicts two boys with their Meccano models. The booklet includes 13 pages of Dinky Toys information	£30-40	☐
2/739/10(1P)	1939	'DINKY TOYS' Catalogue.......	Famous Red/Yellow cover picture of schoolboy with outstretched arm and 17 models. Contains 14 black and white pages..	£200-250	☐
-		'Toys Of Quality'......................	Maroon Express train features on cover plus 'The Hornby Railway Co' logo. 13 pages of Dinky Toys listings are included	£30-40	☐
-	1939	Trade catalogue	Cover depicts boy with Dinky Toys and Hornby pictures with 'MECCANO TOYS OF QUALITY' logo...	£30-40	☐
2/1139/ 20(3P)UK	1939	'DINKY TOYS' Catalogue.......	Superb Red and Yellow cover picture of schoolboy with outstretched arm and 17 models. Catalogue contains 10 Black/White pages of listings & pictures................	£100-150	☐
-	1939	Meccano Magazine...................	Each month contained Dinky Toys listings...	£15-20	☐
16/1040/100	1940	Meccano Price List....................	All products listed but no pictures	NGPP	☐
16/1040/200	1940	'DINKY TOYS' leaflet	Listing of models with pictures	£15-20	☐
-	1940	Meccano Magazine...................	Wartime Dinky aircraft and the Meccano 'Spitfire Fund' are featured	£15-20	☐
16/541/25 UK	1941	'DINKY TOYS' leaflet	Wartime camouflaged aircraft feature in this leaflet	£15-20	☐
16/641/20 UK	1941	'DINKY TOYS' leaflet	Similar to previous leaflet, military models listed...	£15-20	☐
16/1141/20 UK	1941	'DINKY TOYS' leaflet	Listing of models and retail prices...	£15-20	☐

Full Dinky Toys listings also appeared in the toy catalogues of major retailers such as Gamages and Bentalls. These catalogues are themselves highly collectable, difficult to find, and are in the region of £30-40.

Post-War UK Catalogues, booklets, leaflets and listings
Early Post-War period, 1945 - 1951

There were at least two editions per annum so the following listings are not complete. The 'leaflet' approach reflects the shortage of paper in early post-war years.

Ref. No.	Year(s)	Publication	Cover Features & Details	Market Price Range	
16/1145/ 75UK	1945	Meccano leaflet	leaflet lists the models to be reintroduced after the War and features pictures of 23e, 29c, 39a, 62s, 62p. Sepia print on cream paper	£10-15	☐
16/546/30 UK	1946	Meccano leaflet	Sepia printed listing on cream paper featuring pictures of models 70a, 38c, 29c, 23e	£10-15	☐
16/1146/ 65UK	1946	Meccano leaflet	Blue/Black print on cream paper, featuring models 70a, 38c, 70b, 38e	£10-15	☐
16/347/ 50UK	1947	Meccano leaflet	Brown print on light cream paper. Models depicted are 70a, 70b, 70c, 70e, 38c, 38e, 38f, and 153a Jeep	£10-15	☐
16/448/30	1948	Meccano General Products	Booklet with green printing on light cream paper	£10-15	☐
16/948/200	1948		Same as previous issue but with mauve print on light cream paper	£10-15	☐
16/1248/5	1948	'Dinky Toys Tyre Sizes'	Simple Leaflet giving information on Dinky Toys spare tyres	£10-15	☐
16/449/100	1949	Meccano General Products	booklet with brown printing on light cream paper	£10-15	☐
	1949	Independent shop listings	Full Dinky Toys listings and pictures featured in the catalogues published by the larger toy shops such as Bentalls, Gamages, etc	£15-20	☐
16/450/150	1950	Meccano General Products	booklet with pale Blue/Black printing on light cream paper	£10-15	☐
	1950	Independent shop listings	Full Dinky Toys listings & pictures featured in the catalogues of larger toy shops such as Gamages, Bentalls, etc	£15-20	☐
16/251/33	1951	Meccano General Products	booklet with brown printing on light cream paper	£10-15	☐
	1951	Independent shop listings	Full Dinky Toys listings and pictures featured in the catalogues of larger toy shops such as Bentalls, Gamages, etc	£15-20	☐

Meccano Magazines, 1942 - 1952

During the latter part of the war and especially during the early post-war years when Dinky Toys catalogues were not issued, the Meccano Magazine was the main source of new information for collectors. It advised on the reintroduction of models after the war and of the forthcoming new releases. Consequently the Magazines of this period are highly collectable in their own right.

1942 - September 1943 No Dinky Toys adverts or listings appeared
September 1943 - December 1944 Back page adverts for Meccano incorporated listing and pictures of De Havilland Flamingo Aircraft and Buick 'Viceroy' Saloon.
January - November 1945 Back page adverts said 'Sorry, not available but will be ready after the war'.
December 1945 Advert on back page announced 'Ready during December'.
1946 Virtually every month a new model was added to the listing printed on the inside front cover. A picture of each model was shown.
January - September 1947 new models added regularly each month.
October 1947 First advert appears of Dinky Supertoys with pictures of 501 Foden Diesel Wagon, 502 Foden Flat Truck, 503 Foden Flat Truck with Tailboard, 511 Guy 4 ton Lorry, 512 Guy Flat Truck, 513 Guy Flat Truck with Tailboard, and 701 Short 'Shetland' Flying Boat.
1948 Single page advert every month, new models continually introduced
1949, 1950, 1951 Double page advert each month listing new models.
1952 Double page adverts each month. The December issue shows Gift Sets No.1 Farm Gear and No.2 Commercial Vehicles

Prices for Meccano Magazines of this period range between £10-15

UK Catalogue editions, 1952 - 1965

The series included fourteen editions although not all issues were given an edition number. More than one catalogue was issued in some years. It was common for catalogues to be overprinted with the name and address of the toy retailer. In addition to issuing Dinky Toys catalogues, Meccano Ltd continued to issue 'Meccano Toys Of Quality' leaflets which provided a full listing of Dinky Toys with their retail prices plus details of their 'Hornby', 'Hornby-Dublo' and 'Meccano' products. As many as five printings per annum were produced using green, pink, blue or buff paper. When in perfect condition these leaflets sell for £5-8 each.

Ref. No.	Year(s)	Publication	Cover Features & Details	Market Price Range	
15/852/165	1952	(September) 16 pages	Cover shows hands holding 27f Estate Car, 'Dinky Toys' logo	£40-50	☐
	1953	24 page catalogue	Cover shows boy wearing green sweater, 'Dinky Toys' & 'Price 3d'	£40-50	☐
7/953/360	1953	(1st October) 24 pages	Cover features 555 Fire Engine, 522 Big Bedford Lorry and 25x Breakdown Lorry, price '2d'	£40-50	☐

Ref. No.	Year(s)	Model Type	Dinky Toys - continued	Market Price Range	
7/754/600	1954	(1st September) 24 pages...........	Cover features 157 Jaguar, 480 'Kodak' Van, 641 Army Truck, 'Dinky Toys' logo, price '2d'...................	£30-40	☐
7/455/250	1955	(May) 8 page leaflet..................	Cover shows 251, 641, 170 & 401, 'Dinky Toys' & 'Dinky Supertoys'	£15-20	☐
7/755/945	1955	24 page catalogue	'Dinky Toys','Supertoys', 481 'Ovaltine' Van on cover, ('2d')....	£30-40	☐
7/456/800	1956	(June) 32 pages	Cover shows 942 'REGENT' Tanker, 255 Mersey Tunnel 'Police' Land Rover, 157 Jaguar XK120, 'Dinky Toys' & 'Dinky Supertoys', price '2d'..	£30-40	☐
7/657/820	1957	(August) 28 pages	Cover shows 290 'DUNLOP' Double Decker Bus etc, 'Dinky Toys', and 'Dinky Supertoys', price '2d UK'	£30-40	☐
7/458/856	1958	28 page catalogue	Houses of Parliament shown on front cover with 'Dinky Toys' and 'Dinky Supertoys', price '2d UK'	£30-40	☐
7/559/900	1959	28 page catalogue	Red Jaguar XK120 Coupé (157) on front cover with 'Dinky Toys' and 'UK Seventh Edition', price '3d'...............	£20-25	☐
7/3/800	1960	32 page catalogue	Motorway bridge on cover, 'Dinky Toys' & 'UK Eighth Edition'....	£20-25	☐
7/561/700	1961	32 page catalogue	Black/Yellow cover with 6 models, 'Dinky Toys', 'UK 9th Edition'	£20-25	☐
72537/02	1962	32 page catalogue	Cover features 120 Jaguar 'E' type, 'Dinky Toys', price '2d'	£15-20	☐
13/163/200	1963	32 page catalogue	Motor Show stands featured on cover, '11th Edition', 'UK', '2d'	£15-20	☐
7/164/450	1964	16 page catalogue	A large catalogue with 'Widest Range & Best Value In The World' and 'Dinky Toys' logos. Price '3d'	£15-20	☐
7/265/200	1965	16 page catalogue	Rolls Royce (127) on cover with 'Dinky Toys by Meccano'. Price '3d'	£15-20	☐
72557/02	1965	16 page catalogue	Cover features cars 127, 128, 133, 151 and 178	£15-20	☐

UK Catalogue editions, 1966 - 1978

Ref. No.	Year(s)	Publication	Cover Features & Details	Market Price Range	
72561/2	1966	106 page catalogue	'1st Edition', '6d', 'Always Something New From Dinky' on the cover. Accompanied by separate (pink) price list..............	£25-30	☐
72561/2	1966	(after 21st July)..........................	2nd edition, same cover as 1st, 104 pages plus (buff) price list..	£20-25	☐
72571	1967	104 page catalogue	'No.3', '6d'. Cover features 12 models and has same logo as 72561/2. Price list (on green paper) included..............	£20-25	☐
72580	1968	104 page catalogue	'No.4', '6d', Spectrum Pursuit Vehicle (104) on cover. Same logo as 72561/2. Accompanied by (buff) price list.........	£20-25	☐
72585	1969	(1st Sept)...............................	'No.5', '3d', (2nd printing). Cover features 102 'Joe's Car' and has same logo as 72561/2. There are 24 pages.	£15-20	☐
165000	1970	24 page catalogue	'No.6', '3d', many models on cover. Same logo as 72561/2.	£15-20	☐
100103	1971	24 page catalogue	'No.7', '2p', '1971 Meccano Tri-ang Ltd' on rear cover. Same logo as on 72561/2. (Note the change to Decimal Currency in 1971)	£10-15	☐
100107	1972	(1st November) 28 pages...........	'No.8', '2p', 2nd printing, shows 683 Chieftain Tank, 'Dinky Toys'	£10-15	☐
100109	1973	(October) 40 pages	'No.9', '3p', 2nd printing, shows 924 'Centaur', 'Dinky Toys'	£10-15	☐
100113	1974	(May) 48 pages	'No.10', '4p', cover shows 731 S.E.P.E.C.A.T. & 'Dinky Toys'	£10-15	☐
100115 UK	1975	(June) 48 pages	'No.11', '5p', 'Dinky Toys' & 675 Motor Patrol Boat on cover.	£10-15	☐
100118 UK	1976	48 page catalogue	'No.12', '5p', 'Dinky Toys' & 358 'USS Enterprise' on cover.	£10-15	☐
100122 (UK)	1977	44 page catalogue	'No.13' & '5p'. Cover features 357 Klingon Battle Cruiser.	£5-10	☐
100100	1978	44 page catalogue	'No.14', '5p', 'AIRFIX GROUP' & 180 Rover 3500 on cover.	£5-10	☐

Leaflets and Price Lists, 1954 - 1978

Ref. No.	Year(s)	Publication	Cover Features & Details	Market Price Range	
no ref. DT/CF/5	1957	Booklet	Yellow cover, Red lettering 'A NEW SERIES' and 'DUBLO DINKY TOYS'..........	£20-30	☐
16/159/100 DT/CF/7	1959	Illustrated price list........	Colour cover showing 983 Transporter and cars, etc......................	£10-15	☐
16/160/ 100(3P) DT/CF/8	1960	Illustrated price list........	Colour cover with 666 Missile Vehicle and 785 Service Station, etc	£10-15	☐
16/160/ 100(4P) DT/CF/11	1960	Illustrated price list........	Colour cover with 930 Pallet-Jexta plus GS 951 Fire Service, etc	£10-15	☐
8/561/100	1961	Illustrated price list........	(72535/02) Colour cover with 4 cars, 'Purchase Tax Surcharges 26th July 1961'	£10-15	☐
72557/02	1965	Leaflet	Cover with 133, 127, 128, 151, 171, with price list.......................	£10-15	☐
72579	1967	Leaflet	Trade Fair leaflet, 'THUNDERBIRDS'	£10-15	☐
72569	1968	Leaflet	Features 103-105 'Captain Scarlet' vehicles........................	£10-15	☐

Further information. It is known that other leaflets, sales literature and price lists were published.
The Editor would welcome further information to add to these listings.

Meccano Trade Catalogues listing Dinky Toys

These were issued for many years but little information has been recorded (please send any information that you may have). For example:
Ref.100126, 1978 Trade Catalogue with 'Todays World', 'Todays Meccano', Todays Dinky Toys' on the cover plus colour design of late 1970s models on Motorway with 'Meccano' buildings in background.

Overseas Catalogues

Catalogues were often adapted so that they could be switched for use in most countries in the world irrespective of the language or the currency used.
An example of this is the 1965 catalogue:

72257/02UK	1965	UK catalogue	16 pages. Cover depicts 5 cars namely Nos.127, 128, 133 and 171 plus a description of various model features	£15-20	☐
72557	1965	Overseas edition	16 pages. The cover is the same but replacing the features listing is a panel with 'Precision Diecast Scale Models' printed in English, German, French, Spanish, Italian and Swedish. The catalogue pages contain only the basic English model name and number - all the English text having been removed. The models are the same as 72257/02.	£20-25	☐
72559	1965	Overseas edition	24 pages. Whilst the cover is the same as 72557, the listings are entirely different for they feature both English and French Dinky Toys, including the French issues sold in the UK	£40-50	☐

Price lists. Prior to the overseas editions being despatched, price lists in the correct language and currency would be inserted.
The Editor would like to express his thanks to the many collectors around the world who have contributed to this listing. New information would be welcomed.

Dinky Toys Overseas Catalogue editions recorded to date

Ref. No.	Year(s)	Publication	Cover Features & Details	Market Price Range	
NETHERLANDS/HOLLAND Agents: Hausemann & Hötte NV, Kromboomsloot 57-61, Amsterdam.					
Pre-War Editions					
1/736/5	1936		Yellow paper with Black ink	£75-100	☐
13/637/7.5	1937		Yellow paper with Black ink	£75-100	☐
13/738/22	1938		Yellow paper with Black ink	£75-100	☐
Post-War Editions - Some black/white, later coloured as per UK issues					
16/954/108	1954	Illustrated price list	Printed in French	£15-20	☐
8/1255/50	1955	(DT/L/7)		£30-35	☐
16/256/30n	1956	(DT/CL/2)		£20-25	☐
16/256/30n	1956	(DT/L/9)		£20-25	☐
16/1158/20	1958		'Nederland Frs 3-'. Cover same as 1958 UK issue	£30-35	☐
16/256/30	1962	(72538/29)		£20-25	☐
BELGIUM and LUXEMBOURG (French printing). Agents: P. FREMINEUR et Fils, Rue des Bogards 1, Bruxelles 1					
Pre-War Edition					
13/736/26.5	1936	Meccano Catalogue		£75-100	☐
Post-War Editions - Mostly same covers as equivalent UK issues					
16/1053/10	1954	Catalogue	Same cover as 1953 UK issue	£30-40	☐
16/1054/2	1954	Catalogue	Same cover as 1954 UK issue	£30-40	☐
16/656/156	1956	Catalogue	(DT/CL/5) Same cover as 1956 UK issue	£30-40	☐
7/539/-	1959	Catalogue	with Red Jaguar XK140 on cover	£30-40	☐
no ref.	1960	48 page catalogue	English and French models in one catalogue. Printed and issued only in Belgium/ Luxembourg. Cover depicts Land Rover plus two French Dinky Toys cars. Frs 3-.	£75-100	☐
BELGIUM (Flemish printing).					
16/1054/2	1954	Illustrated price list		£15-20	☐
ITALY Agents: Alfredo Parodi, Piazza 8, Marcellino 6, Genova.					
Post-War Editions					
no ref.	1957	Illustrated list	with 101-105 pictured	£30-40	☐
no ref.	1957	Leaflet	with 163, 236 and 238 on racing circuit	£20-25	☐
no ref.	1957	Leaflet	with 237, 661, and 919 'Golden Shred'.	£20-25	☐
16/357/5	1957	Illustrated price list	with 'Italy' printed after the reference number.	£20-25	☐
12/757/50	1957	Leaflet	(DT/CL/15) 642 and 455 'Brooke Bond' shown	£20-25	☐
7/857/50	1957	Catalogue	Same cover as UK issue 7/657/820	£30-40	☐
DT/CL/12	1957	Leaflet	with 677 and 472 on cover	£20-25	☐
7/758/50	1958	Catalogue	Same cover as UK issue 7/458/856	£30-40	☐
U.S.A. Agents: H. Hudson Dobson, PO Box 254, 26th St. and Jefferson Avenue, Kenilworth, NJ. New York showroom: 200, Fifth Avenue, PO Box 255. Models sold by this distributor will often be found with an 'H.Hudson Dobson' label.					
Post-War Editions					
7/753/150	1953	Catalogue	Same cover as 1953 UK issue 7/953/360	£50-75	☐
7/954/150	1954	Catalogue	Same cover as 1954 UK issue 7/754/600	£50-75	☐
no ref.	1955	Catalogue	Yellow/Red cover has Red lined sections displaying English and French models. Red panel with US address of H.Hudson Dobson. 36 black/white pages of English and French models.	£75-100	☐
7/559/250	1959	USA Catalogue	Cover depicts Red Jaguar XK140 etc. 26 pages English models, 6 pages French	£50-75	☐
7/8/125	1959	Leaflet	3 pages of colour pictures plus price list. Cover shows English and French models, eg. 195 Jaguar 3.4, 265 Plymouth Taxi	NGPP	☐
no ref.	1960	Leaflet	6 pages introducing 'Mini-Dinky' models with pictures of complete range	£40-45	☐
no ref.	1965	'Lines Bros' leaflet	4 pages, Yellow/Red cover with 113 MGB	£30-35	☐

Ref. No.	Year(s)	Model Type	Dinky Toys - continued	Market Price Range	

CANADA Agents: Meccano Limited, 675, King Street West, Toronto.

Post-War Editions

Ref. No.	Year(s)	Model Type	Description	Market Price Range	
16/355/90	1955	Illustrated price list........	Printed on Off-White leaflet	£30-35	☐
16/656/18c	1956	Illustrated price leaflet	(DT/CL/4) in colour, featuring 131 Cadillac and 660 Tank Transporter....................	£15-20	☐
16/756/18	1956	Illustrated price leaflet	in colour, featuring 706 Vickers 'Air France' Airliner	£15-20	☐

EIRE & CHANNEL ISLANDS Agents: S.J.Gearey, 1, St.Stephens Green, Dublin. (Ceased trading 1968).
Agents from 1969: Kilroy Bros. Ltd., Shanowen Road, Whitehall, Dublin 9.

Ref. No.	Year(s)	Model Type	Description	Market Price Range	
7/755/20	1955	Catalogue..............	'Eire' and 'C.I.' on cover	£20-25	☐
7/659/75	1959	Catalogue..............	'Eire' on cover	£20-25	☐
7/364/7	1964	Catalogue..............	'Eire' on cover	£20-25	☐
No.5	1969	Catalogue..............	'Irish' on cover. Distributed by Kilroy Bros Ltd	£20-25	☐

HONG KONG Representatives: W.R.Loxley & Co Ltd, Jardine House, 11th Floor, 20, Pedder Street, Hong Kong.

Ref. No.	Year(s)	Model Type	Description	Market Price Range	
DT/CF/5	1959	Illustrated price list........	Same cover as 1959 UK issue DT/CF/5..	£20-25	☐

Meccano Magazines 1952 - 1975

With the introduction of yearly Dinky Toys catalogues from 1952 the Meccano Magazine lost its somewhat unique role as a combined magazine/catalogue. However, with the help of 'The Toyman' and his monthly articles plus superb colour advertising of new models, the Magazine continued to provide a valuable service for collectors.
Meccano Magazines of this period are in the price range of £5-10

Meccano Catalogues 1954 - 1958 with colour 'Dinky Toys' & 'Hornby-Dublo' listings

These contained sections with listings and pictures of 'Dinky Toys' and 'Hornby-Dublo' products. Details known to the compiler relate solely to issues in the mid-1950's period. 'MECCANO TOYS OF QUALITY' logo on each cover.

Ref. No.	Years(s)	Publication	Cover Features & Details	Market Price Range	
13/654/ 995UK	1954-55	24 pages, price '2d'	Cover depicts 4 boys on a desert island. Black/White pictures....................................	£20-25	☐
13/655/ 797UK	1955-56	28 pages, price '2d'	Cover shows boys looking in toyshop window. Black/White pictures	£20-25	☐
13/756/ 525UK	1956	32 pages, price '4d'	Cover depicts Dinky Toys, Hornby-Dublo, and a Meccano helicopter. This is a large catalogue with colour printing..	£30-35	☐
13/757/ 500UK	1957	32 pages, price '4d'	Famous cover showing Meccano Tower, Hornby-Dublo train crossing viaduct and Dinky Toys passing beneath. Large, with colour pictures......................	£50-75	☐
13/758/ 450UK	1958	20 pages, price '4d'	Cover depicts boy, Hornby-Dublo train, 8 Dinky Toys and a Meccano model. Includes some superb engine pictures..	£30-35	☐

Acknowledgements

The Catalogue compiler would like to express his appreciation to the following for their help with the Dinky listings:

John Kinchen, Bedhampton, Hampshire
Ray Pearson, Northwich, Cheshire
Dave Jowett, Toyfair Organiser, Nottingham
Brian Kelly, Glengeary, Eire
Gert Ouderits, Lommel, Belgium
Dr John Beugels, Nijnegan, Netherlands
Geoff Curran, Norwich, Norfolk
Irvin B. Fleegle, Bath, Philadaelphia, USA
Thomas Nolan, Walton, Liverpool

Russ Clark, Southport, Cheshire
D. A. Hobson, Sale, Cheshire
Chris Steele, Tiverton, Devon
Justin Watts, Ferndown, Dorset
Rex Gilroy, St.Albans, Herts
P. Searle, Sutton, Surrey
Graham Mansell,
C.Bell, RAF Sek Fong, BFPO1
Laurie Piddock, Perth, Western Australia

Please note: As we are constantly updating the Catalogue we would be very pleased to hear from collectors who may have new or useful information on any aspect of the hobby. Do please send any information to us in order that we may pass it on to fellow collectors through the medium of future editions of the Catalogue. Thank you.

Trade Boxes

Virtually all Dinky Toys models were supplied in their own individual boxes from around 1954. Before then most small models were supplied to shopkeepers in 'Trade Boxes' containing 3, 4, 6 or 12 identical models separated by strips of card. (Some aircraft and ship models were an exception to this general rule). A single item would be sold without further packaging except perhaps for a paper bag. The Trade Boxes have become collectors items in their own right whether full or empty (the latter selling for between £20 and £50 depending on its rarity and that of its original contents. Most of these boxes that come to auction are full and the listing below derives from a recent survey of such items. It is known that others exist and the Editor would welcome any information regarding Trade Boxes.

YB = Yellow box,   GB = Green box

078	Lansing Bagnall Trailers, Box of 6	£140-170 ☐		105b	Wheelbarrow, YB x 6	£150-200 ☐
12c	Telephone Box, YB x 6	£150-200 ☐		105c	Hand Truck, YB x 6	£40-60 ☐
12d	Telegraph Messenger (post-war) GB x 6	£60-70 ☐		105e	Grass Cutter, YB x 6	£120-150 ☐
12e	Postman (post-war) GB x 6	£80-90 ☐		107a	Sack Truck, YB x 6	£130-170 ☐
13a	Cook's Man, box of 6 (50174)	£30-40 ☐		253	Daimler Ambulance, YB x 4	£150-200 ☐
25p	Aveling Barford Diesel Roller, YB x 3	£150-200 ☐		270	AA Motor Cycle (post-war), YB x 6	£200-300 ☐
25g (405)	Jeep, YB x 3	£150-200 ☐		551	Trailer (Grey/Red), GB x 3	£45-65 ☐
27	Tram Car (pre-war) YB x 6	£900-1200 ☐		551	Trailer (various colours), Blue box x 3	£65-85 ☐
27a	Massey-Harris Tractor, YB x 3	£150-200 ☐		603a	Army Personnel (metal), YB x 12	£80-110 ☐
27c	M.H. Manure Spreader, YB x 3	£85-100 ☐		603a	Army Personnel (plastic), YB x 12	£85-120 ☐
27j	Triple-Gang Mower, YB x 6	£150-200 ☐		687	Field Gun Trailer, YB x 6	£65-85 ☐
27m	Land Rover Trailer, YB x 3	£70-90 ☐		705	Viking Airliner, YB x 6	£200-300 ☐
29a	'Q' type Bus, YB x 6	£1000-1200 ☐		750	Telephone Call Box, YB x 6	£200-300 ☐
29c	AEC Bus (post-war) YB x 6	£300-400 ☐		751	Police Hut, YB x 6	£240-280 ☐
29f	Observation Coach, YB x 6	£400-500 ☐		760	Pillar Box, GB x 6	£150-200 ☐
30j	Austin Wagon, YB x 6	£150-200 ☐		773	Traffic Lights, YB x 12	£150-175 ☐
30m	Dodge Tipping Wagon, YB x 6	£150-180 ☐		777	Belisha Beacon, YB x 12	£65-90 ☐
30s	Austin Covered Wagon, YB x 6	£150-200 ☐		786	Tyre Rack, YB x 6	£120-160 ☐
30r	Thames Flat Truck, YB x 6	£130-160 ☐		788	Spare Bucket for 966, YB x 6	£175-225 ☐
33w	Horse and Wagon, Grey box x 3	£110-150 ☐		994	Loading Ramp, Plain box x 3	£55-80 ☐
34c	Loudspeaker Van, YB x 6	£150-180 ☐		14095	Tyres, YB x 12	£5-10 ☐
35a	Saloon Car, YB x 6	£290-330 ☐				
35b	Racer (Silver/Red) YB x 6	£280-330 ☐				
38e	Armstrong-Siddeley, YB x 6	£450-550 ☐		**Trade Packs of BOXED models**		
40b	Triumph 1800, YB x 6	£320-390 ☐		(See 'Christies' Auction picture in the colour section)		
40f	Hillman Minx, YB x 6	£150-200 ☐				
42a	Police Box, YB x 6	£140-170 ☐		106	'The Prisoner' Mini-Moke, (6)	£600-800 ☐
47c	Two-face Traffic Lights, YB x 12	£40-70 ☐		159	Morris Oxford (3 Green, 3 Tan)	£250-350 ☐
70d	Twin Engined Fighter, YB x 6	£80-120 ☐		161	(40j) Austin Somerset, (6)	£600-800 ☐
70e	Gloster Meteor, YB x 6	£40-60 ☐		195	Jaguar 3.4 Saloon, (6)	£400-500 ☐
70f	Shooting Star, YB x 6	£100-150 ☐		471	Austin Vans 'NESTLE', (6)	£300-400 ☐
105a	Garden Roller, YB x 6	£100-125 ☐				

N.B. See also Gift Sets for 62h & 62d Pre-War Aeroplane Trade Box items.

Dinky Toys Trade Accessories

Trade Display Unit packed in plain cardboard box. Black wooden case with 'Property of Meccano Ltd Liverpool' in black on gold; three shelves in light blue/white/yellow; four gold supports with two yellow and two red supports; four red tin flags 'DINKY TOYS'; three tin flags 'ASK FOR BOOKLET', 'OVER 200 MODELS', and 'ALWAYS SOMETHING NEW'; plus two red and two yellow balls. ..... £400-500 ☐

Glass Display Case. Oak frame with three glass shelves. Size approximately 32″ (80 cm.) wide, 24″ (60 cm.) high, 9″ (22 cm.) deep. With 'DINKY TOYS' in green lettering on glass front ..... £200-300 ☐

Trade Display Stand Large yellow folding cardboard stand which non-erected measures approximately 28″ (70 cm.) x 14″ (35 cm.); three display levels with 'DINKY TOYS' logo in green plus 'MECCANO PRODUCT' in red on top header board. Outer corrugated cardboard packing has green printed instruction leaflet ..... £200-300 ☐

Trade Display Stand Small yellow and red folding cardboard stand which non-erected measures approximately 12″ (31 cm.) x 7½″ (15 cm.); with one 'DINKY TOYS' and two 'DINKY SUPERTOYS' logos in green plus yellow 'MASTERPIECES IN MINIATURE' logo on red background.... £75-100 ☐

Display Stand (circa 1950 - 1960) Large metal stand which measures approximately 36″ x 21″ x 22″ (91.5 x 53 x 56 cm.); with nine display shelves covered in black plastic track. Metal advertisement affixed to top states in yellow/red/black 'A MOTOR SHOW FOR GIRLS AND BOYS', 'PRECISION DIE-CAST MODELS BY MECCANO', 'BEST RANGE', and 'BEST VALUE IN THE WORLD'. Lower large transfer also in yellow/red/black repeats the message £400-500 ☐

Window Sign (plastic), Top half is dark blue with white 'MECCANO' logo, bottom half is yellow with red 'Dinky Toys' logo. Approximately 18″ x 6″ ..... £70-80 ☐

Counter Display (cardboard), Small display stand suitable for a single new model, 'ALWAYS NEW MODELS' logo in white on red background, header states 'DINKY TOYS' in red on yellow ..... £70-80 ☐

Note: This section is far from complete and the Editor would welcome details of other trade stands, posters, display cards, promotional material and advertising signs, for example:
Metal Counter Display Sign, triangular in shape with red 'DINKY TOYS' on yellow background, approximately 8″ x 1″ x 1″ £30-40. (See Ashley Collection picture in colour section).

AUCTION RESULTS 1992-93

(C) = Christies, (S) = Sotheby's, (P) = Phillips, (L) = Lacy Scott, (V) = Vectis, (W) = Wallis & Wallis
MB = mint (boxed), MU = mint (unboxed), NMB = not mint (boxed), NMU = not mint (unboxed).

CARS

22a	Sports Car, Orange-Brown/Cream, Met.Blue wheels, MU	£160 (V)
39cu	Lincoln Zephyr (US) Cream/Brown, NMB	£1,200 (C)
40b	Triumph 1800, Black body & wheels, MU	£4,500 (C)
40g	Morris Oxford, Blue, MU	£2,000 (C)
57-002	Corvair Monza, Red/Black, MB	£60 (W)
57-003	Chevrolet Impala, Yellow/White, MB	£65 (W)
57-005	Ford Thunderbird, Blue/White, MB	£75 (W)
102	MG Midget, Red touring finish, NMB	£100 (V)
105	Triumph TR2 Sports Car, MB	£70 (L)
105	TR2 tourer, Yellow, spun wheels, MB	£175 (V)
106	Austin Atlantic, Light Blue, Red seats, MB	£80 (V)
107	Sunbeam Alpine Sports, NMB	£46 (L)
107	Sunbeam Alpine, Light Blue, '6', MB	£70 (V)
108	MG Midget, White, No.'28', MB	£65 (V)
111	Triumph TR2, Pink, No.'29', NMB	£60 (V)
114	Triumph Spitfire, Red body, MB	£50 (V)
116	Volvo 1800s, Metallic Red, MB	£50 (V)
120	Jaguar, Met.Light Blue/Black, Cream seats, MB	£1,350 (V)
135	Triumph 2000, Black, White roof, MB	£1,700 (V)
145	Singer Vogue, Metallic Green, MB	£40 (L)
148	Ford Fairlane, Greyish Lilac, spun wheels, no base number. South African issue & box	£950 (V)
152	Austin Devon, Cerise/Lime Green, MB	£115 (W)
153	Standard Vanguard, Maroon, Brown wheels, MU	£3,600 (V)
154	Hillman Minx, Olive-Green/Cream, MB	£190 (V)
156	Rover 75, Ivory/Blue body, Beige wheels, MB	£200 (V)
159	Morris Oxford, Cerise/Cream, Beige wheels, MB	£140 (V)
161	Austin Somerset, Black/Cream, MB	£135 (V)
162	Ford Zephyr, Light Green/Cream, MB	£95 (V)
164	Ford Zodiac Mk.IV, Metallic Bronze, MB	£130 (V)
165	Humber Hawk, Maroon/Deep Cream, MB	£89 (-)
168	Singer Gazelle, Green/Grey, MB	£60 (V)
170	Ford Fordor, Red/Cream 'highline', MB	£190 (V)
171	Hudson, Light Grey 'lowline', Blue roof, MB	£250 (V)
171	Hudson, Turquoise 'lowline', Cerise roof, MB	£290 (V)
194	Bentley 'S' Coupé, Avocado Green, South African model & box	£650 (V)
197	Morris Mini Traveller, Dark Green, MB	£670 (V)
199	Austin Countryman, Fluorescent Pink, MB	£210 (V)
238	Jaguar 'D' type, Turquoise body, MB	£50 (L)
448	El Camino Pick-up & Trailers, MB	£180 (V)
No.2	(39 Series) Private Automobiles Set, MB	£1,800 (P)
No.4	(23 Series) Racing Cars Gift Set, NMB	£600 (V)
22	22 Series Set, 6 models, NMB	£1,320 (C)
23	Racing Cars Set, 3 models, NMB	£165 (V)
124	'Holidays' Gift Set, 4 models, MB	£420 (V)
149	Sports Cars Gift Set, 5 cars, MB	£920 (V)
299	Post Office Services Set, MB	£390 (V)

COMMERCIAL VEHICLES

25b	Covered Wagon, 'Carter Paterson', MU	£572 (C)
25f	Market Gardeners Lorry, Orange/Black, MU	£65 (V)
25m	Bedford Tipper, Dark Green, Black wheels, MU	£140 (V)
401	Coventry Fork Lift, Red/Orange, MB	£350 (V)
402	Bedford TK Lorry, 'Coca-Cola', MB	£110 (V)
408	Big Bedford Lorry, Blue/Yellow, MB	£110 (V)
430	Commer Breakdown, Pale Cream/Blue, MB	£130 (V)
438	Ford D800, White/Blue,'Polcarb', MB	£270 (V)
501	Foden 1st cab, Red/Black wings, MU	£2,000 (C)
505	Foden Chains, 1st, Maroon body, MB	£1,300 (V)
512	Guy Flat Truck, Brown/Green, MB	£350 (V)
582	Pullmore Car Transporter, Mid-Blue body/wheels, Dark Grey decks, Dark Blue print, MB	£750 (W)
903	Foden Flat/Tailboard, Blue/Cream, MB	£320 (S)
903	Foden Flat/Tailboard, Blue/Orange, MB	£160 (P)
908	Mighty Antar with Transformer, NMB	£280 (V)
914	AEC Articulated Lorry, 'BRS', Red/Grey, MB	£130 (V)
934	Leyland Octopus, Blue/Yellow, MB	£1,100 (V)

941	Foden Tanker, 'Mobilgas', MB	£280 (V)
944	Leyland Octopus, 'Corn Products', NMB	£1,300 (C)
945	AEC Tanker, 'Lucas' promotional, MB	£110 (V)
972	Jones Mobile Crane, Orange/Red, MB	£65 (W)
No.2	Commercial Vehicles Set, MB	£4,000 (V)
33	Mechanical Horse & 4 Trailers Set, NMB	£380 (C)

VANS

28a	Delivery Van, 1st type, 'Hornby', MU	£385 (C)
40g	Bedford 'Ovaltine', Blue, Grey wheels, MB	£2,000 (V)
274	Mini Van, Yellow 'AA' livery, MB	£78 (L)
450	Bedford TK Box Van 'Castrol', MB	£85 (L)
452	Trojan Van 'Chivers', MB	£105 (W)
455	Trojan Van 'Brooke Bond', Red, MB	£110 (V)
455	Trojan PRM, 'Brooke Bond', roof & box labels: 'Since 1924 more than 5,700 'Little Red Vans supplied. Replaced on a long-life basis.', MB	£650 (V)
465	Morris 'J' Van, 'Capstan', MB	£145 (W)
491	Dairy Van 'Job's Dairy', promotional, MB	£110 (V)
514	Guy Van, 'Weetabix', NMB	£1,000 (V)
920	Warrior Van, 'Heinz Ketchup', MB	£1,700 (V)
No.12	pre-war Postal Set, with 34b Van, NMB	£800 (C)

EMERGENCY VEHICLES

25k	Streamlined Fire Engine, tinplate firemen, MU	£495 (C)
954	Fire Station kit, MB	£220 (V)
956	Berliet Turntable Fire Escape, MB	£180 (V)
No.42	Police Set, Box/Patrol/Policemen, NMB	£210 (W)

FARM AND GARDEN MODELS

No.2	Farmyard Animals Set ('Modelled Miniatures' box)	£400 (C)
No.6	Shepherd Set, with dog & sheep, MB	£380 (C)
22c	Farm Tractor, NMU	£80 (L)

AIRCRAFT AND MILITARY MODELS

62d	Bristol Blenheim Set (6) Green box, MB	£600 (V)
64	Wartime Aircraft Set, 6 planes, MB	£600 (V)
62n	Junkers JU90 Airliner, MB	£270 (V)
63	Mayo Composite, 'Maia' & 'Mercury', MB	£260 (V)
151	Royal Tank Corps Medium Set, NMB	£200 (C)
156	Mechanised Army Set, pre-war, MB	£3,500 (V)
675	(Ford Fordor) US Army Staff Car, MB	£320 (V)
695	7.2" Howitzer and Tractor Set, MB	£290 (W)
992	Vulcan Bomber, MB	£2,200 (V)
61	RAF Aeroplanes Set, 5, pre-war, NMB	£350 (W)
60	Aeroplanes Gift Set, MB	£820 (C)

NOVELTY and FILM & TV-RELATED MODELS

100	'FAB 1', Shocking Pink, MB	£220 (V)
350	Tiny's Mini Moke, MB	£75 (V)
352	Ed Straker's Car, Yellow, MB	£42 (L)

TRAINS, BUSES, CARAVANS, TAXIS, BOATS

29a	Trade Box of 6 Motor Buses, MB	£1,200 (W)
29c	Bus, 'Dunlop', Blue/Cream/Grey, pre-war, NMU	£200 (W)
256	Plymouth Canadian 'Metro Cab', MB	£145 (V)
282	Duple Roadmaster, Cream/Dark Green, MB	£200 (W)
289	Routemaster, 'Thollenbeek', Gold promotional, MB	£150 (V)
289	'Beckenham Hospital', Purple, promotional, MB	£600 (C)

'DINKY DUBLO' MODELS

062	Singer Roadster, MB	£50 (V)
070	AEC Mercury Tanker 'SHELL-BP', MB	£55 (L)

ACCESSORIES and CATALOGUES

44	AA Patrol Set, 4 models/figures, MB	£220 (C)
48	Petrol Station, tinplate, MB	£440 (C)
65/66	US issue Dinky Toys Catalogue (mint)	£75 (V)

CHRISTIES AUCTION RESULTS

See models listed in colour section pictures

Condition abbreviations:
(P) Poor, (F) Fair, (G) Good, (E) Excellent, (M) Mint, (NPA) No price available

Auction Sale, 6th November 1992
p.ii, Top shelf (left to right):
514 Guy Van 'LYONS SWISS ROLLS' (G) **£450**
289 Deep Purple Routemaster Bus (M) **£600**
920 Guy Warrior Van with 'HEINZ' Tomato Ketchup design (NPA)
450 Bedford TK 'CASTROL' Van (NPA)
Second shelf (left to right):
919 Guy Van 'GOLDEN SHRED' (E-M) **£500**
471 Trade Pack for six 'NESTLES' Austin Vans (M) **£260**
514 Guy Van 'WEETABIX' (F-G) **£1,000**
Third and fourth from top (left to right):
Rare flight of seven Armstrong Whitworth Whitley Bombers - six camouflaged 62t and one silver 60v (E) **£1,200**
920 Guy Warrior 'HEINZ' Tomato Ketchup Van (NPA)
No.45 Garage with rare green painted doors (G) **£380**
39cu Lincoln Zephyr Coupé, US export issue, two-tone tan and brown (G) **£1,200**
Second from bottom (left to right):
No.33 pre-war Set, Mechanical Horse and Four Assorted Trailers (P-F) **£286**
23m pre-war 'Thunderbolt' Racing Car with box (E) **£110**
No.12 Postal Set (pre-war), (F - some fatigue) **£350**
Bottom shelf (Trade Packs, left to right):
Six 195 Jaguar 3.4 Saloons (M) **£450**, Six 161 Austin Somerset Saloons (M) **£700**, Six 471 Austin 'NESTLES' Vans (M) **£320**

p.xxvii, Top shelf (left to right):
GS40 Avengers Gift Set (M) **£320,** 481 Trade Pack **£150**
First shelf down:
Zebra 'R.A.C.' Motorcyclist (NPA), 514 Guy 'SPRATTS' Van (E) **£420**, Corgi GS 8 (NPA)
Second shelf down:
1139 Menagerie Truck (NPA), Mettoy 'Castoys' (NPA)
Third shelf down: Early Lesney Rag & Bone Merchants Cart (NPA), Corgi 419 Trade Pack **£185**, Dinky 448 Chevrolet El Camino Pick Up and Trailers **£180**
Bottom shelf:
GS 30 Grand Prix Set (NPA), Corgi 310 Trade Pack (E) **£150**

Auction Sale, 19th May 1992, 'The Ashley Collection' (model gradings shown where possible)
p.iii, Left hand row (front to back):
920 Guy Warrior (G) **£2,860,** 923 Big Bedford (G-E) **£1,650**
934 Leyland Octopus blue/yellow (E) **£2,640,** 935 Leyland Octopus Chain Lorry (E) **£1,540**
989 'AUTO TRANSPORTER' (NPA) plus 152 Austin Devon (blue/yellow) **£220** and 152 Austin Devon (green/pink) **£240**
Middle pairs (front to back):
39bu Oldsmobile Sedan (cream/tan, few chips) **£770** and 39eu Chrysler Royal Sedan (red/yellow) **£935**
157 Jaguar XK120 (grey/yellow) **£286**, 39bu Oldsmobile Sedan in two-tone blue (NPA)
161 Austin Somerset (cream/black) **£143** plus 161 Austin Somerset (yellow/red) **£143**
40b Triumph 1800 in black (G) **£4,950**, 170 Ford Fordor (pink/blue 'lowline') **£308**
157 Jaguar XK120 (pink/blue) **£286**, 161 Austin Somerset (yellow/red) **£93**
159 Morris Oxford (pink/white) **£198**, 159 Morris Oxford (green/cream) **£176**
Right hand row (front to back):
514 Guy Van 'WEETABIX' (G-E) **£1,540**, 514 Guy Van 'LYONS' (G) **£660**
919 Guy Van 'GOLDEN SHRED' **£1,045**, 935 Leyland Octopus with Chains (blue/yellow) (E - few chips) **£2,640**
908 Mighty Antar Transporter with Transformer (G, box E) **£660**
NB Background to picture provides a fine display of various box types

Auction Sale, 20th May 1992
p.iv, Top shelf (left to right):
No.2 Modelled Miniatures and No.6 Shepherd Set (pre-war) sold as a single lot for **£800**
22a Sports Car (red/green) and 22b Sports Coupé (yellow/green) sold as part of unboxed 22 Series Set for **£1,320**
Second shelf down (left to right):
33r 'LMS Railway' Mechanical Horse and Trailer (part of lot, NPA)
25b 'CARTER PATERSON' Covered Wagon (G) **£572**
25k Streamlined Fire Engine with Tinplate Firemen (E) **£495**
34a Royal Air Mail Service Car (F-G, some fatigue) **£160**
28h 'DUNLOP' Delivery Van - 2nd type (F-G, some fatigue) **£143**
28k 'EXIDE BATTERIES' Delivery Van - 2nd type (F-G, some fatigue) **£176**
Third shelf down (left to right):
28a 'HORNBY TRAINS' Delivery Van - 1st type (F-G) **£385**
28b 'PICKFORDS REMOVALS' Delivery Van - 1st type (E) **£1,100**
28e 'ENSIGN CAMERAS' Delivery Van - 1st type (G) **£880**
28k 'MARSH and BAXTERS' Delivery Van - 1st type (G-E) **£660**
28m 'WAKEFIELDS OIL' Delivery Van - 1st type (G) **£495**
Bottom shelf (all pre-war, left to right):
24h Sports Tourer, yellow/blue (NPA)
36a Armstrong-Siddeley (maroon) with Driver and Footman (NPA)
39a Packard Tourer in green (NPA)
39b Oldsmobile Sedan, black (NPA)
39d Buick Viceroy Saloon, maroon (NPA)
39c Lincoln Zephyr Coupé, fawn (NPA)

Auction Sale, 27th November 1992, 'The Great Hornby Dublo Collection'   Bottom shelf: (see Hornby Dublo picture, p.xi)
050 Dinky Toys Railway Staff Set **£220**
054 Dinky Toys Railway Station Personnel Set **£90**

E.F.E. MODELS
Exclusive First Editions

In 1989 a range of models called 'Exclusive First Editions' was introduced with the intention of satisfying a number of requirements that collectors were beginning to express at the time. Initially only commercial vehicles and buses were planned though cars have also made an appearance. The models are collectable as a growing range of vehicles, colours and liveries, a particular strength being the introduction of various bus types not tackled by other model manufacturers. The decision to produce the models to a constant scale of 1:76 ('00' gauge) means that not only do the various vehicles look right together but they can also be used by model railway enthusiasts.

To maintain compatibility with other publications, this listing is divided into three main areas of interest:
1 Buses, Coaches and Trams,   2 Cars,   3 Commercial Vehicles.

Some of the early issues carried no reference numbers. These have been listed first and subsequent issues of the same models which were given references follow in number order. Models enhanced by the addition of 'loads' or extra detail were marketed by EFE as 'Deluxe'. These versions of the original model are listed together following the numbered models in each section.

Gift Sets are listed separately and it should be noted that some liveries and logos only exist in certain sets, the particular model not being available in that form as an individual item.

The listings provide sufficient detail to identify the models for pricing purposes and a 'Market Price Range' is quoted where this information is helpful. Current models still available in shops are generally shown as 'NRP' (the current normal retail price). If a model is listed separately but is only available in a set then 'GSP' (Gift Set Price) is shown and reference to that section will give the price for the set. Collectors wishing for further details (of casting modifications, colour variations, promotional or special productions, etc) are recommended to read:

'EFE - A Collectors Guide', by Ken Benham

This and other publications are available from the EFE Official Collectors Club. The address is at the end of these listings.

Buses, Coaches and Trams

Ref. No.	Year(s)	Model Type	Model Features and Size	Market Price Range	

A.E.C. Regent Double-Deck Bus, (closed top)

Base A is smooth with 'AEC REGENT' in raised lettering,
Base B is textured with 'AEC REGENT' in raised lettering,
Base C is textured with 'RT/RTL' in raised lettering.

'London Transport' fleetname

Ref. No.	Year(s)	Model Type	Model Features and Size	Market Price Range	
-	1989	'STAR GROUP'	Red body, Cream stripe, 'RTW 75', supplied with additional labels and numbered certificate 001 - 288	£100-125	☐
-	1989	'STAR GROUP'	Red body, Cream stripe, 'RTW 75', supplied with additional labels and numbered certificate 289 - 1008	£65-85	☐
-	1989	'STAR GROUP'	Red body, Yellow stripe, 'RTW 75'	£30-40	☐
10101	1989	'DURACELL'	Red body, Cream stripe, 'RT 981', base A	£9-12	☐
10101	1989	'DURACELL'	Red body, Cream stripe, 'RT 206', base A	£15-18	☐
10101	1989	'DURACELL'	Red body, Cream stripe, 'RT 206', base B. Also in Gift Set 99901	£6-9	☐
-	1989	'RT 50 YEARS'	Red body, Cream stripe, 'RT 3254', base A	£35-45	☐
-	1989	'RT 50 YEARS'	Dark Green body, Cream stripe, 'RT 3254', base A	£35-45	☐
-	1989	'RT 50 YEARS'	Dark Green body, Yellow stripe, 'RT 3254', base A	£175-200	☐
-	1989	'FISHERMANS FRIEND'	Red body, Cream stripe, 'RT 3254', special box	NGPP	☐
10104	1990	'SCHWEPPES'	Red body, 'RT 858', base B, also in Gift Set 99901	£6-8	☐
10105	1990	'TATE & LYLE'	Red body, 'RT 4093', base B, part of Gift Set 19901	GSP	☐
10106	1990	'RANK HOVIS'	Red body, 'RT 206', base B, part of Gift Set 19902	GSP	☐
10106 DL	1993	'RANK HOVIS'	'deluxe' version of previous model, with registration plates	NRP	☐
10107	1990	'DULUX'	Red body, 'RT 33', base C	£9-12	☐
10108	1990	'FISHERMANS FRIEND'	Re-issue of 1989 model, base B, in Gift Set 99902	GSP	☐
10109	1990	'BIRDS CUSTARD'	Red body, 'RT 4572', base C	£6-8	☐
10110	1991	'TAYLOR WOODROW'	Red body, 'RT 4331', base C, part of Gift Set 19904	GSP	☐
10111	1991	'BARCLAYS'	Red body, 'RT 4245', base C	£5-7	☐
10112	1991	'VERNONS'	Red body, 'RT 2861', base C	£6-9	☐
10116	1992	'AIR FRANCE'	Red body, 'RT 3402', base C	£5-6	☐

'London Country' fleetname

Ref. No.	Year(s)	Model Type	Model Features and Size	Market Price Range	
-	1989	'BEATTIES'	Green body, 'RT 1044', base A	£16-20	☐
10103	1990	'BIRDS EYE'	Green body, 'RT 4050', base B, singly and in Gift Set 99901	£5-6	☐

'Greenline' fleetname

Ref. No.	Year(s)	Model Type	Model Features and Size	Market Price Range	
-	1990	'PEARL ASSURANCE'	Green body, 'RT 3639', base B	£20-25	☐

148

Ref. No.	Year(s)	Model Type	E.F.E. Models - continued	Market Price Range	
10102	1989	'BUXTED CHICKENS'..........	Green body, 'RT 981', base A............	£7-10	☐
10102	1990	'BUXTED CHICKENS'..........	Green body, 'RT 981', base B............	£5-6	☐
10117	1992	'EFE CLUB 1992'................	Green, 'RT 3254', base B, 'Bullseye' motif....	£25-30	☐

Provincial operators and fleetnames

-	1989	'EVENING DESPATCH'........	'Midland Red', Red body, base A, numbered certificate	£20-25	☐
-	1990	'EFE 1'...............	'Midland Red', Red body, base B, numbered certificate	£5-7	☐
-	1990	'EFE FENCE CLUB'.............	'Midland Red', Red body, base B, 350 only, numbered certificates ...	£110-140	☐
-	1989	'ATKINSONS'..............	'Coventry', Maroon body, base A, with certificate	£40-50	☐
-	1989	'PAIGNTON ZOO'	'Devon General', Maroon body, base A, with certificate	£65-80	☐
-	1990	'SMITHS BEER'..........	'Birmingham', Blue/Ivory body, base A	£30-35	☐
-	1990	'DULUX'................	'Glasgow', Yellow/Green body, base A	£30-35	☐
-	1990	'GARDEN FESTIVAL'	'Northern', Red body, base C, 5,000 only, numbered certificates.	£5-7	☐
10113	1991	'COURIER ADVERTISER'	'Dundee', Green/White body, base C	£16-20	☐
10114	1992	'LONDON/MANCHESTER'..	'Bradford', Blue/White body, base C	£7-10	☐
10118	1993	(no advert)	'St.Helens Corporation', Red/Cream, route '6'	£7-10	☐

A.E.C. Regent Double-Deck Bus, (open top)

-	1990	'EFE 2'	'Birmingham', Blue/Ivory body, base A, with numbered certificate ...	£8-10	☐
-	1990	'COLMANS'................	'London', Red body, base B	£30-35	☐
-	1990	'See The Island'	'Southern Vectis', Cream body, base B	£40-50	☐
10201	1989	'BEACHY HEAD'................	'Eastbourne', Ivory/Blue body, base A	£7-10	☐
10201	1990	'BEACHY HEAD'................	'East Bourne', Ivory/Blue body, base B	£5-7	☐
10202	1989	'COLMANS'	'Great Yarmouth', Dark Blue body, base A	£7-10	☐
10202	1990	'COLMANS'	'Great Yarmouth', Dark Blue body, base B	£5-7	☐
10203	1990	'CORONATION'	'Great Yarmouth', Cream body, base C	£6-9	☐
10204	1991	'TYPHOO'................	'London', Red body, base C	£5-6	☐

AEC Routemaster Double-Deck Bus

'London Transport' fleetname

15601	1993	'B.O.A.C.'	Red body, 'RM 2110', route '8A'	£7-9	☐
15601b	1993	'B.O.A.C.'	Red body, 'RM 1910', route '15'	£7-9	☐
15602	1993	'OVALTINE'................	Red body, 'RM 2103', route '3'	£7-9	☐
15602 b	1993	'OVALTINE'................	Red body, 'RM 1818', route '76'	£7-9	☐
15605	1993	'EVENING STANDARD'	Red body, *TYPHOO*, 'RM 1018', route '16'	NRP	☐
15605 b	1993	'EVENING STANDARD'	Red body, *TYPHOO*, 'RM 1277', route '73'	NRP	☐
15608	1993	'PICKFORDS'	Red body, *WILKINSON SWORD*, 'RM 1768', route '7'	NRP	☐
15608 b	1993	'PICKFORDS'	Red body, *WILKINSON SWORD*, 'RM 966', route '141'	NRP	☐
-	1993	'BRITISH DIECAST MODEL TOYS CATALOGUE	Promotional only available with this Catalogue. Red body, Black side posters with Gold design, plus 'Exclusive Fifth Edition' logo at rear	£9-12	☐

Provincial operators and fleetnames

15603	1993	'BLACK PRINCE'	Red/Yellow body (no advert) route 'X 51'	NRP	☐
15604	1993	'SOUTHEND TRANSPORT'..	Blue/White body, 'ESSEX RADIO', route '29'	NRP	☐
15606	1993	'EAST YORKSHIRE'	Dark Blue/Primrose body (no adverts)	NRP	☐
15607	1993	'CLYDESIDE'	Red/Yellow body, 'THE SCOTSMAN'	NRP	☐
15609	1993	'MANSFIELD & DISTRICT'..	Green/Cream body (no adverts)	NRP	☐

Leyland RTL Double-Deck Bus

11101	1990	'BOAT SHOW'	'London', Red body, 'RTL 815', base C, part of Gift Set 19903	GSP	☐
11102	1990	'WILKINSON SWORD'	'London', Green body, 'RTL 1245', base C, part of Gift Set 19903	GSP	☐
11103	1990	'T. F. BOTT'	'Contractus', Green body, base C, part of Gift Set 19903	GSP	☐
11104	1990	'LOCKEYS'	Black body (no advertising) base C	£9-12	☐
11105	1991	'BRYLCREEM'	'London', Red body, 'RTL 2', base C	£6-9	☐
11106	1991	'FISHERMANS FRIEND'	'London', Red body, 'RTL 285', base C, special box	£8-10	☐
11106 DL	1993	'FISHERMANS FRIEND'	'London Transport', Red body, route '145', extra detail	£8-10	☐
11107	1992	'BARTONS'	Multi-coloured, in Set 99905	GSP	☐
11108	1992	'A.1'	Multi-coloured body	£5-6	☐

Bristol Lodekka FLF

13901	1992	'BRISTOL'	Green/Black, late radiator, no heating vents................	£9-12	☐
13902	1992	'BRISTOL'	As previous model but with *'BEATTIES'* adverts................	£7-10	☐
14001	1992	'BRIGHTON'................	Red and Cream body, late radiator, heating vents	£7-9	☐
14002	1993	'EASTERN NATIONAL'	Green/Cream/Black, late radiator, heating vents	£7-9	☐
14003	1993	'CROSVILLE COACH'............	Cream body (no adverts) Silver detail, Black wheels	£7-9	☐
14004	1993	'CHELTENHAM'................	Red/Cream body, *'GLOUCESTERSHIRE ECHO'*, Red wheels	£7-9	☐
14005	1993	'SOUTHDOWN'	Green/Cream body, *THE BURNLEY*, part of Gift Set 99907	GSP	☐
14006	1993	'LINCOLNSHIRE'	Green/Cream body, *TRUSTEE SAVINGS BANK*, Black wings and wheels............	NRP	☐
14007	1993	'THAMES VALLEY'	Red/Cream body, *'MAIDENHEAD AUTOS'*............	NRP	☐
14101	1992	'UNITED'	Red body & wheels, early radiator, heating vents................	£7-9	☐
14102	1992	'UNITED'	As previous model but with *'BEATTIES'* adverts................	£8-10	☐
14201	1992	'ALEXANDER'	Blue body, White wheels, early radiator, no heating vents	NRP	☐
14202	1993	'MIDLAND GENERAL'........	Blue/Cream body, *'FARMER & STOCKBREEDER'*................	NRP	☐

Leyland National Mk.I and Mk.II Single Deck Bus

There are two versions of this model:
1 - a **short** version having a single pair of doors, and 2 - a **long** version with two pairs of doors.

14401	1992	'GREENLINE'	Green/White body, Green wheels, short, single pair of doors	**£7-10** ☐
14402	1992	'MANCHESTER'	Orange/White/Brown body, Brown wheels, short, single pair of doors	**£7-10** ☐
14403	1993	'UNITED'	Red/White/Blue body, Black wheels, short, single pair of doors	**£7-10** ☐
14701	1993	'McGILLS'	Red/Grey, *'McGILLS BUS SERVICE LTD BARRHEAD'*, Cream wheels, short, single pair of doors	**£7-10** ☐
15101	1992	'HANTS & DORSET'	Red body, Grey wheels, long, two pairs of doors	**£7-10** ☐
15102	1993	'CROSVILLE'	Green body, Grey wheels, long, two pairs of doors	**£7-10** ☐
15103	1993	'NORTHERN'	Yellow body, Grey wheels, long, two pairs of doors	**£7-10** ☐
15104	1993	'BRISTOL CITY'	Green/White body, Grey wheels, long, two pairs of doors	**£7-10** ☐

AEC Reliance Coach - Harrington Cavalier

11901	1991	'YELLOWAYS'	Dark Cream & Orange body with front roof box, Orange wheels, Gold logo	**£25-30** ☐
11903	1992	'GREY-GREEN'	Green and Grey body with front roof box, Green wheels	**£6-9** ☐
12101	1991	'SOUTHDOWN'	Two-tone Green body (no front roof box), Dark Green wheels, Gold logo	**£30-35** ☐
12102	1992	'EAST YORKS'	Cream/Blue, Blue wheels	**£6-9** ☐
12103	1992	'HEBBLE'	Cream/Red, Red wheels	**£6-9** ☐
12104	1992	'SURREY'	Yellow/Brown, in Gift Set 99906	**GSP** ☐
12105	1992	'NEATH & CARDIFF'	Brown/Red, Red wheels	**£6-9** ☐
12106	1993	'VALIANT'	Red/White, Silver detail, White wheels	**£6-9** ☐
12107	1993	'SOUTHDOWN' Touring	Green/Cream body, Gold logo	**£30-35** ☐

AEC Reliance Coach - Harrington Grenadier

12201	1991	'BLACK & WHITE'	Black and White body with front roof box, White wheels, Black logo	**£16-20** ☐
12202	1992	'PREMIER'	Grey-Green & Navy body with front roof box, Navy wheels	**£6-9** ☐
12203	1992	'BARTONS'	Red/Maroon/Cream, roof box, in Set 99905	**GSP** ☐
12204	1992	'ORANGE LUXURY'	Cream/Grey/Orange body with front roof box, *'ESSEX EXPRESS'*	**NRP** ☐
12204 DL	1992	'ORANGE LUXURY'	As previous model but with added detail	**NRP** ☐
12301	1991	'MAIDSTONE'	Cream & Green body (no front roof box), Green wheels, Black logo	**£20-25** ☐
12302	1992	'GREY CARS'	Grey and Maroon body (no front roof box), Maroon wheels	**£7-10** ☐
12303	1992	'TIMPSONS'	Ivory and Maroon body, in Gift Set 99906	**GSP** ☐
12304	1992	'SOUTHDOWN'	Two-tone Green body Dark Green wheels	**£7-10** ☐
12305	1993	'ELLEN SMITH'	White and Maroon body, Maroon wheels	**£7-10** ☐
12306	1993	'B.O.A.C.'	White, Grey and Blue body	**NRP** ☐

Plaxton Panorama Elite Coach

15701	1993	'SOUTH WEST NBC'	White body, 'NATIONAL EXPRESS', Grey wheels	**NRP** ☐
15702	1993	'RIBBLE NBC'	White body, 'NATIONAL', Grey wheels	**NRP** ☐
15703	1993	'EAST KENT'	Red/Beige body	**NRP** ☐
15704	1993	'ABBOTTS of BLACKPOOL'	Red and Grey body	**NRP** ☐
15705	1993	'SHEFFIELD UNITED'	Red and Off-White body	**NRP** ☐
15706	1993	'BRISTOL GREYHOUND'	Red and White body	**NRP** ☐

Leyland PD1 Lowbridge Bus

15801	1993	'WIGAN CORPORATION'	Red/White body	**NRP** ☐
15802	1993	'EAST KENT'	Red/White body	**NRP** ☐

Leyland PD1 Highbridge Bus

15901	1993	'LEICESTER CITY'	Red/White body, 'C.W.S.'	**NRP** ☐

Leyland PD2 Lowbridge Bus

16001	1993	'TODMORDEN'	Dark Green/White body, 'LMS RAILWAY'	**NRP** ☐
16002	1993	'TODMORDEN'	Dark Green/White body, 'BRITISH RAILWAYS'	**NRP** ☐
16003	1993	'EAST KENT'	Red and White body, 'LITTLEWOODS'	**NRP** ☐

Leyland PD2 Highbridge Bus

16101	1993	'WIGAN CORPORATION'	Red and White body	**NRP** ☐
16102	1993	'LEICESTER CITY'	Cream and Red body, 'LEICESTER MERCURY'	**NRP** ☐

Horsfield Double-Deck Tram

13402	1991	'CO-OPERATIVE'	'Leeds City', Red/White body, bow type current collector	**£8-10** ☐
13403	1992	'JACOBS'	'Leeds City', Red/White body, bow type current collector	**£8-10** ☐
14301	1992	'YORKSHIRE POST'	'Leeds City', Blue/White body, pole type current collector	**£8-10** ☐
14302	1993	'WHITBREADS'	'Leeds City', Blue/White body, pole type current collector	**£8-10** ☐

Open Touring Cars

Ref. No.	Year(s)	Model Type	Model Features and Size	Market Price Range	

These models were given individual reference numbers but issued as pairs in a single box and it is to this 'twin-pack' that the price range refers.

Ref. No.	Year(s)	Model Type	Model Features and Size	Market Price Range	
11401	1991	Triumph Roadster	Red body, Red wheels, packed with 11601 Triumph Vitesse	£5-8	☐
11402	1991	Triumph Roadster	Black body, Silver wheels, packed with 11602 Triumph Vitesse	£5-8	☐
11403	1992	Triumph Roadster	Blue body, Silver wheels, packed with 11603 Triumph Vitesse	£5-8	☐
11404	1992	Triumph Roadster	Dark Green body, Green wheels, packed with 11604 Triumph Vitesse	£5-8	☐
11501	1991	MG MGB	Dark Green body and wheels, packed with 11701 Austin-Healey Sprite	£5-8	☐
11502	1991	MG MGB	Red body and wheels, packed with 11702 Austin-Healey Sprite	£5-8	☐
11503	1992	MG MGB	Orange body and wheels, packed with 11703 Austin-Healey Sprite	£5-8	☐
11504	1992	MG MGB	Black body, Silver wheels, packed with 11704 Austin-Healey Sprite	£5-8	☐
11601	1991	Triumph Vitesse	White body, White wheels, packed with 11401 Triumph Roadster	£5-8	☐
11602	1991	Triumph Vitesse	Light Blue body and wheels, packed with 11402 Triumph Roadster	£5-8	☐
11603	1992	Triumph Vitesse	Red body and wheels, packed with 11403 Triumph Roadster	£5-8	☐
11604	1992	Triumph Vitesse	Dark Blue body and wheels, packed with 11404 Triumph Roadster	£5-8	☐
11701	1991	Austin-Healey Sprite	Yellow body and wheels, packed with 11501 MGB	£5-8	☐
11702	1991	Austin-Healey Sprite	White body and wheels, packed with 11502 MGB	£5-8	☐
11703	1992	Austin-Healey Sprite	Green body and wheels, packed with 11503 MGB	£5-8	☐
11704	1992	Austin-Healey Sprite	Red body and wheels, packed with 11504 MGB	£5-8	☐

Commercial Vehicles

Ref. No.	Year(s)	Model Type	Model Features and Size	Market Price Range	

AEC Mammoth Major 6-wheel Box Vans

Ref. No.	Year(s)	Model Type	Model Features and Size	Market Price Range	
-	1989	'FISHERMANS FRIEND'	White body, Red chassis and wheels, special box	NGPP	☐
10201	1989	'LONDON CARRIERS'	Dark Green body and wheels, Black chassis	£5-7	☐
10501	1989	'LONDON CARRIERS'	Re-run of 10201 with darker shade of Dark Green body	£5-7	☐
10502	1989	'START-RITE'	Cream body, Red chassis and wheels	£4-6	☐
10503	1990	'BRS'	Red body and wheels, 'Huddersfield' depot	£5-7	☐
-	1991	'BRS EFE CLUB'	Same model but 'Lincoln' depot, and 'EFE Collectors Club 1991'	£7-10	☐
10504	1990	'PEK PORK'	Blue body and wheels, Black chassis	£4-6	☐
10505	1990	'OXYDOL'	Blue body and wheels, Black chassis	£4-6	☐
10506	1991	'HOOVER'	Blue body, Burgundy wheels and chassis	£4-6	☐
10507	1990	'FISHERMANS FRIEND'	Re-run of 1989 model, singly and in Set 99902	NGPP	☐
10507 DL	1993	'LORD RAYLEIGH's'	Mid-Blue chassis, Pale Blue cab, White/Blue box	£4-7	☐
Deluxe	1991	'LONDON CARRIERS'	Re-run of 10501 with additional printing. In Set 99903	GSP	☐
Deluxe	1991	'BRS'	Re-run of 10503 with additional printing. In Set 99903	GSP	☐
Deluxe	1992	'WELCHES'	Turquoise body and wheels	£5-6	☐

AEC Mammoth Major 8-wheel Box Vans

Ref. No.	Year(s)	Model Type	Model Features and Size	Market Price Range	
11001	1989	'CROFT SHERRY'	White body, Black wheels and chassis	£4-6	☐
11002	1989	'PICKFORDS'	Blue body, Black chassis	£5-6	☐
11003	1990	'TATE & LYLE'	White body, Green wheels and chassis, in Set 19901	GSP	☐
11004	1990	'RANK HOVIS'	Cream body, Brown wheels, in Gift Set 19902	GSP	☐
11005	1990	'LACONS'	Yellow body, Red wheels, Black chassis	£4-6	☐
11006	1991	'ROSES LIME JUICE'	Green body and wheels, Black chassis	£4-6	☐
Deluxe	1991	'PICKFORDS'	Model 11002 with additional printing. In Set 99903	GSP	☐

AEC Mammoth Major 6-wheel Dropside Wagon

Ref. No.	Year(s)	Model Type	Model Features and Size	Market Price Range	
-	1989	'FISHERMANS FRIEND'	White body, Red wheels and chassis, special box	NGPP	☐
10301	1990	'FENLAND AGGREGATES'	Orange body and wheels, Black chassis	£4-6	☐
10302	1990	'CYRIL RIDGEON'	Turquoise body, Black wheels and chassis	£4-6	☐
10303	1990	'J. D. LOWN'	Green body and wheels, Black chassis	£4-6	☐
Deluxe	1991	'FENLAND AGGREGATES'	Model 10301 but with plastic 'load'	£4-6	☐
Deluxe	1991	'CYRIL RIDGEON'	Model 10302 but with plastic 'load'	£4-6	☐
Deluxe	1991	'J. D. LOWN'	Model 10303 but with plastic 'load'	£4-6	☐

AEC Mammoth Major 8-wheel Dropside Wagon

Ref. No.	Year(s)	Model Type	Model Features and Size	Market Price Range	
10801	1989	'BRITISH STEEL'	Dark Blue body and wheels, Black chassis	£4-6	☐
10802	1989	'WHITBREAD'	Brown body and wheels, Black chassis	£4-6	☐
10803	1990	'MARLEY TILES'	Red body and wheels, Black chassis	£5-6	☐
10804	1991	'MACREADYS'	Orange body and wheels, Black chassis	£5-6	☐
10805	1990	'FISHERMANS FRIEND'	White body, Red wheels/chassis, special box (? in Set 99902)	NGPP	☐
10806	1991	'TAYLOR WOODROW'	Yellow/Green body and wheels, Black chassis. In Set 19904	GSP	☐

Ref. No.	Year(s)	Model Type	E.F.E. Models - continued	Market Price Range	
10806 DL	1993	'TAYLOR WOODROW'	Yellow body and wheels, Black chassis, additional 'covered load'	£5-7	☐
Deluxe	1992	'BRITISH STEEL'	Model 10801 but with plastic 'load'	£4-6	☐
Deluxe	1991	'WHITBREAD'	As model 10802 but with plastic 'load'	£4-6	☐
Deluxe	1992	'LACONS'	Mustard Yellow body with plastic 'load', Red wheels	£5-6	☐
Deluxe	1992	'MOBILOIL'	Dark Blue body with plastic 'load', Red wheels	£5-6	☐
Deluxe	1992	'MACREADYS'	As model 10804 but with plastic 'load'	£5-6	☐

AEC Mammoth Major 6-wheel Flatbed Truck

Ref. No.	Year(s)	Model Type		Market Price Range	
10701	1989	'FURLONG Bros.'	Cream body and wheels, Black chassis	£4-6	☐
10702	1989	'BLUE CIRCLE'	Yellow body and wheels, Black chassis	£4-6	☐
10703	1990	'WIMPEY'	Yellow body and wheels, Black chassis	£5-6	☐
10703	1990	'WIMPEY'	Orange body and wheels, Black chassis	£5-6	☐
Deluxe	1991	'FURLONG Bros.'	Model 10701 with plastic 'load'	£4-6	☐
Deluxe	1991	'BLUE CIRCLE'	As model 10702 but with plastic 'load'	£4-6	☐
Deluxe	1992	'WIMPEY'	As 10703 (Orange body) with plastic 'load' added	£4-6	☐
Deluxe	1992	'BRS'	Red body and wheels, plastic 'load'	£5-6	☐

AEC Mammoth Major 8-wheel Flatbed Truck

Ref. No.	Year(s)	Model Type		Market Price Range	
10401	1989	'BATH & PORTLAND'	Dark Blue body and wheels, Black chassis	£4-6	☐
Deluxe	1991	'BATH & PORTLAND'	Same model but with plastic 'load'	£4-6	☐
10402	1989	'LONDON BRICK'	Orange body and wheels, Black chassis	£4-6	☐
Deluxe	1991	'LONDON BRICK'	Same model but with plastic 'load'	£4-6	☐

AEC Mammoth Major 6-wheel Tanker

Ref. No.	Year(s)	Model Type		Market Price Range	
10901	1989	'HEYGATES'	White body, Burgundy cab and wheels, Black chassis	£4-6	☐
10902	1989	'RAYLEIGHS'	White body, Blue cab, Black wheels, Blue chassis	£4-6	☐
10903	1990	'L.P.G.'	White round tank, Yellow cab and wheels	£4-6	☐
10903 DL	1993	'L.P.G.'	As 10903 but 3rd type (oval) tank in Silver, additional detail	£5-6	☐
10904	1990	'RANK HOVIS'	Cream body & cab, Orange wheels & chassis. In Set 19902	GSP	☐
10905	1990	'WELCHS'	Turquoise body, cab and wheels, Black chassis	£4-6	☐
Deluxe	1991	'L.P.G.'	Model 10903 but additional detail. In Set 19904	GSP	☐

AEC Mammoth Major 8-wheel Tanker

Ref. No.	Year(s)	Model Type		Market Price Range	
10601	1989	'CENTURY OIL'	Black body, cab, wheels and chassis	£4-6	☐
10602	1989	'J. & H. BUNN'	Cream body, cab and chassis, Black wheels	£4-6	☐
10603	1990	'TATE & LYLE'	Dark Blue body, cab & wheels, Black chassis. In Set 19901	GSP	☐
10604	1990	'MOBILGAS'	White body, Dark Blue cab & chassis, Red wheels	£4-6	☐
10605	1990	'REGENT'	Red body and cab, Black chassis, White wheels	£6-8	☐
10606 DL	1993	'WHITBREAD'	Brown body and cab, Black chassis. With ladder	£5-6	☐
Deluxe	1991	'CENTURY OIL'	As model 10601 but additional detail. In Set 99904	GSP	☐
Deluxe	1991	'MOBILGAS'	As model 10604 but additional detail. In Set 99904	GSP	☐

AEC Mammoth Major 8-wheel Tipping Wagon

Ref. No.	Year(s)	Model Type		Market Price Range	
12001	1990	'WIMPEY'	Yellow body, cab and wheels, Black chassis	£6-8	☐
12002	1990	'TARMAC'	Green body and cab, Black wheels and chassis	£6-8	☐
12003	1991	'TAYLOR WOODROW'	Yellow/Green body and wheels, Black chassis. In Set 19904	GSP	☐
12004	1991	'KETTON'	Cream body and cab, Red wheels and chassis	£6-8	☐
Deluxe	1992	'TARMAC'	As model 12002 but plastic 'load' added	£5-6	☐
Deluxe	1992	'TAYLOR WOODROW'	As model 12003 but with 'load' and available singly	£5-6	☐

Atkinson Articulated Vehicles (Car transporters)

Ref. No.	Year(s)	Model Type		Market Price Range	
13001	1991	'TLS RECOVERY'	Light Blue body and wheels	£15-18	☐
13002	1991	'SWIFTS'	Yellow body, Blue wheels	£9-12	☐
13003	1992	'MIDLAND CAR'	Maroon/Green/Silver	£8-10	☐
13004	1993	'CLASSIC'	Blue/Maroon body, Maroon wheels	£8-10	☐

Atkinson 6-wheel Rigid Vehicles

Ref. No.	Year(s)	Model Type		Market Price Range	
12501	1992	'WELLS DRINKS'	White/Red body, Red chassis and wheels. (Box Van)	£5-6	☐
12601	1991	'McNICHOLAS'	Brown body, chassis and wheels. (Dropside Wagon)	£5-6	☐
12601 DL	1991	'McNICHOLAS'	As previous model but with 'timber and crate load' and extra detail	£5-6	☐
12701	1991	'CHARRINGTONS'	Dark Blue body and chassis, Red wheels. (Tanker)	£5-6	☐

Atkinson 8-wheel Rigid Vehicles

Ref. No.	Year(s)	Model Type		Market Price Range	
12801	1992	'McPHEES'	Dark Green body, chassis and wheels. (Flatbed Truck)	£20-25	☐
12901	1991	'FYFFES'	Yellow/Blue. (Box Van with AEC pattern wheels)	£5-6	☐
13301	1991	'St.ALBANS'	Silver body, Orange cab and wheels. (Tipping Wagon)	£6-8	☐
13301 DL	1993	'St.ALBANS'	As previous model but with 'load' and extra detail	£6-8	☐
13701	1992	'FINA'	Blue body, Black wheels. (Tanker, 2 type tank)	£5-6	☐

EFE Gift Sets

Ref. No.	Year(s)	Set Name	Contents	Market Price Range	
19901	1990	'TATE & LYLE'	10105 AEC Bus, 11003 8-wheel Van, 10603 8-wheel Tanker	£18-22	☐
19902	1990	'RANK HOVIS'	10106 AEC Bus, 11004 8-wheel Van, 10904 6-wheel Tanker	£14-17	☐
19903	1990	'The RTL Story'	11101 'Boat Show', 11102 'Wilkinson', 11103 'Bott'	£15-18	☐
19904	1991	'TAYLOR WOODROW'	10110 AEC Bus, 10806 8-wheel Dropside, 12003 8-wheel Tipper	£16-20	☐
99901	1990	'London Buses'	10101 'Duracell', 10103 'Birdseye', 10104 'Schweppes'	£20-25	☐
99902	1990	'FISHERMANS FRIEND'	10108 AEC Bus, 10507 6-wheel Van, 6 or 8 wheel Dropside Wagon.		☐
		1st run	in separate boxes (smooth base RT Bus and 6 wheel Dropside Wagon)	£40-50	☐
		2nd run	in separate boxes (textured base RT Bus and 8 wheel Dropside Wagon)	£20-25	☐
		3rd run	in one box, (textured base RT Bus and 8 wheel Dropside Wagon)	£15-18	☐
99903	1991	'Road Transport'	(Deluxe) 'London Carriers', 'BRS', 'PICKFORDS'	£12-15	☐
99904	1991	'Tankers'	(Deluxe) 'L.P.G.', 'CENTURY OIL', 'MOBILGAS'	£12-15	☐
99905	1992	'BARTONS'	Leyland RTL and Harrington Grenadier	£12-15	☐
99906	1992	'Harrington Coaches'	Cavalier 'Surrey' and Grenadier 'Timpsons'	£20-25	☐
99907	1993	'SOUTHDOWN'	Bristol Lodekka and Harrington Cavalier, both in Green/Cream	NGPP	☐

EFE packaging and presentation

Standard issues of single models were packed in rigid card window boxes coloured in two shades of grey, with black and red printing. The contents were secured by a moulded clear plastic inner shell.

Special boxes were made for certain models used for promotional purposes. The models were the 'BRS' Box Van, the 'HEYGATES' Tanker and the 'J.D.LOWN' Dropside Wagon. Their boxes were white with 'COMMERCIAL MOTOR' and 'DAF - LEYLAND' printed on them.
White boxes (with black printing) were used initially for the 'FISHERMANS FRIEND' issues that were part of an 'on-pack offer' promotion, and a subsequent RT bus promotion presented in a pale blue customised box.
The 'Road Transport' Gift Set was issued in a dark blue window box with the three models encased in a flock-covered vac-form with a clear lid.
Certain of the models were designated 'Deluxe' by acquiring additional detail or plastic 'loads' of various kinds. They were packed in a double blister-pack that folded to enclose the model, and was designed to hang on display stand pegs though they could also stand (untidily) on a shelf.
The first of the Gift Sets ('Tate & Lyle') was designed to look like a book (even having 'Volume One' printed on its blue card covering). The inner container was plain white expanded polystyrene - good for insulation but not the nicest form of presentation! Subsequently the 'Rank Hovis' set (designated 'Volume Two') had an inner container of improved appearance with a flock base and clear plastic covering. Standard issues are currently presented a little more assertively in black window boxes with light red printing, with a similar box in royal blue used for the De Luxe range.

The EFE Official Collectors Club

Formed in January 1991, the Club aims to assist its members by way of monthly bulletins and a telephone help-line, to form a complete and as comprehensive collection as possible of all the EFE product range.
Included in this service are the following:

Monthly advice of all new issues,
Bi-monthly updates to the Collectors Guide,
4-monthly colour photo-packs showing selected models from the EFE range,
Telephone help-line (available 12 hours per day)
Sales and promotional material (brochures and badges)
Standing order scheme for the supply of all new issues.

If you are interested in joining then please write to the following address for details:
The EFE Official Collectors Club, 'Farmside', Witham Bank, Martin Dales, Woodhall Spa, Lincolnshire, LN10 6XS.
Please remember to enclose a stamped self-addressed envelope with your initial enquiry. Thank you.

WHEN REPLYING TO ADVERTISEMENTS PLEASE MENTION JOHN RAMSAY'S CATALOGUE

154

THE 'SWAPMEET'
A.E.C. Routemaster Bus

LOOK OUT FOR THE REAL BUS IN CENTRAL LONDON
— OXFORD ST, REGENT ST & PICCADILLY CIRCUS.
N.B. Final poster design may vary from picture shown.

HORNBY DUBLO
MODEL RAILWAYS 1938 - 1964

In any chronicle of the Meccano company the middle of the 1930s stands out as the golden years. Frank Hornby's burgeoning enterprise encompassed the famous Liverpool works, a French factory producing its own distinctly Gallic toys and models and a worldwide network of branches and agents with eager customers everywhere for the growing range of Dinky Toys, Meccano sets, and of course the famous Hornby Series gauge 'O' clockwork and electric trains.

Gauge 'O' (scaled at 7 mm. to the foot) had become the paramount model railway scale supplanting the earlier (and bigger) Victorian gauge '1' and Hornby was the premier British manufacturer of gauge 'O' ready-to run trains. However, even smaller (and thus more convenient model railways were being developed, mainly on the Continent, where as far back as 1921 Bing offered their 'table-top' clockwork railway in 'HO' gauge, with an electric version two years later. 'HO' indicates 'half-O' and is 3.5 mm. to the foot. Other 'HO' models appearing in the 1920s included the Trix-Twin sets which were imported from Germany to England by the British Bassett-Lowke company.

As not every Meccano boy lived in a large house capable of accommodating a reasonable size railway, even in gauge 'O', Meccano were doubtless urged by would-be customers and dealers alike to manufacture something a little smaller - a 'OO' railway - and given the Company's superb marketing skills, would have been quite aware of competitors' developments in the smaller scales. However it was not until 1938 that the first Hornby 'Dublo' models were announced, the decision to produce a 'OO' range having been taken a bare 9 months before. In true Meccano style the new range comprised not merely locomotive models but an extensive choice of goods rolling stock, passenger coaches, railway buildings and signals, as well as the requisite track and controllers.

In 1972 Tri-ang was acquired by the Dunbee-Combex-Marx firm and the Hornby name lives on today as 'Hornby Railways' manufactured by Hornby Hobbies Ltd., of Margate. Study of the present Hornby Railways catalogue reveals a stud of over 30 finely detailed 'OO' locomotives along with a comprehensive range of rolling stock and accessories, tempting railway modellers and collectors alike. In 1966 Mr G.Wrenn negotiated the purchase of many of the original Dublo tools from Tri-ang, and the firm of G. & R. Wrenn continued to employ these tools in producing diecast 'OO' models until 1992 when production ceased. A number of the original Hornby Dublo type locomotives (with detail improvements) feature in the Wrenn range and any prizes for 'OO' longevity must surely go to 'N2' tanks and the 'A4 Sir Nigel Gresley', both seeing the first light of day in 1938 and still available in Wrenn form over fifty years later!

Since the Locomotives section was introduced in the 4th Edition it has become apparent that there is also a need for an easy to understand, non-technical listing of the rolling stock. Consequently a simplified listing has been included in this Edition. The Editor would welcome comment on these listings and how they might be improved. The contents are as follows:

1: **Locomotive models 1938 - 1964**
 - Steam Outline Locomotives
 (Clockwork)
 (Electrically powered)
 - Diesel, Diesel-Electric and Electric
 Outline Locomotives

2: **Rolling Stock 1938 - 1964**
 - Passenger Coaches
 - Vans and Wagons

3: **Gift Sets**

4: **Accessories**
 - 1938 - 1940
 - 1948 - 1958
 - 1959 - 1964

5: **Catalogues**

6: **Model Pricing Guidelines**

7: **Packaging and Box Types**
 - Locomotives
 - Passenger Coaches, Vans, Wagons

8: **Technical Notes**
 - Construction materials
 - Wheel arrangements
 - 'Totem' Motifs, '00' scale
 - Wheel and Coupling types

Abbreviations (Railway Companies, Pre-Nationalisation):
GWR = Great Western Railway,   LMS = London, Midland and Scottish Railway,
LNER = London and North Eastern Railway,   SR = Southern Railway
Abbreviations (Post-Nationalisation (1948) British Railways):
WR = Western region,   MR = Midland Region,   ER = Eastern Region,   SR = Southern Region

1:   Locomotive models 1938 - 1964

Ref. No.	Year(s)	Type	Name	No.	Railway	Colour	RF/ NOR	NOV	Market Price Range
Steam Outline Locomotives (Clockwork)									
DL1	1938-41	4-6-2	'Sir Nigel Gresley'	4498	LNER	Blue			£750-1000 ☐
DL7	1938-40	0-6-2	Tank	2594	SR	Olive Green			£700-800 ☐
DL7	1938-40	0-6-2	Tank	6917	LMS	Black			£400-450 ☐
DL7	1938-40	0-6-2	Tank	2690	LNER	Black			£450-550 ☐
DL7	1938-40	0-6-2	Tank	6699	GWR	Black			£700-800 ☐

156

Steam Outline Locomotives (Electrically powered)

EDL1	1938-41	4-6-2	'Sir Nigel Gresley'	4498	LNER	Blue	3	2	£600-800	☐

Note: Pre-war model had full-depth valances over the wheels

EDL1	1947-53	4-6-2	'Sir Nigel Gresley'	7	LNER	Blue	3	5	£125-150	☐
EDL2	1947-53	4-6-2	'Duchess of Atholl'	6231	LMS	Maroon	3	8	£100-150	☐
			Rare variation with Cream nameplate				3		£250-400	☐
			Rare variation with smoke deflectors on either side of front of boiler				3		£500-800	☐

Note: This variation occurred when models were repaired at Binns Road and were fitted with new 'Duchess of Montrose' bodies painted in 'Duchess of Atholl' livery.

EDL2	....	4-6-2	'Canadian Pacific'	1215		Black	3		£600-700	☐

Notes: (1) - This model was made for the Canadian market.   (2) - Replicas of the Canadian Pacific are currently made using Duchess of Atholl originals.

EDL11	1953-58	4-6-2	'Silver King'	60016	BR	Green	3	2	£100-125	☐
L11/3211	1958-63	4-6-2	'Mallard'	60022	BR	Green	3	2	£125-175	☐
L11	1958-63	4-6-2	'Mallard'	60022	BR	Green	3	2	£125-175	☐
3211	1962-63	4-6-2	'Mallard' (nickel plated wheels)	60022	BR	Green	3	2	£300-350	☐
2211	1959-64	4-6-2	'Golden Fleece'	60030	BR	Green	2	2	£130-175	☐
EDL12/	1953-58	4-6-2	'Duchess of Montrose'	46232	BR	Green	3	4	£95-125	☐
/3212	....	4-6-2	Binns Rd. repair variation, nickel plated wheels, plain Brown box	46232			3		£125-150	☐
EDL7	1938-41	0-6-2	Tank	2594	SR	Olive Green	3		£600-700	☐
EDL7	1938-41	0-6-2	Tank	6917	LMS	Black	3		£300-400	☐
EDL7	1938-41	0-6-2	Tank	2690	LNER	Black	3		£300-400	☐
EDL7	1938-41	0-6-2	Tank	6699	GWR	Green	3		£500-600	☐

The immediate post-war versions (listed below) were fitted with post-war automatic couplings requiring a chamfer in the front buffer beam:

EDL7	1947	0-6-2	Tank (with pre-war body)	2594	SR	Olive Green	3		£550-700	☐
EDL7	1948-53?	0-6-2	Tank	2594	SR	Malachite version			£300-450	☐
EDL7	1947-?	0-6-2	Tank (LMS in serif letters)	6917	LMS	Black	3		£175-250	☐
EDL7	1949-53	0-6-2	Tank (LMS in block letters)	6917	LMS	Black	3	2	£50-100	☐
EDL7	1947	0-6-2	Tank (pre-war body)	2690	LNER	Black	3		NGPP	☐
EDL7	1947	0-6-2	Tank	9596	LNER	Black	3	2	NGPP	☐
EDL7	1948-53	0-6-2	Tank	9596	LNER	Green	3	2	£125-175	☐
EDL7	1947-53	0-6-2	Tank	6699	GWR	Green	3	3	£200-250	☐
EDL7	1948?	0-6-2	Tank	6231	GWR	Green	3		NGPP	☐
EDL7	1953)	0-6-2	Tank	E9560	BR ER	Green	3		NGPP	☐
EDL7	1953-54	0-6-2	Tank (no coal in bunker)	69567	BR ER	Gloss Black	3		£50-70	☐
EDL17/ /L17	1954-58	0-6-2	Tank (no coal in bunker)	69567	BR ER	Matt Black	3	3	£50-70	☐
3217	1961-63	0-6-2	Tank (with coal in bunker)	69567	BR ER	Matt Black	3	2	£200-300	☐
2217	1960-64	0-6-2	Tank	69550	BR ER	Black	2	4	£100-125	☐
EDLT20/ LT20/3220	1957-61	4-6-0	'Bristol Castle'	7013	BR WR	Green	3		£100-150	☐
3221	1961-61	4-6-0	'Ludlow Castle'	5002	BR WR	Green	RF,3		£400-450	☐
2220	1959-59	4-6-0	'Denbigh Castle'	7032	BR WR	Green	2		£175-200	☐
2221	1960-64	4-6-0	'Cardiff Castle'	4075	BR WR	Green	RF,2		£150-175	☐
EDL18	1954-58	2-6-4	Tank (1st issue in plain blue box)	80054	BR	Black	3		£175-200	☐
EDL18	1955-58	2-6-4	Tank (2nd issue in picture box)	80054	BR	Black	3		£125-150	☐
3218	1961-63	2-6-4	Tank	80059	BR	Black	3	2	£350-400	☐
2218	1959-64	2-6-4	Tank	80033	BR	Black	2	2	£95-125	☐
3225/ /LT25	1958-61	2-8-0	BR Class 8F	48158	BR	Black	3		£125-150	☐
3224	1961-63	2-8-0	BR Class 8F	48094	BR	Black	RF,3		£350-450	☐
2225	1959-59	2-8-0	BR Class 8F	48109	BR	Black	2		£180-225	☐
2224	1960-64	2-8-0	BR Class 8F	48073	BR	Black	RF,2		£125-160	☐
2226	1959-64	4-6-2	'City of London'	46245	BR MR	Maroon	2	2	£125-175	☐
3226	1961-63	4-6-2	'City of Liverpool'	46247	BR MR	Maroon	3		£450-600	☐
*2206	1959-64	0-6-0	Tank, Class R1	31337	BR SR	Black	2	2	£50-60	☐
*2207	1959-64	0-6-0	Tank, Class R1	31340	BR SR	Green	2		£40-50	☐
2235	1961-64	4-6-2	'Barnstaple'	34005	BR SR	Green	RF,2		£125-175	☐
3235	1961-63	4-6-2	'Dorchester'	34042	BR SR	Green	RF,3		£325-400	☐

Diesel, Diesel-Electric and Electric Outline Locomotives

*L30/3230	1958-62	D8000	Diesel-Electric 1000 loco, 'Bo-Bo'		BR	Green	3	2	£75-125	☐
*2230	1959-62	D8017	Diesel-Electric 1000 loco, (picture box)		BR	Green	3		£75-125	☐
*2230	1959-62	D8017	Diesel-Electric 1000 loco, (Red box)		BR	Green	2	2	£75-125	☐
*L30/2230			Versions of the above locos, without buffers but otherwise identical, were produced for the Canadian market						NGPP	☐
*2231	1960-64	0-6-0	Diesel-Electric shunter	D3302	BR	Green	RF,2	2	£60-85	☐
*3231	1961-63	0-6-0	Diesel-Electric shunter	D3763	BR	Green	RF,3	2	£150-195	☐

Note: Variations are available with split coupling rods on each side. Expect them to be **£20 to £25 more.**

Ref. No.	Year(s)	Model Type	Hornby Dublo - continued						Market Price Range	
2232	1961-64	'Co-Co'	Deltic Class 3300 hp Diesel-Electric.................	none	BR	Green	RF,2	....	£100-120	☐
3232	1961-63	'Co-Co'	Deltic Class 3300 hp Diesel-Electric.................	none	BR	Green	RF,3	....	£120-135	☐
2234	1962-64	'Co-Co'	Deltic 'Crepello' 3300 hp Diesel-Electric..........	D9012	BR	Green	RF,2	2	£125-250	☐
3234	1962-63	'Co-Co'	Deltic 'St.Paddy' 3300 hp Diesel-Electric..........	D9001	BR	Green	RF,3	2	£275-350	☐
2233	1961-64	'Co-Bo'	1200 hp Diesel-Electric loco	D5702	BR	Green	2	RF,3	£110-140	☐
3233	1961-64	'Co-Bo'	1200 hp Diesel-Electric loco	D5713	BR	Green	RF,3		£150-175	☐
2250	1962-64	....	Suburban Electric loco (Drive Coach and Trailer Car).........................	S65326	BR SR	Green	RF,2	3	£250-300	☐
3250	1962-63	....	Suburban Electric loco (Drive Coach and Trailer Car).........................	S65326	BR SR	Green	RF,3	3	£250-350	☐

Note: Both the above sets were sold with dummy Driving Coach Trailer S77511.

Ref. No.	Year(s)	Model Type							Market Price Range	
*2245	1964	'Bo-Bo'	3300 hp Electric locomotive with twin overhead pantographs......................	E3002	BR	Blue	RF,2	....	£400-500	☐

* **Note:** These models have moulded plastic bodies with diecast metal chassis

2:   Rolling Stock 1938 - 1964

Ref. No.	Year(s)	Type & Export No.		Railway	No.	Livery & Box Ref.	Market Price Range	

Passenger Coaches (pre-war Three-Rail)

Ref. No.	Year(s)	Type & Export No.		Railway	No.	Livery & Box Ref.	Market Price Range	
D1	1938-40	Corridor Coach	1st/3rd........	LNER	42759	Teak finish with White roof (D251)	£100-150	☐
D2	1938-40	Two Coach Articulated Unit			45401 ?		£650-850	☐
			All 3rd and Brake 3rd ...	LNER	45402	Teak finish with White roof (D252)		
D3	-	Corridor Coach	1st/3rd	LMS	4183	Maroon body, Silver Grey roof (not issued pre-war)	NGPP	☐
			Brake/3rd	LMS	26133	Maroon body, Silver Grey roof (not issued pre-war) ...	NGPP	☐

Passenger Coaches (post-war Three-Rail)

Ref. No.	Year(s)	Type & Export No.		Railway	No.	Livery & Box Ref.	Market Price Range	
D1	1948-55	Corridor Coach	1st/3rd.........	LNER	42759	Teak finish with Brown coach ends (32010)............	£30-40	☐
			All 3rd.........	LNER	45401	Teak finish with Brown coach ends (DR361 & 32012)	£50-70	☐
			Brake 3rd	LNER	45402	Teak finish, Brown or Teak coach ends (DR361 & 32011)	£40-60	☐
D2	1948-49	Two Coach Articulated Unit			45401 ?			
			All 3rd and Brake 3rd ...	LNER	45402	Teak finish with White roof (D252) post-war model was only listed for sale overseas	£750-1000	☐
D3	1949-53	Corridor Coach	1st/3rd	LMS	4183	Maroon body, Silver-Grey or Grey roof (DR363 & 32015)	£40-60	☐
			Brake/3rd	LMS	26133	Maroon body, Silver-Grey or Grey roof (32016)..........	£40-60	☐
D11	1953-56	Corridor Coach	1st/3rd	BR (E)	E42759E	Red & Cream body, Grey roof, tinplate windows (32013)	£20-35	☐
			Brake/3rd	BR (E)	E45402E	Red & Cream body, Grey roof, tinplate windows (32014)	£20-35	☐
D12	1953-56	Corridor Coach	1st/3rd	BR (M)	M4183	Red & Cream body, Grey roof, transparent windows (32017)	£20-25	☐
			Brake/3rd	BR (M)	M26143	Red & Cream body, Grey roof, transparent windows (32018)	£20-25	☐
32017	1956-58	Corridor Coach	1st/2nd	BR (M)	M4183	Red & Cream body, Grey roof, transparent windows (32017)	£20-25	☐
			1st/3rd	BR (M)	M4183	As previous model but with Black coach ends (32017)..	£25-35	☐
32018	1956-58	Corridor Coach	Brake/2nd ...	BR(LMR)	M26133	Red & Cream body, Grey roof, transparent windows (32018)	£20-25	☐
			Brake/3rd	BR(LMR)	M26133	As previous model but with Black coach ends (32018)..	£25-35	☐
D13	1954-56	Suburban Coach	1st/3rd	BR	....	Maroon body, Grey roof, tinplate windows (32091)......	£20-25	☐
			Brake/3rd	BR	....	Maroon body, Grey roof, tinplate windows (32091)......	£20-25	☐
32090	1956-57	Suburban Coach	1st/2nd	BR	....	Maroon body, Grey roof, tinplate windows (32090)......	£20-25	☐
			1st/3rd	BR	....	Maroon body, Grey roof, tinplate windows (32090)......	£20-25	☐
32091	1956-57	Suburban Coach	Brake/2nd ...	BR	....	Maroon body, Grey roof, tinplate windows (32091)......	£20-25	☐
			Brake/3rd	BR	....	Maroon body, Grey roof, tinplate windows (32091)......	£20-25	☐
D14	1956-57	Suburban Coach	1st/3rd	BR	....	Maroon body, Grey roof, transparent windows (32092) with windows at one end (as brake van)..........	£20-25	☐
			Brake/3rd	BR	....	Maroon body, Grey roof, transparent windows (32093)	£20-25	☐
32092	1956-58	Suburban Coach	1st/2nd	BR	....	Maroon body, Grey roof, transparent windows (32092)	£20-25	☐
32093	1956-58	Suburban Coach	Brake/2nd ...	BR	....	Maroon body, Grey roof, transparent windows (32093)	£20-25	☐
D21	1957-58	Corridor Coach	1st/2nd	BR (W)	W15862	Brown/Cream body, Grey roof, transparent windows (32094)	£20-25	☐
			Brake/2nd ...	BR (W)	W34481	Brown/Cream body, Grey roof, transparent windows (32095)	£20-25	☐
32094	1957-58	Corridor Coach	1st/2nd	BR (W)	W15862	Brown/Cream body, Grey roof, transparent windows (32094)	£20-25	☐
32095	1957-58	Corridor Coach	Brake/2nd ...	BR (W)	W34481	Brown/Cream body, Grey roof, transparent windows (32095)	£20-25	☐

Ref. No.	Year(s)	Model Type				Market Price Range	
				Hornby Dublo - continued			
D22	1957-58	Corridor Coach	1st/2nd	BR (M)	M4193	Maroon body, Grey roof, transparent windows (32023)..........	£20-25 ☐
			Brake/2nd ...	BR (M)	M26143	Maroon body, Grey roof, transparent windows (32023)..........	£20-25 ☐
32022	1957-58	Corridor Coach	1st/2nd	BR (M)	M4193	Maroon body, Grey roof, transparent windows (32022)..........	£20-25 ☐
32023	1957-58	Corridor Coach	Brake/2nd ...	BR (M)	M26143	Maroon body, Grey roof, transparent windows (32023)..........	£20-25 ☐

Passenger Coaches (post-war Two-Rail)

Ref. No.	Year(s)	Model Type				Market Price Range	
4005	1959-61	Corridor Coach	1st/3rd	BR (M)	M4183	Red & Cream body, Grey roof, transparent windows (36005)..........	£25-35 ☐
4006	1959-61	Corridor Coach	Brake/2nd ...	BR (M)	M26143	Red & Cream body, Grey roof, transparent windows (36006)..........	£25-35 ☐
4009	1959-61	Corridor Coach	1st/2nd	BR (W)	W15862	Brown & Cream body, Grey roof, transparent windows (36009)..........	£20-25 ☐
4010	1959-61	Corridor Coach	Brake/2nd ...	BR (W)	W34481	Brown & Cream body, Grey roof, transparent windows (36010)..........	£20-25 ☐
4013	1959-62	Corridor Coach	1st/2nd	BR (M)	M4193	Maroon body, Grey roof, transparent windows (36013)..........	£20-25 ☐
4014	1959-61	Corridor Coach	Brake/2nd ...	BR (M)	M26143	Maroon body, Grey roof, transparent windows (36014)..........	£20-25 ☐
4021	1959-64	Suburban Coach	1st/2nd	BR	....	Maroon body, Grey roof, transparent windows (36021)..........	£20-25 ☐
4022	1959-64	Suburban Coach	Brake/2nd ...	BR	....	Maroon body, Grey roof, transparent windows (36022)..........	£20-25 ☐
4025	1959-64	Suburban Coach	1st/2nd	BR (SR)	S41060	Green body, Grey roof, transparent windows (36025)...	£25-35 ☐
4026	1959-64	Suburban Coach	Brake/2nd ...	BR (SR)	S43374	Green body, Grey roof, transparent windows (36026)...	£25-35 ☐

Passenger Coaches (with 'Super Detail' features)

Ref. No.	Year(s)	Model Type				Market Price Range	
4035	1961-64	Pullman Car - First Class (4185)........		BR	ARIES	Brown & Cream body, Grey roof, transparent windows (36035)..........	£40-50 ☐
4036	1961-64	Pullman Car - Second Class (4186).....		BR	Car 74	Brown & Cream body, Grey roof, transparent windows (36036)..........	£40-50 ☐
4037	1961-64	Pullman Car - Brake/2nd (4187)		BR	Car 79	Brown & Cream body, Grey roof, transparent windows (36037)..........	£40-50 ☐
4050	1960-64	Corridor Coach - 1st/2nd (4200)		BR (W)	W15870	Brown & Cream body, plastic roof, transparent windows (36050)..........	£20-30 ☐
4051	1960-64	Corridor Coach - Brake/2nd (4201)		BR (W)	W34290	Brown & Cream body, plastic roof, transparent windows (36051)..........	£20-30 ☐
4052	1961-64	Corridor Coach - 1st/2nd (4202)		BR (E)	E15770	Maroon body, Grey roof, transparent windows (36052)..........	£20-30 ☐
4053	1961-64	Corridor Coach - Brake/2nd (4203)		BR (E)	E35173	Maroon body, Grey roof, transparent windows (36053)..........	£20-30 ☐
4054	1962-64	Corridor Coaches - 1st/2nd (4204)		BR (SR)	S15573	Green body, Grey roof, transparent windows..........	£35-45 ☐
4055	1962-64	Corridor Coaches - Brake/2nd (4205)		BR (SR)	S35001	Green body, Grey roof, transparent windows..........	£35-45 ☐
4060	1961-64	Open Corridor Coach - 1st (4210)		BR (W)	W3085	Brown & Cream body, Grey roof, transparent windows (36060)..........	£25-30 ☐
4061	1961-64	Open Corridor Coach - 2nd (4211)		BR (W)	W3984	Brown & Cream body, Grey roof, transparent windows (36061)..........	£25-30 ☐
4062	1961-64	Open Corridor Coach - 1st (4212)		BR (M)	M3002	Maroon body, Grey plastic roof, transparent windows (36062)..........	£25-35 ☐
4063	1961-64	Open Corridor Coach - 2nd (4213)		BR (M)	M3716	Maroon body, Grey plastic roof, transparent windows (36063)..........	£25-35 ☐
4075	1961-64	Passenger Brake Van (4225)		BR (E)	E81312	Maroon body, Grey roof, transparent windows (36075)..........	£20-30 ☐
4076	1963-64	Six-wheel Passenger Brake..................		BR (M)	M32958	Maroon body, Grey roof, transparent windows (34076)..........	£100-125 ☐
4081	1962-64	Suburban Coach - 1st/2nd (4231)........		BR (SR)	S46291	Green body, Grey roof, transparent windows (36081)...	£50-70 ☐
4082	1962-64	Suburban Coach - Brake/2nd (4232)....		BR (SR)	543381	Green body, Grey roof, transparent windows (36082)...	£50-70 ☐
4082	1962-64	variation		BR (SR)	S43381	with correct coach number (rare) (36082)	£110-130 ☐
4083	1962-64	Suburban Coach - 1st/2nd (4233)........		BR (M)	M41012	Maroon body, Grey roof, transparent windows (36083)..........	£40-50 ☐
4084	1962-64	Suburban Coach - Brake/2nd (4234)...		BR (M)	M43277	Maroon body, Grey roof, transparent windows (36084)..........	£40-50 ☐
4150	1962-64	Electric Driving Trailer Coach (4250)		BR (SR)	S77511	Green, Yellow band on drive end, Black rear panel......	£110-130 ☐
4150	1962-64	variation		BR (SR)	S77511	As previous model but Green inner panel on rear........	£130-150 ☐

Note: The Export issues packed in boxes displaying the special Export Numbers are rare - expect to pay an additional **£20 per issue.**

Restaurant Cars and Sleeping Car

Ref. No.	Year(s)	Model Type				Market Price Range	
D20	1957 only	Restaurant Car		BR (W)	W9562	Brown & Cream body, Grey roof, transparent windows (32097)..........	£25-35 ☐
32096	1957-58	Restaurant Car		BR (W)	W9572	Brown & Cream body, Grey roof, transparent windows (32096)..........	£25-35 ☐
32097	1957-58	Restaurant Car		BR (W)	W9562	Red & Cream body, Grey roof, transparent windows (32097)..........	£25-35 ☐
4047	1959-64	Restaurant Car		BR (W)	W9572	Brown & Cream body, Grey roof, transparent windows (36047)..........	£25-35 ☐

HORNBY DUBLO ELECTRIC TRAINS are here again!

Small supplies of these long-awaited trains are now becoming available. Here is your chance to get the Perfect Table Railway.

Complete sets ONLY will be available at first. Of the sets illustrated below the Tank Goods Set is now ready. The L.M.S. "Duchess of Atholl" Set and the L.N.E.R. "Sir Nigel Gresley" Set will follow.

Obtainable only from Meccano Dealers.

EDG7 Tank Goods Set, L.N.E.R., L.M.S., G.W.R., S.R.
Price 135 - (including tax)

EDP1 L.N.E.R. Passenger Set
Price 167/6 (including tax)

EDP2 L.M.S. Passenger Set
Price 190 - (including tax)

Home supplies will be very limited because Export must have preference.

MADE IN ENGLAND BY MECCANO LIMITED

Rear cover of May 1948 'Meccano Magazine'.

Hornby Dublo Railways

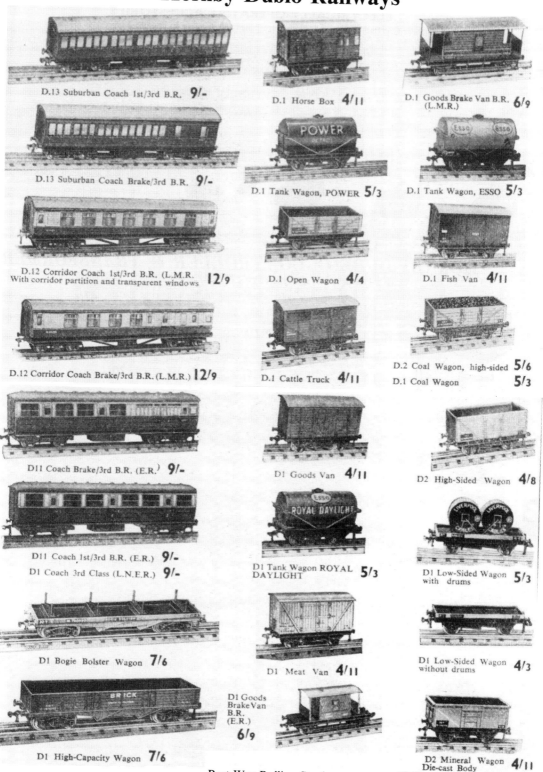

D.13 Suburban Coach 1st/3rd B.R. **9/-**

D.13 Suburban Coach Brake/3rd B.R. **9/-**

D.12 Corridor Coach 1st/3rd B.R. (L.M.R.) **12/9**
With corridor partition and transparent windows

D.12 Corridor Coach Brake/3rd B.R. (L.M.R.) **12/9**

D11 Coach Brake/3rd B.R. (E.R.) **9/-**

D11 Coach 1st/3rd B.R. (E.R.) **9/-**
D1 Coach 3rd Class (L.N.E.R.) **9/-**

D1 Bogie Bolster Wagon **7/6**

D1 High-Capacity Wagon **7/6**

D.1 Horse Box **4/11**

D.1 Tank Wagon, POWER **5/3**

D.1 Open Wagon **4/4**

D.1 Cattle Truck **4/11**

D1 Goods Van **4/11**

D1 Tank Wagon ROYAL DAYLIGHT **5/3**

D1 Meat Van **4/11**

D1 Goods Brake Van B.R. (E.R.) **6/9**

D.1 Goods Brake Van B.R. (L.M.R.) **6/9**

D.1 Tank Wagon, ESSO **5/3**

D.1 Fish Van **4/11**

D.2 Coal Wagon, high-sided **5/6**
D.1 Coal Wagon **5/3**

D2 High-Sided Wagon **4/8**

D1 Low-Sided Wagon with drums **5/3**

D1 Low-Sided Wagon without drums **4/3**

D2 Mineral Wagon Die-cast Body **4/11**

Post-War Rolling Stock
Picture taken from Gamages Catalogue.

161

Ref. No.	Year(s)	Model Type			Hornby Dublo - continued	Market Price Range	
4048	1959-64	Restaurant Car	BR(LMR)	W9562	Red & Cream body, Grey roof, transparent windows (36048)	£25-35	☐
4049	1959-61	Restaurant Car	BR (M)	W9566W	Maroon body, Grey roof, transparent windows (Red frames)	£25-35	☐
4049	1961-64	Restaurant Car	BR (M)	W9566W	As previous model but with White window frames	£25-35	☐

Restaurant Cars and Sleeping Car ('Super Detail')

Ref. No.	Year(s)	Model Type				Market Price Range	
4070	1963-64	Restaurant Car	BR (W)	W1910	Brown & Cream body, Grey roof, transparent windows (34070)	£70-90	☐
4071	1963-64	Restaurant Car	BR (E)	E1939	Maroon body, Grey roof, transparent windows (34071)	£100-120	☐
4078	1961-64	Sleeping Car (4228)	BR (W)	W2402	Maroon body, Grey roof, transparent windows (36078)	£35-60	☐

Vans and Wagons   (pre-war Three-Rail)

Model identification: All have White lettering and Black chassis unless shown differently. See 'Technical Notes' for types of wheels and couplings.

Ref. No.	Year(s)	Model Type	Colour	Market Price Range	

'Great Western Railway' - 'G.W.' issues

D1	1938-40	Open Goods Wagon	Grey body	£25-35	☐
D1	1938-40	Goods Van	Grey body, White roof, 'RETURN TO G.W.R.'	£55-75	☐
D1	1938-40	Goods Brake Van	Grey body, White roof, 'PARK ROYAL' logo	£45-65	☐
D1	1938-40	Coal Wagon	Grey body	£25-35	☐
D1	1938-40	Cattle Truck	Grey body, White roof	£25-35	☐

'London, Midland & Scottish' - 'L.M.S.' issues

D1	1938-40	Open Goods Wagon	Bauxite Brown body	£25-35	☐
D1	1938-40	Goods Van	Bauxite Brown body, Silver-Grey roof	£25-35	☐
D1	1938-40	Goods Brake Van	Bauxite Brown body, Silver-Grey roof	£25-35	☐
D1	1938-40	Coal Wagon	Bauxite Brown body	£25-35	☐
D1	1938-40	'MEAT' Van	Bauxite Brown body, Silver Grey roof	£45-65	☐
D1	1938-40	Cattle Truck	Bauxite Brown body	£25-35	☐
D2	1938-40	High-Sided Coal Wagon	Bauxite Brown body	£25-35	☐

'London & North Eastern Railway' - 'N.E.' issues

D1	1938-40	Open Goods Wagon	Grey body	£25-35	☐
D1	1938-40	Goods Van	Grey body, White roof	£25-35	☐
D1	1938-40	Goods Brake Van	Brown body, White roof	£25-35	☐
D1	1938-40	Coal Wagon	Grey body	£25-35	☐
D1	1938-40	'FISH' Van	Light Brown body, White roof	£60-75	☐
D1	1938-40	High Capacity Wagon	Brown body, White 'BRICK' and 'RETURN TO FLETTON' logos, Black or Brown chassis	£25-35	☐
D1	1938-40	Horse Box	Teak body, White roof	£40-50	☐
D2	1938-40	High-Sided Wagon	Seven-plank Grey body	£40-50	☐
D2	1938-40	High-Sided Coal Wagon	Seven-plank Grey body		☐

'Southern Railway' - 'S.R.' issues

D1	1938-40	Open Goods Wagon	Chocolate Brown body	£40-50	☐
D1	1938-40	Goods Van	Chocolate Brown body, White roof	£75-85	☐
D1	1938-40	Goods Brake Van	Chocolate Brown body, White roof	£125-150	☐
D1	1938-40	Coal Wagon	Chocolate Brown body	£40-50	☐

Tank Wagons

D1	1938-40	'ROYAL DAYLIGHT'	Red tank, Gold logo	£65-85	☐
D1	1938-40	'POWER ETHYL'	Green tank, White and Red logo and 'hand' motif	£65-85	☐
D1	1938-40	'ESSO'	Buff tank with Red stripe, Dark Blue logo with Red shadow	£65-85	☐

Vans and Wagons (post-war Pre-Nationalisation Liveries, Three-Rail)

Model identification: All have White lettering and Black chassis unless shown differently. See 'Technical Notes' for types of wheels and couplings.

'Great Western Railway' - 'G.W.' issues

D1	1948-53	Open Goods Wagon	Grey body	£30-40	☐
D1	1948-53	Goods Van	Grey body, White roof, 'RETURN TO G.W.R.'	£75-100	☐
D1	1948-53	Goods Brake Van	Grey-Green body, White roof, 'PARK ROYAL' logo	£70-90	☐
D1	1948-53	Coal Wagon	Grey body	£20-30	☐
D1	1948-53	Cattle Truck	Grey-Green body, White roof with 2 small windows	£20-30	☐
D1	1948-53	Cattle Truck	Grey-Green body, White roof with one long window	£40-60	☐

'London, Midland & Scottish' - 'L.M.S.' issues

D1	1948-53	Open Goods Wagon	Bauxite Brown body	£30-40	☐
D1	1948-53	Goods Van	Bauxite Brown body, Silver-Grey or Grey roof	£15-20	☐
D1	1948-53	Goods Brake Van	Bauxite Brown body, Silver-Grey or Grey roof	£15-20	☐
D1	1948-53	Coal Wagon	Bauxite Brown body	£10-15	☐
D1	1948-53	Cattle Truck	Bauxite Brown body, Cream interior, 2 small windows, Silver-Grey roof	£100-130	☐
D1	1948-53	'MEAT' Van	Bauxite Brown body, Silver-Grey or Grey roof	£10-15	☐
D1	1948-53	High-sided Coal Wagon	Bauxite Brown body	£10-15	☐
D2	1948-53	High-sided Wagon	Bauxite Brown body	£10-15	☐

'London & North Eastern Railway' - 'N.E.' issues

D1	1948-53	Open Goods Wagon	Grey-Green or Grey body	£15-20	☐
D1	1948-53	Goods Van	Brown body, White roof	£15-20	☐
D1	1948-53	Goods Brake Van	Brown body, White roof	£15-20	☐
D1	1948-53	Coal Wagon	Grey-Green or Grey body	£15-20	☐
D1	1948-53	'FISH' Van	Brown body, White roof	£15-20	☐
D1	1948-53	High Capacity Wagon	Brown body with White 'BRICK' and *RETURN TO FLETTON* logos	£15-20	☐
D1	1948-53	Horse Box	Teak body, White roof	£15-20	☐
D2	1948-53	High-sided Coal Wagon	Seven-plank Grey-Green body	£50-60	☐
			As previous model but with seven-plank Grey body	£25-35	☐

'Southern Railway' - 'S.R.' issues

D1	1948-53	Five Plank Open Goods Wagon	Chocolate Brown body	£80-100	☐
D1	1948-53	Goods Van	Chocolate Brown body, White roof	£100-150	☐
D1	1948-53	Goods Brake Van	Chocolate Brown body, one window on end	£100-150	☐
D1	1948-53	Goods Brake Van	Chocolate Brown body, window each side of end door	£80-100	☐
D1	1948-53	Coal Wagon	Chocolate Brown body	£60-80	☐
D1	1948-53	'MEAT' Van	Buff body, Silver-Grey roof	£100-150	☐
D1	1948-53	'MEAT' Van	Buff body, White roof	£60-80	☐

Tank Wagons

D1	1948-53	'ROYAL DAYLIGHT'	Red tank, Gold logo, (no 'ESSO' or 'PARAFFIN' logos on tank sides)	£60-80	☐
D1	1948-53	'POWER PETROL'	Green tank, Silver logo, Red 'ETHYL' logos, White 'hand' design	£60-80	☐
D1	1948-53	'ESSO'	Buff tank with Red stripe, Dark Blue logo with Red shadow	£60-80	☐

Vans and Wagons
(post-Nationalisation 'British Rail' issues, Three-Rail)

Model identification: All have White lettering and Black chassis unless shown differently. See 'Technical Notes' for types of wheels and couplings.

D1/32020	1954-58	Cattle Truck	Brown body, Grey roof, metal wheels	£10-15	☐
32021	1954-58	Cattle Wagon	Brown body, Grey roof, spoked plastic wheels	£10-15	☐
D1/32025/6	1954-58	Coal Wagon	Grey body, metal or spoked plastic wheels	£10-15	☐
D1/32035	1954-58	Fish Van	Brown body, Grey roof	£10-15	☐
D1/32040	1954-58	Goods Van	Brown body, Grey roof	£10-15	☐
D1/32044/5	1954-58	Goods Brake Van	All Grey body, Grey roof	£10-15	☐
32046	1954-58	Goods Brake Van	Brown body, Grey roof	£10-15	☐
D1/32047	1954-58	Goods Brake Van	All Grey body, 'PARK ROYAL' logo	£10-15	☐
32047	1954-58	Goods Brake Van	All Grey body, 'SOUTHALL' logo	£10-15	☐
D1/32049	1954-58	Caboose	Black body, 'CANADIAN PACIFIC RAILWAY' logo	£75-95	☐
D1/32050	1954-58	High Capacity Wagon	Brown body, 'BRICK - EMPTY TO FLETTON'	£10-15	☐
D1/32051	1954-58	30 ton Wagon	'BOGIE BOLSTER', Grey	£10-15	☐
D1/32058/ /32041	1954-58	Ventilated Van	Brown body, White or Grey roof	£10-15	☐
D1/32060	1954-58	Horse Box	Red body, Grey roof	£10-15	☐
D1/32065	1954-58	Meat Van	White body, Grey roof	£10-15	☐
D1/32068	1954-58	Salt Wagon	Yellow body, Grey roof, Red 'SAXA SALT' logo	£10-15	☐
D1/32069	1954-58	'U.G.B.' Sand Wagon	Yellow body, Black 'United Glass Bottle Co.' logo	£15-20	☐
32070	1954-58	Tank Wagon	Red tank, Red/White/Blue 'ESSO', Gold 'ROYAL DAYLIGHT', Black 'PARAFFIN' logos	£20-25	☐
D1/32076	1954-58	'TUBE' Wagon	Brown body	£10-15	☐
D1/32080	1954-58	Tank Wagon	Green tank with Gold/Yellow 'POWER PETROL' logo	£25-35	☐
D1/32081	1954-58	Tank Wagon	Silver-Grey tank, Red/White/Blue 'ESSO' logo	£25-35	☐
D1/32082	1954-58	Tank Wagon	Yellow tank, Red 'SHELL LUBRICATING OIL' logo	£25-35	☐
D1/32083	1954-58	Tank Wagon	Red tank, White 'VACUUM OIL COMPANY' logo plus two 'MOBILGAS' motifs	£25-35	☐
D1/32084	1956-57	'MOBIL' Tank Wagon	Red tank, White 'MOBIL OIL COMPANY LTD' logo plus two 'MOBILOIL' motifs	£25-35	☐
	1957-58		Red tank, Dark Blue 'MOBIL' logo on White background	£25-35	☐
D2/32030	1954-58	High-sided Coal Wagon	Grey body	£10-15	☐
D2/32052	1954-58	Double Bolster Wagon	Grey body	£10-15	☐
D2/32055	1954-58	High-sided Coal Wagon	Grey body	£10-15	☐
D2/32056	1954-58	Mineral Wagon	Grey body	£10-15	☐

THREE RAIL - TWO RAIL TRANSITION 1958, Box numbering identification

The box numbers changed from their 3-rail reference numbers (e.g. 32048 WR) to their new 2-rail numbers, (32048 WR became 4312 WR, etc). The early models continued to be issued in blue boxes with white stripes and also displayed an 'SD6' number to denote that they were 'Super Detail' models. The 'SD6' reference only appeared on the blue/white box. Eventually the 'SD6' was dropped and the red box (with white lines) was introduced.

WHEN REPLYING TO ADVERTISEMENTS PLEASE MENTION JOHN RAMSAY'S CATALOGUE

Vans and Wagons ('British Rail' issues, Two-Rail)

Cat No	Years	Name	Description	Price	
4300	1959-64	Blue Spot Fish Van	White or Cream body, Grey roof, Blue spot, 'INSUL FISH' logo (SD)	£12-15	☐
4301	1959-64	Banana Van	Brown body, Grey roof with Yellow identification spot (SD)	£12-15	☐
4305	1959-64	Passenger Fruit Van	Maroon body, Black or Grey roof, (SD)	£18-24	☐
4310	1959-64	Goods Brake Van	Grey body, 'M.R.', (SD)	£10-15	☐
4311	1959-64	Goods Brake Van	Brown body, 'B.R.', (SD)	£10-15	☐
4312	1959-64	Goods Brake Van	Grey body, 'W.R.', (SD)	£10-15	☐
4313	1959-64	Gunpowder Van	Brown body, Grey roof, (SD)	£20-30	☐
4315	1959-64	'B.R.' Horse Box	Maroon body, Grey roof, Light Brown plastic horse, (SD)	£75-100	☐
4316	1959-64	'S.R.' Horse Box	Green body, Grey roof, Light Brown plastic horse, (SD)	£100-125	☐
4318	1959-64	Packing Van for Breakdown Train	Red body, Grey roof, (SD)	£25-35	☐
4320	1959-64	Refrigerator Van	White or Cream body, Grey roof, (SD)	£10-15	☐
4323	1959-64	'S.R.' Utility Van	Green body, Grey roof, (SD)	£25-35	☐
4325	1959-64	12 ton Ventilated Van	Brown body, White roof, (SD)	£7-9	☐
4401	1959-64	T.P.O. Mail Van	Maroon body, Grey roof	£30-40	☐
4605	1959-64	40 ton Bogie Well Wagon	Grey body with White 'WELTROL' logo, (SD)	£10-15	☐
4610	1959-64	'BOGIE BOLSTER' Wagon	Grey body, (SD)	£10-15	☐
4615	1959-64	Double Bolster Wagon	with Timber Load, Grey body, Black base, (SD)	£9-12	☐
4620	1959-64	Breakdown Crane Wagon	Red gloss finish, White on Black 'No.133'	£60-80	☐
			Red matt finish, White on Black 'No.133'	£40-50	☐
4625	1959-64	20 ton Wagon	'BULK GRAIN', Grey body, (SD)	£10-15	☐
4626	1959-64	Bulk Cement Wagon	'PRESFLO', Bauxite Brown body, (SD)	£10-15	☐
4627	1959-64	'I.C.I.' 20 ton Salt Wagon	'BULK SALT', all-Blue body, (SD)	£10-15	☐
4630	1959-64	8 ton Cattle Wagon	Brown body, Grey roof, (SD)	£10-15	☐
4635	1959-64	13 ton Coal Wagon	Grey body, (SD)	£10-15	☐
4640	1959-64	12 ton Steel Type Goods Wagon	Brown body, (SD)	£10-15	☐
4644	1959-64	21 ton Hopper Wagon	Grey body, (SD)	£50-75	☐
4645	1959-64	Low-sided Wagon	Grey body, (SD)	£10-15	☐
4646	1959-64	Low-sided Wagon	Grey body, 2 Yellow plastic cable drums, 'ALUMINUM WIRE AND CABLE Co'	£35-45	☐
4646	1959-64	Low-sided Wagon	Grey, 2 Black/Beige wooden cable drums, 'LIVERPOOL CABLES', (Export)	£9-12	☐
4647	1959-64	Low-sided Wagon	Grey body with Red/Grey container, 'BRITISH RAILWAYS', 'FURNITURE'	£9-12	☐
4648	1959-64	Low-sided Wagon	Grey body with White/Grey container, 'BRITISH RAILWAYS', 'INSUL-MEAT'	£9-12	☐
4649	1959-64	Low-sided Wagon	Grey body with Hornby Dublo tractor (Blue)	£35-45	☐
4652	1959-64	Machine Wagon	'LOWMAC', Brown body, (SD)	£10-15	☐
4654	1959-64	'RAIL CLEANING WAGON'	White logo on Black wagon plus six cleaning plugs, (SD)	£300-500	☐
4655	1959-64	Mineral Wagon	Grey metal body with plastic disc type wheels, (SD)	£60-75	☐
			As previous model but with Grey plastic body, plastic wheels	£10-15	☐
4656	1959-64	16 ton Mineral Wagon	Brown plastic body, plastic wheels	£30-45	☐
4657	1959-64	United Dairies Milk Tank	Six-wheeled 'Super Detail' vehicle		
			Off-White tank, Yellow 'U.D.' logo, High and Low supports	£20-25	☐
			Off-White tank, Yellow 'U.D.' logo, plus High supports	£20-25	☐
			Off-White tank, Yellow 'U.D.' logo, plus Low supports	£20-25	☐
			White tank, Yellow 'U.D.' logo, plus High and Low supports	£20-25	☐
			Cream tank, Yellow 'U.D.' logo, plus High supports	£25-35	☐
4658	1959-64	'PRESTWIN' Silo Wagon	Brown body, (SD)	£7-9	☐
4660	1959-64	'U.G.B.' Sand Wagon	Yellow body, Black 'United Glass Limited' logo, (SD)	£35-45	☐
		Private Owners variation	Yellow body, Black 'United Glass Manufacturing Company Ltd' logo	£12-15	☐
4665	1959-64	'SAXA SALT' Wagon	Yellow body, Grey roof, Red logo, (SD)	£12-15	☐
4670	1959-64	13 ton Standard Wagon	Grey body, (SD)	£10-15	☐
4675	1959-64	Tank Wagon	White Chlorine tank, Yellow top, Black 'I.C.I. motif and star, (SD)	£10-15	☐
4676	1959-64	Tank Wagon	Silver-Grey tank with two Red/White/Blue 'ESSO' motifs plus Black star, (SD)	£10-15	☐
4677	1959-64	Tank Wagon	Red tank with Dark Blue 'MOBIL' logo on White background, (SD)	£15-20	☐
4678	1959-64	Tank Wagon	Yellow tank with Red 'SHELL LUBRICATING OIL' logo, (SD)	£15-20	☐
4679	1959-64	Tank Wagon	Silver-Grey tank with Black 'TRAFFIC SERVICES Ltd' logo, 2 Black stars, (SD)	£15-20	☐
4680	1959-64	Tank Wagon	Black tank with Red 'ESSO' motif plus White 'ESSO PETROLEUM COMPANY LTD' logo and 2 Black stars, (SD)	£20-30	☐
4685	1959-64	Tank Wagon	Dark Blue 'I.C.I.' Caustic Liquor Bogie Wagon, (SD)	£65-85	☐
		variation:	As previous model but with Diamond bogies	£100-150	☐

Notes:
'SUPER DETAIL' - Models with the abbreviation '(SD)' have greatly enhanced 'SUPER DETAIL' features
'BLACK STARS' - Two Black stars on a wagon indicates that the vehicle can travel by the fastest freight train
'SILVER TANK' - A Tank Wagon painted Silver indicates that it is carrying an inflammable liquid

WHEN REPLYING TO ADVERTISEMENTS PLEASE MENTION JOHN RAMSAY'S CATALOGUE

3: Gift Sets

Ref. No.	Year(s)	Set Name	Contents	Market Price Range	

Pre-war issues

Ref. No.	Year(s)	Set Name	Contents	Market Price Range	
DP1	1938-40	Clockwork Passenger Train Set	'L.N.E.R.' Contains DL1 'Sir Nigel Gresley' loco and tender plus two Articulated Coaches, 8 curved and 2 straight rails	£1200-1500	☐
DG7	1938-40	Clockwork Tank Goods Train Sets	'G.W.R.', 'L.M.S.', 'L.N.E.R.', 'S.R.' Contains DL7 Tank loco plus Open Wagon, Goods Van and Goods Brake Van	£300-1300*	☐
EDP1	1938-40	Electric Passenger Train Set	'L.N.E.R.' Contains EDL1 'Sir Nigel Gresley' loco and tender plus two Articulated Coaches, 8 curved and 2 straight rails	£900-1500	☐
EDG7	1938-40	Electric Tank Goods Train Sets	'G.W.R.', 'L.M.S.', 'L.N.E.R.', 'S.R.' Contains EDL7 loco plus Open Wagon, Goods Wagon and Goods Brake Wagon	£300-1300*	☐

* **Note:** The Market Price Range for these sets reflects the great variation in market prices for the individual locomotives (see the Locomotives listing).

Post-war issues (Pre-Nationalisation Liveries)

Ref. No.	Year(s)	Set Name	Contents	Market Price Range	
EDP1	1948-53	Electric Passenger Train Set	'L.N.E.R.' Contains EDL1 'Sir Nigel Gresley' loco and tender plus D1 1st/3rd and Brake/3rd Coaches	£150-200	☐
EDP2	1948-53	Passenger Set	'L.M.S.' Contains EDL2 'Duchess of Atholl' loco and tender plus D3 'L.M.S.' Coaches '3rd' and 'Brake 3rd'	£120-160	☐
EDP2	1948-53	Passenger Set	'CANADIAN PACIFIC' Contains EDL2 loco (1215) and tender plus D3 'L.M.S.' Coaches '3rd' and 'Brake 3rd'	£750-1000	☐
EDG3	1948-53	Freight Train Set	'CANADIAN PACIFIC RAILWAY' Contains EDL2 loco and tender plus 32049 'C.P.' Caboose & D1 Bogie Bolster Wagon	£750-1000	☐
EDG7	1948-53	Tank Goods Train Sets	'G.W.R.', 'L.M.S.', 'L.N.E.R.' or 'SOUTHERN' Contains EDL7 0-6-2 loco plus D1 Goods Van, D1 Open Wagon & D1 Goods Brake Wagon	£300-1300*	☐

* **Note:** The Market Price Range for these sets reflects the great variation in market prices for the individual locomotives (see the Locomotives listing).

Post-Nationalisation 'British Railways' issues (Three-Rail)

Ref. No.	Year(s)	Set Name	Contents	Market Price Range	
EDP10	1954-58	Passenger Train Set 'B.R.'	EDL17 0-6-2 Tank loco (69567) D14 Suburban Coaches '1st/3rd' & 'Brake/3rd'	£100-125	☐
EDP11	1954-58	Passenger Train Set 'B.R.'	EDL11 'Silver King' loco and tender plus D11 Coaches '1st/2nd' & 'Brake/2nd'	£100-125	☐
EDP12	1954-58	Passenger Train Set 'B.R.'	EDL12 'Duchess of Montrose' (gloss finish) D11 Coaches '1st/2nd' & 'Brake/2nd'	£120-140	☐
			Same set but with matt finish locomotive	£90-105	☐
EDP13	1954-58	Tank Passenger Set 'B.R.'	EDL18 2-6-4 Tank loco (no.80054) plus D13 Suburban Coaches '1st/3rd' and 'Brake/3rd'	£100-125	☐
EDP14	1954-58	Passenger Train Set 'B.R.'	EDL18 2-6-4 Tank loco (no.80054) plus D14 Suburban Coaches '1st/2nd' & two 'Brake/3rd'	£120-140	☐
EDP15	1954-58	Passenger Train Set 'B.R.'	Contains EDP11 'Silver King' loco and tender plus D12 Coaches '1st/3rd' & 'Brake/3rd'	£100-125	☐
EDG16	1954-58	Tank Goods Set 'B.R.'	EDL17 0-6-2 Tank loco (no.69567) plus D1 issues: 2 Open Wagons and a Goods Brake Van	£100-125	☐
EDG17	1954-58	Tank Goods Set 'B.R.'	EDL17 0-6-2 Tank loco (no.69567) plus D1 issues: Meat Van, Open Wagon, 'MOBIL' Tank Wagon, Goods Brake Van	£100-125	☐
EDG18	1954-58	Tank Goods Set 'B.R.'	EDL18 2-6-4 Tank loco (no.80054) plus D1 issues: High Capacity Wagon, Bogie Bolster Wagon, Goods Brake Van	£100-125	☐
EDG19	1954-58	Tank Goods Set 'B.R.'	EDL18 2-6-4 Tank loco (no.80054) plus D1 issues: Ventilated Van, 'MOBIL' Tank Wagon, Double Bolster Wagon, Tube Wagon, Goods Brake Van	£130-150	☐
EDP20	1954-58	'BRISTOLIAN' Passenger Train Set	Contains LT 20 'Bristol Castle' loco and tender plus D21 Coaches '1st/2nd' & 'Brake/2nd'	£160-180	☐
EDP22	1954-58	Passenger Train Set 'B.R.'	Contains EDL12 'Duchess of Montrose' loco and tender plus D22 Coaches '1st/2nd' & 'Brake/2nd'	£100-125	☐
G 25	1954-58	Freight Train Set 'B.R.'	Contains: 3225/LT25 Class 8F loco (2-8-0, no.48158) plus D1 Refrigerated Van, 'WELTROL' Bogie Wagon, D1 'SHELL' Tank Wagon, D1 Open Wagon & Goods Brake Van	£100-125	☐

Gift Sets - continued

'British Railways' issues (Two-Rail)

Ref. No.	Year(s)	Model Type	Description	Market Price Range	
2001	1959-64	Tank Goods Set	'Ready to Run' Black or Blue 0-4-0 Tank loco plus two open wagons and Goods Brake Van 'B.R.'	£75-100	☐
2004	1959-64	Diesel Shunter Goods Set	'Ready to Run' Contains Yellow 0-4-0 loco plus two open wagons and Goods Brake Van 'B.R.'	£50-75	☐
2006	1959-64	Southern Tank Goods Set	2207 Green loco (0-6-0, no.31340) plus 4660 'U.G.B.' Sand Wagon, 4646 Steel Goods Wagon, 4312 Goods Brake Van 'W.R.'	£100-125	☐
2007	1959-64	Southern Tank Passenger Set	2207 Green loco (0-6-0, no.31340) plus 4025/6 Suburban Coaches '1st/2nd' & 'Brake/3rd'	£100-125	☐
2008	1959-64	Tank Goods Set	2206 Black loco (0-6-0, no.31337) plus 4660 'U.G.B.' Sand Wagon, 4640 Steel Goods Wagon, 4312 Goods Brake Van	£100-125	☐
2009	1959-64	Tank Passenger Set 'S.R.'	2206 Black loco (0-6-0, no.31337) plus 4025/6 Suburban Coaches '1st/2nd' & 'Brake/2nd' 'S.R.'	£100-125	☐
2015	1959-64	'The TALISMAN' Passenger Train Set 'E.R.'	2211 'Golden Fleece' loco and tender plus 4052/3 Coaches '1st/2nd B.R.' & 'Brake/2nd B.R.'	£200-300	☐
2016	1959-64	Tank Goods Set	2217 loco (0-6-2, no.69550) plus 4665 'SAXA SALT' Wagon, 4677 'MOBIL' Tank Wagon, 4646 Cable Wagon (2 drums), 4310 Goods Brake Van 'L.M.R.'	£100-125	☐
2019	1959-64	Tank Goods Set	2218 loco (2-6-4, 80033) 4648/9 Low-sided Wagons (Meat Container & Tractor) Double Bolster Wagon (Timber load) Goods Brake Van 'L.M.R.' or 'E.R.'	£100-125	☐
2020	1959-64	'TORBAY EXPRESS' Passenger Train Set 'W.R.'	2220 'Denbigh Castle' loco & tender, 4050/1 Coaches '1st/2nd' & 'Brake/2nd'	£200-250	☐
2021	1959-64	'RED DRAGON' Passenger Train Set	2221 'Cardiff Castle' loco and tender plus D1 or 4050/1 Coaches '1st/2nd' & 'Brake/2nd'	£200-250	☐
2022	1959-64	'THE CALEDONIAN' Passenger Train Set	2226 'City of London' loco and tender plus D22 Coaches '1st/2nd' & 'Brake/2nd'	£100-150	☐
			As previous set but with updated 4052/3 Coaches '1st/2nd' and 'Brake/2nd'	£100-150	☐
2024	1959-64	Express Goods Set 'L.M.R.'	Contains 2224 loco (2-8-0, no.48073) plus 4605 Bogie Well Wagon, 4678 'SHELL' Tank Wagon, 4670 Standard Wagon, 4310 Goods Brake Van 'L.M.R.'	£100-125	☐
2025	1959-64	Express Goods Set 'L.M.R.'	2225 loco (2-8-0, no.48109) plus same rolling stock as set 2024	£200-250	☐
2030	1959-64	Diesel-Electric Goods Set	Contains 2230 'Bo-Bo' loco (no.8017) plus 4320 Refrigerator Van 'W.R.', 4625 Grain Wagon, 4325 Ventilated Wagon, 4310 Goods Brake Van 'L.M.R.'	£100-125	☐
2033	1959-64	Diesel-Electric Goods Set	2233 'Co-Bo' loco (no.D5702) plus same rolling stock as set 2030	£200-250	☐
2034	1959-64	'THE ROYAL SCOT' Passenger Train Set	2234 Deltic loco 'Crepello' plus 4052/3 Maroon Coaches '1st/2nd' and 'Brake/2nd'	£200-250	☐
2035	1959-64	'BOURNEMOUTH BELLE' Passenger Train Set	Contains 2235 'Barnstaple' loco and tender plus 4035/6/7 Pullman Coaches	£250-300	☐
2045	1959-64	3300 hp Electric Loco Set	Illustrated in 1964 catalogue but not issued	NPP	☐
2049	1959-64	Breakdown Train Set	Contains 2217 loco (0-6-2, no.69550) plus 69550 Crane, 4318 Packing Van and Brake/2nd Suburban Coach	£200-300	☐
2050	1959-64	Suburban Electric Train Set	Contains 2250 Drive Coach and Trailer Car 4150. Shown in Oct.1962 catalogue as 3 x Car Unit but only marketed as a 2 x Car Unit	£200-250	☐

GIFT SET ENCLOSURES: Operating instructions, Track Layout plans, 'Tested' label, Guarantee, Application form to join the 'Hornby Railway Club'.

4:   Accessories

Ref. No.	Year(s)	Accessory	Details	Market Price Range	

Pre-war accessories (1938 - 1940)

Ref. No.	Year(s)	Accessory	Details	Market Price Range	
D1	1938-40	Main Line Station Building	Cream with Red or Green roof, wooden construction	£200-250	☐
D1	1938-40	Goods Depot	Cream with Red or Green roof, wooden construction	£200-250	☐
D1	1938-40	Engine Shed	Cream with Red or Green roof, wooden construction	£200-250	☐
D1	1938-40	Signal Cabin	Cream with Red or Green roof, wooden construction	£50-75	☐
D2	1938-40	Station Building	Cream with Green roof, wooden construction	£300-400	☐
D2	1938-40	Arched roof	Wooden construction, perspex roof	£200-250	☐
D2	1938-40	Centre platform	Wooden construction	£30-40	☐
D2	1938-40	Side platform	Wooden construction	£30-40	☐
D2	1938-40	Centre platform ramps	Wooden construction	£20-30	☐
D2	1938-40	Side platform ramps	Wooden construction	£20-30	☐
D1	1938-40	Cardboard Tunnel (short)		£40-50	☐
D1	1938-40	Cardboard Tunnel (long)		£40-50	☐
D1	1938-40	Footbridge		£30-40	☐
D1	1938-40	Buffers (single)	or D2 Buffers (double)	£15-25	☐
D1	1938-40	Buffer box	Six in a box	£35-50	☐
D1	1938-40	Signal (single)	or D2 Signal (double) or D3 Signal (Junction)	£7-12	☐
D1	1938-40	Railway Staff	6 metal figures: Guard, Porter with luggage, Ticket Collector, Shunter, Engine Driver, Station Master	£75-100	☐
D2	1938-40	Railway Passengers	6 metal figures: 3 males, 3 females	£75-100	☐
	1938-40	Miscellaneous items	include transformers, electrically operated points, switches, etc.	£6-12	☐
	1938-40	'Clockwork' Track Points		£30-40	☐
	1938-40	'Clockwork' Track		£1-2	☐
	1938-40	Electric Track		£1-2	☐

Post-war accessories (1948 - 1958) Three-Rail

D1	1948-58	Through Station	(Diecast Cream with Orange roof, Green doors and windows)	£50-70	☐
D1	1948-58	Island Platform	(Diecast Cream with Orange roof, Green doors and windows)	£30-40	☐
D1	1948-58	Platform extension	with wall for Through Station	£35-45	☐
D1	1948-58	Platform extension	with wall for Island Platform	£35-45	☐
D1	1948-58	Turntable (32180)	Metal, Grey-Green with Orange sideframes	£40-60	☐
D1	1948-58	Footbridge	All Cream three-piece construction	£20-30	☐
D1	1948-58	Level Crossing (3460 3 R)	Metal, White gates with Red warning circles, Green verges	£15-20	☐
		Plastic version:	Cream base & gates, White posts, Red warning circles	£20-25	☐
D1	1948-58	Girder Bridge	Diecast metal, Orange	£40-50	☐
D1	1948-58	T.P.O. Mail Van Set	with Mail Van, lineside apparatus and two mailbags	£20-30	☐
D1	1948-58	Loading Gauge		£10-15	☐
D1	1948-58	Water Crane	Brown	£5-10	☐
D1	1948-58	(051) Station Staff	6 metal figures: Guard, Porter, Ticket Collector, Shunter, Engine Driver, Station Master	£40-50	☐
D2	1948-58	(053) Passengers	6 metal figures: 3 males, 3 females	£40-50	☐
3450	1948-58	Buffers Stop	Box of 2	£10-15	☐

Signals and Switches

32115	1948-58	Colour Light Signal ES6	'Home'	£7-12	☐
32116	1948-58	Colour Light Signal ES6	'Distant'	£7-12	☐
32117	1948-58	Colour Light Signal ES6	'Junction - Home'	£10-15	☐
D1	1948-58	Switch	Red, for electrically operated points and signals	£7-10	☐
D2	1948-58	Switch	Black, for isolating rails	£7-10	☐
G3	1948-58	Switch	Green, for coloured light signals (rare)	£20-30	☐
ED1/5065	1948-58	Signal	Electrically operated, single arm, 'Home'	£7-12	☐
ED1/5066	1948-58	Signal	Electrically operated, single arm, 'Distant'	£7-12	☐
ED2/5070	1948-58	Signal	Electrically operated, double arm, 'Home - Distant'	£12-18	☐
ED3/5075	1948-58	Junction Signal	Electrically operated, two arms, 'Home'	£12-18	☐
ED3/5076	1948-58	Junction Signal	Electrically operated, two arms, 'Distant'	£12-18	☐
D1/5050	1948-58	Signal	Hand operated, single arm, 'Home'	£10-15	☐
D1/5051	1948-58	Signal	Hand operated, single arm, 'Distant'	£7-10	☐
D2/5055	1948-58	Signal	Hand operated, double arm, 'Home - Distant'	£7-10	☐
D3/5060	1948-58	Junction Signal	Hand operated, two arms, 'Home'	£12-18	☐
D3/5061	1948-58	Junction Signal	Hand operated, two arms, 'Distant'	£12-18	☐

Accessories (1959 - 1964) Two-Rail

050	1959-64	Railway Staff	12 moulded plastic figures	£100-125	☐
052	1959-64	Railway Passengers	12 moulded plastic figures	£30-40	☐
790	1959-64	Granite Chippings		£2-3	☐
791	1959-64	Coal (imitation)	per bag	£2-3	☐
1575	1959-64	Lighting Kit		£10-15	☐
2400	1959-64	T.P.O. Mail Van Set	Mail Van plus lineside apparatus, two mailbags	£20-30	☐
2450	1959-64	Buffers Stop		£10-15	☐
2451	1959-64	Illuminated Buffers		£15-20	☐
4620	1959-64	Breakdown Crane	Gloss or Matt, with 2 support wagons each with 2 screw jacks plus match truck (see Wagons listing)	£75-90	☐
5005	1959-64	Engine Shed Kit - Two Road	Cream and Green with Grey roof	£60-70	☐
5006	1959-64	Engine Shed Extension Kit		£20-30	☐
5010	1959-64	Footbridge		£10-20	☐
5015	1959-64	Girder Bridge	Red plastic (rare - only 3,000 made)	£300-400	☐
5020	1959-64	Goods Depot Kit	Cream and Green, Grey roof, Red/Yellow static working jib	£30-50	☐
5025	1959-64	Gradient and Mile Posts	Box of 12	£40-50	☐
5030	1959-64	Island Platform Kit	Cream and Green, Grey roof	£30-40	☐
5035	1959-64	Loading Gauge		£15-20	☐
5037	1959-64	Lineside Notices	Box of six	£25-35	☐
5040	1959-64	Platelayers' Hut	Box of 6	£25-35	☐
5080	1959-64	Signal Cabin	Cream and Green, Orange roof	£10-20	☐
		Rare variation:	As previous model but with Green roof	£150-200	☐
5083	1959-64	Terminal and Through Station Composite Kit		£200-300	☐
5084	1959-64	Station Canopy Extension Kit	(Tri-ang - Hornby). Box with large top opening, Red/Yellow printing	£400-500	☐
R5084	1959-64	Station Canopy Extension Kit	(late Tri-ang - Hornby). Plain White box, Black/White end labels	£200-300	☐
5085	1959-64	Suburban Station Kit	Cream and Green with Grey roof	£30-40	☐
5086	1959-64	Platform extension		£5-10	☐
5087	1959-64	Platform Fence extension		£10-20	☐
5089	1959-64	Platform Side extension		£20-30	☐
5090	1959-64	Telegraph Poles	Box of 12	£50-75	☐
5091/2	1959-64	Tunnel	Single or Double, price for either	£50-100	☐
5095	1959-64	Water Crane	Buff	£25-35	☐

Note: All the Building Kits in the listing above are of plastic construction.

5: Hornby Dublo Catalogues

Ref. No.	Year(s)	Publication	Cover Features & Details	Market Price Range	
7/938/185 UK	1938-39	Catalogue............................	First catalogue dedicated solely to Hornby Dublo. White cover with colour picture of pre-war layout and boy with flag and whistle plus man and seated boy. Lists all pre-war issues with prices and pictures..	£75-100	☐
1/939/27	1939	Leaflet (one page)	Gives details of the new EDP2 'L.M.S.' Electric Passenger Set plus list of rolling stock and prices..	£15-20	☐
12/1039/70 UK	1939	Leaflet (8 pages).................	A large leaflet with Orange cover listing the entire pre-war range	£75-100	☐
7/1053/250	1953-54	Leaflet	Colour cover. Lists new 'B.R.' liveries	£30-40	☐
7/754/200	1954-55	Leaflet	Colour cover, products price list..	£30-40	☐
7/755/550	1955-56	Leaflet	Colour cover depicting attractive layout. Includes superb colour pictures of entire range..	£30-40	☐
7/556/500	1956-57	Leaflet	With colour picture of 'Duchess of Montrose'..	£30-40	☐
7/857/500	1957	Three-fold Leaflet	With excellent centre page layout spread (man with FIVE fingers pointing to layout)..	£20-30	☐
7/858/500	1958	Three-fold Leaflet	Cover depicts 'Duchess of Montrose' 'ROYAL SCOT'	£15-25	☐
HD/CF/1	1959	Three-fold Leaflet	Cover depicts 2236 'City of London' 'THE CALEDONIAN'	£15-25	☐
18/259/300	1959	'Hornby Book of Trains'....	Cover shows green loco (4472) and price '1/6d'. 64 pages	£10-15	☐
92016	1960	24 page Catalogue	The cover depicts a Blue 'English Electric' loco..	£10-15	☐
72236/02	1961	24 page Catalogue	Cover depicts D9002 Diesel Electric loco with excellent pictures of all items manufactured..	£10-15	☐
77250/02	1961	3 fold Leaflet......................	'City of Liverpool' (No.46247) on the cover	£7-12	☐
18/561/500	1961	24 page Catalogue	Cover picture shows 'Barnstaple' loco..	£10-15	☐
13/162/500	1962	28 page Catalogue	Cover picture shows 'Deltic' locomotive..	£10-15	☐
72245/02	1962	4 page Leaflet......................	Excellent cover picture shows the front ends of 'Barnstaple' and 'Crepello' locos	£10-15	☐
7/363/400 ? 722257/02	1963	20 page Booklet	Pocket sized booklet depicting 'Kingfisher' loco, introduces the E3001 Loco with Pantographs..	£10-15	☐
13/464/100	1964	4-fold Leaflet......................	With view of two green locos	£10-15	☐
R 280 S	1965	Tri-ang and Hornby Dublo Amalgamation Issue	Night scene on cover..	£10-15	☐

In addition to the foregoing basic listing of leaflets and catalogues dedicated to Hornby Dublo many other publications listed the products:

Meccano Magazines - pre-war and post-war
Meccano General Products catalogues
Large stores own catalogues - 'Hamleys', 'Gamages', 'Bentalls', etc.
Hornby 'Book of Trains' - pre-war and post-war
'Hornby Trains' leaflets and illustrated price lists - pre-war and post-war from 1948

6: Model Pricing Guidelines

Post-war Locomotives. All were issued both as individual models and in sets. Post-war re-issued models are priced at 20% less than pre-war examples.

Early Boxes. Models EDL1 and EDL2 packed in light powder-blue boxes are priced at 33% more than those in dark blue boxes.

'Gloss' finished Locomotives. The only locomotives to be issued in a glossy paint livery were:
EDL11 'Silver King',   EDL12 'Duchess of Montrose',   N2 69567 Tank Locomotive.

Qualifying Standards. The prices shown in this Catalogue have been based on the following qualifying standards:
Locomotives to be in exceptional condition showing no signs of wear or fingerprints, to be in working order, and to be in its original box.
Boxes to be in pristine, unmarked condition, complete with any original packing or labelling. See the following section on 'Packaging'.

Prices for non-Mint or unboxed models. Models in near mint condition but unboxed are usually priced at approximately 60% to 70% of the mint and boxed price shown.

7: Packaging and Box types

Locomotives, pre-war packaging
A boxed model should include the original corrugated cardboard wrapper which displays a white 'Meccano' sticky label with red printing, plus a small sticker indicating the locomotive's livery. A further sticker indicates whether the model is 'Clockwork' or 'Electric'. The ends of the locomotive should be protected by cardboard core end rings.
Each locomotive was packed with a brown 'TESTED' label together with operating instructions, a track layout guide, plus an application form to join the 'Hornby Railway Company'. A guarantee was also enclosed with the number shown matching the number stamped on the bottom of the box.

Locomotives, post-war packaging
Packing materials should include a cover protector strip which covers the entire length of the boxed model, tucking into the box ends. The ends of the locomotive should be protected by engine housing cores plus top and bottom cardboard strip protectors.
Enclosed with the model should be operating instructions, a track layout leaflet/booklet and a guarantee with the number matching the number stamped on the bottom of the box.
Early post-war models were packed with a brown 'TESTED' label, later issues received just a white rubber stamped label and the last locomotives had a yellow/black label.
A combined 'TESTED AND GUARANTEED' certificate (ref. 16/500) was also used in the early post-war 'long box' sets (the certificate had blue printing on pale blue paper). All sets contained a 'TESTED' label.

Passenger Coaches, Vans and Wagons packaging

All models issued from 1938 until 1955 were housed in strong cardboard boxes. On the side of most boxes was printed a date manufacturing code together with a quantity code plus a prominent Box Number. D3 Corridor Coach, L.M.S. Brake/3rd for example: Box Number 'DR 363', Date '6 49' (June 1949) Manufacturing Code '3.5 N' (3,500). A printing reference was also shown - 'BWW9232'. Stamped on the box, usually on its back, was the date the model was actually issued - often some months later than the manufacturing date shown. It is not always possible to find the release date stamp. In addition the colours of the boxes and the colour of the box lettering were changed at regular intervals.

The main changes were as follows:

1938 - 1940	Pale blue boxes with dark blue printed letters
1948 - 1949	Pale blue boxes with dark blue printed letters. The first post-war models were issued in plain brown cardboard with blue printing.
1950 only	Grey-blue boxes with dark blue printed letters
1951 only	Grey-blue boxes with white printed letters
1952 - 1955	Dark blue boxes with white printed letters
1955 - 1958	Dark blue boxes with white parallel lines and without the date and manufacturing information. The box numbers continued to be shown and were prominently featured in catalogues. Pictures added to boxes in 1958 when 'Super Detail' models introduced.
1958 - 1964	Red boxes with white parallel lines and without date and manufacturing information.

NB Assembly dates and Packers' initials shown on the end flaps of some boxes, for example 'HG 358'.

Model and Box Numbers

When the Hornby Dublo range was launched in 1938 each model reference received a 'D' prefix. This referred to 'Dublo' in order to differentiate the models from existing Hornby trains. In addition each box (as described above) was given a separate reference number. This system continued until 1956 when the box number effectively became the catalogue number. As a consequence the models listed include both the original simple 'D' reference numbers and their box numbers. For the purposes of simplicity the models have been listed on a 'date of release' basis in this Catalogue.

8:   Technical Notes

Model construction materials

Locomotives: Die-cast zinc alloy bodies, wheels and chassis until 1958 when polystyrene features were introduced.

Coaches: The early coaches had die-cast bogies and wheels with lithographed tinplate bodies. From 1959 polystyrene ends, roofs and underframes were introduced.

Vans and Wagons: Die-cast underframes and wheels until 1958 when polystyrene introduced.

Locomotive wheel arrangements

Steam Locomotives are classed by the number of wheels in the order: Leading - Driving - Trailing. Some wheel arrangements have a general type name, for example 4-6-2 'Pacific', or 4-4-2 'Atlantic'. Two leading or trailing wheels are a 'pony truck'. Four leading or trailing wheels are a 'bogie truck'. Diesel and Electric engines have their own classifications.

'BO - BO'	A locomotive fitted with two pairs of wheels at both front and rear
'CO - CO'	A locomotive fitted with three pairs of wheels at both front and rear (Deltic)
'CO - BO'	A locomotive with three pairs of wheels at the front and two pairs at the rear

'Totem' motifs

These refer to the motifs on 'British Railways' locomotive tenders.
1st type: Lion on a wheel,   2nd type: Lion on a Crown.
References to totems facing forwards or backwards indicate the direction the head of the lion is facing.
The tails of the lions in the 1st type of motif have four variations. Each variation is linked to a matching cab number design:

1:   Lion with thin short tail - small thin matching cab number
2:   Lion with thick short tail - small thick matching cab number
3:   Lion with thick long tail - large thick matching cab number
4:   Lion with thin long tail - large thin matching cab number

Hornby Dublo model scale

Double '0' ('00') scale is 4 mm. to the foot (1/76) and is thus slightly larger than the 3.5 mm. 'HO' scale, but still using the same 16.5 mm. rail gauge.

Wheel and Coupling types (Passenger Coaches, Vans and Wagons)

Types of wheels

1938 - 40	Wheels have an inner and outer axle rim and often show signs of fatigue. Axles held by single housing.
1948 - 53	Same as pre-war wheels in shape but not prone to fatigue. Axles retained by clips to mountings.
1953 - 58	Wheels have no pronounced inner or outer axle rim. Axles retained by mounting clips.
1958 - 64	Nylon 'disc' wheels with no spokes. Axles retained by mounting clips (used on coaches).
1958 - 64	Nylon wheel with eight spokes. Axles retained by mounting clips (used on vans and wagons).

Types of couplings

1938 - 40	A flat spring-steel coupling with an oval end plus a small chassis hook.
1948 - 54	A metal coupling with 'RD.No.848012' on shank and without patent ref. 'PAT NO 605283'.
1954 - 58	Same as previous coupling but with both Registered and Patent Numbers on shank.
1956 - 60	Same as previous coupling but with longer vertical 'hook-up' link.
1963 - 64	Same as previous coupling but finer and made of Nylon.

HORNBY DUBLO AUCTION RESULTS 1992-93

Christies auction results (see pictures of models listed in the colour section)

Condition abbreviations: (P) Poor, (F) Fair, (G) Good, (E) Excellent, (M) Mint, (NPA) No price available
Gradings shown refer to condition of models. Boxes are all (G) to (E) unless otherwise described.

Auction Sale, 27th November 1992, 'THE GREAT HORNBY DUBLO COLLECTION'

First shelf:
DL1 Clockwork 'Sir Nigel Gresley' loco '4498'**£1,100**,   EDL1 Electric 'Sir Nigel Gresley' loco '4498' **£900**,   DL7 Clockwork Tank loco 'LNER 2690' **£420**

Second shelf:
EDL2 'Duchess of Atholl' (yellow nameplate) 'LMS' **£200**,   EDL7 Tank loco 'GWR 6699' (green) **£550**,   EDL2 'Duchess of Atholl' (smoke deflectors) 'LMS' **£950**

Third shelf:
EDL2 'Canadian Pacific' loco (black, with caboose) '1215' **£600**,   EDL7 Tank loco (green) 'Southern 2594' **£580**,   3224 2-8-0 Locomotive (black) 'BR 48094' **£400**

Fourth shelf:
3221 'Ludlow Castle' loco '5002' **£500**,   3235 'Dorchester' loco '34042' **£400**,   2245 'Bo-Bo' 3300hp Electric Locomotive **£450**

Fifth shelf:
4070 Restaurant Car (WR) **£80**,   4076 6-wheeled Passenger Brake Van 'BR' **£130**,
4685 'ICI' Caustic Liquor Bogie Wagon (diamond bogies) **£120**,   4654 'RAIL CLEANING WAGON' **£750**

Bottom shelf:
5080 Signal Cabin (green roof) **£220**,   5015 'Red' Girder Bridge **£480**,
050 Dinky Toys Railway Staff **£220**,   054 Dinky Toys Railway Station Personnel **£90**

Locomotives and Train Sets sold at auction 1992 - 1993

(C) = Christies, (V) = Vectis, (W) = Wallis & Wallis.
All items listed below were sold in mint condition and were boxed.

LOCOMOTIVES

2211	4-6-2 BR 'Golden Fleece', MB	**£170** (C)
2217	0-6-2 BR Tank '69550', big valve, MB	**£150** (C)
2217	0-6-2 BR Tank, small valve, MB	**£70** (C)
2221	4-6-0 BR 'Cardiff Castle', MB	**£180** (C)
2224	2-8-0 BR 8F Loco '48073', MB	**£160** (C)
2226	4-6-0 BR 'City of London', MB	**£170** (C)
2231	BR 0-6-0 Diesel Electric Shunter, MB	**£110** (C)
2233	BR Co-Bo 1200hp Diesel-Electric, MB	**£140** (C)
2235	BR 4-6-2 'Barnstaple' Loco, MB	**£260** (C)
2250	BR Suburban Loco/4080/4150 Coach, MB	**£350** (C)
3218	BR 2-6-4 Tank '80059', nickel wheels, MB	**£380** (C)
3221	BR 2-6-4 'Ludlow Castle', MB	**£700** (C)
3224	Goods Loco & Tender, MB	**£460** (V)
3226	BR 4-6-2 'City of Liverpool', MB	**£600** (C)
3231	BR 0-6-0 Shunter, double rods, MB	**£260** (C)
3245	E3002 Bo-Bo, (Meccano conversion), MB	**£850** (C)
BDL1	'Sir Nigel Gresley', (pre-war, clockwork), MB	**£1,100** (C)
EDL1	'Sir Nigel Gresley', (pre-war, electric), MB	**£900** (C)
EDL1	'Sir Nigel Gresley', (pre-war, electric), MB	**£480** (V)
EDL2	LMS 'Atholl' (with 'Montrose' body), MB	**£950** (C)

EDL12	'Duchess of Montrose', gloss finish, MB	**£280** (C)
EDL18	(2nd) BR 2-6-4 Tank loco, '80054', MB	**£200** (C)
LT25	BR 2-8-0 8F Loco, '48158', MB	**£220** (C)

TRAIN SETS

C19	Goods Train Set, MB	**£180** (V)
DG7	SR Tank Goods Set, 2594, pre-war, MB	**£1,400** (C)
DG7	LMS Tank Goods Set, 6917, pre-war, MB	**£650** (C)
DG7	GWR Tank Goods Set, 6699, pre-war, MB	**£1,000** (C)
DP1	LNER 'Sir Nigel Gresley' Set, pre-war, MB	**£700** (C)
EDP10	BR Tank Passenger Set, short tail, MB	**£120** (C)
EDG7	SR Tank Goods Set, 2594, pre-war, MB	**£1,200** (C)
EDG7	SR Tank Goods Set, MB	**£430** (-)
EDG7	LMS Tank Goods Set, 6917, pre-war, MB	**£650** (C)
EDG7	NE Tank Goods Set, 2690, pre-war	**£400** (C)
EDG7	LNER Tank Goods Set	**£260** (C)
EDG7	GWR Tank Goods Set	**£300** (C)
2049	Hornby Dublo Breakdown Set	**£340** (W)

Hornby Dublo information sources:

The Swapmeet Toys and Models Ltd. and the Dick Fawcett 'Hornby Dublo' collections,
Hornby Dublo catalogues 1938 - 1964,
models sold at Christies' London Auction sale in Nov. 1992 'The Great Hornby-Dublo Collection',
models sold at Vectis, Guildford, Auction sales,
models sold at the regular Lacy Scott Auction sales in Bury St.Edmunds,
models sold at Phillips West Two, London, Auction sales, and Wallis & Wallis, Lewes, Sussex, sales.

Acknowledgements

The Compiler of the Hornby Dublo section was the Editor, John Ramsay, who would like to express his personal thanks to Dick Fawcett of Ipswich and to Brian Secker of 'Trains and Olde Tyme Toys', Aylsham Road, Norwich for their invaluable technical assistance in the production of the listings. Further thanks are also due to George Beavis and Albert Chaplin of Lacy Scott, Bury St.Edmunds.

Books and further information.

The following are recommended:
'The Hornby Dublo Post-war 3-Rail Collectors Guide' - Tony Oakes, Mayfield Publishing, 68, Main Road, Wynbunbury, Nantwich, Cheshire, CW5 7LS.
'Hornby Dublo Trains', Hornby Companion Series, Vol.3 - Michael J. Foster, Guild Publishing, London (by arrangement with New Cavendish Books).
The many monographs and notes published by the Dublo Circle of the Hornby Railway Collectors Association in the H.R.C.A. Journal.
Hornby Railway Collectors Association (H.R.C.A.)
Membership Secretary: Bob Field, 2 Ravensmore Road, Sherwood, Nottingham, NG5 2AH.

LLEDO

'Models of Days Gone'

Introduction

One of the founders of Matchbox Toys, Jack Odell OBE formed the Lledo toy company in 1982 and the first 6 models made their appearance at Easter 1983. Successful 'Sunday magazine' type marketing raised public awareness of these delightful new collectables and the number of dedicated collectors grew rapidly.

Lledo introduced the 'Premier Collection' and the 'Military Collection' in 1991 to offer greater choice, more detailed finish and improved appearance of certain models. Both these ranges have their own attractive packaging.

With increasing interest the range has expanded to around sixty models and has generally represented only vehicles made up to the 1930s. 'Days Gone Vanguards' introduced in 1993 enhances and extends the range of interest into the 1950s and 1960s. Rationalisation of output means that some earlier models are now being discontinued and are likely to increase in price.

Part of the success of the Lledo company is due to the demand for use of certain models for promotional purposes. A review of this aspect of Lledo collecting follows the main 'Days Gone' listing.

The Compiler of this Catalogue is indebted to RDP Publications for supplying information on which these lists are based. Details of Club membership and other specialist services to Lledo collectors are given at the end of this chapter.

Lledo - Models of Days Gone

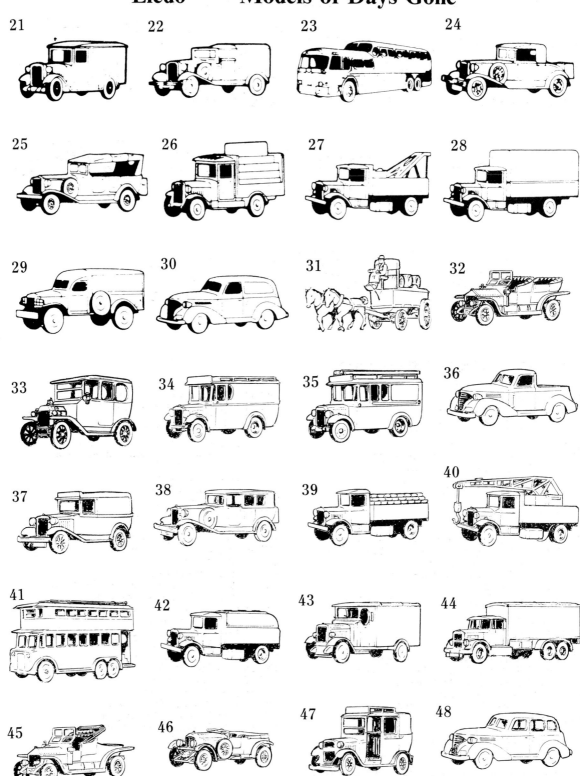

21 22 23 24

25 26 27 28

29 30 31 32

33 34 35 36

37 38 39 40

41 42 43 44

45 46 47 48

Lledo - Models of Days Gone

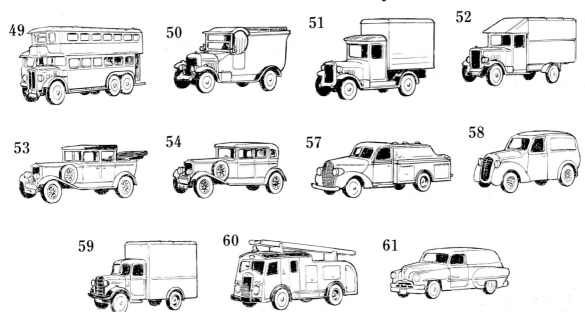

49   50   51   52

53   54   57   58

59   60   61

'Days Gone' Model Numbers & Types

DG 1   Horse-Drawn Tram
DG 2   Horse-Drawn Milk Float
DG 3   Horse-Drawn Delivery Van
DG 4   Horse-Drawn Omnibus
DG 5   Shand Mason Horse-Drawn Fire Engine
DG 6   1920 Ford Model 'T' Van
DG 7   1934 Ford Model 'A', Woody-Wagon
DG 8   1920 Ford Model 'T' Tanker
DG 9   1934 Ford Model 'A' Car (open)
DG 10 1935 Dennis Single-Deck Coach
DG 11 Horse-Drawn Removal Van
DG 12 1934 Dennis Fire Engine
DG 13 1934 Ford Model 'A' Van
DG 14 1934 Ford Model 'A' Car (with hood)
DG 15 1932 AEC Regent Double-Deck Bus
DG 16 1934 Dennis Parcels Van
DG 17 1932 AEC Regal Single-Deck Bus
DG 18 1936 Packard Van
DG 19 1931 Rolls-Royce Phantom II (Brewster)
DG 20 1936 Ford Stake Truck
DG 21 1934 Chevrolet Van
DG 22 1933 Packard Town Van
DG 23 1954 Scenicruiser
DG 24 1934 Rolls-Royce Playboy (Brewster)
DG 25 1925 Rolls-Royce Silver Ghost (Barker)
DG 26 1934 Chevrolet Bottle Delivery Truck
DG 27 1934 Mack Breakdown Truck
DG 28 1934 Mack Canvas-Back Truck
DG 29 1942 Dodge 4 x 4
DG 30 1939 Chevrolet Panel Van
DG 31 Horse-Drawn Brewers Dray

DG 32 1907 Rolls-Royce Silver Ghost
DG 33 1920 Ford Model 'T' Car
DG 34 1932 Dennis Delivery Van
DG 35 1932 Dennis Limousine
DG 36 1939 Chevrolet Pick-Up
DG 37 1932 Ford Model 'A' Van Panel Van
DG 38 1925 Rolls-Royce Silver Ghost Saloon
DG 39 1934 Mack Truck
DG 40 1934 Mack Crane Truck
DG 41 1928 Karrier E6 Trolley-Bus
DG 42 1934 Mack Tanker
DG 43 1931 Morris Van
DG 44 1937 Scammell 6-Wheeler
DG 45 1908 Rolls-Royce Silver Ghost Coupé
DG 46 1930 Bentley 4.5 Litre
DG 47 1933 Austin Taxi
DG 48 1939 Chevrolet Car
DG 49 1931 AEC Renown Double-Deck Bus
DG 50 1926 'Bull-Nose' Morris Van
DG 51 1934 Chevrolet Box Van
DG 52 1935 Morris Parcels Van
DG 53 1926 Rolls Royce Landaulet
DG 54 1929 Rolls Royce 'D' Back
*DG 55 Horse-Drawn Tanker
*DG 56 1934 Ford Model 'A' Van (Raised Roof)
DG 57 1939 Ford Tanker
DG 58 1950 Morris 'Z' Van
DG 59 1950 Bedford 30cwt Truck
DG 60 1955 Dennis F8 Fire Engine
DG 61 1953 Pontiac Delivery Van

* Not issued as a 'Model of Days Gone' — only issued as a promotional to date.

173

'Models of Days Gone'

DG 1 HORSE-DRAWN TRAM. Model features a metal body with plastic horse & seats. It has brass trim and includes a set of figures: 2 lady passengers, a male passenger, a girl and the driver.

000a	1983	'WESTMINSTER'		
		Green chassis, Orange seats, Yellow crest.....	**£15-25**	☐
000b	1983	Green chassis, Orange seats, Cream crest	**£10-15**	☐
000c	1983	Green chassis, Orange seats, White crest......	**£4-6**	☐
		(a,b,c) with no strengtheners on end panel or shafts...	**£100-120**	☐
		(a,b,c) with strengtheners on shafts but not end panels....................................	**£20-30**	☐
000d	1987	Green chassis, Red seats, White crest........	**£3-5**	☐
001a	1984	'MAIN STREET', Green/Grey	**£4-6**	☐
002a	1984	'MAIN STREET', Brown/Cream................	**£4-6**	☐
003		Not allocated		
004a	1984	'CRICH', Blue chassis, Cream roof	**£4-6**	☐
005a	1984	'DOWNTOWN', Cream, Green seats	**£4-6**	☐
005b	1987	Cream chassis, Dark Green seats	**£3-5**	☐
005c	1988	Dark Green seats, no Gold in crest..............	**£3-5**	☐
005d	1992	Dark Green seats, reversed crest	**NRP**	☐
006a	1990	'HERSHEY', Dark Brown & Green	**£3-5**	☐
	1990	Model withdrawn (but re-run for DG1-005d)		

DG 2 HORSE-DRAWN MILK FLOAT. Model features a metal body with a plastic roof section, horse & 3 milk crates. It has 'brass' 12-spoke wheels and a set of Cream plastic figures including a woman, a man, the driver and a dog.

000a	1983	'EXPRESS DAIRY', Blue/White..................	**£4-6**	☐
001a	1984	'CHAMBOURCY', Cream/Blue	**£4-6**	☐
002		Not allocated		
003a	1984	'CLIFFORD DAIRY', Red/Yellow/White...	**£4-6**	☐
004a	1984	'CELTIC DAIRY', Cream/Red	**£4-6**	☐
	1990	Model withdrawn from production		

DG 3 HORSE-DRAWN DELIVERY VAN. Model has a metal body with a plastic horse and roof section. Until 1985 a set of Cream plastic figures was included - a woman, a boy and a driver.

000a	1983	'WINDMILL BAKERY', Yellow body, Cream shafts	**£4-6**	☐
000b	1984	Yellow body, Beige shafts	**£4-6**	☐
001a	1985	'COCA-COLA', Yellow/Black....................	**£4-6**	☐
002a	1984	'FINE LADY BAKERIES', Beige...............	**£4-6**	☐
003a	1984	'ROBERTSONS', Green/Yellow	**£4-6**	☐
003a	1987	re-run, darker Green 'leaves'	**£4-6**	☐
004a	1984	'PEPPERIDGE FARM', White/Tan	**£4-6**	☐
005a	1984	'STAFFS COUNTY SHOW', Pale Green ...	**£4-6**	☐
005b	1984	'STAFFS COUNTY SHOW', Mint Green ..	**£5-7**	☐
006a	1984	'MATTHEW NORMAN', Green	**£4-6**	☐
007a	1985	'ROYAL MAIL', solid Red wheels, SBX	**£4-6**	☐
008a	1984	'LSWR', Dull Pink/Brown........................	**£4-6**	☐
009a	1984	'HAMLEY'S TOYS', (special box).............	**£4-6**	☐
010a	1985	'TRI-SUM POTATO CHIPS', Red	**£4-6**	☐
011a	1987	'LLEDO WORLDWIDE CC', SBX	**£5-7**	☐
012a	1988	'J.SPRATT', Blue, (special box).................	**£3-5**	☐
013a	1990	'ROYAL MAIL', (special box)...................	**£3-5**	☐
014a	1992	'HARRODS', (Set HD1004).......................	**GSP**	☐
015a	1992	'GREAT EASTERN', (Set RSL4003)..........	**GSP**	☐

DG 4 HORSE-DRAWN OMNIBUS. Model consists of metal omnibus body, plastic seats & horses. Cream plastic figures included: 2 ladies, a man, the driver & conductor, (No.'4' moulded-in the surround).

000a	1983	'VICTORIA-KINGS CROSS', Red body, Green seats, Green 'LIPTONS' on Off-White panel........	**£10-20**	☐
000b		As 000a but pure White panel	**£4-6**	☐
000c		As 000a but White logo, Green panel...........	**£4-6**	☐
000d	1984	As 000c but Brown seats	**£4-6**	☐
001a	1984	'BOWERY to BROADWAY' Red body, Black wheels..........................	**£4-6**	☐
002a	1984	'BOWERY to BROADWAY', Green body, Brown seats & wheels................	**£4-6**	☐
002b	1984	Green body & seats, Brown wheels..............	**£4-6**	☐
002c	1984	Dark Green, Brown seats, Gold wheels	**£4-6**	☐

002d	1988	Mid-Green, Brown seats, Gold wheels..........	**£3-5**	☐
003a	1984	'PUTNEY', White body, Red seats...............	**£4-6**	☐
004a	1985	'MASONS PANTRY', Dark Brown body....	**£4-6**	☐
004b	1985	with 'Mrs Beaton' on wrong sides................	**£18-22**	☐
005a	1984	'PEARS', Beige body, Red wheels...............	**£4-6**	☐
005b	1987	'PEARS', Beige body, Black wheels............	**£3-5**	☐
006a	1984	'MADAME TUSSAUDS', Yellow body, Red seats and wheels............	**£4-6**	☐
006b	1987	Yellow body, Red seats, Black wheels..........	**£4-6**	☐
007a	1986	'HIGH CHAPARRAL', Beige body..........	**£4-6**	☐
008a	1984	'HAMLEYS TOYS', Red body, SBX	**£4-6**	☐
009a	1987	'BALMORAL TOURS', Yellow, SBX	**£3-5**	☐
010a	1988	'RADIO TIMES' ('A Million Copies') in special box	**£75-100**	☐
010b	1988	'RADIO TIMES' ('Thomas Tilling) SBX	**£3-5**	☐
011a	1988	'NEWS of the WORLD', SBX	**£3-5**	☐
012a	1989	'COLMANS MUSTARD', Yellow/Red.......	**£3-5**	☐
013a	1991	'STONES GINGER WINE', Cream............	**NRP**	☐
014a	1992	'OXO', Red body, Black seats	**NRP**	☐
015a	1993	'CO-OP TEA'.....................................	**NRP**	☐
016a	1993	'FURNESS RAILWAY', (set RSL4003)	**GSP**	☐

DG 5 SHAND MASON HORSE-DRAWN FIRE ENGINE. The model features a metal main body with plastic horses. A set of 3 (Dark Blue) plastic firemen figures was included up to 1985 (and re-introduced in 1989 partially painted and affixed).

000a	1983	'LONDON', Red body, Black wheels	**£4-6**	☐
000c	1987	Red body, Gold wheels...............................	**£65-80**	☐
001a	1983	'CHICAGO', Red body, Black wheels, Black horses........................	**£4-6**	☐
001b	1985	Gold wheels, Cream horses. (72 only)..........	**£65-80**	☐
002a	1983	'GUILDFORD', Green body, Gold wheels, Black boiler (288 made).................	**£100-150**	☐
002b	1983	Green body, Gold boiler............................	**£4-6**	☐
002c	1984	Dark Green body, Gold boiler	**£4-6**	☐
003a	1984	'HONG KONG', White body, Red wheels, Red boiler (288 issued)	**£100-150**	☐
003b	1984	'HONG KONG', Gold boiler......................	**£4-6**	☐
004a	1984	'GWR', Brown body/wheels, Cream horses..	**£4-6**	☐
004b	1985	Gold wheels, wood plinth, special box	**£7-10**	☐
004c	1985	Gold wheels, Black horses..........................	**£4-6**	☐
005a	1985	'LAKE CITY', Yellow body, Red wheels.....	**£4-6**	☐
005b	1987	Yellow body, Black wheels	**£3-5**	☐
006a	1984	'PHILADELPHIA', Red body....................	**£4-6**	☐
007a	1984	'BIFBAC 2', Maroon body	**£4-6**	☐
008a	1988	'LONDON EAST HAM', Red, SBX..........	**£3-5**	☐
009a	1989	'CARROW WORKS', Red body.................	**£3-5**	☐
	1991	Model withdrawn from production		

DG 6 1920 FORD Model 'T' VAN. A 'Brass' radiator features on this model (except where 'Chrome' noted), along with metal main body and plastic roof section. Later issues cast without cab door imprint. Models 000-035 came with Blue plastic figures: a policeman, man with starting-handle & dog, girl with teddy. There are 4 variations of baseplates: 1st (metal) 'DG6-DG', 2nd (metal) 'DG6-DG8', 3rd (metal 'DG6-8', 4th (plastic) 'DG6-8-33'.

000a	1983	'OVALTINE', Orange body, with 1st baseplate..	**£8-10**	☐
		with 2nd or 3rd baseplate	**£4-6**	☐
001a	1983	'YORKSHIRE POST', (1st Lledo Code 1 Trade Special)...............	**NGPP**	☐
002a	1984	'COOKIE COACH Co', Yellow logo	**£4-6**	☐
002b	1984	'COOKIE COACH Co', White logo...........	**£4-6**	☐
003a	1984	'BRITISH MEAT', Cream body, Brown chassis, Brown roof........................	**£7-10**	☐
003b	1984	Black chassis, Black roof	**£10-15**	☐
004a	1984	'AEROPLANE JELLY', Blue body............	**£4-6**	☐
005a	1984	'BRITISH MEAT', Cream, rear doors	**£4-6**	☐
006a	1984	'MARCOL', Beige/Maroon/Black with Maroon 'Red Dragon'.........................	**£4-6**	☐
006b		'MARCOL', no 'Red Dragon'.....................	**£4-6**	☐
007a	1984	'POLICE AMBULANCE', CLE of 5000	**£30-40**	☐
008a	1984	'I.P.M.S.', Cream and Blue.........................	**£7-10**	☐
009a	1984	'LIVERPOOL GARDEN FESTIVAL'.........	**£4-6**	☐
010a	1984	'ILLINOIS TOYFAIR', Lemon/Tan	**£4-6**	☐
011a	1984	'STRETTON', Blue chassis, Black roof	**£4-6**	☐
012a	1984	'YORKSHIRE EVENING POST'................	**£4-6**	☐
013a	1984	'DAYS GONE C.C.' Black	**£7-10**	☐

014a	1984	'BRITISH BACON', Blue/Black	£4-6	☐
015a	1984	'HARRY RAMSDEN', Cream and Red	£4-6	☐
016a	1985	'OVALTINE 75th', Stone roof, SBX	£5-7	☐
016b	1990	Tan roof, (000a re-run error)........................	£5-7	☐
017a	1984	'DAILY EXPRESS' (in CP1 Pack)...............	GSP	☐
018a	1985	'PERRIER JOUET', Cream and Black	£4-6	☐
019a	1985	'HOME ALES', Green and Black	£4-6	☐
020a	1984	'COCA-COLA' 'At Soda Fountains'.........	£4-6	☐
021a	1984	'COCA-COLA' 'Every Bottle Sterilized' ...	£4-6	☐
022a	1984	'WONDERBREAD', White/Dark Blue	£4-6	☐
023a	1984	'RAILWAY EXPRESS' ('84 USA Pack)......	GSP	☐
024a	1984	'KODAK', Yellow and Black	£4-6	☐
025a	1984	'MARKS & SPENCER', Green/Black..........	£4-6	☐
026a	1984	'MARCOL 2', Yellow body, printed rear doors................	£4-6	☐
027a	1984	'PHILADELPHIA', Cream/Black	£4-6	☐
028a	1984	'PHILADELPHIA', Red/Black	£4-6	☐
029a	1984	'YORKSHIRE BISCUITS', Brown/Black	£4-6	☐
030a	1984	'AUTOMODEL EXCHANGE', Maroon and Black	£4-6	☐
031a	1984	'ECHO 100', Cream and Black	£4-6	☐
032a	1985	'STRETTON', Green chassis & roof............	£7-10	☐
033a	1985	'BARCLAYS', Light Blue body, Cream chassis, Blue headboard letters	£18-20	☐
033b	1985	with Cream headboard letters......................	£4-6	☐
033c	1990	with Black chassis and tyres	£3-5	☐
034a	1984	'MAGASIN Du NORD', Dark Green, with White headboard lettering	£15-20	☐
034b	1984	with Gold headboard lettering......................	£4-6	☐
035a	1984	'HAMLEYS', Dark Green/Red, SBX	£4-6	☐
036a	1985	'AUSTRALIAN Collectors Club', Dark Beige body, Dark Brown chassis, Tan roof ..	£7-10	☐
036b		with Dark Brown roof	£7-10	☐
036c		Beige body, '85 Convention' (36 only)	£450-600	☐
037a	1984	'MURPHYS CRISPS', Yellow/Red	£4-6	☐
038a	1985	'WELLS DRINKS', Lemon/Dark Brown.....	£4-6	☐
039a	1985	'WOODWARDS', Dark Blue body	£4-6	☐
040a	1985	'LINDT', Pale Blue body, Blue roof...........	NRP	☐
040b		Pale Blue body, Pale Blue roof..................	£20-25	☐
041a	1985	'EVENING CHRONICLE', Red/Black	£4-6	☐
042a	1986	'CWM DALE', White, Blue chassis	£4-6	☐
042b		'CWM DALE', White, Red chassis	£7-10	☐
043a	1985	'ROYAL MAIL', Red/Black, SBX	£4-6	☐
044a	1985	'ALTON TOWERS', Dark Brown/Cream, special box	£4-6	☐
045a	1985	'NORTHERN DAILY', Green/Black...........	£4-6	☐
046a	1986	'CADBURYS BOURNVILLE', Red and Cream	£4-6	☐
047a	1986	'JOHN SMITHS', Green/Black....................	£4-6	☐
048a	1986	'BAY to BIRDWOOD RUN', SBX	£4-6	☐
049a	1986	'HARDWARE JOURNAL', Blue, SBX	£20-30	☐
050		'TOY FAIR'. Trade-only models, Red/cream, in White promotional box:		
050a	1986	'TOY FAIR '86, Harrogate'....................	£10-15	☐
050b	1986	'TOY FAIR '86, Harrowgate', (with 'w')....	£60-75	☐
050c	1987	'TOY FAIR '87, Harrogate'.....................	£10-15	☐
050d	1988	'TOY FAIR '88, Harrogate'.....................	£10-15	☐
050e	1989	'TOY FAIR '89, Harrogate'.....................	£10-15	☐
051a	1986	'CADBURYS DRINKING CHOCOLATE', special box	£4-6	☐
052		Not allocated		
053a	1986	'TIZER', Yellow and Black...................	£4-6	☐
054a	1986	'COCA-COLA', Green model, SBX..............	£4-6	☐
055a	1986	'HERSHEYS', Orange/Brown, in SBX........	NRP	☐
056a	1987	'HEDGES & BUTLER', Green/Cream	£3-5	☐
057a	1986	'CANADIAN TRAVEL & GIFT', 500	£60-75	☐
058a	1986	'COCA-COLA', Red/Black van, Red hubs, Chrome radiator, special box	£4-6	☐
058b	1987	with Brass hubs & radiator	£3-5	☐
059a	1986	'CRAFT & HOBBY', 500, Canadian...........	£60-75	☐
060a	1987	'BLACK VELVIT', Pink and Black...........	£3-5	☐
061a	1987	'FAIRY SOAP', White and Dark Green	£3-5	☐
062a	1987	'ROSE & CROWN', Green and White........	£3-5	☐
063a	1987	'ROYAL FLYING CORPS', (RFC/RAF set)	GSP	☐
064a	1988	'HAMLEYS', Green and Black....................	£3-5	☐
065a	1988	'BUDWEISER', Cream/Brown, SBX...........	£3-5	☐
066a	1988	'LLEDO WORLDWIDE CC', Green/ Black..............................	£4-6	☐
067a		Not Allocated		
068a	1988	'GOLDEN SHRED', Red/Green/White	£3-5	☐
069a	1988	'CHARRINGTONS', Red and Brown	£3-5	☐
070a	1988	'MILLBANK BOOKS', Black	£3-5	☐
071a	1990	'HMV', Burgundy/Black/Cream	NRP	☐

072a	1989	'SHELL PUMP SERVICE', Red/Black........	£3-5	☐
073a	1989	'WALLS ICES', Black/Cream, Chrome radiator.................	£3-5	☐
074-	1986	13 Canadian models, each in 'maple-leaf' box, as a set,....................... later available singly:	£40-45	☐
074a	1988	'ONTARIO', White/Red	£3-4	☐
075a	1988	'YUKON', White/Blue/Green	£3-4	☐
076a	1988	'N.W.TERRITORIES', White/Red/Blue	£3-4	☐
077a	1988	'PRINCE EDWARD ISLE', White/Green/Red, wrong date ('1870').........	£8-12	☐
077b	1990	with correct date ('1873')......................	£3-4	☐
078a	1988	'NEWFOUNDLAND', White/Blue/Red	£3-4	☐
079a	1988	'QUEBEC', White/Red/Blue	£3-4	☐
080a	1988	'NOVA SCOTIA', White/Blue/Red	£3-4	☐
081a	1988	'MANITOBA', White/Red	£3-4	☐
082a	1988	'ALBERTA', White/Blue......................	£3-4	☐
083a	1988	'NEW BRUNSWICK', White/Yellow	£3-4	☐
084a	1988	'BRITISH COLUMBIA', White/Yellow/ Blue	£3-4	☐
085a	1988	'SASKATCHEWAN', White/Yellow/Green ..	£3-4	☐
086a	1988	'CANADA', White/Red........................	£3-4	☐
087a	1989	'SELFRIDGES' (in Set LS1004)	GSP	☐
088a	1989	'AU BON MARCHE', Yellow/Black	£3-5	☐
089a	1989	'SCHNEIDERS', Orange and Blue	£3-5	☐
090a	1989	'WINCHESTER CLUB', Green/Black	£3-5	☐
091a	1989	'BRITANNIA FILM' (in 'Gold Set')	GSP	☐
092a	1989	'NESTLES', Pale Red/Black	£3-5	☐
093a	1989	'NORTH YORKS MOORS' (in Set)..........	GSP	☐
094a	1989	'HAMLEYS '89', Blue/Black/Cream, special box	£3-5	☐
095a	1990	'4711', Cyan body, Black chassis & roof.......	NRP	☐
096a	1990	'ROWNTREES COCOA', Red/Black...........	NRP	☐
097a	1990	'JAEGER', (in Set LS2004)......................	GSP	☐
098a	1990	'ROYAL MAIL TELEGRAMS', Red and Black	NRP	☐
099a	1990	'HERSHEY', issued in USA	NGPP	☐
100a	1990	'DAYS GONE' Club Model, Burgundy and Black....................	£4-6	☐
101a	1990	'ARNOTTS' (in Set ABL1003)	GSP	☐
102a	1991	'DAYS GONE' Club Model, Blue/Green.....	£4-6	☐
103a	1991	'JOSEPH LUCAS', Dark Green/Grey..........	NRP	☐
104a	1991	'BLACKPOOL VAN TRANSPORT'............	NRP	☐
105a	1991	'ZEBRA GRATE POLISH'	NRP	☐
106a	1992	'DAYS GONE' Club Model, Pale Metallic Green/Black...................	NRP	☐
107a	1992	'JAMESONS', Cream/Green/Burgundy........	NRP	☐
108a	1992	'HOTEL COLUMBIA', (in Set HLL1003) ..	NRP	☐
109a	1993	'HUNTLEY & PALMERS', Green body	NRP	☐
110a	1993	'MIDLAND', ('Golden Age of Steam')	NRP	☐
111a	1993	'LANCS & YORKS', ('Golden Age of Steam')........................	NRP	☐
112a	1993	'Nth EASTERN', ('Golden Age of Steam')..	NRP	☐
113a	1993	'LMS', ('Golden Age of Steam')................	NRP	☐
114a	1993	'DAYS GONE' Club Model	NRP	☐

DG 7 1934 FORD Model 'A' WOODY WAGON. The model has metal body, plastic roof, seats, radiator & bumper. Cream plastic figures of a woman with 3 poodles were discontinued after 005.

000a	1984	'PATS POODLE PARLOUR', Yellow/Red, with headboard	£4-6	☐
001a	1984	'COCA-COLA', Yellow/Black, headboard ...	£4-6	☐
002a	1984	'FORD', headboard, (set GS1)...................	GSP	☐
002b	1985	no headboard, available singly	£4-6	☐
003a	1984	'WEST POINT TOY SHOW'....................	£4-6	☐
004a	1984	'HAMLEYS', Pale Cream/Red, Chrome radiator, headboard, SBX	£4-6	☐
004b	1985	Brass radiator, headboard, SBX	£4-6	☐
005a	1985	'GODFREY DAVIS', White/Blue	£4-6	☐
006a	1986	'DELLA', Cream body	NRP	☐
007a	1986	'COMMONWEALTH GAMES' (in set)......	GSP	☐
008a	1988	'CASTROL OIL', White/Green	£3-5	☐
009a	1990	'PASCALL SWEETS', White/Green............	NRP	☐
	1990	New baseplate introduced ('7-9-13-14-37')		
	1991	Model withdrawn from production		

175

DG 8 1920 FORD Model 'T' TANKER'. A metal body and plastic tank are the main features of this model. The same Blue plastic figures included with DG 6 were provided with 000 to 004 inclusive.

000a	1984	'ESSO', 'Inflamable' (only 1 'm').....................	£5-7	☐
000b	1984	'Inflammable' (correct spelling)	£4-6	☐
001a	1984	'COCA-COLA', Dark Yellow/Black............	£4-6	☐
002a	1985	'CASTROL', Dark Green/Black/White........	£4-6	☐
003a	1984	'PHILADELPHIA', Red, Black roof...........	£4-6	☐
003b	1985	'PHILADELPHIA', Red, White roof...........	£10-15	☐
004a	1985	'PENNZOIL', Red/Black/Yellow..............	£4-6	☐
005a	1985	'HOFMEISTER', Yellow/Brown	£4-6	☐
006a	1986	'BLUE MOUNTAIN', All Red body	£3-5	☐
007a	1987	'CROW CARRYING', Yellow/Black..........	£3-5	☐
008a	1986	'HERSHEYS', White/Brown, special box.....	£4-6	☐
009a	1987	'WATER WORKS', Blue/Black..................	£3-5	☐
010a	1987	'ZEROLENE', (Dealer promotional, 3,000)	£15-18	☐
011a	1988	'SHELL FUEL OIL', Red/Black/White	£4-6	☐
012a	1988	'HOMEPRIDE', White/Red/Blue	£3-5	☐
013a	1988	'DUCKHAMS OILS', Grey/Black/Green ...	£3-5	☐
014a	1989	'SHELL FRANCE', Red/Black/White	£4-6	☐
015a	1989	'BP MOTOR SPIRIT', Green/Black...........	NRP	☐
016a	1989	'TEXACO', Red and Black	NRP	☐
017a	1989	'ARMY WATER' (part of Army set)..........	GSP	☐
018a	1990	'PRATTS', Green and Black	NRP	☐
019a	1991	'MOBILGAS', Red and Black	NRP	☐
020a	1993	'RUSSIAN OIL', Grey/Red	NRP	☐

DG 9 1934 FORD Model 'A' CAR. This model has a metal open car body with DG 7 baseplate & chassis. White plastic figures (2 bank robbers & seated policeman with gun) included with 001a & b. The same figures (but Black plastic), were with 001c and 002 to 004.

000a	1984	'POLICE' Car, Mid Blue/Dark Blue............	£20-30	☐
000b	1984	All Dark Blue body, Cream seats..............	£4-6	☐
000c	1984	All Dark Blue body, Black seats	£4-6	☐
001a	1984	'NEW YORK - RIO', (in Set GS1)	GSP	☐
002a	1984	'PHILADELPHIA FIRE', Red body	£4-6	☐
003a	1985	'15 MILLIONTH FORD', Black body.........	£4-6	☐
	1991	Model withdrawn from production		

DG 10 1935 DENNIS SINGLE-DECK COACH. This was the first Lledo model to have twin rear wheels. Other features are metal body castings and plastic roof/window section, seats & baseplate. Cream plastic figures included (1984-85) were of: man leaning on bus-stop, man & woman with boy, young woman with dog.

000a	1984	'BRIGHTON BELLE', Maroon body,		
		Beige roof, Chrome radiator	£15-20	☐
000b		Beige roof, Brass radiator	£4-6	☐
000c		Cream roof, Brass radiator	£4-6	☐
001a	1984	'TILLINGBOURNE', Maroon/Black...........	£4-6	☐
002a	1987	'SILVER SERVICE',		
		Silver/Red, Silver 'Matlock'	£3-5	☐
002b	1987	Silver/Red, White 'Matlock'	£3-5	☐
003a	1984	'SOUTHERN VECTIS', Green/Cream,		
		with Yellow logo	£4-6	☐
		with White logo......................................	£12-15	☐
004a	1984	'SCHOOL BUS', Yellow/Black,		
		with Chrome radiator..............................	£7-10	☐
004b	1984	with Brass radiator..................................	£4-6	☐
004c	1987	'OAKRIDGE SCHOOL', Yellow/Black	£3-5	☐
005a	1984	'POTTERIES', Red/Black, Cream roof	£4-6	☐
005b	1986	with Red roof..	£14-16	☐
006a	1985	'GWR', Dark Brown and Cream		
		'150th Anniversary' model, SBX...............	£8-12	☐
007a	1985	'BARTON', Red/Maroon/Cream................	£4-6	☐
008a	1986	'LONDON COUNTRY', Green,		
		with Brass radiator..................................	£3-5	☐
008b	1986	with Chrome radiator..............................	£3-5	☐
008c	1988	Green body, Black chassis	£75-100	☐
009a	1984	'HAMLEYS', Dark Brown/Cream, SBX	£5-7	☐
010		Not allocated		
011		Not allocated		
012a	1985	'TARTAN', Red and Cream	£4-6	☐
013a	1985	'TRAILWAYS', (part of 3-bus Set)	GSP	☐
014a	1985	'IMPERIAL AIRWAYS', Blue roof	£4-6	☐
014b	1987	'IMPERIAL AIRWAYS', Red roof	£12-15	☐
015a	1986	'REDBURNS', Red/Cream.......................	£3-5	☐
016a	1986	'COMMONWEALTH GAMES', (in set).....	GSP	☐
017a	1986	'HERSHEYS', Brown/Cream.....................	£4-6	☐
018a	1988	'E.B.TAYLOR', Red/Black.......................	£3-5	☐

	1989	New baseplate text ('DG10-12-34-35')		
019a	1989	'CITY of COVENTRY', Crimson/Cream.....	£3-5	☐
020a	1990	'BOAC', Dark Blue and Cream....................	NRP	☐
021a	1991	'BEA', Grey and Cream	NRP	☐
	1992	Model withdrawn from production		

DG 11 HORSE-DRAWN REMOVAL VAN. Large metal body, plastic roof, metal base. Cream plastic figures (not included after 1985) were: driver, woman with birdcage, girl with hoop, boy with bag & bulldog. In 1989 a driver figure was re-introduced along with a change in design of horses.

000a	1984	'TURNBULL & Co', White/Red/Green.......	£4-6	☐
001a	1985	'ABELS', Pale Blue/Red/Blue.....................	£4-6	☐
002a	1985	'BIG TOP CIRCUS', Cream/Red/Blue.......	£4-6	☐
003a	1985	'Staffs COUNTY SHOW', Buff/Brown.......	£4-6	☐
004a	1985	'ROYAL MAIL', Red/Black, SBX	£4-6	☐
005a	1985	'WILLIAMS GRIFFIN',		
		Green/Red/Beige, Gold wheels	£4-6	☐
006a	1986	'MacCOSHAMS', Yellow, Black wheels.......	£3-5	☐
007a	1986	'COCA-COLA', White/Red, Hartoy Set......	GSP	☐
008a	1988	'BUDWEISER', White/Red, special box	£3-5	☐
009a	1989	'LLEDO WORLDWIDE CC', Blue/White...	£4-6	☐
010a	1988	'R.P.COOPER', White/Black	£3-5	☐
011a		Not allocated		
012a	1989	'JAMES BROWN & SON', Cream/Green ...	£3-5	☐
013a	1989	'ALBERT DALEY & Co', Yellow body	£3-5	☐
014a	1990	'MARKS & SPENCER', Red/Black, SBX ...	NRP	☐
015a	1990	'ROYAL MAIL', Red/Black, SBX	NRP	☐
016a	1990	'ARNOTTS', Red, (Set ABL1003)	GSP	☐
017a	1991	'ROBERT HEATON & SON', Black	NRP	☐
018a	1991	'DG CLUB SUMMER '91'	NRP	☐
019a	1991	'SAINSBURYS', Blue/Black	NRP	☐
020a	1992	'HARRODS', (in Set HD1002)	GSP	☐
021a	1992	'HAMLEYS', (in Set HAL1004)...............	GSP	☐
022a	1993	'SCHWEPPES', Green/Black/Red..............	NRP	☐
023a	1993	'PEPSI-COLA', White, SBX.....................	NRP	☐
024a	1993	'GREAT NORTHERN', (Set RSL4003)	GSP	☐

DG 12 1934 DENNIS FIRE ENGINE. This model uses the same chassis/baseplate/wheels/radiator as DG 10 with plastic windscreen/ladder mount & ladder. Escape wheels not fitted to 000a, 001a, 003a. 3 Blue plastic firemen included up to 1985.

000a	1984	'LUCKHURST', Red/Green	£4-6	☐
000b	1989	Red body, Red chassis	£4-6	☐
001a	1985	'CARDIFF CITY', Red/White	£4-6	☐
002		Not allocated		
003a	1985	'BERMUDA', Blue body, Cream floor.......	£4-6	☐
003b	1985	'BERMUDA', Blue body, White floor.........	£4-6	☐
004a	1986	'LCC', Red body, Black chassis	£3-5	☐
005a	1986	'CHELMSFORD',		
		Red/Black, Brass radiator	£3-5	☐
005b	1987	Red/Black, Chrome radiator	£3-5	☐
006a	1987	'AUXILIARY', Green body/chassis	£3-5	☐
007a	1987	'ESSEX COUNTY', Red/White	£3-5	☐
007b	1990	same but White 'ESSEX'	£5-8	☐
008a	1987	'WARE FIRE SERVICE', All Red	£3-5	☐
009a	1987	'WINDSOR', All Red, special box	£3-5	☐
010a	1988	'GLASGOW', All Red.............................	£3-5	☐
011a	1988	'BOSTON', Red body..............................	£3-5	☐
012a	1989	'BIRMINGHAM', Red and Black..............	£3-5	☐
	1989	Baseplate with 'DG10-12-34-35' introduced		
013a	1990	'BRADFORD', Red and Black	NRP	☐
014a	1990	'HERSHEY', Red/White, SBX	NRP	☐
015a	1991	'MANCHESTER', Red and Black	NRP	☐
016a	1992	'WEST HAM', Red and Black	NRP	☐
017a	1993	'VALLETTA', (Set MG1003).....................	GSP	☐

DG 13 1934 FORD Model 'A' VAN. Model features metal body and plastic fluted roof with advertising board on some. Cream plastic figures included up to 011 included: a newsboy, a deliveryman, man reading paper.

000a	1986	'CAMP COFFEE', Cream/Brown, SBX	£3-5	☐
001a	1984	'EVENING NEWS', Yellow body	£4-6	☐
002a	1985	'TUCHER BEERS', Cyan/Black, SBX.........	£4-6	☐
003a	1986	'MITRE 10', Caramel/Black, SBX.............	£20-25	☐
004a	1984	'HAMLEYS', Yellow body, SBX.................	£4-6	☐
005a	1985	'MICHELIN', Yellow/Blue (also in Set)......	£4-6	☐
006a	1985	'JERSEY EVENING POST', White/Pink	£10-15	☐
007a	1985	'MARY ANN BREWERY', Blue body	£10-15	☐
008a	1984	'ROYAL MAIL', Red and Black................	£4-6	☐
008b	1992	'ROYAL MAIL', new longer body.............	£3-4	☐

009a	1985	'COCA-COLA', Yellow and Black	£4-6	☐
010a	1985	'BASILDON BOND', White/Blue		
		with matt finish	£6-8	☐
010b	1985	with gloss finish	£4-6	☐
011a	1986	'RYDER', Yellow body..................................	£3-5	☐
012a	1985	'COCA-COLA', All Yellow..........................	£3-5	☐
013a	1985	'EVENING SENTINEL',		
		Blue and Black (with figures).....................	£4-6	☐
014a	1985	'STROH'S', Red body, Black roof.................	£4-6	☐
015a	1985	'ROYAL MAIL 350', Red/Black, SBX	£4-6	☐
016a	1985	'FESTIVAL GARDENS LIVERPOOL'	£4-6	☐
017a	1986	'ROBINSONS', Cream and Green	£3-5	☐
018a	1988	'EVER READY', Blue and White	£3-5	☐
019a	1987	'HP SAUCE', Maroon and White	£3-5	☐
020a	1986	'FDB' (Danish), Grey and Blue.....................	£20-25	☐
021a	1986	'COCA-COLA', Black chassis	£3-5	☐
021b		'COCA-COLA', Yellow chassis....................	£75-100	☐
022a	1988	'J. LYONS', Blue and White	£3-5	☐
023a	1986	'HERSHEYS KISSES', Brown/Cream	£3-5	☐
024a	1986	'HERSHEYS', Cream/Brown	£3-5	☐
025a	?	'ROYAL MAIL', Red and Black, SBX	£3-5	☐
026a	1988	'HEINZ TOMATO SOUP', Red/Cream	£3-5	☐
027a	1988	'CHARLES TATE', Brown and Black	£3-5	☐
028a	1988	'EXCHANGE & MART', White/Black.......	£3-5	☐
029a	1988	'ELIZABETH SHAW', Cream/Blue	£3-5	☐
030a	1989	'OXYDOL', Light and Dark Blue	£3-5	☐
031a	1989	'AQUASCUTUM', (in Set LS1004)	GSP	☐
032		Not allocated		
033a	1989	'ALLENBURYS', Maroon /Cream	£3-5	☐
034a	1989	'EMPIRE', (part of 'Gold Set').....................	GSP	☐
035a	1989	'KLEENEX', White and Blue	£3-5	☐
036a	1991	'AUSTIN REED', (in Set LS2004)	GSP	☐
037a	1989	'BBC', Green and Black	£3-5	☐
038a	1989	'ARMY RECRUITMENT', (BA1003)	GSP	☐
039a	1990	'PERSIL', Green and Black	NRP	☐
040a	1990	'MADAME TUSSAUDS', Blue/White.......	NRP	☐
041a	1990	'MARKS & SPENCER',		
		White and Green, special box	NRP	☐
042a	1990	'ROYAL MAIL', Red and Black	NRP	☐
043a	1990	'HERSHEYS', Silver/Brown, (US issue)......	NGPP	☐
044a	1990	'Nth YORKS MOORS', (NYM Set 2)	GSP	☐
045a	1990	'ARNOTTS', (Set ABL1003)........................	GSP	☐
	1990	Baseplate with '7-9-13-14-37' introduced		
046a	1991	'ROSELLA', Yellow and Green...................	NRP	☐
047a	1991	'CASTROL', Red and Black	NRP	☐
	1991	Steering wheel and seats added		
048a	1992	'HAMLEYS', White and Blue......................	NRP	☐
	1992	Longer body introduced		
049a	1992	'RINSO', Two-tone Blue	NRP	☐
050a	1992	'SOUTHERN RAILWAY', (RSL2003)........	GSP	☐
051a	1992	'HARRODS', (HD1004)...............................	GSP	☐
052a	1992	'QANTAS', (in Set QA1002).......................	GSP	☐
053a	1992	'GODE', (for German market)......................	NGPP	☐
054a	1992	'RAMA', (for German market).....................	NGPP	☐
055a	1993	'GOLDEN SHRED', Red/White	£3-4	☐
056a	1993	'PEPSI-COLA', White, SBX........................	£3-4	☐
057a	1993	'MARKS & SPENCER', (MS2004)	GSP	☐
058a	1993	'Grand Hotel Peking', (HLL2003)................	GSP	☐

DG 14 1934 FORD Model 'A' CAR with HOOD. Model has metal body and raised plastic hood. Cream plastic figures (1 US policeman & 2 firemen), were only issued with 000a/b and 001a.

000a	1985	'SAN DIEGO', 'Fire Chief' in Gold with		
		Black surround	£75-100	☐
000b		'Fire Chief' not in Gold with		
		Black surround	£4-6	☐
001a	1985	'TAXI', Yellow and Black	£3-5	☐
002a	1985	'ACME CLEANERS', White body..............	£4-6	☐
003a	1986	'HAMLEYS', Red and Black, SBX	£3-5	☐
004a	1986	'GRAND HOTEL', Brown/Cream	£3-5	☐
004b	1987	'GRAND HOTEL', Brown/Beige	£3-5	☐
005		Not allocated		
006a	1987	'STATE PENITENTIARY', Light Grey	£4-6	☐
007a	1988	'SAN DIEGO', (US version).........................	NGPP	☐
	1990	Baseplate with '7-9-13-14-37' introduced		
008a	1990	'RALEIGH CYCLES', Green/Black............	NRP	☐
	1991	Model withdrawn from production		

DG 15 1932 AEC REGENT DOUBLE-DECK BUS. The first 'Days Gone' model to be issued without the plastic figures. Components include metal main body, roof, staircase and baseplate; plastic windows, radiator, wheels and upper seats. Lower seats were absent till 1989.

000a	1985	'HALLS WINE', Red/Black,		
		Silver roof, Chrome radiator.....................	£4-6	☐
000b	1985	Silver roof, Brass radiator	£4-6	☐
001a	1985	'COCA-COLA', Red and Black	£4-6	☐
002a	1985	'CASTLEMAINE XXXX', (in 3-bus Set).....	GSP	☐
003a	1985	'HAMLEYS', Red and Black, SBX	£4-6	☐
004a	1985	'LIVERPOOL GARDENS', Cream/Brown..	£4-6	☐
005a	1985	'CINZANO',		
		Cream seats, Chrome radiator	£4-6	☐
005b	1988	Ivory seats, Brass radiator	£3-5	☐
006a	1986	'EVENING ARGUS', Red/Black/Cream	£3-5	☐
007a	1986	'HALLS WINE', Pale Brown body.............	£30-35	☐
007b	1986	'HALLS WINE', bare metal body	£15-20	☐
007	1986	(a & b) in display case with components.....	£100-125	☐
008a	1986	'ROYAL WEDDING', Blue/Red, SBX	£10-13	☐
009a	1987	'MADAME TUSSAUDS',		
		with Chrome radiator	£3-5	☐
009b	1987	with Brass radiator	£3-5	☐
010a	1986	'SWAN VESTAS',		
		with Cream seats, Chrome radiator	£3-5	☐
010b	1987	with Ivory seats, Brass radiator	£3-5	☐
011a	1986	'COMMONWEALTH GAMES', White,		
		Chrome radiator, (in 3-model Set)	GSP	☐
011b	1987	with Brass radiator	£3-5	☐
012a	1987	'HEINZ', Red and Black	£3-5	☐
013a	1987	'STRATFORD BLUE', Blue/Silver, SBX	£3-5	☐
014a	1987	'TV TIMES', Red and Black	£3-5	☐
015a	1988	'HAMLEYS', All Red	£3-5	☐
016a	1988	'BIRMINGHAM MAIL', Blue/Cream	NRP	☐
017a	1988	'GOLDEN WONDER', Blue/Silver............	£3-5	☐
018a	1988	'LLEDO COLLECTORS CLUB'	£10-15	☐
019a	1989	'MAPLES', All Red	£3-5	☐
020a	1989	'TERRY'S GYM', Blue/Cream/Silver..........	£3-5	☐
021a	1989	'St.IVEL CHEESE', Red and Cream	£3-5	☐
022a	1989	'HAMLEYS', Red and Black, SBX	£3-5	☐
023a	1990	'PALMOLIVE', Red and Black	NRP	☐
024a	1990	'RAC', Blue and Cream	NRP	☐
025a	1990	'POST EARLY FOR XMAS',		
		Red body, Red seats, special box	NRP	☐
025b	1990	Red body, Cream seats, special box	NRP	☐
026a	1990	'HERSHEYS', Beige/Brown, (US issue)	NGPP	☐
027a	1990	'Nth.YORKS MOORS', (NYM Set 2)	GSP	☐
028a	1992	'HARRODS', (Set HD1002)........................	GSP	☐
029a	1993	'Mazawattee Tea', Green/Cream	NRP	☐
030a	1993	'Van HOUTENS COCOA', Blue/Cream	NRP	☐

DG 16 1934 DENNIS PARCELS VAN. The model features a single metal body casting, plastic roof and baseplate. The plastic seats and steering wheel did not appear until 1991. Either separate wheel/tyre units or composite wheels can be found.

000a	1985	'MAYFLOWER', Yellow/Black/Green........	£4-6	☐
001a	1985	'ROYAL MAIL', Red and Black, SBX	£4-6	☐
002a	1985	'CROFT ORIGINAL', Cream body............	£4-6	☐
003a	1986	'HAMLEYS', All Black, special box	£3-5	☐
004a	1986	'TREBOR', Green/Black/White	£3-5	☐
005a	1986	'L.N.E.R.', Dark Blue.................................	£3-5	☐
006a	1986	'KIWI', Black hubs, Brass radiator............	£3-5	☐
006b	1987	'KIWI', Cream hubs, Chrome radiator	£3-5	☐
007a	1985	'BUSHELLS', Dark Blue and Black	£4-6	☐
008		Not allocated		
009a	1987	'CADBURYS', Purple and White	£3-5	☐
010a	1987	'FYFFES', Yellow/Blue/White	£3-5	☐
011a	1986	'COCA-COLA', Red and Black, SBX	£3-5	☐
012a	1986	'HERSHEYS GOODBAR', Yellow, SBX	£3-5	☐
013a	1986	'HERSHEYS KRACKEL', Red body		
		with Brass radiator, special box	£4-6	☐
013b	1987	with Chrome radiator, special box.............	£4-6	☐
014a	1988	'PICKFORDS', Blue body	£3-5	☐
014b	1989	'PICKFORDS', Dark Blue body	£3-5	☐
015a	1987	'LLEDO WORLDWIDE CC',		
		Black body, special box.............................	£4-6	☐
016a	1988	'HAMLEYS', All Black................................	£3-5	☐
017a	1989	'ABELS', Pale Blue and Black	£3-5	☐
018a	1990	'MADAME TUSSAUDS', Red/Black	NRP	☐
019a	1989	'ALLIED', Orange/Black/White..................	£3-5	☐
020a	1989	'COSMOS', White and Black	£3-5	☐
021a	1989	'GOODYEAR', Blue/Black/White	£3-5	☐

021b	1990	same model but White 'Goodyear'	£4-6	□
022a	1989	'HAMLEYS', Maroon/Black/Cream	£3-5	□
023a	1990	'OXO', Black body, Chrome radiator	NRP	□
024a	1990	'ROYAL MAIL', Red and Black	NRP	□
025a	1990	'Nth.YORKS MOORS', (NYM Set 3)	GSP	□
026a	1991	'SCHWEPPES', Dark Blue body	NRP	□
	1991	Steering wheel and seats added		
027a	1991	'ATORA FOR XMAS', Green/Black	NRP	□
028a	1991	'LNER East Coast', (Set TPL1003)	GSP	□
029a	1991	'LNER Skegness', (Set RSL1003)	GSP	□
030a	1991	'Y.M.C.A.', (Set HF1003)	GSP	□
031a	1992	'HUDSONS SOAP', Blue/Black	NRP	□
032a	1993	'TUNNOCKS', Red/Black	NRP	□
033a	1993	'NAAFI', (Set DM1003)	GSP	□
034a	1993	'RAF Runway Control', (Set DML1003)	GSP	□

DG 17 1932 AEC REGAL SINGLE DECK BUS. The model features metal body, chassis & roof castings with plastic baseplate, and composite window and seat section.

000a	1985	'SOUTHEND', Blue body, Cream wings, with filler cap casting	£60-75	□
000b		without filler cap casting	£4-6	□
000c	1986	with Red roof, (1,000 only)	£25-35	□
001a	1985	'EUROTOURS', Green/Cream, (in Set)	GSP	□
002a	1985	'CORPORATION TRANSPORT', Yellow/Grey	£4-6	□
003a	1986	'HAMLEYS', Green/Cream, SBX	£25-35	□
004a	1985	'LONDON TRANSPORT', Red/Black	£4-6	□
005a	1986	'OXFORD (MORRELL'S)', Red/Black/Maroon	£3-5	□
006a	1986	'COMMONWEALTH GAMES', White, SBX	£4-6	□
007a	1986	'STRATFORD BLUE', Chrome radiator	£3-5	□
007b	1987	'STRATFORD BLUE', Brass radiator	£6-9	□
008a	1987	'BURNLEY CORPORATION', Blue/White	£3-5	□
009a	1986	'BIG TOP CIRCUS', Cream/Blue	£3-5	□
010a	1987	'PENNINE', Orange and Black	£3-5	□
011a	1987	'ROYAL FLYING CORPS', (in Set)	GSP	□
012a	1988	'HAMLEYS', Two-tone Blue	£3-5	□
	1988	New roof (with 2 hoardings) introduced.		
013a	1988	'HANTS & DORSET', Green/Black	NRP	□
014a	1988	'SUTTONS', Red and Grey	£3-5	□
015a	1989	'ROYAL BLUE', Blue and Black	£3-5	□
015b	1989	'ROYAL BLUE', as 015a but with White background to headboard decal	£3-5	□
016a	1989	'COLCHESTER', Maroon, no hoardings	£3-5	□
017a	1988	'ROYAL NAVY', (in Set RN1003)	GSP	□
018a	1989	'Nth.YORKS MOORS', (NYM Set)	GSP	□
019a	1990	'RED & WHITE', Cream/Black/Red	NRP	□
020a	1991	'BUCKLAND OMNIBUS Co', Red	NRP	□
021a	1992	'SOUTHERN VECTIS', Green	NRP	□
022a	1992	'GREEN LINE', Green/Black/Silver	NRP	□

DG 18 1936 PACKARD VAN. This model has metal body & chassis castings, plastic roof and baseplate. Steering wheel & seats appeared in 1991.

000a	1985	'AMBULANCE', Chrome radiator	£4-6	□
000b	1987	'AMBULANCE', Brass radiator	£3-5	□
001a	1985	'AMERICAN AMBULANCE', as 000a but Red cross in circle	£4-6	□
002a	1986	'COMMONWEALTH GAMES', with Chrome radiator, special box	£5-7	□
002b	1987	with Brass radiator, normal box	£3-5	□
003a	1986	'RAPID CASH', Green/Black/Cream	£3-5	□
004a	1986	'FIRESTONE', with Chrome radiator	£4-6	□
004b	1987	'FIRESTONE', with Brass radiator	£3-5	□
005		Not allocated		
006a	1987	'WHITE STAR', Chrome radiator	£3-5	□
006b	1987	'WHITE STAR', Brass radiator	£3-5	□
007a	1987	'COLMANS', Yellow and Black	£3-5	□
008a	1987	'ROYAL FLYING CORPS', (in Set)	GSP	□
009a	1988	'PERRONI BIRRA', White and Blue	£3-5	□
010a	1988	'NATIONAL WESTMINSTER', Silver/White	£10-15	□
011a	1988	'FOTORAMA', Chrome radiator	£3-5	□
011b	1989	'FOTORAMA', Brass radiator	£3-5	□
012a	1990	'St.IVEL', Yellow/Black/Green	NRP	□
013a	1989	'FORTNUM & MASON', (in Set LS1004)	GSP	□
014a	1989	'B & C FILMS', (in 'Gold' Set)	GSP	□
015a	1988	'St.MARY'S HOSPITAL', (Canadian charity model)	£20-25	□
016a	1989	'LEYLAND PAINTS', Blue/Maroon	£3-5	□
017a	1989	'HAMLEYS', Cream and Blue, SBX	£3-5	□
018a	1990	'ASPREY', (in Set LS2004)	GSP	□
019a	1990	'DAYS GONE CLUB' Autumn model	NRP	□
020a	1991	'McVITIE & PRICE', Burgundy	NRP	□
021a	1992	'CAMP COFFEE', Cream/Brown	NRP	□
022a	1992	'St.JOHN AMBULANCE', in Set MG1003	GSP	□
023a	1993	'FERODO', Green/Black	NRP	□
024a	1993	'IMPERIAL HOTEL' (Set HLL2003)	GSP	□
TBA	1986	'CAMPERDOWN HOSPITAL', (Australian charity)	£75-90	□

DG 19 1931 ROLLS-ROYCE PHANTOM II (BREWSTER). The model has a one-piece metal body and incorporates the DG 18 baseplate. Plastic seats, roof, trunk and radiator. It acquired a steering wheel in 1989.

000a	1985	Burgundy/Black, ('TV Times' offer)	£4-6	□
001a	1986	Yellow/Tan, Chrome radiator	£3-5	□
001b	1986	Yellow/Tan, Brass radiator	£3-5	□
002a	1986	'Basketweave', Beige/Cream, Grey tyres, Brass radiator	£4-6	□
002b	1987	Grey tyres, Chrome radiator	£3-5	□
002c	1987	Beige tyres, Brass radiator	£3-5	□
003a	1988	Metallic Grey/Black, (in 3-car Set)	GSP	□
003b	1988	Not mounted or drilled, (unofficial)	£7-10	□
004a	1987	Gold and White	£3-5	□
005a	1987	'Ruby Wedding', Maroon body, SBX	£4-6	□
006a	1989	Dark Green/ Black/Beige	£3-5	□
007a	1988	'Minder', Gold/White	£3-5	□
008a	1989	'Lledo Worldwide C.C.', Silver/Black	£3-5	□
009a	1989	'Army Staff Car', in Set BA1003	GSP	□
010a	1992	Black/Ivory, Chrome radiator	NRP	□
011a	1992	Silver/Black (for German market)	NGPP	□
TBA	1985	All Cream, Chrome radiator, (108 only)	£30-35	□
	1993	Model withdrawn from the standard range		

DG 20 1936 FORD STAKE TRUCK. Model features one-piece metal cab and cast stake body, plastic baseplate and load (barrels, tyres, cylinders or sacks). The steering wheel and seats appeared in 1991.

000a	1986	'EAGLE ALES', Yellow and Brown	£3-5	□
001a	1986	'COCA-COLA', Yellow/Black, SBX	£3-5	□
001b	1987	same but with Red barrels	£3-5	□
002a	1987	'STROH'S', Red/Black, Brass radiator	£3-5	□
002b		same but with Chrome radiator	£3-5	□
003a	1986	'WHITBREAD', Brown/Black, Brass radiator	£3-5	□
003b	1987	Brown/Black, Chrome radiator	£3-5	□
004a	1986	'GOODRICH', Cream and Blue	NRP	□
005a	1988	'AULD SCOTCH GINGER', Blue	£3-5	□
006a	1987	'UNIROYAL', Red and Black	£3-5	□
007a	1988	'BUDWEISER', White body, SBX	£4-6	□
008a	1988	'IND COOPE', All Green	£3-5	□
009a	1989	'WATNEYS', Green and Black	£3-5	□
010a	1989	'CALOR GAS', Orange/Green/White	£3-5	□
011a	1988	'ROYAL NAVY', (in Set RN1003)	GSP	□
012a	1990	'PIRELLI', Yellow and Black	NRP	□
013a	1990	'BRITISH OXYGEN', Maroon/Black	NRP	□
014a	1990	'HERSHEYS', US issue in SBX	NGPP	□
015a	1990	'RAF', (in RAF Set BB1003)	GSP	□
016a	1990	'WINN DIXIE', Black/Cream	£3-4	□
017a	1991	'DUNLOP TYRES', White/Blue	NRP	□
	1993	'DUNLOP TYRES', 'Brooklands Collection')	NRP	□
018a	1991	'GOODYEAR TYRES', Blue body	NRP	□
019a	1993	'McDOUGALLS', Grey/Blue	NRP	□

DG 21 1934 CHEVROLET VAN. Model has one-piece cast body plus metal chassis mounted on a plastic baseplate. The plastic roof may have front headboard, front & lengthways headboard, or no headboard at all. Seats & steering wheel added in 1991. Baseplate updated in 1992.

000a	1986	'SHARPS', Cream, Chrome radiator	£3-5	□
000b	1987	'SHARPS', Yellow, Brass radiator	£3-5	□
001a	1986	'LLEDO WORLDWIDE CLUB', SBX	£3-5	□
001b	1986	Maroon hubs, Black prototype logo	£3-5	□
002a	1986	'LEICESTER MERCURY', Blue/Black	£3-5	□
003a	1986	'HOSTESS CAKE', White and Red	£3-5	□
004a	1987	'Dr.PEPPER', Red and Black	£3-5	□
005a	1986	'COCA-COLA', Cream and Red, SBX	£3-5	□
006		Not allocated		
007a	1988	'HAMLEYS', Red and Cream	£3-5	□
008a	1988	'BUDWEISER', Green/Black, SBX	£3-5	□
009a	1988	'BIRDS CUSTARD', Yellow/Blue	£3-5	□

010a	1988	'FARRAH'S TOFFEE', Purple/White	£3-5	☐
011a	1988	'VITA-WHEAT', Beige and Brown	£3-5	☐
012a	1989	'SIMPSONS', (in Set LS1004)	GSP	☐
013a	1989	'BENETTONS', Cream and Green	£3-5	☐
014a	1989	'HERSHEYS KISSES', Brown/Cream	£3-5	☐
015a	1989	'CHERRY BLOSSOM', Blue/White	£3-5	☐
016a	1989	'MAJESTIC FILMS', (in 'Gold' Set)	GSP	☐
017a	1990	'TOYFAIR '90', Cream and Green	£8-11	☐
018a	1990	'RECKITTS BLUE', Blue/Black	NRP	☐
019a	1990	'MARKS & SPENCER', Cream/Green	NRP	☐
020a	1990	'LIBERTY'S', (in Set LS2004)	GSP	☐
021a	1990	'CLUB SUMMER '90', Blue/Cream	NRP	☐
022a	1990	'SCOTTISH BLUEBELL', in Set BM1004	GSP	☐
023a	1990	'BRYANT & MAY', in Set BM1004	GSP	☐
024a	1990	'SWAN VESTAS', in Set BM1004	GSP	☐
025a	1990	'ENGLANDS GLORY', set BM1004	GSP	☐
026a	1991	'HAMLEYS', Two-tone Blue	NRP	☐
027a	1991	'EXIDE ', Cream and Green	NRP	☐
028a	1991	'FAIRY SOAP', White and Green	NRP	☐
029a	1991	'BUSHELLS COFFEE', Cream/Blue	NRP	☐
030a	1991	'U.S. MARINES', (in Set PH1003)	GSP	☐
031a	1992	'ELLIMANS', Red/Black	NRP	☐
032a	1992	'MAGGI'S SOUP', Blue/Black	NRP	☐
033a	1991	'SCRIBBANS', (Trade special)	NGPP	☐
034a	1992	'LMS & LNER', in Set RSL2003	GSP	☐
035a	1992	'GRAND HOTEL', in Set HLL1003	GSP	☐
036a	1992	'LNER Country', in Set RSL3003	GSP	☐
037a	1992	'HAMLEYS', in Set HAL1004	GSP	☐
038a	1993	'PEPSI-COLA', Blue, SBX	NRP	☐

DG 22 1933 PACKARD TOWN VAN. The model features a metal box body (with plastic roof) behind a roofless cab. Spare wheels in front wings.

000a	1986	'STAG WHISKY', Cream and Red	£3-5	☐
001a	1986	'LORD TED', Black body	£3-5	☐
002a	1987	'FLORISTS', Brass radiator	£3-5	☐
002b	1987	'FLORISTS', Chrome radiator	£3-5	☐
003a	1987	'WHITMANS', Yellow/Brown/Red	£3-5	☐
004a	1987	'LLEDO WORLDWIDE C.C.', SBX	£5-7	☐
005a	1988	'HAMLEYS', Cream and Black	£3-5	☐
006a	1988	'PIZZA EXPRESS', White/Red	£3-5	☐
007a	1988	'BUDWEISER', Black/Red, SBX	£3-5	☐
008a	1988	'TESCO', White and Red	£20-25	☐
009a	1989	'SOHO DAIRIES', Black body	£3-5	☐
009b	1990	'SOHO DAIRIES', Dark Brown body	£3-5	☐
010a	1990	'HEINZ 57', Cream and Blue	NRP	☐
011a	1991	'SHARPS TOFFEE', Beige body	NRP	☐
012a	1992	'PUNCH', Green/Black	NRP	☐
	1993	Model withdrawn from the standard range		

DG 23 1954 SCENICRUISER. This is the only 'Days Gone' model to feature window glazing. The body is a single metal casting and the baseplate is plastic.

000a	1987	'GREYHOUND', Silver body, pale windows, bare metal chassis	£8-12	☐
000b	1987	dark windows, Silver chassis	£4-6	☐
000c	1987	dark windows, Black chassis	£4-6	☐
001a	1987	'GOLDEN WEST', Gold body	£3-5	☐
002a	1987	'BUFFALO', Red body	£3-5	☐
	1991	Model withdrawn from production		

DG 24 ROLLS-ROYCE PLAYBOY (BREWSTER). A single cast 2-door body and windscreen feature on this model which was fitted with a steering wheel from its introduction. The radiator is that used on the DG 19.

000a	1987	Yellow body, (TV Times offer)	£3-5	☐
001a	1987	Lilac body, Mauve chassis	£3-5	☐
001b	1987	Dark Lilac body, Mauve chassis	£3-5	☐
002a	1988	Metallic Grey body, (in 3-car Set)	GSP	☐
002b	1987	Not mounted or drilled, (unofficial)	£7-10	☐
003a	1987	Red and White, special box	£3-5	☐
004a	1988	Metallic Green body	£3-5	☐
005a	1989	Dark Green body	£3-5	☐
-	1989	24k Gold plated, on plinth, (110 made)	NGPP	☐
	1991	Model withdrawn from production		

DG 25 1925 ROLLS-ROYCE SILVER GHOST (BARKER). The 4-door body on this model is a single casting with wing-mounted spare wheels and plastic roof. Newly introduced with DG 25 was the one-piece plastic seats/ steering wheel moulding.

000a	1987	Dark Blue/Black, ('TV Times' offer)	£3-5	☐
001a	1987	Silver and Blue	£3-5	☐
002a	1988	Metallic Grey, (in 3-car Set)	GSP	☐
002b	1988	Not mounted or drilled, (unofficial)	£7-10	☐
003a	1987	White and Black, (Cream seats)	£3-5	☐
003b	1988	All White body, (White seats)	£3-5	☐
004a	1989	Blue/Black/Tan	£3-5	☐
005a	1989	Dark Green body	£3-5	☐
	1991	Model withdrawn from production		

DG 26 1934 CHEVROLET BOTTLE DELIVERY VAN. This model uses the same baseplate, chassis & radiator as the DG 21. The plastic crate load is mounted in a metal truck body. Steering wheel and seats added in 1991.

000a	1987	'SCHWEPPES', Lemon, Red chassis	£12-16	☐
000b	1987	Yellow body, Red chassis	£3-5	☐
000c	1988	Yellow body, Black chassis	£80-100	☐
001a	1987	'LLEDO WORLDWIDE C.C.', White/Black	£4-6	☐
002a	1987	'COCA-COLA', Brass radiator	£3-5	☐
002b	1989	'COCA-COLA', Chrome radiator	£3-5	☐
003a	1988	'BUDWEISER', in SBX	£3-5	☐
004a	1988	'BARR'S', Red and Black	£3-5	☐
005a	1988	'CORONA', Green and Black	£3-5	☐
006a	1988	'TIZER', Red and Blue	£3-5	☐
007a	1989	'CANADA DRY', (illegible artwork)	£3-5	☐
007b	1989	Legible rear, illegible side	£3-5	☐
007c	1990	Legible rear & side	£3-5	☐
008a	1990	'SCHWEPPES', Red and Black	NRP	☐
009a	1991	'TENNENTS', Green/Black	NRP	☐
010a	1992	'BASS', Blue/Black	NRP	☐
011a	1992	'FYFFES', fleet no. '6' at rear	NRP	☐
011b	1992	'FYFFES', fleet no. '6' at front	NRP	☐
012a	1993	'PEPSI-COLA', Blue, SBX	NRP	☐
013a	1993	'PERRIER', Green/Black	NRP	☐
014a	1993	'BROOKE BOND', Red/Black	NRP	☐

DG 27 1934 MACK BREAKDOWN TRUCK. A metal crane jib features on this model which has metal cab, body and chassis surmounting a plastic baseplate. The steering wheel appeared in 1991.

000a	1987	'A1 RECOVERY', Orange/Black	£3-5	☐
001a	1988	'HANKS AUTO', Green body	£3-5	☐
002		Not allocated		
003a	1988	'MOBILOIL', White and Blue	£3-5	☐
004a	1989	'MOBILOIL', (French issue)	£5-7	☐
005a	1989	'ARTHUR DALEY', Red and Black	£4-6	☐
006a	1991	'US ARMY', (in Set US1003)	GSP	☐
007a	1992	'LONDON CC', Green/Black	NRP	☐
	1993	'BROOKLANDS AUTOMOBILE RACING CLUB', Yellow/Green, (in 'Brooklands Collection')	NRP	☐

DG 28 1934 MACK CANVAS-BACK TRUCK. This model is distinguished by the addition of a large plastic 'tilt' (canvas cover) on the metal truck body. The chassis and the plastic baseplate & radiator are those shared by DG 27. From 1991 the model was fitted with a steering wheel.

000a	1988	'TYPHOO', Red/Black/Cream	£3-5	☐
000b	1988	same but 'leaf' outline in Black	£3-5	☐
001a	1988	'TATE & LYLE', Blue/Cream	£3-5	☐
002a	1988	'LLEDO WORLDWIDE CLUB', SBX	£4-6	☐
003a	1988	'HEINZ BEANS', Chrome radiator	£3-5	☐
003b	1989	'HEINZ BEANS', Brass radiator	£3-5	☐
004a	1989	'DUNLOP', Blue/Black/White	£3-5	☐
005		Not allocated		
006a	1989	'ROYAL NAVY', in Set RN1003	GSP	☐
007a	1990	'STROH'S', Dark Blue and Black	NRP	☐
008a	1989	'NORTH YORKS MOORS', (NYM Set)	GSP	☐
009a	1989	'COCA-COLA', (not released)		
010a	1991	'GREENE KING', Dark Green/Black	NRP	☐
011a	1990	'ROYAL AIR FORCE', (in RAF Set)	GSP	☐
012a	1990	'WINN DIXIE', (US issue)	NGPP	☐
013a	1991	'HAMLEYS', Dark Blue, SBX	NRP	☐
014a	1991	'LNER', in Set TPL1003	GSP	☐

015a	1991	'LMS', in Set RSL1003	GSP	☐
016a	1991	'8th ARMY', in 'Military' box	NRP	☐
017a	1991	'Quartermasters Corps', in Set USA1003	GSP	☐
018a	1991	'REVELL '91', US Trade special	NGPP	☐
019a	1991	'Corps Truck', in Set PH1003	GSP	☐
020a	1992	'GWR', in Set RSL2003	GSP	☐
021a	1992	'HAMLEYS', in SBX	NRP	☐
022a	1991	'Motor Torpedo', in Set PH1003	GSP	☐
023a	1992	'WINCARNIS', Maroon/Black	NRP	☐
024a	1992	'DG Club 91-92', Crimson/Black	NRP	☐
025a	1992	'TOYFAIR '92', Trade Fair model	NGPP	☐
026a	1992	'ROYAL NAVY', in Set MG1003	GSP	☐
027a	1992	'US Marines', in Set GU1003	GSP	☐
028a	1992	'SR Express', in Set RSL3003	GSP	☐
029a	1993	'KAFFEE HAG', Red/Black	NRP	☐
030a	1993	'RAF', in Set DML1003	GSP	☐

DG 29 1942 DODGE 4x4. This unusual choice of model required new components throughout. The plastic baseplate is surmounted by a metal chassis and a one-piece metal body casting incorporating front bumper & radiator.

000a	1988	'US Field Ambulance', Military-Green	£3-5	☐
001a	1989	'RAF Aircrew', Pale Blue	£3-5	☐
002a	1991	'TEXACO', Red body, Black wings	NRP	☐
003a	1991	'US Army Ambulance', in Set USAL1003	GSP	☐
004a	1992	'Bomb Disposal', 'Military' box	£3-5	☐
005a	1992	'Marines Corps', in Set GU1003	GSP	☐
006a	1993	'Police Emergency'	NRP	☐

DG 30 1939 CHEVROLET PANEL VAN. Completely new components were required again with the introduction of this model. They include a one-piece metal body, metal chassis, plastic baseplate, radiator, lights, interior and bumpers.

000a	1988	'JOHN BULL TYRES', Red/Black	£3-5	☐
001a	1989	'FRY'S COCOA', Black body	£3-5	☐
002a	1989	'LIPTONS', Green body	£3-5	☐
002b	1990	'LIPTONS', Dark Yellow print	£3-5	☐
003a	1989	'LLEDO WORLDWIDE CLUB', SBX	£4-6	☐
004a	1989	'HAMLEYS', Maroon body, SBX	£3-5	☐
005a	1990	'SPRATTS', Cream body	NRP	☐
006a	1990	'BROOKE BOND', Red body	NRP	☐
007a	1990	'HERSHEY', (US issue, SBX)	NGPP	☐
008a	1990	'ROYAL AIR FORCE', Set BBL1004	GSP	☐
009a	1991	'NESTLES', Dark Red body	NRP	☐
010a	1991	'GOLDEN STREAM TEA', Gold/Black	NRP	☐
011a	1991	'Polish Army Ambulance', SBX	NRP	☐
012a	1991	'Army Surgical Unit', Set USA1003	GSP	☐
013a	1991	'US Navy', in Set PHL1003	GSP	☐
014a	1992	'STEPHENS INKS', Blue	NRP	☐
015a	1993	'SHELL-BP', Yellow	NRP	☐

DG 31 HORSE-DRAWN BREWERS DRAY. The large/small wheels from DG 4, 5 & 11 came back into use for this model, the first to have a dedicated driver figure and painted detail on the horses. Plastic drivers seat, headboard and barrels.

000a	1988	'WHITBREAD', Brown body	£3-5	☐
001a	1988	'EVERARDS', Red body, (Dealer Promotion)	£12-16	☐
002a	1989	'TAUNTON CIDER', Red body	£3-5	☐
002b	1990	same but tampo on wrong side	£3-5	☐
003a	1989	'GREENE KING', (reversed tampo)	£3-5	☐
003b	1989	'GREENE KING', (correct tampo)	£3-5	☐
004a	1989	'TRUMANS', Red body	£3-5	☐
005a	1991	'COURAGE ALES', Blue body	NRP	☐
006a	1992	'WORTHINGTON', Dark Blue	NRP	☐
007a	1993	'BASS', Dark Blue	NRP	☐

DG 32 1907 ROLLS-ROYCE SILVER GHOST. This model echoes the Odell design of the Lesney Y15-1 version of 1960 with its cast metal body, bonnet, chassis and windscreen. The seats, steering wheel, radiator and headlights assembly are in plastic.

000a	1988	Silver body, Maroon seats	£3-5	☐
001a	1989	Dark Green body, Beige seats	£3-5	☐

002a	1990	Metallic Green body, Black seats	NRP	☐
003a	1990	'Gold-plate' effect	NGPP	☐
004a	1991	Dark Red, Black seats	NRP	☐
005a	1992	Dark Blue, Black seats	NRP	☐
006a	1992	Bronze body, (German market)	NGPP	☐
007a	1992	'Gold' effect, (German market)	NGPP	☐

DG 33 1920 FORD Model 'T' CAR. Existing DG6 & 8 radiator, chassis, baseplate & wheels were used on this model. A new metal body casting was designed with new plastic windscreen, roof, seats & spare wheel mounting.

000a	1989	Black body, chassis and roof	£3-5	☐
001a	1989	'SINGER', Green, Maroon seats	NRP	☐
001b	1989	'SINGER', Green, Black seats	NRP	☐
002		Not allocated		
003a	1990	'HERSHEYS', (US issue, SBX)	NGPP	☐
004a	1991	'GRAND HOTEL', Red/Black	NRP	☐
005a	1992	'HOTEL PARIS', in Set HLL1003	GSP	☐
006a		Gold	NGPP	☐
007a	1993	'PFAFF', Cream body	NRP	☐

DG 34 1932 DENNIS DELIVERY VAN. This model is a modification of DG 10 with the addition of a roof-rack and with reduced seating section. It has 'D' shaped side windows behind cab.

000a	1989	'HOVIS', Cream body	£3-5	☐
001a	1989	'SMEDLEYS', Dark Green body	£3-5	☐
002a	1989	'HAMLEYS', Dark Green/Black	£3-5	☐
003a	1990	'CHEDDAR CHEESE', Yellow/Green	NRP	☐
004a	1990	'ROYAL AIR FORCE', Set BBL1003	GSP	☐
005a	1991	'DAYS GONE CLUB, Spring'	£4-6	☐
006a	1992	'Wartime Library', Dark Green	£3-4	☐
	1993	Model withdrawn from production		

DG 35 1932 DENNIS LIMOUSINE. Another modification of DG 10, this time a utility vehicle using the ladder component from DG 12. The main differences are in the upper body/roof moulding which has a smaller roof-rack than DG 34 and rectangular side windows.

000a	1989	'EDINBURGH Fire Brigade'	£3-5	☐
001a	1990	'POST OFFICE TELEPHONES'	NRP	☐
002a	1990	'ROYAL AIR FORCE', Set BBL1003	GSP	☐
003a	1991	'1st Div. SIGNALS HQ', SBX	NRP	☐
004a	1991	'NFS', in Set HF1003	GSP	☐
005a	1992	'BBC Wartime Outside Broadcasts'	NRP	☐

DG 36 1939 CHEVROLET PICK-UP. Based on the DG30 Panel Van, the major new component in this model is the one-piece cast metal pick-up body. Oil-drums load introduced in 1992.

000a	1989	'BUCK & HICKMAN', Dark Green/Black	£3-5	☐
001a	1990	'CAKEBREAD & ROBEY', Red body	NRP	☐
002a	1991	'AVON TYRES', Dark Blue body	NRP	☐
003a	1991	'US Army Explosives', Set USAL1003	GSP	☐
004a	1992	'DUCKHAMS', White/Black	NRP	☐
005a	1993	'REDEX', Red/Black	NRP	☐
	1993	'CASTROL', Green/Black, oil drums, (in 'Brooklands Collection')	NRP	☐

DG 37 1932 FORD Model 'A' PANEL VAN. The model has a modified DG 9 body with the addition of a plastic van upper body & roof section.

000a	1990	'CANADIAN CLUB', Brown body	NRP	☐
001a	1990	'Mr THERM', Dark Green body	NRP	☐
002a	1991	'USA POLICE', Dark Blue	NRP	☐
003a	1992	'DAYS GONE CLUB '92', Cream	NRP	☐
	1993	'EXIDE', Cream, in 'Brooklands Collection'	NRP	☐

DG 38 1925 ROLLS-ROYCE SILVER GHOST SALOON. Basically a DG 25 with a new plastic roof moulding.

000a	1989	Dark Green body, Gold lining	£3-5	☐
	1991	Model withdrawn from production		

DG 39 1934 MACK TRUCK. The DG 28 with canvas tilt replaced by plastic sack load. The steering wheel appeared in 1991.

000a	1990	'BLUE CIRCLE', Yellow/Blue	NRP	☐
001a	1991	'KETTON CEMENT', White/Black	NRP	☐
002a	1989	'GAS LIGHT & COKE', Black	£3-5	☐
003a	1992	'PORTLAND CEMENT', Yellow/Blue........	£3-4	☐
004a	1992	Military Sand-Bag Truck, SBX	£3-4	☐

DG 40 1934 MACK CRANE TRUCK. The model is basically DG 27 Breakdown Truck but with a new forward-facing crane assembly.

000a	1990	'TARMAC', Black body, Red chassis...........	NRP	☐
001a	1991	'RICHARD COSTAIN', Grey body.............	NRP	☐
002a	1991	Ammunition Crane, in Set PH1003.............	GSP	☐
003a	1992	'US NAVY', in Set GU1003	GSP	☐
004a	1993	'RAF', in Set DM1003	GSP	☐
	1993	Model withdrawn from production		

DG 41 1928 KARRIER E6 TROLLEY BUS. The model features six wheels, new metal body castings, upper & lower plastic seat mouldings. Plastic trolley poles surmount the metal roof. This was the first model in the new **'Premier Collection'** range.

000a	1990	'ROBIN STARCH', Maroon body	NRP	☐
001a	1990	'MARKS & SPENCER', SBX	NRP	☐
002a	1991	'HAMLEYS', Red body, SBX	NRP	☐
003a	1991	'BISTO', Red body	NRP	☐
004a	1991	'BOVRIL', Red body....................................	NRP	☐
005a	1991	'NORTH YORKS MOORS', in NYM Set ..	GSP	☐
006a	1992	'SAXA SALT', Red body	NRP	☐
007a	1992	'SCHWEPPES', Dark Green	NRP	☐
008a	1992	'HAMLEYS', in Set HAL1004	GSP	☐
009a	1992	'SUNMAID RAISINS', Red........................	NRP	☐

DG 42 1934 MACK TANKER. DG 27 again, this time with a plastic tank replacing the original crane assembly. It acquired a steering wheel in 1991.

000a	1990	'NATIONAL BENZOLE', Yellow body	£3-5	☐
001a	1990	'ROYAL AIR FORCE', Set BB1003............	GSP	☐
002a	1991	'REGENT PETROL', Blue/Red	NRP	☐
003a	1991	'US Air Corps', in Set USAL1003	GSP	☐
004a	1991	'US Navy', in Set PHL1003........................	GSP	☐
005a	1992	Army Water Tanker, in Set EAL1003..........	GSP	☐
006a	1992	'SHELL FUEL OIL', (German market).......	NGPP	☐
	1993	'SHELL FUEL OIL',		
		(in 'Brooklands Collection')	NRP	☐
007a	1993	'PENNZOIL', Yellow/Black	NRP	☐

DG 43 1931 MORRIS VAN. Another in the **'Premier Collection'** range. Apart from the use of DG 30 wheels, this model has all-new components: cast metal body, chassis & roof, with plastic baseplate, interior & radiator.

000a	1990	'WEETABIX', All Yellow	£3-5	☐
001a	1990	'CHIVERS JAMS', All Cream	£3-5	☐
002a	1991	'HAMLEYS', Green/Black, SBX	NRP	☐
003a	1991	'DG CLUB Winter 90/91'	NRP	☐
004a	1991	'AC SPARK PLUGS', Yellow/Blue.............	NRP	☐
005a	1991	'LNER', (in Set TPL1003)	GSP	☐
006a	1991	'METROPOLITAN Rly', (Set RSL1003)	GSP	☐
007a	1991	'BIRDS CUSTARD', Blue/White	NRP	☐
008a	1991	'8th Army Ambulance', SBX	NRP	☐
009a	1991	'91 Toyfair', Dealer PRM/SBX	£8-10	☐
009b	1991	no locations printed on door	NGPP	☐
010a	1991	'Cornwall Home Guard', (Set HF1003)	GSP	☐
011a	1992	'HAMLEYS', Cream, SBX...........................	NRP	☐
012a	1992	'AMBROSIA', Dark Green	NRP	☐
013a	1992	'ARNOTTS', Red body	NRP	☐
014a	1992	'GWR', in Set RSL3003	GSP	☐
015a	1992	'HARRODS', in Set HD1004.......................	GSP	☐
016a	1992	'SUNLICHT SEIFE', (German market).......	NGPP	☐
017a	1993	'TATE SUGARS'...	NRP	☐

DG 44 1937 SCAMMELL 6-WHEELER. Realistic 'heavy-duty' wheels distinguish this all-new model in the **'Premier Collection'** range.

000a	1990	'BISTO', (matt and gloss versions)...............	£3-5	☐
001a	1990	'TOBLERONE', Cream/Green......................	£3-5	☐

002a	1991	'MARMITE', Green body..........................	NRP	☐
003a	1991	'FOX's GLACIER MINTS', Dark Blue	NRP	☐
004a	1991	'NORTH YORKS MOORS', NYM Set.......	GSP	☐
005a	1992	'ROWNTREES', Grey body	NRP	☐
006a	1992	'McMULLEN', Dark Brown	NRP	☐
007a	1992	'DG CLUB Spring '92'	NRP	☐
008a	1992	'British Army', Set EAL1003........................	GSP	☐
009a	1993	'BERLINER KINDL', German market	NGPP	☐
010a	1993	'TETLEYS FINE ALES'	NRP	☐

DG 45 1908 ROLLS-ROYCE SILVER GHOST COUPE. Lledo ingenuity applied to the DG 32 resulted in this rather sporty 2-seater.

000a	1992	Metallic Green	£3-4	☐
001a	1991	Crimson body, Black seats.........................	NRP	☐
002a	1993	White body..	NRP	☐

DG 46 1930 BENTLEY 4.5 Litre. Another echo of the past (Lesney Y5-1) in this delightful model with separate wing mouldings and side-mounted spare wheel.

000a	1991	British Racing Green	NRP	☐
001a	1991	Dark Blue body, No.'1'	NRP	☐
002a	1991	'Gold-plate' effect	NGPP	☐
003a	1992	British Racing Green, No.'2'	NRP	☐
004a	1992	Cream body, No.'18'	NRP	☐
005a	1993	Maroon body, No.'10'................................	NRP	☐
	1993	British Racing Green body, No.'85'		
		(in 'The Spirit of Brooklands' Collection)	£4-5	☐

DG 47 1933 AUSTIN TAXI. Introduced at the end of 1991 in the **'Premier Collection'**, the usual Lledo mix of metal and plastic components producing an attractive model taxi.

000a	1991	Dark Blue body..	£3-4	☐
001a	1992	Black body	£3-4	☐
002a	1992	'HAMLEYS', (in Set HA1002)...................	GSP	☐
003a	1992	'HAMLEYS', (in Set HAL1004)	GSP	☐
004a	1993	Maroon body	£3-4	☐

DG 48 1939 CHEVROLET CAR. To broaden their range of model cars Lledo developed the DG 48 from DG 30 & 36 and released it in July 1991.

000a	1991	Cream and Dark Green	£3-4	☐
001a	1991	'DG CLUB Autumn '91', Gold...................	£3-4	☐
002a	1992	Cream and Maroon	£3-4	☐
003a	1992	'British Army', in Set EAL1003.................	GSP	☐
004a	1993	'YELLOW CABS', Yellow taxi...................	£3-4	☐
005a	1993	'RAF', in Set DML1003	GSP	☐

DG 49 1931 AEC RENOWN DOUBLE DECK BUS. The AEC radiator used on DG 15 and 17 came into use again on this 6-wheeled bus introduced in October 1991 in the **'Premier Collection'** range.

000a	1991	'BOURN-VITA', Red................................	NRP	☐
001a	1991	'ROSES LIME JUICE', Red.......................	NRP	☐
002a	1992	'HAMLEYS', Black chassis, SBX	NRP	☐
002b	1992	'HAMLEYS', Red chassis, SBX..................	NRP	☐
003a	1992	'MARTINI', Red	NRP	☐
004a	1992	'JANTZEN', Red...	NRP	☐
005a	1992	'HAMLEYS', in Set HA1002	GSP	☐
006a	1992	'DG CLUB 1992', Red................................	NRP	☐
007a	1992	'HARRODS', in Set HD 1004	GSP	☐
008a	1992	'QANTAS', in Set QA1002	GSP	☐
009a	1993	'PEPSI-COLA', Red, SBX	NRP	☐
010a	1993	'HAMLEYS', Grey advert, SBX	NRP	☐
011a	1993	'LITTLEWOODS'	NRP	☐
012a	1993	'St.MICHAEL', Set MS2004	GSP	☐

DG 50 1926 'BULL-NOSE' MORRIS VAN. This vintage van model was introduced to the standard range in June 1992. It has a cast metal body and plastic roof with goods rack.

000a	1992	'LYONS TEA', Dark Blue	NRP	☐
001a	1992	'BRYANT & MAY', Maroon......................	NRP	☐
002a	1993	'HAMLEYS'	NRP	☐
003a	1993	'H.M.V. - MILLERS'	NRP	☐
004a	1993	'DAYS GONE CLUB'	NRP	☐
005a	1993	'MARKS & SPENCER', Set MS2004	GSP	☐
006a	1993	'RAFFLES Hotel', Set HLL2003.................	GSP	☐

DG 51 1934 CHEVROLET BOX VAN. Another vintage van model in the standard range (introduced April 1992). It has a tall cast metal box body and plastic roof.

000a	1992	'MADAME TUSSAUDS', Black..................	NRP	☐
001a	1992	'STARTRITE', White..................................	NRP	☐
002a	1993	'HOVIS', Cream/Black	NRP	☐
003a	1993	'DAYS GONE CLUB'	NRP	☐
004a	1993	'MARKS & SPENCER', Set MS2004	GSP	☐

DG 52 1935 MORRIS PARCELS VAN. This new van model in the **'Premier Range'** was introduced in October 1992. Although the radiator, baseplate and wheels are of plastic, it is a heavy model with relatively large die-castings.

000a	1992	'ROYAL MAIL', Red/Black	NRP	☐
001a	1992	'PICKFORDS', Dark Blue	NRP	☐
002a	1993	'PEPSI-COLA', White, SBX........................	NRP	☐
003a	1993	'LNER PARCELS'......................................	NRP	☐
004a	1993	'43rd Division'...	NRP	☐
005a	1993	'DAYS GONE CLUB'	NRP	☐
006a	1993	'1993 TOYFAIR'..	NRP	☐
007a	1993	'RAF Ambulance', Set DM1003	GSP	☐

DG 53 1926 ROLLS ROYCE LANDAULET. The first appearance of this model was early in 1992 as a Promotional. It was issued as a standard model in October of that year.

000a	1992	'Days Gone Collector', 'Gold-plate' effect	NRP	☐

DG 54 1929 ROLLS ROYCE 'D' BACK. Again appearing first as a Promotional (in May 1992) this new version of a famous name is scheduled for release in November 1993.

000a	1993	Blue body, Tan roof	NRP	☐

DG 55 HORSE-DRAWN TANKER. Though given a Days Gone number this model has only been used for Promotional purposes, and there are no plans to issue it in the standard range.

DG 56 1934 MODEL 'A' FORD VAN (Raised Roof). Though given a Days Gone number this model has only been used for Promotional purposes, and there are no plans to issue it in the standard range.

DG 57 1939 FORD TANKER. A new 'late pre-war' model scheduled for introduction in April 1993.

000a	1993	'SHELL-BP Aviation'....................................	NRP	☐

DG 58 1950 MORRIS 'Z' VAN. This is the first in a new range of 1950s and 1960s model vehicles called **'Days Gone Vanguards'**. New colourful packaging was designed for this range with DG 58 being scheduled for release in August 1993.

000a	1993	'P.O. TELEPHONES'....................................	£4-6	☐
001a	1993	'MALVERN WATER'...................................	£4-6	☐
002a	1993	'MACKESONS STOUT'..............................	£4-6	☐

DG 59 1950 BEDFORD 30cwt TRUCK. A very popular subject with collectors and the second of the **'Days Gone Vanguards'**, this model was also scheduled for release in August 1993.

000a	1993	'BIRDS CUSTARD'	£4-6	☐
001a	1993	'CANADA DRY'	£4-6	☐
002a	1993	'DUNLOPILLO'...	£4-6	☐

DG 60 1955 DENNIS F8 FIRE ENGINE. Fire appliances also make popular subjects for modelling. This is the third in the **'Days Gone Vanguards'** range with a release date of October 1993.

000a	1993	'ESSEX'..	£4-6	☐
001a	1993	'DERBYSHIRE'..	£4-6	☐
002a	1993	'WESTERN AREA - OBAN'	£4-6	☐

DG 61 1953 PONTIAC DELIVERY VAN. American vehicles of this period are particularly stylish. This fourth introduction in the **'Days Gone Vanguards'** range is scheduled for November 1993.

000a	1993	'Dr. PEPPER'	£4-6	☐
001a	1993	'DETROIT POLICE'	£4-6	☐
002a	1993	'MILWAUKEE' Ambulance........................	£4-6	☐

Miscellaneous models by Lledo

Marathons

These models were introduced in 1987 to balance the vintage feel of 'Days Gone' vehicles with something having a more modern appeal. Although some were used as promotional models (particularly the buses), they did not attract sufficient interest among collectors to warrant continuing the range after 1988.

Ref. No.	Year(s)	Model Type	Model Features and Size	Market Price Range	
M1a 01a	1987	Leyland Olympian Bus.............	'LONDON PRIDE SIGHTSEEING', 'PINDISPORTS', Blue body	£2-3	☐
M1a 01b	1987		same model but 'PINDISPORTS' address printed in Red	£2-4	☐
M1a 02a	1987		'LONDON TRANSPORT' & 'LONDON ZOO', Red body	£2-3	☐
M1a 03a	1987		'CORPORATION TRANSPORT' & 'PAN AM', White/Blue	£2-3	☐
M2a 01a	1987	Setra Coach	'PAN AM', White body, Blue roof	£2-3	☐
M2a 02a	1987		'AIR CANADA', White body, Red roof	£2-3	☐
M2a 03a	1987		'GHANA AIRWAYS', Yellow body and roof...	£2-3	☐
M3a 01a	1987	Neoplan Spaceliner...................	'ISLAND TOURS', Yellow body and roof	£2-3	☐
M3a 02a	1987		'SPEEDLINK', White body and roof..	£2-3	☐
M3a 03a	1987		'GATWICK FLIGHTLINE', Yellow body, White roof...................................	£2-3	☐
M4a 01a	1988	Leyland Rigid Truck	'FEDERAL EXPRESS', White cab, chassis & body.....................................	£2-3	☐
M5a 01a	1988	Leyland Tipper	'LECCA ARC', Yellow cab & chassis, Silver tipper.....................................	£2-3	☐
M6a 01a	1988	Leyland Tanker	'SHELL', Yellow cab, Black chassis, Silver tank..	£2-3	☐

'Fantastic Set-O-Wheels' models

A series of models introduced in 1985 for the US toy market and distributed by Hartoy Inc of Florida. They were blister-packed on card with the legend 'Made in England by Lledo (London) Ltd' on most of the baseplates.

Ref. No.	DG Model	Model Name	Features	Market Price Range	
F1a	DG 6	'MALIBU OR BUST'.............	Yellow/Dark Brown/Tan, 'Made In England by Lledo' on baseplate..........................	£10-15	☐
F1b			same model but with 'Days Gone' on baseplate..........................	£10-15	☐
F2a	DG 7	'TRI-STATE DEALER'	White/Blue with Yellow wheels, 'Made In England' baseplate............................	£10-15	☐
F2b			As previous model but Black wheels, 'Days Gone' baseplate....................	£10-15	☐
F3a	DG 15	'LIQUID BUBBLE'.................	Blue/Pink/White body, 20-spoke Red wheels with Cream tyres.........	£10-15	☐
F4a	DG 10	'OAKRIDGE SCHOOL'.........	Yellow/Black body, Cream tyres on Black wheels............	£10-15	☐
F5a	DG 12	'BOSTON FIRE Dept'	Red body and wheels, Cream floor and tyres, 'Made In England' baseplate..............	£10-15	☐
F5b			As previous model but with 'Days Gone' on the baseplate..........	£10-15	☐
F6a	DG 13	'JOLLY TIME'	Cream/Pink, 'Made In England' baseplate, Red wheels, Cream tyres.......................	£10-15	☐
F6b			same model but with 'Days Gone' baseplate	£10-15	☐
F7a	DG 14	'POLICE' Car............................	Black body, Cream tyres on Black 12-spoke wheels, 'Made In England' base	£10-15	☐
F7b			As previous model but 'Days Gone' baseplate...................	£10-15	☐
F7c			As F7a but with 20-spoke wheels...............................	£10-15	☐
F8a	DG 14	'SAN-DIEGO FIRE'	Red body, Black roof and wheels, Cream tyres, Chrome grille.....................	£10-15	☐
F8b			As previous model but with Brass grille	£10-15	☐

Edocar ('Old-Timer' Series)

A range of eight models made in 1986 for Edor BV (Fred Beheer BV), in the Netherlands and sold there under the name 'EDOCAR'. The baseplates all have the wording 'EDOCAR - Made in England by Lledo' plus the model number. Some models have original Days Gone colours but have been left unprinted (without logos). All but A7 have only Black tyres. The 'double window' boxes were made and printed in Holland.

Ref. No.	DG Model	Model Name	Features	Market Price Range	
A1a	DG 8	Tanker (unprinted)	Red body, Black chassis & roof, Yellow tank, Brass wheels...............	£10-15	☐
A1b		'ESSO BLUE'.............................	Blue body, White roof, (produced for ESSO garages in Holland)	£10-15	☐
A2a	DG 12	Dennis Fire Engine..................	Red body and wheels, White floor, Brass grille	£10-15	☐
A2b			As previous model but with Black floor	£10-15	☐
A3	DG 14	Taxi..	Yellow body, Black roof, Yellow 20-spoke wheels, Chrome grille	£10-15	☐
A4a	DG 16	'HUMBROL'	Green/White with Chrome grille, White wheels	£10-15	☐
A4b			As previous model but with Brass grille	£10-15	☐
A5	DG 17	AEC Single Deck Bus	White body, Blue seats, (box states 'AEC Double Decker Bus')	£10-15	☐
A6a	DG 18	Packard 'AMBULANCE'........	White body, White wheels, Chrome grille	£10-15	☐
A6b			same model but with Brass grille	£10-15	☐
A7	DG 19	Rolls Royce Phantom...............	Silver body, Black chassis and wheels, Black or Cream tyres................	£10-15	☐
A8	DG 21	'EDOCAR'	Blue/Black/White Chevrolet van with Brass grille	£12-18	☐

The 'Grey' Series

Finished in neutral Grey and left unprinted for use as samples of promotionals by sales representatives (mainly in the USA). Only 144 sets of models were produced (in 1986) and all except DG7, DG11 and DG14 have 'Days Gone' baseplates.

Ref. No.	Year(s)	Model Type	Model Features and Size	Market Price Range	
DG 2	1986	Horse-Drawn Milk Float	Cream 20-spoke wheels, Black horse, Pale Blue milk crates....................	£12-18	☐
DG 3	1986	Horse-Drawn Delivery Van	Cream 20-spoke wheels, Black horse and roof..................	£12-18	☐
DG 4	1986	Horse-Drawn Omnibus	Cream horses, Red seats	£12-18	☐
DG 5	1986	Horse-Drawn Fire Engine........	Cream horses, Black wheels, Bronze boiler	£12-18	☐
DG 5	1986		same model but with Gold wheels	£12-18	☐
DG 6	1986	Ford Model 'T' Van.................	Cream 20-spoke wheels, Black tyres, White roof	£12-18	☐
DG 7	1986	Ford Woody Wagon	Cream 20-spoke wheels with Black tyres,'Lledo' and 'DG' baseplates........	£15-20	☐
DG 8	1986	Ford Model 'T' Tanker.............	Cream 20-spoke wheels with Black tyres, Green plastic tank..........	£15-20	☐
DG 10	1986	Dennis Single Deck Bus	Red roof, Brown hubs, Cream tyres & seats............	£15-20	☐
DG 10	1986		same model but with Yellow roof	£15-20	☐
DG 11	1986	Horse-Drawn Large Van...........	Cream horses, Blue roof, 'Lledo' & 'DG' baseplates..........	£12-18	☐
DG 12	1986	Fire Engine	Brown wheels with Cream tyres, Brass radiator, Tan ladder............	£12-18	☐
DG 13	1986	Ford Model 'A' Van	Cream 20-spoke wheels, White roof, Chrome grille	£12-18	☐
DG 14	1986	Ford Model 'A' Car	Cream 20-spoke wheels, roof & seats, 'Lledo' & 'DG' baseplates........	£15-20	☐
DG 15	1986	AEC Double Deck Bus	Yellow wheels and windows	£15-20	☐
DG 16	1986	Dennis Parcels Van	Brown wheels, Cream tyres & roof...........	£12-18	☐
DG 17	1986	AEC Single Deck Bus	Pale Blue wheels, White windows	£15-20	☐
DG 18	1986	Packard Van	Brown roof, Cream wheels & tyres..........	£12-18	☐
DG 19	1986	Rolls-Royce Phantom II	Cream hubs and tyres, Black roof, Tan boot and seats..........	£12-18	☐

American Days Gone models - the '500' series

To generate more interest in the USA a range of six Days Gone models were marketed which were in plain colour finishes having no printed logos or liveries. In each case the standard reference number carried the suffix '500'.

Ref. No.	Year(s)	Model Type	Model Features and Size	Market Price Range	
DG14-500		Ford Model 'A'	Yellow body/chassis and 20-spoke wheels, Black roof, Brass radiator	NGPP	☐
DG22-500		Packard Town Van	Black body/roof, Red chassis, Brass radiator and 12-spoke wheels	NGPP	☐
DG30-500		Chevrolet Van	Red body, Black chassis and wheels, Chrome radiator	NGPP	☐
DG33-500		Ford Model 'T'	Black body/chassis/wheels/tyres, Chrome radiator	NGPP	☐
DG36-500		Chevy Pick-Up	Green body, Black chassis, wheels and tyres, Chrome radiator	NGPP	☐
DG37-500		Ford Model 'A' Van	Blue body/chassis/roof, Brass wheels, Chrome radiator	NGPP	☐

'Days Gone' Gift Sets

The individual models that make up these sets are listed separately in the 'Days Gone' listings. The following list indicates the content of specific sets and prices where available.

Ref. No.	Year(s)	Set Name	Contents	Market Price Range	
AB 1003	1990	Arnotts Biscuits Set	DG6-101a Ford T Van, DG11-016a Horse Drawn, DG13-045a Ford A Van	£20-25	☐
BA 1003	1989	British Army Collection	DG8-017a Tanker, DG13-038a Recruitment, DG19-009a Staff Car	£20-25	☐
BB 1003	1990	RAF Ground Crew Support	DG20-015a Balloon Tender, DG35-002a RAF Riggers, DG42-001a Fuel Tanker	£15-20	☐
BBL 1003	1990	RAF Personnel Transport	DG28-011a Truck, DG30-008a Ambulance, DG34 004a Office. (12,500)	£15-20	☐
BM 1004	1990	Bryant & May Set	Four DG21 vans: 022a Scottish Bluebell, 023a Bryant & May, 024a Swan Vestas, 025a Englands Glory (Limited Edition of 12,500)	£20-25	☐
	1986	Commonwealth Games Set	DG7-007a Woody Wagon, DG10-016a Dennis Coach, DG15-011a AEC Bus	£10-12	☐
CC 1003	1986	Coca-Cola Set	DG6-058a Ford T Van, DG11-007a Horse Drawn, DG13-021a Ford A Van	£20-25	☐
CC 2003	1987	Coca-Cola Set	DG6-054a Ford T Van, DG21-005a Chevrolet, DG26-002a Chevrolet	£20-25	☐
CP 1	1984	Collector Pack	DG3-003a Robertsons, DG4-005a Pears Soap, DG6-017a Daily Express	£10-15	☐
DML 1003	1993	Dambusters Set	DG16-034a Control, DG28-030a RAF, DG48-005a RAF, (7,500)	£12-15	☐
DM 1003	1993	Dambusters Set	DG16-033a NAAFI, DG40-004a RAF, DG52-007a RAF	£10-13	☐
EAL 1003	1992	El Alamein Set	DG42-005a Water, DG44-008a Army, DG48-003a Army, (12,500)	£10-13	☐
GS 1	1984	Gift Set	DG6-023a Railway Express, DG7-002a Ford Sales, DG9-001a New York-Rio	£10-15	☐
GS 2	1985	Gift Set	DG6-033a Barclays, DG11-001a Abels, DG13-005a Michelin	£15-20	☐
GS 3	1985	Bus Gift Set	DG10-013a Trailways, DG15-002a Castlemaine, DG17 001a Eurotour	£10-15	☐
GS 4	1986	Coca-Cola Set	DG6-058a Ford T Van, DG11-007a Woody Wagon, DG13-021a Ford A Van	£20-25	☐
GS 5	1986	Hersheys Set	DG6-055a Ford T Van, DG13-023a Ford A Van, DG16-012a Dennis Van	£20-25	☐
GS 1004	1989	Golden Days Of Film	Early Film Industry vans in 'gold-plate': DG6-091a Britannia, DG13-034a Empire, DG18-014a B & C Films, DG21-016a Majestic. (10,000)	£60-65	☐
GU 1003	1992	Guadalcanal Set	DG28-027a Marines, DG29-005a Marines, DG40-003a Navy	£10-13	☐
	1984	Hamleys Set	DG3-009a, DG4-008a, DG6-035a, DG7-004a, DG10-009a, DG13-004a	£35-40	☐
HA 1002	1992	Hamleys London Set	DG47-002a Austin Taxi and DG49-005a AEC Bus	£8-10	☐
HAL 1004	1992	Hamleys Ltd Ed Set	DG11-021a, DG21-037a, DG41-008a, DG47-003a, (5,000)	£15-20	☐
HD 1002	1992	Harrods Set	DG11-020a Horse Drawn Removals Van and DG15-028a AEC Bus	£8-10	☐
HD 1004	1992	Harrods Set	DG3-014a, DG13-051a, DG43-015a, DG49-007a	£12-16	☐
HF 1003	1991	The Home Front Set	DG16-030a YMCA, DG35-004a NFS, DG43-010a Cornwall	£10-13	☐
HLL 1003	1992	Hotel Labels Set	DG6-108a Colombia, DG21-035a de Paix, DG33-005a de Paris, (12,500)	£10-13	☐
HLL 1003	1993	Hotel Labels Set	DG13-058a Grand, DG18-024a Imperial, DG50-006a Raffles, (7,500)	£12-15	☐
LS 1004	1989	London Stores Set No.1	Four different vans: DG6-087a Selfridges, DG13-031a Aquascutum, DG18-013a Fortnum & Mason, DG21-012a DAKS Simpson. (Not limited)	£12-17	☐
LS 2004	1990	London Stores Set No.2	DG6-097a Jaeger, DG13-036a Austin Reed, DG18-018a Asprey, DG21-020a Liberty. (Not limited)	£12-17	☐
MG 1003	1992	Malta George Cross Set	DG12-017a Valletta, DG18-022a St.John, DG28-026a Royal Navy	£10-13	☐
MS 1004	1990	Marks & Spencer Set	DG11-014a, DG13-014a, DG21-019a, DG41-001a. (Also available singly)	£10-15	☐
MS 2004	1993	Marks & Spencer Set	DG13-057a, DG49-012a, DG50-005a, DG51-004a	£12-16	☐
NYMR1003	1989	Nth Yorks Moors Set 1	DG6-093a Cartage, DG17-018a NYM Railway, DG28-008a Parcels (7,500)	£12-16	☐
NYMR2003	1990	Nth Yorks Moors Set 2	DG13-044a, DG15-027a, DG16-025a (6,000)	£12-16	☐
NYMR1002	1991	Nth Yorks Moors Set 3	DG41-005a Scarborough and DG44-004a NYMR, (6,500)	£9-12	☐
PHL 1003	1991	Pearl Harbor Set 1	DG28-019a Corps, DG30-013a Navy, DG42-004a Navy, (12,500)	£11-14	☐
PH 1003	1991	Pearl Harbor Set 2	DG21-030a Marines, DG28-022a Torpedo, DG40-002a Crane	£10-13	☐
QA 1002	1992	Qantas Set	DG13-052a Ford A Van, and DG49-008a AEC Bus	£7-10	☐
	1987	Royal Flying Corps/RAF Set	DG6-063a and DG-011a '216 Squadron', DG18-008a Ambulance	£35-45	☐
RN 1003	1988	Royal Navy Set	DG17-017a Britannia, DG20-011a Rooke, DG28-006a Devonport (10,000)	£25-35	☐
RR 1003	1988	Rolls Royce Set	DG19-003a, DG24-002a & DG25-002a on wooden plinth, (7,500)	£30-35	☐
RSL 1003	1991	Railway Express Parcels 1	DG16-029a LNER, DG28-015a LMS & DG43-006a Metropolitan, (12,500)	£9-12	☐
RSL 2003	1991	Railway Express Parcels 2	DG13-050a Southern, DG21-034a LMS/LNER & DG43-005a GWR, (10,000)	£10-13	☐
RSL 3003	1991	Railway Express Parcels 3	DG21-036a LNER, DG28-028a Southern & DG43-014a GWR, (10,000)	£10-13	☐
RSL 4003	1993	Railway Road Vehicles 1900s	DG3-015a GER, DG4-016a Furness & DG11-024a Gt.Northern, (7,500)	£12-16	☐
TPL 1003	1991	LNER Express Parcels Vans	DG16-028a Dennis, DG28-014a LNER, DG43-009a Morris, (12,500)	£9-12	☐
USA 1003	1991	US Army Set 1	DG27-006a Mack, DG28-017a Quartermaster & DG30-012a Surgical	£9-12	☐
USAL1003	1991	US Army Set 2	DG29-003a Ambulance, DG36-003a Pick-Up, DG42-003a Air Corps, (12,500)	£9-12	☐
LP 1553	1991	Charles & Diana Set	Two Rolls Royce models in special Purple box (not limited)	£7-10	☐

View Vans & Souvenir Buses

These are a variation on the Promotional theme and include LP6, LP13, LP15, LP17, LP21. They are printed with a standard 'camera' logo and supplied in a choice of three colours for each type. They are finished with adhesive photographic labels featuring various subjects including tourist areas, stately homes, football teams, etc. They are completed by a company independent of Lledo and are packed in distinctive 'dark gold' boxes. Values have yet to exceed the normal retail price of these souvenirs. A detailed Guide is available, see below.

Lledo Reference Material

The intention of this Catalogue is to provide collectors with a useful guide to current prices of this highly collectable range of die-cast models. However, the listings must of necessity be simplified for ease of use. Collectors seeking full details of all the variations of Lledo products are admirably catered for by RDP Publications who provide the books, reference material and services in the following list.

'Days Gone Collector'
This is the official full-colour Journal for 'Models Of Days Gone' collectors. Published quarterly, it contains regular features and up to date information to get the best from Lledo collecting. It includes a pull-out section of high quality photographs depicting 'Models of Days Gone' and will eventually build to a comprehensive full-colour photographic library of the entire 'Days Gone' range.

In recent years subscribers have received special and exclusive models such as a DG 32 Rolls-Royce Silver Ghost in Gold vacuum-metallized finish and a similarly finished DG 46 Bentley.

Lledo Information Service
This is an information club for Lledo enthusiasts, mainly with emphasis on Lledo Promotional Models (although ALL new issues are fully featured). Members receive five high-quality magazines per year packed with Lledo information.

Lledo Days Gone Guide
Lledo Promotional Model Guide
View Vans & Souvenir Bus Guide
The Guides are packed with listings, data, production information, colour variations, etc, and include many photographs. The books are hard-wearing and pocket-size for easy reference.

For further details of these specialist publications and other services offered to Lledo collectors, please send a stamped, self-addressed envelope to:
RDP Publications, Dept BD4, PO Box 1946, Halesowen, West Midlands, B63 3TS.

Model listing information

Only Code 1 models are listed (that is models wholly produced by Lledo PLC and sold through normal retail outlets or by mail-order at normal retail prices).

Promotional Model Issues

To mark the issue of the Catalogue's first Lledo Promotional model, we have deciced to provide more support for promotional collectors by providing a 'Lledo Promotionals Price Guide'. It is hoped that the new guide will become available early in 1994 and full details of its price and availability will be given in the Spring 1994 edition of the 'Model Price Review'. Please send details of all the existing and new Promotionals for inclusion in this listings. Promotional information available at present is shown on page 274.

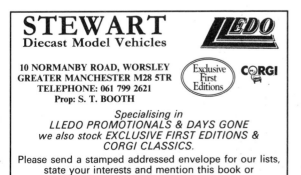

John Ramsay's
5TH EDITION
BRITISH DIECAST
MODEL TOYS CATALOGUE

THE "SWAPMEET" TRUCK

An Exclusive Lledo LP59 Bedford 30 cwt Truck

Livery:- Dark Blue and Black body with rear panels same as Catalogue cover.
One of the very first Promotionals to use this superb new casting.

The first of a unique new series of 100% British Made Promotional models available only through each new Swapmeet Toys & Models Ltd Publication.

To receive your model please complete the order form below.

To avoid damaging your catalogue you may send a photocopy or letter.

I wish to order the following LP 59 Bedford 30 cwt Trucks

Quantity .... models at £5.95 each plus 50p postage & packing for each model.

Overseas postage at cost after making due allowance for VAT.

I enclose payment for £.. in the following manner:
cheque (drawn on a British Bank) or postal or money order.

Payments must be made payable to:
Swapmeet Toys & Models Ltd, Fallowfield House,
Westminster Drive, Bury St Edmunds, Suffolk IP33 2EZ

Credit Cards accepted   ☐ Visa   ☐ Access   ☐ Eurocard   ☐ Mastercard

Credit Card Number ☐☐☐☐☐☐☐☐☐☐☐☐☐☐☐☐

Expiry Date .... Signature ....

Please allow 28 days for delivery from 1st October 1993
Subject to availability this offer remains valid until 1st April 1994
N.B. *Australasian collectors should contact Message Models, N.S.W. — see page 77*

Name and Address (in BLOCK CAPITALS please)

....

....*Postcode*..

THE 'SWAPMEET'
1950 Bedford 30 cwt Truck

LONE STAR

Robert Newson has provided the following information on Lone Star models.

'Lone Star' was the trade name of Die Casting Machine Tools Ltd (DCMT) who started in 1939 as manufacturers of diecasting machines, based at Palmers Green in North London. After the war they started making diecast toys which were distributed by The Crescent Toy Co Ltd. In the Crescent Toys section of this catalogue, the items listed as 'early post-war models' were all made by DCMT with the exception of the Locomotive and the Racing Car. From 1950 DCMT arranged their own distribution direct to wholesalers.

Over the next four decades DCMT Lone Star made several ranges of diecast vehicles including 'Slikka Toys' (early 1950s), 'Modern Army Series' (mainly 1960s), 'Roadmaster Majors' (1960s and 1970s), the miniature 'Tuf-Tots' (1970s) 'Farmer's Boy' (1980s) and the well known 'Lone Star Locos' miniature railway system (later called 'Treble-O-Lectric' or 'Treble-O-Trains'). The three ranges of most interest to collectors are listed here - the original DCMT 'Roadmasters' of 1956, the 1:50 scale 'Roadmasters' (1960s) and the 'Impy' and 'Flyers' series made in various forms from 1966 to the mid 1980s.

DCMT Lone Star Roadmasters

This was a short-lived series introduced in 1956, consisting of three sports cars and four veteran cars, all around 1:35 to 1:40 scale. The models had diecast bodies but all other components were plastic. Plastic drivers and passengers were included with the models. Nowadays the models are hard to find hence NGPP shown below.
See colour section for pictures.

....	1904 Darracq 'Genevieve'	Black or Red body, Yellow plastic chassis	NGPP ☐
....	1904 Daimler 'Windsor' Phaeton	Red body, Yellow plastic chassis. (Illustrated)	NGPP ☐
....	1912 Ford Model 'T'	Silver body, Black plastic chassis	NGPP ☐
....	1912 Morris Oxford 'Bullnose'..	Metallic Blue body, Black plastic chassis	NGPP ☐
....	Daimler Conquest Roadster......	Red, Metallic Light Blue, Pale Yellow or Pale Cream. (Illustrated)	NGPP ☐
....	Ford Thunderbird	Pale Green or Pale Blue. (Illustrated)	NGPP ☐
....	MG Midget TF	Metallic Light Blue	NGPP ☐

Lone Star Roadmasters   -   1:50 scale

In 1960 Lone Star produced four American cars on behalf of the US firm of Tootsietoy. These were the first four models listed below and they had 'Tootsietoy Classic Series' cast underneath. This arrangement only lasted for a couple of years, as by 1962 there were eight models available, all now marked 'Lone Star Roadmasters'. The models featured plated grilles, bumpers and wheels, and had windows but no interior detail. Around 1964 the plated parts were replaced by less attractive painted or self-coloured plastic, and vacuum-formed interiors were fitted. Five further numbers were added to the range before they were withdrawn around 1966.

1470	....	Chevrolet Corvair	NGPP ☐
1471	....	Rambler Rebel Staion Wagon ..	NGPP ☐
1472	....	Cadillac 62	NGPP ☐
1473	....	Ford Sunliner Convertible.......	NGPP ☐
1474	....	Chevrolet El Camino Pick-Up ..	NGPP ☐
1475	....	Dodge Dart Phoenix	NGPP ☐
1476	....	Rolls-Royce Silver Cloud II	NGPP ☐
1477	....	Dodge Dart Police Car............	NGPP ☐
1478	....	Rambler Ambulance..............	NGPP ☐
1479	....	Chevrolet Corvair	'FIRE CHIEF' in Black on Red body .... NGPP ☐
1480	....	Chevrolet Corvair	Army Staff Car (continued after 1966 as no.1273 in 'Modern Army' series)............ NGPP ☐
1481	....	Rambler Military Ambulance ...	(continued after 1966 as no.1274 in 'Modern Army' series) .... NGPP ☐
1482	....	Citroën DS19......................	NGPP ☐

Lone Star Impy and Flyers

In the following listing the year shown is the date of introduction. Most models remained in production until 1976. The models are priced at £10 - £20 in the Market Price Range column but rare examples also exist.

7	1971 -	Vauxhall Firenza	Flyers wheels, right and left hand drive versions	£10-20 ☐
8	....	Ford Capri	Not issued..	NPP ☐
9	1970 -	Maserati Mistral	Flyers wheels	£10-20 ☐
10	1966 -	Jaguar Mk.X	Impy or Flyers wheels	£10-20 ☐
11	1966 -	Chevrolet Corvette Stingray......	'Gran Turismo', Impy or Flyers wheels	£10-20 ☐
12	1966 -	Chysler Imperial	Impy or Flyers wheels	£10-20 ☐
13	....	Ford Thunderbird	Not issued..	NPP ☐
13	1971 -	Toyota 2000 GT	Flyers wheels	£10-20 ☐
14	1966 -	Ford Zodiac Mk.III Estate	Impy or Flyers wheels	£10-20 ☐
15	1966 -	Volkswagen Microbus	Impy or Flyers wheels	£10-20 ☐
16	1966 -	Ford Zodiac Mk.III Estate	'POLICE' Car, Impy or Flyers wheels	£10-20 ☐
16	....	Chrysler Imperial	'POLICE' Car, Impy wheels	£10-20 ☐
16 M	....	Mercedes-Benz 220 SE	'POLIZEI' Car, Impy wheels	£10-20 ☐
17	1966 -	Mercedes-Benz 220 SE	Impy or Flyers wheels	£10-20 ☐
18	1966 -	Ford Corsair	Impy or Flyers wheels	£10-20 ☐
19	1967 -	Volvo 1800 S	Impy or Flyers wheels	£10-20 ☐
20	1967 -	Volkswagen Ambulance	Impy or Flyers wheels	£10-20 ☐
21	1967 -	Fiat 2300 S Coupé	Impy or Flyers wheels	£10-20 ☐
22	1967 -	Rolls-Royce Silver Cloud III.....	Convertible, Impy or Flyers wheels	£10-20 ☐

Ref. No.	Year(s)	Model Type	Model Features and Size	Market Price Range	
23	1967 -	Alfa Romeo Giulia 1600 Spider	Impy or Flyers wheels	£10-20	☐
24	1967 -	Foden Tilt-cab 8w Tipper	Black plastic or Hi-Speed wheels	£10-20	☐
25	1967 -	Tractor Shovel	International Harvester	£10-20	☐
26	1967 -	Foden Petrol Tanker	Tilt-cab, 8 wheels, 'MOBIL' labels, Black plastic or Hi-Speed wheels	£10-20	☐
27	1967 -	Ford Taunus 12M	Impy or Flyers wheels	£10-20	☐
28	1967 -	Peugeot 404 Saloon	Impy or Flyers wheels	£10-20	☐
29	....	Cement Mixer Lorry	Not issued	NPP	☐
29	1971	Foden Tilt-cab 8w Box Van	'LUCAS BATTERIES' labels, Black plastic or Hi-Speed wheels	£10-20	☐
29	1972	Foden Tilt-cab 8w Box Van	'EXPRESS FREIGHT' labels, Black plastic or Hi-Speed wheels	£10-20	☐
30	1967 -	AEC Merryweather Fire Engine	Black plastic or Hi-Speed wheels	£10-20	☐
31	1967 -	Breakdown Lorry	Ford Transit, with towing cradle, 'ESSO' labels, Black plastic or Hi-Speed wheels	£10-20	☐
32	1968 -	'FIRE CHIEF' Car	Ford Corsair, Red body, roof light, Impy or Flyers wheels	£10-20	☐
32	1968 -	'FEUERWEHR' Car	Ford Corsair, Red body, roof light, Impy wheels	£10-20	☐
33	1968 -	Austin-Western Mobile Crane	Elevating jib	£10-20	☐
34	1968 -	Euclid Crawler Tractor	Rubber tracks	£10-20	☐
35	....	Articulated Flat Truck	Not issued	NPP	☐
36	1969 -	Lotus Europa	Flyers wheels	£10-20	☐
37	....	Ford GT	Not issued	NPP	☐
38	1971 -	Chevrolet Corvette Stingray	Flyers wheels	£10-20	☐
39	1971 -	Ford Mustang	Flyers wheels	£10-20	☐
40	1973 -	Cadillac Eldorado	Flyers wheels	£10-20	☐
41	1972 -	Builders Supply Lorry	Leyland 8 wheel flat lorry, 4 girders, Hi-Speed wheels	£10-20	☐
41	1972 -	Builders Supply Lorry	Leyland 6 wheel flat lorry, 4 girders, Hi-Speed wheels	£10-20	☐
41	1972 -	Builders Supply Lorry	Foden half-cab 6 wheel flat lorry, 4 girders, Hi-Speed wheels	£10-20	☐
42	1972 -	Foden Half-cab 8w Tipper	'TILCON' labels, Hi-Speed wheels	£10-20	☐
43	1973 -	Flat Lorry with Pipes	Leyland 6 wheel flat lorry, Hi-Speed wheels	£10-20	☐
43	1973 -	Flat Lorry with Pipes	Foden half-cab 6 wheel flat lorry, Hi-Speed wheels	£10-20	☐
44	1972 -	Marine Transport Lorry	Leyland 8w flat lorry, Speedboat, Hi-Speed wheels	£10-20	☐
44	1972 -	Marine Transport Lorry	Leyland 6w flat lorry, Speedboat, Hi-Speed wheels	£10-20	☐
44	1972 -	Marine Transport Lorry	Foden half-cab 6w flat lorry, Speedboat, Hi-Speed wheels	£10-20	☐
46	1973 -	Leyland 6w Dropside Lorry	Hi-Speed wheels	£10-20	☐
47	1973 -	Leyland High-Side Lorry	6 wheel lorry, Hi-Speed wheels	£10-20	☐
47	1973 -	Foden High-Side Lorry	Half-cab, 6 wheel lorry, Hi-Speed wheels	£10-20	☐
48	1973 -	Hopper Lorry	Leyland 6 wheel chassis, Hi-Speed wheels	£10-20	☐
48	1973 -	Hopper Lorry	Foden half-cab 6 wheel chassis, Hi-Speed wheels	£10-20	☐
49	1973 -	Foden Tipper	Half-cab 6 wheel chassis, Hi-Speed wheels	£10-20	☐

IMPY series, post-1976

The Market Price Range is shown as £5 - £10 but as yet there is little collectors' interest in these recent models.

50	Six-wheel Tipper	£5-10	☐
51	Six-wheel High Side Lorry	£5-10	☐
52	Six-wheel Flat Lorry with Crane	£5-10	☐
53	Six-wheel Flat Lorry with Speedboat	£5-10	☐
54	Six-wheel Cement Mixer	£5-10	☐
55	Six-wheel Luton Van	£5-10	☐
56	Six-wheel Dropside Lorry	£5-10	☐
57	Six-wheel Flat Lorry with Water Tank	£5-10	☐
58	Six-wheel Hopper Lorry	£5-10	☐
59	Six-wheel Flat Lorry with Pipes	£5-10	☐
60	Six-wheel Flat Lorry with Planks	£5-10	☐
61	Six-wheel Petrol Tanker	£5-10	☐
71	Range Rover	£5-10	☐
72	Cadillac Eldorado	£5-10	☐
73	Chevrolet Corvette Stingray	£5-10	☐
74	Toyota 2000 GT	£5-10	☐
75	Range Rover Police Car	£5-10	☐
76	Chevrolet Corvette Stingray 'GT Rally'	£5-10	☐
77	Jaguar Mk.X	£5-10	☐
78	Maserati Mistral	£5-10	☐
79	Ford Mustang	£5-10	☐
80	Lotus Europa	£5-10	☐
81	Volvo Coupé	£5-10	☐
82	Mercedes-Benz	£5-10	☐
181	Articulated Flat Lorry with Crane	£5-10	☐
182	Articulated Petrol Tanker	£5-10	☐
183	Articulated Low Loader with Tuf-Tots car	£5-10	☐
184	Articulated Flat Lorry with Pipes and water tank	£5-10	☐
185	Cadillac Eldorado with Tuf-Tots Speedboat on trailer	£5-10	☐
185	Range Rover with Tuf-Tots Speedboat on trailer	£5-10	☐
185	Range Rover 'RNLI' with boat on trailer	£5-10	☐
185	Jaguar Mk.X with Cabin Cruiser on trailer	£5-10	☐
186	Crane Lorry (no.52) with Impy car	£5-10	☐
187	Luton Van (no.55) with Trailer	£5-10	☐
188	Articulated Low Loader with Cabin Cruiser	£5-10	☐
189	Articulated Flat Lorry with Planks	£5-10	☐

190	Petrol Tanker (no.61) with Trailer	£5-10	☐
191	High Side Lorry (no.51) with Trailer	£5-10	☐
192	Cement MIxer (no.54) with Flat Trailer	£5-10	☐
1251	Articulated Car Transporter	£5-10	☐
1252	AEC Merryweather HTTL Fire Engine (re-packaging of no.30)	£5-10	☐
1256	Car Transporter (no.1251) with four Impy cars	£30-40	☐

GIFT SETS

All are scarce, hence NGPP

301	1967 Six-piece Gift Set	NGPP	☐
302	1967 Six-piece Gift Set	NGPP	☐
303	1968 'MOBIL' Gift Set	NGPP	☐
304	1968 Five-piece Commercial Vehicle Gift Set	NGPP	☐
309	1968 Twelve-piece Gift Set	NGPP	☐

IMPY ACCESSORIES

401	1967 Car Lifting Ramp	£5-10	☐
402	1967 Lock-Up Garage (plastic)	£5-10	☐
403	Service Station (not issued)	NGPP	☐
404	1968 'MOBIL' Petrol Pump Island with Canopy and Forecourt Sign	£5-10	☐
406	Fire House (not issued)	NGPP	☐

IMPY TWO-PACKS

422	VW Ambulance (no.200) and Mercedes-Benz 'Polizei' (no.16M)	£15-20	☐
423	Fiat 2300s (no.21) and Breakdown Lorry (no.31)	£15-20	☐
424	Foden Tanker (no.26) and Ford Taunus (no.27)	£15-20	☐
425	Ford Zodiac (no.14) and Tractor (no.25)	£15-20	☐
427	Alfa Romeo (no.23) and 'MOBIL' Petrol Pumps (no.404)	£15-20	☐
431	Chevrolet Corvette (no.11) and Fiat 2300s (no.21)	£15-20	☐
432	Fire Engine (no.30) and Ford Corsair 'FEUERWEHR' (no.32)	£15-20	☐

THANKS are due to the following who also contributed information on Lone Star models:
Mrs S. Clark, Farnham, Surrey, Barry McDowell, Maidstone, Kent, Brian Price, Trowbridge, Wiltshire, R. F. Pearson, Northwich, Cheshire, Ian Dorrell, Attleborough, Norfolk, G.West, Nuneaton, Warwickshire, G. V. Norrington, Romford, Essex, Bill Bateson, Scunthorpe, South Humberside, Peter Jeeves, Horningsea, Cambridge.

WHEN REPLYING TO ADVERTISEMENTS PLEASE MENTION JOHN RAMSAY'S CATALOGUE

MATCHBOX TOYS

INTRODUCTION

The company was founded in 1947 by the unrelated Leslie and Rodney Smith who combined their names to form 'Lesney' Products Ltd. They were soon joined by Jack Odell a recognised die-casting expert. The most famous of the various early products was the 'Coronation Coach'. During the 1950s the company developed the highly successful Matchbox '1-75' and 'Models of Yesteryear' ranges.

Following a difficult trading period Lesney Products Ltd was bought in 1982 by the Universal Toy Co. of Hong Kong.

On the 7th May 1992 it was announced in the 'New York Times' that 'Tyco Toys Inc.' had acquired by merger the 'Universal Matchbox Group'. Since this merger Matchbox is now referred to as 'Tyco-Matchbox' although the products are still marketed under the famous Matchbox brand name. Late in 1992 Tyco Toys announced the formation of a new division called Matchbox Collectibles which will be responsible for the future sales and marketing of Matchbox 'Models of Yesteryear'.

'MoKo' Products

'MoKo' Products was a toy distribution firm founded by Moses Kohnstam who came to Britain from Nuremburg, Germany at the turn of the century. 'MoKo' provided the distribution and storage facilities and, irrespective of the supplier, all toys were marketed as 'MoKo' products. The early issues after the Second World War were housed in plain cardboard boxes with 'tuck in' ends, usually with single colour printing and no model picture. During the early 1950s the packaging became much more attractive with colour boxes displaying a picture of the model inside. 'MoKo' will best be remembered for their distribution of the early Matchbox '1-75' Toys under the name of 'MoKo-Lesney'. Moses Kohnstam was succeeded by Richard Kohnstam in 1953.

The following listing of 'MoKo' items constitutes all the information available to publish at present. Additional information would be welcomed by the Editor.

Ref. No.	Year(s)	Model Type	Model Features and Size	Market Price Range	
i)	c1948-53	Mechanical Tractor	Probably early Lesney. Orange body, Green rubber tracks, Black wheels, Green/Black driver. (Early issue in plain box - see picture in colour section).........................	£125-150	☐
	1950-55	Mechanical Tractor	As previous model but with Orange wheels, (later issue in picture box).......................	£125-150	☐
ii)	1947-50	Excavator (with open cab)	Orange body and jib, Black digger and chassis, Green rubber tracks, Orange handle. Early card box has *MoKo TOYS OF DISTINCTION* logo (see colour section picture)	NGPP	☐
iii)	1950-55	'RUSTON BUCYRUS' Excavator	Yellow over Red body with Black '10 RB' logo. Black or Dark Grey chassis, jib, digger, crank wheel and rubber tracks. Later card box with full colour picture	NGPP	☐
iv)	1950-55	Builders Crane	All Blue crane base and jib with unpainted metal hook. Later card box with full colour picture (see colour section)	NGPP	☐
v)	1950-55	Drummer Boy (Mechanical).......................	Red body with Gold trim and wearing a Black busby. Cream/Yellow drum with Gold trim and drumsticks...	NGPP	☐
vi)	1947-50	Crawler Bulldozer.....................	Red body and dozer blade (possibly early Lesney). Early plain card box	£125-150	☐
vii)	1947-50	Hayrick	Yellow/Green body	NGPP	☐
viii)	1947-50	Fairground Carousel	Blue/Red base and centre column, Maroon/Blue roof, 2 Red and 2 Blue seated figures. Plain card box (see picture in colour section)	NGPP	☐
ix)	1947-50	Mechanical Mouse.....................	Grey body with Red eyes plus curling tail. Early plain card box...............................	NGPP	☐
x)	1950-55	Model Motor Scooter................	Dark Red scooter with Black seat. Female figure has blonde hair, blue sweater, red trousers. Later box with full colour picture	NGPP	☐

MoKo 'Farmette Series' (circa 1950 - 1953)

Miniature size models packed in end-flap type boxes with colour picture of the model. The horses are die-cast with dark brown bodies and white feet.

Ref. No.	Year(s)	Model Type	Model Features and Size	Market Price Range	
?	1950-53	Tumbrel type Cart with Single Horse..............	Blue cart body, large Red 12-spoke wheels. Dark Brown 'trunk' design box	£90-110	☐
No.2	1950-53	Farm Cart with two Horses.................	Blue cart body with Red raves, four Red 12-spoke wheels...	£90-110	☐
No.3	1950-53	Bull Wagon with two Horses.................	Green wagon body, two horses in tandem, Brown metal bull, four Red 12-spoke wheels...	£90-110	☐

NB Models No.2 and No.3 sold at Wallis & Wallis's June 1993 auction for £92 apiece.

The Early 'Lesney' Toys

Lesney Products first produced diecast toys in 1948. Whilst production ceased during the Korean war period (1950-52), the models produced formed the basis from which the 1-75 series was launched in 1953 and were sold in boxes under the name of 'MOKO' who were ultimately to also market all the early 1-75 series models.

Ref. No.	Year(s)	Model Type	Model Features and Size	Market Price Range	
i)	....	Road Roller..............................	All Green body and flywheel, unpainted wheels	£250-300	☐
			As previous model but with Red roller wheels and Yellow flywheel............................	£250-300	☐
		casting change:...........	With a driver but without a flywheel...	£175-200	☐
		casting change:...........	Without a driver and without flywheel..	£150-175	☐
ii)	....	Cement Mixer...........................	All Green body, Red wheels	£150-175	☐
			Pale Green body, Red mixer and wheels...	£125-150	☐
			Dark Green body, Red mixer and wheels	£100-150	☐
			Red body, Green mixer and wheels	£125-150	☐
iii)	....	Caterpillar Tractor	Orange or Yellow body, Red roller wheels, Black rubber tracks, driver...................	£125-150	☐
iv)	....	Caterpillar Bulldozer	Green, Orange or Red body, driver, Black rubber tracks	£125-150	☐
			Yellow body, Red dozer blade and wheels	£125-150	☐
v)	....	Prime Mover...........................	Orange tractor (Green engine on some), Beige or Blue trailer, Red/Yellow dozer, 'BRITISH ROAD SERVICES'...	£800-1000	☐
			As previous model but with Beige trailer	£500-600	☐
vi)	....	'MASSEY HARRIS' Tractor ...	Red body, Cream hubs, Black rubber tyres	£300-400	☐
vii)	....	Milk Cart...............................	Orange body, White driver and 6 crates, Black or Brown horse, Black or Grey wheels, 'PASTEURISED MILK' cast into cart sides..	£400-500	☐
			As previous model but with Blue body	£600-700	☐
viii)	....	Breadbait Press........................	1st type: Red body, unpainted 'butterfly' press	£40-50	☐
			2nd type: As 1st type but with Green press.......................................	£50-60	☐
			3rd type: As 2nd type with 'MILBRO' cast onto Red body...........................	£60-70	☐
ix)	....	Quarry Truck...........................	Yellow body, Black tyres, 'LAING'. Only one example known to exist...............	NGPP	☐
x)	....	Covered Wagon with Barrels	Green body, White cover, 2 Red barrels, 6 Mid-Brown horses (with White tails), with postilion rider and wagon driver	£200-250	☐
xi)	....	Covered Wagon without Barrels...........................	As previous model but with Chocolate Brown horses and no barrels...................	£200-250	☐
xii)	....	'RAG & BONE MERCHANTS' Cart	Yellow body, Red wheels, Black horse, Brown driver, with 7 pieces of 'junk': mangle-wheel, bike frame, bedhead, bath, bucket, box, cistern...............	£750-1000	☐
			As previous model but Green body, Red wheels	NGPP	☐
xiii)	....	Soap-Box Racer........................	Brown box, Grey spoked wheels (16 and 9), Dark Blue boy with Pink face	NGPP	☐
xiv)	....	Coronation Coach (large)...........	Gold coach with King & Queen, eight White horses, Gold/Red trappings, 4 Red riders. 200 issued..	£750-850	☐
xv)	....	Coronation Coach (large)...........	Gold, Silver or Gilt coach with just the Queen inside. Horses and riders as for previous model	£150-200	☐
xvi)	....	Coronation Coach (small)........	Silver or Gold coach, 8 White horses, Red/Gold trappings, 4 Red riders, 'A MOKO TOY BY LESNEY' cast into horsebar (1,000,000 sold).......	£85-100	☐
xvii)	....	'Muffin The Mule'	White body, Red/Gold harness, Black trim	£175-200	☐

Other early Lesney toys. Collectors should be aware that in addition to die-cast models some tin-plate items were also produced, namely: a clockwork 'JUMBO' elephant, 'PEREGRINE' puppet, and a Red drummer-boy.

Matchbox Model identification

Many models have common identifying features and these are shown below to avoid any unnecessary repetition.

Model Number is always cast into the base, chassis or body. Obvious exceptions are the early models which were not numbered.

'Lesney' is cast into the base, chassis or body of all issues between 1953 and 1982.

'Matchbox' or 'Matchbox Series' is shown on the base or chassis of all issues after 1965.

Model name. All issues after 1957 had the model name on the base or chassis. Exceptions include those without a base (No.24 Excavator for example).

Suspension and windows. All car models were fitted with windows after 1961 and with suspension after 1965.

Windscreen, seats and steering wheels are usually made of plastic (though some earlier open cars, dump trucks, etc have metal seats).

Length of models is shown in mm. and is taken from Matchbox publications or from actual models.

Boxes often have differing designs for the same model and provide additional collecting interest.

Baseplates are metal castings until the late 1970s when plastic bases introduced. From 1983 they are marked 'Made in Macau' and from 1986 'Made in China'.

Wheels were metal castings on early models gradually changed to grey, silver or black plastic. Superfast wheels introduced in late 1960s and issues from 1968-69 may be found with either type. Novelties such as 'Laser Wheels' introduced in the late 1980s.

Rolamatics were introduced in the 1970s having working parts that were operated by pushing.

Model descriptions. This Catalogue tries to give original makers description of model names and colours but early matchbox listings are known to be inaccurate graphically. Makers catalogue photographs are often taken of mock-ups months before production starts and model designs are changed before release.

Matchbox Miniatures

Ref. No.	Year(s)	Model Type	Model Features and Size	Market Price Range	

MB 1

1a	1953	Diesel Road Roller (Aveling Barford)................	Type 1: curved lower canopy ends & thin braces above canopy supports, Type 2: straight ends & thick braces above supports, brace extension. Dark Green body, Type 1 or 2, Red metal roller wheels, Gold trim, Tan driver cast-in, no number, crimped axles, tow hook, 49 mm.	£40-50	☐
		colour change:.............	As previous model but Type 2 with Light Green body	£30-40	☐
1b	1956	Diesel Road Roller (Aveling Barford)................	Pale Green body, Red metal roller wheels, Light or Dark Tan driver, high peaked canopy, no number, crimped axles, hook, 57 mm.	£30-40	☐
1c	1958	Diesel Road Roller (Aveling Barford)................	Light or Dark Green body and driver, Red metal roller wheels, number cast-in, high peaked canopy, hook, 62 mm.	£30-40	☐
1d	1962	Diesel Road Roller (Aveling Barford)................	Green body and driver, Red plastic rollers, 67 mm.	£15-20	☐
1e	1967	Mercedes Truck	Turquoise body, Orange canopy, Black plastic wheels, 75 mm.	£10-15	☐
	1970	colour change:.............	Gold body, Yellow canopy, Blue windows, Superfast wheels..................	£8-12	☐
		colour change:.............	Red body, Yellow canopy, 'Transcontinental', Superfast	£8-12	☐
1f	1972	'Mod Rod'	Yellow body, Silver exposed rear engine, Superfast wheels, 73 mm.	£4-6	☐
		colour change:.............	Same as previous model but with 'flower' label	£10-15	☐
		colour change:.............	As previous model but with Red interior or wheels............................	£8-11	☐
		note:	Other variations exist		
		'Silver Streak'	US issued version of model 1f..	£8-11	☐
1g	1976	Dodge Challenger	Red body, White roof, Red or Silver interior, Superfast, 74 mm.	£8-11	☐
		colour change:.............	Blue body with Red interior	£8-11	☐
		colour change:.............	Dark Blue body with Red interior...	£5-8	☐
	1982	design change:.............	Blue or Orange body, 'Revin Rebel', clear windows, Superfast, 74 mm.	£2-4	☐
	1983	design change:.............	Yellow body, Black roof, 'Toyman', clear windows, Superfast	£2-4	☐
1h	1988	Jaguar XJ6..............................	Red body, Silver trim, authentic radiator....................................	£2-4	☐
	1989	colour change:.............	White body	£2-4	☐
	1988	Promotional:.............	Green body, 'REDOXON' on bonnet, Superfast, (Hong Kong model)	NRP	☐
	1988	Promotional:	'WHYTE & MACKAY', Black body, Gold bonnet design	NRP	☐
	1991	Jaguar XJ6 (Police)	White body, Yellow 'Police' logo on Blue background, 2 Blue rooflights ...	NRP	☐
	1992	design change:.............	Same but 'Police' crests on doors & bonnet, Red band on sides............	NRP	☐

MB 2

2a	1953	Muir Hill Site Dumper.............	Dark Green body, Red dumper, Green metal wheels, 42 mm.	£35-40	☐
		colour change:.............	As previous model but with unpainted metal wheels	£25-30	☐
2b	1957	Muir Hill Site Dumper.............	Same but Tan driver, metal wheels, 46 mm.	£20-25	☐
		wheel change:..............	As previous model but with Grey plastic wheels.	£20-25	☐
2c	1962	Muir Hill Dumper Truck	Red body, Green dumper, 'LAING' logo, Black plastic wheels, 54 mm.	£15-20	☐
		decal change:..............	With 'MUIR HILL' logo & picture-box (72 only known to exist)	£50-60	☐
2d	1967	Mercedes Trailer......................	Turquoise body, Orange canopy, Black plastic wheels, 89 mm.	£5-8	☐
	1970	colour change:.............	Gold body, Yellow canopy, Superfast wheels	£5-8	☐
		colour change:.............	Red body, Yellow canopy, 'Transcontinental', Superfast	£5-8	☐
		colour change:.............	Military Green body & canopy	£5-8	☐
2e	1972	Jeep Hot Rod	Pink with Green base, Cream seats, Superfast wheels	£5-8	☐
		variants:	Pink with White base	£20-25	☐
			Red with Green base	£20-25	☐
			Red with White Base	£5-8	☐
		note:	Other variations exist		
2f	1977	Rescue Hovercraft	Green/Fawn body, 'Rescue', Superfast wheels, 77 mm.	£4-7	☐
		colour change:.............	Metallic Green/Tan body, Chrome/Red top, 'Rescue', Superfast, 77 mm. ...	£5-8	☐
		colour change:.............	Pale Green/Black body, Chrome/Red top, '2000'	£5-£8	☐
		Note:	Many other variations exist		
2g	1980	Mazda RX7	Yellow or Green body, Japanese issued model	£5-8	☐
2h	1981	S-2 Jet	Black/Yellow body, Red or Yellow cockpit, folding wing-tips, 76 mm.	£3-5	☐
		colour change:.............	Black/Red body, Red flash, 'VIPER'	£3-5	☐
		colour change:.............	Blue/White body, Silver wings	£3-5	☐
	1989	colour change:.............	Camouflage paintwork	NRP	☐
2i	1985	Pontiac Firebird......................	Black body, 'Halleys Comet', US issued model...............................	£3-5	☐
2j	1985	Pontiac Fiero	White/Blue/Orange body, racing number '85'	£3-5	☐
	1986	colour change:.............	Blue body, Yellow/Red panels...	NRP	☐
	1987	colour change:.............	White/Red body	£2-4	☐
2k	1987	Rover Sterling	Maroon body, Black chassis, Superfast wheels	NRP	☐
	1987	Laser Wheels issue:.....	Silver body	NRP	☐
	1992	design change:.............	Silver body, Black chassis, 'ROVER STERLING' logo	NRP	☐
2L	1993	BMW 850	All Silver body	NRP	☐

MB 3

Ref. No.	Year(s)	Model Type	Description	Price
3a	1953	Cement Mixer	Blue body, Orange metal or Grey plastic wheels, 40/41 mm.	£25-35 ☐
3b	1961	Bedford Tipper Truck	Grey cab, Maroon opening tipper, Grey or Black plastic wheels, 64 mm.	£25-35 ☐
		colour change:	Grey cab, Bright Red tipper, Grey or Black plastic wheels	£45-55 ☐
3c	1967	Mercedes Benz 'BINZ' Ambulance	Cream, Red Cross, opening tailgate, Black plastic wheels, 74 mm.	£12-16 ☐
	1970	colour & wheel change:	As previous model but Off-White body with Superfast wheels	£10-14 ☐
3d	1973	Monteverdi Hai	Orange body, RN '3', tinted windows, opening doors, Superfast, 74 mm.	£5-8 ☐
		label change:	Red body, racing number '16'	£5-8 ☐
3e	1979	Porsche Turbo	Brown or Silver body, opening doors, Superfast, 74 mm.	£3-5 ☐
	1981	colour change:	Green body, Yellow interior, opening doors, Superfast	£3-5 ☐
		colour change:	As previous model but with Red interior	£6-9 ☐
	1982	colour change:	Red body, White RN '90' and 'Porsche', opening doors, Superfast	£3-5 ☐
	1985	colour change:	Black body, Red 'Turbo', racing number '90'	£2-4 ☐
	1987	colour change:	White body	£1-3 ☐
	1989	colour change:	Metallic Blue body, Yellow design	NRP ☐
	1990	colour change:	Red body	NRP ☐
	1992	colour change:	Red body, '911' on doors, large crest on bonnet	NRP ☐
		note:	Other variations exist	

MB 4

Ref. No.	Year(s)	Model Type	Description	Price
4a	1954	Massey Harris Tractor	Red, Tan driver, Gold trim, spoked front metal wheels, 40 mm.	£35-40 ☐
4b	1957	Massey Harris Tractor	Same but with solid front metal wheels, number cast-in, 40 mm.	£30-35 ☐
		wheel change:	As previous model but with Grey plastic wheels, 40 mm.	£25-30 ☐
4c	1960	Triumph T110 Motor Cycle	Steel Blue bike/sidecar, 11 mm. Silver wheels, Black plastic tyres, 54 mm.	£30-40 ☐
		colour variant:	As previous model but Copper body, 9.5 mm.	£30-40 ☐
4d	1967	Dodge Stake Truck	Yellow/Blue, with or without hook, Black plastic wheels, 74 mm.	£50-60 ☐
	1970	colour change:	Yellow/Green stake body, Black plastic or Superfast wheels	£10-15 ☐
4e	1972	'Gruesome Twosome'	Gold body, Pink roof, Silver exposed engine, Superfast, 73 mm.	£5-8 ☐
4f	1976	Pontiac Firebird	Metallic Blue body, Silver trim, Orange tinted windows, Superfast, 73 mm.	£5-8 ☐
4g	1981	'57' Chevy	Metallic Mauve body, Silver trim and engine, opening doors, Superfast, 75 mm.	£3-5 ☐
	1982	colour change:	All Red body, 'Cherry Bomb' labels, Superfast, 75 mm.	£3-5 ☐
	1983	colour change:	Black/Red/Yellow, 'flames' effect, Superfast, 75 mm.	£3-5 ☐
	1989	US issue:	'HEINZ' promotional model	£2-4 ☐
4h	1985	Chrysler Daytona	White body, (US issued model)	£3-5 ☐
4i	1988	FX4-R Taxi	Black body, Silver trim	NRP ☐
	1989	Australian issue:	Black body, 'LONDON TO SYDNEY', promotional model	£3-5 ☐

MB 5

Ref. No.	Year(s)	Model Type	Description	Price
		No. 5 London Bus		
5a	1954	'Buy MATCHBOX SERIES'	Red, Gold grille, 'No.5' cast-in, Yellow/Green paper label, metal wheels, 52 mm.	£40-50 ☐
5b	1957	'Buy MATCHBOX SERIES'	Red, Gold grille, Yellow decal, metal or Grey plastic wheels, 57 mm.	£40-50 ☐
		'PLAYERS PLEASE'	Red, Silver grille, Grey plastic wheels	£75-90 ☐
		'BP VISCO-STATIC'	Red, Silver grille, Grey plastic wheels, rivetted axles	£30-35 ☐
5c	1960	'PLAYERS PLEASE'	AEC Routemaster, Red body, No.5 on Baseplate, Grey plastic wheels, 66 mm.	£75-85 ☐
		'PEARDRAX'	As previous model but with Grey or Black plastic wheels	£25-30 ☐
		'VISCO-STATIC'	As previous model but with Grey or Black plastic wheels	£20-25 ☐
5d	1965	'BP LONGLIFE'	Red body, Black plastic wheels, Cream or White interior, 70 mm.	£15-20 ☐
		'BP VISCO-STATIC'	As previous model	£15-20 ☐
	1961-66	Promotional issues:	'The Baron of Beef' (beware fakes), 'Mecca Ltd', 'Pegram'	£25-35 ☐
5e	1969	Lotus Europa	Metallic Blue, Silver trim, opening doors, hook, Superfast, 71 mm.	£7-10 ☐
			Pink body with '20' labels	£10-12 ☐
		Bulgarian issue:	Green or Metallic Green body	£20-25 ☐
		Bulgarian issue:	Metallic Blue body	£20-25 ☐
		note:	Many other variations exist	
5f	1976	Seafire Motor Boat	White/Blue body, 'Seafire', 75 mm.	£5-8 ☐
		colour change:	Red/White body, 'Seafire'	£5-8 ☐
		colour change:	White/Brown body, 'Seafire'	£5-8 ☐
		colour change:	Red/Blue body, 'Seafire'	£3-5 ☐
5g		Nissan Fair Lady 2802X	Red or Metallic Red body (Japanese issued model)	£6-8 ☐
		Police Car variant:	White/Black body	£5-8 ☐
5h	1980	U.S. Mail Truck	Blue roof, White body, 'U.S. Mail' logo, Superfast, 59 mm.	£3-5 ☐
		variants:	Pale blue, sleet and snow base, US issue, 'No. 38 Jeep'	£7-9 ☐
			Yellow body, 'GLIDING CLUB' logo	£7-9 ☐
5i	1982	4 x 4 Jeep	Bronze body, large wheels, Black roll-bar and bumpers	£2-4 ☐
	1989	colour change:	Camouflage paintwork	NRP ☐
5j	1984	**Peterbilt Tanker**		
		'SHELL'	White/Grey body, Yellow/Red design	£3-5 ☐
		'AMOCO'	Black body, Black exhaust pipes, etc.	£3-5 ☐
	1985	'AMOCO'	Black body, Chrome exhausts, etc.	£12-15 ☐
		'AMPOL'	Australian issued model	£8-11 ☐
		'SUPERGAS'	Black/Yellow (US issued model)	£3-5 ☐
		'GETTY'	Red/Chrome (US issued model)	£3-5 ☐
	1988	'SHELL'	White/Chrome body, Yellow/Red design	£2-4 ☐

MB 6

Ref. No.	Year(s)	Model Type	Description	Market Price Range	
6a	1954	Quarry Truck	Orange body, Grey tipper with 6 ribs, metal wheels, 55 mm.	£25-30	☐
		wheel change:	With Grey plastic wheels, domed/crimped axles	£20-25	☐
6b	1959	Euclid Quarry Truck	Yellow body, 4 ribs, decals, 6 Black plastic wheels, 63 mm.	£18-22	☐
		wheel change:	With Grey plastic wheels, rivetted axles	£26-32	☐
6c	1963	Euclid Quarry Truck	Yellow body, 6 Black plastic wheels, 67 mm.	£8-11	☐
6d	1968	Ford Pick Up	Red body, White detachable canvas, Black plastic wheels, 71 mm.	£8-11	☐
	1970	wheel change:	As previous model but with Superfast wheels	£4-6	☐
6e	1974	Mercedes 350SL	Orange/Black body, Yellow interior, Superfast, 75 mm.	£3-5	☐
	1976	colour change:	Yellow/Black body, Superfast	£2-4	☐
	1978	G15 Gift Set model:	Metallic Silver/Black body, 'Rennservice'	£15-20	☐
	1978	colour change:	Metallic Bronze body, Black roof	£1-2	☐
	1980	colour change:	Red body, White roof	£1-2	☐
6f	1982	Mercedes 350SL Open Top	Metallic Blue body, White interior, Superfast, 75 mm.	£2-4	☐
	1982	colour change:	Maroon body, White interior	£2-4	☐
6g	1986	F1 Racer	Red body, racing number '3', Superfast	£1-2	☐
	1987	colour change:	Blue body, racing number '20', (US issue)	£2-4	☐
	1988	colour change:	Yellow body, racing number '5'	NRP	☐
	1989	colour change:	White body, 'MR JUICY' design	NRP	☐
6h	1991	Alfa Romeo SZ	Red body, Black roof, 'ALFA ROMEO' logo	NRP	☐

MB 7

Ref. No.	Year(s)	Model Type	Description	Market Price Range	
7a	1954	Horse Drawn Milk Float	Brown horse varies in shade, Gold & White trim is hand-applied.		
		'PASTEURISED MILK'	Orange body, White driver & logo, metal spoked wheels, 57 mm.	£45-55	☐
		wheel change:	With Grey plastic wheels, White driver & logo	£70-80	☐
		colour change:	Same but Pale Orange body, White driver & logo, metal wheels	£75-85	☐
		variant:	Pale Orange body and logo, Orange driver with White hat, Grey plastic wheels	£75-85	☐
7b	1961	Ford Anglia	Light Blue, Green windows, metal or Grey plastic wheels, 67 mm.	£60-70	☐
		wheel change:	With Silver plastic wheels	£45-55	☐
		wheel change:	With Black plastic wheels	£25-30	☐
7c	1967	Ford Refuse Truck	Orange or Red body, Silver dumper, Black plastic wheels, 76 mm.	£8-11	☐
	1970	wheel change:	As previous model but with Superfast wheels	£4-6	☐
7d	1973	'Hairy Hustler'	Metallic Orange body, RN'5', clover-leaf wheels, Purple or Yellow windows	£3-5	☐
		colour change	White body, Amber windows, 'streaker' design	£3-5	☐
		colour change:	Yellow body, 'flame' design	£3-5	☐
		note:	Many other variations exist.		
7e	1977	VW Golf with Surfboards	Light or Dark Green body, 2 Black surfboards, hook, Superfast	£3-5	☐
	1979	colour change:	Red body	£2-4	☐
	1981	colour change:	Yellow body, Red seats, Black base, hook, Superfast	£2-4	☐
	1982	colour change:	Silver body, Green flash 'Golf', Red interior, Superfast	£2-4	☐
		colour change:	With Tan interior	£20-25	☐
		Export issues:	'ADAC' German and Japanese issued models	£15-20	☐
7f	1983	IMSA Mazda	Blue body, Orange/White flash, 'Mazda', 76 mm.	£2-4	☐
7g	1986	Porsche 959	Silver body, 'Porsche' logo	£1-3	☐
	1988	colour change:	Metallic Dark Grey body, Red interior	NRP	☐
	1991	design change:	Silver body, Red design, Yellow 'Porsche' logo on doors	NRP	☐
	1992	design change:	As previous model but Yellow 'Porsche 959' logo on doors	NRP	☐
7h		'Rompin' Rabbit'	US issued model	£5-8	☐
7i		'Ruff Rabbit'	Yellow/Black body, 'VW rabbits' tampo print design, US issued model	£5-8	☐
7j		London Bus	'Nice to Meet You'. Japanese issued model	£5-8	☐
	1984	logo change:	'1984 Yokohama'. Japanese issued promotional	£35-45	☐

MB 8

Ref. No.	Year(s)	Model Type	Description	Market Price Range	
8a	1955	Caterpillar Tractor	Yellow body (various shades), Red driver, Green tracks, 41 mm.	£25-30	☐
		colour change:	As previous model but Orange body and driver, Gold grille	£40-50	☐
			Same but Yellow body and driver, Silver or Yellow grille, Green or Grey tracks.	£25-30	☐
8b	1958	Caterpillar Tractor	Yellow body and driver, no. '8' cast-in, Green rubber tracks, 42 mm.	£25-30	☐
8c	1961	Caterpillar Tractor	Yellow body and driver, no. '8' or '18' cast on some, 48 mm.	£12-16	☐
		wheel change:	with Silver or Black plastic roller wheels, indistinct or no number	£35-40	☐
8d	1964	Caterpillar Tractor	Yellow body, No driver, Green rubber tracks, 51 mm.	£12-15	☐
8e	1966	Ford Mustang Fastback	White body, Red seats, Black plastic wheels, 74 mm.	£30-35	☐
		wheel change:	Same but Silver hubs, Black tyres	£20-25	☐
			Same but with Superfast wheels	NGPP	☐
		colour change:	Orange body, Silver hubs, Black plastic tyres,	NGPP	☐
	1970	wheel change:	Same but fitted with Superfast wheels	£10-15	☐
8f	1970	Wildcat Dragster	Orange or Pink, base in various colours, 'Wild-Cat', Superfast, 74 mm.	£8-11	☐
8g	1975	De Tomaso Pantera	White or Blue body, Red seats, racing number '8' and 'Pantera'.	£3-5	☐
		colour change:	As previous model but with Orange interior	£5-7	☐
		label change:	As previous model but with 'SUN' label	£7-10	☐
8h	1981	Rover 3500	Red body, Cream seats, Black base, Superfast, 73 mm.	£2-4	☐
8i	1983	Rover 3500 'POLICE' Car	White body, Yellow/Black decal, 2 Blue flashing lights, 73 mm.	£2-4	☐
	1984	variant:	As previous model but with the addition of a rooflight bar	£2-4	☐
		variant:	As previous model but with Red/Black stripes	£2-4	☐

Ref. No.	Year(s)	Model Type	Matchbox Miniatures - continued	Market Price Range
8j	1986	'Greased Lightnin'	Red body, racing number '31', US issued model	£4-6
8k	1986	1962 Corvette	Orange body	£3-5
	1988	colour change:	Metallic Green body	£3-5
8L	1988	Astra Police	White body, Red/Blue side stripes, Blue light bar on roof	£1-2
	1992	design change:	As previous model but Yellow/Blue side stripes	NRP

MB 9

Ref. No.	Year(s)	Model Type	Matchbox Miniatures - continued	Market Price Range
9a	1955	Fire Escape (Dennis)	Red body, Gold trim on some, metal wheels on crimped axles, 57 mm.	£30-35
9b	1958	Fire Escape (Dennis)	Red body, Gold trim, metal wheels, 58 mm.	£40-45
		wheel change:	As previous model but with Grey plastic wheels	£100-125
9c	1959	Merryweather Marquis Series III Fire Engine	Red body with Tan ladder, Grey plastic wheels, 64 mm.	£15-20
		ladder change:	As previous model but with Gold ladder	£35-45
		wheel change:	With Gold ladder and Black plastic wheels	£15-20
		ladder change:	With Silver ladder, Black plastic wheels	£60-70
9d	1966	Boat and Trailer	Blue/White boat (76 mm.), with Blue trailer (77 mm.), Black plastic wheels	£10-12
	1970	wheel change:	As previous model but fitted with Superfast wheels	£4-6
9e	1972	AMX Javelin	Metallic Lime Green body, Yellow interior, Superfast, 77 mm.	£5-8
		interior change:	With Cream or Orange interior	£5-8
	1980	colour change:	Blue body, Yellow interior, 'Cam Cracker', RN '1', Superfast	£4-6
9f	1978	Ford Escort RS2000	White body, 'Shell' and 'Ford' decals, Superfast, 74 mm.	£6-10
	1981	colour change:	Metallic Green, White grille, 'Seagull', Superfast, 74 mm.	£6-10
		rare variant:	As previous model but with Red interior	£75-85
9g		'Cam Cracker'	Blue body, (US issued model).	£4-6
9h	1990	Caterpillar Bulldozer	Dark Red body, 'Dr.PEPPER' design	NRP
		colour change:	Yellow body, Black cab roof	NRP
	1992	colour change:	Yellow body, Red cab and stripes on blade	NRP

MB 10

Ref. No.	Year(s)	Model Type	Matchbox Miniatures - continued	Market Price Range
10a	1957	Scammell Mechanical Horse	Red cab, Gold trim, Grey trailer, crimped axles, 56 mm.	£35-40
10b	1957	Scammell Mechanical Horse	Dark Red Cab, Brown trailer, crimped axles, 75 mm.	£35-40
10c	1960	Foden 8-wheel Truck 'TATE & LYLE'	Dark Blue body, Yellow logo (inc. crown), Grey plastic wheels, 67mm.	£60-70
		design change:	Same but without crown in logo. Grey, Silver or Black plastic wheels	£45-55
10d	1966	Leyland Pipe Truck	Red, Silver base & grille, 6 or 7 Grey pipes, Black plastic wheels, 73 mm.	£10-15
		colour change:	Same model but with White base & grille	£7-10
	1970	wheel change:	As previous model but with Superfast wheels	£4-6
		colour change:	Orange body, Grey or Yellow pipes, Blue tinted windows	£4-6
10e	1973	'Piston Popper'	Metallic Blue, Silver exposed engine, Rolamatic, Superfast, 75 mm.	£5-8
		colour change:	White body	£50-60
		'Hot Popper'	US issued model. No details available.	£7-10
10f	1979	Plymouth Gran Fury	White body, Black 'POLICE' logo, 2 warning lights, Superfast, 75 mm.	£2-4
	1981	logo change:	White body, Black 'METRO POLICE' logo, Superfast	£1-3
	1983	colour change:	White body, Blue Police shield, Superfast	£1-3
	1985	new logo:	White body, 'SFPD' logo, Superfast, (US issue)	£1-3
	1987	new logo:	White body, Red logo, 'SHERIFF', Superfast, (US issue)	£1-3
10g	1988	Buick Le Sabre	Black body, racing number '4', '355 CID'	£1-2
	1989	colour change:	Yellow body, Red skirt, racing number '10', Superfast wheels	NRP
	1989	Laser Wheels issue:	Metallic Red body, 'KEN WELLS' logo	NRP
10h	1993	Chevy Van	Yellow body, Blue and Red design	NRP

MB 11

Ref. No.	Year(s)	Model Type	Matchbox Miniatures - continued	Market Price Range
11a	1955	E.R.F. Road Tanker	Green, Gold trim, 'ERF' cast-in, no logo, metal wheels, 52 mm.	NGPP
		colour change:	Dark or Light Yellow body, 'ERF' cast-in, Silver trim, no logo	£60-70
		colour change:	Red body, Gold trim, large or small 'ESSO' decal	£55-65
11b	1958	'ESSO' Petrol Tanker (E.R.F.)	Red, Silver trim; metal, Grey, Silver or Black plastic wheels, 63 mm.	£30-40
11c	1965	Jumbo Crane	Yellow/Red body, Red or Yellow weight box, Black plastic wheels, 82 mm.	£7-10
11d	1969	Mercedes Scaffolding Truck	Silver body, Red base, Yellow poles, 'Builders Supply Company', Black plastic or Superfast wheels, 62 mm.	£7-10
11e	1973	'Flying Bug'	Red/Yellow body, Silver helmet, Superfast, 73 mm.	£3-5
11f	1977	Car Transporter	Orange/Cream body, 3 cars, Superfast, 75 mm.	£3-5
	1980	colour change:	Red/Cream body	£2-4
	1983	colour change:	Orange/Grey body, Silver grille	£2-4
11g		Cobra Mustang	Orange body, US issued model	£4-6
11h		IMSA Mustang	Green/White US issued model	£4-6
11i		Ferrari 308 GTB	Yellow body, US issued model	£4-6
11j	1985	Lamborghini Countach	Red body, Yellow seats	£1-3
	1986	colour change:	Black/Orange body, Red racing number '5'	£1-3
	1988	colour change:	Yellow body, 'COUNTACH' in Black	£1-2
	1987	Laser Wheels issue:	Silver body, 'LP 5005' logo	NRP

MB 12

Ref. No.	Year(s)	Model Type	Matchbox Miniatures - continued	Market Price Range
12a	1955	Land Rover	Green body, Silver trim on some, Tan driver, metal wheels, 43 mm.	£25-30
12b	1959	Land Rover Series II	Olive Green body, no driver, Black plastic wheels	£20-25
		wheel change:	As previous model but with Grey plastic wheels, rivetted axles	£25-30
12c	1965	Land Rover Safari	Green or Blue body, Black plastic wheels, Tan luggage, 71 mm.	£10-14
	1970	colour change:	Metallic Gold body, Black plastic or Superfast wheels, 71 mm.	£7-10

Ref. No.	Year(s)	Model Type	Matchbox Miniatures - continued	Market Price Range	
12d	1971	Setra Coach	Gold body with Grey roof, Red lights, clear windows, Superfast, 76 mm.	£9-12	☐
		colour change:	Gold body, White roof, Superfast	£8-11	☐
		colour change:	Gold body, Light Brown roof, Superfast	£8-11	☐
	1972	colour change:	Yellow body, White roof, Superfast	£8-11	☐
	1973	colour change:	Maroon body, White roof, Green tinted or clear windows, Superfast	£5-8	☐
	1973	colour change:	Green body, White roof.	£5-8	☐
12e	1975	'Big Bull'	Orange body, Green dashboard, Red Superfast wheels, 63 mm.	£3-5	☐
		wheel change:	As previous model but with Black wheels	£30-40	☐
		wheel change:	Same but with Orange wheels, shiny metal dashboard, Black wheels	£3-5	☐
12f	1979	Citroën CX	Metallic Blue body, Yellow interior, hook, Superfast, 77 mm.	£2-4	☐
	1980	interior change:	With Red interior	£50-60	☐
	1980	colour change:	Metallic Light Blue, Superfast	£1-3	☐
	1982	'TEAM MATCHBOX'	Yellow body, Black or Blue logo, Superfast	£2-4	☐
	1983	'AMBULANCE'	White body, Black/White cross, Superfast	£1-3	☐
12g	1986	Pontiac Firebird Racer	Yellow body, Blue chassis, racing number '55' or '56' (US issue model)	£4-6	☐
	1987	colour change:	Blue body, racing number '10', (US issue model)	£1-3	☐
	1987	colour change:	White body, Blue chassis, racing number '15', Superfast	NRP	☐
	1987	Laser Wheels issue:	Metallic Blue, racing number '10'.	NRP	☐
12h	1986	Chevy Prostocker	White body (US issued model)	£4-6	☐
12i	1988	Modified Racer	Orange body, Red racing number '12'	NRP	☐
	1990	design change:	White body, 'TOMY' or 'JAMIE' logo, racing number '1'	NRP	☐
		design change:	Red body, 'MIKE' logo, racing number '15'.	NRP	☐
		design change:	Yellow body, 'REGGIE', racing number '44'	NRP	☐
	1991	colour change:	Orange body, 'GOODYEAR', racing number '12'	NRP	☐
12j	1992	Cattle Truck	Green cab, Yellow stake rear body, 2 Black plastic cows	NRP	☐

MB 13

Ref. No.	Year(s)	Model Type		Market Price Range	
13a	1955	Wreck Truck (Bedford)	Tan body, Red crane and hook, metal wheels on crimped axles, 51 mm.	£25-30	☐
13b	1958	Wreck Truck (Bedford)	Tan, Red crane, '13' cast-in, metal or Grey plastic wheels, 53 mm.	£60-70	☐
13c	1960	Thames Trader Wreck Truck	Red body, Red or Silver hook, Yellow decal, Grey plastic wheels, 63 mm.	£40-45	☐
		wheel change:	Same but with Black plastic wheels, Silver or Grey hook	£30-35	☐
13d	1965	Dodge Wreck Truck	Yellow/Green, 'BP' logo, Grey or Red hook, Black plastic wheels, 77 mm.	£9-12	☐
	1970	wheel change:	As previous model but fitted with Superfast wheels	£4-6	☐
		Beware fakes:	Unknown to Lesney, some 'Green cab' versions were made in their factory and sold as original. (Crudely crimped axles and self-adhesive labels)		☐
13e	1972	Baja Buggy	Green body with Black/Red trim, Silver engine, Superfast wheels, 66 mm.	£7-9	☐
		design change:	As previous model but with 'Police' shield label	£10-12	☐
13f	1978	Snorkel Fire Engine	Red body, Yellow or White hoist, Superfast, 78 mm.	£3-5	☐
	1982	new version:	Merryweather (35) casting with altered cab	£1-2	☐
	1982	'METRO FIRE DEPT'	Red body, White hoist, Superfast	£1-2	☐
	1982	'LOS ANGELES FIRE'	Red body, White hoist, Superfast	£1-2	☐
	1986	'FIRE DEPT'	Red body, White hoist, Superfast	£1-2	☐
13h	1985	Volvo Container	Blue body, White container 'COLDFRESH'	£2-3	☐

MB 14

Ref. No.	Year(s)	Model Type		Market Price Range	
14a	1955	Ambulance (Daimler)	Cream body, Silver trim, Red cross on roof, metal wheels on crimped or domed/crimped axles, no number, 'Ambulance' cast onto sides, 49 mm.	£30-35	☐
14b	1958	Daimler Ambulance	Cream body, Silver trim, Red cross on roof, 'Ambulance', 59 mm.	£25-30	☐
		colour change:	Off white body, metal or Grey plastic wheels	£25-30	☐
		wheel change:	As previous model but with Silver plastic wheels	£40-45	☐
14c	1962	Bedford Lomas Ambulance	Off-White body, 'LCC Ambulance' in Blue, Red cross on roof, 66 mm.	£25-30	☐
		colour change:	White with Red cross on sides; Grey, Silver or Black plastic wheels	£15-20	☐
		colour change:	Off-White body; Grey, Silver or Black plastic wheels	£15-18	☐
		logo colour change:	Same but 'LCC Ambulance' in Black, White interior, Black plastic wheels	£15-18	☐
14d	1968	Iso Grifo	Mid or Dark Metallic Blue, Blue interior, Silver hubs, Black plastic tyres, 76 mm.	£5-7	☐
		interior change:	As previous model but with White interior	£5-8	☐
	1969	wheel change:	As previous models but with Superfast wheels	£3-5	☐
	1972	colour change:	Same but (non-metallic), Light Blue body, Superfast	£3-5	☐
		Note:	Iso Grifo reissued as 'Super GT' models (1986/7), in Metallic Blue or Green	NRP	☐
14e	1977	'Mini-Ha-Ha'	Red body, Blue seats, Silver trim, driver, 60 mm.	£3-5	☐
14f		Rallye Royale	Silver or White body (US issue model)	£4-6	☐
14g	1982	Leyland Petrol Tanker	Red/White body, Blue or Turquoise 'ELF' logo, Superfast, 77 mm.	£3-5	☐
	1989	colour change:	Same but military version in camouflage paintwork	NRP	☐
14h	1985	Jeep Laredo	Black body, White roof (US issue model 20)	£4-6	☐
	1986		Red body, White roof, Grey seats & bonnet	£1-2	☐
14i	1986	BMW Cabriolet	White body (US issue model)	£4-6	☐
14j	1988	Grand Prix Racing Car	Blue/White body, Red driver	£1-2	☐
	1990	colour change:	Red Ferrari, 'FIAT', White driver, no racing number	NRP	☐
		colour change:	Red Ferrari, racing number '27', no logo	NRP	☐

MB 15

Ref. No.	Year(s)	Model Type		Market Price Range	
15a	1955	Diamond T Prime Mover	Yellow body, 6 metal wheels, hook, no number, 55 mm.	£150-200	☐
		colour change:	Orange body, 6 metal wheels	£25-30	☐
			As previous model but with Grey plastic wheels	£50-60	☐
15b	1959	Super Atlantic Tractor	Orange body, Black base, hook, Grey or Black plastic wheels, 67 mm.	£15-20	☐
15c	1963	Dennis Refuse Truck	Blue/Grey, 'Cleansing Service', Black plastic wheels, 64 mm.	£11-15	☐
		tyre change:	As previous model but with knobbly-tread tyres	£20-25	☐
15d	1968	Volkswagen 1500 Saloon	Off-White body, RN '137', 'Monte Carlo Rallye' plaque, Silver hubs, Black tyres	£15-20	☐
	1969	wheel change:	As previous model but with Superfast wheels	£10-15	☐
	1970	colour change:	Red body, Superfast	£10-15	☐

Ref. No.	Year(s)	Model Type	Matchbox Miniatures - continued	Market Price Range	
15e	1973	'LANSING BAGNALL' Fork Lift Truck	Red body, Yellow forks, horse design faces front	£2-4	☐
		label design change:	With horse design facing rear	£1-3	☐
		colour change:	Red body, Black/Grey forks.	£2-4	☐
		colour change:	Red body with White forks, 'Hi-Lift'.	£1-3	☐
15f	1985	Peugeot 205 Turbo 16	White body with racing number '205'	£1-2	☐
	1986	design change:	Blue/Red print, 'SHELL' advert on lifting rear section	£1-2	☐
15g	1988	UK (69) Corvette	Yellow body	NRP	☐
	1990	colour change:	Metallic Blue, White band on roof/bonnet, RN '15' on doors/boot/bonnet	NRP	☐
	1992	design change:	As previous model but with 'CORVETTE' on doors, (no racing number)	NRP	☐
	1993	colour change:	White body with central Red stripe	NRP	☐

MB 16

16a	1955	Transporter Trailer	Tan body, 6 metal wheels (crimped or domed & crimped axles), 80 mm.	£15-20	☐
16b	1960	Super Atlantic Trailer	Tan body and drawbar, Grey plastic wheels, 78 mm.	£25-30	☐
		colour change:	Orange body; Orange, Black or unpainted drawbar, Grey or Black plastic wheels	£60-70	☐
16c	1963	Scammell Snowplough	Grey/Orange body, Red/White or Orange/White blade, Grey or Black plastic wheels, 74 mm.	£11-15	☐
16d	1969	Case Bulldozer Tractor	Red/Yellow body, Green rubber tracks, hook, 64 mm.	£7-9	☐
16e	1974	Badger Truck	Red body; White, Cream or Silver Radar, 6 Black plastic wheels, Rolamatic	£5-8	☐
		colour change:	As previous model but Metallic Red body	£5-8	☐
		colour change:	As previous model but Military Green issue	£15-18	☐
16f	1980	Pontiac Saloon	Metallic Gold body with 'eagle' design, Superfast wheels, 77 mm.	£2-4	☐
	1982	colour change:	Metallic Bronze or White body, 'eagle' design	£2-4	☐
	1983	open top 'T' issue:	Black body, 'Turbo' logo, Superfast	£2-4	☐
	1985	colour change:	Silver body, Red/Orange design, Superfast	NRP	☐
	1986	colour change:	Black body, Orange striped design, Superfast	NRP	☐
16g	1988	Land Rover Ninety	Blue body, White roof, Orange flash	NRP	☐
	1989	colour change:	Red/white body, Yellow bonnet emblem	NRP	☐
	1989	colour change:	Camouflage paintwork	NRP	☐
	1990	colour change:	Yellow body, White roof, Green 'PARK RANGERS' logo	NRP	☐
	1992	colour change:	Yellow body, Grey roof, Black 'PARK RANGERS' logo	NRP	☐

MB 17

17a	1955	Bedford Removals Van	Light Blue body, Silver trim, metal wheels, no number, White logo 'MATCHBOX REMOVALS SERVICE', 55 mm.	£50-60	☐
		colour change:	As previous model but Maroon body, Silver or Gold trim	£125-150	☐
		colour change:	Green body, open or closed cab window	£35-45	☐
17b	1958	casting change:	Green body with slight roof curve, number '17' cast into cab roof of some, black outline around 'REMOVALS' on some, metal or Grey plastic wheels	£35-45	☐
	1959	colour change:	Dark Green body, Silver trim, Grey plastic wheels	£50-60	☐
17c	1960	Austin FX3 Taxi	Maroon body, Mid-Grey interior, Tan driver, Grey plastic wheels, 60 mm.	£45-55	☐
		wheel change:	As previous model but with Silver plastic wheels, Mid-Grey interior	£75-90	☐
		US issue:	With Pale Grey interior & Silver plastic wheels	NGPP	☐
17d	1964	Foden Tipper	Red cab, Orange back, 'HOVERINGHAM' logo, 74 mm.	£9-12	☐
17e	1969	AEC Horse Box	Red or Orange cab, Cream or Green box, 2 White horses, Black plastic or Superfast wheels, hook, 72 mm.	£9-12	☐
17f	1972	**LONDONER BUS (1st type)**	**LEYLAND 'ATLANTEAN' Double Decker.** Unless otherwise shown each has a Red body, White interior, painted metal base or plastic base, one set double opening doors, 2 open rear windows, 5-spoked Superfast wheels, 78 mm.		
	1972	'SWINGING LONDON'	Red body with multi-coloured label 'CARNABY ST'	£10-15	☐
		'THE BARON OF BEEF'	Red body, White logo.	£75-85	☐
		'PRESTON M.G.'	Red body, Green label, 'MERCHANT GUILD'	£60-70	☐
		'BUSCH GARDENS'	Red/White body, 'BRITISH AIRWAYS'	£60-70	☐
		'SELLOTAPE'	Red body, 2 different labels	£60-70	☐
		'SELLOTAPE	Red body, 'SELBESTKLEBEBANDER', German issue	£60-70	☐
		'TYPHOO'	White and Black decals, metal baseplate, 'VJ' emblem	£60-70	☐
		'CHAMBOURCEY'	Multicoloured decal with countryside scene	£10-15	☐
		'IMPEL 73'	Red/White body, Red/Black logo	£10-15	☐
		'IMPEL 76'	Off-White body, Brown upper deck, White label	£25-30	☐
		'ESSO EXTRA'	Red, White and Blue decals, metal baseplate	£30-35	☐
		'AIM BUILDING'	Black and White decal. Metal baseplate	£10-15	☐
		'JACOBS BISCUITS'	Orange or Red body, Black/White decals	£10-15	☐
		'SILVER JUBILEE'	Silver or Red body	£5-10	☐
		'MATCHBOX 1953-78'	Red, Blue or Brown body, Red/Yellow/Orange/Black decals, metal base	£25-35	☐
		'KENSINGTON HILTON'	Red body, Black logo on White label	NGPP	☐
		colour variation:	Silver body, Black logo on White label	£50-60	☐
		'LONDON HILTON'	Red body, Black logo on White label		☐
		'BISTO'	Red body, 'BISTO KIDS' on Yellow labels	£10-15	☐
		'AVIEMORE CENTRE'	Red body, Blue logo/emblem	£65-75	☐
		'SELFRIDGES'	Red body, White label, Black logo	£10-15	☐
		'BARCLAYS BANK'	Red body, Blue/White label	£40-50	☐
		'ILFORD HPS'	Red body, Black/White label	£50-60	☐
		'AMCEL'	Red body, White label, Orange logo	£40-50	☐
		'LONDON MUSEUM'	Red body, Black/White label with 'new' logo	£30-35	☐
		'ARAL'	Blue body, White/Blue label 'DEUTSCHLANDS AUTO PARTNER'	£35-45	☐

LONDONER BUS (1st type) – continued

Ref. No.	Year(s)	Model Type		Market Price Range	
		'BERGER PAINTS'.............	Red body, Purple/Orange/Gold lower body........................	£5-8	☐
			Silver body	£20-25	☐
			Gold body	£20-25	☐
			Coffee/Cream body	£15-20	☐
			Red/Yellow body (this version made in Brazil).....................	£30-35	☐
			Red/White body (this version made in Brazil).....................	£30-35	☐
			Blue/White body (this version made in Brazil)....................	£30-35	☐
		note:............................	'Paint brushes' may be either end of label.		
		'KEDDIES' 'No. 1 in ESSEX'	Blue body, White interior, White paper (round end) labels, sold in Blue box (900).....	£35-40	☐
		note:............................	Beware fakes with square cut label ends, sold in white boxes.		
	1982	LONDONER BUS (2nd type)...	(new casting), LEYLAND 'TITAN' Double Decker. The model is Red with 2 sets double opening doors and 3 open rear windows unless differently described.		
		'LAKER SKY TRAIN'	Red, White and Blue label..	£5-8	☐
		'CHESTERFIELD'	Green body, Green and White label................................	£5-8	☐
		'YORK FESTIVAL'	Red body, Purple lower body, 'MYSTERY PLAYS'	£4-7	☐
		'RAPPORT'	Maroon body, Yellow lower body, 'SALES FROM WALES'	£4-7	☐
		'JAPAN 84'......................	Red body, 'NICE TO MEET YOU', Japanese issue model	£15-20	☐
		'NESTLES'	Red body, 'MILKY BAR' label......................................	£4-7	☐
		colour change:......	As previous model but with Blue body.............................	£10-15	☐
		'ROWNTREES'	Red body, 'FRUIT GUMS' label....................................	£4-7	☐
		colour change:......	As previous model but with Cream body............................	£10-15	☐
		'KEDDIES'	Blue body, White label, Red logo 'No. 1 in ESSEX'	£35-40	☐
		'MB' London Bus	Red body, Red/Yellow/White/Blue label............................	£4-7	☐
		'YOU'LL LOVE NEW YORK'	Red body, White label, 'USA' and 'TWA'	£4-7	☐
		'MATCHBOX No. 1'..........	Blue/White body, White label.....................................	£10-15	☐
		colour change:......	As previous model but with Red body..............................	£10-15	☐
		'YOKOHAMA FAIR'	Red body, Yellow label, Japanese issue model	£15-18	☐
		'STAFFS POLICE'	White/Blue body, 'CHARITY APPEAL' logo	£15-18	☐
		'CITYRAMA'....................	All Blue body, multicoloured labels depicting flags.............	£5-7	☐
		'MIDLAND MUSEUM'	Brown/White body, 'Bus & Transport - Wythall'	£5-7	☐
		'TRAMWAY MUSEUM'.....	All Blue body, Red logo, 'THE NATIONAL CRICH'	£5-7	☐
		'BAND AID'	Red body, White label 'Playbus'.................................	£5-7	☐
		'W. H. SMITH & SONS	Orange/White body..	£10-14	☐
		'WEST MIDLANDS TRAVEL'	Blue/Cream body, White label, Blue logo.........................	£5-8	☐
		'AROUND LONDON'	Red body, 'TOUR BUS' label......................................	£3-5	☐
		'MICA' Commemorative.......	All White body, Red/White/Blue/Yellow label, (Promotional in special box)	£12-16	☐
		'DENNY'........................	White body, Red/Blue labels, Blue tampo print...................	£3-5	☐
	1993	'MARKFIELD PROJECT' ..	Code 1 model...	NRP	☐
	1989	'TOUR BUS'	Red body, Red/White/Blue design.................................	NRP	☐
	1989	'COKE'	Yellow body, 'ITS THE REAL THING'	NRP	☐
	1990	'CORNING GLASS'............	US issue..	NRP	☐
	1992	'TOUR BUS'	Red bus, 'London Guide Tour Bus' on Black/Yellow background	NRP	☐

MB 18

Ref. No.	Year(s)	Model Type		Market Price Range	
18a	1955	Caterpillar Bulldozer	Yellow body, Red dozer blade, Green tracks, metal roller wheels, 46 mm	£28-33	☐
18b	1958	larger casting:............	Yellow body, no. '8' or '18' cast-in, Yellow blade ('18'), Green tracks, 50 mm..........	£35-40	☐
18c	1961	larger casting:............	Yellow body & blade, Green tracks; metal, Silver or Black plastic rollers, 58 mm.	£10-14	☐
18d	1964	no driver casting:	Yellow body, Green rubber tracks, Silver or Black plastic rollers, 62 mm..............	£7-9	☐
18e	1969	Field Car..........................	Yellow body, Tan roof, Red plastic wheels, unpainted or Black baseplate...............	£7-9	☐
		wheel change:............	with Green plastic wheel hubs, Black plastic tyres, unpainted base	£150-175	☐
	1970	wheel change:............	As previous model but with Superfast wheels....................................	£5-8	☐
		colour change:...........	Military Green issue, with or without star......................................	£12-15	☐
		note:............................	Several variations were issued in the 'Twin-Pack' series		
18f	1975	'Hondarora'	Red body, Black seat, Silver trim, 'Honda', spoked wheels, 63 mm.	£5-8	☐
		colour change:...........	As previous model but with White seat...	£45-55	☐
		colour change:...........	Same but Black front forks, seat and handlebars................................	NGPP	☐
		colour change:...........	Yellow body, Silver engine, Black seat, forks & handlebars	NGPP	☐
		colour change:...........	Dark Military Green..	£14-18	☐
		colour change:...........	Orange body, 'Honda'...	£12-16	☐
		colour change:...........	Metallic Green, Black handlebars, 'Honda'	£4-6	☐
18g	1984	Fire Engine	Red body, White ladder, flashing light bar on roof.............................	NRP	☐
	1987	design change:............	'FIRE DEPT' livery	NRP	☐

MB 19

Ref. No.	Year(s)	Model Type		Market Price Range	
19a	1956	MG Midget TD......................	Cream body, Brown driver, Red seats, metal wheels, no number, 51 mm.	£60-70	☐
		colour change:...........	Off-White body, metal wheels...	£65-75	☐
19b	1958	MG 'MGA' Sports Car............	Off-White body, Tan driver, Red/Gold or Red/Silver trim, metal wheels, 56 mm.......	£55-65	☐
		colour change:...........	Off-White body, Red/Silver trim, Grey plastic wheels	£60-70	☐
		wheel change:............	With Silver plastic wheels on rivetted axles	£80-90	☐
19c	1962	Aston Martin Racing Car	Metallic Green, Grey or White racing driver, Black base, racing numbers: '3' '5', '19', '41' or '52', wire wheels, Black plastic tyres, 63 mm.	£20-25	☐
19d	1965	Lotus Racing Car	Racing numbers may be transfers or stick-on labels, or a mixture of both. Dark Green, White driver, Yellow hubs, Black plastic tyres, RN '3', 70 mm.	£9-12	☐
	1967	colour change:...........	Orange body, Yellow hubs, Black plastic tyres.................................	£18-22	☐
	1970	colour change:...........	Purple body, Superfast wheels..	£7-9	☐

Ref. No.	Year(s)	Model Type	Matchbox Miniatures - continued	Market Price Range	
19e	1971	Road Dragster	Red body, Silver exposed engine, clear windows, Superfast, 76 mm.	£5-8	☐
		design change:	With 'Scorpion' labels	£30-35	☐
		design change:	Pink with 'WYNNS' labels	£30-35	☐
19f	1976	Cement Truck	Red body, Orange barrel, Red or Black stripes, Superfast, 75 mm.	£3-5	☐
	1978	barrel change:	Red body, Grey barrel, Red stripes, Superfast	£3-5	☐
	1981	barrel change:	Red body, Yellow barrel, Red stripes, Superfast	£6-9	☐
19g	1982	Peterbilt Cement Truck	Metallic Green/Orange/Blue, 'BIG PETE', Green door design	£1-3	☐
	1984	colour change:	As previous model but with Yellow door design	£1-3	☐
	1985	'CEMENT COMPANY'	Blue body, Yellow mixer drum	£1-3	☐
	1988		Yellow body, Silver mixer drum	NRP	☐
	1990	colour change:	Pink/grey body. Australian issue.	£4-6	☐
	1991	'READYMIX'	Blue cab, Red circular designs on roof/doors, Yellow/Black drum, various logos	NRP	☐
	1992	design change:	Yellow cab, Red design, Red drum & logos on doors/bonnet	NRP	☐

MB 20

Ref. No.	Year(s)	Model Type	Matchbox Miniatures - continued	Market Price Range	
20a	1956	E.R.F. Lorry	Light Green body, Silver trim, metal wheels, crimped axles, 57 mm.	£200-300	☐
		colour change:	Maroon body, Gold fuel tank, metal wheels, crimped axles	£20-30	☐
		colour change:	Maroon body, Silver fuel tank, metal or Grey plastic wheels	£30-40	☐
		colour change:	Dark Red body, metal or Grey plastic wheels	£20-30	☐
20b	1959	E.R.F. 68g Truck 'EVER READY FOR LIFE'	Dark Blue body, Orange advert outline, Grey plastic wheels, 66 mm.	£50-75	☐
		wheel change:	As previous model but with Silver plastic wheels on rivetted axles	£100-150	☐
		colour change:	With Red outline to advert, Grey or Black plastic wheels	£50-75	☐
20c	1965	Chevrolet Impala Taxi	Orange-Yellow body, Cream or White interior, 'Taxi', Grey plastic wheels	£30-35	☐
		wheel change:	Black plastic wheels, Cream, White or Red interior	£10-12	☐
		colour change:	Yellow body, Cream, White or Red interior, Black plastic wheels	£10-12	☐
20d	1969	Lamborghini Marzal	Metallic Dark Red, White seats, Silver trim, Superfast, 70 mm.	£8-11	☐
		colour change:	Pink body	£8-11	☐
		colour change:	Yellow body	£14-18	☐
	1971	colour change:	Orange body	£5-8	☐
20e	1975	Police Range Rover	White body, Orange flash, 'Police', flashing light, 82 mm.	£3-5	☐
	1981	colour change:	White body, Red/Yellow/Black flash	£2-4	☐
	1983	colour change:	Gold body, 'Securit Rallye Paris Dakar 83'	£6-8	☐
	1984		As previous model but no design on bonnet, unpainted chassis	£4-6	☐
		colour change:	Military Green body, 'AMBULANCE' and Red crosses	£20-25	☐
		colour change:	Military Green body, 'POLICE'	£20-25	☐
		colour change:	White body with 'SHERIFF', US issue model	£4-6	☐
		colour change:	Orange body, 'SITE ENGINEER'	£10-12	☐
		note:	There are many other variations		☐
20f		'Desert Dawg'	White body, Red roof, 'JEEP' logo	£4-6	☐
20g		**Volvo Container Truck**	Blue body, White box	£1-3	☐
	1985	'COLD FRESH'	White cab and container, (US issue model)	£3-5	☐
	1986	'FEDERAL EXPRESS'	Blue body, Red/Yellow design, 'No. 1 Selling Toy 86-5-4-3'	£30-35	☐
	1987	MATCHBOX 'MB 75'	White body and container	£1-3	☐
	1987	'SCOTCH CORNER'	Dark Blue body, Red/White design	£1-3	☐
	1987	'CROOKES HEALTHCARE'			
	1987	'SUPERSAVE DRUGSTORES'	Grey cab and container	£1-3	☐
	1988	'ALLDERS'	Dark Blue body, Gold tampo, promotional	£1-3	☐
	1989	'COMMA OIL COMPANY'	Dark Blue body, promotional	£1-3	☐
	1990	'YORKIE'	White body, Blue panel, Yellow logo	NRP	☐
		'BIG TOP CIRCUS'	Red/White body, Yellow/Red design	NRP	☐
		'KIT KAT'	White body, Red/White design	NRP	☐
20h	1988	VW Transporter	White body, Orange stripe and cross	NRP	☐
	1989	colour change:	Camouflage paintwork	NRP	☐
	1989	'AMBULANCE'	White body, Red stripe & cross, Blue dome light on roof	NRP	☐

MB 21

Ref. No.	Year(s)	Model Type	Matchbox Miniatures - continued	Market Price Range	
21a	1956	Bedford Duple Luxury Coach	Green body & base, Red/Yellow 'LONDON-GLASGOW', metal wheels, 57 mm.	£50-60	☐
21b	1958	Bedford Duple Luxury Coach	Green, Black base, 'LONDON-GLASGOW', metal or Grey plastic wheels, 68 mm.	£35-45	☐
		colour change:	Dark Green body, Black base, Grey plastic wheels	£45-55	☐
21c	1961	Commer Milk Float 'DRINK MORE MILK'	Pale Green body, Cream or White load, Green or clear windows, 'bottle' decal on doors, Silver plastic wheels, 57 mm.	£50-60	☐
		decal change:	Same but with 'cow' decal on doors, Silver plastic wheels	£30-35	☐
		wheel change:	Same but with Grey or Black plastic wheels, Green windows	£20-25	☐
21d	1968	Foden Concrete Truck	Yellow body and revolving drum, Red base, Black plastic wheels, 76 mm.	£14-17	☐
21e	1973	Road Roller	Yellow body, Green or Black base, Black plastic roller wheels, 70 mm.	£5-7	☐
21f	1978	Renault 5TL	Blue body, Silver trim, Tan seats, Superfast wheels, 65 mm.	£5-7	☐
		colour change:	With Red interior and Silver or Black base	£12-16	☐
	1980	colour change:	Yellow body, 'Le Car' decals, opening tailgate	£2-4	☐
	1981	colour change:	Silver body with Orange flash, 'Le Car', opening tailgate	£2-4	☐
	1982	colour change:	White body with Green labels, 'MICHELIN' decals, etc	£2-4	☐
	1983	colour change:	White body, 'RADIO MONTE CARLO' design	£1-3	☐
	1984	colour change:	Black body, Red/Yellow design 'ROLOIL'.	£1-3	☐
21g	1986	Chevy Breakdown Van	Red body, White hoist '24hr SERVICE'	NRP	☐
	1989		Yellow body, Black hoist, '24 HOURS' logo	£3-5	☐
21h		Corvette Pace Car	US issued model	NRP	☐
21i	1991	Nissan Prairie	Two-tone Blue and Grey body	NRP	☐
	1992	colour change:	Metallic Silver body with 'NISSAN' logos on sides	NRP	☐

MB 22

Ref. No.	Year(s)	Model Type	Description	Price	
22a	1956	Vauxhall Cresta	Maroon body, Off-White roof, metal wheels, 63 mm.	£35-40	☐
22b	1958	Vauxhall Cresta	Pale Pink body, Green windows or none, Grey plastic wheels	£90-120	☐
		colour change:	Same but Cream body, with or without windows, Grey plastic wheels	£90-120	☐
		colour change:	Pale Pink body, Blue-Green side panels, Green windows, Grey plastic wheels	£250-300	☐
		colour change:	Light Metallic Brown, Blue-Green panels, Green windows, Grey plastic wheels	£90-120	☐
		colour change:	Light Grey body, Lilac side panels, Silver or Grey plastic wheels	£90-120	☐
		colour change:	Light Metallic Gold body, Silver or Grey plastic wheels	£90-120	☐
		colour change:	Dark Metallic Gold body, Silver plastic wheels	£90-120	☐
		colour change:	Metallic Copper body, Silver, Grey or Black plastic wheels	£90-120	☐
22c	1965	Pontiac GP Sports Coup	Red body, Grey interior, Black plastic wheels, 76 mm.	£15-20	☐
		casting change:	As previous model but without patent number on base	£35-45	☐
	1970	wheel change:	Red body, Superfast wheels	NGPP	☐
		colour change:	Metallic Purple body, Superfast wheels	£10-15	☐
22d	1971	Freeman Inter City	Maroon or Purple body, White seats, 'Arrow' motif, Superfast, 76 mm.	£5-8	☐
		colour change:	As previous model but Metallic Gold body, Off-White interior, 'arrow' motif	£4-6	☐
22e	1976	'Blaze Buster'	Red body, 'Fire', Yellow ladder, Silver or White seats, 77 mm.	£3-5	☐
		ladder change:	With Black ladder	£7-9	☐
22f		'BIG FOOT'	Grey body, White roof, '26', US issued model	£4-6	☐
22g	1984	Jaguar XK120	Green body, Red seats, windscreen	£3-5	☐
	1986	colour change:	White body, racing number '414', Red seats	£1-3	☐
	1993	colour change:	Cream body, Red seats	NRP	☐
22h	1988	Saab 9000 Turbo	Red body, opening doors	NRP	☐
	1990	colour change:	White body, Red/Yellow design, 'SAAB' and 'No.22' logos	NRP	☐

MB 23

Ref. No.	Year(s)	Model Type	Description	Price	
23a	1956	Berkeley Cavalier Caravan	Pale Blue, 'On Tow MBS 23', metal wheels, slight body outlines, 65 mm.	£33-38	☐
23b	1957	casting change:	As previous model but with strong body outlines	£20-25	☐
		colour change:	Same but Lime Green body, metal or Grey plastic wheels	£75-100	☐
		colour change:	Metallic Lime Green body, Grey plastic wheels	£100-130	☐
23c	1960	Bluebird Dauphine Caravan	Metallic Lime Green body, Grey plastic wheels, 64 mm.	£150-200	☐
	1962	colour change:	Metallic Mauve body and base, Grey plastic wheels, clear windows	£25-30	☐
		wheel change:	Same but with Black or Silver plastic wheels, clear windows	£40-50	☐
		window change:	Same (with Black, Silver or Grey plastic wheels), but with Green windows	£40-50	☐
23d	1965	Trailer Caravan	Yellow/White or Pink/White, Black plastic wheels, 74 mm.	£8-11	☐
23e	1970	Volkswagen Camper	Blue/Orange body, Orange or White interior, Superfast, 67 mm.	£8-11	☐
	1972	with labels:	As previous model but with 'yacht' labels	£5-8	☐
	1973	colour change:	Orange body with 'yacht' labels, Superfast	£5-8	☐
	1980	US issue:	White body, 'PIZZA VAN' logo	£5-8	☐
23g	1976	Atlas Dump Truck	Metallic Blue/Orange, Silver or Grey seats, Superfast, 71 mm.	£4-6	☐
	1981	colour change:	Red cab and chassis, Silver dumper, Superfast	£2-4	☐
23h	1983	Peterbilt Quarry Truck	Yellow/Grey body, 'DIRTY DUMPER', Superfast	£2-4	☐
	1985	design change:	As previous model plus Blue/White 'PACE' design	£1-3	☐
	1992	colour change:	Yellow cab with Red design, Red rear tipper	NRP	☐
23i	1986	GT350 Wildcat Dragster	White/Grey body, US issued model	£4-6	☐
23j	1987	Honda ATC 250R	US issued model	£4-6	☐

MB 24

Ref. No.	Year(s)	Model Type	Description	Price	
24a	1956	'Hydraulic' Excavator	Orange-Yellow body, metal wheels, 'WEATHERILL', 58 mm.	£20-25	☐
		colour change:	Same but Yellow body, metal wheels, 'WEATHERILL'	£20-25	☐
24b	1959	'Hydraulic' Excavator	Yellow body, 'WEATHERILL', Grey or Black plastic wheels, 67 mm.	£15-18	☐
24c	1967	Rolls-Royce Silver Shadow	Metallic Red body, Cream interior; Black, Green, Pink or Grey base (patent numbers on some), Silver plastic wheels or Silver hubs/Black plastic tyres	£12-15	☐
	1970	colour change:	Metallic Gold body, Black base, Superfast wheels	£10-12	☐
24d	1973	'TEAM MATCHBOX'	Metallic Red body, racing number '8', White driver, Superfast	£5-8	☐
		colour change:	Metallic Green body, racing number '5', driver, Superfast	£15-20	☐
		colour change:	Metallic Blue body, racing number '1', driver, Superfast	NGPP	☐
		colour change:	Yellow body, racing number '8', driver, Superfast	NGPP	☐
24e	1979	Diesel Shunter	Green or Yellow body, 'Railfreight' or 'D1496RF'	£2-4	☐
24f	1983	Datsun 280 ZX	Black body, Gold flashes, opening doors, clear windows, Superfast. 74 mm.	£2-4	☐
	1984	logo change:	As previous model plus gold 'TURBO ZX' on bonnet	£1-3	☐
24g	1986	Nissan 3002X	Silver body with Black/Yellow stripes	£1-3	☐
	1987	design change:	'FUJI FILM' design	£1-3	☐
	1987	US issue:	Red body, Orange/Yellow design	£4-6	☐
	1987	Laser Wheels issue:	Metallic Purple body, Orange/Yellow design	NRP	☐
24h	1989	Lincoln Town Car	White body	NRP	☐
24i	1992	Fire Tender	Red body, Blue design with 'FIRE' and 'No.5' logos	NRP	☐

MB 25

Ref. No.	Year(s)	Model Type	Description	Price	
25a	1956	Bedford 12 cwt Van	Dark Blue body, 'DUNLOP', metal or Black plastic wheels, 56 mm.	£30-35	☐
		wheel change:	As previous model but with Grey plastic wheels	£35-45	☐
25b	1960	Volkswagen 1200	Silver Blue body, Grey plastic wheels, 62 mm.	£22-26	☐
		window change:	As previous model but with Green tinted windows, Grey plastic wheels	£18-24	☐
		wheel change:	As previous model but with Silver plastic wheels	£18-24	☐
25c	1964	Bedford Petrol Tanker	Yellow cab, Green chassis, White tank, 'BP', Grey or Black plastic wheels	£10-13	☐
	1964	German issue:	Dark Blue cab and chassis, White tank, 'ARAL', Black plastic wheels	£65-80	☐

Ref. No.	Year(s)	Model Type	Matchbox Miniatures - continued	Market Price Range	
25d	1968	Ford Cortina Mk.II..................	Metallic Light Brown body, Cream interior, Black plastic wheels, 71 mm.	£10-15	☐
		Gift Set issue:.............	As previous models but fitted with Yellow plastic roof rack...................................	GSP	☐
	1970	wheel change:...........	As previous model but with Superfast wheels..	£30-40	☐
		colour change:...........	Metallic Blue body..	£10-15	☐
		colour change:...........	Metallic Dark Brown body...	£25-35	☐
		Bulgarian issue:...........	As previous models but with Gold or Green body..	£25-35	☐
25e	1972	Mod Tractor.....................	Purple or Red body, Silver engine, Superfast. 57 mm...	£5-8	☐
		casting change:...........	As previous model but headlamps on mudguards	£13-16	☐
25f	1979	Flat Car and Container............	Black chassis, Red/Beige container, 'NYK' and 'USL', 72.5 mm.	£4-6	☐
25g		Toyota Celica....................	US issued model.	£4-6	☐
25h		'Yellow Fever'....................	US issued model.	£4-6	☐
25i	1982	Audi Sport.......................	White body, Brown/Red panels, racing number, 'AUDI SPORT', 76 mm.	£1-3	☐
	1985	colour change:...........	Black body, Gold 'TURBO' design	£1-3	☐
	1986	colour change:...........	Maroon body, White 'QUATTRO' design	NRP	☐
	1989	colour change:...........	Metallic Grey body, 'AUDI QUATTRO' logo	NRP	☐
25j	1987	'Paramedics' Ambulance	US issued model.	£4-6	☐
25k	1991	Peugeot 205 Turbo 16	Red body, Blue/White racing number '48'	NRP	☐
	1992	colour change:...........	Yellow body, Blue logos 'PEUGEOT' and number '48'	NRP	☐
25L	1993	Model 'A' Ford	White body, Red chassis/wings, 'flame' design..................................	NRP	☐

MB 26

26a	1956	E.R.F. Cement Mixer	Orange body, Gold trim, metal wheels, crimped axles, 45 mm.	£30-35	☐
		trim colour change:.....	As previous model but with Silver trim, metal wheels............................	£30-35	☐
		wheel change:.............	With Grey plastic wheels, Silver trim...	£40-50	☐
		wheel change:.............	With Silver plastic wheels, Silver trim	NGPP	☐
26b	1961	Foden Cement Mixer	Orange body, Dark Grey barrel, Grey plastic wheels, 66 mm...........................	£200-250	☐
		colour change:...........	As previous model but with Light Grey barrel, Grey plastic wheels. 66 mm...........	£200-250	☐
		colour change:...........	Orange body, Orange barrel, Silver plastic wheels......................................	£35-45	☐
		wheel change:...........	Orange body, Orange barrel, Grey or Black plastic wheels...........................	£15-20	☐
26c	1968	G.M.C. Tipper Truck..............	Red cab, Green chassis, Silver tipper, Black plastic wheels, 67 mm.	£6-9	☐
	1970	wheel change:.............	As previous model but with Superfast wheels...	£5-8	☐
26d	1972	'BIG BANGER'	Red or Brown body, Silver exposed engine and trim, Superfast, 76 mm.	£5-8	☐
26e		'Brown Sugar'.....................	US issued model.	£7-10	☐
26e	1976	Site Dumper.......................	Yellow body, Black base, Superfast, 64 mm.	£3-5	☐
	1981	colour change:...........	Red body, Silver dumper, Superfast, 64 mm. Many other variations exist	£2-4	☐
26f	1982	Cable Truck........................	Yellow body, Black/Grey cable drums, tinted windows, Superfast, 77 mm.	£1-3	☐
	1984	colour change:...........	Yellow/Red body	£1-3	☐
26g		'Cosmic Blues'	White body, Blue 'stars' design, US issue model	£4-6	☐
26h		**Volvo Tilt Truck**			
	1985	'FRESH FRUIT'	Blue body, Yellow tilt	£1-3	☐
	1986	'FERRYMASTERS'	Yellow body, White cab & side panel, contains Collector Card......................	£2-4	☐
	1986	'HI BRAN'	White/Green body, Red design..	£1-3	☐
	1986	'TT86 ISLE OF MAN'	Two-tone Blue body with Red roof...	£1-3	☐
	1987	'FEDERAL EXPRESS'	All White body, Dark Blue design...	NRP	☐
	1988	'PIRELLI'..........................	White body, 'GRIPPING STUFF' logo..	NRP	☐
	1989	'MICHELIN'	Blue/Yellow body..	NRP	☐
		Military version	With Camouflage paintwork..	NRP	☐
	1990	'PIRELLI'..........................	White body..	NRP	☐
26i	1993	Jaguar XJ-220......................	Deep Blue body..	NRP	☐

MB 27

27a	1956	Bedford Low Loader......≈........	Pale Blue cab, Dark Blue trailer, 6 metal wheels, crimped axles, 78 mm.	£120-150	☐
		colour change:...........	Pale Green cab, Light Brown trailer...	£40-50	☐
27b	1958	Bedford Low Loader	Pale Green cab, Light Brown trailer, metal or Grey plastic wheels, 95 mm.	£80-90	☐
		colour change:...........	Dark Green cab, Light Brown trailer, Grey plastic wheels................................	£80-90	☐
27c	1960	Cadillac Sixty Special	Metallic Pale Green/White, Crimson base, Silver plastic wheels, 69 mm.	£80-90	☐
		colour change:...........	Silver Grey body, Off-White roof, Silver plastic wheels..................................	£40-50	☐
		colour change:...........	Metallic Lilac/Pink, Crimson base, Grey or Silver plastic wheels	£20-25	☐
		base colour change:	Same model but with Black base; Grey, Silver or Black plastic wheels	£20-25	☐
27d	1966	Mercedes 230 SL	Off-White body, Red seats, Black plastic wheels, 74 mm.	£8-11	☐
	1970	wheel change:.............	As previous model but with Superfast wheels..	£7-10	☐
	1970		Yellow body, Red or Black seats, Superfast	£7-9	☐
27e	1973	Lamborghini Countach	Yellow or Orange/Red main body, RN '3' or '8', Superfast, 74 mm.	£3-5	☐
27f	1981	Swing Wing Jet.....................	Red/White main body, retractable wings, 'JET', 76 mm.	£1-3	☐
		design change:...........	White body with 'Jet Set' in Red on wings...	£1-3	☐
27g	1986	Jeep Cherokee.....................	White body, multi-coloured side panels, contains Collector Card	£1-2	☐
		'FOREST RANGER'........	Yellow/Green body..	NRP	☐
	1988	'Mr FIXER'	Yellow body, logo in Red..	NRP	☐
		'BP'	Yellow body, Dutch promotional model...	NRP	☐
		'HOLIDAY CLUB'	Beige body...	NRP	☐
27h	1990	Mercedes Benz Tractor............	Lime Green & Dark Green body	NRP	☐

MB 28

28a	1956	Bedford Compressor................	Orange/Yellow body, Silver trim, metal wheels, 47 mm.	£25-30	☐
		colour change:...........	Yellow body, Silver trim, metal wheels, domed/crimped axles	£15-24	☐
28b	1959	Ford Thames Compressor........	Yellow body, Silver trim on some, Black plastic wheels, 59 mm.	£18-24	☐

202

Ref. No.	Year(s)	Model Type	Matchbox Miniatures - continued	Market Price Range	
28c	1964	Jaguar Mk.10..................	Pale Metallic Brown, Cream seats, Black plastic wheels, 74 mm..................	£15-20	☐
		rare variant:	With Grey plastic wheels and without *Matchbox Series* on base	NGPP	☐
28d	1968	Mack Dump Truck	Orange or Light Green body, Orange, Red or Yellow hubs, 68 mm.	£5-8	☐
	1970	wheel change:	As previous model but with Superfast wheels..................	£3-5	☐
		colour change:............	Military Green issue..................	£14-17	☐
28e	1974	Stoat..................	Gold body, driver rotates, Rolomatic, Superfast, 67 mm.	£4-6	☐
		colour change:............	Olive Green body, Chrome hubs	£10-15	☐
		colour change:............	Olive-Drab (Military Matt-Green) body	£45-55	☐
		note:..................	Base may plastic and metal or all plastic. Many other variations exist.		☐
28f	1979	Lincoln Continental..................	Red body, White roof, Tan seats, Superfast, 72 mm..................	£2-4	☐
28g	1982	Formula Racing Car	Gold and Black, RN '8', White driver, Superfast, 75 mm.	£2-4	☐
	1983	colour change:............	Metallic Green and Black body	£1-3	☐
28h	1985	Dodge Daytona	Brown/Grey body, opening bonnet	£1-2	☐
	1986	colour change:............	Silver/Red/Black body	NRP	☐
	1988	colour change:............	Red body, Blue/Yellow design	NRP	☐
28i	1989	1987 Corvette..................	Yellow body, Red/Black design	NRP	☐
28j	1991	BMW 323i Cabriolet	Red body, Brown interior, Black trim..................	NRP	☐
28k	1992	Thunderbird Coupé	Dark Metallic Blue with Red body design	NRP	☐

MB 29

Ref. No.	Year(s)	Model Type		Market Price Range	
29a	1956	Bedford Milk Delivery Van......	Light Brown body, White bottle load, metal wheels, 57 mm.	£22-27	☐
		wheel change:	Same but Grey plastic wheels, White or Cream bottles	£20-25	☐
29b	1961	Austin A55 Cambridge..............	Two-tone Green body, Green tinted windows, Grey plastic wheels, 68 mm.	£30-35	☐
		wheel change:.............	Same but Silver or Black plastic wheels, clear or tinted windows	£18-24	☐
29c	1966	La France Fire Pumper..............	Red body, Orange *'Denver'*, Black plastic wheels, 76 mm.	£6-9	☐
	1970	wheel change:............	As previous model but with Superfast wheels	£4-6	☐
29d	1971	Racing Mini..................	Metallic Bronze body, racing number '29' on Yellow label, 57 mm.	£9-12	☐
		colour change:............	Deep Orange body with Cream interior and racing number '29'	£5-8	☐
		colour change:............	Pale Orange body, racing number '29'	£5-8	☐
		label change:	Orange models issued with RN '29' on Yellow labels with Green border	£5-8	☐
		colour change:............	Red body, racing number '29'	£5-8	☐
29e	1977	Shovel-Nose Tractor..................	Yellow body, Red shovel, Black trim, 72 mm.	£2-4	☐
	1981	colour change:............	Orange body, Black shovel, Grey trim	£1-3	☐
	1982	colour change:............	Yellow body, Black shovel	£1-3	☐
	1989	German issue:	Lemon Yellow body, *'THOMAS MUCOSLVAN'*, promotional	£4-6	☐
	1992	colour change:............	Yellow body with Red shovel and design..................	NRP	☐

MB 30

Ref. No.	Year(s)	Model Type		Market Price Range	
30a	1956	Ford Prefect..............................	Light Brown body, Red & Silver trim, metal or Grey plastic wheels, 58 mm.	£25-30	☐
		colour change:............	As previous model but Light Blue body, Grey plastic wheels, 58 mm.	£120-150	☐
30b	1961	Magirus-Deutz Crane Lorry	Light Brown body, Red jib & hook, six Grey plastic wheels, 66 mm.	NGPP	☐
		colour change:............	As previous model but with Orange jib and hook	NGPP	☐
		colour change:............	Silver body, Orange jib and hook, six Silver or Grey plastic wheels..........	£35-40	, ☐
		hook colour change: ...	Silver body, Orange jib, Silver hook, six Silver plastic wheels..........	£25-35	☐
		wheel change:.............	Silver body, Orange jib, Silver or Grey hook, Black plastic wheels..........	£25-30	☐
		wheel change:.............	Silver body, Orange jib, Grey hook, six Grey plastic wheels..........	£25-30	☐
30c	1965	Faun Crane Lorry	Green/Orange, Yellow or Red hook, eight Black plastic wheels, 77 mm.	£8-12	☐
	1970	design change:............	Red body, Gold jib, Yellow hook base, Superfast wheels	£4-6	☐
	1966	Gift Set model:	Turquoise body, Yellow hook, Black plastic wheels, (Gift Set G6)	GSP	☐
30d	1970	Beach Buggy	Metallic Mauve or Yellow, 'Clover' motif on some, Superfast, 65 mm.	£4-7	☐
30e	1976	'SWAMP RAT'	Olive Green body, Superfast, 77 mm.	£2-4	☐
	1989		Camouflage paintwork	NRP	☐
30f	1981	Leyland Articulated Truck	Blue cab, Silver trailer, *'Leyland'* on front, Superfast, 77 mm.	£2-4	☐
30g	1983	colour change:............	Blue cab, Yellow trailer, *'International'*..................	£2-4	☐
	1984	logo change:..........	Blue body, White radiator grille, flashing light, *'PAULS'*..................	£25-30	☐
30h	1985	Mercedes-Benz 280GE Truck....	Red body with White roof, 3 warning lights, *'RESERVE'*..................	£1-3	☐
	1988	Police version:............	Green/White body, 3 Blue beacons, *'POLIZEI'*	£4-6	☐
	1990	Fire Set issue:..........	Red body, *'FIRE RESCUE'* livery (MC 15)	GSP	☐

MB 31

Ref. No.	Year(s)	Model Type		Market Price Range	
31a	1957	Ford Station Wagon..................	Yellow body, metal wheels, hook, 66 mm.	£30-35	☐
			Yellow body, Grey plastic wheels	£45-55	☐
31b	1959	Ford Station Wagon..................	Yellow, Black base, clear windows, Grey or Silver plastic wheels, 69 mm.	£70-80	☐
		base change:..............	Same but Crimson base; clear, tinted or no windows, spare wheel	£20-15	☐
		colour change:............	Metallic Green/Pink, Black or Crimson base; Grey, Silver or Black plastic wheels	£20-24	☐
31c	1964	Lincoln Continental..................	Metallic Blue body, Black plastic wheels, 73 mm..................	£15-20	☐
		colour change:............	As previous model but Light Sea Green body, Black plastic wheels..........	£8-12	☐
		colour change:............	As previous model but Metallic Lime Green body, Black plastic wheels..........	£8-12	☐
		wheel change:............	As previous model but with Superfast wheels	£5-8	☐
31d	1972	'Volks-dragon'	Red body, Silver exposed engine, 'eyes' decal, 66 mm.	£5-8	☐
31e	1977	Caravan	White, Yellow door and windows, opening door, 70 mm.	£4-6	☐
	1981	colour change:............	White with Blue door, Orange tinted windows	£2-4	☐
		with logo:..............	White with Blue door, *'MOBILE 500'*	£1-3	☐
31f	1983	'MAZDA RX7'	Metallic Gold and Black, Red seats, opening doors, Superfast wheels, 76 mm.	£1-3	☐
		colour change:............	Black body, Gold shape, US issued model..................	£5-7	☐
31g		'Lady Bug'	US issued model..................	£4-6	☐

Ref. No.	Year(s)	Model Type	Matchbox Miniatures - continued	Market Price Range	
31h	1985	Rolls-Royce Silver Cloud ('James Bond' model)........	Silver or Cream body, (linked to the film 'View To A Kill'), special box	£4-6	☐
31i	1989	BMW 5 series	Dark Blue body	NRP	☐
	1991	rally version:	White body, Red/Blue design, *BMW TEAM* logo, rally number '31'........................	NRP	☐

MB 32

32a	1957	Jaguar XK-140	Off-White body, Black base, metal or Grey plastic wheels, 60 mm.	£35-40	☐
		colour change:............	Red body, Black base, Grey plastic wheels	£120-140	☐
32b	1962	Jaguar 'E'-type..........................	Metallic Red body, Green or clear windows, wire wheels, Black or Grey plastic tyres, 66 mm.	£35-45	☐
32c	1968	Leyland Tanker 'BP'	Green/White, Silver grille & base, Black plastic wheels, 77 mm.	£8-11	☐
		colour change:............	As previous model but with White grille and base	£15-20	☐
	1970	wheel change:	As previous model but with Superfast wheels	£5-8	☐
		Leyland Tanker 'ARAL'..........	Blue body, White tank, Silver grille & base, Blue logo	£75-85	☐
		Leyland Tanker 'NAMC'........	Red cab, White tank with *NAMC* logo	NGPP	☐
32d	1972	Maserati Bora.......................	Metallic Pink body, Yellow interior, RN '8', Superfast wheels, 76 mm.	£5-8	☐
		design change:..............	As previous model but with racing number '3'	£10-15	☐
32e	1977	Field Gun and Diorama............	Military Green and Black, 2 figures, 4 shells, 77 mm.	£2-4	☐
32f	1981	Atlas Excavator	Orange cab, Black base and grab, 80 mm.	£2-4	☐
	1982	colour change:............	Yellow cab, Black base and grab..	£1-3	☐
	1992	colour change:............	Yellow cab, Black base and arm with Red grab	NRP	☐

MB 33

33a	1957	Ford Zodiac..............................	Dark Green body, hook, no windows, metal wheels, 68 mm.	£30-35	☐
	1958	colour change:............	Blue body, hook, no windows, metal wheels...	£150-200	☐
	1958	colour change:............	Sea-Green body, hook, no windows, metal or Grey plastic wheels	NGPP	☐
	1959	colour change:............	Metallic Mauve body, Orange panels, no windows, Grey plastic wheels	£50-60	☐
	1960	window change:	Same but with Green tinted windows, Grey or Silver plastic wheels	£25-30	☐
33b	1963	Ford Zephyr 6	Sea-Green body; Grey, Silver or Black plastic wheels, 67 mm.	£15-20	☐
33c	1968	Lamborghini Miura	Yellow body, Red interior, Cream seats, Black plastic tyres, 71 mm.	£12-15	☐
		colour change:............	Metallic Gold body, Cream interior	£10-12	☐
	1969	wheel change:.............	As previous model but with Superfast wheels	£7-10	☐
	1971	Bulgarian issue:..........	Bronze body	£40-50	☐
33e	1973	Datsun 126X..........................	Yellow body, with or without flame design, 76 mm.	£2-4	☐
		US issue:	Gold body, 'Golden X' on base.	£4-6	☐
		note:	Datsun 126X reissued as a 'Super GT' in 1986		
33f	1977	Honda 'POLICE' Motor Cycle	White body, Green or White seat, wire wheels, 74 mm.	£2-4	☐
	1980	wheel change:.............	As previous model but with Black plastic wheels	£1-3	☐
		US Issue:.....................	Black body, White seat, *Los Angeles Police Department* decal	£5-7	☐
	1982	colour change:............	White body with Black seat, or vice versa	£1-3	☐
	1984	colour change:............	Black body, White panniers, Yellow stripes	£1-3	☐
33g	1989	Renault 11	Dark blue body, Silver stripe, *TURBO*	NRP	☐
33h	1989	Mercury Sable Wagon............	White body...	NRP	☐
33i	1990	Mercedes-Benz 500 SKL	Silver body, Blue interior	NRP	☐
	1992	colour change:............	White body, Green base, White *500 SL* logo	NRP	☐

MB 34

34a	1957	Volkswagen 15cwt Van	Blue body; metal or Grey, Silver or Black plastic wheels, 55 mm.	£30-35	☐
34b	1962	Volkswagen Caravette	Pale Green, Mid-Green interior/base; Grey, Silver or Black plastic wheels ...	£15-20	☐
34c	1967	Volkswagen Camper.................	Silver body, roof rack on some, Black plastic wheels, 65 mm.	£20-30	☐
		casting change:	As previous model but lower (windowless), raised roof.	£15-20	☐
34d	1971	Formula 1 Racing Car	Metallic Pink or Orange body, RN '16' on Yellow design, Superfast	£5-8	☐
		Promotional issue:	As previous model but with *WYNNS* logo	£7-9	☐
	1974	colour change:.............	Yellow body, racing number '16' on 'arrow' design, Superfast	£3-5	☐
		colour change:............	Metallic Blue body, racing number '15' on 'arrow' design, Superfast	£3-5	☐
34e	1976	'Vantastic'..............................	Orange body, White baseplate and interior, RN '34', Superfast	£3-5	☐
34f	1981	Pro-Stocker	White/Blue body, RN '34' on some, *Lightning* , Superfast, 76 mm.	£2-4	☐
	1983	design change:..............	Yellow body, Orange/Black stripes, RN '4', *Chevy*, 76 mm.	£2-4	☐
	1984	'PEPSI'	Red/White body, racing number '14'...	£1-3	☐
	1986	'7 UP'	Green/White body	£1-3	☐
	1987	Laser Wheels issue:....	White body, racing number '21'..	NRP	☐
34g	1988	Ford RS 2000	White body, Blue design, racing number '7'	NRP	☐
	1989	colour change:.............	Camouflage paintwork	NRP	☐
	1991	design change:.............	White body, Red design, racing number '7'	NRP	☐
34h	1990	Dodge Challenger.....................	Yellow/Black, Red design & interior, *TOYMAN* & *D/174 PRO*	NRP	☐

MB 35

35a	1957	E.R.F. Marshall Horse Box	Red cab, Light Brown box, metal wheels, 52 mm..	£30-35	☐
		wheel change:.............	Same but with Grey plastic wheels	£30-35	☐
		wheel change:.............	With Silver plastic wheels	£75-100	☐
		wheel change:.............	With Black plastic wheels	£75-100	☐
35b	1964	Snow-Trac Tractor	Type 1 has short straight ridge under track guards, Type 2 has curved ridge.		
		1st casting:	Dark Red, Type 1, White rubber tracks, *Snow-Trac* cast-in, 60mm.	£20-25	☐
		design change:.............	Dark or Mid-Red, (1 or 2) White or Cream tracks, 22 mm. *Snow-Trac* decal	£15-20	☐
		decal change:..............	As previous model but *Snow-Trac* on 25 mm. decal......................................	£15-20	☐

Ref. No.	Year(s)	Model Type	Matchbox Miniatures - continued	Market Price Range	
35c	1969	Merryweather Fire Engine	Metallic Red body, 'London Fire Service'..............................	£8-11	☐
		colour change:............	With Cream base..	£10-12	☐
	1975	Promotional issue:	Red body, 'FLAME-PROOF WOOL' logo	£35-40	☐
	1981	US issue:	'Los Angeles City Fire Department'	£5-8	☐
35d	1975	'Fandango'......................	White or Red body, racing number '35', Superfast, 75 mm.	£2-4	☐
	1977	label change:	White body, RN '6', Red base, clear windows, Superfast	£10-12	☐
	1979	window change:	Red body, Purple windows, racing number '35'.....................	£4-6	☐
35e	1982	Zoo Truck......................	Red body, Blue cage, Yellow lions, tinted windows, Superfast, 77 mm.	£1-3	☐
	1985	Pick Up Camper....................	Red/White body, 'Aspen Ski Holidays'.	£1-2	☐
	1988	'SLD Pumps'....................	Promotional model with White body	£1-2	☐
35f	1986	Pontiac T.Roof.....................	Black body, US issued model	£3-5	☐
35g	1988	Ford Bronco II......................	White/Orange body, big wheels	NRP	☐
	1990	colour change:............	White body, 'COASTGUARD'.	NRP	☐
	1992	colour change:............	Dark Blue body, Red 'BRONCO' & '4x4' logos	NRP	☐

MB 36

Ref. No.	Year(s)	Model Type	Matchbox Miniatures - continued	Market Price Range	
36a	1957	Austin A50 Cambridge............	Blue-Green body, Black base, metal wheels, 60 mm.	£20-25	☐
		wheel change:..............	As previous model but with Grey plastic wheels..................	£20-25	☐
		colour change:............	Pale Blue body, Grey plastic wheels	£15-20	☐
36b	1961	Lambretta & Sidecar	Pale Metallic Green Scooter and side-car, Black plastic wheels, 49 mm.	£35-40	☐
36c	1966	Opel Diplomat..........................	Metallic Gold body, White interior, Black plastic wheels, 74 mm.	£15-20	☐
	1970		As previous model but with Superfast wheels......................	£10-12	☐
36d	1970	Hot Rod 'Draguar'....................	Metallic Red or Pink body, Silver engine, 'Draguar', Superfast, 72 mm.	£5-8	☐
36e	1976	Formula 5000	Orange body, Blue driver, RN '3', 'Formula 5000', Superfast.	£3-5	☐
		colour change:............	As previous model but Red body, racing number '3' and '5000'	£3-5	☐
	1977	colour change:............	Red body, racing number '11', 'MARLBORO', Superfast	£3-5	☐
	1978	label change:	Red body, racing number '11', 'CHAMPION', Superfast	£3-5	☐
36f	1980	Refuse Truck	Metallic Red and Yellow body, 'Collectomatic'	£2-4	☐
		design change:..............	As previous model but without 'Collectomatic'....................	£20-25	☐
		colour change:............	Metallic Blue/Yellow body, with 'Collectomatic'..................	£1-3	☐
	1982	colour change:............	Blue and Orange body	£1-3	☐
	1983	colour change:............	Blue and Cream body	£1-3	☐
	1984	colour change:............	Blue/Grey body with 'Collectomatic'.	£1-3	☐
	1987	colour change:............	Green/Yellow body	NRP	☐
	1989	colour change:............	Orange body, Silver tipper, Blue logo	NRP	☐
	1992	colour change:............	Green body, Yellow tipper, Green wastebin/person design	NRP	☐
	1993	design change:..............	Orange-Yellow cab, White rear, 'DISPOSAL' logo	NRP	☐

MB 37

Ref. No.	Year(s)	Model Type	Matchbox Miniatures - continued	Market Price Range	
37a	1957	Karrier Bantam 2 ton Lorry	Yellow body, UNEVEN crate load, metal wheels, large or small 'COCA-COLA' side decals, 57 mm.	£100-130	☐
		colour change:............	Same (with UNEVEN load), but Orange/Yellow body............	£60-75	☐
	1958	casting change:	Yellow body, EVEN crate load, metal or Grey plastic wheels, large or small 'COCA-COLA' decals, 57 mm.	£35-40	☐
		colour change:............	Same (with EVEN load), but Orange-Yellow, metal or Grey plastic wheels	£35-40	☐
37b	1960	Karrier Bantam 2 ton Lorry	Yellow body, EVEN load, small 'COCA-COLA' side decals, large or small rear decals, Black base, Grey, Silver or Black plastic wheels, 61 mm.	£40-50	☐
37c	1966	(Dodge) Cattle Truck	Yellow cab, Mid-Grey box, 2 cows, Black plastic wheels, 66 mm.	£7-10	☐
		base change:.................	Same but unpainted metal baseplate, Mid or Dark Grey box........	£5-8	☐
		colour change:............	Orange cab, Grey body...	£7-10	☐
		colour change:............	Orange/Silver body..	£75-90	☐
	1970	wheel change:..............	As previous models but with Superfast wheels......................	£4-6	☐
37d	1973	'Soopa Coopa'	Metallic Pink, Blue or Purple body, flower decal, Superfast, 74 mm.	£5-8	☐
		colour change:............	Orange body, 'JAFFA-MOBILE'..	£60-75	☐
37e	1977	Skip Truck	Red Cab and chassis, Yellow skip, Silver trim, 69 mm...........	£2-4	☐
		colour change:............	Red with Blue skip...	NGPP	☐
	1981	colour change:............	Blue/Yellow body, Black or Silver base	£2-4	☐
37f	1982	Matra Rancho	Blue or Yellow body, hook, opening tailgate, Superfast, 74 mm.	£2-4	☐
37g	1985	Ford Escort Cabriolet XR3i	White or Blue body with 'XR3i' logo, Superfast.....................	£1-3	☐
	1986	colour change:............	Red body, Black seats, 'FORD' logo, Superfast	£1-2	☐
	1987	Laser Wheels issue:.....	Blue body, racing number '3', Superfast	NRP	☐
		US issue:	White body, racing number '3', Superfast	NRP	☐
37h	1990	Nissan 300 ZX......................	Yellow body, Black '300 ZX' logos, White interior, clear windows	NRP	☐

MB 38

Ref. No.	Year(s)	Model Type	Matchbox Miniatures - continued	Market Price Range	
38a	1957	Karrier Refuse Wagon	Grey/Brown body, Silver trim, metal wheels, 61 mm.	NGPP	☐
		colour change:............	Grey body, metal wheels or Grey plastic wheels	£25-30	☐
		colour change:............	Silver body, Silver or Grey plastic wheels	£35-45	☐
38b	1963	Vauxhall Victor Estate	Pale Yellow, Red seats; Grey, Silver or Black plastic wheels, 67 mm.	£15-18	☐
		interior change:...........	as previous model but with Light Green seats.......................	£18-22	☐
38c		Honda Motorcycle & Trailer	Motorcycle is 49 mm. long, Trailer is 74 mm. long.		
	1967	1st issue:.....................	Metallic Blue-Green bike, Orange trailer, Black plastic wheels	£15-20	☐
	1969	labels added:	As previous model but Yellow trailer with 'HONDA' labels	£8-11	☐
	1971	colour change:............	Metallic Purple or Pink body, 'HONDA' labels, Superfast	£5-7	☐
38d	1973	'Stingeroo'................................	Metallic Pink with Purple, Blue or chrome bars, Superfast, 78 mm.	£4-7	☐
38e	1977	Jeep	Military-Green body, with 'star' label, Black gun, 61 mm.	£2-3	☐
38f	1981	Camper	Red and Cream body, tinted windows, Superfast, 76 mm.	£2-3	☐

Ref. No.	Year(s)	Model Type	Matchbox Miniatures - continued	Market Price Range
38g		**Ford Model 'A' Van**		
1	1982	'CHAMPION'	Blue body, White roof, Black chassis with number '73', tinted windows......................	NGPP ☐
			As previous model but without '73' on base, in UK box	**£6-8** ☐
			As previous model but with Brown base..	NGPP ☐
			As previous model but with clear windows, in Macau box	**£6-8** ☐
4	1984	'PEPSI COLA'	White/Blue/Red body, with or without 'COME ALIVE' on doors, 3 rivets..................	**£7-10** ☐
			Without 'COME ALIVE' and with 2 base rivets..	**£10-15** ☐
			'Matchmates' blister packed version...	**£8-12** ☐
		Spanish issue:..............	Without 'COME ALIVE', with second body casting and 2 base rivets	**£10-15** ☐
16	1986	'MATCHBOX SPEED SHOP'	Blue/Black body, large rear wheels...	**£2-4** ☐
53		'MATCHBOX SERIES'	Yellow body, printed in the style of eaarly Lesney boxes...	**£4-6** ☐

MB 38 Vans have been issued in great numbers for various promotional purposes around the world. Because of the volume of issues it has become necessary to list them in a computer based 'Specialist Series' publication that will be regularly updated. Details of how to obtain the publication are given at the end of the Matchbox chapter. In the meantime to bridge the gap an updated 4th Edition listing will be available as from 1st November from Swapmeet Toys & Models Ltd, price £3.00 including P&P (UK & EEC).

Ref. No.	Year(s)	Model Type		Market Price Range
38h	1986	Flareside Pick-Up	Red body, White interior	NRP ☐
	1987	colour change:............	Yellow body, Blue design	NRP ☐
38i	1992	Ford Courier Van		
		'MATCHBOX'	Dark Blue body, 'The Ideal Premium'. 1000 only. (German issue)............................	NGPP ☐
	1992	'MILKA'	Purple body, White 'MILKA' logo..	NRP ☐
	1992	'COURIER'	White body, Yellow/Green/Purple side flash. Ford garages Limited Edition..............	NGPP ☐

MB 39

Ref. No.	Year(s)	Model Type		Market Price Range
39a	1957	Zodiac Convertible	Pale Peach body, Light Brown base/interior/driver, metal wheels, 68 mm..................	**£100-150** ☐
		colour change:............	Same but with Light Green base and interior, metal wheels	**£50-60** ☐
		wheel change:.............	Light Green base, Grey plastic wheels...	**£30-35** ☐
		colour change:............	Dark Peach body, Blue-Green base & interior, Grey plastic wheels.	**£20-25** ☐
		wheel change:.............	As previous model but with Silver plastic wheels..	**£35-45** ☐
		base change:...............	Dark Peach body with Sea-Green base, Grey plastic wheels..	**£25-30** ☐
39b		Pontiac Convertible	Type 1 has separate Red steering wheel, Type 2 is moulded into dashboard	
	1962	1st issue:......................	Metallic Violet, Type 1, Crimson base, Grey or Silver plastic wheels, 70 mm.	**£50-60** ☐
		colour change:............	Yellow body, Type 1 or 2, Crimson base, Green tinted windows, Silver or Grey plastic wheels	**£20-25** ☐
		base colour change:	Yellow body, Type 2, Black base, Grey, Silver or Black plastic wheels........................	**£15-20** ☐
39c	1967	Ford Tractor............................	Blue body, Yellow engine cover and wheels, Black plastic tyres, 55 mm.	**£10-15** ☐
	1968	colour change:............	Same but All Blue body, issued with K20 Transporter	GSP ☐
	1972	colour change:............	Orange body, Yellow wheels, issued with BM-2 Transporter	GSP ☐
39d	1973	Clipper	Metallic Pink, Yellow interior, Rolamatic feature, 77 mm.	**£4-7** ☐
39e	1979	R.R. Silver Shadow Mk.II	Metallic Silver body, Red seats, opening doors, Superfast, 75 mm.	**£2-4** ☐
	1981	colour change:............	Metallic Red body, Cream seats	**£2-4** ☐
	1982	colour change:............	Metallic Gold body, White seats	**£2-4** ☐
	1984	colour change:............	Metallic Maroon body, Silver base...	**£1-3** ☐
39f	1985	BMW 323i Cabriolet	Metallic Blue body	**£1-2** ☐
	1986	colour change:............	All Red body	**£1-2** ☐
	1987	colour change:............	White body, '323i' logo, Superfast...	NRP ☐
	1987	Laser Wheels issue:......	White body, 'ALPINA' logo..	NRP ☐
	1989	colour change:............	Green body, flame design 'BP' (Dutch promotional)...	**£1-2** ☐
39g	1990	Mach CH 600 Tractor.............	White body, Red/Blue stripes..	NRP ☐
39h	1992	Mercedes-Benz 600 SEL	Metallic Silver body. (Catalogue picture not seen)	NRP ☐

MB 40

Ref. No.	Year(s)	Model Type		Market Price Range
40a	1957	Bedford 7 Ton Tipper	Red body, Brown tipper, metal wheels, 53 mm..	**£25-30** ☐
		wheel change:.............	Same but with Grey plastic wheels, domed crimped axles...	**£15-20** ☐
		axle change:	As previous model with Grey plastic wheels on rivetted axles	**£15- 20** ☐
40b	1961	Leyland Royal Tiger Coach	Steel Blue body, Black base, clear or Green windows, Grey, Silver or Black plastic wheels, 75 mm.	**£10-15** ☐
40c	1967	Hay Trailer	Blue body, Yellow plastic hay racks and wheels, Black plastic tyres, 86 mm.	**£2-4** ☐
		note:	Model deleted in 1972 but appeared in Two-Packs between 1976-1981:	
		Twin-Pack model:......	Red body	**£8-10** ☐
		Twin-Pack model:......	Lemon body	**£5-7** ☐
		Twin-Pack model:......	Pale Blue body	**£5-7** ☐
		scarce colour:	Tan body with Black racks	**£50-60** ☐
40d	1972	Vauxhall Guildsman..................	Pink body, Green windows, Cream interior, hook	**£5-8** ☐
		colour change:...........	Red body, Green windows, racing number '40'	**£5-8** ☐
		colour change:...........	Gold body (Bulgarian issue)...	**£25-30** ☐
		note:...........................	Many other variations exist	
40e	1976	Horse Box...............................	Orange and Cream body, Tan ramp, 2 White horses, Superfast, 72 mm.	**£3-5** ☐
	1981	colour change:............	Green and Cream body, Brown drop-down ramp	**£2-4** ☐
	1983	colour change:............	Orange and Brown body, White drop-down ramp	**£2-4** ☐
		colour change:............	Brown and Yellow body, White drop-down ramp	**£1-3** ☐
		colour change:............	Cream and Black body, Brown drop-down ramp	**£1-3** ☐
40f	1982	Corvette 'T' Roof	White body..	**£1-3** ☐
40g	1985	Rocket Transporter	White body, Red logo 'NASA'	NRP ☐
	1989	colour change:............	As previous model but in Camouflage finish...	NRP ☐

MB 41

Ref. No.	Year(s)	Model Type	Matchbox Miniatures - continued	Market Price Range	
41a	1957	Jaguar 'D'-type	Dark Green, driver, RN '41' or '52', metal or Grey plastic wheels, 55 mm.	£35-40	☐
41b	1960	Jaguar 'D'-type	Dark Green body, RN '5', '6' or '41', Grey plastic wheels, 62 mm.	£30-35	☐
		wheel change:	As previous model but with Red wheel hubs, Black plastic tyres	NGPP	☐
		wheel change:	As previous model but with White wheel hubs, Black plastic tyres	£75-100	☐
		wheel change:	With unpainted cast metal 'spoked' wheels, Black or Grey plastic tyres	£30-35	☐
41c	1965	Ford GT	White body, RN '6', Yellow hubs, Black plastic tyres, 67 mm.	NGPP	☐
		wheel change:	As previous model but Red wheel hubs	£70-80	☐
		colour change:	As previous models but Yellow body and wheels	£15-20	☐
	1969	wheel change:	White body, Black or Green base, Superfast wheels	£10-15	☐
		colour change:	Metallic Red body, Black, Yellow or Cream base, Superfast	£10-15	☐
41d	1973	Siva Spyder	Metallic Red, Black or Silver band on roof, Superfast	£4-7	☐
		colour change:	Blue body, 'GOODYEAR'	£3-5	☐
		colour change:	Blue body, stars on bonnet, Red/White stripe, 'S'	£3-5	☐
		colour change:	Blue body, spider-web print, 'Black Widow' on base, Superfast	£3-5	☐
41e	1979	'AMBULANCE'	White body, Red/Yellow/Black decal, opening rear door, Superfast, 75 mm.	£2-4	☐
	1981		White body, Blue/Yellow decal	£2-4	☐
		colour change:	Silver body, White doors	£25-30	☐
		colour change:	Red 'NOTARTZ', German model	£10-15	☐
		logo change:	Small 'Ambulance' on labels	£8-11	☐
41f	1982	Kenworth Aerodyne	Orange, Black or Green body (issued with Convoy sets)	£1-3	☐
41g	1983	Racing Porsche	Two-tone Blue body, 'Team Porsche', 'Elf', etc, Superfast	£2-4	☐
	1986	colour change:	White body, Red RN '10', 'PORSCHE', (box also contains Collector Card)	£1-3	☐
	1987	Laser Wheels issue:	Metallic Red body, racing number '35'	NRP	☐
	1989	colour change:	Red body, White design, Red racing number '4'	NRP	☐
41g	1990	Vauxhall Cavalier Gsi 2000	Metallic Dark Pink body	NRP	☐
41h	1991	'Sunburner'	Yellow body with Black seats, Orange/Red 'fire' design	NRP	☐
	1993	colour change:	Blue body with double White stripe	NRP	☐

MB 42

Ref. No.	Year(s)	Model Type	Matchbox Miniatures - continued	Market Price Range	
42a	1957	Bedford CA Van	Yellow body, 'EVENING NEWS', metal wheels, 57 mm.	£35-40	☐
		wheel change:	As previous model but with Grey plastic wheels	£35-40	☐
		wheel change:	As previous model but with Black plastic wheels on rivetted axles	£50-60	☐
42b	1965	Studebaker Lark Wagonaire	Light or Dark Blue body, 'hunter & dog' figures, Black plastic wheels, 76 mm.	£12-15	☐
42c	1969	Iron Fairy Crane	Red body, Yellow or Green boom & hook, Black plastic wheels	£10-15	☐
	1971	colour change:	Orange body, Gold boom, Superfast	£20-25	☐
42d	1972	'Tyre Fryer'	Metallic Blue body, Yellow interior, Superfast, 76 mm.	£5-8	☐
		colour change:	Orange body, 'Jaffa Mobile' logo	£45-55	☐
42e	1978	Mercedes Container Truck	'MATCHBOX', Red body, Cream or White container, Superfast	£3-5	☐
		'MAYFLOWER'	Metallic Dark Green body and container	£3-5	☐
		'SEALAND'	Red body, Cream container	£3-5	☐
		'KARSTADT'	Blue body, Blue container. (German issue model)	£10-15	☐
		'DEUTSCHE BUNDESPOST'	Yellow body and container. (German issue model)	£10-15	☐
		'CONFERN'	Red body, Cream/Red container. (German issue model)	£10-15	☐
		'NYK'	Red body, Cream container	£3-5	☐
		'OCL'	Red body, Cream container	£3-5	☐
		'MODEL TRANSPORTSBETRIEBE'	Red/White body, (German issue)	£4-6	☐
42f	1983	'57 'T-Bird'	Red and White body, Red seats	£2-4	☐
		US issue:	Black body	£4-6	☐
42g	1984	Mobile Crane	Yellow body, Black crane, Red logo 'REYNOLDS CRANE HIRE'	£1-3	☐
	1992	colour change:	Yellow body, Red cab with Yellow design	NRP	☐

MB 43

Ref. No.	Year(s)	Model Type	Matchbox Miniatures - continued	Market Price Range	
43a	1958	Hillman Minx	Light Green body, Silver/Red trim, metal wheels, hook, 66 mm.	£200-250	☐
		colour change:	Blue/Grey body, Pale Grey roof, metal or Grey plastic wheels	£30-35	☐
		colour change:	Turquoise body, Cream roof, Grey plastic wheels	£25-30	☐
43b	1962	A.B. Tractor Shovel	Yellow body, Yellow shovel, Red or Yellow driver, Black plastic wheels, 65 mm.	£20-25	☐
		colour change:	As previous model but with Red shovel, Yellow or Red driver	£8-11	☐
43c	1968	Pony Trailer	Yellow/Grey, 2 horses, Brown or Green base, Black plastic wheels, 67 mm.	£5-8	☐
	1970	wheel change:	As previous model but with Superfast wheels	£5-8	☐
	1971	colour change:	Light Brown body, Dark Brown drop-down ramp	£4-7	☐
43d	1973	'Dragon Wheels'	Green main body, Red decal, Silver engine, Superfast wheels, 72 mm.	£3-5	☐
43e	1979	Steam Locomotive	Red/Black body, Yellow number '4345', 0-4-0, hook, 68 mm.	£1-3	☐
	1989	'NORTH YORKSHIRE MOORS'	Red body, Promotional	NRP	☐
	1989	'WEST SOMERSET RAILWAY'	Green body, Promotional	NRP	☐
	1989	'ISLE of MAN RAILWAY'	Blue body, 'HUTCHINSON', Promotional	NRP	☐
	1989	'BLUE TRAIN'	A Promotional model commissioned by M/s K.H.Norton of Leicester	NRP	☐
	1990	'BRITISH RAIL'	Black body with 'lion' emblem. Promotional	NRP	☐
	1990	'G.W.R.'	Matt Green/Black body, Gold design, Promotional	NRP	☐
	1990	'KELLOGGS'	Green/Black body, White design, Promotional	NRP	☐

Ref. No.	Year(s)	Model Type	Matchbox Miniatures - continued	Market Price Range
43f	1982	Peterbilt Conventional..............	Black body (US issue)..	NRP ☐
	1984	Convoy Set issues:	Red, Black, White or Yellow. Various logos	NRP ☐
43g	1984	Mercedes 500 SEC AMG.........	All White body..	£1-3 ☐
	1985	colour change:..........	All Red body..	£1-3 ☐
	1987	colour change:..........	Black body	£1-3 ☐
	1987	Laser Wheels issue:.....	Red body, 'AMG 500 SEC' logo	NRP ☐
	1988	colour change:..........	White body, Silver stripe, (German issue)	£1-3 ☐
	1989	colour change:..........	Black body, 'REDOXON' on bonnet. Hong Kong promotional issue	£4-6 ☐
43h	1990	'57 Chevy	Blue body, White logo 'MILKY WAY', (Mars on-pack offer)......	£1-2 ☐
	1990	design change:..........	Black body with Red/Yellow 'fire' design covering front, 'CHEVY' on boot..............	NRP ☐
	1993	design change:..........	Red body with 'flame' effect	NRP ☐

MB 44

44a	1958	Rolls-Royce Silver Cloud	Metallic Mid-Blue body, Red trim, metal wheels, 67 mm........	£28-33 ☐
	1960	colour change:..........	Metallic Light Blue body, metal or Grey plastic wheels	£25-30 ☐
		wheel change:..........	As previous model but with Silver plastic wheels............	£35-40 ☐
44b	1964	Rolls-Royce Phantom V	Metallic Light Mauve, Cream interior, Grey, Silver or Black plastic wheels	£20-25 ☐
		colour change:..........	Silver-Grey body, Silver or Black plastic wheels	£15-20 ☐
		colour change:..........	Crimson Red body, Cream interior, Silver plastic wheels	£15-20 ☐
		colour change:..........	With Metallic Bronze body	£75-100 ☐
44c	1967	GMC Refrigerator Truck.........	Red cab, Green box, Grey, Black plastic wheels, 76 mm........	£8-11 ☐
	1970	wheel change:..........	As previous model but with Superfast wheels..................	£8-11 ☐
	1971	colour change:..........	Yellow and Red body, Superfast	£7-9 ☐
44d	1972	Boss Mustang	Yellow/Black or Green body, Superfast wheels, 75 mm.	£5-8 ☐
44e	1979	Passenger Coach	Red/Black body, Green tinted windows, '431-432', 73 mm.	£2-4 ☐
44f	1983	Citroën 15cv	Black body, Tan seats, Silver trim, Superfast	£1-3 ☐
	1986	colour change:..........	Deep Blue body	NRP ☐
44g	1988	Skoda 130LR......................	White body, Blue 'SKODA' on roof, racing number '44'	NRP ☐
44h	1982	4 x 4 Chevy Van......................	Green body and windows, 'RIDIN' HIGH' decal	NRP ☐
44i		**1921 Ford Model 'T' Van**	Promotional issues introduced in 1990.	
44i	1990	'5th MICA UK CONVENTION'	White/Blue body with UK and E.E.C. flags design	£5-7 ☐
	1990	'3rd MICA USA CONVENTION'	White/Blue body with US and UK flags design..................	£5-7 ☐
	1990	'BIRDS CUSTARD'	Yellow/Red/Blue body, 'ORIGINAL FLAVOUR' logo	NRP ☐

MB 44i Vans have been issued in great numbers for various promotional purposes around the world. It has become necessary to list them in a separate computer based 'Specialist Series' publication that will be regularly updated. Details of how to obtain the publication are given at the end of the Matchbox chapter.

MB 45

45a	1958	Vauxhall Victor	Dark Red body, Black base, metal wheels, 61 mm.	£300-400 ☐
		colour change:..........	Pale Yellow body, Silver/Red trim, metal wheels..............	£30-35 ☐
		wheel change:..........	Pale Yellow body; Grey, Silver or Black plastic wheels........	£15-20 ☐
45b	1965	Ford Corsair with Boat............	Cream body, Green boat, Red seats, Grey or Black plastic wheels, 68 mm.	£8-11 ☐
		interior change:	As previous model but with White interior, Black plastic wheels	£5-8 ☐
45c	1970	Ford Group Six	Metallic Green body, Cream interior, RN '7' or '45', Pink or Black base, 75 mm......	£10-13 ☐
	1973	colour change:..........	Lime Green body, RN '45', Amber engine, Dark Grey or Black base	£5-8 ☐
	1974	colour change:..........	Red body, tinted windows, racing number '45'	£4-6 ☐
45d	1976	BMW 3.0 CSL	Red body, Yellow interior, 'BMW', opening doors, Superfast, 74 mm.	£2-4 ☐
	1979	colour change:..........	Orange body, White interior, 'BMW'	£2-4 ☐
	1977	colour change:..........	White body, 'POLIZEI' and '123' logos, Superfast	£2-4 ☐
		colour change:..........	White body, 'MANHAULTER'	£20-25 ☐
45e	1982	Kenworth Cabover	White/Blue body, Amber tinted windows, Superfast, 71 mm.	£2-4 ☐
	1984	colour change:..........	Silver Grey body, '45' design	£1-3 ☐
	1985	colour change:..........	Black body	NRP ☐
	1986	colour change:..........	Red body, Yellow/White/Orange design, (with Collector Card).	NRP ☐
		US Issue:..................	'Chef Boyardee'	£12-15 ☐
45f	1988	Skip Truck	Yellow body, Grey/Orange skip	NRP ☐
	1992	colour change:..........	Yellow body/chassis, Red skip	NRP ☐

MB 46

46a	1958	Morris Minor 1000.....................	Pale Brown body, no windows, metal wheels, 53 mm............	NGPP ☐
		colour change:..........	Dark Green body, Black base, domed crimped axles	£50-60 ☐
		colour change:..........	Dark Blue/Green body, metal or Grey plastic wheels	£125-175 ☐
		colour change:..........	Blue body, Grey plastic wheels	£125-175 ☐
46b	1960	(Guy) Removals Van.....................	Dark Blue, White opening rear door, Grey or Silver plastic wheels, 66 mm.	
		'PICKFORDS'	'Removers & Storage, Branches in all Large Towns' on THREE lines......	£55-75 ☐
		logo change:..........	'Pickfords Removers & Storage' on TWO lines..................	£100-140 ☐
		colour change:..........	Green body (logo on 3 lines), Grey, Silver or Black plastic wheels............	£55-75 ☐
		'BEALES-BEALESONS'	Light Brown body, White decals, Black plastic wheels. Promotional in White card box with Black 'Sun' design plus the logo 'Its A Pleasure'.	£250-350 ☐
46c	1968	Mercedes-Benz 300 SE	Green body, Cream seats, clear windows, Black plastic wheels, 74 mm.	£9-12 ☐
	1969	colour change:..........	Metallic Blue body, Black plastic wheels......................	£8-11 ☐
	1970	colour change:..........	Gold body, Superfast	£5-7 ☐
		colour change:..........	Silver body, Superfast	£15-18 ☐
		Bulgarian issue:..........	Metallic Blue or Red body, Superfast	£20-25 ☐

Ref. No.	Year(s)	Model Type	Matchbox Miniatures - continued	Market Price Range	
46d	1973	'Stretcha Fetcha'	White body, Red baseplate and cross, Blue tinted windows and beacons, 70 mm.	£3-5	☐
		window change:	With Amber windows	£3-5	☐
		design change:	With small Red cross label	£12-15	☐
		German issue:	Red body	£12-15	☐
		note:	Other variations exist.		
46e		'Viper' Van	No details	£2-4	☐
46f	1979	Ford Tractor and Harrow	Blue body, Silver engine, Yellow harrow and seat, hook, 52 mm.	£2-4	☐
		colour change:	Metallic Green body, with or without 'FORD' on engine cover, US issue	£1-3	☐
46g	1984	Sauber Group 'C' Racer	Red body, 'BASF', (with Collector Card)	NRP	☐
	1986	colour change:	White body, Black racing number '61'	NRP	☐
	1988	colour change:	White/Blue body, racing number '46', 'SHELL', Superfast	NRP	☐
	1989	colour change:	Two-tone Blue body, racing number '46'	NRP	☐
	1989	colour change:	White body	NRP	☐
	1991	colour change:	White/Blue body, 'Grand Prix' & 'Sauber' logos, racing number '46'	NRP	☐
46h	1987	'Hot Chocolate'	US issue	£4-6	☐
46i	1987	'Big Blue'	Metallic Blue lift-up Volkswagen body, racing number '39'	£4-6	☐

MB 47

Ref. No.	Year(s)	Model Type	Matchbox Miniatures - continued	Market Price Range	
47a	1958	Trojan Van	Red body, 'BROOKE BOND TEA', metal or Grey plastic wheels, 58 mm.	£33-38	☐
47b	1963	Commer Mobile Shop	Metallic Blue body, 'LYONS MAID' decals, Black plastic wheels, vendor (with legs), 58 mm.	£50-60	☐
		colour change:	Non-Metallic Blue body, Black or Grey plastic wheels, vendor (legs on some)	£35-45	☑
		colour change:	Cream body, Black plastic wheels, vendor with or without legs	£45-55	☐
		design change:	Cream body, Red/White side labels 'LORD NIELSENS ICE CREAM VAN'	£50-60	☐
47c	1968	DAF Container Truck	Sea Green body, Grey roof, Yellow container, Black plastic wheels, 77 mm.	£35-45	☐
		colour change:	Silver body, Grey or Silver roof, Yellow container, Black plastic wheels	£10-12	☐
	1970	wheel change:	Same but Superfast wheels, 'Patent app. for' on base of some	£10-15	☐
47c	1974	Beach Hopper	Metallic Blue body, Yellow design, Rolomatic, Superfast, 66 mm.	£3-5	☐
47e	1980	'G.W.R.' Pannier Locomotive	Green/Black body, Gold decals, 0-6-0, hook, 77 mm.	£2-4	☐
47f	1982	Jaguar SS100	Red body, Silver trim, Beige seats & steering wheel, Superfast, 76 mm.	£2-4	☐
	1986	colour change:	Blue body, Grey bonnet, White seats, (includes Collector Card)	£2-4	☐
	1990	colour change:	Green/Red body, (Brooke Bond promotional model)	NRP	☐
47g	1988	School Bus	Yellow body, US issue model, 'School District'	£4-6	☐
	1988	Army version:	Olive Green bus celebrating U.S.A. Matchbox Club's 7th Anniversary	£4-6	☐

MB 48

Ref. No.	Year(s)	Model Type	Matchbox Miniatures - continued	Market Price Range	
48a	1958	Meteor Sports Boat on Trailer	Blue/Cream boat, Black trailer, metal or Grey plastic wheels, 59/66 mm.	£15-20	☐
48b	1961	Sports Boat and Trailer	Cream or White deck, Red hull, Dark Blue trailer, Grey or Black Plastic wheels, 66/67 mm.	£15-20	☐
	1964	colour change:	Red deck, Cream or White hull, Light Blue trailer	£15-20	☐
48c	1966	(Dodge) Dumper Truck	Red body, Silver trim, wide or narrow Black plastic wheels, 76 mm.	£8-10	☐
	1970	colour change:	Blue cab and chassis, Yellow tipper, Superfast wheels	£5-8	☐
48d	1973	'Pie-Eyed Piper'	Metallic Blue, Silver engine, tinted windows, Superfast wheels	£3-5	☐
	1981	US issue:	Red body, 'RED RIDER' logo	£5-8	☐
	1983	US issue:	White body, racing number '48'	£5-8	☐
48e	1978	'White Lightning'	US issued model	£4-6	☐
48f	1978	Sambron Jacklift	Yellow/Black or Yellow/Orange body, 78 mm.	£2-4	☐
48g	1983	(Mercedes) Unimog	Yellow/White/Black body, Red 'Rescue', snowplough, Superfast, 64 mm.	£2-3	☐
		variant:	With White blade	£9-11	☐
	1987	colour change:	White body, Yellow blade, 'ROAD RAIDER' logo	NRP	☐
48h	1986	Vauxhall Astra GTE	Red body, opening doors, (includes Collector Card)	£2-3	☐
	1987	design change:	With 'A.C. Delco' tampo print	£2-3	☐
	1987	colour change:	White body, racing number '48'	NRP	☐
	1988	design change:	White/Blue/Red/Yellow body with 'STP' logo, racing number '7'	NRP	☐

MB 49

Ref. No.	Year(s)	Model Type	Matchbox Miniatures - continued	Market Price Range	
49a	1958	M3 Personnel Carrier	Military Green, White star, Grey tracks, metal wheels & rollers, 62 mm.	£25-35	☐
		wheel change:	Same but Grey plastic wheels; metal, Grey or Silver plastic rollers	£30-40	☐
		wheel change:	Same but Black plastic wheels and rollers	£15-25	☐
		track change:	Same (Black plastic wheels and rollers), but with Green rubber tracks	£20-25	☐
49b	1967	(Mercedes) Unimog	Tan body, Green or Red base Yellow hubs, Black plastic tyres, 61 mm.	£8-11	☐
	1968	colour change:	Pale or Mid-Blue body with Red base, Yellow hubs	£6-8	☐
		wheel change:	As previous models but with Superfast wheels	£6-8	☐
49c	1973	'Chop Suey'	Metallic Red body, Silver engine and handlebars, 72 mm.	£3-5	☐
	1974	colour change:	Metallic Red body, Red handlebars	£3-5	☐
49d	1977	Crane Truck	Yellow/Black body, Purple windscreen, 76 mm.	£2-4	☐
		colour change:	Yellow/Black body, 'SAFETY FIRST' decal	NRP	☐
		colour change:	Red/Yellow body	NRP	☐
		colour change:	All Yellow body, Orange jib, Red hook, Green tinted windows, Superfast	NRP	☐
49e	1983	'SAND DIGGER'	Green body, exposed engine, Yellow logo	£2-4	☐
	1985	'DUNE MAN'	Red body, Yellow design on bonnet	NRP	☐
49f	1987	Peugeot Quasar	White body, Chrome interior, (with Collector Card)	NRP	☐
	1987	Laser Wheels issue:	Metallic Blue body	NRP	☐
	1988	colour change:	Maroon body, Yellow design, exposed engine	NRP	☐
49g	1992	Lamborghini Diablo	Yellow body with Red 'DIABLO' on doors	NRP	☐

MB 50

Ref. No.	Year(s)	Model Type	Description	Price
50a	1958	Commer Pick-Up Mk.VIII.......	Pale Brown body, metal or Grey plastic wheels, 64 mm.	£20-25
		colour change:............	Light Brown body, Grey or Silver plastic wheels	£50-60
	1961	colour change:............	Red body, Cream cab, Silver plastic wheels	£100-125
	1962	colour change:............	Red body, Grey cab, Silver or Black plastic wheels	£45-55
		wheel change:............	Red body, Grey cab, Grey plastic wheels	£60-70
50b	1964	John Deere Lanz Tractor.........	Green body, Silver/Yellow trim, Yellow wheels, Black tyres, 50 mm.	£10-15
50c	1969	Ford Kennel Truck	Metallic Green body, Black plastic wheels, 71 mm.	£8-11
	1971	wheel change:............	As previous model but Superfast wheels, Yellow or Black base.	£5-8
50d	1974	Articulated Truck	Yellow cab, Blue trailer, tinted windows, Superfast wheels	£4-6
	1974	colour change:............	As previous model but with Blue/Yellow labels.	£2-4
50e	1981	Harley Davidson Motor Cycle..	Metallic Bronze body, Silver engine, Black seat and handlebars, 70 mm.	£2-4
	1982	colour change:............	Metallic Plum body, Brown rider, Black seat & forks	£2-4
50f	1985	Chevy Blazer	Red/White body, 'SHERIFF' crest, 'ISP7'.	NRP
50g	1988	Dodge Dakota	Red pick-up body, side stripes, 2 spotlights	NRP
50h	1991	Auxiliary Power Truck	Yellow/White body, 'Floodlight Heavy Rescue' logo	NRP
	1992	Auxiliary Power Truck	Red/White body, Blue 'No.2', 'Fire', 'Rescue Dept.' logos	NRP

MB 51

Ref. No.	Year(s)	Model Type	Description	Price
51a	1958	Albion Chieftain	Yellow body, Beige load, metal wheels, 'PORTLAND CEMENT'	£38-45
		logo change:...............	As previous model but with 'BLUE CIRCLE' added, metal or Grey or Silver plastic wheels	£30-35
	1962	colour change:............	Light Brown body, Grey or Black plastic wheels	£30-35
51b	1964	Tipping Trailer	Green body, 3 Yellow or Brown barrels, Yellow wheels, Black plastic tyres	£4-6
			As previous model but with Grey plastic tyres	£8-10
51c	1969	AEC Mammoth Major	Orange cab, Silver tipper, White base, 'DOUGLAS', 8 Black plastic wheels	£15-20
		colour change:............	Orange cab with Grey tipper	£11-14
		base change:................	As previous models but with Silver base and grille	£15-20
		colour change:............	Yellow cab, Silver tipper and base, 'DOUGLAS'.	£15-20
	1970	logo change:...............	Yellow cab, Silver tipper and base, Green/Yellow label, 'POINTER'.	£15-20
		wheel change:............	Superfast issue.	£10-15
51d	1973	Citroën SM............................	Metallic Red body, Cream seats, clear windows, Superfast, 78 mm.	£3-5
		colour change:............	Metallic Orange body	£3-5
		colour change:............	Metallic Blue body	£3-5
		Bulgarian issues:	Green, Gold or Blue body	£10-15
	1977	colour change:............	Blue body, Red flash, racing number '8'	£2-4
51e	1978	Combine Harvester...................	Red body, Yellow moving parts. Superfast or ordinary plastic wheels.	£2-4
51f	1982	'Midnight Magic'.....................	Black/Silver, Chrome interior, US issued model	£4-6
51g	1983	Pontiac Firebird	Red body, White decals, Tan seats, Superfast, 76 mm.	NRP
	1983	design change:............	Red or Black body, 'Firebird' design	NRP
	1986	US issue:	Black body, 'HALLEYS COMET' logo	NRP
	1987	Laser Wheels issue:.....	Metallic Blue body	NRP
	1987	Matchbox/Dinky issue: ..	Blue body, racing number '18'.	NRP
51h	1988	Ford Police Car	White body, Black tampo, Red 'PD-21'.	NRP

MB 52

Ref. No.	Year(s)	Model Type	Description	Price
52a	1958	1948 Maserati 4 CLT	Red body, Cream driver, RN '52' on some, Black plastic wheels, 61 mm.	£20-25
		wheel change:............	Red body, racing number '52', wire wheels, Black plastic tyres	£70-85
		wheel change:............	Red body with Red wheels	NGPP
		colour change:............	Yellow body, RN '52', '5' or '3', wire wheels, Black plastic tyres	£35-45
52b	1965	B.R.M. Racing Car	Blue body, RN '5' or '3', Yellow wheels, Black plastic tyres, 67 mm.	£8-11
		colour change:............	Red body, racing number '5'	£20-25
52c	1970	Dodge Charger Mk.III.............	Red body, Black/Yellow flash on some, Superfast, 76 mm.	£7-9
	1973	colour change:............	Purple body, racing number '5' on some, Superfast	£5-8
	1974	colour change:............	Lime Green body, decal on some, Red base, Superfast	£5-8
52d	1977	'POLICE' Launch	Blue and White boat, Blue tinted windows, 2 policemen, 77 mm.	£2-4
	1989	colour change:............	Military version with Camouflage paint finish	NRP
52e	1981	BMW MI................................	Silver body, Black racing number '52', Red seats, Superfast, 75 mm.	£2-4
	1983	colour change:............	White body, Black RN '52', Red 'BMW MI', Superfast wheels	NRP
	1984	design change:............	Red/Yellow body, racing number '5'.	NRP
	1985	design change:............	Black body, racing number '59'.	NRP
	1986	design change:............	Yellow/White body, Red racing number '11'.	NRP
	1988	design change:............	Red body, Blue/Red/White design.	NRP
52f	1991	Isuzu Amigo	Blue body, spare wheel on rear, 'ISUZU' logo	NRP
	1992	colour change:............	Red body, slanting side designs on Blue/Orange	NRP

MB 53

Ref. No.	Year(s)	Model Type	Description	Price
53a	1958	Aston Martin DB2-4 Mk.I.......	Metallic Green body, metal or Grey plastic wheels, 65 mm.	£20-25
		colour change:............	Metallic Red body, Grey plastic wheels	£60-70
		wheel change:............	Metallic Red body, Black plastic wheels	£100-130
		colour change:............	Non-Metallic Red body, Black plastic wheels	£75-90
53b	1963	Mercedes-Benz 220SE..............	Maroon body, Cream seats; Grey, Silver or Black plastic wheels, 69 mm.	£12-15
		colour change:............	Dark Red body, Grey or Black plastic wheels	£9-12

Ref. No.	Year(s)	Model Type	Matchbox Miniatures - continued	Market Price Range	
53c	1968	Ford Zodiac Mk.IV..................	Metallic Light-Blue body, Cream seats, Black plastic wheels, 71 mm.	£12-15	☐
	1970	colour change:.............	Metallic Light-Green body, Black plastic wheels	NGPP	☐
		wheel change:.............	As previous model but with Superfast wheels	£5-8	☐
		colour change:.............	Lime Green body	£15-20	☐
53d	1973	'Tanzara'.........................	Orange body, 'Clover-leaf' decal on some, Superfast, 76 mm.	£3-5	☐
	1976	colour change:.............	White body, Blue/Red stripes, racing number '53', Superfast	£3-5	☐
	1981	US issue:	Black body, Silver design, 'MIDNIGHT MAGIC'.	£6-8	☐
53e	1977	CJ6 Jeep...........................	Red body, Fawn seats and roof, Superfast, 75 mm.	£2-4	☐
		seat change:...............	With Black seats.	£7-9	☐
		colour change:.............	Green body, with Black seats	£7-9	☐
		colour change:.............	Yellow body, with Brown roof	£5-7	☐
	1981	colour change:.............	Green body, Yellow seats, Fawn roof	£2-4	☐
53f	1982	Flareside Pick-Up	Blue or Orange body, 'Baja Bouncer' logo, Superfast	£2-4	☐
	1986	design change:.............	Yellow/Blue body, 'FORD'.	NRP	☐
	1987	colour change:.............	Military-Green body, 'STICK-UP PICK-UP' logo	NRP	☐
53g	1989	Dump Truck...........................	Yellow body, Grey tipper, Red stripes	NRP	☐
	1992	colour change:.............	Yellow cab and chassis, Red tipper	NRP	☐

MB 54

Ref. No.	Year(s)	Model Type	Matchbox Miniatures - continued	Market Price Range	
54a	1958	Saracen Personnel Carrier	Olive Green body, 6 Black plastic wheels, 57 mm.	£15-20	☐
54b	1965	Cadillac Ambulance	White, Red cross & roof lights, Black plastic wheels, 72 mm.	£8-11	☐
	1970	wheel change:.............	As previous model but with Superfast wheels	£5-8	☐
54c	1971	Ford Capri.........................	Red body, Red or Black bonnet, Cream or White seats, Superfast, 77 mm.	£2-4	☐
		colour change:.............	As previous model but Orange body	£2-4	☐
	1974	colour change:.............	Metallic Purple body, Cream or White seats	£2-4	☐
	1985	colour change:.............	Pink body with Pink or Black bonnet	NRP	☐
54d	1977	Personnel Carrier......................	Green body, Brown figures, Superfast wheels, 76 mm.	£2-4	☐
54e	1980	Mobile Home...........................	Cream or White body, Orange interior, Superfast, 76 mm.	£2-4	☐
54f	1982	'NASA' Tracking Vehicle..........	White body, Blue/Red decal, with or without 'Space Shuttle' logo	£2-4	☐
54g	1984	Airport Unit	Red/White body, Black/White design	NRP	☐
	1985	design change:.............	Red/Yellow body, 'METRO', 2 Blue warning lights................	NRP	☐
	1989	colour change:.............	Red body, 'AIRPORT FOAM PUMPER'.	NRP	☐
	1989	colour change:.............	Yellow body, Red tampo 'FOAM'.	NRP	☐
	1989	colour change:.............	Military version in Camouflage paintwork	NRP	☐
54h	1990	Chevrolet Lumina......................	Blue body, 'MATCHBOX MOTORSPORTS', Yellow racing number '35'.	NRP	☐
	1992	colour change:.............	Green body, Yellow 'MATCHBOX MOTORSPORTS', and RN '35'	NRP	☐
	1993	design change:.............	Red body, racing number '12', Yellow 'Performance' logo.	NRP	☐

MB 55

Ref. No.	Year(s)	Model Type	Matchbox Miniatures - continued	Market Price Range	
55a	1958	DUKW Amphibian..................	Olive Green body, Black base; metal, Grey or Black plastic wheels, 71 mm.	£15-20	☐
55b	1963	Ford Fairlane 'POLICE' Car....	Dark Blue body and crests, Black plastic wheels, 66 mm.	£125-150	☐
		colour change:.............	Metallic Blue body, Black plastic wheels	£14-18	☐
		wheel change:.............	With Silver or Grey plastic wheels	£25-30	☐
55c	1966	Ford Galaxie 'POLICE' Car.....	White body, Red/Blue crests, Black plastic wheels, 77 mm.	£12-15	☐
	1970	wheel change:.............	As previous model but with Superfast wheels	£5-8	☐
55d	1968	Mercury 'POLICE' Car............	White body, Red/Black crests, Black plastic tyres, 77 mm.	£8-11	☐
	1982	US issue:	White body, 'LOS ANGELES POLICE', Superfast wheels	NRP	☐
	1986	US issue:	Black body, 'HALLEYS COMET' logo, Superfast	NRP	☐
	1987	Laser Wheels issue:.....	White body, 'R-15' logo.	NRP	☐
55e	1971	Mercury 'POLICE' Estate Car..	White body, Police crest, Superfast wheels, 77 mm.	£6-9	☐
55f	1976	'Hell Raiser'...........................	White body, Silver exposed engine, Red seats, 75 mm.	£3-5	☐
	1978	colour change:.............	Metallic Blue body, stars and stripes decal	£2-4	☐
55g	1980	Ford Cortina 1600 GL............	Metallic Green body, Red seats, opening doors, Superfast wheels, 75 mm.	£2-4	☐
	1981	colour change:.............	Metallic Red body, Yellow seats, opening doors, Superfast	£2-4	☐
	1982	colour change:.............	Metallic Bronze and White body, Yellow seats, (many other variations)	£2-4	☐
	1983	colour change:.............	Metallic Tan body with Dark Blue racing stripes	£2-4	☐
55h	1983	Ford Sierra XR4i	Metallic Silver & Black body, Red seats, Superfast wheels, 76 mm.	£2-4	☐
	1984	colour change:.............	Silver/Grey body, Red/Black design	NRP	☐
	1985	colour change:.............	Silver/Red body, Red 'XR4i' design	NRP	☐
	1987	colour change:.............	Cream body, racing number '55', Superfast	NRP	☐
	1987	colour change:.............	White body, 'VIRGIN' logo, Superfast	NRP	☐
	1987	Laser Wheels issue:.....	Metallic Green, racing number '85' logo	NRP	☐
	1989	design change:.............	Black body, 'TEXACO' logo, racing number '46'	NRP	☐
55i	1986	Ford Sierra XR44......................	Yellow body, Black chassis, spoiler, tampo-print design	NRP	☐
		design change:.............	Yellow body, Red interior	NRP	☐
	1989	design change:.............	Yellow body, Black bonnet stripes	NRP	☐
	1991	design change:.............	Black body, White/Red 'TEXACO' and star logos, RN '6'	NRP	☐
	1992	design change:.............	White body, Red racing number '1', plus various Blue logos................	NRP	☐

MB 56

Ref. No.	Year(s)	Model Type	Matchbox Miniatures - continued	Market Price Range	
56a	1958	London Trolley Bus	Red body, 2 Red roof poles, 'PEARDRAX' and destination board decals, metal wheels, or Grey, Silver or Black plastic wheels, 67 mm.	£30-40	☐
			As previous model but with Black poles	£75-90	☐
56b	1965	Fiat 1500..............................	Green body, Red seats, Light or Dark Brown luggage, hook, 65 mm.	£10-15	☐
		colour change:.............	Red body, Light Brown luggage.	£35-45	☐

Ref. No.	Year(s)	Model Type	Matchbox Miniatures - continued	Market Price Range	
56c	1969	B.M.C. 1800 Pininfarina	Gold body, White seats, opening doors, Superfast wheels, 70 mm..........	£8-11	☐
	1970	colour change:............	Orange body, White seats, wide or narrow Superfast wheels	£5-8	☐
	1971	colour change:............	Bronze body, White seats, Superfast	£5-8	☐
		colour change:............	Off-White body and seats, metal base, wide or narrow Superfast	£5-8	☐
56d	1975	Hi-Tailer	White body, Blue/Orange driver, racing number '5', 'TEAM MATCHBOX'	£3-5	☐
		logo change:..............	As previous model but with Red base, 'MARTINI RACING'	£3-5	☐
56e	1980	Mercedes 450 SEL....................	Metallic Blue body, Tan or Red interior, clear windows..........	£2-4	☐
	1981	Taxi version:	Cream body, Red 'Taxi' on roof	£2-4	☐
	1983	Police Car version:......	Green and White body, 'Polizei', 2 Blue warning lights, Superfast	£2-4	☐
	1981	colour change:	White body	£2-4	☐
	1992	Taxi version:	Yellow body, Red 'Taxi' on White roof sign, Black '56' on bonnet	£2-4	☐
56f	1982	Peterbilt Tanker......................	Blue/White body, 'MILKS THE ONE'..........	£2-4	☐
	1989	colour change:...........	Camouflage paint	NRP	☐
56g	1985	VW Golf Gti................................	Red body, opening bonnet	NRP	☐
	1986	design change:............	as previous models but White body with 'GTI' design	NRP	☐
	1987	design change:............	Blue/White body, 'QUANTUM', racing number '66', promotional	NRP	☐
	1987	design change:............	White body, 'FEDERAL EXPRESS' or 'QUANTUM' logo	NRP	☐
	1989	colour change:...........	Two-tone Metallic Grey body..........	NRP	☐
56h	1989	4 x 4 Jeep..................................	Red body and seats, 'GOLDEN EAGLE' logo in Yellow	NRP	☐

MB 57

Ref. No.	Year(s)	Model Type	Matchbox Miniatures - continued	Market Price Range	
57a	1958	Wolseley 1500..........................	Pale Green body, Grey plastic wheels, 55 mm.	£28-33	☐
57b	1961	Chevrolet Impala....................	TT Blue body, Dark Blue or Black base, Silver plastic wheels, 69 mm.	£30-35	☐
		window change:	Same but with Green windows, Grey, Silver or Black plastic wheels	£15-20	☐
		base colour change:	Same but Pale or Mid-Blue base, Green windows, Silver wheels	£12-16	☐
57c	1966	Land Rover Fire Truck............	Red body, 'KENT FIRE BRIGADE', Black plastic wheels, 64 mm.	£12-16	☐
		wheel change:.............	As previous model but with Grey plastic wheels..........	£20-24	☐
	1970	wheel change:.............	As previous model but with Superfast wheels	£10-14	☐
57d	1970	Eccles Caravan	Pale Yellow body, Orange roof, Maroon stripe, Superfast, 75 mm.	£7-10	☐
		colour change:............	Same but Brown stripe, White interior, 'flower' decal on some	£5-8	☐
	1971	colour change:............	Off White body, with or without 'flower' decal	£5-7	☐
	1973	colour change:............	Cream body, Brown stripe and 'flower' decal on some, Green interior	£3-5	☐
57e	1974	Wild Life Truck......................	Yellow body, 'Ranger decal, clear cover, Rolamatic, 70 mm.	£2-4	☐
	1981	colour change:............	White body, Black stripes	£2-4	☐
57f	1982	Carmichael Police Vehicle	White body, Black roof, 'Police Rescue'..........	£2-4	☐
57g	1983	Carmichael Fire Vehicle	Red/White body, 'FIRE', Black plastic ladder	NRP	☐
		'Mountain Man'	Blue body, 'CIBIE', 4 x 4, US issued model	£4-6	☐
57h	1986	Mission Helicopter	Blue body, White rotor and tail	NRP	☐
	1987		Red body, 'SHERIFF' tampo-print	NRP	☐
	1989	colour change:............	Camouflage paint finish	NRP	☐
	1992	Police version:.............	White with Dark Blue side panels, White 'POLICE' logo, Red trim..........	NRP	☐

MB 58

Ref. No.	Year(s)	Model Type	Matchbox Miniatures - continued	Market Price Range	
58a	1958	AEC Coach 'BEA'	Dark Blue body, Black base, White logo, Grey plastic wheels, 65 mm..........	£30-35	☐
		decal change:..............	'BEA' in Red panel at forward end of White decal, Grey, Silver or Black plastic wheels	£20-25	☐
	1959	decal change:..............	Same but 'BEA' in Red panel at rearward end of White decal	£20-25	☐
		mismatched decal:.......	with 'BEA' panel at forward end on one side and at rear on other side..........	£100-150	☐
58b	1962	Drott Excavator	Red or Orange body, Green rubber tracks, 65 mm.	£8-10	☐
58c	1968	DAF Girder Truck....................	Cream body, Red base & girders, 6 Black plastic wheels, 75 mm.	£8-10	☐
	1970	wheel change:.............	as previous model but with Superfast wheels	£4-6	☐
		colour change:............	Same but Metallic Lime Green body, Red plastic base	£4-6	☐
58d	1973	'Woosh-N-Push'	Yellow body, racing number '2', Superfast wheels, 77 mm.	£2-3	☐
		design change:............	Yellow body with 'flower' label	£10-12	☐
		design change:............	Purple body with '8' label	£3-5	☐
		design change:............	Metallic Dark Red body, Pale Yellow interior, metal base, RN '2'	£4-6	☐
58e	1977	Faun Dumper............................	Yellow body, 'Cat' logo on some, Superfast wheels, 71 mm.	£1-3	☐
58f	1983	'RUFF TREK' (Pick Up)........	Gold/Brown body, Red trim, Black load, spare wheel, 74 mm.	NRP	☐
	1985	design change:............	White body, Red/Yellow tampo-print design, racing number '217'	NRP	☐
	1989	colour change:............	White body, 'flame' design, (James Bond Set)	NRP	☐
	1987	colour change:............	Brown body, 'CAR POW' logo, Superfast wheels	NRP	☐
58g	1988	Mercedes 300e	Metallic Blue body with Silver trim..........	NRP	☐
	1991	'POLIZEI' version:.....	White and Green body with Black logo	NRP	☐

MB 59

Ref. No.	Year(s)	Model Type	Matchbox Miniatures - continued	Market Price Range	
59a	1958	Ford Thames Van 'SINGER' ...	Light Green body, Red Seats and logo, Grey plastic wheels, 56 mm.	£35-40	☐
		wheel change:.............	As previous model but with Silver plastic wheels, rivetted axles	£65-75	☐
		colour change:............	Mid-Green body and Grey plastic wheels, rivetted axles	£65-75	☐
		wheel change:.............	Mid-Green body and Silver plastic wheels, rivetted axles	£100-125	☐
59b	1963	'FIRE CHIEF' Car	(Ford Fairlane), Red body, Yellow logo, Black plastic wheels, 66 mm.	£15-20	☐
		wheel change:.............	As previous model but with Silver plastic wheels.	£25-30	☐
		wheel change:.............	With Grey plastic wheels.	£20-25	☐
59c	1966	'FIRE CHIEF' Car	(Ford Galaxie), Red body, Yellow logo, Black plastic wheels, 73 mm.	£11-15	☐
	1970	wheel change:.............	As previous model but with Superfast wheels	£8-11	☐
59d	1970	'FIRE CHIEF' Car	Red body, Yellow logo, driver and passenger, Superfast wheels, 73 mm.	£8-11	☐

Ref. No.	Year(s)	Model Type	Matchbox Miniatures - continued	Market Price Range	
59e	1976	Planet Scout......................	Two-tone Green body, tinted windows, 2 warning lights, 70 mm.	£3-5	☐
	1979	colour change:............	Red body, Cream chassis	£2-4	☐
	1981	colour change:............	Green/Black body, Purple windows	£6-8	☐
	1983	colour change:............	Metallic Blue with Purple windows	£15-18	☐
59f	1980	Porsche 928....................	Metallic Brown body, 'PORSCHE', opening doors, Superfast wheels, 75 mm...........	£2-4	☐
	1981	colour change:............	Blue body	£2-4	☐
	1982	colour change:............	Black body, White stripes, crest on bonnet	£2-4	☐
	1984	colour change:............	Grey/Blue body, 'PORSCHE'	£1-3	☐
	1985	colour change:............	Black with Tan interior	£1-3	☐
	1986	colour change:............	Silver/Blue body, Blue 'PORSCHE'	NRP	☐
59g	1988	Porsche '944 Turbo'	All Red body, Yellow design	NRP	☐
	1989	colour change:............	Red body, Black print 'CREDIT CHARGE'	NRP	☐
	1989	colour change:............	Black body, bonnet design	NRP	☐
	1990	colour change:............	White body, 'DUCKHAMS OIL'.	NRP	☐
	1991	colour change:............	White body & interior, Yellow '944' on doors, 'PORSCHE' bonnet crest	NRP	☐

MB 60

Ref. No.	Year(s)	Model Type	Matchbox Miniatures - continued	Market Price Range	
60a	1958	Morris J2 Pick Up.....................	Light Blue body, Red and Black logo 'BUILDERS SUPPLY COMPANY', with cab rear window, Black base, Grey plastic wheels......................	£35-40	☐
		logo change:...............	Same but with Red/White logo; Grey, Silver or Black plastic wheels	£20-25	☐
		casting change:............	As previous model but without cab window, Grey or Black plastic wheels................	£35-45	☐
60b	1966	Leyland Site-Office Truck.........	Blue body, Yellow/Green office, Black plastic wheels, 65 mm.	£8-11	☐
	1970	wheel change:............	As previous model but with Superfast wheels	£5-8	☐
60c	1972	Lotus Super Seven.....................	Light Brown body, Black seats, Black plastic wheels, 74 mm.	£6-9	☐
	1976	colour change:............	Yellow body, Red stripes racing number '60'	£4-6	☐
		design change:............	Orange body, Black seats, metal base, 'devil' logo	£5-8	☐
60d	1977	Holden Motorcycle Pick-Up	Metallic Red body, 2 Yellow motorcycles, '500', Superfast wheels	£2-4	☐
	1978	colour change:............	Orange body, 2 Yellow motorcycles, '500', Superfast	NRP	☐
	1981	colour change:............	Red body, 2 Green or Yellow motorcycles, '500', Superfast	£2-4	☐
	1982	colour change:............	Cream body, 2 Red motor-bikes, 'SUPERBIKE' logo	NRP	☐
60e	1983	'TOYOTA RACING'	White/Black body, racing number '41' in Red, Superfast wheels, 76 mm.	£2-4	☐
	1985	logo change:............	As previous model but without racing number, with 'SUPRA' logo	£2-4	☐
	1987	Matchbox/Dinky issue: ..	White body, Blue/Red/Yellow design, bubble packed	NRP	☐
60f	1986	**Ford Transit Van**			
	1986	'MOTORSPORT'	Red body with Blue design, promotional	NRP	☐
	1987	'AMBULANCE'...................	White body, promotional	NRP	☐
	1987	'UNICHEM'.........................	White body	NRP	☐
	1987	'FEDERAL EXPRESS'	White body	NRP	☐
	1987	'AUSTRALIA POST'	Red body, Australian issue	NRP	☐
	1987	'XP'....................................	White body	NRP	☐
	1988	'GREAT ORMOND St HOSPITAL'.............................	White body, 'WISHING WELL APPEAL'	NRP	☐
	1988	'WELLA'.............................	White body, Brown/Red design, German promotional model	£4-6	☐
	1988	'FORD MOTOR Co.'..........	All Green body, Ford box, Dutch issue model	£4-6	☐
	1988	'AUSTRALIAN POST'	Bright Orange/White body, 'WE DELIVER' logo	NRP	☐
	1989	'PETER COX'	White body, Blue/Red stripe (K.H.Norton promotional)	NRP	☐
	1990	'D.C.S.'	White body, 'TECHNICAL SERVICES COMPANY'.	NRP	☐
	1990	'RYDER TRUCK RENTALS'.........................	Yellow body with Black logo	NRP	☐
	1992	'CADBURYS FLAKE'.........	Yellow body with Purple logo	NRP	☐

MB 60 Ford Transit Vans have been issued in large numbers for various promotional purposes and it has become necessary to list them in a computer based 'Specialist Series' publication that will be regularly updated. Details of how to obtain the publication are given at the end of the Matchbox chapter.

MB 61

Ref. No.	Year(s)	Model Type	Matchbox Miniatures - continued	Market Price Range	
61a	1959	Ferret Scout Car......................	Olive Green body, Tan driver Silver or Black plastic wheels, 57 mm.	£15-20	☐
61b	1966	Alvis Stalwart 'BP'	White/Yellow body, Green hubs, Black plastic tyres, 65 mm.	£9-12	☐
		wheel change:............	As previous model but with Yellow plastic wheel hubs.	£12-15	☐
	1978	military version:.........	Camouflage finish, Black plastic wheels. (In 'Two-Pack' TP 16).	NRP	☐
61c	1972	'Blue Shark'	Metallic Blue body, White driver, racing number '86' Superfast, 77 mm.	£2-4	☐
		design change:............	With 'SCORPION' label.	£12-16	☐
		design change:............	With '69' label.	£12-16	☐
		design change:............	With '86' label and Silver/Grey base	£6-9	☐
61d	1978	Ford Wreck Truck	Red body with Red or White jibs, Superfast wheels	£2-4	☐
	1981	colour change:............	Yellow body with Red or Green jibs	£2-4	☐
	1982	colour change:............	Red body, White jibs, '24 HOUR TOWING' logo	NRP	☐
61e	1982	Peterbilt Wreck Truck	Red body, 2 Black jibs, 'Eddies Wrecker', Superfast	£2-4	☐
	1982	colour change:............	White body, Black jibs, 'DIAL 911'	NRP	☐
	1984	colour change:............	White body, Blue jibs, 'DIAL 911'	NRP	☐
	1985	colour change:............	Orange jibs and 'SFPD' logo	NRP	☐
	1987	colour change:............	Orange body, Green jibs, 'TOWNAILER' logo	NRP	☐
	1989	colour change:............	Camouflage paint finish	NRP	☐
61f	1991	Fork Lift Truck	Yellow/Black body and forks	NRP	☐
	1991	colour change:............	Lime or Mid-Green body, Red/White stripes, Black chassis & forks	NRP	☐
61g	1988	T-Bird Turbo	All Red body, Black band	NRP	☐

MB 62

Ref. No.	Year(s)	Model Type	Description	Price	
62a	1959	AEC General Service Lorry	Olive Green body, tow hook, 6 Black plastic wheels, 68 mm.	£20-25	☐
62b	1963	Commer TV Van			
		'RENTASET'	Cream body, Red logo, ladder/aerial/3 TVs, Black plastic wheels, 64 mm.	£40-50	☐
		wheel change:.............	As previous model but with Grey plastic wheels..	£50-60	☐
	1967	'RADIO RENTALS'............	Cream body, Green logo, ladder/aerial/3 Tvs, Black or Grey plastic wheels............	£75-85	☐
62c	1968	Mercury Cougar	Cream body, White interior, Silver hubs with Black plastic tyres, 78 mm.	NGPP	☐
		colour change:............	Metallic Lime Green body, Red interior, Black plastic wheels	£10-15	☐
	1969	wheel change:.............	As previous model but with Superfast wheels	£5-8	☐
62d	1970	'RAT ROD' Dragster................	Lime Green body, Red decal, Silver exposed engine, Superfast, 76 mm.	£2-4	☐
		design change:............	With 'WILD CAT' design	£10-14	☐
62e	1974	Renault 17 TL	Red body, White seats, Blue tinted windows, RN '9', Superfast, 76 mm.	£2-4	☐
		window change:	As previous model but with Green tinted windows	£2-4	☐
62f	1980	Chevrolet Corvette	Metallic Red body, White stripe, Superfast wheels, 74 mm.	£2-4	☐
	1981	colour change:............	Black body, Orange stripe or '54' logo...............................	£2-4	☐
	1983	US issue:	Silver body, 'PACE CAR' logo	£4-6	☐
	1986	Laser Wheels issue:.....	Black body, 'TURBOVETTE' logo	NRP	☐
62g	1982	Chevrolet Corvette T Roof	White body, Orange/Black stripes, racing number '09', Superfast	NRP	☐
	1985	colour change:............	Blue body, Red interior, Red/White/Yellow design, Superfast	NRP	☐
	1987	colour change:............	Yellow body, 'CORVETTE' logo, Superfast	NRP	☐
62h	1989	Volvo Container Truck	White body, Purple/Red print 'FEDERAL EXPRESS'.	NRP	☐
	1991	design change:............	Red body, White container with 'BIG TOP CIRCUS' design	NRP	☐
62i	1986	Volvo 760........................	Silver body, opening doors	NRP	☐
	1988	colour change:............	Red body	NRP	☐

MB 63

Ref. No.	Year(s)	Model Type	Description	Price	
63a	1959	Service Ambulance (Ford)........	Olive Green body, Red crosses, Black plastic wheels, 63 mm.	£20-25	☐
63b	1963	Alvis Foamite Crash Tender	Red body, Silver hose nozzle, 6 Black plastic wheels, 63 mm.	£35-40	☐
		hose change:.............	With Gold hose nozzle.	£15-20	☐
63c	1968	Dodge Crane Truck...................	Yellow body, Red or Yellow hook, Black plastic wheels, 76 mm.	£8-11	☐
	1970	wheel change:.............	as previous models but with Superfast wheels	£5-8	☐
63d	1973	Freeway Gas Tanker	78 mm. long with Red cab, White/Red tank unless otherwise stated:		
		'BURMAH'	Black logo, Red/Blue company motif, Superfast wheels..................	£2-4	☐
		'ARAL'.............................	Blue cab, Blue and White logo, Superfast, German issue..............	£30-35	☐
		'SHELL'.............................	White/Yellow body, Red logo, Superfast..................	£2-4	☐
		'CHEVRON'........................	Red cab, Red/White/Blue logo, Superfast..................	£2-4	☐
		'BP SUPER'........................	White cab, White/Green tank, Yellow logo, Superfast..................	£2-4	☐
		'EXXON'...........................	US issued model	£4-6	☐
		Army issue	Dark Military Green body with French Flag............	£30-40	☐
		Army issue	Military Green, '95 High Octane'	£3-5	☐
		'CASTROL'.........................	Red/White body	£25-35	☐
63e	1980	Dodge Challenger	Metallic Green, 'SPEEDSTICKS', (US issued model)	£4-6	☐
	1981	logo change:.............	Metallic Green, 'HOT POINTS' logo, (US issued model)	£4-6	☐
63f	1982	4 x 4 Pick-Up Truck................	Orange body, racing number '24' with '4 x 4' or 'FWD' logo, 71 mm.	NRP	☐
	1984	colour change:............	Yellow body, Orange panels, racing number '24'	NRP	☐
	1986	colour change:............	White/Blue body, racing number '63' logo	NRP	☐
63g	1988	Volvo 480 ES	All White body, '480 ES'.	NRP	☐
	1988	Laser Wheels issue:.....	Silver body, '480' logo	NRP	☐
	1989	colour change:............	White body, with or without 'VOLVO' on bonnet	NRP	☐
63h	1991	Volkswagen Golf GT	White body with 'flower' design, 'ABSTRACT'................	nrp	☐
63i	1992	Steam Locomotive	Green body with Black tank and chassis, with 'British Railways' crest	NRP	☐

MB 64

Ref. No.	Year(s)	Model Type	Description	Price	
64a	1959	Scammell Breakdown Truck	Olive Green body, metal or plastic hook, Black plastic wheels, 64 mm.	£20-25	☐
64b	1966	MG 1100........................	Green body, White seats, driver, dog, Black plastic wheels, 67 mm.	£11-15	☐
	1970	colour change:............	Metallic Blue body, Superfast wheels	£7-9	☐
64c	1972	'Slingshot' Dragster	Pink body, racing number '9', driver, Superfast, 76 mm.	£6-9	☐
	1974	colour change:............	Green body, Silver/Red exposed engine	£6-9	☐
		colour change:............	Orange body	£50-60	☐
		colour change:............	Metallic Green body, racing number '3'	£15-20	☐
	1975	colour change:............	Blue body, Silver/Red exposed engine	£2-4	☐
64d	1976	Fire Chief Car	Red body, Yellow/Black 'Fire', Blue tinted windows, 77 mm.	£2-4	☐
64e	1979	Caterpillar D8H Bulldozer	Yellow body & dozer blade, Brown canopy	£2-4	☐
	1982	colour change:............	Yellow body & blade, Black canopy	NRP	☐
	1983	colour change:............	Yellow body, Black blade & canopy, 'C' or 'CAT' logo	NRP	☐
64f	1984	Dodge Caravan.....................	Silver body, Black stripes, Red interior, chrome trim, sliding door	£1-3	☐
		colour change:............	Black body, Silver stripes	NRP	☐
		colour change:............	Red body, Black stripe	NRP	☐
	1985	colour change:............	Black body, Silver/Gold design.	NRP	☐
	1987	colour change:............	White with 'CARAVAN', 'PAN-AM' or 'VIRGIN' logo	NRP	☐
64g	1989	Oldsmobile Aerotech	All Silver or Red body	NRP	☐

MB 65

Ref. No.	Year(s)	Model Type	Description	Price	
65a	1959	Jaguar 3.4 litre........................	Blue body, Silver number-plate on some, Grey plastic wheels, 62 mm.	£30-40	☐
		colour change:............	Metallic Blue body and number-plate, Grey plastic wheels....................	£75-85	☐

Ref. No.	Year(s)	Model Type	Matchbox Miniatures - continued	Market Price Range	
65b	1962	Jaguar 3.4 Sedan	Metallic Red body, Black base, Silver plastic wheels, 68 mm.	£20-25	☐
		colour change:.............	Non-Metallic Red body, Black, Grey or Silver plastic wheels	£15-20	☐
65c	1967	Claas Combine Harvester..........	Red body, Yellow blades and front hubs, Black plastic tyres/wheels, 76 mm.............	£6-9	☐
65d	1973	Saab Sonnet...............................	Metallic Blue body, Orange seats, Superfast wheels, 73 mm.	£2-4	☐
65e	1978	**Airport Coach**	Model has painted lower body (colour as listed), White plastic upper body, Amber or clear windows, Yellow or Ivory interior, Superfast wheels, 78 mm.		
		'BRITISH AIRWAYS'.........	Metallic Blue lower body, Red/White/Blue labels...	£5-7	☐
		'AMERICAN AIRWAYS' ...	Metallic Blue lower body, Red/White/Blue labels...	£5-7	☐
		'LUFTHANSA'.....................	Metallic Blue body, Black/Blue/Orange/White labels...	£5-7	☐
	1980	'TWA'..................................	Metallic Red/White, Yellow interior, Amber windows..	£5-7	☐
		'QUANTAS'.........................	Metallic Red, Yellow interior, Amber windows..	£5-7	☐
	1982	'ALITALIA'.........................	Green/Red/Black body..	£5-7	☐
		'SCHULBUS'	Orange lower body, White upper body, German issue model	£5-7	☐
		'PAN AM'	White body...	£5-7	☐
		'GIROBANK'......................	Blue/White body, *'SIMPLY MORE CONVENIENT'*	£5-7	☐
		'STORK SB'.........................	White/Blue body, Australian issue..	£5-7	☐
		'VIRGIN'............................	Red body	£2-3	☐
65f		Kenworth 'Tyrone Malone'			
	1982	US issue:	Black body, *'Bandag Bandit'* logo	£4-6	☐
	1987	colour change:.............	Tan body, *'Barrel Bomber'* logo	NRP	☐
65g		Indy Racer	Yellow body, (US issue model)...	£2-4	☐
65h	1985	Plane Transporter	Yellow body, Red/White plane, *'RESCUE'*, (includes Collector Card)	NRP	☐
	1989	colour change:.............	Camouflage paint finish	NRP	☐
65i	1987	Cadillac Allante	Silver body, Red seats, opening doors	NRP	☐
	1987	Laser Wheels issue:.....	Black body	NRP	☐
	1989	colour change:.............	All Pink body, White interior	NRP	☐
	1989	US issue:	Silver body	£4-6	☐
	1991	design change:.............	Pink body, White interior, Yellow side stripe, Black design...............................	NRP	☐

MB 66

Ref. No.	Year(s)	Model Type		Market Price Range	
66a	1959	Citroën DS 19...........................	Yellow body, Silver trim, Grey plastic wheels, 64 mm.	£25-30	☐
		wheel change:.............	Same but with Silver plastic wheels, rivetted axles...	£50-60	☐
66b	1962	Harley Davidson Motor Cycle..	Metallic Bronze bike & sidecar, 3 spoked wheels, Black plastic tyres, 66 mm.	£40-50	☐
66c	1966	'GREYHOUND' Coach	Silver body (slanted decal), Black plastic wheels, 76 mm.	£40-50	☐
		window change:	Amber windows, slanted decal or label, or square-ended label...........................	£8-10	☐
	1970	wheel change:.............	as previous models but with Superfast wheels...	£5-8	☐
66d	1972	'Mazda' RX500	Orange body, White baseplate, Superfast wheels, 74 mm.	£4-6	☐
	1976	colour change:.............	Red body, White baseplate, *'CASTROL'*.	£10-12	☐
		colour change:.............	Dark Green body, Yellow racing number '66'	£15-18	☐
		colour change:.............	Red body, racing number '77' and *'RX500'* design...	£10-12	☐
		Bulgarian issue:..........	Gold body	£15-20	☐
66e	1978	Ford Transit Pick Up................	Orange body, Yellow or Green interior, Green tinted windows, Tan crate	£5-7	☐
		window change:	As previous model but with Amber tinted windows...	£2-4	☐
66f	1983	Tyrone Malone	White body, Red & Blue design *'SUPERBOSS'*, Superfast	NRP	☐
66g		Rolls-Royce Silver Spirit	Brown body and interior, opening doors, Superfast	NRP	☐
	1988	colour change:.............	Metallic Greenish-Gold body	NRP	☐
	1990	colour change:.............	Metallic Red body	NRP	☐

MB 67

Ref. No.	Year(s)	Model Type		Market Price Range	
67a	1959	Saladin Armoured Car	Olive Green body, 6 Black plastic wheels, 61 mm.	£15-20	☐
67b	1967	Volkswagen 1600 TL................	Red body, White seats, Black plastic wheels, 68 mm.	£12-15	☐
		wheel change:.............	As previous model but with Black plastic tyres on Silver hubs	£12-15	☐
		colour change:.............	Metallic Light Purple body, Silver hubs, Black plastic tyres	£12-15	☐
	1969	wheel change:.............	as previous models but with Superfast wheels...	£5-8	☐
	1968-69	Gift Set model:	Red body, Maroon roof rack, Black plastic tyres, (Set G4)	GSP	☐
	1969	wheel change:.............	As previous model but with Superfast wheels..	£25-35	☐
	1970	colour change:.............	Pink body, Superfast...	£4-7	☐
67c	1974	'Hot Rocker'............................	Metallic Green body, White seats, Rolamatic, Superfast wheels, 77 mm.	£2-4	☐
	1976	colour change:.............	Red body	£2-4	☐
	1981	US issue:	Yellow body, *'MAXI TAXI'*	£4-6	☐
67d	1979	Datsun 260 Z............................	Metallic Purple body, Yellow interior, hook, Superfast wheels, 75 mm.	£2-4	☐
	1981	colour change:.............	Metallic Silver, Red stripes & *'2 x 2'* on some, Superfast................................	£2-4	☐
	1982	colour change:.............	Black body, with or without *'2 x 2'* logo	£2-4	☐
	1983	colour change:.............	Metallic or plain Blue body, Pale Yellow interior...	£2-4	☐
67e	1983	IMSA 'FORD MUSTANG'	Black body, Red/White/Blue stripes tinted windows, Superfast	£2-4	☐
	1985	window change:	As previous model but with luminous *'Glo'* windows..	NRP	☐
67f	1986	'IKARUS' Coach......................	White body, *'GIBRALTAR'* (Spanish issue)	£4-6	☐
	1986	design change:.............	White body, Orange roof, *'VOYAGER'*, (with Collector Card)	£2-4	☐
	1988	design change:.............	White with Green stripes, *'TOURIST CITY LINE'*	NRP	☐
	1988	design change:.............	White body, *'I LOVE CANARY ISLAND'*, promotional	NRP	☐
	1992	design change:.............	White body, *'ESPANA'* logo	NRP	☐

MB 68

Ref. No.	Year(s)	Model Type		Market Price Range	
68a	1959	Austin Radio Truck Mk.II........	Olive Green body and base, Black plastic wheels, 62 mm.	£15-20	☐
68b	1965	Mercedes Coach	Turquoise/White body, Black plastic wheels, 73 mm.	£175-200	☐
		colour change:.............	Orange/White body, Black plastic wheels..	£7-10	☐

Ref. No.	Year(s)	Model Type	Matchbox Miniatures - continued	Market Price Range	
68c	1970	Porsche 910	Metallic Red, White seats racing number '68', Superfast, 76 mm.	£2-4	☐
		design change:	With '68' labels on sides	£10-12	☐
		colour change:	White body	£15-17	☐
68d	1976	'Cosmobile'	Metallic Blue and Yellow body, Silver trim, tinted windows, 73 mm.	£2-4	☐
	1979	colour change:	Metallic Red and Brown body	£2-4	☐
		colour change:	Green/Black body	£6-8	☐
		colour change:	Blue/Black body	£15-18	☐
68e	1980	Chevrolet Van	Orange body, Red and Black flashes, Superfast wheels, 77 mm.	£2-4	☐
	1981	colour change:	Green body, Orange flash, 'Chev.', Superfast	£2-4	☐
	1982	colour change:	Silver body, Black/Blue/Red flashes 'Vanpire', Superfast	£2-4	☐
	1983	colour change:	White body, Orange flashes, 'Matchbox Racing'	£2-4	☐
		colour change:	Orange body, 'Matchbox Collectors Club'	£10-15	☐
		colour change:	White body, 'Adidas', (German issued model)	£10-15	☐
		logo change:	White body with 'USA' logo	£5-7	☐
	1985	logo change:	White body with 'Dr. PEPPER' logo	NRP	☐
		logo change:	Yellow body with 'PEPSI' logo	NRP	☐
68h	1991	Road Roller	Orange body, Black roller wheels	NRP	☐
	1992	colour change:	Yellow body with Red body design	NRP	☐
68f	1982	Chevy 4 x 4 Van	Metallic Green body with 'RIDIN' HIGH' logo	NRP	☐
	1983	colour change:	White body, 'RACING' logo	NRP	☐
	1984	Japanese issues:	White body with 8 various designs	NRP	☐
	1985	Australian issue:	White body with 'CASTROL' logo	NRP	☐
68g	1987	Camero Iroc-Z	Blue or Pale Green body, (with Collector Card)	NRP	☐
	1987	Laser Wheels issue:	Red body, 'GOODYEAR' logo	NRP	☐
	1988	design change:	Yellow body, Blue/Red design	NRP	☐
	1988	design change:	Blue body, Yellow 'BP' print, Dutch promotional	NRP	☐
	1988	Laser Wheels issue:	Metallic Bronze body, racing number '12'	NRP	☐
	1989	design change:	Yellow body, Blue or Green stripes	NRP	☐

MB 69

Ref. No.	Year(s)	Model Type	Matchbox Miniatures - continued	Market Price Range	
69a	1959	Commer Van 'NESTLES'	Maroon body, driver, Yellow logo, Grey plastic wheels, 56 mm.	£33-38	☐
		colour change:	Red body, Grey plastic wheels	£50-60	☐
69b	1965	Hatra Tractor Shovel	Orange body; Orange, Red or Yellow hubs, Grey or Black plastic tyres, 78 mm.	£7-9	☐
	1967	colour change:	Yellow body, Yellow or Red hubs, Black plastic tyres	£6-8	☐
69c	1970	Rolls-Royce Silver Shadow	Metallic Blue body, Red seats, Tan hood, Superfast wheels	£5-8	☐
	1973	colour change:	Metallic Gold body, White seats, Black hood	£5-8	☐
69d	1974	Turbo Fury	Red body with flash, RN '69', White driver, Rolamatic, Superfast	£2-4	☐
		decal change:	As previous model but with '86' label	£10-12	☐
69e		Security Truck	Metal body, plastic roof, Superfast wheels, 73 mm.		☐
	1979	'WELLS FARGO'	Red body, White roof & logo, special lights, Superfast	£2-4	☐
	1980	'DRESDNER BANK'	Green body, White roof, German issue model	£5-8	☐
69f	1982	Willys Street Rod	White or Blue body, '313' logo. (US issue)	£4-6	☐
69g	1983	'83 Corvette	Silver body, Red bands, '83 Vette' logo	NRP	☐
	1984	colour change:	Red/Grey body, 'Vette'.	NRP	☐
	1986	US issue:	White body, racing number '7' or 'BOYARDEE' logo	£4-6	☐
	1987	colour change:	Grey/Blue body, 'THUNDER GUNNER' logo	NRP	☐
	1987	Matchbox/Dinky issue:	Red/Silver body, bubble packed	NRP	☐
69h	1990	Snow Plough	Yellow body, Black/Yellow plough, '45' in Blue	NRP	☐
	1992	Maintenance Truck	Yellow body, Red tipper and plough. (This is 69h Snow Plough renamed 'Maintenance Truck' in the 1992 Matchbox catalogue)	NRP	☐

MB 70

Ref. No.	Year(s)	Model Type	Matchbox Miniatures - continued	Market Price Range	
70a	1959	Ford Thames Estate Car	Sea-Green and Yellow body, no windows, Grey plastic wheels, 55 mm.	£20-25	☐
		window change:	Same but with clear windows and Grey or Silver plastic wheels	£28-34	☐
		window change:	With Green windows and Grey, Silver or Black plastic wheels	£20-25	☐
70b	1966	Ford Grit Spreader	Red/Yellow body, Pale Lemon container, Black plastic wheels, 68 mm.	£12-15	☐
		colour change:	Red/Yellow body, Yellow container, Black or Grey slide, Black plastic wheels	£8-11	☐
	1971	wheel change:	As previous model but with Superfast wheels	£5-8	☐
70c	1972	Dodge Dragster	Pink body, 'snake' decal, Superfast, 78 mm.	£3-5	☐
	1978	US issue:	Yellow body, 'HOT SMOKER'.	£4-6	☐
	1980	US issue:	White body, 'ORANGE PEEL'.	£4-6	☐
70d	1977	SP Gun	Olive Green body, Black gun, Tan tracks, 68 mm.	£1-3	☐
	1989	colour change:	Camouflage paint finish	NRP	☐
70e	1981	Ferrari 308 GTB	Orange body, Black flash, Black interior, Superfast wheels, 75 mm.	£2-4	☐
	1982	colour change:	Same colours with 'Ferrari' decal, Superfast	£2-4	☐
	1983	colour change:	Red body, White chassis, Superfast	£1-3	☐
	1985	colour change:	Red/Blue body, racing number '39', 'Pioneer'.	NRP	☐
	1987	Laser Wheels issue:	Yellow body, 'FERRARI'.	NRP	☐
70f	1989	Ferrari F40	All Red body, Ferrari badges front & sides	NRP	☐

MB 71

Ref. No.	Year(s)	Model Type	Matchbox Miniatures - continued	Market Price Range	
71a	1959	200 gallon Water Truck	Olive Green, Black plastic wheels, 61 mm. With first 'Matchbox Collectors' badge	£35-40	☐
		alternative version:	Same model but without badge	£15-20	☐
71b	1964	Jeep Gladiator Pick-UP	Red body, White interior, Black plastic wheels, 66 mm.	£8-11	☐
		colour change:	As previous model but with Green interior	£20-25	☐
71c	1969	Ford Heavy Wreck Truck	Red/White body, Green or Amber windows, 'ESSO', Black plastic wheels, 75 mm.	£8-11	☐
		colour change:	Military Green, Black hubs	£6-8	☐
		component change:	As previous model with Chrome hubs	£6-8	☐
		colour change:	Blue body	£60-70	☐

Ref. No.	Year(s)	Model Type	Matchbox Miniatures - continued	Market Price Range	
71d	1973	Jumbo Jet Motor Cycle............	Metallic Blue body, Light or Dark Blue handlebars..	£3-5	☐
71e	1977	Dodge Cattle Truck...................	Bronze cab, Yellow cage, 2 Black cows..	£2-4	☐
	1979	colour change:............	Red cab, Yellow or Ivory cage, 2 Black cows...	£2-4	☐
	1981	colour change:............	Red cab, White cage, 2 Black cows..	£20-25	☐
	1982	colour change:............	Yellow cab, Brown cage, 2 Brown cows...	£3-5	☐
		colour change:............	Metallic Orange cab, Yellow cage, 2 Brown cows...	£8-11	☐
		colour change:............	Non-Metallic Green cab, Brown cage, 2 Brown cows....................................	£15-20	☐
		colour change:............	Metallic Lime Green, Cream cage, 2 Brown cows...	£3-5	☐
	1983	colour change:............	Green and White body, 2 Brown cows, Superfast...	£2-4	☐
		note:............................	Many other variations exist, for example with either Amber, Orange, Red, Blue, Purple or Green windows!		
71f	1987	Corvette	Blue, Red or White body (USA issued model)	£4-6	☐
	1987	Laser Wheels issue:.....	Orange or Metallic Green body, racing number '11'	NRP	☐
71g	1985	Scania T142	White/Blue body, Black bumper..	NRP	☐
	1987	colour change:............	Blue body	NRP	☐

Note: 71g was reissued many times as part of the 'Convoy' series. Logos include 'Amoco', 'Duckhams', 'Readymix', 'Varta', 'Sealink', 'Kit Kat', 'Tizer', 'Weetabix', 'Walls', 'Heinz', 'Signal', 'Shell', '7 Up', 'Beefeater', 'Golden Wonder' and 'Michelin'.

71h	1987	'Blue Flame 'Vette'	White body (USA issued model)	£4-6	☐
71i	1988	GMC Wrecker..........................	White Red body, 'FRANKS'	NRP	☐

MB 72

72a	1959	Fordson Major Tractor............	Blue body, Orange hubs with Grey or Black plastic wheels/tyres, 50 mm.	£28-36	☐
		wheel change:............	Yellow hubs with Grey or Black tyres front & rear	£28-36	☐
		wheel variant:............	Black front hubs, Yellow rear hubs with Black or Grey tyres........................	£50-75	☐
72b	1966	CJ5 Jeep.................................	Yellow body, Red seats, Silver plastic wheels, Black tyres, 61 mm.	£10-15	☐
		wheel change:............	As previous model but with Yellow hubs and Black plastic tyres...................	£10-15	☐
	1970	colour change:............	With Yellow and Orange body, Superfast wheels	£10-15	☐
		seat colour change:	Yellow body with White seats	£50-75	☐
72c	1972	'SRN6' Hovercraft	White/Red/Black body with Union Jack, 77 mm.	£2-4	☐
72d	1979	Bomag Road Roller	Yellow body, Red engine and interior, Superfast wheels, 71 mm.	£2-4	☐
		wheel change:............	With Silver rear hubs	£9-12	☐
72e		Dodge Commando Truck			
	1982	'PEPSI'......................	Red and White body, Red/White/Blue decal, Superfast, 72 mm.	NRP	☐
	1984	'KELLOGGS'..........................	Red and White body	£2-4	☐
		wheel change:	With Gold hubs	£8-11	☐
	1984	'SMITHS CRISPS'...................	With 'crisp packet' design	£8-11	☐
	1984	'STREETS ICE CREAM'.....	Australian issue	£8-11	☐
	1985	'HERTZ'..................................	All Yellow body	NRP	☐
	1986	'ROYAL MAIL'........................	Red body	NRP	☐
	1987	'RISI'	All Yellow body	NRP	☐
	1987	'JETPRESS'...........................	White body, Australian issue	£8-11	☐
	1988	'YORKIE'.................................	Blue body, Red/Yellow design, promotional...	NRP	☐
	1988	'KIT KAT'................................	Red Body, Red/White design, promotional..	NRP	☐
	1989	'MATCHBOX CONVENTION USA'	Red/White body	£4-6	☐
	1990	'C-PLUS ORANGE'	Green and Orange body...	NRP	☐
72f	1986	Sand Racer	US issue model	£3-5	☐
72g	1986	Ford 'SUPERVAN 2'	White/Blue body & tampo print, (includes Collector Card)	NRP	☐
	1987	colour change:............	Mid or Dark Blue body	NRP	☐
	1988	design change:............	White body, Blue/Red design 'STARFIRE'.	NRP	☐
	1989	design change:............	Yellow body with Green design 'BP', Dutch promotional	NRP	☐
72h	1990	Sprint Racer	Red/Grey or Red/Silver body, racing number '2' in Yellow...........................	NRP	☐

MB 73

73a	1959	R.A.F. 10 ton Refueller	(Leyland) Airforce-Blue body, roundel, 6 Grey plastic wheels, 66 mm.	£30-35	☐
		wheel change:............	Same model but with Black plastic wheels	£30-35	☐
73b	1962	Ferrari F1 Racing Car	Red body, Grey or White driver, RN '73', 'spoked' metal hubs, Black plastic tyres ...	£8-11	☐
73c	1968	Mercury Commuter...................	Metallic Lime Green body, Silver hubs, Black plastic tyres, 78 mm.	£8-10	☐
	1970	wheel change:............	As previous model but with Superfast wheels	£5-8	☐
	1972	colour change:............	Red body version, bonnet motif, filler cap on some	£2-4	☐
73d	1974	Weasel....................................	Metallic Green body, Rolamatic, Superfast, 72 mm.	£2-4	☐
		colour change:............	Dark Military Green body	£50-60	☐
		colour change:............	Light Military Green, Chrome hubs...	£10-15	☐
	1989	colour change:............	Camouflage paint finish	NRP	☐
73e	1980	Ford Model 'A' Car	Cream body, Green chassis, spare wheel on some, Superfast	£5-8	☐
	1981	colour change:............	TT Green body and chassis, some, Superfast	£4-6	☐
	1982	colour change:............	Cream/Black body, Brown chassis, Orange tinted windows, Superfast........	£2-4	☐
	1984	colour change:............	Brown body, Black wings & roof	£2-4	☐
	1985	colour change:............	Red body	NRP	☐
	1986	colour change:............	Black body, Yellow/Red 'fire' design	NRP	☐
		Promotional:	Metallic & non-metallic Green, 'CLIMAT' label	£25-30	☐
	1990		Red/Green body, (Brooke Bond promotional)..	£1-3	☐
73f	1989	TV News Truck	Blue/Grey body, Red camera, 'MB TV 75'.	NRP	☐
	1991	design change:............	White body, Blue roof with Red 'SKY SATELLITE TELEVISION'................	NRP	☐

MB 74

74a	1959	Mobile 'REFRESHMENTS' Bar	White body, Pale Blue base, Blue interior, opening hatch, Grey plastic wheels	£70-90	☐
		colour change:............	Cream body, Light Blue base, Grey plastic wheels...............................	£70-90	☐
		colour change:..........	Pink body, Light Blue base, Grey plastic wheels...............................	£125-175	☐
		colour change:..........	Silver body, Light, Mid or Dark Blue base, Grey plastic wheels..................	£25-30	☐
		wheel change:.............	Silver body, Light Blue base, Silver plastic wheels...........................	£17-22	☐
		base change:.............	Silver body, Green base, Grey or Silver plastic wheels........................	£17-22	☐
74b		Daimler Fleetline	Double Decker Bus		
	1966	'ESSO EXTRA'........................	Cream, Red/White/Blue decals or labels, Black plastic wheels, 76 mm.	£20-24	☐
	1968	colour change:.............	Green body with labels	£20-24	☐
	1969	colour change:.............	Red body, Black plastic wheels..	£14-16	☐
	1970	wheel change:.............	Red body, Superfast wheels..	£5-8	☐
	1970	label change:	Red body with 'INN ON THE PARK' labels, Superfast.......................	£60-70	☐
	1970	label change:	Red body with 'THE BARON OF BEEF' labels, Superfast......................	£60-70	☐
74c	1973	Tow Joe Breakdown Truck.......	Metallic Green body, Dark Green jibs, Superfast, 75 mm......................	£2-4	☐
		colour change:............	Green/White body	£50-60	☐
		colour change:............	Yellow/Red body, 'HITCH HIKER'...	£50-60	☐
		note:............................	Other variations exist.		
74e	1979	Cougar Villager	Metallic Green body, Yellow interior, 76 mm...................................	£2-4	☐
		variants:	Metallic Blue body, Orange/Yellow interior....................................	£15-20	☐
		Bulgarian issue:..........	Metallic Blue with Black interior	£15-20	☐
		Bulgarian issue:..........	Metallic Green with Black interior	£15-20	☐
		note:	Many other variations exist.		
74f	1982	'FIAT' Abarth.......................	White body with 'Matchbox Toys' logo, RN '45', Superfast wheels, 76 mm.	£1-3	☐
	1983	design change:.............	White body, racing number '3', 'ALITALIA'..................................	NRP	☐
	1987	Matchbox/Dinky issue: ..	White body, Yellow/Red design, bubble-packed.................................	NRP	☐
74g	1984	Mustang..............................	(US issued model), Orange body, 'GT' logo....................................	£4-6	☐
	1986	colour change:.............	Silver body, racing number '427'..	NRP	☐
74h	1986	'TOYOTA' MR 2....................	White body, 'MR 2' and 'PACE CAR' logos, (with Collector Card)...........	NRP	☐
	1987	Laser Wheel issue:	Metallic Blue body, 'MR 2' logo..	NRP	☐
74i	1989	Utility Truck........................	Green/White body, 'CHERRY PICKER'......................................	NRP	☐
	1990	design change:.............	Red bonnet with Grey cab and body plus White boom	NRP	☐
	1992	colour change:.............	Yellow body with various Blue logos plus White boom	NRP	☐

MB 75

75a	1960	Ford Thunderbird	Cream body, Peach sides, Blue base, Silver plastic wheels, 67 mm.	£30-35	☐
		base/wheel change:......	with Black base and Silver, Grey or Black plastic wheels....................	£20-25	☐
75b	1965	Ferrari Berlinetta...................	Metallic Green, Silver base, 'wire' wheels, Black plastic tyres, 75 mm.	£13-16	☐
		base colour change:	with unpainted base, 'wire' wheels or Silver hubs with Black plastic tyres ..	£10-12	☐
		colour change:...........	Red body, Cream or White seats, Silver hubs, Black plastic tyres	NGPP	☐
	1970	wheel change:.............	As previous model but with Superfast wheels	£10-12	☐
75c	1971	Alfa Carabo	Pink body, Yellow baseplate, Superfast wheels, 76 mm.......................	£2-4	☐
		colour change:............	Red body, 'Streetcar' design, Yellow baseplate..............................	£2-4	☐
		note:............................	There are many other variations.		
75d	1977	Seasprite Helicopter................	Red and White body, 'Rescue', Black rotors, 74 mm.........................	£2-4	☐
75e	1982	'MB TV NEWS' Helicopter......	Orange/White body fitted with tinted windows, 76 mm.......................	NRP	☐
75f	1983	'POLICE' Helicopter	Black/White body, Black rotors...	NRP	☐
	1984	colour change:............	Orange body, 'Rescue' logo..	NRP	☐
75g	1986	Ferrari Testarossa....................	Red or Silver body, Superfast wheels	NRP	☐
	1988	Laser Wheels issue:......	Red body with Ferrari badges on front & sides................................	NRP	☐
	1989	Promotional:................	Orange body, 'REDOXON' on roof, (Hong Kong issue)......................	NRP	☐
75h	1985	Dodge Caravan.......................	Black or Maroon body	NRP	☐

WHEN REPLYING TO ADVERTISEMENTS PLEASE MENTION JOHN RAMSAY'S CATALOGUE

Matchbox Gift Sets
and multi-model Packs

Ref. No.	Year(s)	Set Name	Contents	Market Price Range	

Presentation Sets

The first presentation set was sold in the USA in 1957 and consisted of an enlarged normal 'Matchbox' containing eight of the sixty-four models that Lesney manufactured at that time. The first sets were not sold in the UK until 1959.

Ref. No.	Year(s)	Set Name	Contents	Market Price Range	
PS 1	1957	Matchbox Presentation Set	Contains models 1 - 8 (only available in USA).................	£500-600	☐
PS 2	1957	Matchbox Presentation Set	Contains models 9 - 16 (only available in USA).................	£500-600	☐
PS 3	1957	Matchbox Presentation Set	Contains models 17 - 24 (only available in USA).................	£500-600	☐
PS 4	1957	Matchbox Presentation Set	Contains models 25 - 32 (only available in USA).................	£500-600	☐
PS 5	1957	Matchbox Presentation Set	Contains models 33 - 40 (only available in USA).................	£500-600	☐
PS 6	1957	Matchbox Presentation Set	Contains models 41 - 48 (only available in USA).................	£500-600	☐
PS 7	1957	Matchbox Presentation Set	Contains models 49 - 56 (only available in USA).................	£500-600	☐
PS 8	1957	Matchbox Presentation Set	Contains models 57 - 64 (only available in USA).................	£500-600	☐
PS 1	1959	Private Owner Set....................	Contains 19 MGA, 43 Hillman Minx, 45 Vauxhall Victor, A-3 Garage....................	£150-175	☐
PS 2	1959	Transporter and 4 Cars Set.......	Contains 30 Ford, 31 Ford Station Wagon, 33 Ford Zodiac, 36 Austin A50 and an A-2 Transporter	£150-175	☐
PS 3	1959	Transporter and 6 Cars Set.......	Contains 22 Vauxhall Cresta, 32 Jaguar XK, 33 Ford Zodiac, 43 Hillman Minx, 44 Rolls-Royce Silver Cloud, 45 Vauxhall Victor and A-2 Transporter	£200-250	☐
PS 4	1959	Commercial Vehicle Set.............	Contains No.5 Bus, 11 Petrol Tanker, 21 Long Distance Coach, 25 'Dunlop' Van, 35 Horse Box, 40 Bedford Tipper, 47 'Brooke Bond' Van, 60 Morris Pickup	£400-450	☐
PS 5	1959	Army Personnel Carrier Set	Contains M3 Personnel Carrier, 54 Saracen, 55 DUKW, 61 Ferret, 62 General Service Lorry, 63 Ambulance, M-3 Tank Transporter................................	£150-175	☐

Gift Sets

The packaging for the first UK issued sets consisted of a frail blue box with a yellow lid panel on which were displayed (in red) the models which made up the set. Sets in similar packaging were issued for the German market.

Ref. No.	Year(s)	Set Name	Contents	Market Price Range	
G 1	1960-61	Commercial Motor Set..............	Contains: 5b 'Players Please', 47a 'Brooke Bond' Van, 69a 'Nestles' Van, 60a 'Builders Supply' Pick Up, 37a 'Coca Cola' Lorry (even load), 59a Ford 'Singer' Van, 20a 'Ever Ready' Truck, 51a Albion 'Portland Cement' Lorry. (All models in G 1 had Grey plastic wheels).	£350-450	☐
G 1	1962-63	Commercial Vehicle Set............	Contains 5c 'Visco-Static', 10c, 12b, 13c, 14c, 21c, 46b, 74a.	£250-300	☐
G 1	1965	Motorway Set......................	Contains 6, 10, 13, 33, 34, 38, 48, 55, 71 and R-1 layout	£125-175	☐
G 1	1967	Service Station Set..............	Contains Service Station, 32c, 13d, 64b.....................	£45-55	☐
G 1	1970	Service Station Set..............	Contains 13e, 32d, 15e and Service Station......................	£45-55	☐
G 1	1981	Transporter Set....................	Contains Transporter and 5 Superfast Cars	£15-20	☐
G 1	1984	Transporter Set....................	Contains K10 plus 4 cars	£8-11	☐
G 2	1960-61	Car Transporter Set...............	Contains A-2 Transporter with cars 22, 25, 33, 39, 57 & 75	£175-225	☐
G 2	1962-63	Car Transporter Set...............	Contains models 25b, 30b, 31b, 39b, 48b, 65b and Accessory Pack No.2	£225-275	☐
G 2	1965	Car Transporter Set...............	Contains 22c, 28c, 36c, 75b and Major Pack 8b	£80-90	☐
G 2	1967	Transporter Set...................	Contains Transporter, 14d, 24c, 31c, 53c	£55-65	☐
G 2	1970	Transporter Set...................	Contains Transporter and 5 Superfast models	£45-55	☐
G 2	1973	Transporter Set...................	Contains Transporter and 5 Superfast models	£45-55	☐
G 2	1981	Railway Set.......................	Contains 43e, 2 x 44e, 25f.....................	£10-15	☐
G 2	1987	Car Transporter Set.................	Contains K120 Transporter plus MB25 Audi Quattro, MB33 Renault 11, MB55 Ford Sierra 4x4, MB74 Toyota MR2, MB75 Ferrari Testarossa	NGPP	☐
G 3	1960-61	Building Constructors Set	Contains 2, 6, 15, 16, 18, 24, 28 and M-1	£150-175	☐
G 3	1962-63	Constructional Plant Set	Contains 2, 6, 15, 16, 18, 24, 28 and M-1	£200-250	☐
G 3	1965	Vacation Set	Contains 12c, 23c, 27d, 42b, 45b, 56b, 68b, and Sports Boat on Trailer	£90-120	☐
G 3	1968	Farm Set	Contains 12c, 37d, 40c, 43c, 65c, 72b, 47c, 39c.................	£55-65	☐
G 3	1970	Racing Specials Set..................	Contains 5e, 20d, 45c, 56c, 52c, 68c	£45-55	☐
G 3	1973	'WILD ONES' Set	Contains 5 Superfast Cars	£10-15	☐
G 3	1981	Racing Car Set	Contains Transporter and 4 Racing Cars........................	£10-15	☐
G 3	1987	JCB Gift Set	No details	NGPP	☐
G 4	1960-61	Farm Set	Contains 12, 23, 31, 35, 50, 72 & M-7	£125-150	☐
G 4	1963	Agricultural Implements and Farm Vehicles Set....................	Contains 12, 23, 31, 35, 50, 72 and M-7	£175-225	☐
G 4	1963	Grand Prix Set..................	Contains 13c, 14b, 19c, 41b, 47b, 52a, 32b, 73b, Major Pack No.1, R-4 Racetrack	£300-350	☐
G 4	1965	Racetrack Set................	Contains 13d, 19d Green, 19d Orange, 41c White, 41c Yellow, 52b Blue, 52b Red, 54b, Major Pack M-6 29c...................	£120-160	☐
G 4	1968	Race 'N' Rally Set....................	Contains 19d Orange, 19d Green, 52b Blue, 52b Red, 29d, 3c, 41c, 67b, 25d, 8e.........	£100-125	☐
G 4	1970	Truck SuperSet..................	Contains 47c, 63c, 58c, 49b, 16d, 21d, 11d, 51c.................	£55-65	☐
G 4	1973	Team Matchbox Set	Contains Racing Car Transporter and 4 Racing Cars..................	£40-50	☐
G 4	1981	Military Assault..................	Contains Landing Craft and 6 military models..................	£10-15	☐
G 5	1960-61	Military Vehicles....................	Contains 54, 62, 63, 64, 67, 68 and M-3	£125-150	☐
G 5	1963	Army Gift Set..................	Contains 54a, 62a, 63a, 67a, 68a, 64a and Major Pack No.3........	£125-150	☐
G 5	1965	Army Gift Set..................	Contains 12, 49, 54, 61, 64, 67, M-3.....................	£125-140	☐
G 5	1965	Fire Station Set..................	Contains Fire Station, 29c, 54b, 59c....................	£130-150	☐
G 5	1981	Construction Set..................	Contains 5 construction models........................	£10-15	☐

Ref. No.	Year(s)	Model Type	Matchbox Toys - continued	Market Price Range	
G 6	1965	Commercial Trucks Set	Contains 6, 15, 16, 17, 26, 30, 58 and 62	£80-100	☐
G 6	1970	Truck Set	Contains 1e, 10d, 21d, 30c, 60b, 70b, 49b, 26c	£65-75	☐
G 6	1973	Drag Race Set	Contains 6 Superfast Cars	£40-50	☐
G 6	1981	Farm Set	Contains 6 farming models	£10-15	☐
G 7	1973	Ferry Boat	Contains Plastic Boat and 4 Superfast Cars	£15-20	☐
G 7	1978	Car Ferry Set	Contains 3 Cars and Sports Boat	£15-20	☐
G 7	1981	Emergency Set	Contains 5 Rescue models	£10-15	☐
G 7	1984	Emergency Set	Contains models 8, 12, 22, 57, 75	£8-11	☐
G 8	1984	Turbo Charged Set	Contains Turbo Charger plus 7, 9, 52, 60 and 68	£8-11	☐
G 9	1963	Major Series Set	Contains Major Packs 1, 2, 4 and 6	£150-200	☐
G 9	1965	Service Station Set	Contains 13, 33, 71, A-1, MG-1	£65-75	☐
G 10	1963	Service Station Set	Contains Service Station, 13c, 25b, 31b, and Accessory Pack No.1 ...	£65-75	☐
G 10	1965	Fire Station Set	Contains MF-1, 14, 59, 2 of No.9	£65-75	☐
G 10	1986	'PAN-AM' Set	Contains 10, 54, 64, 65 and 'Sky-Buster' Boeing	£15-18	☐
G 11	1978	Strike Force Set	Contains 6 Army Vehicles	£45-50	☐
G 11	1986	'LUFTHANSA' Set	Contains 30, 54, 59, 65 and 'Sky-Buster' A300 Airbus	£15-18	☐
G 12	1978	Rescue Set	Contains 6 Rescue Vehicles	£20-30	☐
G 13	1978	Construction Set	Contains 6 Construction Vehicles	£20-25	☐
G 14	1978	Grand Prix Set	Contains Transporter and 4 Racing Cars	£20-25	☐
G 15	1978	Transporter Set	Contains Transporter and 5 Superfast Cars	£20-25	☐
G 40	1988	40 years Set...............................	Contains Aveling Barford Road Roller, London Bus, Horse Drawn Milk Float, Massey Harris Tractor, Dennis Fire Engine. (These models may be distinguished from the original issues as they have 'Made in China' cast into the underside).	£8-12	☐
	1960-61	Garage Set 'C'	Contains 8 various models, a garage, R-1 (roadway), A-1 Esso pumps, A-2 Transporter and M-6 'Pickfords'..	£300-350	☐

'Motorcity' Sets and Accessories Introduced in 1988

Ref. No.	Year(s)	Model Type		Market Price Range	
MC 1		Car Wash......................	with two Miniatures	NRP	☐
MC 2		Petrol Station............................	with two Miniatures	NRP	☐
MC 3		Pit Stop....................................	with two Miniatures	NRP	☐
MC 4		Garage	with two Miniatures	NRP	☐
MC 5		Construction Crane	with MB 23	NRP	☐
MC 6		Conveyor Loader........................	with MB 9, 23, 29 and 32	NRP	☐
MC 7	1990	Farm Set	Contains Convoy CY20 Kenworth Tipper, MB27 Jeep (and Horsebox), TP103, TP108, and Harrow and Combine Harvester....................................	NRP	☐
MC 8	1990	Construction Set	Convoy Peterbilt Low Loader plus Yellow Miniatures MB 9, 19, 23, 32, 42, 48	NRP	☐
MC 9		Gear Shift Garage	Gear lever operates car lift and 4 other functions....................	NRP	☐
MC 10		10 Pack	10 assorted Miniatures	NRP	☐
MC 11		Car Transporter Set....................	Contains CY1 Car Transporter plus two MB37 Escort Cabriolet (1 Red, 1 Blue).......	NRP	☐
MC 12		Aerobatic Team Set	Contains CY21 DAF Transporter plus MB57 and MB 75 Helicopters	NRP	☐
MC 13		'POLICE' Set	Contains Convoy Kenworth Low Loader plus Miniatures MB51 Ford Police Car ('G12' logo), MB61 and MB75 Helicopter....................................	NRP	☐
MC 15	1990	Fire Set	Contains CY13 Fire Engine plus Miniatures MB13, MB16, MB18, MB54 Pumper, Skybuster SB26 'FIRE'..	NRP	☐
MC 17		British Airways Set	Contains 747 Airliner and Concorde plus 3 Miniatures	NRP	☐
MC 18	1990	Ferrari Set.................................	Contains CY24 plus MB70e, MB70f, MB75 and MB14.....................	NRP	☐
MC 19	1990	British Airways..........................	A Sky-Busters set	NRP	☐
MC 20		20 Pack	Contains 20 assorted Miniatures	NRP	☐
MC 23		Porsche Set...............................	Contains CY24 plus MB3, MB7, MB41 & MB59	NRP	☐
MC 24		Red Arrows Set	See the 'Colour Section' picture......................................	NRP	☐
MC 30		30 Pack	Contains 30 assorted Miniatures	NRP	☐
MC 50		Bucket of Cars...........................	Contains 50 assorted Miniatures	NRP	☐
MC 100		Garage Set	A complete mini-garage and equipment.................................	NRP	☐
MC 150		Airport Set................................	Contains complete mini-airport layout and outfit	NRP	☐
MC 155		Motorcity Airport	International airport plus two airliners	NRP	☐
MC 160		Red Arrows Squadron HQ	Includes HQ building, control tower and two 'Red Arrows' (Skybusters).......	NRP	☐
MC 200		Playtrack.................................	Includes bridge, petrol station, road signs, etc.	NRP	☐
MC 250		Railway Set	no details	NRP	☐
MC 300		Playtrack.................................	Includes car park and accessories	NRP	☐
MC 330		Playtrack Set	Minitronic unit with voice and sound effects	NRP	☐
MC 370		Super Spin Car Wash	Conveyor belt moves cars under water spray	NRP	☐
MC 400		Playtrack.................................	Includes garage, car park and accessories	NRP	☐
MC 410		Deluxe Playtrack Set	Includes working bridge, dual lane track and accessories	NRP	☐
MC 420		High Rise Park	A multi-storey car park with super fast roll-down ramps..............	NRP	☐
MC 500		Multi-Storey Car Park	With working lift and roll-down ramps plus accessories	NRP	☐
MC 510		Transport Set............................	Roadway, buildings, roadway track, train, carriages, goods yard, airport, playmat	NRP	☐
MC 520	1992	Construction Zone	A complete building set with crane, scaffolding and playmat...........	NRP	☐
MC 550	1992	Electronic Service Centre...........	A complete Matchbox garage with electronic sound effects	NRP	☐
MC 560		Intercom City	Computerised communications system with sounds and voices, plus 4 models	NRP	☐
MC 570		Message Vehicles Sets...............	Four sets of vehicles which activate different sounds and messages when used with Intercom City	NRP	☐
MC 580		Intercom City Grand Prix Set...	Similar system to MC 560 plus 3 racing cars	NRP	☐
MC 585		Intercom City Mega Set............	Super Pack as per MC 560	NRP	☐
MC 590		Intercom City Airport Set.........	Similar to MC 560 plus 2 vehicles and an airliner....................	NRP	☐
MC 610		Container Port	Includes dockside equipment	NRP	☐
MC 620		Construction Yard	Yard with working features	NRP	☐
MC 630		Fold 'n' Go Garage....................	Includes garage plus pumps, parking lot and moving barriers	NRP	☐
MC 640		Fold 'n' Go Garage....................	Includes ramps, multi-level parking, moving lift and barriers	NRP	☐

Ref. No.	Year(s)	Model Type	Matchbox Toys - continued	Market Price Range	
MC 660		Electronic Rescue Centre	Portable Rescue Unit with building, 2 working sirens, search beam, lights, etc	NRP	☐
MC 700		Mini Tronics Sets	1: Car Wash, 2: Petrol Station, 3: Construction Site, 4: Conveyor Site	NRP	☐
MC 803		Circus Set..................................	CY24 'Circus', MB16 and caravan, animal cage truck plus 2 horses.........................	NRP	☐
MC 804		Circus Set..................................	Big Top, tent, CY24 'Circus', MB16 and caravan, animal cage truck, Skybusters biplane, Model 'A' car, booking office van	NRP	☐

Miscellaneous Sets

C 6		Japanese Emergency Gift Set	All Japanese Set	£15-20	☐
C 11		Japanese Airport Gift Set.........	Japanese Foam Pump, Ikarus Coach & Aircraft	£20-25	☐
		Japanese Cars Gift Set	JPS Lotus, Volkswagen, Gold Rolls-Royce and Mercedes...	£30-35	☐
		Las Vegas Dodge Set	Car and Van	£120-140	☐
MG 9		Gear Shift Garage	Gear lever operates car lift and 4 other functions..	NRP	☐
MP 804	1990	Porsche Set	Contains MB3 (911 Turbo), MB7 (959), MB59 (944 Turbo)	NRP	☐
SS 100		Smash 'n' Crash......................	Action Playset with two vehicles	NRP	☐
		Multi-Pack Gift Sets.................	Contains 5 Superfast models...	£15-20	☐
		'Days Of Thunder'	Film-related sets issued in the US only:		
			i) Modified MB10 Buick Le Sabre in 5 liveries	NGPP	☐
			ii) Modified MB54f Chevrolet Lumina in 5 liveries...	NGPP	☐

Early Accessory Packs

A1a	1957	'ESSO' Petrol Pump Set...........	Red pumps, White figure	£15-20	☐
A1b	1963	'BP' Petrol Pump Set...............	White pumps, Yellow/White decal	£15-20	☐
A2	1957	Car Transporter.......................	1st type: All Blue body with 'MATCHBOX' logo..	£35-40	☐
			2nd type: Red cab, Grey trailer, 'MATCHBOX' logo...	£90-110	☐
A3	1957	Garage	Yellow/Green/Red, opening doors, all metal	£15-20	☐
A4	1960	Road Signs Set	Eight Red/White/Black signs 'Lesney' on base...	£15-20	☐
A5	1960	'HOME STORES'......................	Food shop with window display and opening door...	£20-25	☐

Note: In 1959 the first of a continuing series of 'MATCHBOX GARAGES' was issued (MG1A). In 1963 a 'MATCHBOX FIRE STATION' was issued (MF1A). The models are made in plastic and a price of **£35 - £45** should be expected on each.

Major Series models

M 1 (a)	1960	Caterpillar Earthmover	Yellow body, Silver metal wheels, Black plastic tyres. 99 mm.	£25-35	☐
M 1 (b)	1963	'BP' Petrol Tanker....................	Green/Yellow/White main body, tinted windows, Black plastic tyres, 102 mm.	£20-25	☐
M 2 (a)	1960	Bedford Articulated Truck 'WALLS ICE CREAM'..........	Light Blue cab, Cream trailer, metal or Grey plastic wheels, 101 mm.	£45-50	☐
			As previous model but with White trailer	£55-60	☐
M 2 (b)	1963	York Trailer 'DAVIES TYRES'	Red cab, Grey trailer, Yellow/Black/Red decals, 10 wheels, 117 mm..........................	£35-40	☐
M 2 (c)	1966	LEP International Transport	Silver cab, Maroon trailer, Yellow/Black/Red decals, 10 wheels, 117 mm.	£40-45	☐
M 3	1960	Centurion Tank on Transporter............................	Olive Green transporter and tank, drop-down ramps, 10 wheels, 155 mm.	£30-35	☐
M 4 (a)	1960	'RUSTON BUCYRUS'	Brown/Yellow, Green rubber tracks, plastic rollers, 99 mm.	£40-50	☐
M 4 (b)	1966	'FREUHOF' Hopper Train	Maroon trailer, 2 Silver hoppers, Red wheels, Black plastic tyres, 286 m....................	£30-35	☐
M 5	1966	'MASSEY FERGUSON' Combine Harvester	Red body, Tan driver, Yellow blades, 117 mm.	£50-60	☐
M 6 (a)	1960	'PICKFORDS' Transporter......	Dark Blue tractor, Dark Red low-loader, Black plastic wheels, 279 mm.	£50-60	☐
			Light or Dark Blue tractor, Bright Red low-loader	£80-90	☐
M 6 (b)	1966	'BP Racing Transporter'	Green body, Yellow/Green decal, Red hubs, Black plastic tyres, 127 mm.	£30-35	☐
M 7	1960	'Jennings' Cattle Truck.............	Red cab, Light Tan box trailer, Grey plastic wheels, 121 mm.	£30-45	☐
			Red cab & ramp, Dark Tan box trailer, Grey plastic wheels	£40-45	☐
			As previous model but with Black plastic wheels	£50-55	☐
M 8 (a)	1960	'MOBILGAS' Petrol Tanker.....	Red, Silver trim, Black/White decal, Grey or Black plastic wheels, 99 mm.	£55-65	☐
M 8 (b)	1964	Car Transporter.......................	'FARNBOROUGH - MEASHAM', Blue cab, Orange trailer and wheels, 'Car Auction Collection', drop-down ramps, Grey plastic tyres, 209 mm.	£30-35	☐
M 9	1962	Inter-State Double Freighter	Dark Blue cab, 2 Silver trailers 'COOPER-JARRETT Inc'	£40-50	☐
			Same but Orange label 'COOPER-JARRETT INTERNATIONAL'.............................	£50-60	☐
M 10	1963	Dinkum Rear Dumper	Yellow body, 'DD70', Red hubs with Black plastic tyres, 108 mm.	£20-25	☐

WHEN REPLYING TO ADVERTISEMENTS PLEASE MENTION JOHN RAMSAY'S CATALOGUE

'Two Packs', '900' Series, 'Twin Packs', 'Team Matchbox'

Ref. No.	Year(s)	Model Type	Model Features and Size	Market Price Range	

The 'Two Pack' series was launched in 1976. Each issue consists of two 'Miniatures' but with new 'TP' numbers on the base.
The series was renamed the '900 Series' in 1979 when the 'Long Haul Cab' vehicles were introduced as follows:
TP 22 Long Haul Double Container Truck,   TP 23 Long Haul Covered Container Truck,
TP 24 Long Haul Box Container Truck,   TP 25 Long Haul Pipe Truck

These models were popular and led to the introduction in 1982 of the 'Convoy' series which was based on Long Haul Trucks. This development resulted in the '900 Series' being renamed 'Two Packs'.

Ref. No.	Year(s)	Model Type	Model Features and Size	Market Price Range	
TP 1	1976	Mercedes Truck and Trailer	Blue/Yellow body, 'IMS' logo (Nos. 1e & 2d)	£10-15	☐
			Red/Yellow body, 'TRANSCONTINENTAL'	£5-10	☐
TP 2	1976	Mod Tractor and Hay trailer	Red tractor, Yellow trailer (Nos 25e & 40c)	£10-15	☐
TP 2	1979	Police Car and Fire Engine	Either 22e or 35c with 59d	£10-15	☐
TP 2	1981	'EXXON' Tanker	Red Cab and chassis, Red & White tank	£10-15	☐
TP 3	1976	Javelin & Pony Trailer	Green Javelin, Orange or Cream trailer, 2 horses	£10-15	☐
TP 3		French issue:	Jeep and pony trailer	£10-15	☐
TP 4	1976	Car and Caravan	Metallic Blue car, Yellow/Red caravan No. 57	£10-15	☐
TP 5	1976	Car towing Boat	Orange Ford Capri (other cars may be substituted)	£10-15	☐
	1981	colour change:	Blue car 'PHANTOM', and Blue boat & trailer	£10-15	☐
TP 5	1976	Lotus Set	2 Black 'JPS' Lotus racing cars	£20-25	☐
TP 6	1976	Breakdown Set	Nos. 61 or 74 with 15d Volkswagen or 65d Saab or 20e Range Rover	£10-15	☐
TP 7	1976	Emergency Set	'Stretcha Fetcha' No. 46 with either 59d or 64d	£10-15	☐
TP 7	1978	Jeep and Glider Set	Yellow Jeep No. 38c plus trailer	£10-15	☐
	1981	Red Jeep and trailer		£10-15	☐
TP 7	1978	Escort & Glider Set	No. 9f plus trailer	£10-15	☐
TP 8	1976	Bus & Hovercraft	No. 17d (with 'CARNABY St.' labels), and No. 72c	£10-15	☐
TP 8	1977	Field Car & Motorcycle	Orange No. 18c (with Silver base), plus Honda 38c	£10-15	☐
	1981	colour change:	Yellow car and trailer, Green motor-cycle	£10-15	☐
TP 9	1978	Field Car & Racing Car	No.18c with 'Team Matchbox' No.24	£10-15	☐
	1981	colour change:	Orange car and racing car	£10-15	☐
TP 10	1978	Ambulance & Fire Chief	Mercedes Ambulance & Fire Chief's car with 'Fire' labels, (No.59d with 3c)	£10-15	☐
TP 11	1977	Jeep and Motorcycle	Military Green No.38c with 'JEEP' on baseplate, plus 18f	£25-35	☐
		model change:	As previous model but with No.2c plus 18f Hondarora	£10-15	☐
TP 11	1979	Tractor & Hay Trailer	Red tractor and trailer Nos.25e and 40c	£10-15	☐
	1981	colour change:	Green tractor, Yellow trailer	£10-15	☐
TP 12	1977	Military Police & Field Car	Dark Military Green 'POLICE' labels (Nos.20e and 18c).	£25-35	☐
			As previous model but with 'AMBULANCE' labels.	£25-35	☐
TP 12	1977	Field Car & VW Ambulance	Military Green	£25-35	☐
TP 13	1977	Weasel & Stoat	Dark Military Green	£100-125	☐
TP 13	1978	Unimog & Gun	No.49b in Military Green plus 32e	£10-15	☐
TP 14	1977	Tanker & Badger	Dark Military Green, (French flag on tanker)	£50-60	☐
TP 14	1978	Ambulance & Staff Car	Mercedes Ambulance No.3c plus No.46, both in Military-Green	£10-15	☐
TP 15	1977	Mercedes Truck & Trailer	Military Green Nos.1e and 2d, 'USA 48350' labels	£35-40	☐
TP 16	1977	Dump Truck & Bulldozer	28d Mack truck in Dark Military Green	£35-40	☐
		colour change:	In normal Military Green livery	£10-15	☐
TP 16	1979	Wreck Truck & Stalwart	Military Green finish Nos.71c and 61b	£10-15	☐
TP 16	1980	Artic Truck & Trailer	Yellow/Blue body for each model	£10-15	☐
		colour change:	Red/Silver body for each model	£20-25	☐
TP 17	1979	Tanker and Trailer	Red/White body with 'CHEVRON' logo (No.63)	£10-15	☐
		colour change:	White/Yellow body with 'SHELL' logo (No.63)	£5-10	☐
TP 18	1979	'Water Sporter'	Red 7e Volkswagen Golf, Red/White 5f Seafire Motor Boat	£5-10	☐
TP 19	1980	Cattle Truck & Trailer	Red/Cream body for each model, plus 2 cows	£5-10	☐
TP 20	1980	Shunter & Side Tipper	Cream/Red 24e Diesel Shunter, Red or Black side tipper	£5-10	☐
	1981	colour change:	Yellow/Red bodies, 'D1496-RF' logo	£5-10	☐
TP 21	1980	Datsun & M/C Trailer	Metallic Blue 24f (Datsun 280 ZX) with 3 Cream or Red motor-bikes	£5-10	☐
TP 21	1980	Citroën & M/C Trailer	Metallic Blue 12f with roof-rack, 3 Cream or Red motor-bikes	£5-10	☐
TP 22	1980	Container Truck	Metallic Red cab, Cream containers	£5-10	☐
	1981	with logo:	As previous model but with 'OCL' logo in Blue	£5-10	☐
TP 23	1980	Covered Truck	Red/White body, (articulated vehicle) 'FIRESTONE'	£5-10	☐
TP 24	1980	Box Truck	All Red body, 'FIRESTONE' in White, 8 wheels	£10-15	☐
		colour change:	Yellow cab, Yellow box, 'KODAK', 8 wheels	£150-175	☐
		colour change:	Cream cab, Red trailer base 'MATCHBOX'	£5-10	☐
		colour change:	Cream cab, Black trailer base 'MATCHBOX'	£8-12	☐
		colour change:	Red cab, Red trailer base	£8-12	☐
TP 25	1980	Pipe Truck	Metallic Green cab, Black trailer base, 3 Red pipes	£5-10	☐
		colour change:	Yellow cab version	£16-20	☐
TP 26	1981	Boat Transporter	Blue cab, Silver trailer, Red/Cream boat	£5-10	☐
TP 27	1981	Steam loco & Caboose	Green/Black logo, Green/Cream/Black Caboose	£5-10	☐
TP 28	1982	Cortina & Caravan	Bronze/White 25d, Red/White 'SUN SET' caravan 57d	£5-10	☐
TP 29	1982	Flareside Pickup & Boat	Blue 57f plus Blue/White boat	£5-10	☐
TP 30	1982	Datsun and Speed Boat	Silver/Red 24f, Yellow/Black 5f	£5-10	☐
TP 31	1982	Citroën & M/C Trailer	Yellow 12f and trailer with 3 Red bikes	£5-10	☐
TP 32	1982	Wreck Truck & Dodge	Green 61d with Orange/Blue 1g Dodge Challenger, 'Revin' Rebel'	£5-10	☐
TP 102	1984	Escort & Pony Trailer	Green Escort and 'SEAGULL' trailer	£5-10	☐
TP 103	1984	Cattle Truck & Trailer	Yellow cab and chassis, Brown cages, 4 cows	£5-8	☐
TP 103	1987	new design:	Blue truck and trailer with Brown stake sides, plus 4 Black cows	£5-8	☐
TP 103	1989	new design:	Green truck and trailer with Yellow stake sides, plus 4 Black cows	£5-8	☐

Ref. No.	Year(s)	Model Type	Matchbox Toys - continued	Market Price Range	
TP 106	1984	Renault 5 & M/C Trailer	Black car, Yellow/Red panels, Yellow/Red motor-cycle trailer	**£5-10**	☐
TP 106	1987	new design:	White/Orange/Black car *'Scrambles'*, White trailer, 3 motorbikes	**£5-10**	☐
TP 107	1984	Datsun & Caravan	Silver/Blue car, White caravan	**£5-10**	☐
TP 108	1984	Tractor & Hay Trailer	Blue tractor, Red/Black trailer	**£5-10**	☐
TP 108	1987	new design:	Orange tractor and trailer with Black raves	**£5-10**	☐
TP 108	1989	new design:	Green tractor, Yellow trailer with Black raves	**£5-10**	☐
TP 109	1984	Citroën & Boat	White/Blue car, Black/White boat, Red trailer	**£5-10**	☐
TP 110	1984	Matra Rancho & Boat	Black Rancho, Yellow logo, Orange inflatable	**£5-10**	☐
TP 110	1987	new design:	Red Rancho, *'SURF 2'* logo, Black boat on White trailer	**£5-10**	☐
TP 111	1984	Cortina & Horsebox	Red car, Yellow *'SILVERSHOES'* horsebox, 2 horses	**£5-10**	☐
TP 112	1985	Unimog & Trailer	Yellow body, White covers, Red *'ALPINE RESCUE'*	**£5-10**	☐
TP 112	1987	new design:	Red truck and trailer, White rear covers, 'UNFALL - BETTUNG'	**£5-10**	☐
TP 112	1989	new design:	White truck and trailer, Orange rear covers, Blue 'GB 5' logo	**£5-10**	☐
TP 113	1985	Porsche & Caravan	Black car, White/Orange caravan	**£5-10**	☐
TP 114	1986	VW Golf and Horsebox	Black car, Beige/Brown horsebox *'Silvershoes'*, 2 White horses	**£5-10**	☐
TP 115	1987	Ford Escort and Boat	White car with *'XR4i'* logo, plus White/Blue boat on trailer	**£5-10**	☐
TP 116	1987	'Holiday Club'	Yellow vehicle *'HOLIDAY CLUB'* plus trailer with Green *'500'* logo	**£5-10**	☐
TP 117	1987	Mounted Police Land Rover	White *'POLICE'* Land Rover and horsebox with 2 Black horses	**£5-10**	☐
TP 117	1989	Mercedes G Wagon and Horsebox	Green/White *'POLITIE'* car and horsebox with 2 Black horses	**£5-10**	☐
TP 118	1987	BMW and Glider	Red/White car and glider trailer, White glider	**£5-10**	☐
TP 119	1987	Flareside and Seafire	Blue/Yellow vehicle and motorboat with *'FORD'* and *'60'* logos	**£5-10**	☐
TP 120	1989	VW Golf and Inflatable	Blue/Silver car *'GTI'*, Orange boat on trailer	**£5-10**	☐
TP 121	1989	Land Rover and Seafire	White and Red vehicle and speedboat	**£5-10**	☐
TP 122	1989	Porsche and Glider	Blue and Yellow car and glider trailer, White Glider	**£5-10**	☐
TP 123	1989	BMW and Caravan	Metallic Blue car, Grey caravan with Red design on lower part	**£5-10**	☐
TP 124	1989	Zoo Truck, Caravan Trailer	White and Red truck and caravan, 'All Stars Circus' logo	**£5-10**	☐
TP 124	1991	Locomotive and Carriage	Green and Cream loco and carriage with British Railways crest	**£5-10**	☐
TP 125	1991	Shunter and Tipper	Yellow and Red models with Red logo on shunter	**£5-10**	☐
TP 127	1991	BMW and Dinghy	White open top car plus Blue dinghy on White trailer	**£5-10**	☐
TP 128	1992	Dodge Truck and Trailer	Red truck and trailer with White rear covers, 'Big Top Circus'	**£5-10**	☐
TP 129	1992	Isuzu and Powerboat	Red and White models with Gold logo and Blue stripes	**£5-10**	☐
TP 130	1992	Land Rover and Pony Trailer	Green and White models plus 2 Black horses	**£5-10**	☐
TP 131	1992	G Wagon and Dinghy	White and Orange models with Blue *'Marine Rescue'* logos	**£5-10**	☐
TP 131	1992	G Wagon and Dinghy	White and Orange models with Blue *'Marine Rescue'* logos	**£5-10**	☐

Matchbox 'King-Size' Models

Following the successful sales of Major Series, Lesney Products decided to further develop the range by introducing a larger scale toy and a suitable name was 'King-Size'. Ultimately the popular Major Models were themselves built into the King-Size series when the Major Model series was discontinued in 1966.

K1-1	1960	Hydraulic Shovel	All Yellow body, Grey plastic wheels, *'WEATHERILL'*	**£18**	☐
K1-2	1963	Tipper Truck	Red cab and chassis, Orange tipper, 8 wheels, *'HOVERINGHAM'*	**£18-20**	☐
K1-3	1970	Excavator	Red body, Silver shovel, tinted windows, *'O & K'* logo, Black plastic tyres	**£10-12**	☐
K2-1	1960	Dumper Truck	Red body, *'MUIR HILL 14B'*, Black or Green, metal wheels	**£18-20**	☐
K2-2	1964	Dumper Truck	Yellow body, *'KW DART'* logo, 6 Red wheels, Black plastic tyres	**£14-16**	☐
K2-3	1968	Scammell Wreck Truck	White body, Red jib & wheels, Grey hook, *'ESSO'* logo	**£14-16**	☐
		colour change:	Gold body version	**£14-16**	☐
K3-1	1960	Caterpillar Bulldozer	Yellow body, Red engine, Grey metal rollers	**£14-16**	☐
		colour change:	As previous model but with Red metal rollers	**£10-12**	☐
		colour change:	As previous model but with Yellow metal rollers	**£10-12**	☐
K3-2	1965	Tractor Shovel	Orange body, Red wheels *'HATRA'*	**£14-6**	☐
K3-3	1970	Tractor & Trailer	Each has Red body, Yellow trim, *'MASSEY FERGUSON'* logo	**£10-12**	☐
K4-1	1960	Tractor	Red body, Green wheels, *'McCORMICK INTERNATIONAL'*	**£20-22**	☐
		colour change:	As previous model with Orange or Red wheel hubs	**£14-16**	☐
K4-2	1967	G.M.C. Tractor & Hoppers	Dark Red cab, 2 Silver hoppers, *'FREUHOF'* logo	**£20-22**	☐
K4-3	1969	Leyland Tipper	Dark Red cab and chassis, Silver tipper *'W. WATES'*	**£14-16**	☐
		colour change:	As previous model but with Yellow/Green body colours	**£14-16**	☐
		colour change:	With Red cab and chassis, Green tipper	**£14-16**	☐
		colour change:	With Blue cab and chassis, Silver tipper *'Miner'* label	**£14-16**	☐
		colour change:	With Silver tipper and *'LE TRANSPORT'* logo	**£20-22**	☐
K5-1	1961	Tipper Truck	Yellow body and tipper, Red wheels, *'FODEN'* logo	**£14-16**	☐
K5-2	1967	Racing Car Transporter	Green body, Silver drop down rear door, Red wheels	**£24-26**	☐
K5-3	1970	Tractor and Trailer	Each has Yellow body, Red chassis, *'MUIR HILL'*	**£12-14**	☐
K6-1	1961	Earth Scraper	Orange body, Red engine, *'ALLIS CHALMERS'*	**£14-16**	☐
K6-2	1967	Mercedes Ambulance	White body, Silver grille, Red badge, ambulance-man, stretcher	**£14-16**	☐
K7-1	1961	Rear Dumper	Yellow body, Red engine, *'CURTISS-WRIGHT'*	**£10-12**	☐
K7-2	1967	Refuse Truck	Red body and wheels *'CLEANSING DEPARTMENT'*	**£10-12**	☐
		colour change:	Blue body version	**£10-12**	☐
K8-1	1962	Prime Mover & Transporter with Crawler Tractor	Orange bodies, Yellow tractor *'LAING'* logo in Black/Yellow, (6 x 6 wheels)	**£40-45**	☐
K8-2	1967	Guy Warrior Transporter	Blue cab, Yellow car transporter *'FARNBOROUGH - MEASHAM'*	**£20-24**	☐
		colour change:	Orange cab, Orange or Yellow transporter	**£20-24**	☐
K8-3	1970	'CATERPILLAR TRAXCAVATOR'	Yellow body and shovel, Blue or White driver	**£20-22**	☐
K9-1		Diesel Road Roller	Green body, Red wheels and driver 'AVELING BARFORD'	**£10-12**	☐
K9-2	1967	Combine Harvester	Red body, Yellow blades and wheels, *'CLAAS'*	**£15-18**	☐
		colour change:	Green body, Red blades and wheels *'CLAAS'*	**£15-18**	☐
K10-1	1963	Tractor Shovel	Blue-Green body, Red seat and wheels *'AVELING BARFORD'*	**£16-18**	☐
K10-2	1966	Pipe Truck	Yellow body, Red wheels, 6 Grey pipes	**£14-16**	☐
		colour change:	('Super-Kings' issue) Purple body, Grey or Yellow pipes	**£10-12**	☐
K11-1	1963	Tractor & Trailer	Blue tractor, Grey/Blue trailer *'FORDSON SUPER MAJOR'*	**£24-26**	☐

Ref. No.	Year(s)	Model Type	Matchbox Toys - continued	Market Price Range	
K11-2	1969	DAF Car Transporter	Yellow body, Yellow/Red decks, 'DAF' logo........................	£14-16	☐
		colour change:............	Metallic Blue body, Gold trailer decks..............................	£14-16	☐
K12-1	1963	Breakdown Truck	Green body, Yellow jib, 'MATCHBOX SERVICE STATION'	£24-26	☐
K12-2	1969	Scammell Crane Truck	Yellow body and chassis, 'LAING' on crane........................	£10-12	☐
K13-1	1963	Concrete Truck.........................	Orange body and barrel, 'READYMIX' logo	£16-18	☐
		logo change:...............	As previous model but with 'RMC' logo	£16-18	☐
K14-1	1964	Jumbo Crane	Yellow body and crane, 'TAYLOR JUMBO CRANE'............	£10-12	☐
K15-1	1964	Merryweather Fire Engine	Red body, Silver ladder, 'KENT FIRE BRIGADE'	£16-18	☐
K15	1973	**'THE LONDONER'**	**Double Decker Bus**		
K15-1	1973	'CARNABY STREET'.........	Red body, 'SWINGING LONDON' & 'CARNABY STREET' labels	£14-16	☐
K15-2	1977	Jubilee Bus	Silver body, 'SILVER JUBILEE', '1952 E II R 1977' labels	£14-16	☐
K15-3	1978	'HARRODS'.........................	Red body, 'ENTER A DIFFERENT WORLD - HARRODS'	£12-14	☐
K15-4	1978	'HAMLEYS'........................	Red body, 'HAMLEYS THE FINEST TOY SHOP' labels........	£12-14	☐
K15-5	1979	Tour Bus	Red body, 'TOURIST LONDON - BY BUS' labels	£10-12	☐
K15-6	1980	'LONDON DUNGEON'	Red body, 'VISIT THE LONDON DUNGEON' labels	£12-14	☐
K15-7	1981	'DUNGEON MUSEUM'	Red body, 'LONDON DUNGEON MUSEUM' labels	£12-14	☐
K15-8	1981	'ROYAL WEDDING'	Silver body, 'THE ROYAL WEDDING 1981' labels	£10-12	☐
K15-9	1985	'NESTLES'	Red/White body, 'NESTLE MILKY BAR' labels	£6-10	☐
K15-10	1986	Tour Bus	Red body, 'LONDON-WIDE TOUR BUS' labels	£6-10	☐
K16-1	1966	Tractor & Twin Tippers............	Green cab, Yellow tippers, 'DODGE TRUCKS' in Red	NGPP	☑
		colour change:...........	Yellow cab, Blue tippers same logo (22w)........................	£30-35	☐
K17-1	1967	Low Loader & Bulldozer	Green cab and loader, Red/Yellow Bulldozer	£24-26	☐
K18-1	1966	Artic Horse Box	Red cab, Brown box, 4 White horses 'ASCOT STABLES'......	£14-16	☐
K19-1	1967	Scammell Tipper......................	Red body, Yellow tipper, Silver trim...............................	£14-16	☐
K20-1	1968	Tractor Transporter..................	Red body, Yellow rack, 3 Blue tractors (39c)	£24-26	☐
		colour change:...........	As previous model but with Orange tractors......................	£70-75	☐
K21-1	1969	Mercury Cougar	Gold body, Cream seats..	NGPP	☐
K22-1	1969	Dodge Charger	Blue body, Yellow seats..	NGPP	☐
K23-1	1969	Mercury 'POLICE' Car.............	White body with 'HIGHWAY PATROL' logo	NGPP	☐
K24-1	1969	Lamborghini Miura..................	Red body, Cream seats	NGPP	☐

GIFT SETS   (King-Size models)

	1963	King-Size Set	Contains K1-1, K2-1, K3-1, K5-1, K6-1	£60-65	☐
	1965	Construction Set	Contains K16-1, K7-1, K10-1, K13-1, K14-1	£75-80	☐
	1966	King-Size Set	Contains K16-1, K11-1, K12-1, K15-1	£40-45	☐

After 1970 the 'King-Size' range developed into the larger **'SUPER-KINGS'** Series.
Collectors requiring more information of the large number of 'SUPERKINGS' issues (or 'SPEED KINGS', 'BATTLE KINGS', 'SEA KINGS' and 'SPECIALS') should send for the **Specialist Series** publication. Details are given at the end of the Matchbox chapter.

Convoy Series

The model range was launched in 1982 and the early issues were made in England before manufacture was transferred to Macau. The basic listing of models issued up to 1988 is as follows:

CY1	Kenworth Boat Transporter	CY21	DAF Aircraft Transporter
CY2	Kenworth Rocket Transporter	CY22	DAF Power Boat Transporter
CY3	Peterbilt Container Truck	CY23	Scania Covered Truck
CY4	Kenworth Boat Transporter (MB 41f)	CY24	DAF Box Car
CY5	Peterbilt Covered Truck	CY25	DAF Box Truck
CY6	Kenworth Horse Box	CY26	DAF Container Truck
CY7	Peterbilt Petrol Tanker	CY27	Mack Box Truck
CY8	Kenworth Box Truck (MB 45e)	CY28	Mack Container Truck
CY9	Kenworth Box Truck (MB 41f)	CY29	Mack Aircraft Transporter
CY10	Kenworth Racing Transporter (MB 66f)	CY35	Mack Tanker
CY11	Kenworth Helicopter Transporter (MB 75e)	CY36	Kenworth Box Car
CY12	Kenworth Aircraft Transporter	CY104	Kenworth Aerodyne Cab and Box Car Trailer
CY13	Peterbilt Fire Engine	CY105	Kenworth Aerodyne Tanker
CY14	Kenworth Boat Transporter (MB 45e)	CY106	Peterbilt Tipper Truck
CY15	Peterbilt Tracking Vehicle	CY107	Mack CH-600 Box Car
CY16	Scania Box Truck	CY109	Ford Aeromax Box Car
CY17	Scania Petrol Tanker	CY110	Kenworth Box Car
CY18	Scania Container Truck	CY201	Fire Rescue Set
CY19	Peterbilt Box Car	CY202	Police Set
CY20a	Scania Tipper	CY203	Construction Set
CY20b	Kenworth Tipper	CY204	NASA Set

Convoy models have been issued in a large number of variations and increasingly for promotional purposes. It is therefore not possible to provide an up-to-date list of them in this Catalogue. Collectors requiring this information should obtain a copy of the **Specialist Series** publication. Details are at the end of the Matchbox chapter.

Matchbox Catalogues

1957	Folded Leaflet	Yellow cover has Blue edging and depicts No.1 Diesel Roller. Colour pictures of nos. 1 - 42 of '1-75' series........................		£50-75	☐
1957	Folded Leaflet	Blue/Yellow cover featuring MOY No.1 Allchin 7nhp Traction Engine 1st series box. Contents list first nine Yesteryears.................		£75-100	☐
1958	16-page catalogue.........................	Cover features Rolls-Royce (44), emerging from box in colour, plus early 'Major Packs' and Accessory Packs. Contents illustrate models 1 - 60 in colour...............		£50-75	☐
	Reprints.....................................	Catalogue reprinted for DTE in 1982		£15-20	☐
1959	Folded Leaflet	Features first fourteen Models Of Yesteryear in colour............		£75-100	☐
1959	16-page catalogue.........................	Same cover as 1958 catalogue with '1959 Edition'. Lists 1-75's, Major Packs and accessories. Colour pictures		£50-75	☐

Ref. No.	Publication	Cover details	Market Price Range	
1959	24-page catalogue	'UK' & '2d' on cover featuring MOY No.9, 1-75 series, No.'43', and Accessory No.'2'. Colour contents show 1-75's Nos 1 - 72 plus MOY 1 - 14 plus Accessories and Major Packs..	£50-75	☐
1960	32-page catalogue	'UK' & '3d' on cover featuring logo *ALL THE MATCHBOX POCKET TOYS BY LESNEY* plus semi-circle picture of MOY & 1-75's. Contents illustrate all ranges.	£50-75	☐
1961	32-page catalogue	*'International Pocket Catalogue'* on cover with picture of 1-75 model No.5 Bus. New style smaller catalogue listing all issues in colour plus International price list.	£50-75	☐
1962	20-page catalogue	'2d', *'International Pocket Catalogue'* and *'1962 Edition'* on cover. All issues listed, European price list included.	£35-45	☐
1963	20-page catalogue	No.53 Mercedes-Benz printed on cover with '2d' and *'1963 Edition'*. Contents include good Gift Set pictures and listings.	£10-14	☐
1964	32-page catalogue	'3d' on cover depicting Blue Mk.10 Jaguar (No.28). *'1964 Matchbox Prices'* on back cover. Contents include superb Gift Set pictures and listings.	£8-11	☐
1965	32-page catalogue	Cover features Motor Racing Cars. *'1965 Matchbox Prices'* on back cover. Excellent full colour Gift Set pictures. (Price 3d).	£8-11	☐
1966	40-page catalogue	London scene and *'Price 3d'* on cover. Excellent pictures of mid-sixties Gift Sets plus history of Matchbox.	£8-11	☐
1967	40-page catalogue	Cover features flags and 1-75 issues, *'Price 3d'*. Contents list and depict Veteran Car Gifts	£8-11	☐
1968	40-page catalogue	1968 car picture & *'Price 3d'* on cover. Includes details of manufacturing processes.	£8-11	☐
1969	48-page catalogue	Cover features Motorway scene. Contents include detailed history of the real cars making up the MOY range.	£8-11	☐
	2nd edition:	A second edition of the 1969 catalogue includes the first reference to *'Superfast'* issues.	£8-11	☐
1970	64-page catalogue	Only drawings of models (no photographs) throughout. Superfast track featured. '6d', *'MATCHBOX SUPERFAST'* and a collage of models on cover.	£5-8	☐
1971	64-page catalogue	'2$p' on Blue/Red cover with scorpion design. 'Speed Kings' listed plus pictures of first Superfast Gift Sets.	£5-8	☐
1972	72-page catalogue	Yellow *'MATCHBOX'* and '3p' on cover. Contents feature launch of 'Scream'n Demon' bikes and excellent Gift Set pictures.	£5-8	☐
1973	80-page catalogue	'5p' and '1973' on cover of the largest Matchbox catalogue produced. Contents include good 'Super Kings' and Aircraft Kit listing.	£5-8	☐
1974	64-page catalogue	'2p' and '1974' on cover. Includes first 'SKYBUSTERS' listing.	£5-8	☐
1975	64-page catalogue	'2p' and '1975' on cover. Contents feature 'Rolamatics' and 'Battle Kings'.	£5-8	☐
1976	64-page catalogue	'1976' on cover. Contents feature 'Sea Kings' plus 'Baby Dolls' & 'Disco Girl Dolls'	£5-8	☐
1977	80-page catalogue	'1977' on cover. Contents list the 'Two Pack' (TP) range of 1-75's. Good Gift Set pictures and listings of 1-75's.	£5-8	☐
1978	64-page catalogue	'1978' on cover. Includes good 'SKYBUSTERS' and 1-75 Gift Set pictures.	£5-8	☐
1979-80	80-page catalogue	'5p' and '1979-80' on cover. The contents feature good pictures of Gift Sets G1 - G8. '900' TP series introduced.	£4-6	☐
1980-81	80-page catalogue	'5p' on cover. All ranges listed including 'Walt Disney' & 'Power Track' equipment	£3-4	☐
1981-82	64-page catalogue	'5p' and '1981-82' on cover. 'Adventure 2000' space models pictured. 'Playtrack', 'Popeye' and 'Streak Sets' listed.	£2-3	☐
1982-83	64-page catalogue	'1982-83' on cover. 'Convoy' series introduced, good MOY pictures, 'Streak Sets' listing.	£2-3	☐
1984	64-page catalogue	'1984' on cover. 'MATCHBOX SPECIALS' introduced, good Gift Set pictures, 'Burnin' Key Cars', 'Rough Riders' and 'Lock Ups' listed.	£2-3	☐
1985	48-page catalogue	'1985' & 'chequered flag' design on cover. All ranges listed plus introduction of 'Trickshifters', 'Power Blasters', 'Matchmates' and 'Carry Cases'. (Printed in Italy)	£1-2	☐
1986	48-page catalogue	'1986' on cover. 'High Riders', 'Twin-Pack' and 'Action Packs' listed inside. 'Motor City' feature introduced	£1-2	☐
1987	72-page catalogue	'1987' on cover. Listing includes 'Superfast Lasers', 'Pocket Rockets', 'Speed Riders', 'Streak Racing', 'Hot Rod Racers', 'Turbo 2', 'Turbo Specials' and 'Demolition Cars'.	£1-2	☐
1988	88-page catalogue	'1988' on cover. Listing includes Miniatures Gift Sets pictures, 'Lasers', 'Super GT Sport' and 'Super Miniatures', 'Team Convoy', 'Road Blasters', 'Motor City' and 'Action Matchbox'. Also includes 'MICA' and 'Junior Matchbox Club' membership details.	£1-2	☐
1989	80-page catalogue	'1989' on cover. Listings include 'Miniatures', 'Twin-Pack', 'Motor City' Gift Sets, 'Dinky Collection', 'World Class', 'Conn-Nect-Ables', 'Flashbacks', 'Super ColourChangers' and 'Skybusters ColourChangers'.	50p	☐
1990	48-page catalogue	'1990' on cover. Contents include 'Superfast Minis' listing plus normal range of products.	50p	☐
1991	56-page catalogue	'1991' on cover. Includes 'Graffic Traffic', 'Action Series', 'Lightning Series', 'Matchbox 2000' range and Matchbox 'Railways'.	NRP	☐
1991	A4 leaflet	Full-colour sheet with MOY on one side and the Dinky Collection on the other	50p	☐

Overseas Catalogue Editions

During the 1960's there were normally six editions of each catalogue; British, International, U.S.A., German, French and French-Canadian. The catalogues were usually of the same format as the UK editions but with the appropriate language and currency. *'INTERNATIONAL CATALOGUE'* was shown on the front cover together with the edition, e.g. *'EDITION FRANCAISE'*, *'INTERNATIONAL'* or *'U.S.A. EDITION'*. The 1960 *'International Pocket Catalogue'* listed the national prices for every product in Australia, Austria, Belgium, Spain, Denmark, Eire, France, Germany, Great Britain, Holland, Hong Kong, Italy, Kenya & East Africa, Singapore & Malaysia, South Africa, Sweden and Switzerland. From 1972 the country-specific editions only listed the model range available in that country.

Market Price Range - Prices are equivalent to those asked for UK editions.

Other Matchbox literature

'Mike and The Modelman' (1st edition 1970), was a childrens' book issued by Lesney telling the Matchbox story. A copy in perfect condition should cost between **£10 - £15**.

Trade Catalogues have been published for many years and occasionally become available for sale. Those before 1970 are scarce and no value information is possible at present. Those from the 1970-80 period tend to be in the region of **£10-15** while post-1980 editions sell for **£2-5** depending on content and condition.

The Matchbox Collectors Passport (introduced in 1987), also served as a catalogue providing a full colour listing of the MOY range available in the years in which it was current. In 1991 the Dinky Collection then available was also pictured with the Special Editions and the Passport scheme model offer.

TYCO-Matchbox issues

The following listings are in respect of the intended new release programme as shown in the 1993 Trade Catalogue. However, it is possible that not all the models listed will be released. See the 1994 'Model Price Review' for the latest news of actual issues.

MW 500 'Motor Show' Series

Two models alternately displayed in a showcase setting with a mirror-back finish and plinth.

Showcase 1	1993	2 BMWs	A Red '5' series and a White '850i'	NRP	☐
Showcase 2	1993	2 Lamborghinis	A Yellow 'Diablo' plus a Green 'Countach'	NRP	☐
Showcase 3	1993	2 Ferraris	A 'Testarossa' and an 'F-40' (both Red)	NRP	☐
Showcase 4	1993	2 Mercedes-Benz	A Metallic Bronze 'SEL' plus a Red '500 SL'	NRP	☐
Showcase 5	1993	2 Porsches	A Red '959' and a White '911'	NRP	☐
Showcase 6	1993	2 Jaguars	A Blue 'XJ-6' and a Metallic Silver 'XJ-220'	NRP	☐

'Masterclass' series 1:24 scale

'In a class of its own'. Each model has highly detailed features and is packaged in an excellent box.

LS 001	1993	Jaguar XJ-220	Silver body	NRP	☐
LS 002	1993	Lamborghini Diablo	Red body	NRP	☐
LS 003	1993	Porsche 911 Carrera Cabriolet		NRP	☐

Farming Series (Miniatures) Farming Action Packs

1	1993	Tractor and Seeder	plus 2 cows	NRP	☐
2	1993	Tractor and Trailer	plus 3 pigs	NRP	☐
3	1993	Kenworth Horsebox	plus 4 horses	NRP	☐
4	1993	Tractor-Shovel	and Tiptrailer plus 3 sheep	NRP	☐
5	1993	Ford Tractor	plus Haytrailer and 2 horses	NRP	☐
6	1993	Ford Tractor	and Rotovator plus 8 ducks	NRP	☐
FM 110	1993	Mobile Farm Set	Contains 2 Tractors, Trailer, Harrow, Land Rover and accessories	NRP	☐
FM 120	1993	Farm Yard Set	Contains 2 Tractors, Combine Harvester, Horsebox, farm equipment, animals, accessories	NRP	☐
FM 130	1993	Big Farm Set	Contains Barn, Grain Silo, Land Rover & Pony Trailer, 2 Tractors, 2 Trailers, Tanker, Horsebox, Seeder, Harrow, accessories	NRP	☐

Farming Series (Large Scale) Each vehicle includes working features

FM 1	1993	Range Rover	Green body with 'ORGANIC FARMS' logo, plus farmer, dog and 2 sheep	NRP	☐
FM 2	1993	Muir Tractor & Back Shovel	Green/Yellow tractor plus 8 chickens	NRP	☐
FM 3	1993	Shovel Tractor	Red/White/Silver tractor plus 3 pigs	NRP	☐
FM 4	1993	Toyota Hilux	Red body, Brown load plus cow and 2 milkchurns	NRP	☐
FM 5	1993	Muir Tractor & Trailer	Green/Yellow tractor/trailer with log load	NRP	☐
FM 6	1993	Massey Ferguson Tractor	Red/White tractor, Red/Brown trailer with 4 crates	NRP	☐
FM 7	1993	Massey Ferguson Tractor	Green/Black tractor plus Yellow/Green implement	NRP	☐
FM 9	1993	Farm Set	Models FM 1 to FM 7 combined	NRP	☐

Construction Series (Miniatures and Convoys)

'ACTION TEAM'

CS 81	1992	Bulldozer & Tractor Shovel	Miniatures plus signs	NRP	☐
CS 82	1992	Tipper & Excavator	Miniatures plus scaffolding and 2 ladders	NRP	☐
CS 83	1992	Road Roller & Crane	Miniatures plus 8 bollards	NRP	☐

'TRUCK TEAM'

CS 61	1992	Transporter & Shovel	Convoy Mack Transporter plus Shovel and 8 bollards	NRP	☐
CS 62	1992	Pipe Transporter	Convoy Mack Pipe Transporter plus 2 road signs	NRP	☐
CS 63	1992	Kenworth Tipper	Convoy Kenworth Tipper plus 2 road signs	NRP	☐
CS 64	1992	Grove Crane	plus 8 bollards	NRP	☐
CS 71	1993	Mobile Squad Set	Contains Convoy Kenworth Transporter plus Miniatures 11, 25 and 45	NRP	☐
CS 75	1993	Heavy Duty Squad	Contains Grove Crane plus Miniatures 5, 19, 23, 25, 45, in Red/Yellow	NRP	☐
CS 90	1992	Carry Pack	30 pieces including vehicles and accessories from previous sets	NRP	☐

Construction Series (Large Scale) Highly detailed Construction Vehicles

CS 1	1993	Bulldozer	Yellow/Red body and shovel	NRP	☐
CS 2	1993	Leyland Cement Truck	Yellow body, Grey barrel, Red/White stripe design	NRP	☐
CS 4	1993	Skip Truck	Yellow/Red body and skip plus Red/White stripe design	NRP	☐
CS 5	1993	Unimog Tar Sprayer	Yellow/Red body with Red/White stripe design	NRP	☐
CS 6	1993	Tipper Truck	Yellow/Red body with Red/White stripe design	NRP	☐
CS 7	1993	Digger and Plough	Yellow/Red body with Red/White stripe design	NRP	☐
CS 8	1993	Mobile Crane	Yellow/Red body with Red/White stripe design	NRP	☐
CS 9	1993	JCB 808 Excavator	Yellow/Red body, Black tracks, Red/White stripe design	NRP	☐
CS 10	1993	Digger Transporter	Yellow/Red models with No.'9' on digger engine	NRP	☐
CS 11	1993	Pipe Transporter	Yellow/Red vehicle with 3 Grey plastic pipes	NRP	☐

'Emergency' Series (Miniatures and Convoys)

'ACTION TEAM'

EM 81	1992	Snorkel and Foam Pumper	MB13 Snorkel plus MB 54 Pumper	NRP	☐
EM 82	1992	Matra Rancho and Truck	Matra Rancho 'Rescue' plus Ford Wreck Truck	NRP	☐
EM 83	1992	Ambulance & Power Truck	American Ambulance plus MB 50 Auxiliary Power Truck	NRP	☐

Ref. No.	Year(s)	Model Type	Matchbox Toys - continued	Market Price Range	

'TRUCK TEAM'

Ref. No.	Year(s)	Model Type	Matchbox Toys - continued	Market Price Range	
EM 61	1992	Helicopter Transporter	Mack Helicopter Transporter (CY29) 'Police' plus road signs	NRP	☐
EM 62	1992	Fire Engine	Red CY13 with Blue 'FIRE' logo	NRP	☐
EM 63	1992	Coastguard Launch Transporter	White/Red CY22 with 'RESCUE' logo	NRP	☐
EM 64	1992	Peterbilt Rescue Centre	CY15 with road signs	NRP	☐
EM 71	1992	Helicopter Transporter	CY29 with MB18 and MB1 plus road signs	NRP	☐
EM 72	1992	Helicopter Transporter	CY29 with MB18 and Mercedes 280 GE, German issue	NRP	☐
EM 74	1992	Helicopter Transporter	CY29 with MB18 and Land Rover, Dutch issue	NRP	☐
EM 75	1992	Action 'FIRE' Set	CY13 plus TP131, MB18, MB51, MB 75 Helicopter	NRP	☐
EM 80	1992	30 Carry Pack	30 pieces including vehicles and accessories from previous sets	NRP	☐

'Emergency' Series (Large Scale) 'Emergency Vehicles to the Rescue!'

Ref. No.	Year(s)	Model Type	Description	Price	
EM 1	1993	US 'POLICE' Car	Yellow body with Blue stripe, '69' logo on roof	NRP	☐
EM 2	1993	Matra Rancho	Red body with White design and 'Fire Control Unit' logo	NRP	☐
EM 3	1993	Jaguar XJ-6 'POLICE'	White body with Red side stripe and lightbar on roof	NRP	☐
EM 4	1993	BMW 730 'POLICE'	White body with Red side stripe and 2 Blue roof lights	NRP	☐
EM 5	1993	Fire Engine	Red body with White extending ladders, '201 FIRE' logo	NRP	☐
EM 6	1993	Range Rover 'POLICE'	White body with Red side stripe and one Blue light	NRP	☐
EM 7	1993	Transit 'Air Ambulance'	White body, Yellow/Red stripe, Red cross, 2 Blue lights	NRP	☐
EM 8	1993	PB Wreck Truck & Car	Black/White truck 'POLICE', plus Silver Porsche 959	NRP	☐
EM 9	1993	Helicopter Transporter	White/Blue vehicle and White 'Coastguard' helicopter	NRP	☐
EM 10	1993	Snorkel Fire Engine	Red/White body 'County Fire' logo, plus a fireman	NRP	☐
EM 11	1993	Fire Spotter Transporter	Red vehicle with Yellow 'FIRE' logo, plus Silver/Red spotter plane	NRP	☐
EM 12	1993	Power Launch Transporter	White/Blue vehicle with 'Coastguard' logo, plus Orange/White boat	NRP	☐
EM 13	1993	Helicopter	Red/Yellow helicopter with Yellow 'FIRE' logo	NRP	☐
EM 14	1993	Suzuki Santana	White body, Orange/Blue design, Blue 'POLICE' logo	NRP	☐

SB 830 - Airforce Series, SB 840 - Airport Series see the Skybusters listing (below)

Harley-Davidson Motor Cycle Series

Ref. No.	Year(s)	Model Type	Description	Price	
HD 210	1993	4 Motor Cycles Set	Includes Silver/Red, Silver/Turquoise, Silver/Blue and All-Silver models with 'Rev-Up' action	NRP	☐
HD 230	1993	Road Riders Set	Yellow/Silver motor cycle plus Black 'Harley-Davidson' transporter	NRP	☐
HD 250	1993	Hog Riders Set	Includes high detail Red/Silver and Blue/Silver motor cycles	NRP	☐

WS 700 'World Sports' Series 'The Greatest Sports Cars in the World'

Ref. No.	Year(s)	Model Type	Description	Price	
i)	1993	Ferrari 512 BB	White/Black body with Pink 'flame' design	NRP	☐
ii)	1993	Porsche 959	White body with 'KONI' logo and 'PORSCHE 959'	NRP	☐
iii)	1993	Ferrari F4	Red body with Yellow/Black Ferrari emblem	NRP	☐
iv)	1993	Jaguar XJ-220	Red body	NRP	☐
v)	1993	Ford Thunderbird	Black body, RN '28', 'HAVOLINE' logo	NRP	☐
vi)	1993	Chevrolet Lumina	Black body, RN '3', 'GOODRICH' logo	NRP	☐

WS 100 'World Class' Series 'The Finest Saloon Cars in the World'

Ref. No.	Year(s)	Model Type	Description	Price	
WS 101	1993	Porsche 944	Yellow body, Black opening tailgate	NRP	☐
WS 102	1993	Mercedes-Benz 190	Metallic Silver body	NRP	☐
WS 103	1993	Jaguar	White body	NRP	☐
WS 104	1993	BMW 750	Metallic Blue body	NRP	☐
WS 105	1993	Ferrari Testarossa	All Red body	NRP	☐
WS 106	1993	Lamborghini Diablo	Yellow body, Red 'DIABLO' logo, 'J68 TGL' registration	NRP	☐
WS 107	1993	Ford Sierra Cosworth	Black body, Red 'TEXACO' logo	NRP	☐
WS 108	1993	Ford Sierra Cosworth	White body, RN '1', 'GEMINI' logo	NRP	☐
WS 109	1993	Porsche 911 Carrera	Red body, Black 'CARRERA' logo	NRP	☐
WS 110	1993	Mercedes-Benz 500 SL	Metallic Brown body	NRP	☐

'City Life' Series Detailed city service-vehicles

Ref. No.	Year(s)	Model Type	Description	Price	
CL 1	1993	London Bus & Taxi	Red Londoner Bus with 'The Planetarium' logo, plus MB4 taxi	NRP	☐
CL 2	1993	Refuse Truck	All White body, 'ABF HAMBURG' logo	NRP	☐
CL 3	1993	Leyland Recovery Truck	White/Blue body, six-wheel truck with ramp	NRP	☐
CL 4	1993	Leyland Skip Truck	Red cab and chassis, Yellow skip	NRP	☐
CL 5	1993	Iveco Petrol Tanker	Red cab and tank with 'TEXACO' logo	NRP	☐

TR 50 'Transporters' Series 'The Kings of the Highway'

Ref. No.	Year(s)	Model Type	Description	Price	
TR 1	1993	DAF Car Transporter	Yellow cab and rear, 'EXPRESS COURIER' logo	NRP	☐
TR 2	1993	Container Truck	Blue/White cab and rear, 'MATEY BUBBLE BATH' logo	NRP	☐
TR 3	1993	Helicopter Transporter	Blue transporter with 'RN' logo, plus Blue/Orange helicopter	NRP	☐
TR 4	1993	Mercedes Petrol Tanker	White cab and tank, 'TOTAL' logo	NRP	☐
TR 5	1993	DAF Aircraft Transporter	Blue/White 'ALPHA ONE' aircraft on White/Red trailer	NRP	☐
TR 6	1993	Mercedes Racing Car Transporter	White and Dark Blue body with 'GOODYEAR' logo	NRP	☐

'Matchbox Originals' Series

Each model perfectly duplicated from the original Matchbox classics and packed in a replica 'MOKO LESNEY' box.

SERIES I

1	1993	Diesel Road Roller	Blue body, Red wheels, Gold trim	NRP	☐
4	1993	Massey Harris Tractor	Green body, Cream driver, Silver wheels	NRP	☐
5	1993	London Bus	Red body, Silver wheels, 'MATCHBOX ORIGINALS' logo	NRP	☐
7	1993	Horse-Drawn Milk Float	Blue body, White driver and milk crates, Brown horse	NRP	☐
9	1993	Dennis Fire Escape	Red body, Yellow ladder wheels, Silver road wheels	NRP	☐

SERIES II

6	1993	Quarry Truck	Blue cab with Grey tipper	NRP	☐
13	1993	Bedford Wreck Truck	Red body, Yellow crane and hook	NRP	☐
19	1993	MG 'TD' Midget	Dark Green body, White driver, Grey wheels	NRP	☐
26	1993	E.R.F. Cement Mixer	Orange body, Grey wheels and mixer barrel	NRP	☐
32	1993	Jaguar XK-140	Black body, Grey wheels	NRP	☐

'Thunderbirds' Series 'International Rescue Services'

TB 1	1993	Thunderbird I	Pilot Scott Tracey, Steel Grey/Blue/Red model, bubble-pack	NRP	☐
TB 2	1993	Thunderbird II	Pilot Virgil Tracey, Green/Red model plus Yellow Thunderbird IV	NRP	☐
TB 3	1993	Thunderbird III	Astronaut Alan Tracey, Red/Black model with No.'3' logo	NRP	☐
TB 4	1993	Lady Penelope's 'FAB 1'	Pink 'Rolls-Royce' with Silver radiator, Cream interior	NRP	☐
TB 79	1993	Thunderbirds Action Set	Redesigned Thunderbirds I, II, III & IV with powerful wind-back motors	NRP	☐
TB 700	1993	Thunderbirds Rescue Pack	Contains the entire Thunderbirds diecast model range	NRP	☐
TB 710	1993	Tracey Island Electronic Playset	All the Thunderbirds models, with voice commands and rocket sounds	NRP	☐
TB 720	1993	Thunderbirds II Playset	Thunderbirds II and IV models with voice commands and rocket sounds	NRP	☐
TB 750	1993	Thunderbirds Figures	95 mm. tall figures of Parker, John, Virgil, Jeff, Brains, Lady Penelope, Hood, Alan, Scott, Gordon	NRP	☐

'Stingray' Series 'Defends the World from the evil Aquaphibians'

SR 200	1993	Stingray and Terrafish	Blue/Silver/Yellow 'Stingray', plus Green/Silver Terrafish	NRP	☐
SR 210	1993	Marineville	Stingray HQ. Contains 2 'Wasp' rockets plus 'Stingray' model	NRP	☐
SR 220	1993	Stingray Action Playset	Highly detailed 'Stingray' model with lift-off top, fires torpedoes. Colours as SR 200	NRP	☐
SR 250	1993	Stingray Figures	Commander Shore, Titan, Marina, Captain Troy Tempest	NRP	☐

'Swop Tops' Series Exotic cars which switch from classic hardtops to sporting convertibles

1	1993	Nissan 300 ZX	Deep Pink body with Blue '300 ZX'	NRP	☐
2	1993	Porsche 968	Dark Red body, Black top with Silver 'PORSCHE' logo	NRP	☐
3	1993	Corvette	Pink/White/Blue body with Black 'CORVETTE' logo	NRP	☐
4	1993	Ford Mustang GT	Yellow body with Black 'MUSTANG' logo	NRP	☐
5	1993	Ferrari Testarossa	Red body with 2 Ferrari emblems in Yellow/Black	NRP	☐
6	1993	Mercedes-Benz 500 SL	Silver body with Black lower part	NRP	☐

'The Nigel Mansell Collection'

Three sets make up the collection and each contains one of the following four models - MB 246 Nigel Mansell's Car, MB 14 Grand Prix Racing Car (a Red Ferrari), MB 57 Mission Helicopter (Yellow/Blue/White), and MB 68 Chevy Van (White/Yellow/Blue).

NM 820	1993	Grand Prix Set	Contains MB 246, MB 68, MB 57, and MB 70	NRP	☐
NM 830	1993	Formula 1 Set	Contains MB 246, MB 68, MB 74, plus CY24 DAF Box Car with MB 57	NRP	☐
NM 860	1993	Williams F1 Transporter	Contains MB 246 plus the Superkings Iveco Transporter	NRP	☐

Skybusters Aircraft series introduced in 1973

SB 1	Lear Jet	SB 17	Ramrod	SB 35	Mil Mi Hind-D
SB 2	Corsair A7D	SB 18	Wildwind	SB 36	F-117a Stealth
SB 3	A300 Airbus	SB 19	Piper Comanche	SB 38	BAE 146 Airliner
SB 4	Mirage F1	SB 20	Helicopter	SB 39	Boeing Stearman Biplane
SB 5	Starfighter F104	SB 21	Lightning	SB 40b	Boeing 737-300
SB 6	MIG 21	SB 22	Tornado		
SB 7	Junkers	SB 23	Supersonic Jet	**Skybusters Gift Sets**	
SB 8	Spitfire	SB 24	F16 Fighter	and sets containing Skybusters	
SB 9	Cessna 402	SB 25	Helicopter	G 5	'Federal Express'
SB 10	Boeing 747	SB 26	Cessna Float Wing	G 6	'Virgin Airways'
SB 11	Alpha Jet	SB 27	Harrier Jet	G 8a	Thunderjets
SB 12	Skyhawk A-4F	SB 28	A300 Airbus	G 8b	Thunderjets
SB 12	Pitts Special	SB 29	SR-71 Blackbird	G 10	'Pan Am' Set
SB 12	Mission Helicopter	SB 30	F14 Tomcat	G 11	'Lufthansa' Set
SB 13	Douglas DC-10	SB 31	Boeing 747-400	G 18	Sky Giants
SB 14	Cessna 210	SB 32	A10 Thunderbolt	CY108	Lowloader & Hawk
SB 15	Phantom F4E	SB 33	Bell Jet Ranger	MC 17	'British Airways'
SB 16	Corsair	SB 34	Lockheed A130	MC 24	'Red Arrows' Set

Many variations of this popular series exist and collectors requiring full details and prices should send for the **'Specialist Series'** publication. Full details are given at the end of the Matchbox chapter.

Lesney Products - Souvenirs
Prices are in the region of £20-35 for most of those listed.

005	London Bus on tray
014	Rolls-Royce on Blue ash tray
016	Boeing 747 on ash tray
018	Rolls-Royce on ash tray
019	Rolls-Royce on ceramic 'office tidy'
024	Rolls-Royce on stainless-steel ash tray
121	Rolls-Royce on cigarette box
123	Packard on trinket box
127	1922 London Bus on trinket box
205	Boeing 747 on onyx penstand
206	Crossley coal truck on onyx penstand
211	Spitfire on penstand
212	Concorde on penstand
221	Packard on double penstand
222	Concorde on double penstand
302	Rolls-Royce on pipe-rack
505	Rolls-Royce Vintage Car double gift pack
621	Street Rod on penstand/calendar
623	Concorde on penstand/calendar
624	Rolls-Royce on penstand/calendar

Walt Disney Characters
A series of models produced by Lesney in 1971 and again in 1979.
The models are quite collectable and prices range from **£15** to **£25**.

Space Series 1971 issues, (127 mm.)

W1	Astrocar with Donald Duck
W2	Astrotracker with Mickey Mouse
W3	Astrocat with Mickey Mouse

Hot Rod Series 1971 issues, (127 mm.)

W7	Hotcar with Donald Duck
W8	Dragon with Mickey Mouse
W9	Fun Bug with Donald Duck

Disney Characters 1979, (73 mm.)

WD1-A	Mickey Mouse Fire Engine
WD2-A	Donald Duck's Beach Buggy
WD3-A	Goofy's Beetle (ears attached to shoulders on some)
WD4-A	Minnie Mouse Lincoln
WD5-A	Mickey Mouse Jeep:
	i) 'Mickey Mouse' logo on bonnet
	ii) 'Mickeys Mail Jeep' on bonnet
	iii) 'Police' logo/crest on bonnet
WD6-A	Donald Duck's Jeep
WD7-A	Pinnochio's Travelling Theatre
WD8-A	Jimminy Cricket's Old Timer
WD9-A	Goofy's Sports Car
WD10-A	Goofy's Train
WD11-A	Donald Duck's Ice Cream Van
WD12-A	Mickey Mouse Corvette

'Adventure 2000' models
Space age models (issued 1977-82), and based on the year 2000.
Three plastic spacemen with guns were included with each model.

K2001	Radar Command	Contains Metallic Green tracked vehicles with '2000' logo
K2002	Flight Hunter	Contains Metallic Green vehicle with Red wings and '2000' logo
K2003	Crusader	Contains Metallic Green vehicle on Black tracks, 2 Red guns
K2004	Rocket Striker	Contains Green/Red rocket-firing vehicle (Black tracks), plus 3 rockets
K2005	Command Force	Contains K2004 plus MB2 Hovercraft and 2 smaller vehicles (MB59 & MB68)
K2006	Shuttle Launcher	Metallic Blue body, Black tracks, Orange launcher, White shuttle. '2000'

Note: In 1980 some of the models were issued in Metallic Blue but apart from the Shuttle Launcher no details are available. The models were featured for the last time in the 1981/82 catalogue. Price range **£10 - £15**.

Matchbox 1-75 Models issued 1983 - 1990
The object of this Catalogue is to provide collectors with basic identification of models and their market prices. For collectors requiring a more detailed tabulation of the 900 variations of 1-75 models issued in this 7 year period we would recommend an excellent checklist which can be obtained from MICA member Geoffrey Leake, 38 Park Avenue, Worcester, WR3 7AH, England. (Remember to include a SAE if requesting details).

Matchbox Toys sold at auction 1992 - 1993
(V) = Vectis, (L) = Lacy Scott, (W) = Wallis & Wallis
All the items listed below were sold in mint condition and were boxed.

Accessory Packs & Gift Sets

A2	Car Transporter, Red/Grey	**£140** (V)
G1	Motorway Set, 7 models, Roadway	**£210** (V)
G2	Car Transporter Set, inc. 6 cars	**£210** (V)
G2	Transporter Set, Orange/Grey, 6 cars	**£280** (V)
G3	Building Set, Earthmoving/Dumping	**£140** (V)
G5	Military Set, (Tank & Transporter)	**£150** (V)
G9	Service Station Set	**£150** (V)
G10	Fire Station Set	**£230** (V)

Miniatures (1-75 Series)

MB10c	Foden 8 wheel Truck 'Tate & Lyle'	**£42** (L)
MB17a	Bedford Van, Light Blue, metal wheels	**£90** (V)
MB17a	Bedford Van, Maroon	**£175** (V)
MB19a	MG TD Midget, Cream, Red seats	**£45** (V)
MB19b	MGA, Cream, Red seats, Grey wheels	**£50** (V)
MB20a	ERF Lorry, Light Green, metal wheels	**£320** (V)
MB22b	Vauxhall, Metallic Brownish-Pink	**£65** (V)
MB23b	Berkeley, Metallic Brownish-Green	**£120** (V)
MB26b	ERF Cement Lorry	**£240** (V)
MB27b	Bedford Low Loader, Green/Tan	**£52** (L)
MB32a	Jaguar XK140, Red body	**£210** (V)
MB37a	Coca-Cola, Yellow, uneven load	**£40** (V)
MB38g	Ford A Van, 2nd MICA Convention	**£90** (-)
MB39a	Zodiac, Pale Peach, Light Brown seats	**£120** (V)
MB43a	Hillman Minx, Light Green	**£250** (V)
MB45a	Vauxhall Victor, Dark Red	**£440** (V)
MB46a	Morris 1000, Mid-Blue, Grey wheels	**£130** (V)
MB46b	Removal Truck, 2-line decal	**£120** (V)
MB50a	Commer Pick-Up, Red/Grey	**£140** (V)
MB53a	Aston-Martin, Metallic Red, Black wheels	**£95** (V)
MB59a	Ford Van, 'Singer', Dark Green	**£140** (V)
MB68b	Mercedes Coach, Turquoise, (US)	**£150** (V)
MB74a	'Refreshments', Pink, Light Blue base	**£190** (V)

Models Of Yesteryear

Y1-2	Ford Model 'T', Black textured roof	**£100** (V)
Y3-1	Benz, (version 2), 'Chartreuse' roof	**£170** (L)
Y4-1	Sentinel, (version 4), Grey plastic wheels	**£160** (V)
Y4-2	Shand Mason, (versions 2 & 3), 'KENT'	**£95** (W)
Y4-2	Shand Mason, (version 5), 'LONDON'	**£175** (V)
Y4-3	Opel, White, rear window	**£450** (-)
Y5-2	4½ litre Bentley, Red seats	**£200** (V)
Y6-1	AEC 'OSRAM' Lorry, Dark Grey	**£150** (V)
Y7-1	Leyland Van, (version 1), Dark Brown	**£75** (V)
Y11-3	Lagonda, Metallic Gold/Metallic Purple	**£380** (V)
Y11-3	Lagonda, Metallic Gold/Light Red	**£200** (V)
Y12-3	Ford 'T' Van, 'ARNOTTS'	**£130** (V)
Y12-3	Ford 'T' Van, 'SUNLIGHT'	**£80** (W)
Y15-1	Rolls-Royce, (version 1), Metallic Green	**£40** (V)
Y16-1	Spyker, Maroon body, Green seats	**£1,200** (W)
Y47	Antiques Roadshow Van, auctioned at MICA Convention	**£1,000** (-)
G7	Yesteryear Gift Set	**£210** (W)

229

Matchbox
Models of Yesteryear

The objective of this listing is to provide guidance in respect of all the main model variations. Collectors requiring details of the many minor variations issued should obtain a copy of the excellent reference book produced by the Matchbox Club, namely 'The Yesteryear Book 1956-1993', which contains fine pictures of all issues. See the Matchbox Club page for details.

Common features. Many models have common identifying features and these are shown below to avoid unnecessary repetition in the Features column.

Model name and number. Both **'Models of Yesteryear'** & **'Made in England by Lesney'** are cast underneath all models issued up to the end of 1982. With the change of ownership this was replaced by **'Matchbox Intl Ltd.'** From 1987 **'Made in Macau'** appears on the base. All models have their 'Y' number shown underneath.

Wheels. All the wheels prior to 1970 were of metal construction. From 1972 (approximately), plastic wheels were used on all models. Nevertheless the models issued at this changeover period are to be found with either metal or plastic wheels. The varieties of wheels are:

- Metal Spoked Wheels
- Metal or Plastic Spoked Wheels
- Plastic Bolt Head Wheels
- Plastic Spoked Wheels
- Solid Spoked Wheels

Scale of models rangess from 1:34 to 1:130 across the range. The scale of each model is usually shown on its box.

Logos and designs. The early models had waterslide transfers. Labels have also been used and currently models are tampo printed.

Catalogue listings. Do not place too much reliance on the model colours shown in catalogues. Very often the pictures shown are from mock-ups in colours never actually issued. E.g., the 1969 catalogue showed a picture of a blue Y-5 Peugeot that was issued in yellow. Similarly the 1973 catalogue showed a silver Hispano Suiza which was then issued in Red.

Bumpers, dashboards, headlights, radiator shells and windscreens. All assumed to be of metal construction prior to 1974 (approx.), after which plastic was increasingly used.

Base plate and chassis are usually of metal construction. Exceptions include the Y30 Mack Truck.

Tyres are of treaded black plastic unless otherwise indicated.

Seats are all made of plastic unless otherwise indicated.

Boxes

1956-60	All card box with line drawing of model used for first 15 models issued, blue number shown on white circle on endflap.
1960-61	As first box but with a red number. All card box with coloured picture of the model (3 varieties of this box exist). All card box with model pictures on the box endflaps.
1968-69	Pink and yellow box with clear window.
1968-70	As previous box with hanging display card (developed in the US market and led to blister-pack design).
1969-70	Mauve and yellow box with window.
1974-78	'Woodgrain' window box in various colours.
1979-83	'Straw' (light cream), window box.
1984-90	'Red' (maroon), window box.
1990	'New-style red'. Bigger, folded clear plastic

Matchbox Models of Yesteryear

Ref. No.	Year(s)	Model Type	Model Features and Size	Market Price Range	
Y1-1		**ALLCHIN TRACTION ENGINE**	Scale 1:80. The main variations are the rear wheel treads, the early models having a straight-across pattern, the second a diagonal and the third a smooth tread		
	1956	1	Green body, Red wheels (10 spokes front, 16 rear, unpainted 'straight across' treads), copper boiler door, 9 slats on cab floor, full Gold trim	£175-200	☐
		2	Same as version 1 but rear wheels with unpainted 'diagonal' treads, Copper boiler	£80-100	☐
		3	As 2 but Red diagonal rear wheel treads	£100-135	☐
		4	As 2 Dark or Bright Red diagonal treads	£120-170	☐
		5	As 2 but painted or unpainted rear treads, Gold boiler door	£80-100	☐
		6	As 5 but with Mid-Green boiler door	£200-250	☐
		7	As 6 but with rivetted axles and less Gold trim	£200-250	☐
	1983	8	As version 7 but with Gold boiler door	£80-100	☐
		9	As version 8 but with 11 slats to cab floor	£80-100	☐
		10	As 9 but with Silver boiler door	£100-125	☐
		11	As 10 but smooth unpainted wheel treads, Gold boiler door	£500-750	☐
Y1-2		**1911 MODEL 'T' FORD**	Henry Ford's famous car in a scale 1:42.		
	1964	1	Red body and steering wheel, smooth Black roof and seats, single-lever handbrake, Brass trim, two holes in baseplate, 14 mm. brass wheels	£18-20	☐
		2	As version 1 but with twin-lever handbrake	£140-150	☐
		3	As 1 but without holes in baseplate	£18-20	☐
		4	As 3 but Black steering wheel and column	£15-20	☐
		5	As version 4 but 11 mm. brass wheels	£15-20	☐
		6	As 4 but with Black 'textured' plastic roof	£150-200	☐
	1974	7	Cream body, Red wings, bare metal windscreen frame, Chrome 12-spoke wheels, Dark Red textured roof. Seats & grille may be Red, Dark Red or Black	£12-20	☐
		8	As 7 but seats and textured roof in Black	£140-160	☐
		9	As version 8 but brass windscreen surround	£40-50	☐
	1975	10	White body, Red wings, bare metal windscreen frame, Red or Dark Red textured roof, Chrome 12-spoke wheels, Black seats and grille	£20-30	☐
		11	As 10 but Red seats, textured roof, 12 or 24-spoked Chrome wheels	£12-20	☐
	1984	12	Gloss Black body, Gold trim on running boards, Gold wheels, Fawn seats, 'LIMITED EDITION' under roof and baseplate, in 'Connoisseurs' set	GSP	☐

Y1-3   **1936 SS 100 JAGUAR** .... The model (in a scale of 1:38) is of a two-seater sports car with metal body and folded-down hood in black plastic. It has chrome 24-spoke wheels, radiator and headlights, and a spare wheel on the petrol tank.

	Year	No.	Description	Price	
	1977	1...............	White body and chassis with small sidelights (2 mm.), 'Lesney' on baseplate...............	£155-175	□
		2...............	As 1 but with large sidelights (4 mm.), on front mudguards	£12-15	□
	1978	3...............	As 2 (with large sidelights), but Steel-Grey body and chassis...............................	£50-60	□
	1979	4...............	As 2 but Light Steel Blue body, 24-spoke or 12-spoke or solid chrome wheels, with plain or whitewall tyres..	£8-10	□
		5...............	As 4 (24 or 12-spoke wheels), plus 5 ribs under running boards..................................	£8-9	□
	1981	6...............	As version 5 but Dark Green body...	£6-9	□
	1986	7...............	As 5 but Talbot Yellow body and chassis, whitewall tyres, 'Lesney England' base......	£60-80	□
		8...............	As 7 but (Yellow), body components oversprayed Dark Green	£12-15	□
	1987	9...............	As 7 but Darker Yellow body and chassis, baseplate reads 'MATCHBOX INT'L (c) 1977, MADE IN MACAU'. Diorama box	NRP	□
Y1-G	1991	10.............	Red body, Black seats, Brown steering wheel, 'MADE IN CHINA' on baseplate	NRP	□
		11.............	Unpainted pewter version on wooden plinth (1991/1992 UK Passport Scheme)..........	£35-45	□

Y2-1   **1911 'B' TYPE LONDON BUS**   The scale of this vintage bus model is 1:100 and its diecast driver may be found in any shade of mid or dark blue, sometimes black.

	Year	No.	Description	Price	
	1956	1...............	Red body, Grey wheels (8 spokes front, 16 rear), Silver radiator, 4 small window frames above 4 main window frames, 'GENERAL'...	£150-200	□
		2...............	As 1 but with 8 small window frames above 4 main window frames...........................	£75-95	□
		3...............	As 2 but minor changes, e.g. Black wheels and rivetted axles	£75-95	□

Y2-2   **1911 RENAULT TWO SEATER** .... Scale 1:40. (The Red pigment in the seats is prone to fading in bright ligh

	Year	No.	Description	Price	
	1963	1...............	Metallic Green body. Windscreen, lights, handbrake & 4-prong spare wheel carrier in Silver. Windscreen panel is above bonnet and radiator...................................	£60-80	□
		2...............	As 1 but windscreen, lights, 4-prong spare wheel carrier etc in brass trim	£40-50	□
		3...............	As 2 but windscreen panel runs down sides of bonnet...	£15-20	□
		4...............	As 3 but spare wheel carrier with 3 prongs, brass plating	£15-20	□
	1965	5...............	As 4 but with Black plastic steering wheel and column...	£12-14	□

Y2-3   **1914 PRINCE HENRY VAUXHALL** .... An open car modelled in 1:47 scale with a metal body and plastic seats and steering wheel. The radiator surround, headlights, windscreen and toolbox is gold trimmed. It has 24-spoke wheels with a spare on the offside unless described differently.

	Year	No.	Description	Price	
	1970	1...............	Red body, Silver bonnet, Red radiator grille, Brass 26-spoke wheels & tank	£15-20	□
		2...............	As version 1 but with Copper petrol tank...	£90-110	□
		3...............	As version 1 with Black radiator grille...	£15-20	□
	1975	4...............	Blue body, Silver bonnet, Cream seats, Brass tank, Chrome 24-spoke wheels............	£15-20	□
		5...............	As version 4 but with Copper petrol tank...	£25-35	□
		6...............	As 4 (Brass tank), but with additional lateral floor braces	£10-12	□
		7...............	As 6 (with floor braces), but with Copper petrol tank	£20-30	□
		8...............	As 7 but with Red seats, (2,000 only, distributed in E.Europe)	£600-700	□
		9...............	As 6 (Cream seats), but with Chrome 12-spoke wheels..	£8-10	□
	1979	10.............	Red body, Black chassis, Red 12-spoke wheels, small spare wheel rivet......................	£8-10	□
	1984	11.............	As 10 but Lighter Red body, large headed rivet retains spare wheel	£8-10	□

Y2-4   **1930 4$ LITRE BENTLEY** ...... Based on the 1930 Le Mans winning car, this model is in 1:40 scale.

	Year	No.	Description	Price	
	1985	1...............	Dark Green body, Green 24-spoke wheels, spare on nearside. Chrome trim, Brown seats & straps. Union Jack on sides, 'MADE IN ENGLAND' on base	£6-8	□
		2...............	As version 1 but dark Green Nylon mudguards	£10-15	□
		3...............	As 2 but light Brown bonnet straps, dashboard and seats	NRP	□
	1988	4...............	As 3 but lighter Green body and wheels, 'MADE IN MACAU' on base	NRP	□
	1990	5...............	Dark Blue body and wheels, Tan steering wheel and column, RN '7'	£10-15	□
		6...............	As 5 but with hole cast in base for self-tapping screw...	£8-10	□
		7...............	As 6 but with Olive-Green steering wheel and column..	£8-10	□
	1992	8...............	Maroon body, Chrome wheels, Black seats, wings, straps & folded hood....................	NRP	□

Y3-1   **1907 'E' CLASS TRAMCAR** .... All versions have a bright Red body with Yellow 'LONDON TRANSPORT' fleetname and 'NEWS OF THE WORLD' decals. Scale 1:130.

	Year	No.	Description	Price	
	1956	1...............	Cream roof, Silver trim, thin Grey cow-catcher and unpainted wheels, cut-out in luggage area beneath the stairs	£200-275	□
		2...............	Same as 1 but with double thick cow-catcher brace	£90-110	□
		3...............	Same as 2 but with Powder Grey base plate and Silver trim	£200-275	□
		4...............	Same as 3 (with Powder Grey base plate), but with Gold trim...................................	£200-275	□
		5...............	With no cut-out beneath the stairs, Cream or White roof, metal or Black plastic wheels	£70-80	□
	1985	6...............	As 5 but Black plastic wheels and White cow-catcher	£90-110	□

Y3-2   **1910 BENZ LIMOUSINE** .... The model has a metal body with Dark Green or Dark Red seats and radiator grille, Brass trim and spare tyre mounted on handbrake casting. Scale 1:54.

	Year	No.	Description	Price	
	1965	1...............	Cream body, Dark Green roof, Cream metal steering wheel, Green or Red seats	£50-60	□
		2...............	As 1 but with 'Chartreuse' Yellow roof	£200-250	□
	1969	3...............	As 2 but with Light Green body, Dark Green roof. (Black grilles exist)......................	£200-250	□
		4...............	Light Green body (as 3), but with 'Chartreuse' roof	£30-35	□
		5...............	As 4 but with Black plastic steering wheel	£30-35	□
		6...............	As version 5 but with Matt Black roof	£100-125	□
		7...............	Metallic Dark Green body with Matt Black roof	£15-20	□
		8...............	Metallic Dark Green body with Chartreuse roof	£200-250	□
		9...............	Black body and roof, Blue side panels, 'LIMITED EDITION' on baseplate, in 'Connoisseurs' set	GSP	□

Y3-3

1934 RILEY MPH ...... A two-seater sports car model with a metal body, plastic seats and steering wheel, Chrome radiator surround, windscreen, headlights and wheels. Scale 1:35.

	1973	1	Metallic Purple/Red body and chassis with Black seats and grille, Chrome 12-spoke wheels	£150-200 ☐
		2	As 1 but seats and grille in White and with 12 or 24-spoke wheels	£20-25 ☐
		3	As 2 but reddish-Purple body and chassis	£10-15 ☐
		4	As version 2 but with Dark Red body and chassis	£10-15 ☐
		5	As 4 but Light Red body & chassis, Red 12-spoke wheels	£30-40 ☐
	1979	6	Light Blue body, White seats and grille, 24-spoke wheels, RN '6' or '9'	£8-10 ☐
		7	As 6 but with RN '3' on door	£25-35 ☐
		8	As version 6 but with Red 12-spoke wheels	£20-25 ☐
		9	As version 8 but with racing number '6'	£20-25 ☐

Y3-4

1912 FORD MODEL 'T' TANKER ...... The model features a small tanker with an all metal body and tank with simulated brass filler pipes and 12-spoke plastic wheels. Scale 1:35.

	1981	'BP' 1	Dark Green body, Black chassis, White roof, Red tank, Gold trim, Gold 'BP' logo on tank with Black shadow effect, '1978 No. Y12' on baseplate	£110-120 ☐
		2	As version 1 but baseplate number blanked-out	NRP ☐
		3	As 2 but without the shadow effect around the 'BP' logo	NRP ☐
		4	As version 3 but matt-Black filler caps	£45-55 ☐
		5	As 3 but with Gold 12-spoke wheels	£20-30 ☐
		6	As 3 but Chrome 12-spoke wheels, with shadow effect	£20-30 ☐
	1982	'ZEROLENE'	20,000 issued in UK, 15,000 issued elsewhere in Europe	
		1	Bright Green body, gloss-Black chassis, White logo. Brass 12-spoke wheels	£40-50 ☐
		2	As version 1 but matt-Black chassis	£40-50 ☐
		3	As version 1 but with Red 12-spoke wheels	£50-75 ☐
	1983	'EXPRESS DAIRY'	90,000 made.	
		1	Blue body, Gloss Black lower body, White roof and logo, brass trim	NRP ☐
		2	As 1 but with Red 12-spoke wheels	£10-15 ☐
		3	As 1 but with Chrome 12-spoke wheels	£8-10 ☐
	1984	'CARNATION'	This model has different prints below each cab window.	
		1	Cream body, Plum Red tank & chassis, Red 12-spoke wheels, White-wall tyres	NRP ☐
		2	As version 1 but with Red 24-spoke wheels	£14-18 ☐
		3	As 1 but with Gold 12-spoke wheels and Black tyres	£14-18 ☐
	1986	4	As 1 but Plum-coloured 12-spoke wheels, modified baseplate	£25-30 ☐
	1985	'MOBILOIL'	40,000 issued in UK, 40,000 elswhere.	
	1986		Blue body and tank, Red bonnet and wheels, White logo, Red design	NRP ☐
	1986	'CASTROL'	109,000 made.	
		1	Dark Green body and tank, White roof, Black chassis, Tan seats, Plum 12-spoke wheels, Gold grille, 'LESNEY PRODUCTS & Co.Ltd. (c) 1978' on base	£10-12 ☐
		2	As 1 but 'MATCHBOX INT'L (c) 1985' on base	£6-9 ☐
		3	As 2 but with Chrome radiator grille	£20-30 ☐
		4	As version 2 but with Black seats	£20-30 ☐
		5	As 2 but with Gold 12-spoke wheels, 'MATCHBOX 1986 ENGLAND' base	NRP ☐
	1986	'RED CROWN'	35,000 issued in UK, 35,000 elswhere.	
		1	Red body, tank and side panels, Gold 12-spoke wheels with Black tyres, 'MATCHBOX INT'L (c) 1986 MADE IN ENGLAND LIMITED EDITION' on base	£8-10 ☐
		2	with 'LESNEY PRODUCTS & Co.Ltd. (c) 1978 MADE IN ENGLAND' on base	£15-20 ☐
		3	As version 2 but with 'MATCHBOX 1985 ENGLAND' on base	£40-50 ☐
	1989	'SHELL MOTOR SPIRIT'	Yellow body, White roof, Red 12-spoke wheels, 'MADE IN MACAU' on base	NRP ☐

Y4-1

SENTINEL STEAM WAGON ...... **'SAND & GRAVEL SUPPLIES'**. Scale 1:100.

	1956	1	Bright Blue body & tool-box, Black chassis & boiler, Grey metal spoked wheels, domed & crimped axles. Yellow logo with Red border	£80-90 ☐
		2	As version 1 but with Gold tool-box	£80-90 ☐
		3	As 2 but with rivetted axles	£90-110 ☐
		4	As 3 but with Black plastic wheels (24 treads front & rear)	£160-190 ☐

Y4-2

SHAND MASON FIRE ENGINE ...... All metal body and 2 horses with 3 plastic firemen, metal wheels (13 spokes front, 15 rear). Gold pump and boiler appliance. Scale 1:63.

	1960	'KENT FIRE BRIGADE' 1	Bright Red body, 2 Grey horses with Grey manes, 2 locating hose locker ribs. Three firemen with Gold helmets and breastplates	£450-550 ☐
		2	As version 1 but with White horses	£145-175 ☐
		3	As 2 but firemen have only Gold helmets, (plain breastplates)	£145-175 ☐
	1963	'LONDON FIRE BRIGADE'	'No.72'.	
		4	As 3 but with new logo as above and no locating hose locker ribs	£145-175 ☐
		5	As 4 but Black horses with White manes	£145-175 ☐
		6	As 5 but Brown horses with White manes, fireman with no Gold trim	£325-375 ☐
		7	As version 5 but with minor modifications	£145-175 ☐

Ref. No.	Year(s)	Model Type	Matchbox Models of Yesteryear - continued	Market Price Range	
Y4-3		**1909 OPEL CAR**..........	The model features an open fronted metal bodied car with plastic roof, seats and steering wheel. It has 12-spoked wheels. Scale 1:38.		
	1967	1..............	White body and chassis, smooth Tan roof, Brass trim and wheels with Maroon seats and grille	£30-40	☐
		2..............	As 1 but with bright Red seats and grille..	£16-20	☐
		3..............	As 2 with no body pins and roof secured to seat..	£16-20	☐
		4..............	As version 3 but with Maroon seats..	£16-20	☐
		5..............	with window in rear of Tan textured roof, Bright Red or Maroon seats........	£300-350	☐
	1974	6..............	Orange body with Black chassis and roof, White grille, Maroon seats, 12 or 24-spoke wheels..	£10-15	☐
	1984	7..............	Bright Red body with Darker Red lower body, Tan roof with 'LIMITED EDITION', in 'Connoisseurs' set..	GSP	☐
Y4-4		**1930 DUESENBERG 'J' TOWN CAR**.........	The model features a superb large car with an open drivers area and enclosed passenger seats. It has a metal body, plastic roof, seats and trunk, chrome spoked wheels and two spares set into the running boards. Scale 1:43.		
	1976	1..............	White main body, Orange/Red lower body, Yellow roof and seats, small roof window, 'X' shaped roof support, hollow chrome horns..................................	£1200-1500	☐
	1976	2..............	As 1 but seats and roof in Black	£1200-1500	☐
		3..............	Metallic Red body, Black roof with larger window, Black seats...................	£10-15	☐
		4..............	As 3 with solid horns and chrome 12-spoke wheels, Black tyres..................	£10-15	☐
		5..............	As 4 but with Maroon seats and roof, Chrome 24-spoke wheels..................	£200-225	☐
	1979	6..............	Two-tone Green body and rear panel, Dark Green seats and roof.................	£60-75	☐
		7..............	As 6 but rear body panel is in Metallic Light Green....................................	£10-15	☐
		8..............	As version 7 but with Black seats and roof...	£10-12	☐
	1983	9..............	As 3 but Dark Brown upper body, sides & chassis, Cream or Beige seats and roof, 24-spoke wheels, 'LESNEY' or 'MATCHBOX' base........................	NRP	☐
		10............	As 9 but 'solid' chrome wheels with White-wall tyres..................................	NRP	☐
		11............	As version 9 but Brown seats and roof..	£5-8	☐
	1986	12............	As 3 but Metallic Silver body, Royal-Blue chassis, wheels and (tampo-printed), side panels, 'MADE IN ENGLAND' on baseplate..................	NRP	☐
		13............	As 12 but tampo-printed side panels are Dark Blue.....................................	NRP	☐
	1988	14............	As 12 but darker Blue (side panels mask-sprayed), 'MADE IN MACAU'	NRP	☐
	1989	15............	Two-tone Blue, Tan steering wheel, improved detailing, no baseplate hole....	£15-20	☐
	1990	16............	As 15 but with baseplate hole, White-wall tyres	NRP	☐
		17............	As 16 but with Olive-Green steering wheel...	£10-12	☐
Y5-1		**1929 LE MANS BENTLEY**	A famous sports racing car modelled in a scale of 1:55.		
	1958	1..............	British Racing Green body and tonneau (which has Grey rear end), unpainted solid spoked wheels (spare on nearside), Silver radiator, RN '5', Red metal seats..........	£100-125	☐
		2..............	As 1 but with Green radiator grille..	£100-125	☐
		3..............	As version 2 but with Gold radiator surround	£160-180	☐
		4..............	As 3 but with an all Green tonneau	£75-85	☐
		5..............	Minor changes: Green radiator surround and steering wheel, rivetted axles	£75-85	☐
Y5-2		**1929 4½ LITRE BENTLEY**......	The model features a metal body with plastic seats and tonneau. It has Union Jacks and racing numbers on its sides, chrome trim, folded windscreen and silver 24-spoke wheels, (spare on nearside). Scale 1:52.		
	1962	1..............	Metallic 'Apple Green' body, Dark Green seats and tonneau, Black RN '5'	£325-375	☐
		2..............	As 1 but with Dark Red seats and tonneau..	£325-375	☐
		3..............	As 1 but British Racing Green body/seats, additional holes in baseplate.....	£45-55	☐
		4..............	As 3 but with Dark Red seats and tonneau...	£50-60	☐
		5..............	As 4 but seats and tonneau in bright Red plastic..	£25-35	☐
		6..............	As 5 but racing number '6' or '3' in White circle...	£60-70	☐
		7..............	As version 5 but no holes in baseplate...	£30-40	☐
		8..............	As version 7 but with racing number '5'...	£30-40	☐
Y5-3		**1907 PEUGEOT**..............	A large car modelled in a scale of 1:43 with metal body and plastic seats, grille and steering wheel. It has 12-spoke wheels and a spare tyre.		
	1969	1..............	All Yellow body, matt Black roof with Dark Orange windows, Red seats and grille, no front seat beading..	£90-110	☐
		2..............	As version 1 but with seat beading, Dark or Pale Orange windows	£10-15	☐
		3..............	As version 2 but with clear windows..	£180-200	☐
	1974	4..............	Orange-Gold body, roof & wheels, matt Black lower body, Red seats & grille...........	£145-170	☐
		5..............	As 4 with Matt Black roof, seats and grille, Chrome 12-spoke wheels	£90-100	☐
		6..............	As version 4 with Black seats and grille...	£10-15	☐
		7..............	As version 5 with Light Gold body and roof...	£10-15	☐
		8..............	As version 7 with clear windows, Chrome 12-spoke wheels	£120-140	☐
		9..............	As version 7 with clear windows, Chrome 24-spoke wheels	£80-90	☐
Y5-4		**1927 TALBOT VAN**	A model van in a scale of 1:47. It has a metal body with side windows, opening rear doors, plastic seats and steering wheel and spoked wheels.		
	1978	**'LIPTON'S TEA'**	(with Royal Crest)		
		1..............	Dark Green body and 12-spoke wheels, matt Black roof & lower body, Yellow logo & crest	£30-40	☐
		2..............	As version 1 but gloss Black chassis..	£10-12	☐
		3..............	As 2 but without Black 'shadow' effect to logo...	£30-35	☐
		4..............	With gloss Black chassis and either 12 or 24-spoke Chrome wheels	£10-12	☐

Y5-4 TALBOT VANS – continued

Ref. No.	Year(s)	Model Type	Description	Market Price Range	
	1978	'LIPTON'S TEA'	(without royal crest, with 'CITY ROAD' logo)		
	1978	1................	Dark Green body, Gloss Black chassis, Matt Black roof, Green 12-spoke wheels, Yellow logo with shadow effect	£20-30	☐
		2................	As 1 with Chrome 12 or 24-spoke wheels, no shadow effect	£9-12	☐
		3................	As version 2 but with Olive-Green 12-spoke wheels	£9-14	☐
		4................	As version 2 but Gloss Black roof	£20-30	☐
	1979	'CHOCOLATE MENIER'	First issued in 'woodgrain' box with light blue labels bearing French text.		
		1................	Royal Blue body, Black roof and chassis, Yellow logo, Chrome 12-spoke wheels	£8-10	☐
		2................	As 1 but with Chrome 24-spoke wheels	£10-15	☐
		3................	As 1 but with Off-White logo (both sides)	£16-18	☐
		4................	As 1 but Red or Dark Green 12-spoke or Red solid wheels	£10-15	☐
	1980	'TAYSTEE BREAD'			
		1................	Yellow body, Black roof, Red wheels, whitewall tyres, Red/White design	NRP	☐
		2................	As version 1 but with Black lower body	£8-10	☐
		3................	As 1 but with Red solid wheels	£20-25	☐
	1981	'NESTLES'			
		1................	Blue body, Black roof and chassis, Red wheels, White-wall tyres............................	£140-160	☐
		2................	As version 1 but with Dark Grey roof	£12-15	☐
		3................	As version 1 but with Light Grey roof	£40-50	☐
	1982	'CHIVERS & SONS LTD'			
		1................	Cream body & roof, Dark Green wings, Red or Dark Red wheels	NRP	☐
	1982	'WRIGHT'S SOAP'			
		1................	Dark Brown body with Cream roof and chassis, Chrome 12-spoke wheels..................	NRP	☐
		2................	As version 1 but with Brass 12-spoke wheels ....£8-10......		☐
	1983	'EVER READY BATTERIES'			
		1................	Dark Blue body, White roof and Black chassis, Tan seats, White/Orange logo	£8-10	☐
		2................	As version 1 but with Black seats	NRP	☐
	1984	'DUNLOP TYRES'			
		1................	Black and Yellow, Dark Yellow 12-spoke wheels, Tan or Black seats	NRP	☐
		2................	Black and Yellow, Pale Yellow 12-spoke wheels, Tan or Black seats	NRP	☐
	1985	'ROSES LIME JUICE'			
		1................	Light Cream body, Green roof, chassis & wheels, 'MADE IN ENGLAND' on base	£8-10	☐
		2................	As 1 (Black seats), but Pale Cream/Dark Green body & chassis	£8-10	☐
		3................	As version 2 but with Tan seats	£30-40	☐
		4................	As version 1 but with Red 12-spoke wheels	£15-20	☐
	1988	5................	As 1 but 'MADE IN MACAU' on baseplate	£15-20	☐
	1989	'LYLES SYRUP'			
		1................	Green body, Black chassis, Gold wheels, White logo	NRP	☐
		2................	As 1 but with Black wheels, improved (softer) tyres	£15-20	☐

Y5-5 **LEYLAND TITAN BUS**

Ref. No.	Year(s)	Model Type	Description	Market Price Range	
	1989	'ROBIN STARCH'	Green/Cream body in 'SOUTHDOWN' livery	£8-10	☐
	1990	'SWAN FOUNTPENS'	Blue/Cream. Passport Scheme model AVAILABLE ONLY IN CABINET.................	£45-55	☐
Y5-C	1991	'NEWCASTLE BROWN ALE'	Maroon/Cream body, 'COVENTRY CORPORATION'	NRP	☐

Y6-1 **1916 A.E.C. 'Y' TYPE LORRY** ....

'OSRAM LAMPS'. Scale 1:100.

Ref. No.	Year(s)	Model Type	Description	Market Price Range	
	1957	1................	Duck Egg Blue body, Grey metal spoked wheels (8 front/16 rear), White logo	£1000-1200	☐
	1957	2................	Mid-Blue body, driver, steering wheel, grille, seat, Grey wheels.............................	£750-1000	☐
		3................	As 1 but with Light Grey body, painted bonnet handles on some.............................	£120-130	☐
	1959	4................	As 3 but Dark Grey body, with or without painted bonnet handles	£175-225	☐
	1961	5................	As 4 but with unpainted bonnet handles and Black plastic wheels (having 24 treads front, 30 treads rear)	£1000-1200	☐

Y6-2 **1926 TYPE 35 BUGATTI** ....

The model (in a scale of 1:48) has a metal body and seats, Black baseplate and Gold 8-spoke wheels with a spare on the nearside. Racing number '6' may be upside-down and appear as '9'.

Ref. No.	Year(s)	Model Type	Description	Market Price Range	
	1961	1................	Light Blue body, Grey tyres, Red floor, dashboard and RN '6', Gold radiator	£100-125	☐
		2................	As version 1 but with Black tyres..	£40-45	☐
		3................	As version 2 but with Blue radiator	£150-175	☐
		4................	As 2 but with narrow wheel rims..	£40-45	☐
		5................	As version 2 but with White dashboard and floor	£250-300	☐
	1965	6................	Red body, White dashboard & floor, Black seats & tyres, Gold radiator....................	£40-45	☐
		7................	As version 6 but with Red radiator	£100-120	☐
		8................	As 6 but Black dashboard and floor	£250-300	☐

Y6-3 **1913 CADILLAC** ....

The model features a metal bodied two seater car with a plastic roof and seats. It has 12-spoke wheels with a spare at the rear. Scale 1:48.

Ref. No.	Year(s)	Model Type	Description	Market Price Range	
	1968	1................	Light Gold body, smooth Dark Red hood, seats and grille, brass trim. (Hoods on early issues were not secured to windscreen)..	£17-22	☐
		2................	Dark Gold body, smooth Dark Red hood and seats...	£20-30	☐
		3................	As 2 but with textured Dark Red roof, seats and grille...	£60-70	☐
		4................	Dark Gold body, Bright Yellow seats and grille, textured Black hood........................	£60-70	☐
		5................	Metallic Green body, Bright Yellow seats and grille, textured Black hood, Chrome 12-spoke wheels...	£14-17	☐
		6................	As version 5 but with Light Green seats and grille...	£100-150	☐
		7................	As version 5 but with Blue or Pink seats and grille..	£100-150	☐

Y6-4

1920 ROLLS ROYCE FIRE ENGINE ....

The model features a metal vehicle body with plastic ladders, brass 12-spoke wheels and trim, spare wheel mounted on offside. Scale 1:48.
1st type ladders have square ended lug, 2nd type larger round ended

	1977	1...............	Bright Red body, White 1st type ladders, Gold 12-spoke wheels...............................	£100-120 ☐
		2...............	As version 1 but with Brown or Reddish-Brown ladder............................	£80-100 ☐
		3...............	As version 1 but with Chrome 24-spoke wheels....................................	£10-12 ☐
		4...............	White or Brown 2nd type ladders, Y6 & Y7 on baseplate	NRP ☐
	1983	5...............	Dull Red body, Red/Brown 2nd type ladders	£8-10 ☐
		6...............	As version 5 but with Red 12-spoke wheels	£8-10 ☐
		7...............	As 6 but with Chrome 12-spoke wheels	NRP ☐
		8...............	As version 7 but crew seat in Black plastic	NRP ☐
		9...............	As 7 but bright Red plastic front seat, Brown double 2nd type ladder.........................	£250-300 ☐

Y6-5

1932 MERCEDES L5 LORRY ....

A brewery truck capable of carrying 6 tons, modelled in 1:69 scale.

	1988	'STUTTGARTER HOFBRAU'	Cream body, Red logo & wheels. Later issues have smooth truck body sides.............	NRP ☐
	1992	'HOLSTEN-BIER'	White body and tilt, Red wheels, Red/Black logos. Not issued	NPP ☐

Y7-1

FOUR TON LEYLAND 'W & R JACOB & Co.Ltd' ....

'by Royal Appointment to His Majesty the King'. Scale 1:100.

	1957	1...............	Dark Brown body, White or Cream roof, metal wheels, Silver radiator......................	£100-125 ☐
		2...............	As versions 1 but with Light Brown body...	£100-125 ☐
		3...............	As 2 but without *'By Royal Appointment to His Majesty the King'*	£600-800 ☐
		4...............	As 2 but with Reddish/Brown body and radiator surround..........................	£100-125 ☐
		5...............	As 3 but with Black plastic wheels (24 treads front, 32 treads rear)	£800-900 ☐

Y7-2

1913 MERCER RACEABOUT ....

Scale 1:46. The main variations are with the mudguards and their chassis fittings. The first issues had no struts/strengtheners.

	1961	1...............	Lilac body, Brass 12-spoke wheels & trim, 2 spare wheels, no struts......................	£30-40 ☐
		2...............	As version 1 but with mudguard struts...	£30-35 ☐
		3...............	As 2 but Yellow body, Lilac grille, Brass 12-spoke wheels & trim......................	£30-40 ☐
		4...............	As 2 but Yellow body and grille, Brass 12-spoke wheels & trim......................	£30-35 ☐

Y7-3

1912 ROLLS ROYCE..............

A large car modelled in a scale of 1:48. It has a metal body open at the rear with plastic seats, a spare tyre on the offside and brass trim. Thirty-two variations of this model exist so only the main ones are listed. Normally all the fittings (including the fire extinguisher), are brass plated, however variations exist with copper plated extinguisher. Three types of spare tyre carrier exist.

	1968	1...............	Silver body, Red chassis & smooth roof, seats & grille, brass 12-spoke wheels............	£20-25 ☐
		2...............	As 1 but with smooth Grey roof	£20-25 ☐
		3...............	As 2 but with Yellow seats	£300-350 ☐
		4...............	As 2 but with ribbed rear section to Grey roof	£150-175 ☐
		5...............	As 4 but with ribbed rear section to Red roof	£20-25 ☐
		6...............	As 5 but Gold body, Silver bonnet, Black or Red seats, Copper extinguisher	£150-200 ☐
	1973	7...............	Gold body & bonnet, ribbed Red roof, Chrome wheels, Dark Red seats & grille	£10-15 ☐
		8...............	As 7 but with Black seats & grille, Chrome 12-spoke wheels	£10-15 ☐
		9...............	As 7 but with early spare tyre carrier, Black or Dark Red seats......................	£40-50 ☐
		10..............	As 7 but with Green seats and grille	£100-150 ☐
		11..............	As 7 but with Black seats & grille, Red 12-spoke wheels	£30-35 ☐
		12..............	Bright Yellow body, Black chassis & ribbed roof, Red 12-spoke wheels	£10-15 ☐
		13..............	As 11 but having Chrome wheels with either 12 or 24 spokes	£20-25 ☐

Y7-4

1930 FORD MODEL 'A' BREAKDOWN TRUCK ......

This model, based on the Y21 Woody Wagon, has a metal body with a plastic roof and lifting gear. It has plastic solid wheels, whitewall tyres and a large plastic front bumper. It was made to a scale of 1:40.

		'BARLOW MOTOR SALES'		
	1985	1...............	Orange body, bumpers & wheels, Black roof & chassis, Dark Green crane	£8-10 ☐
		2...............	As 1 ('MADE IN ENGLAND' base), but Light Green crane	£35-45 ☐
	1987	3...............	As 1 but 'MADE IN MACAU' on base..	£20-30 ☐
	1988	'SHELL'	Yellow body, Black chassis, Red/Black logo, 'MADE IN MACAU' base..................	NRP ☐

Y8-1

1926 MORRIS COWLEY ....

The 'Bullnose Morris' was the first saloon car to appear in the series and was modelled in a scale of 1:50.

	1958	1...............	Tan body, Dark Brown chassis, metal wheels, domed/crimped axles......................	£80-100 ☐
		2...............	As 1 but with Dark Tan body and rivetted axles	£80-100 ☐

Y8-2

1914 SUNBEAM MOTORCYCLE & SIDECAR

Model features unusual plated finish and a scale of 1:34.

	1962	1...............	Chrome machine and sidecar, Black cycle seat, Dark Green sidecar seat....................	£40-50 ☐
		2...............	As 1 but all Gold machine and sidecar	£500-600 ☐
		3...............	As version 1 but Emerald Green sidecar seat..	£250-350 ☐
	1967	4...............	As 1 but Black plastic sidecar seat	£300-400 ☐

Y8-3

1914 STUTZ..........................

The model features a metal bodied two seater car with plastic seats and roof. It has a spare wheel at rear and brass trim. Scale 1:48.

	1969	1...............	Metallic Red body, Tan smooth roof, Copper petrol tank, Green seats and grille	£13-18 ☐
		2...............	As 1 (12-spoke Brass wheels), but with Tan textured roof............................	£40-50 ☐
		3...............	As version 1 but with Brass petrol tank...	£50-60 ☐

Ref. No.	Year(s)	Model Type		Matchbox Models of Yesteryear - continued	Market Price Range	

Y8-3 1914 STUTZ – continued

	1973		4	Metallic Blue body, Black roof, White seats & grille, Chrome 12-spoke wheels	£10-15	☐
			5	As 4 but with Red seats and grille	£30-40	☐
			6	As version 4 but with Chrome 24-spoke wheels	£10-15	☐

Y8-4 — 1945 M.G. TC — A two seater sports car modelled in a scale of 1:35. Many variations exist.

	1978		1	Dark Green body, Tan roof and seats, RN '3', Chrome 24-spoke wheels	£70-80	☐
			2	As version 1 but with Red seats	£15-20	☐
			3	As version 2 but with Red 12-spoke wheels	£20-25	☐
			4	As 3 but Pink or Black seats, Chrome 24-spoke wheels	£35-50	☐
	1981		5	Bright Red body, Black seats, Tan or Rust roof, Chrome 24-spoke wheels	£8-10	☐
			6	As version 5 but with Bright Red seats	£20-25	☐
	1983		7	Mid-Blue body, Black seats, Tan roof, Chrome 24-spoke wheels	£8-10	☐
			8	As 7 but with Fawn seats, Tan or Rust roof	£8-10	☐
	1984		9	Cream body, Dark Brown lower body, Tan seats and roof	£8-10	☐
			10	As 9 but with Dark Tan seats & roof, Tan or Pink/Brown seats	NRP	☐

Y8-5 — YORKSHIRE STEAM WAGON — A 1917 steam lorry (with transverse boiler), modelled in a scale of 1:61.

	1987	'JOHNNIE WALKER'	1	Dark 'strawberry'-Red body, Grey cab roof, Cream tilt, Black chimney. 'JOHNNIE WALKER WHISKY' in bright Red on tilt sides plus striding figure logo	£200-300	☐
			2	As 1 but 'JOHNNIE WALKER WHISKY' in light or dark Maroon	£6-8	☐
			3	As version 2 but with non-striding figure	£150-200	☐
	1989	'SAMUEL SMITH'		Green & Beige. Passport scheme model ONLY IN CABINET. (12,000 made)	£75-85	☐
	1989	'WILLIAM PRICHARD'		Dark Blue body, Grey cab roof, Cream wheels and sack load, White logo	NRP	☐
	1992	'FYFFES'		Yellow body and wheels, Cream tilt & roof, Blue 'Banana Merchant' logo	£10-12	☐

Y9-1 — 1924 FOWLER SHOWMANS ENGINE — *'LESNEYS MODERN AMUSEMENTS'.* Scale 1:80. Different colour shades exist, not affecting price.

	1958		1	Dark Maroon body with a Cream roof, Gold cylinder block & chimney, smooth Orange/Yellow metal wheels. Copper boiler door. Brass canopy supports	£150-180	☐
			2	As 1 but Dark Maroon cylinder block, Copper or Gold boiler door	£75-90	☐
			3	As 2 but Pale Maroon body; Copper, Gold or Silver boiler door	£75-90	☐
			4	As 3 but Bright Red body with White roof & Silver boiler door	£75-90	☐
			5	As 4 but modified Black base casting, Silver or Brass supports	£100-110	☐
			6	As 4 but with 'T' shaped fire-box ends	£90-110	☐

Y9-2 — 1912 SIMPLEX — The model features a metal body with a plastic roof and seats. It has 12-spoke wheels and spare tyre on offside and was modelled in a scale of 1:48.

	1968		1	Lime Green body, smooth Tan roof, Brass wheels & trim, Red seats and radiator	£30-40	☐
			2	As version 1 but with Mid-Green body	£15-20	☐
			3	As version 2 but with textured Tan roof	£40-50	☐
	1970		4	Dark Metallic Gold body, Dark Red wings, seats and grille, Black textured roof	£25-35	☐
			5	As 4 but with Chrome 12-spoke wheels	£25-35	☐
			6	As 5 but Metallic Mid-Gold body	NGPP	☐
	1973		7	Bright Red body, Black textured roof, Brass trim, Yellow seats & grille	£13-16	☐
	1979		8	Dark Red body, Black chassis, textured Yellow or Black roof, Yellow seats & grille, Red wheels	£8-11	☐
	1986		9	Yellow body, Black chassis & grille, textured Yellow or Black roof, Brown seats, Gold 12-spoke wheels	NRP	☐
			10	As version 9 but Dark Yellow body	NRP	☐

Y9-3 — 1920 3-Ton LEYLAND LORRY — 'LUFF & SONS'. Featuring a high-sided lorry in a scale of 1:62. It has a plastic underframe, mudguards and front bumper, solid wheels and tyres.

	1985		1	Dark Green body, Red chassis & wings, Pale Tan seats, Black grille	£20-30	☐
			2	As 1 but with 'mushroom' coloured seats	£20-30	☐
			3	As version 1 but with Black wings, Red seats	£80-100	☐
			4	As version 3 but with Red radiator grille	£80-100	☐

Y9-4 — 1936 LEYLAND 'CUB' FIRE ENGINE FK-7 — Special Limited Edition model in 1:49 scale. 60,000 produced.

| | 1989 | | 1 | Red body & wheels, Black roof, detachable Brown extending ladders | £50-60 | ☐ |

Y10-1 — 1908 'GRAND PRIX' MERCEDES — An early 12-litre chain-driven racing car modelled in a scale of 1:54

	1958		1	Cream body, Pale Green seats, plated 12-spoke wheels, crimped axles	£80-90	☐
			2	As 1 but with White body	£160-180	☐
			3	As 1 but tooling insert modification to seat side, unplated wheels	£80-90	☐
			4	As 2 but with Dark Green seats, crimped or rivetted axles	£80-90	☐
			5	As 2 but Dark Green seats, White trim, rivetted axles	£130-140	☐

Y10-2 — 1928 MERCEDES BENZ 36-220 — The model features a metal body with one or two spare wheels, plastic seats and tonneau and Chrome spoked wheels. It was modelled in 1:52 scale.

	1963		1	White body, Black seats & tonneau, 2 spare wheels, Silver trim, 2 holes in base	£800-1000	☐
			2	As version 1 but with Red seats and tonneau	£30-40	☐
			3	As version 2 but with only one spare wheel	£20-25	☐
			4	As 3 but there are no holes in the baseplate, 2 spare tyres	£40-50	☐
			5	As 4 but there is only one spare tyre	£20-25	☐

Y10-3

1906 ROLLS-ROYCE SILVER GHOST .... Open four seater car modelled in 1:51 scale. It has a spare tyre on the offside and 12-spoke wheels. Many variations exist.

1969	1..............	Metallic Lime body, Metallic Brown wings, Brass wheels & trim, Red seats & grille ..	£15-20	☐
1974	2..............	White body, Metallic Purple wings, Chrome wheels, Red seats and grille..................	£13-18	☐
	3..............	As 2 but with Red wings, Black seats and grille..	£13-18	☐
	4..............	As version 2 but with Red wheels	£13-18	☐
1979	5..............	Metallic Silver body and wings, Black seats and grille, Chrome wheels...................	£6-9	☐
	6..............	As 5 but Red seats, grille and wheels, plain or White-wall tyres...........................	£6-9	☐
	7..............	As 6 but with Yellow seats and grille, plain or White-wall tyres...........................	£15-20	☐
	8..............	As 5 but with White seats, Black grille, Red wheels	£150-200	☐

Y10-4

1957 MASERATI 250 F .... One of four 'Grand Prix Yesteryears' modelled in a scale of 1:35.

	1..............	Bright Red body, Chrome 12-spoke or Aluminium 24-spoke wheels, baseplate wording: 'MATCHBOX INT'L LTD MADE IN ENGLAND', Black RN '12'.........	£10-15	☐
	2..............	As 1 but '(c) 1986' added to baseplate legend, modified suspension	NRP	☐

Y10-5

1931 DIDDLER TROLLEY BUS 'LONDON TRANSPORT' ... 55,000 of this Special Limited Edition were made (in Macau). The model (in a scale of 1:76) has no less than 36 separate components.
Red/Cream body, Grey roof, 'RONUK', 'JEYES', 'JOHNNIE WALKER' .... £15-20 ☐

Y11-1

1920 AVELING & PORTER STEAM ROLLER................ A popular model in a scale of 1:80.

1958	1..............	Mid-Green body, Brown or Black flywheel, Black or Green canopy supports, makers plate in Gold..	£130-150	☐
	2..............	As 1 but makers plate not in Gold...	£90-100	☐

Y11-2

1912 PACKARD LANDAULET .... The model features a metal body with plastic seats and spare tyre on offside, heraldic shield logo, brass 12-spoke wheels. It was made in a scale of 1:50.

1962	1..............	Dark Red body, Black bonnet & seats, metal steering wheel	£25-35	☐
	2..............	Minor changes include 3-prong tyre carrier & plastic steering wheel......................	£15-20	☐
	3..............	As 2 but Orange-Red body, Black bonnet & plastic steering wheel..........................	£20-25	☐
1984	4..............	Cream body, Brown chassis, Black roof, baseplate logo '1984 LIMITED EDITION', in 'Connoisseurs' set..	GSP	☐

Y11-3

1938 LAGONDA DROPHEAD COUPE .... The model features a luxury 4-seat tourer with spare wheel covers in each of the front wings. Made in the '0'-gauge scale of 1:43.

1972	1..............	Metallic Gold main body, metallic Purple lower body, Black seats & plastic parts	£600-750	☐
	2..............	As 1 but Dark Red lower body, Brass 24-spoke wheels, bumpers & lugs	£250-300	☐
	3..............	As version 2 but with Strawberry-Red lower body	£250-300	☐
	4..............	As version 2 but Dark Maroon lower body...	£45-50	☐
1974	5..............	Metallic Orange body, Gold wings, Black seats, Brass 24-spoke wheels	£30-40	☐
	6..............	As version 5 but Metallic Copper body, Chrome 24-spoke wheels	£10-12	☐
	7..............	As 6 but Maroon seats and other plastic parts, Red 12-spoke wheels	£14-18	☐
	8..............	As 6 but seats, roof, trunk and grille are in bright Red plastic	£200-250	☐
1979	9..............	Cream body, Black wings, Maroon seats & grille, solid chrome wheels	NRP	☐
	10..............	As version 9 but with Black radiator grille	NRP	☐
	11..............	As 10 but with Chrome 24-spoke wheels and White-wall tyres	NRP	☐
	12..............	As 10 but the seats, tonneau and trunk are in Brown	NRP	☐
	13..............	As 12 but with Dark Red 12-spoke wheels, White-wall tyres	NRP	☐
	14..............	As 12 but the seats, tonneau and trunk are in Black...	£30-40	☐
1985	15..............	Deep Red body, Black seats, Brass 24-spoke wheels, (in 'Father's Day' Set)............	GSP	☐
	16..............	As 15 but with seats, hood and trunk in Dark Brown	NRP	☐

Y11-4

	1932 BUGATTI Type 51		Scale 1:35. Wheels vary in brightness (not affecting price).		
		1..............	Blue body, Brown seats, painted bonnet straps, Grey exhaust pipes, RN '4'	£15-20	☐
		2..............	As 1 but wider rear axle housing and larger dashboard lug	NRP	☐
1990	**1927 BUGATTI Type 35**		Blue body, Black seats, plastic bonnet straps, Chrome exhaust, RN '6'......................	NRP	☐

Y12-1

1899 HORSE DRAWN BUS .... 'LIPTONS TEA'. The first horse-drawn model in the series, (scale 1:100).

1959	1..............	Red body, Black 16-spoke metal wheels, Beige driver and metal seats, Brown horses (White manes/tails, Gold collars), 'VICTORIA & KINGS-CROSS', single drawbar rivet...	£75-85	☐
..	2..............	As 1 but Dark Brown horses, partial Gold collars	£75-85	☐

Y12-2

1909 THOMAS FLYABOUT ... The model is scaled at 1:48 and features a metal body with plastic roof and seats, 12-spoke wheels, spare tyre on offside and Black plastic steering wheel.

1967	1..............	Metallic Blue body, smooth Tan hood, Brass wheels, Yellow seats & grille................	£700-900	☐
	2..............	As 1 (roof fixed to body pins), but with Dark Red seats and radiator grille...............	£20-25	☐
	3..............	As 2 but the smooth Tan hood is fixed to seat pins..	£10-15	☐
	4..............	As 3 but the Tan hood has a textured finish..	£32-39	☐
	5..............	As 3 but Black textured hood, White seats...	£20-25	☐
	6..............	Metallic Purple body, Black textured hood & grille, White seats, Chrome 12 or 24-spoke wheels...	£12-15	☐
	7..............	As 6 but Dark Red seats, Chrome 12-spoke wheels	£20-25	☐
	8..............	Metallic Ruby Red body, Black textured roof & grille, White seats, Chrome 12 or 24-spoke wheels...	£15-20	☐

Y12-3   1912 FORD MODEL 'T' VAN

This model is in a scale of 1:35 and features a metal bodied van with oval side windows and a ribbed roof. It has plastic seats (usually Black), 12 or 24-spoke wheels and left hand drive steering wheel. Three different types of rear door design were produced as illustrated:

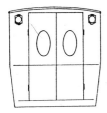

1st Type

2nd Type

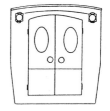

3rd Type cast in

1979	'COLMANS MUSTARD'	Yellow body, Matt-Black chassis and Black roof, Red or Black rear lights.	
	1	Type 1 Yellow doors, 12-spoke Red wheels, 'Y12' on base	£6-8
	2	As version 1 but with Chrome 12-spoke wheels	£6-8
	3	As version 1 but with Chrome 24-spoke wheels	£20-25
	4	As 1 but with Black rear lights and Type 2 doors in Red	£6-8
	5	As 4 but 'Y12' is not present on baseplate, Red rear lights	£10-12
	6	As 5 but Gloss-Black roof, Black rear lights.	£20-25

1980	'COCA-COLA'	Off-White body, Black chassis and roof, Black or Red rear lights.	
	1	Type 1 doors in Red, 5 vertical Red body lines, Red 12-spoke wheels, plain tyres	£250-300
	2	As 1 but with only 4 vertical Red body lines	£35-45
	3	As 2 but Chrome 12 or 24-spoke wheels	£50-60
	4	As 2 but Gold 12-spoke wheels, Red rear lights	£50-60

1980	'SUZE'	Yellow body, Black chassis and matt Black roof, Black & Red logo.	
	1	Type 1 doors in Black, 'No. Y12' on baseplate, Red 12-spoke wheels	NRP
	2	As version 1 with Chrome 12 or 24-spoke wheels	NRP
	3	As 1 but with Red rear lights instead of Black	NRP
	4	As version 3 but with Type 2 doors in Black	£30-40
	5	As 4 but with 'No. Y12' blanked out from baseplate	NRP
	6	As 5 but with Type 2 doors in Red and with Gloss Black roof	£110-120

1981	'SMITHS CRISPS'	Dark Blue body, White roof, Black chassis, Red 12-spoke wheels, whitewall tyres.	
	1	Type 1 doors and rear lights in White, Black seats, 'No. Y12' on baseplate	£15-20
	2	As version 1 but with Tan seats	£8-10
	3	As version 2 but without 'No. Y12' on baseplate	NRP
	4	As version 3 but with Type 2 doors in White	£15-20
	5	As version 4 but with 'No. Y12' on baseplate	£20-30
	Note:	500 'Code 3' issues of version 3 exist in 'Smiths Jubilee' livery.	

1981	'25th ANNIVERSARY OF YESTERYEARS'	(A white version of the standard box was provided for this model). Mid-Green body, darker Green chassis, Grey roof, Yellow 12-spoke wheels.	
	1	Type 2 doors in Silver-Grey, 'No Y12' on base, whitewall tyres, Silver '25' logo	NRP
	2	As version 1 but with Type 1 doors in Grey	£400-500
	3	As version 1 but 'No. Y12' not present on baseplate	NRP
	4	As version 3 but Chrome or Red 12-spoke or Yellow 24-spoke wheels	£12-15

1982	'BIRDS CUSTARD'	Blue body, Yellow roof, Black chassis, Red 12-spoke wheels, White-wall tyres	
	1	Type 2 doors in Yellow, Black seats, Chrome trim	£10-12
	2	As version 1 but with a Metallic Blue body	£40-50
	3	As version 1 but the seats are Tan plastic	£10-15
	4	As version 1 with Yellow 12-spoke wheels	£30-40
	5	As 3 (with Tan seats) but with Type 3 doors	£8-10
	6	As 5 but with Black seats, Chrome trim, Chrome 12-spoke wheels	£25-30
	7	As 5 but with Black seats	£7-10
	8	As 6 (with Black seats), but with Brass radiator grille, windscreen and lamps	£90-115
	9	As 1 but without tampo printing on rear doors	NGPP

1982	'CEREBOS TABLE SALT'	Blue body, Black chassis, Red 12-spoke wheels, Black/White/Gold design	
	1	Yellow roof and type 2 doors, Brass trim, Black tyres and seats	£180-200
	2	As 1 but with Chrome trim and White-wall tyres	£180-200
	3	As 1 but with Gold 12-spoke wheels, Black or White-wall tyres	£180-200
	4	As 2 but White roof, Gold trim, Black seats	NRP
	5	As 2 but White roof, Gold trim, Tan seats	£60-70

1982	'ARNOTTS BISCUITS'	Orange/Red body, gloss Black chassis & roof, Gold trim & 12-spoke wheels.	
	1	Type 2 doors in Gold, label with Cream logo, wheatsheaf & parrot designs	£180-200
	2	As version 1 but with Matt Black chassis and roof	£180-200
	3	As version 1 but with double labels	£180-200
	4	As version 2 but with double labels	£180-200

Y12-3 1912 FORD MODEL 'T' VANS – continued

	1982	'HARRODS EXPRESS DELIVERY'........	Dark Green body, Cream panel & roof, Black chassis, Gold 12-spoke wheels, in special Cream and Green version of the standard box.	
		1	Type 2 doors in White, Gold logo, Black seats..	£10-12 ☐
		2..............	As 1 but Type 3 doors and Green border around oval side windows......................	£8-10 ☐
		3..............	As version 2 but the seats are in Tan plastic	£8-10 ☐
		4..............	As version 3 but the seats are in Pale Cream plastic	£15-20 ☐
	1983	'SUNLIGHT SEIFE'	Yellow body, Black chassis, roof and plastic seats, Red 12-spoke wheels.	
		1..............	Type 2 doors in Red, multicoloured design (on label) covers side window..................	£125-150 ☐
	1983	'ROYAL MAIL'	Gold 'G R' logo and George V crown, Black chassis, roof & plastic seats.	
		1..............	Red, Type 2 doors printed in Yellow, Bright Red 12-spoke wheels, Gold trim............	£180-200 ☐
		2..............	As version 1 but with Gold 12-spoke wheels	£180-200 ☐
		3..............	As 1 but with Post-Office Red body, Type 3 doors, Bright Red 12-spoke wheels	NRP ☐
		4..............	As version 3 but with Chrome trim...	£20-30 ☐
		5..............	As 3 but with Gold trim, Chrome 24-spoke wheels	£10-12 ☐
	1983	'CAPTAIN MORGAN'...........	Black body and chassis, White roof, Gold 12-spoke wheels, Tan seat	
		1..............	Type 3 doors, Black 1-piece label (small 'rum', Gold border, 'pirate' cameo, White logo)	NRP ☐
		2..............	As version 1 but Black seat, Bright Red 12-spoke wheels	£40-50 ☐
		3..............	As version 1 but 2-piece label with large 'rum'	NRP ☐
		4..............	As version 2 but 2-piece label with large 'rum'	£40-50 ☐
	1983	'HOOVER'	Orange body, Black chassis and roof, Chrome trim. Special box.	
		1..............	Type 3 doors, Black rear lights and wheels, Black logo, lady/cleaner cameo	NRP ☐
		2..............	As version 1 but with Tan seat	£20-30 ☐
		3..............	As version 1 but with Black 24-spoke wheels..	£10-15 ☐
		Note:............................	See also 'Code 2 models' section.	
	1984	'PEPSI-COLA'	White body, Red roof, rear lights & logo, Blue chassis, Chrome trim	
		1..............	Type 3 doors, Chrome 12-spoke wheels, 'LESNEY PRODUCTS 1978' on base........	NRP ☐
		2..............	As 1 but with Red 12-spoke wheels	NRP ☐
		3..............	As 1 but with Chrome 24-spoke wheels and White-wall tyres	NRP ☐
	1987	4..............	As 1 but with 'MATCHBOX INT.LTD (c) 1985' on baseplate.............................	NRP ☐
	1985	'MOTOR 100'	Metallic Bronze body, Dark Brown chassis and roof and rear lights.	
		1..............	Type 3 doors, Red 12-spoke wheels, Red *MOTOR 100* 'Globe' has Blue water & Cream land. With certificate 1-2,300	£25-40 ☐
		2..............	As version 1 but without certificate	£6-8 ☐
		3..............	As version 2 but 'globe' has Cream water, Blue land	£200-250 ☐
	1985	'IMBACH'................................	A unique version of Y12-3 having an open truck body instead of a van.	
		1..............	Dark Blue body, Black chassis, Gold wheels, Tan seats, 65,000 made	£10-15 ☐
		2..............	As version 1 but with Red 12-spoke wheels, Pinkish-Tan seats	£12-18 ☐
	1986	'H.J.HEINZ & Co'..................	Model has Green 'gherkin' on roof, *'57 Varieties'* logo, Type 3 doors.	
		1..............	Greenish-Cream body, Dark Green chassis, Gold trim, Maroon 12-spoke wheels, *'Varieties'* printed with thin letters	£4-6 ☐
		2..............	As version 1 but with *'Varieties'* printed with thick letters................................	£4-6 ☐
		3..............	As version 1 but with Bright Red 12-spoke wheels..	£4-6 ☐
		4..............	As version 1 but with Chrome grille and trim	£4-6 ☐
	1987	'ROSELLA'.............................	Blue body, Yellow roof, Black chassis and seats, Type 3 doors.	
		1..............	Gold 12-spoke wheels and trim, Black tyres, 'MATCHBOX 1986' on base.............	£8-10 ☐
		2..............	As version 1 but with 'LIMITED EDITION' on base......................................	£8-10 ☐
		3..............	As version 1 but 'MATCHBOX 1985' on base...	£20-30 ☐
		4..............	As 1 but 'LESNEY PRODUCTS & Co. Ltd (c) 1978' on base	£8-10 ☐
		5..............	As 4 but with Maroon 12-spoke wheels, Black tyres	£8-10 ☐

Y12-4 1987 1829 STEPHENSONS ROCKET ....

			A Special Limited Edition of 60,000 pieces. Scale 1:64 ('S' gauge) Yellow ribbed engine, tender & barrel, Black chassis and components, White chimney, Gold trim. Yellow 12-spoke wheels on loco, 8-spoke on tender	£16-18 ☐

Y12-5

		1937 G.M.C. Van	A 1930s delivery van in a scale of 1:45. ('MADE IN MACAU' on base).	
	1988	'GOBLIN' 1	Black body, light Grey roof, 'acorn'-shaped headlights, solid Chrome wheels	£15-20 ☐
		2................	As version 1 but Black body and Black roof..	£8-10 ☐
		3................	As version 2 but with streamlined headlights...	NRP ☐
	1989	'BAXTERS' 1	Cream body, Green 'MACAU' base, 'acorn' shaped lights, Chrome wheels	£15-20 ☐
		2................	As version 1 but with streamlined headlights...	NRP ☐
Y12-C	1991	'GOANNA' 1	Blue body, Black base ('MADE IN MACAU') Dark Red solid wheels. Advert is Bright Red/Dark Blue/White..	NRP ☐
		2................	As version 1 but advert is Mid-Red/Mid-Blue/White, Mid-Red wheels..................	NRP ☐
		3................	As version 2 but advert is Orange-Red/Pale Blue/White	NRP ☐

Y13-1

		1862 'SANTE FE' Locomotive ..	A popular model (in a scale of 1:112) with hand-applied trim.	
	1959	1................	Dark Green and Maroon body, metal wheels, Gold trim, Silver lens...................	£85-100 ☐
		2................	As 1 but no Gold trim on walkway	£85-100 ☐
		3................	As 2 but Maroon headlight lens and no trim on condensers	£75-85 ☐
		4................	As version 3 but no Gold trim	£75-85 ☐
		5................	Light Green body, Maroon headlight lens, no Gold trim	£700-800 ☐

239

Ref. No.	Year(s)	Model Type		Matchbox Models of Yesteryear - continued	Market Price Range
Y13-2		**1911 DAIMLER**		The model features a metal body and 26-spoke wheels with plastic seats, external handbrake lever and spare wheel on offside. Modelled in 1:45 scale.	
	1966		1...............	Yellow body, Black wings & seats, '1911 DAIMLER' & 'No. Y13' in 2 lines on base.................	£35-45 ☐
			2...............	As version 1 but with Dark Red seats.........................	£15-20 ☐
			3...............	As 1 (Black seats), but with spare wheel open at base.....................	£25-35 ☐
			4...............	As 2 (Dark Red seats), but spare wheel open at base..................	£14-18 ☐
			5...............	As 4 but steering wheel has 4 instead of 5 spokes, no pedals................	£25-35 ☐
			6...............	As 5 but '1911', 'DAIMLER' & 'No. Y13' in 3 lines on base.................	£30-35 ☐
	1984		7...............	Mid-Blue main body, Light Blue lower body 'LIMITED EDITION' on baseplate, in 'Connoisseurs' set..............	GSP ☐
Y13-3		**1918 CROSSLEY**		The model features a small metal truck with plastic cab cover & tilt. It has chrome spoked wheels with a spare on the offside. Scale 1:47.	
	1979	'R.A.F. TENDER'		Airforce Blue body, Red cross on White square label plus 'R.A.F.' roundel.	
			1...............	Flat baseplate with 'LTD' complete, Tan canopy, tilt and grille, Maroon seat...........	£325-375 ☐
			2...............	As version 1 but seat in White plastic...................	£300-350 ☐
			3...............	As 2 but additional brace to front wings, two side panel cleats..........	£40-50 ☐
			4...............	As 3 but 2 discs (8 mm.), on baseplate and 'LTD' incomplete................	£20-30 ☐
			5...............	As version 4 but seat in Green plastic.................	£160-180 ☐
			6...............	As version 4 but with 24-spoke Chrome wheels.................	£25-35 ☐
			7...............	As version 4 but with Maroon seat.................	£25-35 ☐
			8...............	As 6 but with Olive-Green cab cover, tilt and grille................	£70-80 ☐
			9...............	As version 8 but with 12-spoke Chrome wheels................	£70-80 ☐
			10............	As 7 but with Black cab cover, tilt and grille.................	£300-350 ☐
	1979	'EVANS Bros COAL & COKE'		Dark Red body, Black lower body, seats and roof.	
			1...............	With 'CROSSLEY RAF TENDER' on baseplate, 24-spoke Chrome wheels..........	£50-60 ☐
			2...............	As version 1 but with 12-spoke Chrome wheels..............	£15-20 ☐
			3...............	As version 1 but with 12-spoke Red wheels................	£50-60 ☐
			4...............	As 3 but without 'RAF TENDER' on baseplate................	£10-12 ☐
			5...............	As 4 but brighter Red body and large Chrome stud on spare wheel........	£15-20 ☐
Y13-4	1983	**1918 CROSSLEY LORRY** ...... 'CARLSBERG'		Scale 1:47. Cream body, Black lower body, Green cab cover and tilt.	
			1...............	With Chrome 12-spoke wheels, Brass trim, Maroon seats, Green or Black grille, 'Lesney 1973 England' base.................	£10-15 ☐
			2...............	As version 1 but with Brass 12-spoke wheels................	£10-15 ☐
			3...............	As version 2 but 'Matchbox 1973 England' on base..................	NRP ☐
			4...............	As 3 but Darker Green grille, Gold 12-spoke wheels..............	NRP ☐
	1985	'WARINGS'	1...............	Dark Green body, textured cab cover and tilt in White plastic. White tilt labels with 'LONDON W.G. MADRID PARIS' in Brown.................	£8-10 ☐
			2...............	As version 1 but with Cream labels................	£8-10 ☐
			3...............	As 1 (White labels), but textured Cream plastic cab cover and tilt..........	£8-10 ☐
			4...............	As 3 (Cream cab cover and tilt) but labels are Cream................	£8-10 ☐
	1985	'KOHLE & KOKS'	1...............	Lemon-Yellow body, Black cab roof, wheels, chassis & coal load..............	NRP ☐
			2...............	As version 1 but with Dark Green 12-spoke wheels................	£20-30 ☐
Y14-1	1959	**'DUKE OF CONNAUGHT'** **Locomotive (1903)**		Scale 1:130.	
			1...............	Dark Green & Brown body, metal 12-spoked wheels, Gold trimmed sandbox on walkway (not joined to main wheel arch). Gold trim on other main features........	£100-125 ☐
			2...............	As 1 but walkway sandbox has no Gold trim................	£85-95 ☐
			3...............	As 2 but walkway boxes joined to main wheel arches................	£85-100 ☐
			4...............	As version 3 but with combined wheels and axles................	£85-100 ☐
			5...............	As version 4 but with boiler door in Silver................	£100-110 ☐
Y14-2		**1911 MAXWELL ROADSTER**		The model features a metal body, petrol tank and 12-spoke wheels with spare wheel on boot. It has plastic seats and roof and is modelled in a scale of 1:49.	
	1965		1...............	Turquoise body, smooth Black roof, Red seats, Brass wheels, Brass petrol tank........	£60-70 ☐
			2...............	As version 1 but with Copper petrol tank..................	£12-17 ☐
			3...............	As version 2 with textured roof................	£12-17 ☐
	1984		4...............	Dark Cream body, Dark Green lower body, Brass 12-spoke wheels, Black textured roof with 'LIMITED EDITION' on underside, in 'Connoisseurs' set........	GSP ☐
Y14-3		**1931 STUTZ BEARCAT**		The model features an open 2 seater tourer with metal body and plastic seats. It has Chrome 24-spoke wheels and 2 spares. Scale 1:44.	
	1974		1...............	Metallic Light Green main body, Metallic Green lower body. Rear bumper open on left hand side, Red seats and grille, '1973' on baseplate.................	£100-125 ☐
			2...............	As version 1 but rear bumper closed on both sides................	£100-125 ☐
			3...............	As version 2 with '1974' on baseplate................	£8-10 ☐
			4...............	As version 3 but with Dark Red seats................	£75-100 ☐
	1979		5...............	Cream/Red body, Red door tops, Red seats and grille................	£30-35 ☐
			6...............	As version 5 but radiator grille in Black plastic................	£25-35 ☐
			7...............	As 5 but seats and grille are both in Maroon plastic................	£25-35 ☐
			8...............	As version 7 but with Cream door tops................	£8-10 ☐
	1981		9...............	Cream and emerald-Green body, Black seats, Chrome 24-spoke wheels................	£6-8 ☐
			10............	As 8 but with Red 12-spoke wheels, White-wall tyres................	£15-20 ☐
	1985		11............	French Blue and Grey body, Brown or Beige seats................	NRP ☐
	1990		12............	Pale Cream/Blue, Dark Red seats, Tan or Olive steering wheel, Chrome 24-spoke wheels................	£6-8 ☐

Ref. No.	Year(s)	Model Type	Matchbox Models of Yesteryear - continued	Market Price Range
Y14-4		**1936 E.R.A. Type R1-B**	A famous British racing car reproduced in a scale of 1:35.	
	1986	1	Black body, Chrome 24-spoke wheels, RN '7', 'MADE IN ENGLAND' on base	NRP □
		2	As 1 but with 'aluminium' effect 24-spoke wheels	NRP □
	1988	('Romulus') 3	Blue body, Dark Yellow chassis & springs, RN '4', 'MADE IN MACAU' on base ...	£8-10 □
		4	As version 3 but with darker Yellow chassis and springs	£8-10 □
Y15-1		**1907 ROLLS-ROYCE SILVER GHOST**	The first Yesteryear to be finished in metallic paint. Scale 1;55.	
	1960	1	Metallic Light Green body, Silver 12-spoke wheels, Grey knobbly tyres, Black seats, Gold radiator, Silver number plate, Red rear light	£40-50 □
		2	As 1 but Metallic Light Green rear lights and number plate	£35-40 □
		3	As version 2 but with Black knobbly tyres	£20-25 □
		4	As version 2 but with Black smooth tyres	£20-25 □
		5	As version 4 but with Gold 12-spoke wheels	£20-25 □
		6	As 5 but rear running boards filled-in, two holes in baseplate	£20-25 □
		7	As version 6 but with Green seats	£50-60 □
		8	As 6 but baseplate is extended and cross-member removed	£20-25 □
Y15-2		**1930 PACKARD VICTORIA** ...	The model features a metal body, 12 or 24-spoked wheels, with 2 spares (1 in each wing]. It has a plastic roof and luggage trunk. Components are easily interchanged and many combinations exist (both fake and genuine]. Scale 1:46.	
	1969	1	Metallic brownish-Gold upper, dark Brown lower body, Maroon grille, seats and textured hood, Brass 24-spoke wheels, cross chassis brace	£20-30 □
		2	As 1 but Bright Red seats	£20-30 □
		3	As 2 but with Chrome 24-spoke wheels	£40-50 □
	1974	4	Metallic greenish-Gold body, dark Brown chassis, Maroon hood, Bright or Dark Red grille, Chrome 12 or 24-spoke wheels	£10-15 □
		5	As 4 but Black hood & trunk, Dark Red seats & grille, Chrome 24-spoke wheels	NGPP □
		6	As 5 but with raised coachline round body rear, Black trunk	£50-60 □
		7	As version 6 but with Gloss-Black chassis	£200-250 □
		8	Black body with Red panels, Black hood, Dark Red seats, solid Chrome wheels.......	£8-10 □
		9	As 8 but with White hood and Chrome solid or 24-spoke wheels	£8-10 □
		10	As version 9 but with Bright Red seats	£40-45 □
	1984	11	Dark Cream body, Brown or White textured hood, Red wheels, Mushroom seats........	£8-10 □
		12	As 11 but with Orange/Brown hood, Tan seats..	£8-10 □
Y15-3		**1920 'PRESTON' TYPE TRAM CAR**	The model features a double decker tram with metal lower & upper decks, plastic window sections, chassis, roof, seats and staircase. Scale 1:87.	
	1987	'SWAN VESTAS' 1	Red body, White window sections, Grey chassis and roof, 'LONDON TRANSPORT'	NRP □
		2	As 1 but modified resistor box and letter 'A' added to baseplate	NGPP □
	1988	'SWAN SOAP' 1	Blue lower body & roof, Cream upper, 'DARLINGTON CORPORATION'	£10-12 □
		2	As 1 but additional letter 'A' on baseplate	NRP □
	1989	'GOLDEN SHRED'	Cream upper & Orange lower body, 'PAISLEY DISTRICT TRAMWAYS'	NRP □
Y15-D	1991	'ZEBRA GRATE POLISH'	Dark Brown body, Grey roof, 'NEWCASTLE CORPORATION TRANSPORT'	NRP □
		2	As version 1 but with Orange tampo print	NRP □
Y16-1		**1904 SPYKER**	Large open car with huge single headlamp and round grille. Scale 1:45.	
	1961	1	Pale Cream body, Brass 12-spoke wheels, Grey knobbly tyres, Gold radiator surround, Green seats, spare wheel, curved brake/gear lever	£200-250 □
		2	As version 1 but with Pale Yellow body	£50-60 □
		3	As 2 but with Black knobbly tyres and straight brake/gear lever	£25-30 □
		4	As 3 but with two unthreaded holes in baseplate and 'MODELS OF YESTERYEAR No.16' removed, Brass 12-spoke wheels	£90-110 □
		5	As 3 but four braces on Gold wheels with fine tread tyres	£25-30 □
		6	As 5 but with Maroon body, Brass 12-spoke or Y6-2 Bugatti wheels	£1200-1500 □
		7	As 5 but section between running boards and chassis filled-in	£25-30 □
		8	As version 7 but finished in Dark Yellow	£25-30 □
		9	As version 8 but no Gold radiator trim	£25-30 □
Y16-2		**1928 MERCEDES-BENZ SS COUPE**	The model is in 1:45 scale and features a metal body with a spare wheel in each front wing, plastic roof & trunk, exposed manifold exhaust pipes in Brass.	
	1972	1	Metallic Silver body, Metallic Red chassis/differential casting, Black grille, textured roof & smooth trunk, Brass 24-spoke wheels.	£50-75 □
		2	As 1 but without the differential detail, Black trunk	£25-30 □
	1974	3	Metallic Lime Green body, Black textured roof, boot & seats, Chrome wheels...........	£15-20 □
		4	As version 3 but with Chrome 12-spoke wheels	£15-20 □
		5	Metallic Light Green main body with 'Stutz Bearcat'-Green lower body, Chrome 24-spoke wheels.	£200-250 □
		6	As 3 with Dark Green seats, grille, textured roof & textured trunk.............	£60-75 □
		7	As version 6 but with 12-spoke Chrome wheels.	£45-60 □
		8	As 6 but the exhaust pipe is incorporated into baseplate casting	£55-65 □
		9	As 8 with Black seats, grille, textured roof, textured trunk	£14-18 □
		10	As 9 but with Green 12-spoke wheels on plain Black tyres	£90-100 □
	1979	11	White body, Black textured roof, Chrome 24-spoke wheels and exhaust pipes, White-wall tyres	£10-15 □
		12	As version 11 but with Black chassis.	£350-400 □

Y16-2 MERCEDES-BENZ SS COUPE – continued

	Year(s)	No.	Description	Price	
	1981	13	Mid-Blue body, Grey side panels, Black roof, Chrome 24-spoke wheels	**£7-10**	☐
		14	As 13 but with Red 12-spoke wheels, White-wall tyres	**£14-18**	☐
		15	As 13 but with Duck Egg Blue body and side panels	**£75-90**	☐
		16	As 13 but with milky-White body and side panels	**£20-30**	☐
		17	As 13 but with Fawn body and side panels, Black or White-wall tyres	**£16-20**	☐
	1985	18	Bright Red body, Silver chassis, Red 24-spoke wheels, White-wall tyres	NRP	☐
		19	As version 18 but with Red 12-spoke wheels	NRP	☐
	1990	20	Light Grey body, Black chassis, 24-spoke Chrome wheels, Tan steering wheel	NRP	☐
		21	As 20 but with Olive-Green steering wheel with Black painted spokes	NRP	☐

Y16-3 **1960 FERRARI DINO 246/V12**

One of four 'Grand Prix' Yesteryears modelled in a scale of 1:35.

	Year(s)	No.	Description	Price	
	1986	1	Bright Red body, Chrome 24-spoke wheels, Black RN '17' in White disc	**£15-20**	☐
		2	As version 1 but with wider brake drums	NRP	☐
		3	As version 2 but with aluminium-effect wheels	**£10-15**	☐

Y16-4 1988 **1923 SCANIA-VABIS POST BUS**

		No.	Description	Price	
		1	Yellow body & skids, Grey roof, Brass trim and 12-spoke front wheels, Black rear wheels & track, Special Edition Model (60,000), Scale 1:49.	**£14-20**	☐

Y16-5 1989 **SCAMMELL 100 TON TRUCK AND TRAILER WITH G.E.R. E4 CLASS 2-4-0- LOCOMOTIVE**

An impressive Special Limited Edition pair of models in 'S' gauge (1:64)
Blue truck & trailer, White cab roofs & 'PICKFORDS' logo, Red chassis & wheels.
Very dark Blue loco with Red bodylines, Gold trim & number '490'. .... **£70-80** ☐

Y17-1 **1938 HISPANO SUIZA** ....

A stylish sports two-seater modelled in 1:48 scale.

	Year(s)	No.	Description	Price	
	1975	1	Dark Red body, Black wings, roof, seats & grille, Chrome 24-spoke wheels, 'LESNEY PRODUCTS & Co.Ltd. (c) 1973 MADE IN ENGLAND' on base	**£10-15**	☐
	1980	2	As 1 but Two-tone Metallic Silver Blue body, chassis and mudguards	**£8-11**	☐
		3	As 2 but with solid Chrome wheels and White-wall tyres	**£8-11**	☐
		4	As version 3 but with Black chassis and mudguards	**£8-11**	☐
	1981	5	As 4 but with Metallic Silver upper body, Powder-Blue sides	NGPP	☐
		6	As 5 but with Metallic Silver chassis and mudguards	NGPP	☐
	1986	7	Emerald Green body, Dark Green chassis & wings, Brass 24-spoke wheels, Black roof	NRP	☐
		8	As version 7 but with Dark Green radiator grille	**£10-12**	☐
		9	As 7 but 'MATCHBOX INTL' and 'MADE IN ENGLAND' on base	**£20-30**	☐
		10	As 7 but 'MATCHBOX INTL' and 'MADE IN MACAU' on base	NRP	☐
	1990	11	Metallic Green body with Pale Lime-Green panels, Pale Cream hood, Chrome 24-spoke wheels with White-wall flanges, 'MADE IN MACAU' on base	**£10-15**	☐
		12	As 11 but with cast hole in base for self-tapping screw	**£8-10**	☐
		13	As version 12 but with Dark Lime-Green panels	**£8-10**	☐
		14	As version 12 but the wheels are on press-fit axles	**£10-12**	☐

Y18-1 **1937 CORD 812** ....

An unusual American car of the 1930s modelled in 1:48 scale.

	Year(s)	No.	Description	Price	
	1979	1	Bright Red body, Chrome 24-spoke wheels, White-wall tyres, White roof & seats, 'MADE IN ENGLAND (c) 1978 LESNEY PRODUCTS & Co.Ltd.' on base	**£8-11**	☐
		2	As version 1 but with Red solid wheels	**£8-11**	☐
		3	As version 1 but with Chrome solid wheels	NRP	☐
		4	As 3 but with Dark Orange bonnet, front wings & baseplate	NRP	☐
	1981	5	As version 3 but darker Red body and grille	**£10-12**	☐
	1983	6	As version 5 but Plum Red body	**£8-11**	☐
		7	As version 6 but with Chrome 24-spoke wheels	**£10-12**	☐
	1990	8	Yellow body, Brown hood, solid Chrome wheels, 'MADE IN MACAU' on base	**£8-10**	☐

Y18-2 **1918 ATKINSON 'D' TYPE STEAM WAGON** ....

The model (scaled at 1:60) has a metal body & plastic underframe, chrome chimney and boiler, and smooth plastic tyres on 8-spoke wheels. (65,000 made).

	Year(s)	Name	No.	Description	Price	
	1985	'LAKE GOLDSMITH'		Emerald Green body & wheels, Red underframe, Black rounded mudguards	**£8-12**	☐
	1986	'BLUE CIRCLE'	1	Pale Yellow body, Yellow wheels, Pale Blue logo, Black underframe	**£10-12**	☐
			2	Deeper Yellow body, Darker Blue logo	NRP	☐
	1987	'BASS & Co'		Blue body with 7 barrels, Red transmission & wheels. (60,000 made)	**£8-12**	☐
	1988	'BURGHFIELD MILLS'		Red truck body and wheels, Black underframe, Yellow sack load	NRP	☐

Y19-1 **1936 AUBURN SPEEDSTER** ..

An American classic car in a scale of 1:42.

	Year(s)	No.	Description	Price	
	1979	1	Light Beige main body, bonnet & sides, Dark Brown wings & chassis, Dark Orange seats, Cherry-Red solid wheels, Black or WWT	**£8-11**	☐
		2	As 1 but with Red solid wheels with Black or White-wall tyres	**£8-11**	☐
		3	As version 2 but with Bright Red seats	NRP	☐
		4	As 1 but with very Dark Beige wings & chassis	**£10-12**	☐
	1983	5	Light Cream body, Black wings, Bright Red seats, Red solid wheels, Black or White-wall tyres	**£12-15**	☐
		6	As version 6 but Off-White body, Black wings	NRP	☐
		7	As 6 but with Red 12-spoke wheels, Black or White-wall tyres	NRP	☐
	1985	8	White body & wings, Blue panels, seats & 24-spoke wheels	NRP	☐
	1990	9	Dark Tan upper body & wings, Cream sides, Chrome 24-spoke wheels	NRP	☐

Y19-2 1986   **FOWLER B6 SHOWMANS ENGINE**   'Hey-Ho Come To The Fair'. Special Limited Edition of 65,000 models.

1................. Blue body, Black smoke-box, White roof, Red wheels, Scale 1:68 .... £30-35 ☐

2................. As 1 but with off-White (almost Light Cream) roof .... £30-35 ☐

Y19-3   **1929 MORRIS COWLEY VAN**   The model is in 1:39 scale and has a metal van body with oval side windows. It has 12-spoke wheels and a spare wheel on the nearside.

1987   'BRASSO'   1................. Blue main body, Black wings, White roof, Red wheels, Chrome radiator .... NRP ☐

2................. As 1 but underside of roof has additional strengthening webs .... NRP ☐

3................. As 2 but darker Brown seats, press-fit wheels, screw hole in base, 'CHINA' .... £8-10 ☐

1988   'MICHELIN'   1................. Blue body, Black wings, Chrome wheels, Yellow roof & designs, *'Too small a tyre is soon ruined!'* on nearside, *'Pump up every Friday'* on offside .... NRP ☐

2................. As version 1 but with Lemon-Yellow designs .... NRP ☐

1990   'J. SAINSBURY'   1................. Brown body, Black wings, White roof, Chrome wheels & radiator, 'DELICIOUS DAIRY BUTTER' in Dark Blue on roof sides .... NRP ☐

2................. As 1 but 'DELICIOUS DAIRY BUTTER' in lighter shade of Blue .... NRP ☐

Y20-1   **1937 MERCEDES-BENZ 540K**   A luxurious open tourer modelled in 1:45 scale with opening dickey seat.

1981   1................. Metallic Silver body, Black wings, Chrome 24-spoke wheels, Red 28 mm. seats .... £12-15 ☐

2................. As 1 but with Red 30 mm. wide seats .... £8-11 ☐

3................. As version 2 but with Amber seats .... £8-11 ☐

4................. As version 2 but with Chrome solid wheels .... £8-11 ☐

5................. As version 2 but with Red 12-spoke wheels .... £8-11 ☐

1985   6................. White body with Red side stripe, seats and 24-spoke wheels .... NRP ☐

1987   7................. Bright Red body, Brown seats, Chrome 24-spoke wheels, White-wall tyres .... £8-10 ☐

1989   8................. Black body, Maroon seats, Chrome 24-spoke wheels, Tan steering wheel .... £20-30 ☐

1990   9................. As 8 but with cast hole in baseplate and '540K' nearer to rear axle .... NRP ☐

10............... As 9 but with press-fit Chrome 24-spoke wheels & White-wall flanges .... NRP ☐

11............... As 10 but with Light Olive-Green steering wheel .... NRP ☐

Y21-1   **1930 FORD MODEL 'A' WOODY WAGON** .... This model has metal bonnet, wings and baseplate but the main 'utility' body is in plastic. It has a Black roof and Chrome wheels. Scale 1:40.

1981   1................. Yellow bonnet, Dark Brown wings, Red seats, 24-spoke wheels, 'LESNEY' base .... £10-12 ☐

2................. As 1 but seats and steering wheel in Orange .... £35-45 ☐

3................. with Black chassis and 'FORD A' on base changed to 'FORD MODEL A' .... £20-25 ☐

4................. As 3 but Red seats & steering wheel, 'Matchbox 1981' on base .... £20-25 ☐

1983   5................. Dark Orange bonnet, Brown wings, Red seats, 12-spoke wheels, 'Matchbox' base ..... NRP ☐

Y21-2   **1930 FORD MODEL 'A' WOODY WAGON** .... A development from Y21-1 with side windows filled in. Scale 1:40.

1983   'A & J BOX'   1................. Copper bonnet, Dark Brown wings & chassis, White seats, Chrome 12-spoke wheels, White-wall tyres, 'LESNEY' base, windscreen without Chrome finish .... £8-10 ☐

2................. As 1 but the windscreen surround has Chrome finish .... £18-24 ☐

3................. As version 1 but Dark Orange bonnet .... £8-10 ☐

4................. As 1 with Yellow bonnet, Red seats, 24-spoke wheels, Black tyres .... £35-45 ☐

5................. As 3 but 'MATCHBOX INT'L LTD' on underside of o/s running board .... NRP ☐

6................. As 5 but with Red seats, Chrome 12-spoke wheels, White-wall tyres .... £35-45 ☐

7................. Dark Orange Copper bonnet, Off-White seats, 12 or 24-spoke wheels .... £8-10 ☐

1985   'CARTERS SEEDS'   1............... Blue bonnet, Black wings, Cream and Dark Blue wagon sides, Blue 'Carters', Brown seats, Chrome 12-spoke wheels, White-wall tyres .... NRP ☐

2................. As 1 but with Chrome 24-spoke wheels on White-wall tyres .... NRP ☐

3................. As 1 but White body panels, Pale Blue logo, Brown seats .... £8-10 ☐

Y21-3   **AVELING AND PORTER ROAD ROLLER** .... 'James Young & Sons, Edinburgh' A Special Limited Edition of 60,000 models. Scale 1:60.

1987   1................. Emerald Green body & wheels, very Light Grey roof & roller surfaces. Baseplate reads: '(C) 1987 Y21 MATCHBOX AVELING PORTER ROAD ROLLER' .... £700-900 ☐

2................. As 1 but with Light Grey roof and mid-Grey roller surfaces. .... £400-600 ☐

3................. As 2 but underside of roof has 'MATCHBOX INT'L LTD., MADE IN MACAU, LIMITED EDITION' cast-in .... £18-25 ☐

Y21-4 1988   **1955 BMW 507** .... Blue body, removable Black hood, opening bonnet, Chrome engine and solid wheels, '681 313', Special Limited Edition of 60,000 models. Scale 1:38 .... £8-10 ☐

Y21-5   **1926 FORD Model 'TT' VAN** ... A large van in 1:41 scale with a metal body and plastic underframe.

1989   'OSRAM'   1................. Green body, Red roof and 12-spoke wheels, Grey seats, Chrome grille .... £8-10 ☐

2................. As 1 but with Black printed grille, lug under some cab roofs .... £20-30 ☐

1990   'MY BREAD'   1................. Beige body, Lilac-Grey seats, Red 12-spoke wheels .... £20-30 ☐

2................. As version 1 but with Mid-Grey seat .... NRP ☐

3................. As 1 but lighter Beige body, press-fit wheels .... NRP ☐

1992   'DRAMBUIE'   1................. Black body, Gold 12-spoke wheels, Red/Gold logo, heraldic shield on doors .... £10-12 ☐

Y22-1

FORD MODEL 'A' VAN .... Developed from the Y21-1 Woody Wagon, the model features an all metal van body with spare wheel on nearside. Scale 1:40.

	1982	'OXO'	1 .... Red body & seats, Black smooth roof & wings, Chrome 24-spoke wheels	£80-90 ☐
			2 .... As version 1 but with Fawn seats	£8-10 ☐
			3 .... As 2 but raised edge to cab roof, Chrome 12-spoke wheels	£10-12 ☐
			4 .... As version 2 but with gloss Black roof	£14-16 ☐
			5 .... As 4 but 'MATCHBOX' on base instead of 'LESNEY'	£8-10 ☐
	1984	'MAGGI SOUPS'	1 .... Yellow body, Black chassis, Red van roof, Chrome 24-spoke wheels, short 'Suppen & Speisen' logo, 'LESNEY' or 'MATCHBOX 1981' on base................................	£30-40 ☐
			2 .... As 1 but long 'Suppen & Speisen', 'LESNEY' on base, Chrome 24-spoke or Red 12-spoke wheels..	£20-25 ☐
			3 .... As version 2 but with 'MATCHBOX 1981' on base	£8-10 ☐
	1984	'TOBLERONE'	1 .... Beige body, Dark Brown wings, Red roof, Chrome 24-spoke wheels	£8-12 ☐
			2 .... As version 1 but with projecting edge on van roof......................................	NRP ☐
	1984	'PALM TOFFEE'	1 .... Off-White main body, Red wings and roof, Gold 24-spoke wheels, Black tyres..........	NRP ☐
	1984	'POSTES CANADA POST	1 Red body, Black wings, special 'limited edition' box with English & French wording for issue in Canada..	£8-10 ☐
			2 .... As version 1 but packed in standard UK box	NRP ☐
	1986	'SPRATTS'	1 .... Reddish-Brown body, Dark Brown wings, White roof, Chrome 24-spoke wheels........	NRP ☐
	1987	'LYONS TEA'	1 .... Dark Blue body, Black wings, White roof, Chrome 12-spoke wheels	NRP ☐
			2 As version 1 but with Light Gold wheels..	£35-45 ☐
			3 .... As 1 but with bright Red 12-spoke wheels	NRP ☐
			4 .... As 1 but with press-fit wheels	£10-12 ☐
	1989	'CHERRY BLOSSOM'	1 .... White body, Black roof & wings, Red wheels, 'MADE IN MACAU'	NRP ☐
			2 .... As 1 but 'MADE IN CHINA' on base which has cast screw-hole	£40-60 ☐
Y22-i	1991	'PRATTS OIL'	.... White body, Orange wheels, Black roof, 'Anglo-American Oil Co'	NRP ☐

Y23-1

1922 AEC OMNIBUS .... The model features a metal lower body, with a plastic staircase, upper deck, seats, safety bars and 12-spoke wheels on smooth black tyres. Scale 1:72.

	1983	'SCHWEPPES'	1 .... Red main body and wheels, Black lower body, Dark, Mid or Light Brown seats and safety bars. Logo in Red on White label with round ends, Chrome grille..................	£120-130 ☐
			2 .... As version 1 but with Black and White label...	NRP ☐
			3 .... As 2 but safety bars on 3 are mid-Brown, Light Brown on 4	NRP ☐
			4 .... As 3 but Red upper deck/single rail, White/Black logo on Yellow label	NRP ☐
			5 .... As version 4 but with unplated radiator surround	£8-10 ☐
	1985	'R.A.C.'	.... Red main body, Black wings & chassis, Blue/White label, Chrome grille	NRP ☐
	1985	'MAPLES'	.... Red main body, Black wings & chassis, (part of 'Fathers Day' gift set)........	GSP ☐
	1986	'HAIG'	1 .... Dark Brown lower body, Brown seats, Dark Red wheels	NRP ☐
			2 .... As version 1 but with Tan seats	NRP ☐
			3 .... As versions 1 & 2 but with Light Red wheels	NRP ☐
	1988	'RICE KRISPIES	.... Red body, Black chassis, Gold 'GENERAL', 'KELLOGGS' logo on White panel.....	NRP ☐
	1989	'LIFEBUOY SOAP'	1 .... Dark Blue/Cream body, Gold 'EAST SURREY' logo, 'COPTWORNE' destination	NRP ☐
			2 .... As version 1 but 'COPTHORNE' on destination board	£10-12 ☐

Y23-2

MACK BULLDOG TANKER .. A substantial model in 1:60 scale.

	1989	'TEXACO'	1 .... Red body & wheels (12 mm. hub design at front), Black base	£15-20 ☐
			2 .... As 1 but 10 mm. hub design & larger centre recess in front wheels	NRP ☐
Y23-C	1991	'CONOCO'	.... Red body & wheels, White tank, Red logo, Black underframe	NRP ☐

Y24-1

1928 BUGATTI T44 .... One of the largest cars ever made, modelled in 1:72 scale.

	1983		1 .... Black body, Yellow panels, Chrome 24-spoke wheels, Tan or Brown seats	NRP ☐
			2 .... As 1 but with Green or White seats..	£100-150 ☐
			3 .... As 1 but rear number plate joined to mudguards...	£8-10 ☐
	1984		4 .... As 3 but with Pale Yellow panels with Black bar above handles......................	£8-10 ☐
			5 .... As version 4 but with White seats...	£60-80 ☐
			6 .... As version 4 but with Black seats	£40-50 ☐
			7 .... As 6 but with Chrome 12-spoke wheels on Black tyres..................................	£80-90 ☐
	1987		8 .... Light Grey body, Red wings and chassis, Chrome solid wheels, Black tyres..............	NRP ☐
	1990		9 .... Black body, Maroon panels, Chrome 24-spoke wheels, White-wall flanges.................	NRP ☐
			10 .... As version 9 but with Dark Red panels	NRP ☐
			11 .... As version 10 but with press-fit wheels...	NRP ☐

Y25-1

1910 RENAULT 'AG' VAN ..... The model is in a scale of 1:38 and features an open cab with side mounted spare tyre.

	1983	'PERRIER'	1 .... Two tone Green body, White seats & roof with 3 rear struts, raised sidelamp lens, open grab handles	£225-275 ☐
			2 .... As 1 but with 4 struts at rear of roof rack...	NRP ☐
			3 .... As version 2 but with Red seats...	£8-10 ☐
			4 .... As 2 but with flat sidelamp lens...	NRP ☐
	1985		5 .... As 2 but with closed grab handles..	NRP ☐
	1985	'JAMES NEALE'	1 .... Yellow body & wheels, Blue chassis, White roof, 'closed' grab handles	£20-25 ☐
			2 .... As 1 but with hole in right side of cab floor...	£20-25 ☐
			3 .... As version 1 but with 'open' grab handles	£45-55 ☐
			4 .... As 3 but with hole in right side of cab floor...	£45-55 ☐
			5 .... As version 1 but with Navy Blue chassis and mudguards	£45-55 ☐
			6 .... As version 5 with 'open' grab handles..	£60-70 ☐

Y25-1 1910 RENAULT 'AG' VAN – continued

	1985	'DUCKHAMS OILS'	Only available in 'Fathers Day' Gift Set (40,000 made).	
		1..............	Metallic Silver body, Blue chassis, Red wheels, 'open' grab handles	GSP ☐
		2..............	As version 1 but with 'closed' grab handles	£60-70 ☐
	1985	'EAGLE PENCILS' 1	Light Blue body, Dark Blue wings/chassis, White roof, 'open' grab handles	NRP ☐
		2..............	As version 1 but with 'closed' grab handles	£60-70 ☐
		3..............	As 1 but logos printed lighter, '1986' on base	NRP ☐
		4..............	As version 3 but with '1983' on base...	NRP ☐
	1986	'AMBULANCE'	Unique version of Y25 as a Special Limited Edition.	
		1..............	Military-Green body & wheels, Black chassis, 'LIMITED EDITION' on base	£8-10 ☐
		2..............	As 1 but without 'LIMITED EDITION' on base	£8-10 ☐
	1987	'TUNNOCKS' 1..............	Red body, Black chassis, seats and 12-spoke wheels, White roof, 'MATCHBOX 1986' on base, open grab handles, Brass trim	£10-15 ☐
		2..............	As 1 but with 'MATCHBOX 1986' on base	£6-8 ☐
		3..............	As version 1 but with Silver and Brass trim	£6-8 ☐
		4..............	As 2 but with Gold 12-spoke wheels	£40-60 ☐
		5..............	As 2 but with closed grab handles..	£6-8 ☐
	1987	'DELHAIZE' 1..............	Dark green body, White roof, Light Grey van sides with Gold logo.......................	£15-20 ☐
		2..............	As 1 but with strengthened number plate braces	NRP ☐
	1989	'SUCHARD CHOCOLATE'....	Lilac/White body, Brass trim, 'St.Bernard dog' design	NRP ☐

Y26-1

CROSSLEY DELIVERY TRUCK..
The model features a metal body with a plastic cab canopy and a plastic 3-barrel load. Note that the canopies and loads are easily interchangeable. Scale 1:47

	1984	'LOWENBRAU' 1..............	Blue body, Tan canopy, 'RENAULT No.Y25 1983' on base, mid-Brown barrels.......	£60-75 ☐
		2..............	As 1 but baseplate reads: 'CROSSLEY No.Y13 1973'	£40-50 ☐
		3..............	As 1 but baseplate reads:'CROSSLEY No.Y13/Y26 1973'	NRP ☐
		4..............	As version 3 but canopy in light Tan plastic	NRP ☐
	1986	5..............	As 3 but Light Cream canopy and very Dark Brown barrels	NRP ☐
	1986	'ROMFORD BREWERY' 1....	Black body & canopy, Brown chassis, Brass wheels, Brown seats	NRP ☐
		2..............	As version 1 but with Ruby Red seats	£12-15 ☐
	1987	'GONZALEZ BYASS' 1	White body, Red wings & canopy, no 'SHERRY' on barrels, Brass wheels	NRP ☐
		2..............	As 1 but with 'SHERRY' in White on barrel sides	NRP ☐
		3..............	As version 2 but with Chrome 12-spoke wheels	NRP ☐

Y27-1

1922 FODEN STEAM LORRY ....
A popular model in 1:72 scale featuring a metal main body with a plastic tilt, cab roof & solid-tyred wheels, Black smoke-box with Gold chimney.

	1984	'PICKFORDS' 1..............	Blue body, Red chassis & wheels, light Grey roof & tilt, baseplate reads: 'MATCHBOX INT'L LTD (C) 1984', truck body butted up to cab........................	£20-25 ☐
		2..............	As 1 but front edge of truck body intrudes onto cab sides and ends 5 mm. from bottom of cab panel..	£60-70 ☐
		3..............	As 2 but truck body extends to bottom of cab panel	£8-10 ☐
		4..............	As 3 but with Dark Grey cab roof & tilt	£8-10 ☐
	1987	5..............	As 4 but baseplate reads: 'MATCHBOX INT'L LTD (C) 1986'......................	£8-10 ☐
		6..............	As 5 but with 'LIMITED EDITION' cast into shank of towing hook	£15-18 ☐
		7..............	As version 6 but with Dark Grey roof & tilt	£15-18 ☐
		8..............	As version 5 but with Dark Grey roof & tilt	£8-10 ☐
		9..............	As 5 or 8 but rivet without tow hook	£50-60 ☐
	1985	'HOVIS'..................................	Dark Brown truck body, Black lower body, Light Brown cab roof & canopy............	£5-8 ☐
	1986	'TATE & LYLE'S' 1..............	Light Brown body, thick side panel dividing strut (under letter 'E' of 'TATE').........	£17-24 ☐
		2..............	As 1 but with thinner strut giving a smoother side panel...........................	NRP ☐
	1986	'FRASERS'	Dark Green truck & trailer bodies, White tilts & cab roof, Red chassis. Special Limited Edition, box 'stretched' to accommodate trailer..............................	£15-25 ☐
	1987	'SPILLERS' 1..............	Pale Cream body, Dark Green panels & chassis, Red wheels, Cream sack load	NRP ☐
		2..............	As 1 but tow-hook rivet is in centre of rear diagonal crossmembers	£15-20 ☐
		3..............	As version 1 but Mid-Green body panels..	NRP ☐
	1989	'GUINNESS'............................	Dark Blue lorry, Black roof & chassis, Red wheels, 5 barrels. (Also a PRM)............	£10-12 ☐
	1990	'JOSEPH RANK' 1..............	Dark Green body, Brown chassis & cab roof, 2 holes cast in truck floor	£40-50 ☐
		2..............	As 1 but without holes in truck floor, Dark Brown cab roof........................	£20-25 ☐
		3..............	As 2 but wheels have closed ended hubs (axle ends not visible)...................	NRP ☐
		4..............	As version 3 but with Brown cab roof	NRP ☐
		5..............	As 3 but with Dark Tan chassis, mudguards and water tank	£20-25 ☐
	1992	'McMULLEN & SONS'	Black body, Red chassis & wheels, Gold logos, 5 barrels..................................	£20-25 ☐

Y28-1

		1907 UNIC TAXI	The model is in 1:42 scale and features a metal body with a plastic roof, 12-spoke wheels, spare tyre attached to handbrake/gear lever casting.	
	1984	1..............	Dark Red body, Black wings & roof, Red wheels, Tan seats, plastic meter	£7-10 ☐
		2..............	As 1 but with canopy securing pins at rear of body, metal meter....................	£7-10 ☐
		3..............	As 2 but Dark Red or Maroon wheels	£7-10 ☐
	1987	4..............	Dark Blue body, Black chassis and roof, Maroon wheels	£6-8 ☐
		5..............	As version 4 but with Dark Red or Chrome 12-spoke wheels.......................	£6-8 ☐
Y28-C	1991	6..............	White body, Black wings, roof, coachlining & 'LONDON', Brass 12-spoke wheels	NRP ☐

Ref. No.	Year(s)	Model Type	Description	Market Price Range	
Y29-1		**1919 WALKER ELECTRIC VAN**	The model has a metal body, plastic canopy/tilt, solid wheels. Scale 1:51.		
	1985	'HARRODS'	Olive-Green body, Cream canopy/tilt, Gold logo, smooth Black tyres, special Olive-Green version of standard box	NRP	☐
	1986	'JOSEPH LUCAS'	Bright Green body and canopy/tilt, Red solid wheels, White logo	NRP	☐
	1988	'HIS MASTERS VOICE'	(1) Dark Blue body and wheels, Grey canopy/tilt, 'Nipper' logo	NRP	☐
	1989	'HARRODS' 1	Olive-Green, Pale Yellow panels, 'SPECIAL BREAD DELIVERY', Green box	NRP	☐
		2	As 1 but brighter Yellow panels, Green box	NRP	☐
Y30-1		**1920 MACK TRUCK**	Metal body, plastic chassis, roof and 5-spoke wheels. Scale 1:60.		
	1985	'ACORN STORAGE Co' 1	Blue main body, Grey cab and van roof, Dark Blue chassis & mudguards, Red seats, '1984 MADE IN ENGLAND' on baseplate	NRP	☐
		2	As 1 (Dark Blue chassis) but with Grey mudguards and cab steps	£18-22	☐
		3	As 1 but with '1985 MADE IN ENGLAND' on baseplate	£18-22	☐
		4	As 3 but with small retaining lug under roof front	£6-8	☐
		5	Pale Grey body, Dark Grey van roof, '1985 MADE IN MACAU' on base	NGPP	☐
	1985	'CONSOLIDATED' 1	Yellow body, Dark Brown chassis & mudguards, Tan canopy, Red wheels	NRP	☐
		2	As version 1 but Olive-Green canopy	£40-60	☐
	1987	'ARCTIC ICE CREAM'	Cream body & wheels, Dark Green chassis & mudguards, Beige roof	NRP	☐
	1988	'KIWI POLISH' 1	Red body, Beige roof, very Dark Brown 'kiwi' design & logo coachlines	NRP	☐
		2	As 1 but with Light or Mid-Brown 'kiwi' design & logo coachlines	NRP	☐
Y31-1		**1931 MORRIS COURIER VAN**	A large van modelled in 1:59 scale without window glazing.		
	1990	'KEMPS BISCUITS' 1	Red body & wheels, Black mudguards, White roof, Gold design	£60-80	☐
		2	Lighter Red body, horizontal body lines are 2 mm. short of vertical lines	NRP	☐
	1992	'WEETABIX' 1	Yellow body, Black mudguards & bumper, Red wheels, Chrome radiator	NRP	☐
Y32-1		**YORKSHIRE STEAM WAGON**	Based on Y8-5 (without tilt), and presented as a brewery vehicle. Scale 1:54.		
	1990	'SAMUEL SMITH' 1	Maroon body, White roof and 6-spoke wheels, 5 Brown barrels, 'Y8' on base	£8-10	☐
		2	As version 1 but with Cream cab roof	£8-10	☐
		3	As version 1 but with 'Y32' on base	£6-8	☐
		4	As version 3 but with Cream cab roof	£6-8	☐
Y33-1		**1920 MACK AC TRUCK**	A version of Y30-1 with doors and pneumatic tyres. Scale 1:60.		
	1990	'GOODYEAR' 1	Cambridge Blue body, Aqua Blue wheels, Dark Blue chassis, Grey roof	£40-60	☐
		2	As version 1 but Aqua Blue body and wheels	£8-10	☐
Y34-1	1990	**1933 CADILLAC V-16**	A magnificent car modelled in 1:46 scale with generous detailing.		
		1	Navy Blue body, White hood, Light Olive-Green steering wheel, Chrome wheels	£40-60	☐
		2	As version 1 but with Cream hood	NRP	☐
		3	As version 2 but with Brown steering wheel	£10-12	☐
		4	White body, Navy Blue chassis, Black hood, Chrome wheels, White-wall flanges	NRP	☐
Y35-1		**1930 FORD 'A' PICK-UP**	Y7 and Y22 components provide the basis for this model in 1:40 scale.		
	1990	'W. CLIFFORD & SONS' 1	White/Black body, 5 milk-churns, Yellow wheels, 'Fresh Farm Milk' & logo in Red	£6-8	☐
		2	As 1 but 'Fresh Farm Milk' and oval logos in Orange	NGPP	☐
	1992	'AMBROSIA'	Blue/Cream body, 'From our Devon Creamery' logo	£10-12	☐
Y36-1	1990	**1936 ROLLS-ROYCE PHANTOM I** 1	A 1:46 scale model based on a car once owned by Rudyard Kipling. Red body, Black roof, Chrome disc wheels, 'MADE IN CHINA' on base	NRP	☐
	1992	2	As 1 but with Blue body, Black chassis & roof	NRP	☐
Y37-1		**1931 GARRETT STEAM WAGON**	Unusual steam wagon with vertical boiler, modelled in 1:59 scale.		
	1990	'CHUBB'S SAFE DEPOSITS'	Pale Blue body & wheels, White roof, 'MADE IN MACAU' on base	£8-10	☐
	1992	'MILKMAID'	Black cab & chassis, Pale Yellow sides to Cream box body, Red wheels	£15-20	☐
Y38-1	1990	**1920 ROLLS-ROYCE ARMOURED CAR**	A Special Limited Edition model in 1:48 scale		
		1	Light 'desert sand' body, Black gun, RAF roundels, 'HMAC AJAX'	£12-16	☐
		2	As 1 but darker shade of 'desert sand' finish	£12-16	☐
Y39-1	1990	**1820 PASSENGER COACH**	'York To London'. A Special Limited Edition model in 1:43 scale.		
		1	Black body, Red doors, chassis & wheels, 4 diecast horses, 6 plastic figures	£18-25	☐
Y40-1	1991	**1931 MERCEDES-BENZ 770**	A massive car (weighing more than 3 tonnes), modelled in 1:48 scale.		
		1	Grey body, Blue hood, Chrome solid wheels with 2 spares, Maroon seats	NRP	☐
Y41-1		**1932 MERCEDES L5 LORRY**	A development from Y6-5 with the addition of a load. Scale 1:69.		
	1991	'HOWALDTSWERKE' 1	Olive-Green body, Grey roof & load, matt Silver radiator surround	£20-25	☐
		2	As version 1 but with Chrome radiator surround	£8-10	☐

Ref. No.	Year(s)	Model Type	Matchbox Models of Yesteryear - continued	Market Price Range	
Y42-1		**1939 ALBION 10 ton CX27**......	A 6-wheel heavy goods vehicle in a scale of 1:60.		
	1991	'LIBBY'S' 1............	White cab, Blue flat-bed & wheels, 28 milk-churns, matt Silver radiator surround......	£8-10	☐
		2...............	As version 1 but with Chrome radiator surround..	£8-10	☐
Y43-1	1991	**1905 BUSCH STEAM FIRE ENGINE** 1............	Black body, Red wheels, 5 firemen, Special Edition model, scale 1:43..........	£25-35	☐
		2...............	As 1 but with Copper pipes and collars..	£90-100	☐
Y44-1	1991	**1910 RENAULT T45 BUS** 1..	Yellow body, Black roof & wings, Red wheels, scale 1:38......................	£8-10	☐
		2...............	Same but bright Red roof (Est. 1,100 UK, 800 elswhere in Europe)	£70-90	☐
Y45-1	1991	**1930 BUGATTI ROYALE**.......	Black body with Blue bonnet sides, Chrome disc wheels, scale 1:46	NRP	☐
Y46-1	1991	**1868 MERRYWEATHER FIRE ENGINE**	Red body & wheels, 3 firemen, 2 White horses, Special Edition model, scale 1:43.......	£25-30	☐
Y47-A		**1929 MORRIS COWLEY VAN**................	Similar to Y19-2, but without the oval side windows. Scale 1:39.		
	1991	'CHOCOLAT LINDT'	Black body, Yellow roof and logo, Chrome 12-spoke wheels	NRP	☐
Y61	1992	**1933 CADILLAC FIRE ENGINE**................	Use of Y34 components has produced this Swiss fire appliance in 1:46 scale. Red body, Brown ladders on roof, *'Feuerweht Aarau'* logo on doors..........	£8-10	☐
Y62	1992	**1932 FORD 'AA' TRUCK**	A lorry developed from the Ford Model 'A' car, modelled in 1:46 scale. Lime Green body, Black chassis, Grey roof, Red wheels, Brown sack load	£10-12	☐
Y63		**1939 BEDFORD 'KD' TRUCK**..................	A popular subject presented in 1:46 scale.		
	1992	'GEORGE FARRAR'	Red cab, Black chassis, Brown truck body, real stone load	£25-30	☐
Y64	1992	**1938 LINCOLN ZEPHYR**	A stylish car with a V12 4.4 litre engine, modelled in 1:43 scale. Off-White body, Brown seats, Cream folded hood & steering wheel	£8-10	☐
Y65	1992	**1928 AUSTIN 7 (Set)**................	A Special Limited Edition Set comprising Austin 7 Van (Red body, 'CASTROL'), BMW Dixi 3/15 (Blue body, Black roof), ROSENGART 3-seater Tourer (White body). All three have Black chassis, Tan seats and Chrome wheels. Scale 1:43..........	£25-30	☐
Y66	1992	**H.M. QUEEN ELIZABETH'S GOLD STATE COACH**	A Special Limited Edition model in 1:100 scale. Gold body and wheels, 8 Grey horses (4 with Red jacketed riders with Black boots and hats) Brown drawbar..........	£16-20	☐

Models of Yesteryear - Gift Sets

Ref. No.	Year(s)	Set Name	Contents	Market Price Range	
G 6	1960	Gift Set	Contains Nos 1, 2, 5, 10 & 13	£325-375	☐
G 7	1960	Gift Set	Contains Nos 3, 8, 9, 12 & 14	£325-375	☐
G 6	1962	Veteran & Vintage Car Set	Contains Nos 5, 6, 7, 15 & 16	£325-375	☐
G 7	1962	Gift Set	Contains Nos 3, 4, 11, 12 & 13	£450-500	☐
G 7	1965	Veteran & Vintage Set.............	Contains Y2, Y5, Y10, Y15, Y16..	£100-125	☐
G 7	1966	Gift Set	Contains Y1-2 Model T Ford, Y3-2 Benz, Y11-2 Packard, Y14-2 Maxwell	£75-100	☐
G 5	1968	Gift Set	Contains Y4-3 Opel White, Y6-3 Cadillac, Y9-2 Simplex Yellow Green, Y9-2 Simplex Green	£55-65	☐
G 5	1970-72	Gift Set	Contains Y8-3 Stutz Red, Y14 Maxwell, Y16-1 Spyker (Dark Yellow) Y7-3 Rolls Royce Silver and Red	£45-55	☐
Y-50	1982	Gift Set	Contains Y3-4 'BP' Tanker, Y5-4 Talbot Van 'Chivers', Y10-3 Rolls Royce, Y12-3 Model T Van, Y13-3 Crossley Coal Lorry	£35-40	☐
	1984	Connoisseurs Collection	Contains Y1-2 Black 1911 Model 'T' Ford, Y4-3 Red/Beige 1909 Opel, Y3-2 Blue/Black 1910 Benz Limousine, Y11-2 White/Black 1912 Packard Landaulet, Y13-2 Blue 1911 Daimler, Y14-2 Beige/Black 1911 Maxwell. 30,000 certificated & numbered sets issued in beechwood display case	£65-85	☐
	1985	'Fathers Day' Set....................	Y11-3 Red Lagonda, Y23-1 'MAPLES' Bus, Y25-1 Renault Van 'DUCKHAMS'	£15-18	☐
	1987	30 years Set (A)	Y6-4 Rolls Royce Fire Engine, Y25-1 'Eagle Pencils', Y29-1 'Harrods'	£15-20	☐
	1987	30 years Set (B)	Y4-4 Blue Duesenberg, Y28-1 Red Unic Taxi, Y29-1 'Harrods' Van	£15-20	☐
	1987	Starter Kit...............................	(5 for 4 Set) Australian Gift Set	£25-30	☐
Y65	1992	**1928 AUSTIN 7 (Set)**................	A Special Limited Edition Set comprising Austin 7 Van (Red body, 'CASTROL') BMW Dixi 3/15 (Blue body, Black roof) ROSENGART 3-seater Tourer (White body). All three have Black chassis, Tan seats and Chrome wheels. Scale 1:43..........	£25-30	☐

Models of Yesteryear 'Code 2' models

A system of categorising models has evolved among collectors to distinguish between authentic manufacturers output and acceptable but unauthorised alteration of their models for later resale. The explanation which follows refers to a coding system adopted generally (but not officially) throughout the model collecting fraternity in the UK and elswhere, and may be applied to models produced by any manufacturer.

CODE 1 Applies to models which have been originated and totally produced by an established manufacturer.
CODE 2 As CODE 1 but labelled or finished outside the factory WITH the manufacturer's permission.
CODE 3 Same as CODE 2 but model re-labelled, altered or re-worked WITHOUT authorization or permission from the manufacturer.

Ref. No.	Year(s)	Model Type	Model Features and Size	Market Price Range	
Y1-2	1976	**1911 MODEL 'T' FORD CAR**	Black body, textured roof, grille and seats, Chrome 12-spoke wheels, brass trim, bare windscreen frame. 900 models made for the USA.	**£300-400**	☐
Y5-4		**1927 TALBOT VAN**	With 12-spoke wheels and Chrome trim.		
	1978	'2nd A.I.M. CONVENTION'	Dark Green body & wheels, *Toy Show, Harrisburgh P.A. May 27, 28 1978*.	**£80-100**	☐
	1981	'CRAWLEY SWAPMEET 1981'	Royal Blue body, Black roof & chassis, *Follow Us To Crawley*	**£130-150**	☐
	1981	'VARIETY CLUB' 1	Yellow body & chassis, Black roof, Red wheels, *Sunshine Coach Appeal*	**£180-200**	☐
		2	As 1 but with Black chassis, mudguards and running boards	**£180-200**	☐
	1980	'MERITA BREAD'	Yellow body, Black roof, Red wheels, *Old Fashioned Enriched Bread*	**£40-50**	☐
	1980	'LANGENDORF'	Yellow body, Black roof, Red wheels, *Old Fashioned Enriched Bread*	**£40-50**	☐
	1980	'TAYSTEE BREAD'	Yellow body, Black roof, Red wheels and Pale Yellow *Taystee* on Red oval	**£60-80**	☐
	1981	'IRONBRIDGE' 1	Yellow body, matt Black roof, Red wheels, *The Worlds First Iron Bridge*	**£150-175**	☐
		2	As 1 with gloss Black chassis and mudguards	**£140-160**	☐
	1981	'BEES' 1	Yellow body, Black roof, Red wheels, White-wall tyres, *Bees Art & Model Service*	**£85-100**	☐
		2	As 1 but Black chassis & mudguards	**£85-100**	☐
		3	As 1 but with plain tyres	**£85-100**	☐
	1981	'DUTCH MATCHBOX MEET'	Blue & Grey body, Black roof & chassis, *Stoevclaar*, with Certificate	**£200-250**	☐
		'LAWRENCE FRASER TOYS'	Blue body, Black roof and wings, Pale Blue/White logo	**£300-400**	☐
Y7-3	1982	**1912 ROLLS-ROYCE**	Celebrating the wedding of Prince Charles and Princess Diana Bright Yellow body, Black roof & chassis, Red wheels, *Duchy Of Cornwall*	**£140-180**	☐
Y12-3		**FORD MODEL 'T' VAN**			
	1981	'BANG & OLUFSEN'	White body, Red bonnet, Black roof & chassis, with certificate	**£300-400**	☐
	1981	'RAYLEIGH SWAPMEET'	Yellow body, Black roof, *Model Collectors Extravaganza*	**£75-90**	☐
	1982	'CADA TOYS'	Yellow body, Black chassis, roof & side panels, *Cada Toys Have Moved*	**£160-180**	☐
	1982	'DEANS of LEEDS'	Yellow body, Black roof, Red *Deans for Toys*, telephone no. on some	**£100-130**	☐
	1980	'CAMBERLEY NEWS'	Yellow body, Black roof, *75th Anniversary*, 750 made	**£120-140**	☐
	1983	'HOOVER' 1	Blue body, White roof, Black chassis, WITH CERTIFICATE	**£600-800**	☐
		2	As version 1 but without certificate	**£300-350**	☐
Y13-3		**1918 CROSSLEY**			
	1979	'U.K. MATCHBOX CLUB'	Red body & wheels, Yellow tilt & canopy, *800 Members*	**£175-225**	☐
	1981	'ASPECTS and IMAGES'	Red body & wheels, Light Brown tilt & canopy	**£140-160**	☐
	1981	'SURREY MODEL FAIR'	Red body, Grey cover, *Tangley Model Workshop*	**£140-160**	☐
Y21-5	1992	**1926 FORD 'TT' VAN** 'ANTIQUES ROADSHOW'	Black body, Gold 12-spoke wheels, *The Next Generation - BBC*	**£600-1000**	☐
	1992	'MODELS of AUSTRALIA ART SET'	2 models. 1: Royal Blue body, 'Jenny Kee' and face logos (multicoloured one side, Gold outline other side). 2: Dark Green body, 'Pro Hart' and insect design (multicoloured one side, Gold outline other side). 1,000 numbered sets, special box	**£600-800**	☐
Y47-A	1991	**1929 MORRIS VAN** 'ANTIQUES ROADSHOW'	Black body, Yellow roof, Chrome 12-spoke wheels, *Going Live - BBC Television*	**£600-1000**	☐

1990 USA Enhanced Models ('Great Motor Cars of the Century')

Because of the poor wholesale distribution in the USA and a consequent lack of market penetration, a series of twelve models was offered direct to the public via Matchbox Collectibles.

The models were enhanced by giving them detailed dashboards, number plates and rear lights plus mask-sprayed trim and authentic colours. They were issued in white cardboard boxes with black printing which had no need of a screw to retain the model. Models destined for the USA therefore did not have a screw hole cast in the base.

The twelve models included two new issues (Rolls Royce Phantom I and Cadillac V16) and ten re-colours: Y4-4 Duesenberg 'J' Town Car, Y20-1 1937 Mercedes 540K, Y-17 Hispano-Suiza, Y19-1 Auburn Speedster, Y18-1 Cord 812, Y24-1 Bugatti Type 44, Y14-3 Stutz Bearcat, Y6-2 Bugatti Type 35, Y16-2 Mercedes Benz SS Coupé, Y2-4 Bentley.

The models were also sold through retail outlets outside the USA but in the standard 'new style red' boxes which required a cast hole in each base for a self-tapping screw. Total production was 25,000 for UK collectors and a similar amount for those elsewhere in the world.

Models of Yesteryear Giftware series

Models specially plated to adorn giftware (e.g. cigarette boxes, ashtrays, penstands, boxes and pipestands. Non-plated versions of the models listed will also be found with the two baseplate holes used for fixing the plated models to the various items.

<table>
<tr><td colspan="4">SILVER PLATED MODELS</td><td colspan="4">GOLD PLATED MODELS</td></tr>
<tr><td>Y1-2</td><td>1911 Model 'T' Ford</td><td>£20-30</td><td>☐</td><td>Y1-2</td><td>1911 Model 'T' Ford</td><td>£30-40</td><td>☐</td></tr>
<tr><td>Y2-2</td><td>1911 Renault 2 seater</td><td>£20-30</td><td>☐</td><td>Y2-3</td><td>1914 Prince Henry Vauxhall</td><td>£15-20</td><td>☐</td></tr>
<tr><td>Y2-3</td><td>1914 Prince Henry Vauxhall</td><td>£20-30</td><td>☐</td><td>Y4-3</td><td>1909 Opel Coupé</td><td>£15-20</td><td>☐</td></tr>
<tr><td>Y3-3</td><td>1934 Riley M.P.H.</td><td>£20-30</td><td>☐</td><td>Y5-2</td><td>1929 4.2 Litre Bentley</td><td>£35-40</td><td>☐</td></tr>
<tr><td>Y4-3</td><td>1909 Opel Coupé</td><td>£20-30</td><td>☐</td><td>Y7-2</td><td>1913 Mercer Raceabout</td><td>£100-120</td><td>☐</td></tr>
<tr><td>Y5-2</td><td>1929 4.2 Litre Bentley</td><td>£30-40</td><td>☐</td><td>Y7-3</td><td>1912 Rolls-Royce</td><td>£15-20</td><td>☐</td></tr>
<tr><td>Y6-2</td><td>1926 Type 35 Bugatti</td><td>£75-95</td><td>☐</td><td>Y10-2</td><td>1928 Mercedes-Benz 36-220</td><td>£75-95</td><td>☐</td></tr>
<tr><td>Y7-2</td><td>1913 Mercer Raceabout</td><td>£45-65</td><td>☐</td><td>Y10-3</td><td>1906 Rolls-Royce</td><td>£20-30</td><td>☐</td></tr>
<tr><td>Y7-3</td><td>1912 Rolls-Royce</td><td>£20-30</td><td>☐</td><td>Y12-2</td><td>1909 Thomas Flyabout</td><td>£20-30</td><td>☐</td></tr>
<tr><td>Y10-2</td><td>1928 Mercedes-Benz 36-220</td><td>£30-40</td><td>☐</td><td>Y13-2</td><td>1911 Daimler</td><td>£20-30</td><td>☐</td></tr>
<tr><td>Y10-3</td><td>1906 Rolls-Royce</td><td>£20-30</td><td>☐</td><td>Y13-3</td><td>1918 Crossley</td><td>£200-250</td><td>☐</td></tr>
<tr><td>Y12-2</td><td>1909 Thomas Flyabout</td><td>£20-30</td><td>☐</td><td>Y14-2</td><td>1911 Maxwell Roadster</td><td>£15-20</td><td>☐</td></tr>
<tr><td>Y13-2</td><td>1911 Daimler</td><td>£20-30</td><td>☐</td><td>Y15-1</td><td>1907 Rolls-Royce Silver Ghost</td><td>£40-50</td><td>☐</td></tr>
<tr><td>Y13-3</td><td>1918 Crossley</td><td>£175-225</td><td>☐</td><td></td><td></td><td></td><td></td></tr>
<tr><td>Y14-2</td><td>1911 Maxwell Roadster</td><td>£15-20</td><td>☐</td><td></td><td></td><td></td><td></td></tr>
<tr><td>Y15-1</td><td>1907 Rolls-Royce Silver Ghost</td><td>£15-20</td><td>☐</td><td></td><td></td><td></td><td></td></tr>
</table>

Prices for plated models. The market for plated models is quite a small one. Consequently it is difficult to give a more precise or smaller range of likely prices. Some dealers put a high price on plated models when they get them and simply wait till a determined buyer appears even if this takes a long time. Others offer them for sale at a much lower price just to pass them on quickly. The lower prices are usually to be seen at swapmeets. However, in the case of rarer issues, it really is a case of the collector having to pay the price being asked as a similar model may not be seen again for some time.

Gold plated sets:

GOLDEN VETERAN Set with 3 models, Y7-3, Y13-2, Y14-2	**£50-65**	☐
HERITAGE GIFTS with 2 models Y7-3, Y10-3	**£35-50**	☐

Matchbox Trade Display Stands

Since the first wooden display stand was issued in the 1950s with the logo *FROM 1/6 YOUR MATCHBOX TOYS'* a large variety of display units have been released. In the 4th Edition (page 183), a large representation of the 1964 trade display units is shown. All are very scarce and are keenly sought after by collectors. Various pieces are on display in the Chester Toy Museum Matchbox collection. In addition many of the rare early dealer display units are pictured in the excellent book 'Collecting Matchbox Diecast Toys' details of which are at the end of the chapter.

Collectors Passport Scheme 1988 - 1991

In 1987 Matchbox launched a promotional scheme designed to encourage regular purchases from its nationwide 'Appointed Stockists'. MOY collectors were issued with a 'passport' which was stamped each time they purchased a model. The purchase of six normal 1987 issues plus three Special Edition models, qualified the collector to buy a special framed cabinet containing the component parts of the Preston Type Tramcar (in its original standard issue livery). This special framed cabinet was only obtainable under the passport scheme. The scheme continued in 1988-89 and 1989-90 with models Y8-5 and Y5-5 respectively but these were in a livery unique to the promotion (they were not available as standard issues).
In the 1991 continuation of the scheme, Yesteryears were joined by Matchbox Dinky and purchase of either type of model gained a passport stamp. A complete passport now required the purchase of ten standard models plus either of the 1991 Special Editions (Y43 or Y46 Fire Engines). Application could then be made for the 'Exclusive Pewter Model of the 1936 Jaguar SS100' (a re-worked Y1-3 on a wooden plinth).

Y15-3	1987-88	Preston Type Tram Car	'SWAN VESTAS', Red/Cream livery, complete model plus components	**£60-75**	☐
Y8	1988-89	Yorkshire Steam Wagon	'SAMUEL SMITH'S', Green/Beige livery, complete model plus components	**£75-85**	☐
Y5	1989-90	1930 Leyland Titan Bus	'SWAN FOUNTPENS', Blue livery, complete model plus components	**£45-55**	☐
Y1-3	1990-91	1936 Jaguar SS100	Solid pewter (unpainted), body/seats/wheels/tyres, wooden plinth, special box	**£25-35**	☐

'Swapmeet Specialist Series'

No 1. The Matchbox Specialist Listing.

It is not possible to provide listings of all the Matchbox product ranges planned with the catalogue itself.
The 'Specialist Listing' is designed to overcome this problem and it is to include the following listings in the first issue:-
MB38 Ford Model 'A' Vans; MB44 Ford Model 'T' Vans; MB60 Ford Transit Vans; Convoy models - Regular issues; Convoy models - Promotional models (Superstar Transporters); 'Super Kings', 'Battle Kings', 'Speed Kings', Sea Kings', 'Specials'; Skybusters model aircraft; Superstar Cars, Superstar Team Convoy, US Baseball, College and Hockey issues.
Details of how and when the 'Specialist Listing' may be obtained will be given in the Spring 1994 issue of the 'Model Price Review'.

The Matchbox International
Collectors Association (MICA)

M.I.C.A. was founded in 1985 and provides its members with a bi-monthly magazine which is full of useful information about past, present and future issues across the whole Matchbox and 'Dinky Collection' range of products.

All aspects of collecting are included and cover such topics as new releases, variations, past issues and a members advertisement section etc.

Once a year a social convention is held where talks on Matchbox are held and Matchbox auctions take place. A special 'members model' is issued to commemorate the event.

HOW TO JOIN

● NORTH AMERICA

The Membership Secretary, Ms Rita Schneider, 585 Highpoint Avenue, Waterloo, Ontario, Canada N2L 423
Telephone: 519 885-0529

● AUSTRALIA, NEW ZEALAND AND SOUTH PACIFIC

The Membership Secretary, MATCHBOX TOYS PTY LTD, 5 Leeds St, Rhodes, Sydney, New South Wales 2138

● UNITED KINGDOM, EUROPE and REST OF THE WORLD

The Membership Secretary, 13a, Lower Bridge Street Row, Chester CH1 1RS.
Telephone: (0244) 346297

Please note that all enquiries requiring a response must contain a stamped self-addressed envelope.

Recommended reading for Matchbox collectors:

'The Yesteryear Book 1956-1993'

Kevin McGimpsey and Stewart Orr, joint editors of the MICA magazine, assisted by several club members have produced the ultimate book for collectors of Models of Yesteryear. It contains 250 pages packed with full details of every variation issued plus superb colour photographs and International model values. Available from Major Productions, 13a, Lower Bridge Street Row, Chester, CH1 1RS. The price (including p&p) is £23-00 in the UK, £25-00 elsewhere in Europe, or £28-00 outside Europe.

'Collecting Matchbox Diecast Toys - The First Forty Years'

This important book was published in 1989 and contains chapters on every aspect of Matchbox production since 1947, with MICA members providing much of the technical input. Now out of print.

STOP PRESS . . . .

'MODELS OF YESTERYEAR' to be flagship of Tyco-Matchbox new diecast range.

Models to be packed in traditional closed cardboard boxes with high collector appeal. Thirteen models to be issued.

- 1947 Citroën - 'Taste of France' theme,
- 'Great Beers of the World' series, logos to be used will include:
  'BECKS' and 'HOLSTEIN' (Germany)   'FULLERS' (United Kingdom)
  'CARLSBERG' (Denmark)   'SWAN', 'XXXX' and 'CASTLEMAINE' (Australia)
- 'Horsedrawn Carriage' issues
  'Old Bill' London Omnibus,
  Wells Fargo Stage Coach,
  Gipsy Caravan.

Models to be sold via selected retail outlets and direct by mail order.

'Model of Yesteryear'
Y16 1904 Spyker, Maroon body, Green seats, Gold trim, Black knobbly tyres, mint. Sold by Wallis & Wallis for £1200.
Picture reproduced by their kind permission.

MORESTONE, MODERN PRODUCTS, BUDGIE and SEEROL

The following history and listings have been provided by Robert Newson.

The history of these makes is a fascinating story of inter-linked companies, take-overs and bankruptcies reflecting the ups and downs of the toy trade. In the late 1940s Morris & Stone was a toy wholesaler selling the products of many small toy manufacturers including those from Modern Products who had started as die-casters. Morris and Stone decided to have their own exclusive 'Morestone' branded lines and some were made by Modern Products, who increasingly relied on Morestone for the sole marketing and distribution of their own toys. Morestone continued to use several suppliers but in 1954 set up a die-casting company jointly with Rodney Smith (one of the founders of Lesney Products).

From the mid-1950s to 1966 the Morestone and Budgie ranges contained models that came either from the in-house factory or from Modern Products. Morestone's production expanded with new ranges of models, such as the 'Noddy' and 'Big-Ears' vehicles in 1956 and the Esso Petrol Pump Series of miniatures, launched at Christmas of that year. In 1958, the 'Trucks of the World International Series' was introduced, but only ran to three models.

Some of the earlier Morestone and Modern Products models were re-issued as part of the Budgie range which was introduced in 1959. Model numbers were allocated in 1960 and new additions to the range continued every year up to 1966. During 1961, Morris & Stone was taken over by S. Guiterman & Co. Ltd., who changed the name of their new subsidiary to Budgie Models Ltd. Although the range included many interesting and unusual subjects, they failed to compete with Corgi, Dinky and Matchbox, and losses in Budgie Models Ltd. contributed to losses in the Guiterman group. In March 1966 these companies went into voluntary liquidation.

Modern Products was badly hit by this but eventually were able to set up a new company called Budgie Models (Continuation) Ltd and purchase the Budgie trade mark from the receiver. They wanted the Budgie dies as well, but these were destroyed in a fire while negotiations were in progress. The only dies to survive were those in their own factory. Thus the main range of Budgie commercial vehicles came to an end in 1966.

Modern Products continued to produce the Budgie miniatures, mainly for the USA, until 1969 when the stronger competition this time was from Mattel's 'Hot Wheels'. Modern Products' direction for the 1970s was to produce models for H. Seener Ltd., distributors of toys and souvenirs to London's tourist shops. The old Budgie Routemaster bus was reintroduced for Seener, followed by a new FX4 Taxi and Rolls-Royce Silver Cloud.

In 1983, following the death of one of the partners in Modern Products, the business was sold to a neighbouring engineering company called Starcourt Ltd (some boxes say Merracroft Ltd - an associate company of Starcourt). The new owners reintroduced several models from the original moulds, starting with the Aveling Barford Road Roller. However, a disagreement developed with Seener who withdrew the dies for the Taxi and Rolls-Royce (which he had paid for), and arranged for these to be made by Corgi together with a completely new Routemaster bus. These 'Seerol' models appeared in 1985 and are still available. Starcourt ceased toy production in 1985.

Some unpainted castings for no.204 Volkswagen Pick-Up and some empty boxes were sold to a Dutch firm and have since appeared in various liveries. These are classed as 'Code 3' models and have not been listed. The die-casting moulds were sold to Autocraft (Dave Gilbert) in 1988, and these include most of the 1950s Modern Products and part of the 1960s Budgie range. Autocraft are now in the process of adapting dies for a range of some 35 various models. Only one model has so far been reintroduced - a run of 1000 of no.258 Daimler Ambulance in kit form. The Wolseley 6/80 Police car and the Open Fire Engine are scheduled to appear next. It is expected that further production will include finished and tampo-printed standard and promotional models as well as kits.

A complete history of these companies and their products is contained in the book 'Budgie Models' by Robert Newson. This hardback book also has full descriptions of all the models, 58 pages of colour photographs illustrating over 180 models, and reproductions of Budgie leaflets.

Morestone and Modern Products

Ref. No.	Year(s)	Model Type	Model Features and Size	Market Price Range	
	c.1946	Racing Car	One piece casting including driver. No identification on model. 135 mm.	£30-40	☐
	c.1947	Stage Coach with 4 horses	English mail coach with driver and trunk, Yellow body, Red wheels, 173 mm. 'Ye Olde Coach & Four' on box.	£60-70	☐
	c.1948-56	Fire Escape (large)	Brass bell and wheel hubs. Base consists of sump and prop shaft only. Extending wheeled escape ladder. 108 mm. (excluding ladder)	£60-80	☐
	c.1950	Fire Escape (smaller)	Plain flat base, wheeled escape ladder, 66 mm. (excluding ladder)	£40-50	☐
	c.1948	Fire Engine	Clockwork motor and bell underneath, 'Morestone Series' cast-in, 135 mm.	£80-90	☐
	1948-58	0-6-0 Tank Locomotive	Green or Red, 'British Railways', re-issued as Budgie 224, 119 mm.	£25-35	☐
	1949-51	Horse Drawn Snack Bar	'SAM'S' cast on side below counter, removable roof, separate man, tea urn and two mugs, 117 mm. Wide range of colours.	£65-85	☐
	1949-59	Horse Drawn Hansom Cab	Black/Yellow, driver, elastic band for reins, 118 mm. (Budgie 100)	£35-45	☐
	1948-61	Horse Drawn Covered Wagon with Four Horses	Green, Red or Orange, driver, cloth canopy plain or printed, later with 2 barrels, 'Made in England' cast transversely under, 190 mm. (Budgie 404)	£50-60	☐
	1949	'Wells Fargo' Stage Coach with two 'Galloping' Horses	Brown/Yellow, eccentric wheel for 'galloping' effect, 164 mm.	£70-90	☐
	c.1950	'Wells Fargo' Stage Coach	Various colours, four horses, driver, 160 mm.	£70-90	☐
	1952-58	Stage Coach with 2 horses	Red or Orange (no lettering), Black plastic horses, wheels, figures, 165 mm.	£70-90	☐
	1954-59	Horse Drawn Covered Wagon with Six Horses	Red, Yellow wheels, printed cloth canopy, driver, 2 barrels, 'Made in England' cast transversely under, 265 mm.	£70-90	☐

251

Ref. No.	Year(s)	Model Type	Morestone & Budgie – continued	Market Price Range	
	1950-51	Road Sweeper	'City Cleansing Dept.' cast-in, clockwork motor in some, 91 mm.	£80-100	☐
	c.1950	Compressor	With man and pneumatic drill. No identification cast on model. 76 mm.	£40-50	☐
	1953	State Landau with 6 horses	Coronation souvenir, 3 figures cast-in. No identification on model. 111 mm.	£30-40	☐
	1953	Prime Mover with Trailer	Red prime mover, 'British Road Services', 'NO 311' and 'MAX 20 MPH' cast-in, Black plastic wheels, 83 mm. Orange plastic trailer, 136 mm.	£30-40	☐
	1953	Sleigh with Father Xmas	One reindeer. No identification on model. About 140 mm.	£65-85	☐
	1953-55	RAC Motorcycle and Sidecar	Cast wheels/tyres & rider, no windscreen, hinged lid on sidecar, 70 mm.	£75-100	☐
	1954-55	AA Motorcycle and Sidecar	Cast wheels/tyres & rider, windscreen, non-opening sidecar, separate rails, 70 mm.	£75-100	☐
	1956-57	RAC Motorcycle and Sidecar	Cast rider, windscreen, separate rails & hinged lid on sidecar, steering front forks, rubber tyres, plain number plates, 82 mm.	£75-100	☐
	1956-57	AA Motorcycle and Sidecar	Cast rider, windscreen, separate rails & hinged lid on sidecar, steering front forks, rubber tyres, plain number plates, 82 mm.	£75-100	☐
	1956-57	Solo Motorcycle	Cast rider, steering front forks, rubber tyres, plain number plates, 82 mm. 4 versions: Police Patrol, Despatch Rider, GPO Messenger and TT Rider.	£50-75	☐
	1954-55	Horse Drawn Gipsy Caravan	Yellow/Green, tinplate roof and base, separate driver & rear steps, 190 mm.	£125-175	☐
	1954-56	Bedford Dormobile	Red body. 90 mm.	£100-150	☐
	1955-58	Leyland Double Deck Bus	Red or Green, route '7', 103 mm. 'Motor Oil - ESSO - Petrol'.	£80-100	☐
			Same but with 'Finest Petrol - ESSO - in the World'	£80-100	☐
			Same but with 'ESSO - for Happy Motoring - ESSO'	£80-100	☐
	1955-56	Aveling-Barford Road Roller	Green, Yellow or Red, driver, 117 mm. Re-issued as Budgie 701	£30-40	☐
	1955-59	Wolseley 6/80 Police Car	Black, loudspeaker, aerial, 113 mm. No maker's name. (Budgie 246)	£50-60	☐
1	1955-57	Foden 8-wheel Petrol Tanker	Red body, 'Motor Oil Esso Petrol' transfers, 136 mm.	£75-90	☐
2	1955-56	Foden 8-wheel Open Lorry	Light brown cab and chassis, Red truck body, 138 mm.	£75-90	☐
3	1955-56	Foden Flat Lorry with chains	Green cab and 8-wheel chassis, Beige flatbed, brass chain, 138 mm.	£75-90	☐
4	1955-57	Foden 8-wheel Flat Lorry	Yellow or Orange cab and chassis, Grey flatbed, 138 mm.	£75-90	☐
	1956-57	Bedford Car Transporter	Orange cab, Grey trailer, collapsible top deck, 2 loading ramps, 243 mm.	£75-90	☐
	1956	Daimler Ambulance	White or Cream body (no transfers), Silver base, opening rear doors, no maker's name, 110 mm. Re-issued as Budgie 258	£75-90	☐
	1955-57	AA Land Rover (large)	Yellow/Black, 'AA ROAD SERVICE' cast-in, opening rear doors, driver, passenger, 108 mm.	£100-125	☐
	1957-58	AA Land Rover (medium)	Yellow/Black, driver, 79 mm. 'AA ROAD SERVICE' transfers, no rear windows	£75-100	☐
			Same but 'AA ROAD SERVICE' cast-in, two rear windows	£75-100	☐
	1958	Military Police Land Rover	Olive Green, driver, 'MP Military Police' cast on sides, 79 mm.	£150-200	☐
	1958	Breakdown Service Land Rover	Red body, driver, 'Breakdown Service Unit' cast on sides, 79 mm.	£75-100	☐
	1958	Foden Dumper	Orange cab and chassis, Grey dumper, 108 mm. Re-issued as Budgie 226	£30-40	☐

Morestone 'Trucks of the World International'

	Year	Model	Description	Price	
	1958	Klückner Side Tipper	Red cab, Black chassis, Cream tipper, 81 mm. (with 'Drivers Licence')	£40-50	☐
	1958	Scammell Articulated Tanker	Orange cab, Cream tank. 'LIQUID IN BULK' cast on sides, 114 mm.	£35-45	☐
	1958	International Articulated Refrigerator Lorry	Red/Blue cab, Silver trailer, 'COAST to COAST REFRIGERATION' transfers, 153 mm. Re-issued as Budgie 202	£35-45	☐

'Noddy' items by Morestone and Budgie

Ref. No.	Year(s)	Model Type	Model Features and Size	Market Price Range	

The Noddy items were given numbers when incorporated in the Budgie range around 1960.

Ref. No.	Year(s)	Model Type	Model Features and Size	Market Price Range	
301	1956-61	Noddy and his Car (large)	Yellow/Red, windscreen, solid rubber wheels, metal or plastic 'Noddy', 98 mm.	£100-150	☐
	1957-58	Big Ears on Bicycle (large)	Red bicycle (64 mm.), metal 'Big Ears' with legs that move as the model is pushed along. No maker's name on model.	£100-150	☐
	c.1959	Clown on Bicycle (large)	Metallic Light Brown bicycle (64 mm. as previous model), metal clown figure with moving legs. No maker's name on model	£100-125	☐
	1958	Noddy's Garage Set	331 Noddy's Car & 'Esso' series nos. 7, 13, 16 & 20. Box folds into garage	£150-175	☐
303	c.1961	Noddy and his Car (large) with Big Ears	As 301 but with additional Big Ears Figure (presumably plastic)	£125-175	☐
305	1959-61	Noddy's Gift Box	Contains numbers 331, 333 and plastic Mr. Plod the Policeman	£150-200	☐
307	1959-61	Locomotive and Wagon with Noddy & Big Ears	Yellow loco with red cab. Red wagon. Plastic figures, 104 mm.	£75-100	☐
309	c.1961	Noddy and Locomotive	As no.307 but without wagon, 57 mm.	£60-80	☐
311	1960-61	Noddy on Bicycle with Trailer	Yellow bicycle, red trailer, plastic figure, 81 mm.	£80-100	☐
331	1958-61	Noddy and his Car (small)	Yellow car, red base and wheels, plastic figure, 52 mm.	£80-100	☐
333	1958-61	Big Ears on Bicycle (small)	Red. No maker's name on model. Plastic figure, 48 mm.	£80-100	☐

Morestone and Budgie Miniatures

Ref. No.	Year(s)	Model Type	Model Features and Size	Market Price Range	

The miniatures were packaged in 'Esso' Petrol Pump boxes from 1956 to around 1959, then in Budgie bubble packs with a yellow backing card till 1964, and from 1965 in bubble packs with a blue backing card. In the early 1960s conventional boxes marked 'Mobile Vehicle Series' or 'Modern Vehicle Series' were also used.

Ref. No.	Year(s)	Model Type	Model Features and Size	Market Price Range	
1	1956-58	AA Motorcycle and Sidecar	Rider, separate windscreen, 'MADE IN ENGLAND' under sidecar lid, 46 mm.	£30-40	☐
2	1956-58	RAC Motorcycle and Sidecar	Rider, separate windscreen. 'MADE IN ENGLAND' under sidecar lid, 46 mm.	£30-40	☐
3	1956-58	AA Land Rover	'AA ROAD SERVICE' cast-in, spare wheel (on bonnet) on some, 54 mm.	£25-35	☐
4	1956-58	AA Bedford Van	AA badge and 'ROAD SERVICE' cast-in, 57 mm.	£25-35	☐
5	1956-70	Wolseley 6/80 Police Car	Black or green body, 65 mm.	£15-20	☐
6	1956-58	Cooper-Bristol Racing Car	Blue body, Off-White base and driver, 58 mm.	£15-20	☐
7	1956-65	Mercedes-Benz Racing Car	Silver body, Red base and driver, 60 mm.	£15-20	☐
8	1956-70	Volkswagen 1200 Saloon	Metallic Light Blue body, 58 mm.	£15-20	☐
9	1956-58	Maudslay Horse Box	Red body, 'HORSE BOX SERVICE' cast-in, 57 mm.	£20-30	☐
10	1956-58	Karrier GPO Telephones Van	Dark green body, 57 mm.	£20-30	☐
11	1957-65	Morris Commercial Van	Red body, 'ROYAL MAIL' and 'E-II-R' cast-in, 58 mm.	£15-20	☐
12	1957-70	Volkswagen Microbus	Light Brown, Pale Blue or Metallic Dark Blue, 61 mm.	£15-20	☐
13	1957-64	Austin FX3 Taxi	Black body, Silver base and driver, 58 mm.	£15-20	☐
14	1957-70	Packard Convertible	Beige body, Red base and seats, Light Brown or Gold driver, 66 mm.	£15-20	☐
15	1957-70	Austin A95 Westminster Countryman	Blue or Orange, (Silver flash on some); or Metallic Mauve, 66 mm.	£15-20	☐
16	1957-64	Austin-Healey 100	Red body, Off-White base and driver, 57 mm.	£20-25	☐
17	1957-58	Ford Thames 5 cwt. Van	Blue body, 60 mm.	£40-50	☐
18	1957-66	Foden Dumper	Red cab and chassis, Lemon-Yellow or Grey dumper, 60 mm.	£14-18	☐
19	1957-70	Rover 105R	Green or Gold body, 65 mm.	£10-15	☐
20	1957-64	Plymouth Belvedere Convertible	Pale Pink or White body, Red base and driver, 64 mm.	£20-30	☐
20	1968-70	Austin A95 Westminster Emergency Vehicle	White with Orange beacon & 'EMERGENCY' transfer, Red base, 66 mm.	£35-45	☐
21	1963-66	Bedford TK Tipper Lorry	Dark Green tipper. Yellow, Off-White or Orange cab, 58 mm.	£15-20	☐
21	1968-70	Oldsmobile Town Sedan	Gold body, 66 mm.	£20-25	☐
22	1963-66	Bedford TK Crane Lorry	Dark Green cab, Orange crane, Orange or Dark Green platform, 56 mm.	£15-20	☐
22	1968-70	Cattle Transporter	Adapted from no.58. Light Brown body, Dark Brown rear door, 61 mm.	£20-25	☐
23	1963-66	Bedford TK Cement Mixer	Off-White mixer. Green, Yellow, Red or Orange cab & chassis, 59 mm.	£15-20	☐
24	1963-66	Bedford TK Refuse Lorry	Green, Orange, Red or Yellow cab, Silver back, 59 mm.	£15-20	☐
25	1963-66	Bedford TK Cattle Lorry	Light Brown body. Off-White, Orange or Yellow cab, 58 mm.	£15-20	☐
26	1963-66	Aveling-Barford Road Roller	Similar to Lesney Matchbox no.1c. Green body, Red wheels, 55 mm.	£10-15	☐
27	1963-70	Wolseley 6/80 Fire Chief Car	Same as no.5 with altered base lettering. Red body, 65 mm.	£15-20	☐

50 - 55 These models were designated the 'Road Tanker Series'.

Ref. No.	Year(s)	Model Type	Model Features and Size	Market Price Range	
50	1963-66	'BP Racing Service' Tanker	Green with White tank, 61 mm.	£15-20	☐
51	1963-66	'Shell' Tanker	Yellow, 61 mm.	£15-20	☐
52	1963-64	'Shell BP' Tanker	Green or Yellow; White tank, 61 mm.	£15-20	☐
53	1963-66	'National' Tanker	Blue with Yellow tank, 61 mm.	£15-20	☐
54	1963-66	'BP' Tanker	Green with White tank, 61 mm.	£15-20	☐
55	1963-66	'Mobil' Tanker	Red body, 61 mm.	£15-20	☐
56	1966 ?				
56	1968-70	GMC Box Van	'HERTZ TRUCK RENTAL' transfers and 'TRUCK RENTAL' cast-in. Light Green or Pale Blue body, 61 mm.	£15-20	☐
57	1966-70	International Parcels Van	Green body, 'REA EXPRESS' transfers, 67 mm.	£15-20	☐
58	1966-70	'Modern Removals' Van	'MODERN REMOVALS' transfers. Light Brown or Metallic Green, 61 mm.	£15-20	☐
59	1967-70	AEC Merryweather Fire Engine	Copied from Lesney Matchbox no.9c. Red body, Gold ladder, 65 mm.	£15-20	☐
60	1966-70	Rover 105R Squad Car	As no.19 but with altered base lettering. Black or Red body, 65 mm.	£15-20	☐
61	1966-70	Austin A95 Westminster Countryman 'Q Car'	As no.15 but with altered base lettering. Black body, 66 mm.	£15-20	☐

Sets of 3 Vehicles (Bubble-packed)

Ref. No.	Year(s)	Model Type	Model Features and Size	Market Price Range	
94	1966	Interpol Set	Intended to contain no.5 Police Car, 60 Squad Car, 61 Q Car. Not issued	NPP	☐
95	1966	Road Haulage Set	Intended to contain no.56 Hertz Van, 57 REA Van, 58 Removals Van. Not issued	NPP	☐
96	1965-66	Road Construction Set	Contains no.18 Dumper, 23 Cement Mixer, 26 Road Roller	£50-75	☐
97	1965-66	Truck Set	Contains no.21 Tipper, 22 Crane, 25 Cattle Lorry	£50-75	☐
98	1965-66	Utility Vehicle Set	Contains no.12 VW Microbus, 24 Refuse Lorry, 55 Mobil Tanker	£50-75	☐
99	1965-66	Traffic Set	Contains no.8 Volkswagen, 15 Austin, 27 Fire Chief	£50-75	☐
95	1968-70	Town Set	Contains no.20 Emergency Vehicle, 21 Oldsmobile, 56 Hertz Van	£50-75	☐
96	1967-70	Service Set	Contains no.5 Police Car, 19 Rover, 59 Fire Engine	£50-75	☐
97	1967-70	Truck Set	Contains no.12 VW Microbus, 57 REA Van, 58 Removals Van	£50-75	☐
98	1967-70	Utility Vehicle Set	Contains no.27 Fire Chief, 60 Squad Car, 61 Q Car	£50-75	☐
99	1967-70	Traffic Set	Contains no.8 Volkswagen, 14 Packard, 15 Austin	£50-75	☐

Gift Sets

Ref. No.	Year(s)	Model Type	Model Features and Size	Market Price Range	
No.8	1962	Gift Set No.8	Contains numbers 5, 8, 11, 12, 13, 15, 18 and 19	£100-130	☐
No.12	1962	Gift Set No.12	Contains 5, 7, 8, 11, 12, 13, 14, 15, 16, 18, 19 and 20 (Plymouth)	£120-150	☐

Budgie Models

Ref. No.	Year(s)	Model Type	Model Features and Size	Market Price Range	
100	1972-84	Horse Drawn Hansom Cab......	With driver, elastic band for reins. Re-issue of a Morestone/Modern Products model. 'Gold' plated or Metallic Light Brown, 118 mm.	**£10-15**	☐
101	1977-84	Austin FX4 Taxi	Also issued as no.703. Re-issued by Seerol. Black or Maroon body. 106 mm.	**£10-15**	☐
101	1984	Austin FX4 Taxi	Silver body, *'LONDON VINTAGE TAXI ASSOCIATION'*. Limited (1,000) commemorative marking 25 years of the FX4. Normal box	**£20-25**	☐
102	1981-84	Rolls-Royce Silver Cloud	Re-issued by Seerol. Gold (painted or 'plated'), Black, Silver, Cream, Red, Blue, Metallic Light Blue or Metallic Dark Pink, 107 mm.	**£15-20**	☐
202	1959-66	International Articulated Refrigerator Lorry	Re-issued 'Trucks of the World' model. Red/Blue or Red cab (windows later). Silver trailer, 'COAST TO COAST REFRIGERATION', 153 mm.	**£40-50**	☐
204	1959-64	Volkswagen Pick-Up	Blue body, Cream base, cloth tilt 'EXPRESS DELIVERY', 92 mm.	**£35-45**	☐
206	1959-64	Leyland Hippo Coal Lorry	Green cab, Light Brown body, 'COAL AND COKE' cast-in, coal load, 92 mm.	**£45-55**	☐
208	1959-61	RAF Personnel Carrier	RAF blue, roundels, White tilt. 'A MORESTONE PRODUCT', 104 mm.	**£75-85**	☐
210	1959-61	US Army Personnel Carrier	As 208 but Army brown body with star, Light Brown tilt, 104 mm.	**£75-85**	☐
212	1959-61	British Army Personnel Carrier	As 208 but Dark Green with Red/Yellow square, Light Brown tilt, 104 mm.	**£75-85**	☐
214	1959-64	Thornycroft Mobile Crane.......	Red cab and chassis, Yellow crane engine, Light Blue crane, 100 mm.	**£50-60**	☐
216	1959-64	Renault Truck	Yellow cab, Red body. Cloth tilt, 'FRESH FRUIT DAILY', 103 mm.	**£35-45**	☐
218	1959-63	Seddon 'Jumbo' Mobile Traffic Control Unit..........	Yellow cab and trailer with Black flash and catwalk. 'AUTOMOBILE ASSOCIATION' and AA badge transfers, 168 mm.	**£100-120**	☐
220	1959-66	Leyland Hippo Cattle Transporter.............	Orange cab, Light Brown body, Dark Brown base and ramp, 97 mm.	**£35-45**	☐
222	1959-65	International Tank Transporter with Centurion Tank	Army brown with star transfers. Cab as no.202. 155 mm. (with ramps up)	**£45-55**	☐
224	1959-66	0-6-0 Tank Locomotive	As Modern Products model. Red, 'BRITISH RAILWAYS' cast-in, 119 mm.	**£25-35**	☐
224	1971-84	0-6-0 Tank Locomotive............	Red, Metallic Brown, Black or Dark Green, 'BRITISH RAILWAYS' on transfers or labels, 119 mm.	**£10-15**	☐
226	1959-66	Foden Dumper	Re-issue of a Morestone model. Orange cab and chassis, Grey dumper. 'BUD 123' number plate transfers, 108 mm.	**£30-40**	☐
228	1959-64	Karrier Bantam Bottle Lorry	Orange-Yellow, 12 maroon plastic crates. 'DRINK COCA-COLA' transfers, 'COMMER LOW LOADER' cast underneath, 134 mm.	**£125-175**	☐
230	1959-66	Seddon Timber Transporter......	Orange cab (no windows), or Green cab (with windows), Yellow trailer with 5 logs (wood dowel). 178 mm. (fully extended)	**£45-55**	☐
232	1960-66	Seddon Low Loader..................	Red cab (windows later), Orange trailer, 3 wooden cable drums. 167 mm.	**£60-70**	☐
234	1960-65	International Low Loader with Caterpillar Tractor.....	Orange cab, Light Brown trailer, Orange tractor, 155 mm. (with ramps up)	**£40-50**	☐
236	1960-66 and 1969-84	AEC Routemaster Bus	Also issued as nos.704, 705 and 706. All models have destination transfers for route '9' and 'LONDON TRANSPORT' transfers or labels. Most versions came with or without windows. 108 mm.		
			Red, 'Esso GOLDEN Esso'............	**£10-20**	☐
			Red, 'Esso UNIFLO - the tuned motor oil'........	**£10-20**	☐
			Red, 'GO ESSO - BUY ESSO - DRIVE ESSO'.......	**£10-20**	☐
			Red, 'UNIFLO sae 10W/50 Motor Oil'............	**£10-20**	☐
			Red, Green or Gold, 'Houses of Parliament Tower Bridge'............	**£10-20**	☐
236	1973	Promotional issue:	Red body (with windows), 'Sheraton-Heathrow Hotel' on sides, *'OPENING 1st FEBRUARY 1973'* on roof, Special box	**£60-70**	☐
238	1960-63	Scammell Scarab Van................	Crimson/Cream cab & trailer. *'BRITISH RAILWAYS'* & *'CADBURYS'*, **150 mm.**	**£75-85**	☐
238	1964-66	Scammell Scarab Van................	Yellow cab, Black chassis, Yellow trailer. 'Railfreight', *'CADBURYS'*	**£65-75**	☐
238	1985	Scammell Scarab Van................	Maroon cab, Maroon/Cream trailer. *'BRITISH RAILWAYS'* and *'CADBURYS'*	**£15-20**	☐
238	1985	Scammell Scarab Van................	Yellow cab and trailer. 'Railfreight' and *'CADBURYS'* transfers. Most of these were issued in original 1960s boxes. 150 mm.	**£15-20**	☐
240	1960-64	Scammell Scarab Wagon..........	Red/Cream cab, Yellow chassis, Red trailer, Green cloth tilt, 150 mm.	**£55-65**	☐
242	1960-66	Euclid Dumper	Red cab, Orange chassis and dumper. 114 mm.	**£35-45**	☐
244	1961-65	Morris Breakdown Lorry	Blue body, Yellow base, tool box and jib. 'BUDGIE SERVICE', 120 mm.	**£45-55**	☐
246	1960-63	Wolseley 6/80 Police Car..........	Re-issued Modern Products model. Black, loudspeaker, aerial, 'BUDGIE TOYS' cast under, 'POLICE' transfers on grille and boot, 113 mm.	**£35-45**	☐
246	1983	Wolseley 6/80 Police Car..........	Light Blue, 'POLICE' labels, spotlights & roof sign replace the loudspeaker & aerial. Trial run of models - did not go into full production.	**£45-55**	☐
248	1961	Stage Coach with 4 horses	Different from previous coaches. 'WELLS FARGO' above windows, 'STAGE LINES' on doors, luggage cast on roof, Red or Blue, 198 mm.	**£70-90**	☐
250	....	....	This number was used for packs of one dozen of the Budgie miniatures	NGPP	
252	1961-63	Austin Articulated Lorry with Railway Container.....	Crimson/Cream, windows, 'BRITISH RAILWAYS' transfers, 128 mm.	**£65-75**	☐
	1964	design change:	Crimson/Light Blue, windows, 'Door to Door' transfers, 128 mm.	**£65-75**	☐
254	1961-64	AEC Merryweather Fire Escape.......................	Red, windows, Silver extending turntable ladder. 97 mm. (excluding ladder)	**£65-75**	☐
256	1961-64	Foden Aircraft Refuelling Tanker 'Pluto'	Red, with windows. 'ESSO AVIATION PRODUCTS' transfers, 149 mm.	**£100-125**	☐
258	1961-63	Daimler Ambulance	Re-issued Modern Products model. Cream body, Red base ('BUDGIE TOYS' cast-in), 'AMBULANCE' and 'EMERGENCY' transfers, 110 mm.	**£65-75**	☐
258	1992	Daimler Ambulance Kit............	Re-issued as a kit of unpainted castings (by Autocraft)	**£10-20**	☐
260	1962	Ruston-Bucyrus Excavator.......	Yellow/Red cab, '10-RB', Beige or Olive-Green base and jib, 73 mm.	**£100-125**	☐
262	1962-64	Racing Motorcycle	No maker's name on model. Unpainted cycle, tinplate fairing in Metallic Blue, Metallic Lilac, Metallic Brown or Lime Green, Black plastic rider, 104 mm.	**£75-100**	☐
264	1962-64	Racing Motorcycle & Sidecar ...	Cycle as 262, sidecar and tinplate fairing in Metallic Blue, Metallic Pinkish-Red, Metallic Green, Metallic Brown or Lime Green. Black plastic rider and passenger, no maker's name, 104 mm.	**£75-100**	☐
266	1962-64	Motorcycle & Delivery Sidecar................................	Blue cycle as 262, Red sidecar, 'EXPRESS DELIVERY' cast-in, no maker's name, Black plastic rider. 108 mm.	**£75-100**	☐

Ref. No.	Year(s)	Model Type	Budgie Models - continued	Market Price Range	
268	1962-64	AA Land Rover........................	Different from Morestone AA Land Rovers. Yellow body, Black roof, windows, opening rear doors, 'AA ROAD SERVICE' transfers, 97 mm.	£75-95	☐
270	1962-66	Leyland Articulated Tanker	Red, windows, 'ESSO PETROLEUM COMPANY LTD' labels, 132 mm.................	£50-60	☐
272	1962-64	Supercar....................................	From TV series. Red/Silver body, Red wings (or colours reversed), clear plastic canopy, 'SUPERCAR' transfers, 122 mm.	£175-225	☐
274	1962-66	Ford Thames Refuse Lorry.......	Blue cab/Silver body, or Yellow cab/Metallic blue body, windows, 101 mm..............	£45-55	☐
276	1962-66	Bedford LWB Tipper	Red cab with windows, Yellow tipper, 'HAM RIVER GRIT', 128 mm...................	£40-80	☐
278	1963-64	RAC Land Rover.....................	Casting as 268, Blue, windows, 'RAC RADIO RESCUE' transfers, 97 mm.	£65-75	☐
280	1963-64	AEC Super Fueller Tanker	White cab & trailer, windows, Green base & canopy, 'AIR BP', 219 mm..............	£300-400	☐
282	1963-66	Euclid Scraper	Yellow or Lime Green, windscreen, 'EUCLID', Black plastic wheels, 163 mm..........	£35-45	☐
284	1962	Euclid Crawler Tractor	Not issued...	NPP	☐
286	1962	Euclid Bulldozer	Not issued...	NPP	☐
288	1963-66	Leyland Bulk Flour Tanker	Red cab, windows, Off-White silos, Yellow hopppers, 'BULK FLOUR', 107 mm.	£45-55	☐
290	1963-64	Bedford Ice Cream Van	No maker's name on model. Blue body and base, windows, 'Tonibell' transfers, Pink plastic cow on roof, 103 mm.	£85-110	☐
292	1963-66	Leyland Bulk Milk Tanker.......	Blue or Red cab, windows, White tank, 'MILK', 107 mm.	£45-55	☐
294	1963-66	Bedford TK Horse Box.............	Off-White cab, windows, Brown body, Light Brown doors. 2 Brown plastic horses. 'EPSOM STABLE' transfer, 109 mm.	£45-55	☐
296	1963-66	Motorway Express Coach	Midland Red livery: Red body, Black roof, 'BIRMINGHAM-LONDON MOTORWAY EXPRESS' transfers, windows, 121 mm.	£80-100	☐
		USA livery:	Light Blue body, Cream roof, 'WASHINGTON D.C.' and 'BLUE LINE SIGHTSEEING CO.' transfers, phone number 'LA9-7755' at rear	£300-400	☐
298	1963-66	Alvis Salamander Crash Tender......................	Red body, windows, Silver plastic ladder, Yellow engine cover at rear, Black plastic wheels. 'FIRE SERVICE' transfers, 92 mm.	£65-75	☐
300	1963-65	Lewin Sweepmaster	Blue/Silver, windows, Black plastic wheels, Black sweeping brush, 99 mm.	£45-55	☐
302	1963-66	Commer Cabin Service Lift Truck...........................	Blue cab, windows, Silver body, 'BOAC CABIN SERVICES', 104 mm.	£45-55	☐
304	1964-66	Bedford TK Glass Transporter	Off-white cab and chassis, windows, Green body. 'TOWER GLASS CO.' transfers. Four clear plastic 'glass' sheets, 108 mm.	£45-55	☐
306	1964-66	Fiat Tractor with Shovel...........	Orange tractor, Metallic Blue shovel, 108 mm.	£75-100	☐
308	1964-66	Seddon Pitt Alligator Low Loader......................	Green cab, windows, Yellow trailer with Black ramp, 163 mm.	£45-55	☐
310	1964-66	Leyland Cement Mixer..............	Orange cab, windows, Silver mixer, 'INVICTA Construction Co.', 98 mm.	£45-55	☐
312	1964-66	Bedford Super Tipmaster	Dark Green cab, windows, Silver tipper. 'SUPER TIP-MASTER', 127 mm.	£45-55	☐
314	1965-66	Fiat Tractor with Dozer Blade..	As 306 but enclosed cab, Orange tractor, Metallic Blue blade, 81 mm.	£45-55	☐
316	1965-66	Albion Overhead Maintenance Vehicle	Green body, windows, Silver/Black boom assembly, 107 mm.	£40-50	☐
318	1965-66	Euclid Mammoth Articulated Dumper	Modified from no.242. Green cab, Yellow chassis, Orange tipper, 201 mm.	£75-95	☐
322	1965-66	Scammell Routeman Pneumajector Transporter	Light Blue cab, Cream or White tipping tank, 'THE ATLAS CARRIER CO.'	£50-60	☐
324	1965-66	Douglas Prospector Duomatic Tipper................	Tips in two directions. Blue cab and chassis, windows, Grey tipper, 112 mm.	£55-65	☐
326	1965-66	Scammell Highwayman Gas Transporter.............	Green cab, windows, Dark Green trailer, 6 White/Red gas cylinders, 146 mm.	£125-150	☐
328	1966	Scammell Handyman Artic.	Planned but not issued..	NPP	☐
330	1966	Land Rover	Modified 268, planned but not issued	NPP	☐
332	1966	'Kenning' Breakdown Lorry	Planned but not issued..	NPP	☐
334	1966	Austin Gipsy Fire Tender	Planned but not issued..	NPP	☐
404	1960-61	Horse Drawn Covered Wagon..	with Four Horses. For details see Morestone and Modern Products entry.		☐
410	1961	Stage Coach with 4 Horses	Blue or 'Gold plated' coach, no lettering cast on sides but 'WELLS FARGO STAGE COACH' and 'A BUDGIE TOY' cast underneath, plastic horses and driver, bubble-packed, 118 mm.	£70-90	☐
430	1960-61	Wagon Train Set	Contains 3 of no.432 plus 2 more horses with riders, bubble-packed.	£100-150	☐
432	1960-61	Horse Drawn Covered Wagon with Two Horses...............	Red wagon, ('A BUDGIE TOY' on floor), Grey, White or Lemon metal canopy, 2 barrels, plastic horses, driver and passenger, bubble packed, 82 mm.	£35-45	☐
452	1958-63	AA Motorcycle & Sidecar........	Initially in Morestone box. Windscreen, plastic rider, integral rails & hinged lid on sidecar, steerable, rubber tyres, plain number plates, 82 mm.	£75-100	☐
452	1964-66	AA Motorcycle & Sidecar........	New design. Sidecar with transfers and 'BUDGIE' underneath, plastic rider, windscreen and leg guards, plain number plates, 84 mm.	£75-100	☐
454	1958-63	RAC Motorcycle & Sidecar	Initially in Morestone box. Windscreen, plastic rider, integral rails & hinged lid on sidecar, steerable, rubber tyres, plain number plates, 82 mm.	£75-100	☐
454	1964-66	RAC Motorcycle & Sidecar	New design. Sidecar with transfers and 'BUDGIE' underneath, plastic rider, windscreen and leg guards, plain number plates, 84 mm.	£75-100	☐
456	1958-66	Solo Motorcycle	Initially in Morestone boxes. Two casting versions as 452 and 454 above but 'Silver plated'. Plastic riders:		
			Police Patrol (Blue uniform)	£40-50	☐
			Despatch Rider (Light Brown uniform)	£40-50	☐
			GPO Messenger (Light Blue uniform)...	£40-50	☐
			'Tourist Trophy' Rider (White racing overalls)...	£40-50	☐
701	1983	Aveling-Barford Road Roller....	Re-issued Modern Products model. Dark Green body cast in two halves, Silver/Red wheels, very Dark Blue driver, 117 mm.	£10-15	☐
702	1984-85	Scammell Scarab Van...............	Re-issue of 238		
			Very Dark Blue cab and trailer, White 'RN' on doors, 'ROYAL NAVY' on tilt........	£15-20	☐
			Very Dark Blue cab and trailer, 'HALLS MENTHO-LYPTUS' labels.......................	£15-20	☐
			Maroon cab and trailer, 'LMS LIVERPOOL ROAD' transfers...............................	£15-20	☐
			Maroon cab and trailer, 'SPRATTS BONIO' transfers..	£15-20	☐
			Maroon cab and trailer, 'REA EXPRESS' transfers	£15-20	☐
703	1984	Austin FX4 Taxi	As no.101 but in window box packaging. Black, Silver, Metallic Dark Pink, Gold, Dark Green, Light Grey or White body, 106 mm.	£15-20	☐

Ref. No.	Year(s)	Model Type	Budgie Models - continued	Market Price Range	
		AEC Routemaster Bus.............	Casting as no. 236.		
704	1984	'SHOP LINKER'.................	Yellow and Red body, windows, 'SHOP LINKER' labels, 108 mm............................	£8-11	☐
705	1984	'25 FAITHFUL YEARS'......	Silver body, with windows, '25 FAITHFUL YEARS' labels, 108 mm.	£8-11	☐
706	1984	'WATFORD FA CUP FINAL'.................................	Yellow and Red body, windows, 'Watford FA Cup Final '84' labels, 108 mm.	£8-11	☐
	1955-58	Leyland Double Deck Bus	Red or Green, route '7' cast, 'Finest Petrol (Esso) in the World', 103 mm.	NGPP	☐
	1955-58	Leyland Double Deck Bus.......	Red, with '(Esso) For Happy Motoring (Esso)'...	NGPP	☐
	1955-58	Leyland Double Deck Bus.......	Red, with 'Motor Oil (Esso) Petrol'	NGPP	☐

Gift Sets

| No. 4 | 1961 | Gift Set No.4 .... | Contains four models. Price depends on contents which vary...................................... | £125-165 | ☐ |
| No. 5 | 1961 | Gift Set No.5 .... | Contains five models. Price depends on contents which vary.................................... | £150-200 | ☐ |

Seerol Models

	1985	Austin FX4 Taxi	Re-issue of Budgie no.101 with amended base lettering and low friction wheels. Black body, 106 mm. Still available..	£8-11	☐
	1985	Rolls-Royce Silver Cloud	Re-issued Budgie 102, amended lettering, low friction wheels. Black, Silver, White, Yellow, Dark Blue, Pink or Maroon, 107 mm. Still available	£8-11	☐
	1985	AEC Routemaster Bus..............	New design, 1:76 scale, 108 mm., still available.		
			Red, Light Green or Dark Green, 'Houses of Parliament Tower Bridge' labels	£8-11	☐
			Red, 'The Original London Transport Sightseeing Tour' labels..............................	£8-11	☐
			Red, 'Greetings from London' tampo print	£3-5	☐
			Red, 'Tower of London' tampo print..	£3-5	☐
			Red, 'Petticoat Lane' tampo print..	£3-5	☐
			Red, 'Buckingham Palace' tampo print..	£3-5	☐

Budgie Leaflets and Catalogues

A leaflet was included in the box with most Budgie Toys. Dates are not shown on any except the 1964 catalogue.

Ref. No.	Year(s)	Publication	Cover Features & Details	Market Price Range	
	1959	Leaflet	Printed on one side only. 'Budgie Toys Speak for Themselves' at top.		
		1st version:	Includes the 6-horse Covered Wagon	£10-20	☐
		2nd version:............	Timber Transporter replaces the Covered Wagon..	£10-20	☐
	1960	Leaflet	Printed on both sides. 'Budgie Toys Speak for Themselves' on front, 'Budgie Toys for Girls and Boys' on reverse..	£10-20	☐
	1961	Leaflet	'Budgie Toys Speak for Themselves' on Black background	£5-10	☐
	1961	Trade catalogue	Fold-out leaflet showing Noddy items, Wagon Train and Budgie miniatures as well as the main Budgie range. Separate price list marked 'Price List 1961' showing wholesale and retail prices	£30-40	☐
	1962	Leaflet	'Die-Cast Models by Budgie They Speak for Themselves' on Black.		
		1st version:	268 AA Land Rover on front, 258 Daimler Ambulance on reverse...........................	£5-10	☐
		2nd version:...........	214 Mobile Crane on front, 266 Express Delivery Motorcycle on reverse....................	£5-10	☐
	1963	Leaflet	'Die-Cast Models by Budgie They Speak for Themselves' on Black.		
		1st version:	278 RAC Land Rover on front, 258 Daimler Ambulance on reverse...........................	£5-10	☐
		2nd version:...........	278 RAC Land Rover on front, 266 Express Delivery Motorcycle on reverse.............	£5-10	☐
	1963	Trade Catalogue (8 pages)	Landscape format, includes retail price list	£30-40	☐
	1964	Trade Catalogue (8 pages)	'Budgie Models' on cover (portrait format). Includes retail price list	£30-40	☐

Budgie models sold at auction 1992 - 1993

All the items listed below were sold by Vectis Model Auctions and were in mint condition and boxed.

232	Seddon 'Jumbo' Traffic Control...	**£100**
272	Mike Mercury Supercar	**£185**
302	BOAC Cabin Service Lift Truck	**£100**
331	Noddy & his Car, (small version)	**£100**
333	Big Ears on his Bicycle, (small)...	**£100**

The Editor would like to thank Peter Saphier of the Moat House Hotel, Telford, Shropshire, for his assistance with the listings.

FINE DIECASTS & TOYS AT PHILLIPS

For further information on selling Diecasts or Toys at auction please contact
Neil-John Leonard, tel : (071) 229 9090.

MINIC SHIPS

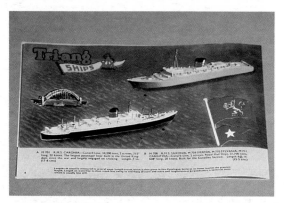
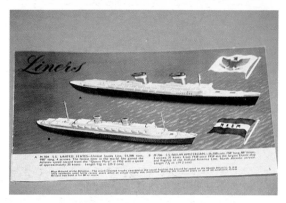

The pictures of catalogue pages are taken from the 1960 2nd Edition.

SPOT ON MODELS

New Zealand issue
Note the different box.
*Picture has been supplied by Gerry Savage of the
'Model and Collectors Mart' and is shown by his kind
permission.*

New Zealand Issue 401
V W Variant (£500)
Vectis Sale April 1993

SPOT ON MODELS

No 260 Royal Rolls Royce with Royal Standard and pennant which are often missing.
(Swapmeet photo)

No 260 Royal Rolls Royce
Note the box accessories.
(Swapmeet photo)

Picture reproduced by kind permission of Christie's of South Kensington, London.
For auction results of models shown see end of section.

BRITAINS TOYS

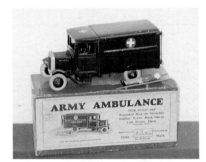

1512 Army Ambulance
Pre-war (£110)

1513 Volunteer Corps Ambulance
Pre-war (£450)

1334 Four wheel Army Lorry (£130)

1885 Lorry with winch & balloon
1879 Gas cylinder Lorry (£160)

1335 Post-war six wheel Lorry (£130)
1512 Post-war Army Ambulance (£90)
2102 Austin Champ (£50)

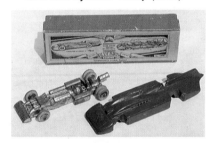

Bluebird Racing Car
*Picture kindly supplied by Mike
and Sue Richardson*

"Lilliput" Vehicle Series Set
Set (£210)

Fordson Major Tractor
Sold by Lacy Scott's Bury St Edmunds Nov. 1992
(£150)
Picture reproduced by their kind permission

Models with prices shown sold by Vectis Model and pictures reproduced by their kind permission.

BRITAINS TOYS

Model sold by Lacy Scott of Bury St Edmunds in November 1992 (£350).
Swapmeet Studio Photo.

Pre-war 'Royal Mail' Van £6,600 (World Record)
60F Farm Lorry £680; 1398 Open Two Seater £1,450; Red and White Saloon £1,050.
Models sold by Phillips, West Two, Salem Road, London in October 1992.
Picture supplied by Mike & Sue Richardson and reproduced by the kind permission of Phillips.

E.F.E. – EXCLUSIVE FIRST EDITIONS

12204 Harrington Grenadier

15604 A.E.C. Routemaster Bus

14006 Bristol Luddeka FLF Bus

15605 & 15605B A.E.C. Routemaster Bus

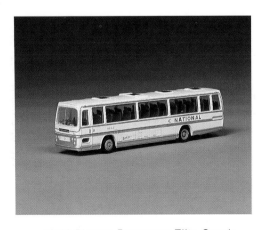

15702 Plaxton Panorama Elite Coach

E.F.E. – EXCLUSIVE FIRST EDITIONS

14701 Leyland National Short MkI

13402 Horsfield Double-Deck Tram

12501 Atkinson 6 wheel Rigid Vehicle

Deluxe – AEC Mammoth 8-wheel Tipping Wagon

15104 Leyland National Long MkI Bus

LLEDO 'MODELS OF DAYS GONE'

DG 61 1953 Pontiac Delivery Van
No 61002 Milwaukee Ambulance

DG 48 Chevrolet Car
No 48004 Yellow Cab

DG 60 1955 Dennis F8 Fire Engine
No 60000 'Essex County Fire Brigade'

DG 60 1955 Dennis F8 Fire Engine
No 60001 'Derbyshire Fire Service'

DG 8 Model 'T' Ford Tanker
No 8020 Russian Oil Products

DG 16 1934 Dennis Parcels Van
No 16032 'Tunnock's Bakery'

LLEDO 'MODELS OF DAYS GONE'

DG 58 1950 Morris 'Z' Van
No 58000 'Post Office Telephones'

DG 58 1950 'Z' Van
No 58002 'Mackeson Stout'

DG 51 1934 Chevrolet Box Van
No 51002 'Hovis Bread'

DG 59 1950 Bedford 30cwt Truck
No 59000 'Birds Custard'

DG 4 Horse Drawn Bus
No 4015 'Co-operative Tea'

DG 49 1931 A.E.C. Renown Double Deck Bus
No 49011 'Littlewoods'

BUDGIE & MORESTONE

No 280 Air BP Superfueller

No 266 Express Delivery Sidecar outfit

L-R 333 Big Ears, 303 & 311

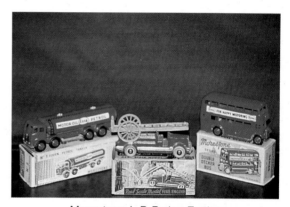

Morestone L-R Foden Tanker,
Fire Engine & 'Happy Motoring Bus'

The above models form part of the Peter Saphier Collection and are shown by his kind permission.

Morestone Land Rovers
1. 'A.A' £200, 2. 'Breakdown' Unit £210,
3. 'Military Police' £160

Morestone Trucks
Open Lorry £110, Flat Truck £95

Models sold by Vectis Model Auctions, Cowes, Isle of Wight and the pictures reproduced by their kind permission.

CORGI TOYS
(ZEBRA TOYS, DINKY TOYS & METTOY CASTOYS)

1st row Corgi, 2nd row Zebra, Dinky & Corgi, 3rd row Corgi & Mettoy 'Castoy' tractor, 4th row Early Lesney, Corgi & Dinky, 5th row Corgi.

Picture reproduced by kind permission of Christie's of South Kensington, London. Models sold at auction in November 1992 and the results are given on page 147.

CORGI TOYS

Mettoy 'C.W.S.' Van and the Corgi casting of
455 Karrier Bantam Van
(Swapmeet photo)

Major Pack 1139 'Chipperfields'
Menagerie Transporter
(Swapmeet photo)

Bedford Carrimore 'S' type Tankers
L-R 1129, 1110 & 1134
(Swapmeet photo)

Rare Mettoy 'Castoy' Coach
*Picture kindly supplied by
Peter Cook of Essex*

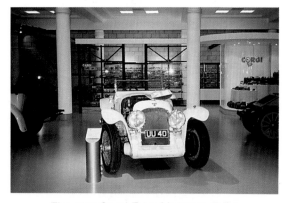

The new Corgi Toys Museum at the
Heritage Motor Centre, Gaydon, Nr Warwick
(Swapmeet photo)

CORGI TOYS – CLASSICS

96847 Morris 1000 Van

96891 Morris 'J' Van

96742 London to Peking

96682 Jaguar MkII – 'Morse' TV Series Car

97126 Bedford 'O'Van

97950   Foden Tanker

97002 AEC Regent

97203 Guy Arab

CORGI TOYS – CLASSICS

97706 Jaguar XK 120 Set

97079 Premier 70th Anniversary Set

97911 Scammell Scarab

97300 Bedford 'O' Articulated

97951 Foden Tanker

Burlingham Coach, Stratford Blue.
Sold at Corgi Collector's Club Convention 1993

97091 Bedford 'O' Pantechnican

97069 The Whittles Set
Burlingham Seagull & A.E.C. Regal Coach

ROSSLYN MODEL CENTRE

2 Hillary Road, Penenden Heath,
Maidstone, Kent ME14 2JP
Telephone/Fax 0622 762218

KENT'S FRIENDLY LEADING MAIL ORDER EXPERT
CORGI GOLD STAR RETAILER

Suppliers of:
Britains, Burago, Corgi Toys, Days Gone, Dinky, Ertl, Onyx,
Solido and Yesteryear etc.
Buying old Corgi Toys.

"BRITISH DIECAST"
MODEL TOYS CATALOGUE
APPROVED DISPLAY CABINETS

D·M·S

DISPLAY CABINETS

BRITAINS LEADING MANUFACTURERS OF TRADITIONAL QUALITY HANDMADE DISPLAY CABINETS

18″ x 24″   15″ x 18″

36″ x 24″

Doll Cabinet 15″ x 22″, Octagonal 20″ x 20″
Base Unit 36″ x 36″ (inc. legs)

If you appreciate fine traditional furniture, hand made from solid hardwood, we feel sure you will be interested in our range of display cabinets.

They are designed as a piece of furniture with fully glazed doors and shelves, brass fittings and hessian lined interiors. However, mirror or baize interiors are also available. Naturally, our base units have toughened safety glass fitted as standard.

All of our cabinets are available in dark oak, medium oak, light oak or a mahogany finish.

Viewing arrangements are as per our brochure, or see us at most large Toyshows.

For full details of the D.M.S. range send a 9ins x 6ins s.a.e. to:-
D.M.S. Offer, Fallowfield House, Westminster Drive, Bury St Edmunds, IP33 2EZ

Collector's Accessories
MAGNIFIERS & LOW VISION AIDS
"Don't miss any of the clues"

IDEAL FOR MODEL MAKERS/RESTORERS,
MODEL IDENTIFICATION
OR AS A READING AID

HAND MAGNIFIERS – BUDGET RANGE
Ref Code
1. Bar Magnifier (just placed over print) 125x25 mm lens £6.95
2. Round Glass lens 3"/76 mm, nickel plated rim, 2 x magnification £6.95
3. Rectangular shape lens 4"x2"/100x50 mm with plastic handle £7.95

HAND MAGNIFIERS – DELUXE RANGE
with 75mm lenses, 2.5 x magnification
4. Quality magnifier with gilt rim and leather handle £35.95
5. Quality magnifier with gilt rim and polished wood handle £29.95
6. Chrome plated rim with polished wood handle £26.95

LOW VISION AIDS
7. Peak light Loupe, 15 x magnification. Batteries not included £39.95
8. Torch mangifier 5 x magnification. Batteries not included £26.95
9. Flatfield magnifier, solid glass, 5 x magnification £59.95

FLEXIBLE ARM MAGNIFIERS
10. Swan neck magnifier 2.5"/63mm lens, 2.5 x magnification £26.95
11. Best quality magnifier with glass lens, 3"/75mm lens, 2.5 x magnification
.... £62.95

POCKET MAGNIFIERS
12. Chrome folding magnifier with 23 mm lens, 10 x magnification £26.95
13. Chrome folding mangifier with 16 mm lens, 20 x magnification £29.95

COMBINATION MAGNIFIER
14. Combined chest/hand/stand magnifier, 102 mm lens, 2 x magnification £13.95

WATCHMAKERS EYE GLASS
15. Double lens type, focal length 35 mm/20 mm, magnification 5x/10x £8.95

PRICES INCLUDE POSTAGE AND PACKING FOR UK — OTHER COUNTRIES AT COST.

PLEASE ALLOW 28 DAYS FOR DELIVERY

Payment by cheque (payable on British Bank), Postal Order or International Money Order made payable to: Swapmeet Publications. Credit Cards accepted Visa, Access, Eurocard, Mastercard.

Send to: Swapmeet Publications, Department SCA, Fallowfield House, Westminster Drive, Bury St Edmunds, Suffolk, IP33 2EZ

WHEN REPLYING TO ADVERTISEMENTS PLEASE MENTION JOHN RAMSAY'S CATALOGUE

SHACKLETON MODELS

The company was formed by Maurice Shackleton and traded as James Shackleton & Sons Ltd. from 1939 to 1952. They had premises in Cheshire and originally produced wooden toys such as lorries and dolls houses. The toy lorries were only made pre-war and had four wheels, a simple wooden chassis and body with a green name badge on the rear of the cab, and were fitted with a highly detailed aluminium radiator grille. Known models are a Chain Lorry, Breakdown Lorry and a Sided Wagon. Their price today is around £100 each.

In 1948 having expanded its staff to nearly 40 people, the company started to produce diecast constructional models based on the Foden FG six-wheel platform lorry. The models consisted of separate parts all of which were, incredibly, made 'in house', including the clockwork motor, its key, and the wheels and tyres. The model was advertised in the 'Meccano Magazine' with the slogan 'You can dismantle it - Just like the real thing', and it was originally priced at £2/19/6. Eventually the range was extended to include a Dyson Drawbar Trailer and a Foden Tipper. Each model was packed in its own distinctive box which displayed a black and white picture of the model inside.

In 1952, whilst in the midst of producing the David Brown Trackmaster 30″ Tractor, a shortage of materials coupled with difficult trading conditions brought about the end of the company. The unique models produced by the Shackleton company are now highly collectable and difficult to find.

Ref. No.	Year(s)	Model Type	Model Features and Size	Market Price Range	
i)	1948-52	Foden FG 6-wheel Platform Lorry	Yellow, Blue, Grey or Green body with Red wings, Grey chassis and Red or Grey fuel tanks, 12½ inches (305 mm.) long, initially in Blue/Yellow box, later in mottled Green box, (20,000 made)	£200-300	☐
			Same colours as above but with Grey or Black wings and Red chassis	£300-400	☐
			Same casting but with Red, Orange or Brown cab	£300-400	☐

Note. Box difficult to find: Blue box with paper label having picture of chassis.

ii)	1949-52	Dyson 8-ton Drawbar Trailer	Yellow, Blue, Grey or Green body, packed in Red and Yellow box, (15,000)	£50-100	☐
iii)	1950-52	Foden FG 6-wheel Tipper Lorry	Yellow, Blue, Grey or Green body with Red wings, Grey chassis and Red or Grey fuel tanks, Silver wheels, (5,000)	£250-350	☐
			As previous models but with Grey wings and Red chassis	£250-350	☐
			As previous models but with Blue wings, Grey chassis, Grey wheels	£250-350	☐
			Orange or Red body	£275-375	☐
iv)	1952	David Brown Trackmaster 30″ Tractor	No details available of body colours but the model had Black rubber tracks, exhaust pipe and headlights. It is thought that only 50 models were sold.	£750-950	☐

Note: It is known that some prototype models were made of Ploughs and Harrows, though it is not known if any were produced for sale.

v)	1958-60	Foden S.21 8-wheel Platform Lorry	Dark Blue, Dark Green or Light Turquoise fibreglass cab with Red metal chassis and wheels, wooden flatbed, length overall 18½ inches (470 mm.), plastic injection moulded springs and axle parts, powered by 'Minimax' electric motor. (250 made as a promotional for Foden)	£750-950	☐

The information in this listing has been taken from an original article written by John Ormandy in the 'Modellers World' magazine, Volumes 12 and 13, and is used by kind permission of the Editors, Mike and Sue Richardson. Robert Taylor provided additional information.

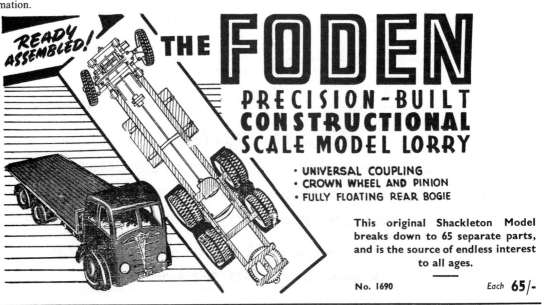

READY ASSEMBLED!

THE **FODEN**

PRECISION-BUILT CONSTRUCTIONAL SCALE MODEL LORRY

- UNIVERSAL COUPLING
- CROWN WHEEL AND PINION
- FULLY FLOATING REAR BOGIE

This original Shackleton Model breaks down to 65 separate parts, and is the source of endless interest to all ages.

No. 1690   Each **65/-**

Rear cover of original leaflet.

Front cover of original leaflet.

Taylor and Barrett Lead Vehicles and the Postwar Re-issues

by Mike Richardson

The firm of Taylor and Barrett dates from the early 1920s when they started producing mainly figures but with a few odd carts. The vehicles themselves were only introduced in about 1935. These were rather crude by comparison with the Dinky Toys of the day as the lead gravity casting process was incapable of working to the fine limits possible with pressure diecasting as used by Meccano Ltd. The majority of the vehicles use a basic chassis incorporating the bonnet and wings. Different bodies are attached to this base unit by tabs and a radiator is plugged into the front. Some versions have the grille cast integrally with the bonnet, and most of these use plain metal wheels instead of having rubber tyres. These vehicles have a tremendous amount of charm as toys while they are only a generic representation of the types of vans and small trucks of the time. A wide variety of types were made including petrol tankers, a pick-up truck and a couple of mail vans. The breakdown truck is particularly attractive with a working crane on the rear. These toys were made until the production was halted in 1940 when the factory was bombed out of existence. All salvageable tools, moulds and stock was moved to a new location in North Finchley but production stopped very soon after because of the munitions requirements of the war effort.

During the war the tools were split between the Taylors and the Barretts for safe keeping but they did not join up again afterwards and two separate companies, F.G.Taylor & Sons and A.Barrett & Sons, started up in 1945. The main part of the range, the small commercial vehicles and the cars, does not seem to have survived the War, only the trolley buses, which became Barretts, and the Leyland coach which appeared in one-piece casting form as a Taylor. It is interesting to note that the trolleybus carries a route board '621 Finchley' which probably means that they went past the factory.

A range of very nice fire engines came along in the late 1930s with a super turntable ladder appliance as the top of the range. These were longer than the main range and had many parts. To mark the advent of the Home Office Fire Precautions scheme (where fire appliances were made available to local areas by central government), Taylor and Barrett painted their range in grey as well as the more traditional red. These grey models are highly sought after now. Personnel were also available to go with these fire engines. A Decontamination Squad being a particular favourite with their gas masks and chemical-proof overalls. There is also a fire engine in the short chassis range but it is not very impressive.

The trolley buses came in two sizes. The large one has a separate driver figure (and conductor as well in the T & B version but not the later Barrett), and the body is in two pieces, upper and lower decks. The small one is in one piece and has no driver. Needless to say there is a vast difference in the values of the two sizes.

There are generic cars, roadster, coup, saloon, on the short base but there is also quite a good model of the 1935 Singer Airstream saloon. This is also the poor man's Chrysler Airflow but never really caught on, the styling made the car look too tall to be appealing. A rather crude one-piece Austin Seven racer was the final car but this was to a larger scale.

Dinky Toys were not the only factory to make a model of the Air Mail Service Car based on the Morris Commercial chassis. T & B also made one and a nice chunky toy it is too. A couple of aeroplanes, a De Havilland Comet and an air liner, completed the range of powered vehicles. A modified version of the Comet seems to have been made by Barrett later but it differs a lot from the T & B, which is a much better model.

Some of the moulds were still around a few years ago and some attempts were made to make models again. These were fairly unsuccessful as casting techniques had changed and the new metals did not have the same flow characteristics as the early lead. Some models are definitely known to have been re-made as they have been seen at a swapmeet some time back, so collectors are advised to be wary.

Editor's note: All the models are rare - any auction prices that become available will be published in the next 'Model Price Review'.

The following listing is of models issued by Taylor and Barrett between 1920 and 1939. Post war production was split between F. G. Taylor & Sons and A. Barrett & Sons, each firm inheriting some moulds and continuing to make some but not all of the models until about 1952.
(FGT) = produced by F. G. Taylor after 1945, (AB) = produced by A. Barrett after 1945

14	Trotting Pony Racer (FGT)	NGPP
15	Turntable Fire Escape (AB)	NGPP
16	Fire Engine and Escape (FGT)	NGPP
17	Fire Engine and Men (FGT)	NGPP
20	Horse Drawn Water Cart (FGT)	NGPP
21	Horse Drawn Brewer's Cart (FGT)	NGPP
22	Horse Drawn Window Cleaner's Cart (FGT)	NGPP
23	Horse Drawn Baker's Cart (FGT)	NGPP
26	Roman Chariot (FGT)	NGPP
27	Donkey Drawn Coster Cart with Dog and Boy (FGT)	NGPP
28	Donkey Drawn Coster Cart, Plants load, Walking Coster (FGT)	NGPP
28a	Donkey Drawn Coster Cart, Vegetable load, Walking Coster (FGT)	NGPP
29	Ice Cream Bicycle, 'ICE BRICKS' logo (FGT)	NGPP
36	Milk Float and Milkman (AB)	NGPP
42	Fire Escape and Team of Firemen (FGT)	NGPP
43	Air and Land Postal Service Set (-)	NGPP
49	Street Cleaning Barrow with two Bins (FGT)	NGPP
92	Llama Cart (FGT)	NGPP
92a	Donkey Cart (FGT)	NGPP
109	Pony Drawn Governor's Cart (AB)	NGPP
109a	Pony Drawn Cart (AB)	NGPP
111	Saloon Car (-)	NGPP
112	Transport Lorry (-)	NGPP
113	'ROYAL MAIL' Van (-)	NGPP
114	'AMBULANCE', Grey (Wartime civilian) (-)	NGPP
114a	'AMBULANCE', Khaki (Army] (-)	NGPP
115	Sports Car (-)	NGPP
116	Coupé (-)	NGPP
117	'AMBULANCE', (Street, civilian) (-)	NGPP
119	Racer (AB)	NGPP
120	Fire Engine (AB)	NGPP
123	Atlanta Touring Plane (AB)	NGPP
124	'AIR MAIL' Van (AB)	NGPP
128	Petrol Tanker (-)	NGPP
129	Breakdown Lorry (-)	NGPP
137	DH 'Comet' Aeroplane (AB)	NGPP
138	'AIR MAIL' Streamline Van (-)	NGPP
139	Saloon Car (-)	NGPP
152	Streamline Motor Coach (-)	NGPP
163	Streamline Fire Engine (-)	NGPP
197	Trolley Bus (small) (AB) (see picture in colour section)	NGPP
204	Trolley Bus (large) (AB)	NGPP
302	Horse Drawn Covered Wagon (-)	NGPP
304	Sledge and Dogs (FGT)	NGPP
306	Aeroplane Set (Comet and Atlanta aircraft and pilots) (FGT)	NGPP
307	Fire Brigade Set (-)	NGPP
310	Rickshaw pulled by Chinese Coolie (FGT)	NGPP
311	Light Trailer Fire Pump in Action Set (-) (see black/white picture)	NGPP
?	Space Ship (-)	NGPP
?	Coronation Coach (small] (AB)	NGPP
?	State Landau Coach (-)	NGPP
?	Farmer's Gig (FGT)	NGPP
?	Farm Cart with Trotting Horse (-)	NGPP
?	Mobile Animal Trailer and Vet (-)	NGPP

The listing has been compiled from original manufacturer's records by Mr Norman Joplin to whom the Editor would like to express his grateful thanks.
For pictures, see the Lacy Scott auction advertisement.

Taylor & Barrett – continued

Models sold by Phillips, West Two, Salem Road London for £400.
Picture reproduced by their kind permission.

Early Cars — picture kindly supplied by Mike & Sue Richardson.

TIMPO TOYS

Timpo Toys were manufactured by TOY IMPORTERS LTD, Devonshire Works, Dukes Avenue, London W4. The firm was founded in 1938 by Mr Gawry Lowicz and also used the trade names 'TIMPOLIN' and 'GOODY TOYS'.

The Timpo Toys slogan was 'ASK FOR THE BEST - LOOK FOR THE NAME, IT'S TIMPO'.

Ref. No.	Year(s)	Model Type	Model Features and Size	Market Price Range	

1/42 scale models

1	c1948	Jowett Javelin Roadster	Various colours	NGPP	☐
2	c1948	Lea-Francis Airflow Saloon	Various colours	NGPP	☐
3	c1948	Jaguar 2.4 litre Saloon	Various colours	NGPP	☐
4	c1948	Morris Ten Saloon	Various colours	NGPP	☐
5	c1948	Dennis Fire Engine...................	Red body...........	NGPP	☐
6	c1948	Armstrong-Siddeley Sapphire....	Various colours	NGPP	☐

The models listed above are rarely seen in collectable condition so no guide prices are available at present (NGPP).

Model Farm Series (hollow cast, unboxed)

-	-	Two-wheel Farm Cart	with Horse, various colours	NGPP	☐
-	-	Two-wheel Water Cart	with Horse, various colours	NGPP	☐
-	-	Four-wheel Log Wagon	with Horse, various colours	NGPP	☐
-	-	Farm Roller............................	with Horse and Farmer, various colours...........	NGPP	☐
-	-	Farm Harrow	with Horse and Farmer, various colours...........	NGPP	☐

Aeroplane and Ship Sets (hollow cast)

-	1948-50	Bomber Station Set	Contains three camouflaged Bombers with US markings plus four pilots..................	£50-75	☐
-	1948-50	Battle Fleet Set	Four unpainted Warships. 2 x Battleship, 1 x Destroyer, 1 x Submarine, 'TIMPO TOYS' logo cast-in..................	£30-40	☐

Miscellaneous Timpo models

-	c1948	Articulated Furniture Van 'PICKFORDS'..............	Black cab with White 'PICKFORDS' above windscreen, Black semi-trailer van with Grey roof and White 'PICKFORDS REMOVERS and STORERS EVERYWHERE', Red hubs, rubber tyres	£40-50	☐

Note: Prices in the Market Price Range column refer to mint items (that is, in original condition). It should be noted however that in the early post-war years some diecast products (including Timpo Toys) were aimed specifically at the cheap end of the toy market and were painted with very little surface preparation (etching, priming, undercoating, etc).
Consequently the paint tends to flake off the model even if it is not played with, and it is now difficult to find Timpo Toys in really fine condition.

Typical battered survivor from the 1950's.

TRI-ANG
MINIC SHIPS
Accurately detailed waterline models

The original catalogue listings as compiled by Ian Clarke have been carefully revised by Brian Smart, Simon Kesley and Bob Faye of Sevenoaks Models. The Editor would like to express his appreciation for all the assistance given.

Brief history

The models were in the shops between 1958 and 1964, a comparatively short life, but production figures must have been high and this factor coupled with 'low play value' (they could not be raced like Dinky Toys), has meant that a reasonable number have survived for collecting purposes.

Six sales catalogues were published which nowadays are quite hard to find. No single catalogue shows the full range as additions, deletions and alterations were a regular occurrence.

Minic ships were re-introduced in 1976 and they are listed here after the first issues.

General notes on specific models

M702, M703: Queens came with and without funnel detail
M708, M709: Towards the end of their run Saxonia and Ivernia were renamed Franconia and Carmania (following Cunards refurbishment of the actual ships). They kept their original catalogue number but their sterns were slightly recast at that time to remove cargo handling gear and add swimming pools. They

were painted green with green masts. Only 480 of each were made and are very hard to find.

M716, M717: Port Auckland/Port Brisbane - short run resulting in scarce models.
M718, M719, M720: Amazon, Arlanza, Aragon - scarce.
M726 Pilot, M727 Lifeboat - very hard to find.
M740 Barge, (designed to match up with M731 tugboat), appears in catalogue but was not issued.
M754 Commando ship. Same casting as other carriers, it was grey and had a helicopter landing deck (a sticker applied the full length of the ship). Not generally known and not appearing in any catalogues; very rare.
M783 Hampshire, **M784** Kent, **M785** Devonshire, **M786** London. Missile Destroyers in grey. Short run; hard to find.
M853 Factory, **M854** Tanker, **M880** Whales (white & grey); all hard to find.

Also produced but not appearing in any catalogue is the Helicopter. It is possible this was designed to go with the limited issue Commando ship. It is a very small and basic item manufactured to a very high technological standard by taking an M880 Whale and nailing a 4-blade rotor to its head (same rotor used on missile destroyers)!

Ocean Liners   1:1200 scale (1 in to 100 ft)

Ref. No.	Model Type	Model Features and Size	Market Price Range	
M701	R.M.S. 'Caronia'	Green body, one plain Red/Black funnel, one mast, 178 mm. 'Painted in the correct Cunard green she is a most striking vessel'	£35-45	☐
M702	R.M.S. 'Queen Elizabeth'	Black/White, 2 plain Red/Black or detailed funnels, 2 masts, 262 mm. 'The worlds largest ship and the pride of the Cunard fleet'	£55-65	☐
M703	R.M.S. 'Queen Mary'	Black/White, plain Red/Black or detailed funnels, 2 masts, 259 mm. 'Her three funnels make her the most easily recognisable'	£40-45	☐
M704	S.S. 'United States'	Black/White body, two Red/White/Blue funnels, 252 mm. 'The present holder of the Blue Riband of the Atlantic'	£35-45	☐
M705	R.M.S. 'Aquitania'	Black/White body, four Red/Black funnels, two masts, 231 mm.	£80-100	☐
M706	S.S. 'Nieuw Amsterdam'	Grey/White body, two Yellow funnels, two masts, 231 mm.	£45-55	☐
M707	S.S. 'France'	Black/White, 2 Red/Black funnels, 5 masts, 262 mm. 'The longest ship in the world 1035ft being 4ft longer than Queen Elizabeth'	£80-100	☐
M708	R.M.S. 'Saxonia'	Black/White body, one Red/Black or detailed funnel, nine masts	£35-40	☐
M708/2	R.M.S. 'Franconia'	Green body, one Red/Black funnel, nine masts, 155 mm.	£500-550	☐
M709	R.M.S. 'Ivernia'	Black/White body.	£35-40	☐
M709/2	R.M.S. 'Carmania'	Green body, one Red/Black funnel, nine masts, 155 mm.	£500-550	☐
M710	R.M.S. 'Sylvania'	Black/White, one Red/Black funnel, nine masts, 155 mm.	£30-40	☐
M711	R.M.S. 'Carinthie'	Black/White, one Red/Black funnel, nine masts, 155 mm.	£35-40	☐
M712	N.S. 'Savannah'	White, no funnels (nuclear powered), four masts, 149 mm.	£45-50	☐
M713	S.S. 'Antilles'	Black/White, one Red/Black funnel, ten masts, 152 mm.	£45-60	☐
		All White body, one Red/Black funnel, ten masts	£65-70	☐
M714	'Flandre'	Black/White, one Red/Black funnel, ten masts, 152 mm.	£35-45	☐
		All White body, one Red/Black funnel, ten masts	£45-55	☐
M715	R.M.S. 'Canberra'	White body, one Yellow funnel, three masts, 189 mm.	£55-65	☐
M716	M.S. 'Port Brisbane'	Grey/White, one Red/Black funnel, eight masts, 140 mm.	£90-110	☐
M717	S.S. 'Port Auckland'	Grey/White, one Red/Black funnel, seven masts, 140 mm.	£90-120	☐
M718	R.M.S. 'Amazon'	White, Yellow funnel, 19 masts, 10 lifeboats, 149 mm.	£115-130	☐
M719	R.M.S. 'Arlanza'	White, Yellow funnel, 19 masts, 149 mm.	£130-150	☐
M720	R.M.S. 'Aragon'	White, Yellow funnel, 19 masts, 149 mm.	£115-130	☐
M721	R.M.S. 'Britannia' Royal Yacht	Blue/White body, Yellow/Black funnel, 3 masts, 105 mm.	£15-18	☐
M721/H	R.M.S. 'Britannia' Hospital Ship	White body, three masts, 105 mm.	£15-18	☐
CHANNEL ISLANDS STEAMERS				
M722	'Isle of Jersey'	Black/White body, 2 Yellow/Black funnels, 2 masts, 78 mm.	£18-24	☐
M723	'Isle of Guernsey'	Black/White body, 2 Yellow/Black funnels, 2 masts, 78 mm.	£18-24	☐
M724	'Isle of Sark'	Black/White body, 2 Yellow/Black funnels, 2 masts, 78 mm.	£18-24	☐
M726	Pilot Boat	Black/White/Yellow body, 'PILOTS', 45 mm.	£65-75	☐
M727	Lifeboat	Blue body.	£15-20	☐
PADDLE STEAMERS				
All the Paddle Steamers are 78 mm. in length.				
M728	'Britannia'	Black/White, 2 funnels (Black/Blue, Red/Black or Yellow/Black), 2 masts	£20-25	☐
M729	'Bristol Queen'	Black/White, 2 funnels (Black/Blue, Red/Black or Yellow/Black), 2 masts	£20-25	☐
M730	'Cardiff Queen'	Black/White, 2 funnels (Black/Blue, Red/Black or Yellow/Black), 2 masts	£20-25	☐

Ref. No.	Model Type	Tri-ang Minic Ships – continued	Market Price Range	
TUGBOATS				
M731	Tugboat	Black/Grey/Red body, Red/Black funnel, 38 mm.	**£5-7**	☐
M731	Tugboat	Black/Grey/Red body, Yellow/Black funnel, 38 mm.	**£5-7**	☐
M731	Tugboat	Black/Blue/Red body, Yellow/Black funnel, 38 mm.	**£5-7**	☐
M731	Tugboat	Black/Grey/Yellow body, Yellow/Black funnel, 38 mm.	**£5-7**	☐
M810	Navy Tug H.M.S. 'Turmoil'	Black/Blue or Grey body, Black funnel, 50 mm.	**£5-8**	☐
OIL TANKER				
M732	S.S. 'Varicella'...........................	Black/White body, Black/Yellow funnel ('SHELL' logo), 2 masts, 169 mm.	**£20-30**	☐
WHALE FACTORY SHIPS				
M733	T.S.S. 'Vikingen'	Grey body, six masts, 125 mm..	**£25-30**	☐
M734	Whale Chaser	Grey body, Yellow/Black funnel, 39 mm.	**£12-15**	☐
LIGHTSHIPS				
M735	'SUNK'...........................	Red body, White logo/name, 33 mm..	**£7-10**	☐
M736	'SHAMBLES'........................	Red body, White logo/name, 33 mm..	**£7-10**	☐
M737	'CORK'	Red body, White logo/name, 33 mm..	**£7-10**	☐
M738	'VARNE'	Red body, White logo/name, 33 mm..	**£7-10**	☐
M739	'St.GOWAN'	Red body, White logo/name, no number on base, 33 mm..	**£7-10**	☐

Warships   1:1200 scale (1 in to 100 ft)

Ref. No.	Model Type	Model Features and Size	Market Price Range	
BATTLESHIPS				
M741	H.M.S. 'Vanguard'	Grey or Blue body with two masts, 206 mm.	**£30-35**	☐
AIRCRAFT CARRIERS				
M751	H.M.S. 'Bulwark'	Grey or Blue body with one mast, 186 mm.	**£20-25**	☐
M752	H.M.S. 'Centaur'	Grey or Blue body with one mast	**£20-25**	☐
M753	H.M.S. 'Albion'.........................	Grey or Blue body with one mast	**£20-25**	☐
COMMANDO SHIP				
M754	H.M.S. 'Albion'	Grey ship with 12 Cream or Brown plastic helicopters. 1000 models issued and given to H.M.S. 'Albion' crew members (Capt. Adams in command)..................	**£400-500**	☐
CRUISERS				
M761	H.M.S. 'Swiftsure'	Blue or Grey body with one crane jib, 145 mm.	**£15-18**	☐
M762	H.M.S. 'Superb'........................	Blue or Grey body with one crane jib, 145 mm.	**£15-18**	☐
DESTROYERS, FLEET ESCORT, 'DARING' CLASS				
M771	H.M.S. 'Daring'	Blue or Grey body with one mast, 98 mm.	**£5-8**	☐
M772	H.M.S. 'Diana'........................	Blue or Grey body with one mast, 98 mm.	**£5-8**	☐
M773	H.M.S. 'Dainty'.......................	Blue or Grey body with one mast, 98 mm.	**£5-8**	☐
M774	H.M.S. 'Decoy'.......................	Blue or Grey body with one mast, 98 mm.	**£5-8**	☐
DESTROYERS, FLEET, 'BATTLE' CLASS				
M779	H.M.S. 'Alamein'	Blue or Grey body with one mast, 97 mm.	**£5-8**	☐
M780	H.M.S. 'Jutland'	Blue or Grey body with one mast, 97 mm.	**£5-8**	☐
M781	H.M.S. 'Anzac'	Blue or Grey body with one mast, 97 mm.	**£5-8**	☐
M782	H.M.S. 'Tobruk'.......................	Blue or Grey body with one mast, 97 mm.	**£5-8**	☐
DESTROYERS, GUIDED MISSILE, 'COUNTY' CLASS				
M783	H.M.S. 'Hampshire'	Grey body with two masts, 136 mm.	**£20-25**	☐
M784	H.M.S. 'Kent'	Grey body with two masts, 136 mm.	**£30-35**	☐
M785	H.M.S. 'Devonshire'..................	Grey body with two masts, 136 mm.	**£20-25**	☐
M786	H.M.S. 'London'	Grey body with two masts, 136 mm.	**£20-25**	☐
FRIGATES, FAST ANTI-SUBMARINE, 'V' CLASS				
M787	H.M.S. 'Vigilant'	Blue or Grey body with one mast, 92 mm.	**£5-8**	☐
M788	H.M.S. 'Venus'	Blue or Grey body with one mast, 92 mm.	**£5-8**	☐
M789	H.M.S. 'Virago'	Blue or Grey body with one mast, 92 mm.	**£5-8**	☐
M790	H.M.S. 'Volage'	Blue or Grey body with one mast, 92 mm.	**£5-8**	☐
FRIGATES, ANTI-SUBMARINE, 'WHITBY' CLASS				
M791	H.M.S. 'Whitby'	Blue or Grey body, 94 mm.	**£5-7**	☐
M792	H.M.S. 'Torquay'	Blue or Grey body, 94 mm.	**£5-7**	☐
M793	H.M.S. 'Blackpool'	Blue or Grey body, 94 mm.	**£5-7**	☐
M794	H.M.S. 'Tenby'.........................	Blue or Grey body, 94 mm.	**£5-7**	☐
MINESWEEPERS, 'TON' CLASS				
M799	H.M.S. 'Repton'	Blue or Grey body	**£5-7**	☐
M800	H.M.S. 'Dufton'	Blue or Grey body	**£5-7**	☐
M801	H.M.S. 'Ashton'	Blue or Grey body	**£5-7**	☐
M802	H.M.S. 'Calton'	Blue or Grey body	**£5-7**	☐
M803	H.M.S. 'Picton'	Blue or Grey body	**£5-7**	☐
M804	H.M.S. 'Sefton'........................	Blue or Grey body	**£5-7**	☐
M805	H.M.S. 'Upton'	Blue or Grey body	**£5-7**	☐
M806	H.M.S. 'Weston'	Blue or Grey body	**£5-7**	☐
SUBMARINES, 'A' CLASS				
M817	Sub 'A' Class	Blue or Grey body, 61 mm.	**£5-7**	☐
M818	Sub Recon	Blue or Grey body, 61 mm.	**£7-10**	☐

DOCKSIDE ACCESSORIES and MISCELLANEOUS

Ref. No.	Model Type	Description	Market Price Range	
M827	Breakwater Straights	Grey	£3-4	☐
M828/L	Breakwater Angle, Left	Grey	50p	☐
M828/R	Breakwater Angle, Right	Grey	50p	☐
M829	Breakwater End	Grey	50p	☐
M836	Quay Straights	Tan	£3-4	☐
M837	Crane Units	Tan, Brown or Green cargo	£3-4	☐
M838	Storage Tanks	Grey/Silver and Red	£2-3	☐
M839	Customs Shed	Green	£3-4	☐
M840	Warehouse	Brown	£3-4	☐
M841	Ocean Terminal	White with Black windows	£5-6	☐
M842	Swing Bridge	Red, no description on base	£2-3	☐
M843	Terminal Extension	White with Black windows	£5-6	☐
M844	Lock Gates (pair)	Brown	£1-2	☐
M846	Lift Bridge	Silver/Tan	£2-3	☐
M847	Pier centre section	White	£2-3	☐
M848	Pier entrance section	White	£2-3	☐
M849	Pier head	White	£12-14	☐
M850	Pier Shelter	Green, 35 mm.	£5-6	☐
M852	Pier archway	Red, 35 mm.	£2-3	☐
M853	Factory Unit	Brown/Tan	£25-30	☐
M854	Tanker Wharf Straight	Tan and Red	£65-75	☐
M854	Tanker Wharf Berth	Red and Green	£2-3	☐
M857	26″ Sea	Blue plastic	£14-18	☐
M857	52″ Sea	Blue plastic	£25-30	☐
M861	Lifeboat set	Grey with Blue shed and one lifeboat	£35-40	☐
M878	Lighthouse	White	£1-2	☐
M880	Whales	White or plain Grey	£12-15	☐
M882	Beacon	White/Red or Green	£1-2	☐
M884	Statue of Liberty	Green/Grey	£15-20	☐
M885	Floating Dock	Grey dock with four Black plastic cranes	£20-25	☐
M -	Helicopter	Cream or Brown plastic body	£20-25	☐

GIFT SETS and SPECIAL PRESENTATION PACKS

Ref. No.	Model Type	Description	Market Price Range	
M891	'Queen Elizabeth'	Gift Set	£75-100	☐
M892	'United States'	Gift Set	£150-175	☐
M893	'Task Force'	Gift Set	£30-40	☐
M894	'Royal Yacht'	Gift Set	£80-100	☐
M895	'Nieuw Amsterdam'	Gift Set	£600-700	☐
M702s	'Queen Elizabeth'	Presentation Set	£80-100	☐
M703s	'Queen Mary'	Presentation Set	£100-120	☐
M704s	'S.S. United States'	Presentation Set	£100-120	☐
M705s	'R.M.S. Aquitania'	Presentation Set	£125-150	☐
M707s	'S.S. France'	Presentation Set	£125-150	☐
M741s	'H.M.S. Vanguard'	Presentation Set	£50-60	☐

Hong Kong 'Blue Box' issues 1976 - 1980

Minic ships were re-introduced in 1976 and manufactured in Hong Kong. The colours are slightly different from the original models. All these 'second issues' were given wheels and have 'HONG KONG' on the base.

SINGLE BOXED MODELS

'Queen Mary', 'Queen Elizabeth', 'United States', 'Canberra', HMS Vanguard', HMS 'Bulwark', 'Missouri', 'Bismark', 'Scharnhorst', 'Yamato'. Each			£15-20	☐
	R.M.S. 'Canberra'		£25-30	☐

SETS OF MODELS

1	Fleet Anchorage Set		£25-30	☐
2	Quay Set		£25-30	☐
3a	Ocean Terminal Set	with box lid showing stern of R.M.S. 'Queen Mary'	£45-50	☐
3b	Ocean Terminal Set	with box lid showing bow of R.M.S. 'Queen Mary'	£35-40	☐
4	Naval Task Force Set	with H.M.S. 'Bulwark and H.M.S. 'Vanguard'	£35-40	☐
5	Naval Task Force Set	with ships 'Bismark' and 'Scharnhorst'	£50-55	☐

Minic Catalogues 1958-64

1	Leaflet	with first Minic Ships listed	£75-100	☐
2	Booklet	with first Minic Ships listed	£25-30	☐
3	Booklet	with Ships and other Tri-ang products	£60-75	☐
4	Booklet	with Minic Ships only	£25-30	☐
5	Booklet	with Minic Ships only	£25-30	☐
6	Booklet	with Tri-ang range	£30-35	☐
M862	Minic illustrated leaflet		£10-15	☐

Acknowledgement   Thanks are due to Richard Lines of Hornby Hobbies and Richard Capon of Colchester for their contribution to the Minic Ships listing.

Minic Ships sold at auction 1992 - 1993

All the items listed below were sold by Vectis Model Auctions and were in mint condition.

M 704 SS 'United States'	£38	
M 707 SS 'France'	£65	
M 708 RMS 'Saxonia'	£40	
M 709 RMS 'Ivernia'	£38	
M 708/2 'Franconia'	£540	
M 710 RMS 'Sylvania'	£30	

M 713 SS 'Antilles'	£48
M 716 MS 'Port Brisbane'	£120
M 718 RMS 'Amazon'	£120
M 720 RMS 'Aragon'	£120
M 732 SS 'Varicella'	£30

TOY and MODEL MUSEUMS

Arundel Toy and Military Museum   High Street, Arundel, Sussex.   Old toys, dolls, games, etc.

Bamford Toy Museum   19 Tyrone Road, Rochdale, Lancs. Tel (0706) 360002.   A superb display of rare toys and items of interest.

Chester Toy Museum   13a Lower Bridge Street Row, Chester CH1 1RJ.   Open most days. Matchbox Toys (particularly 1-75 series and Models of Yesteryear).

Corgi Toy Collection   British Motor Industries Heritage Trust Museum, Gaydon, near Warwick, England.   The Corgi company's permanent collection of Corgi products.

David Cooke Dinky Toys Collection   Beeston Hall, Rackheath, near Norwich, Norfolk.   Superb collection of rare Dinky Toys.

House on Hill Toy Museum   Stanstead, Essex.   One of the largest toy displays in the UK.

Ironbridge Toy Museum   Shropshire   Excellent display of all groups of toys and models.

Lamberhurst Toy and Train Museum   Forstal Farm, Gaudhurst Road, Lamberhurst, Kent.   An excellent day out for the whole family. Mixed collection.

London Toy and Model Museum   21 Craven Hill, London W2 3EN.   Open most days. General collection of toys and models.

Merley House Model Museum   Merley, Wimborne, Dorset.
Open Easter till end of September (telephone 0202 - 886533).   Most model ranges represented, very good display of railway and white-metal models.

Museum of British Road Transport   Hales Sreet, Coventry, CV1 1PN.   Home of the world famous 'TIATSA' collection. Open daily 10:00 - 4:30 (telephone 0203 - 832425).

Sussex Toy and Model Museum   52-55 Trafalgar Street, Brighton, East Sussex, BN1 4EB.   Open most days (telephone 0273 - 749494).   The museum is close to Brighton Station and has a good selection of toys and models.

Tintagel Toy Museum,   Tintagel, Cornwall.   Excellent display of toys and models.

Vintage Toy and Train Museum, 1st Floor, Field's Department Store, Market Place, Sidmouth, Devon, EX10 8LU.   Easter to October. Strong on railway models (particularly Hornby) plus unusual selections of Dinky Toys.

MODEL CLUBS

Maidenhead Static Model Club   21a High Street, West Wickham, Kent, BR4 0LP.   The oldest and widest-based toy and model collectors club. Founded in 1969. WINDSOR SWAPMEET organisers. 12 magazines a year. Monthly meetings, Trips, Quizzes, Discounts, Promotions, Charity fund raising. Telephone (0895) 673386.

The Coventry Diecast Model Club   22 Edingale Road, Walsgrave Park, Coventry, CV2 2RF.   The fastest growing club in the country! Six quality magazines a year, monthly meetings, lectures, outings, discounts, badges, stickers, ties, Club models, etc.

Ulster Model Club   D. R. Nicholl, 74 Old Westland Road, Belfast, BT14 6TE.

Ashford Model Collectors Club   Towers Garage Showroom, Faversham Road, Ashford, Kent. Telephone (0233) 641636.

Havant Model Club   Havant, Hampshire.

East Anglian Diecast Model Club   David Cooke, Norwich (0603) 300800.   Club meetings at 'The Norfolk Dumpling', Hall Road, Norwich, last Tuesday of every month (except December).
new members welcome!

Beccles Model Club   Frank Clarke, 1 St Marys Road, Beccles, Suffolk, NR34 9NQ.   Thriving club with varied and regular programme of events.

TRI-ANG
SPOT-ON
MODELS

INTRODUCTION

Spot-On Models were introduced in 1959 by Tri-ang Toys to gain a foothold in that area of the market dominated at the time by Dinky Toys and their recently established rivals Corgi Toys.

Tri-ang realised that they had to offer not only a range of features similar to those on their competitors products but something more besides. They decided that collectors would appreciate models that were all made to the same precise scale right across the range. They would thus look right together and qualify as models as much as toys. Most Dinky and Corgi cars were made to a scale of 1:43 (with a few exceptions). Tri-ang advertised the precise nature of their (larger) chosen scale as being 'spot-on' at 1:42.

A large modern factory in Belfast, Northern Ireland, produced the models. A coloured picture of the real vehicle was included in the box of most early issues. Well over a hundred different models were designed and production continued till about the time that Tri-ang bought up Dinky Toys in 1967. It has been confirmed for us by Mr Richard Lines (of Tri-ang's parent company Lines Brothers), that the Spot-On company was wound up as a normal business process and not (as was previously thought) as a result of fire damage. After the cessation of UK production, some Spot-On dies went to New Zealand where some interesting versions were produced for a couple of years.

All Spot-On models are highly collectable today particularly commercial vehicles, buses and the Presentation and Gift Sets.

Spot-On model identification

Makers Name and Trade Mark are clearly marked on base of the model ('SPOT-ON' and 'Models by Tri-ang'). Some New Zealand produced versions have nothing at all on the base.

Model name is shown on base, for example: 'Ford Zodiac' (except some New Zealand versions).

Model number is usually shown on box but not always on the model.

Scale of models is 1:42 (with very few exceptions) and is usually (but not always) shown on the base.

Wheel hubs on cars are usually spun or turned aluminium with a raised 'hub cap'.

Wheel hubs on trucks are usually diecast and more accurate representations of the real things. Rear twin wheels have special 'double tyres'.

Number plates are represented on most Spot-On models with the exception of those having plastic chassis (such as 266 Bull Nose Morris and 279 MG Midget).

Windscreens and windows are included in all vehicle models.

Tyres are of black rubber on all the vehicle models.

Other features include seats and steering wheel on most models, suspension on most cars, driver, other figures and lorry loads with some.

Colours are all listed where known though different and previously unknown colours still come to light occasionally.

Prices shown in the 'Market Price Range' column are for mint models in pristine boxes. These models are rare hence their high market prices. The condition of models generally encountered usually tends towards the average and consequently command lower prices. Similarly, rare colours or combinations of colours puts the price into the higher part of the range with common colours achieving a more moderate price level.

Spot-On Cars

Ref. No.	Year(s)	Model Type	Model Features and Size	Market Price Range	
100	1959	Ford Zodiac (without lights).....	Red/Cream or Blue/Cream body, 107 mm.	£60-80	☐
			Red or Cream body	£60-80	☐
			Light Blue, Yellow, Salmon-Pink or Green body	£65-90	☐
			Bluish-Grey and Brownish-Pink body	£75-100	☐
			Grey/Blue body	£65-90	☐
100sl	1959	Ford Zodiac with lights............	Grey/Turquoise or Grey/Pink body, 'TRI 100' or 'LBL 100'	£75-90	☐
			Grey/White, Grey/Light Blue, or Green/White body	£65-85	☐
			Yellow/White, Grey/Green, or Two-tone Blue body	£65-85	☐
101	1959	Armstrong Siddeley 236 Sapphire	Blue/Grey, Turquoise/Black, Blue/Black, Pink or Mauve body, 'TRI 101'. 108 mm. ..	£100-130	☐
			Metallic Green, Metallic Green/Black, or Bluish-Grey	£65-95	☐
			Light Blue body	£95-120	☐
			Light Blue/Black, Grey/Black body	£95-120	☐
			Pale Green/Metallic Charcoal, or Deep Lilac/Black roof	£80-100	☐
			Cream/Metallic Charcoal or Metallic Blue/Black	£65-95	☐
102	1959	Bentley Continental 4-door Sports	Metallic Green/Silver 'SGM 102', or Metallic Grey/Blue. 127 mm.	£100-130	☐
			Metallic Maroon/Silver, 'BML 821'	£175-195	☐
			Two-tone Grey or Silver/Grey body	£95-120	☐
			Silver/Light Blue or Grey/Light Blue body	£120-145	☐
103	1959	Rolls Royce Silver Wraith........	Metallic Silver and Maroon body (White seats), Metallic Silver and Metallic Light Blue (Cream seats), or Metallic Silver and Metallic Green body, 'LTP 103' or 'FTZ 102', 131 mm.	£140-180	☐

Ref. No.	Year(s)	Model Type	Tri-ang Spot-On Cars - continued	Market Price Range	
104	1959	M.G. 'MGA' Sports Car..........	Beige or Blue body, 95 mm...	**£100-140**	☐
			Red body (Grey seats), or Pale Blue (White seats)	**£110-135**	☐
			Turquoise or Cream body (White seats)................................	**£100-130**	☐
			Salmon Pink (Grey seats), or Bluish-Green (Lemon seats)..............	**£140-170**	☐
			Deep Green body (White seats).......................................	**£175-200**	☐
105	1959	Austin Healey 100/6	Yellow (White or Grey seats), Grey (Red seats), Beige (Grey seats), 89 mm.	**£130-160**	☐
			Blue, Green, Cream, Turquoise, Metallic Blue, Metallic Green, or Pink body............	**£125-155**	☐
			Light Blue body (Royal Blue seats)...................................	**£150-180**	☐
107	1960	Jaguar XK-SS...........................	Metallic Blue body, Lemon seats, Black folded hood..................	**£150-195**	☐
			Cream or Red body, ('FTZ 107'), or Light Green body, ('WTB 647')	**£100-140**	☐
			Dark Olive (Light Grey seats/hood), or Pale Blue (Pale Grey seats/hood)........	**£150-175**	☐
			Lilac body with Grey seats, Black folded hood.......................	**£175-225**	☐
			Light Blue with Dark Blue seats and folded hood....................	**£135-195**	☐
			Light Grey body, Pale Blue seats and folded hood...................	**£195-235**	☐
108	1960	Triumph TR3a Sports	Light Blue or Red body, Grey seats, 'WTB 647'. 88 mm.	**£100-140**	☐
			Cream body with Dark Brown seats..................................	**£175-200**	☐
			Light Brown body (White seats), or Pale Green body (Grey seats)	**£140-160**	☐
			Sea Green body with Grey seats.....................................	**£120-150**	☐
			Grey body (White seats), or Metallic Green (Lemon seats).............	**£125-160**	☐
112	1960	Jensen 541..................................	Grey, Mauve, Pink, Red/Black or Metallic Green body, 106 mm.	**£75-95**	☐
			Light Blue or Pale Greenbody.......................................	**£85-125**	☐
			Lemon body (Black roof), or Yellow body (Red seats).................	**£85-125**	☐
113	1960	Aston Martin DB3 Saloon.......	Light Blue, Grey, Red, Light or Dark Green body, 104 mm.	**£125-150**	☐
			Very Pale Pink or Deep Pink body	**£100-130**	☐
			Deep Lilac or Light Brown body	**£140-160**	☐
			White or Metallic Dark Green body	**£130-160**	☐
			Metallic Silver Blue body...	**£130-160**	☐
114	1960	Jaguar 3.4 Mark 1 Saloon........	Metallic Blue, Maroon, Mauve, Metallic Green, or Pink, 108 mm.	**£125-150**	☐
			Light Grey or Mid-Green body......................................	**£140-175**	☐
			Light Blue, Yellow or Red body	**£110-140**	☐
			White body	**£160-180**	☐
115	1960	Bristol 406 Saloon	Orange, Red, or Grey body, 116 mm.	**£100-130**	☐
			Metallic Dark Steel body...	**£160-180**	☐
			Yellow or Metallic Greenbody.......................................	**£100-160**	☐
118	1960	BMW Isetta Bubble Car	Pale Blue, Beige or Turquoise, 'BML 112' or 'CMO 118'. 56 mm.	**£65-75**	☐
			Green or Metallic Green, Red, Pink or Yellow body...................	**£75-95**	☐
119	1960	Meadows Frisky Sport	Orange/Grey, Blue/Grey or Turquoise/Grey, 'MIP 119' or 'OVM 163'	**£45-65**	☐
			Red/Light Grey, Red/Black, or Light Blue/White, 69 mm.	**£75-95**	☐
			Bluish-Green/Black or Red/White body................................	**£80-100**	☐
120	1960	Fiat Multipla Estate	Blue (Cream seats), or Mauve body, 'TXY 120', 85 mm.	**£70-80**	☐
			Pink, Light Blue, Yellow, Red or Dark Red body.....................	**£85-105**	☐
			Sea Green or Pale Green body.......................................	**£95-115**	☐
131	1960	Goggomobil 'Super' Regent......	Grey/Black, Yellow/Black, Mauve/Black, Blue/Grey, Blue, Green, Grey, Red or Turquoise, 'SGM 102' or 'VYD 121'.	**£60-70**	☐
			Metallic Green, Beige, Light Grey, Pink or Deep Salmon Pink body...........	**£55-65**	☐
			Light Blue/Black, Red/Black, Dark Blue/Black, Green/Black, 70 mm.	**£55-65**	☐
154	1961	Austin A40 Farina Saloon	Green, Grey, White, Blue/White or Grey/Blue, 'SGM 102'...............	**£50-60**	☐
			Light Grey, Metallic Blue, Beige, Light Blue or Turquoise body........	**£55-75**	☐
			Red/Black, Blue/Black, Green/Black, Lavender/Black, 88 mm.	**£60-80**	☐
157	1963	Rover 3-litre (without lights).....	Mid Blue, Mauve or Yellow, 'BTW 115' or 'TRL 157'..................	**£70-90**	☐
			Grey, Pale Grey, Sea Green, Dark Green, Light Blue, 107 mm.	**£85-115**	☐
			Dark Blue or Dark Grey body.......................................	**£120-150**	☐
			White body	**£95-125**	☐
157sl	1963	Rover 3-litre with lights	Mid Blue, Mauve, Red or Yellow	**£90-120**	☐
			Grey, Pale Grey, Sea Green, Dark Green, Light Blue, 107 mm.	**£85-115**	☐
			Dark Blue or Dark Grey body.......................................	**£120-150**	☐
			White body	**£95-125**	☐
165/1	1961	Vauxhall PA Cresta Saloon	Beige, Red, Maroon, Pink, Turquoise or Yellow, 'WXD 219', 115 mm.	**£80-100**	☐
			Blue, Light Blue, Grey or Light Grey	**£90-120**	☐
			Plum Red or Sea Green body..	**£100-120**	☐
165/2	1961	PA Cresta with roof rack	Beige, Red, Maroon, Pink, Turquoise or Yellow, 'JPO 113', 115 mm.	**£80-100**	☐
			Blue, Light Blue, Grey or Light Grey	**£90-120**	☐
			Plum Red or Sea green body..	**£110-140**	☐
166	1962	Renault Floride Convertible......	Blue, Green or Grey body, 'SLT 105', 101 mm.	**£70-90**	☐
			Dark Red, White or Yellow body....................................	**£80-100**	☐
183	1963	Humber Super Snipe Estate	Beige/White, Blue/White, Green/White, Blue/Black, Beige, Blue, Metallic Bronze or TT-Blue, with or without wing mirrors..	**£90-120**	☐
184	1963	Austin A60 (with skis)..............	Beige, Green or White body, 'LBL 100', 106 mm.	**£65-85**	☐
			Red, Light Blue or Light Grey (Grey rack)	**£75-100**	☐
			Lime Green or Greyish-Blue (Black or Grey roof-rack).................	**£85-120**	☐
185	1963	Fiat 500....................................	Light Blue, Green, Red or Grey body, 'TXY 120'	**£80-100**	☐
191/1	1963	Sunbeam Alpine Convertible.....	Beige, Mid-Blue, Green, Red, Mauve, Pink or Yellow, 'SLT 105', 95 mm.	**£65-85**	☐
			Turquoise or Grey (Cream seats), or Light Blue (White seats)	**£90-110**	☐
			Deep Salmon Pink or White with Red seats	**£100-130**	☐

Ref. No.	Year(s)	Model Type	Tri-ang Spot-On Cars – continued	Market Price Range	
191/2	1963	Sunbeam Alpine Hardtop	Red/White, Turquoise/White, Blue/Black, Blue/Cream, Beige/White, Grey/Black body and hardtop, 'BML 112', 95 mm..............	£65-85	☐
			Dark Green (Red seats), or Metallic Green	£95-130	☐
			Pink (Cream seats)	£85-120	☐
			Mauve (Cream seats), or Yellow body (Cream seats)..........................	£120-140	☐
			Light Blue, Light Blue/White, Pale Blue/White	£80-110	☐
193	1963	N.S.U. Prinz	Turquoise, Beige, Pale Blue, Light or Dark Blue, Cream, Grey or Red body, 'PJL 114', 84 mm.	£50-70	☐
			White body..................	£80-90	☐
195	1963	Volkswagen Rally Car..............	Beige, Cream, Maroon, or Orange body, roof light, flags on bonnet, racing number '9' or '23', 110 mm.	£140-170	☐
			Red body, racing number '11'	£240-280	☐
			Light Blue ('6'), Turquoise ('9'), or Metallic Bronze.................	£175-220	☐
210	1960	Morris Mini Minor..................	Shown catalogue but not issued	NPP	☐
211	1963	Austin Seven (Mini)	Light Blue, Grey, Red or Yellow body, 'LRT 145', 73 mm.	£120-150	☐
			Pink body	£200-250	☐
			White body	£160-180	☐
213	1963	Ford Anglia Saloon..................	Cream, Grey or White body 'MLP 119', 95 mm.	£70-90	☐
			Turquoise, Light Blue, Dark Blue or Pink	£130-160	☐
215	1961	Daimler Dart SP250	Beige, Green or Yellow body, 'MLP 119', 75 mm.	£80-120	☐
			White (Red seats), or Light Blue (Blue seats)	£140-160	☐
			Turquoise (White seats), or Red (Cream seats).................	£90-125	☐
216	1963	Volvo 122s	Red or Orange body, 'YYO 131', sliding roof, 110 mm.	£80-100	☐
			Blue, Grey, Turquoise, Yellow Ochre, Dark Green or Lime Green	£90-125	☐
217	1963	Jaguar 'E' Type	Beige, Cream, Light or Dark Green, Red, White or Yellow/Black, 'PML 511'	£90-120	☐
			Mid-Blue or Light Grey body	£95-130	☐
			Light Blue body	£200-240	☐
218	1963	Jaguar Mk.10..........................	Metallic Brown, Blue, Bronze or White, 'RBG 218', 122 mm.	£90-120	☐
			Dark or Mid-Green.................	£110-150	☐
219	1963	Austin-Healey Sprite Mk.III	Red (White seats), Blue (Red seats), Beige (White seats); Brown driver, Yellow scarf, 'WXD 219' or 'CMO 118', 84 mm.	£80-100	☐
			Off-White or Light Blue body	£95-125	☐
259	1963	Ford Consul Classic	White (Blue seats), Beige (White seats); or Blue, Light Blue, Red, Grey or Green body, 'PZL 108', 105 mm.	£80-100	☐
260	1963	Royal Rolls-Royce Phantom V	Maroon body, Blue interior, 2 flags on roof, Queen & Prince Philip in rear seats, driver & passenger in front. 143 mm.	£300-400	☐
261	1963	Volvo P1800	1: bonnet & boot open, spare wheel, Light Blue, Red, Turquoise	£80-100	☐
			2: only bonnet opens, Blue, Grey or Metallic Bronze	£80-100	☐
262	1963	Morris 1100	Dark Blue or Red (Grey seats), Green or Beige (Red seats), 'LXQ 216', 89 mm.	£60-80	☐
			Lime Green or Light Blue body	£65-85	☐
263	1964	Bentley 4½ Litre (Supercharged)........................	Green body, racing number '27', '11' or '15', 108 mm.	£55-75	☐
266	1965	Bull Nose Morris 1923	Red/Black or Yellow/Black, Brown driver, (scale 1:48)	£40-50	☐
267	1964	M.G. 1100 Saloon	White/Dark Green (Red seats), Red (Cream seats), or Red/White or Beige/Cream, 'PML 511', 88 mm.	£55-70	☐
			Royal Blue/White	£350-450	☐
268	1965	Vauxhall PB Cresta	Shown in catalogue but not issued under this number, see 280	NPP	
270	1965	Ford Zephyr 6 Mk.III..............	Blue, Cream, Green, Greyish-Green or Grey (Red seats); or Red (Grey seats), 'LXO 913' or 'TXY 120', 110 mm.	£65-90	☐
274	1965	Morris 1100 and Canoe.............	Green, Grey, Light Blue, Dark Blue or Red car, Brown canoe on roof, 'DCY 472' ...	£45-65	☐
			Light Blue or Two-tone Blue (Red canoe) or Red (Red/White canoe)	£60-85	☐
276	1964	Jaguar 'S' type	Metallic Gold body, 'RBG 218' or 'VYD 131', 114 mm.	£120-150	☐
			Metallic Green	£120-150	☐
278	1965	Mercedes-Benz 230 SL	Metallic Red, Cream, or Maroon body, 'RUN 163', 100 mm.	£75-100	☐
			Metallic Blue or Metallic Bronze	£85-115	☐
279	1965	M.G. PB Midget 1935..............	Dark Blue or Red body, Black wings & seats, 'CMY 749', 79 mm.	£50-65	☐
280	1963	Vauxhall PB Cresta	Red/Beige, Dark Blue/Cream or Grey/Green body 'VCS 165' or 'BVM 163'	£55-70	☐
281	1966	M.G. Midget Mk.II..................	Blue or Red body, Driver with scarf, Policeman, 83 mm.	£75-100	☐
		New Zealand issue:........	Dark Green body	NGPP	☐
286	1965	Austin 1800..............................	Light or Dark Blue, Cream, Green or Beige (all with Red seats); or Red (Grey seats), 'BVM 163' or 'VCS 165', 100 mm.	£60-75	☐
287/1	1965	Hillman Minx (with roof-rack)	Pale Green, Beige, Cream or Green (all with Red seats) Red (Grey seats) or Greyish-Green body, 'NTB 647' or 'LXQ 973', Two brown suitcases, 84 mm.	£60-85	☐
289	1963	Morris Minor 1000....................	Metallic Blue or Light Blue body	£120-150	☐
			Red or Metallic Green body	£160-200	☐
306	1964	Humber Super Snipe Estate	Same casting as 183 but with roof-rack and two suitcases.		
			Beige, Blue, Green or Red body, 'SGM 501', 113 mm.	£100-140	☐
			Metallic Bronze	£100-150	☐
			Light Blue (White roof-rack) or Turquoise (White roof-rack)	£110-145	☐
			White and Turquoise body, Grey roof-rack, 113 mm.	£120-140	☐
307	1965	Volkswagen Beetle 1200	Metallic Blue or Metallic Red body, 'RBG 218', 110 mm.	£145-195	☐
401	1966	Volkswagen Variant with Skis ..	(New Zealand issue). Dark Blue body, roof rack, 'FYS 799' or 'EDU 458C', 100 mm.	£500-750	☐
405	1966	'B.E.A.' Vauxhall Cresta	Dark Grey body with Red 'B.E.A.' logo	£60-70	☐
407	1966	Mercedes-Benz 230 SL	Brown body, Red interior, 103 mm.	£50-60	☐
408	1966	Renault Caravelle	Not issued.	NPP	☐
410	1966	Austin 1800 and Rowboat	Green, Blue, Beige or Red car with Red or Orange boat on roof, 'ETW 566B'	£60-70	☐

269

Spot-On Commercial Vehicles and Vans

Ref. No.	Year(s)	Model Type	Model Features and Size	Market Price Range	
106a/0c	1960	Austin Prime Mover with MGA Sports Car in Crate	Light Blue, Dark Blue, or Orange cab. 234 mm.	£350-400	☐
106a/1	1959	Austin Prime Mover and Flat Float with Sides	Light Blue, Green or Orange cab and float sides, 234 mm.	£170-200	☐
106a/1c	1960	Austin Prime Mover and Float with Crate Load	Light Blue, Green or Orange cab. 234 mm.	£200-250	☐
			Turquoise body	£225-300	☐
109/2	1960	E.R.F. 68g with Flat Float	Turquoise body with Black cab roof or Green body with Grey cab roof. 210 mm.	£160-190	☐
109/2p	1960	E.R.F. 68g and Flat Float (without Sides, with Planks)	Turquoise body with Black cab roof, Turquoise body or Yellow body. 210 mm.	£160-190	☐
109/3	1960	E.R.F. 68g and Flat Float (with Sides)	Dark Blue cab (Pale Blue float), Yellow body (Metallic Grey roof), Green body (Green roof), Blue body or Green body (Black roof), 210 mm.	£160-190	☐
			Deep Blue body (Silver chassis), or Orange-Red (Light Grey chassis)	£250-300	☐
			Lemon, Pale Green or Turquoise body, Silver chassis.	£190-250	☐
109/3b	1960	E.R.F. with sides, Barrel load	Turquoise, Light Blue or Red body with or without Silver float bed, 210 mm.	£200-300	☐
110/2	1960	A.E.C. Mammoth Major 8 and Flat Float (without sides)	Red, Blue or Maroon body (with or without Black roof), 210 mm.	£170-200	☐
110/2b	1960	A.E.C. Mammoth Major 8 'London Brick Co Ltd'	Red body, Black cab roof, Brown 'brick' load, 210 mm.	£200-250	☐
110/3	1960	A.E.C. Mammoth Major 8 'British Road Services'	Red body, with or without Black cab roof. 210 mm.	£200-250	☐
110/3d	1962	A.E.C. Mammoth Major 8 and Oil Drums Load	Red body, Black cab roof, Silver trim. 210 mm.	£300-400	☐
110/4	1961	A.E.C. Mammoth Major 8 'SHELL-BP' Tanker	Green cab, Red tank, Black chassis and catwalk, 210 mm.	£400-500	☐
110/4	1963	A.E.C. Mammoth Major 8 'SHELL-BP' Tanker	Yellow cab, White/Yellow tank, Silver chassis and catwalk, 210 mm.	£500-750	☐
111/a0g	1962	Ford Thames with Garage Kit	Orange cab and truck body, Silver chassis. 219 mm.	£250-300	☐
			Light Blue cab and truck body, White garage	£250-300	☐
111/a0t	1961	Ford Thames Trader with Log Load	Two tone Blue or Red cab and truck body, 3 logs, 219 mm.	£250-300	☐
			Light Blue cab and truck body.	£200-275	☐
			Light Yellow cab and truck body	£300-375	☐
111a/1	1959	Ford Thames Trader 'British Railways'	Maroon and White body, '4884 BG M' and 'M 1741 GT6' logo on cab. 219 mm.	£200-250	☐
111a/1	1960	Ford Thames Trader 'R.Hall & Son Ltd. Fulham'	Green body, logo on door. Doubtful if model issued.	NPP	☐
111a/1s	1960	Ford Thames with Sack Load	Dark Blue cab, Pale Blue truck body, Black chassis, 219 mm.	£250-300	☐
			Light Blue and Silver	£275-325	☐
			Bluish-Green body	£300-350	☐
117	1963	'JONES' Mobile Crane	Cream cab & jib, Red body & wheels, Black chassis, Grey base	£150-200	☐
			Dark Red cab & body, White jib, Light Grey chassis & base, Silver wheels	£300-400	☐
122	1961	'UNITED DAIRIES' Milk Float	Red/White body, chains, 'Lada and New Yoghurt', 98 mm.	£75-95	☐
158a/2	1961	Bedford 'S' Type 2000 Gallon 'SHELL-BP' Tanker	Green cab, Red tank, Black chassis, 'P33A37' logo. 202 mm.	£450-500	☐
158a/2	1962	Bedford 'S' Type 2000 Gallon 'SHELL-BP' Tanker	Yellow cab, White tank, Silver trim, 'P33A37' logo. 202 mm.	£800-1000	☐
158a/2C	1961	Bedford Low Loader	Red low-loader with cable drum load. Doubtful if issued	NPP	☐
161	1961	Land Rover (long wheelbase)	Grey/White, Light Grey/White or Blue/White, 108 mm.	£65-80	☐
210	1961	Morris Mini Van	Bright Yellow, seats/steering wheel, suspension	£90-120	☐
210/1	1962	Morris Mini Van 'Royal Mail'	Red body, Post Office crest, 'E-II-R', suspension	£70-90	☐
210/2	1962	'Mini Van 'P.O. Telephones'	Olive-Green body, Gold crown logo	£90-100	☐
258	1963	'R.A.C.' Land Rover	Dark Blue body, 'RADIO RESCUE', 108 mm.	£90-120	☐
265	1964	'TONIBELL' Ice Cream Van	Blue body, Red flash, attendant, 'Soft Ice Cream', 107 mm.	£90-125	☐
		New Zealand issue:	Turquoise body	£125-150	☐
271	1965	'EXPRESS DAIRIES' Milk Float	Blue/White body, 3 wheels, driver, 'Drink Express Milk'	£90-120	☐
273	1965	Commer Van 'SECURITY EXPRESS'	Green/Gold, driver and seated guard, coin slot in roof, 126 mm.	£80-100	☐
308	1965	Land Rover and Trailer	Green body, Beige hood, Brown trailer, 107 mm.	£70-80	☐
315	1965	'GLASS & HOLMES' Commer Van	Blue/Yellow, ladder, figures, 'Window Cleaning Company Est 1891'	£80-100	☐
402	1966	Crash Service Land Rover	Orange body, 'MOTORWAYS CRASH SERVICE', logo in Blue, 125 mm.	£70-90	☐
404	1966	Morris Mini Van 'SHELL'	Yellow body, suspension, ladder, 79 mm.	£500-600	☐
404	1966		As previous model but without decals	£325-395	☐

Spot-On Buses, Coaches and Taxis

Ref. No.	Year(s)	Model Type	Model Features and Size	Market Price Range	
145	1963	Routemaster Bus	Red 'London Transport' bus, route '284', 'Ovaltine - The Worlds Best Nightcap', 'LTR 145' or 'BML 112'. 198 mm.		
			1st type has chrome moulded radiator	£500-600	☐
			2nd type has transfer print on plastic background	£400-500	☐

270

Ref. No.	Year(s)	Model Type	Spot-On Buses, Coaches and Taxis – continued	Market Price Range	
155	1961	Austin FX4 Taxi	Maroon body, Cream steering wheel, Green base 'PQT 155', Tin hubcaps.................	NGPP	☐
			Black body, Red steering wheel, Grey base, 'SLT 105'	£65-80	☐
156	1961	Mulliner Luxury Coach............	Pale Blue/Grey, Red flash, 'Triang Tours', 'LMC 156', 213 mm.	£300-400	☐
			Yellow/White body, Brown side flash	£1000-1250	☐
			Sea Green/Cream, Red flash	£400-500	☐
			Silver/Red/Dark Blue..	£250-350	☐

Miscellaneous Spot-On models

Military and R.A.F. models

415	1965	R.A.F. Land Rover	Blue/Grey, R.A.F. roundel, hose/pump/attendant, 111 mm.	£80-100	☐
416	1965	Leyland Army Ambulance	Olive Green body. Not issued	NPP	☐
417	1965	Military 'FIELD KITCHEN' ...	Olive Green body, squadron markings, suspension, 108 mm.	£80-90	☐
418	1965	Leyland Military Bus................	Olive Green body, 'Army Personnel'. Not issued	NPP	☐
419	1965	Land Rover and Missile Carrier..................	Olive Green body, 3 White Missiles	£200-250	☐

Roadmaking vehicles and Tractors

116	1959	Caterpillar Tractor D9	Brown/Silver body, White rubber tracks, 153 mm.	£500-750	☐
123	1959	Bamford Excavator	Red/Yellow, 'J.C.B.'. Intended model but not issued	NPP	☐
137	1962	'MASSEY HARRIS' Tractor ...	Red/Silver/Blue body, driver and steering wheel, 79 mm.	£500-750	☐

Fire, Police and Ambulance models

207	1964	Wadham Ambulance	Cream body without Red crosses	£200-300	☐
			White body with Red crosses...	£350-450	☐
256	1966	Jaguar 3.4 'POLICE' Car.........	White or Black. Very few with undamaged aerial or roof sign	£200-275	☐
309	1965	Police 'Z' Car	Ford Zephyr police car from the BBC-TV series 'Z-Cars'		
			1st type with aerial and 'POLICE' sign, White body..	£100-130	☐
			2nd type with no aerial or police sign. Black body...	£600-700	☐
			2nd type, White body..	£500-600	☐
316	1966	'FIRE DEPT' Land Rover	Red body, suspension, 2 firemen, 112 mm.	£80-100	☐
402	1966	Land Rover 'MOTORWAYS' ..	Orange/Blue body, hook, Blue 'CRASH SERVICE' logo	£70-90	☐
409	1966	Leyland 'Black Maria'..............	Blue body, 'Police', policeman & villain. Not issued	NPP	☐

Caravans, Boats, Motor Scooter

135	1961	14ft Sailing Dinghy/Trailer........	Blue/Grey, Dark Blue/Red, Dark Blue/White or Red/White boat (with or without cover), plastic trailer 117 mm.	£40-55	☐
135	1964	14ft GP Sailing Dinghy	Brown or Yellow boat on trailer, 128 mm.	£35-45	☐
139	1960	Eccles E.16 Caravan	Blue body, White roof, 146 mm.	NPP	☐
229	1966	Lambretta	Blue body, Red or White rear casing	£150-200	☐
264	1962	Tourist Caravan	Blue body, White roof, 152 mm.	£45-55	☐

'Cotswold Village' series

Buildings and larger items:

1 School, 2a Haystack, 3 'Cornerstones' Cottage, 4 'Fourways' Cottage, 'The Cot' Cottage, 5 Antique Shop, General Store, 7 Bourton Town Hall, 8 Barn, 9 Public House, 10 Farm House, 11 Manor House, 12 Post Office, 13 Church, 14 Forge

Miscellaneous items:

Stocks, Memorial Stone, Set of Trees, Stone Bridge Sides

All the 'Cotswold Village' items are rare and it is suggested that larger buildings (church, shop, etc) are likely to be in the region of £100 - £150, while smaller buildings and miscellaneous items might be anything from £10 - £50 depending on size, complexity, etc. Note however that these price levels can only be applied to items in pristine condition having no appreciable 'sag' or softness caused by ageing or sunlight.

Garage and Equipment

L146/7/8		'SHELL' items...........................	L146 Lamp standard, L147 'SHELL' sign, L148 Red/Yellow petrol pump. Each	£10-15	☐
L148		Trade pack...............................	Blue card box containing 6 of L148 pumps	£80-100	☐
L149		Oil Dispenser Rack..................		£10-15	☐
L159		'BP' Lamp Standard.................		£10-15	☐
162		'BP' or 'SHELL' Filling Station	Each...	£35-45	☐
162/1/2/3		Garages....................................	Each...	£15-20	☐
163		'BP' Petrol Pump.....................		£10-15	☐
164		'BP' Forecourt Sign.................		£10-15	☐
172a		'SHELL' Garage Set		£50-75	☐
172b		'BP' Garage Set		£50-75	☐

Road Signs and accessories   (see also Gift Sets)

		Road Traffic Signs....................	Twenty different signs were issued, each	£10-15	☐
L1271/		Road Direction Signs	/1 Portsmouth, /2 Guildford, /3 Bristol, /4 Birmingham, /5 Biggar, /6 Dumfries. Each...	£10-15	☐
		Road sections	Straights, curves, T-junctions. Each..	£6-8	☐
		Plastic Figures	In groups set on a card. Figures include Garage Personnel, Newspaperman, Milkman, Postman, Doctor, Policeman, Schoolboys, Children, 3 Roadmen & Brazier or 3 Roadmen & Road Drill/Planks/Walls. Per card...........................	£5-10	☐

Spot-On Presentation and Gift Sets

Ref. No.	Year(s)	Set Name	Contents	Market Price Range

Presentation Sets

Ref. No.	Year(s)	Set Name	Contents	Market Price Range	
No.0	1960	Presentation Set	106a/1 Austin Prime-Mover and Flat Float, 100 Ford Zodiac, 103 Rolls-Royce Silver Wraith, 104 MGA and 113 Aston Martin	£500-600	☐
No.1	1960	Presentation Set	100 Ford Zodiac, 101 Armstrong-Siddely, 103 Rolls-Royce and 104 MGA	£600-700	☐
No.2	1960	Presentation Set	109/3 ERF with Flat Float, 101 Armstrong-Siddely, 102 Bentley Continental and 105 Austin-Healey 100/6	£600-700	☐
No.3	1960	Presentation Set	Contains 111a/1 Ford Thames Trader, 101 Armstrong-Siddely, 104 MGA, 108 Triumph TR3a, 112 Jensen 541, 113 Aston Martin, 114 Jaguar 3.4	£600-750	☐
No.4	1960	Presentation Set	106a/1 Austin Prime-Mover and Flat Float, 109/3 ERF with Flat Float, 100 Ford Zodiac, 107 Jaguar XK-SS, 112 Jensen 541	£400-500	☐
No.4a	1963	Presentation Set	Contains 104 MGA, 105 Austin-Healey, 107 Jaguar XK-SS and 108 Triumph TR3a	£400-500	☐
No.5		Presentation Set	118 BMW Isetta, 119 Meadows Frisky Sport and 131 Goggomobil Super Regent	£200-250	☐
No.6		Presentation Set	131 Goggomobil, 185 Fiat 500, 193 NSU Prinz and 211 Austin Seven	£300-400	☐
No.6a		Presentation Set	131 Goggomobil, 185 Fiat 500, 119 Meadows Frisky and 211 Austin Seven	£350-450	☐
No.7		Presentation Set	Contains 166 Renault Floride, 191 Sunbeam Alpine, 211 Austin Seven, 213 Ford Anglia, 215 Daimler Dart, 217 Jaguar 'E'-type	£500-600	☐
No.8		Presentation Set	Contains 157 Rover 3 litre, 191 Sunbeam Alpine, 213 Ford Anglia, 216 Volvo 122s, 258 RAC Land Rover	£500-600	☐
No.9		Presentation Set	Contains 122 Milk Float, 145 Routemaster Bus, 193 NSU Prinz, 207 Wadham Ambulance, 211 Austin Seven, 256 Jaguar Police Car	NGPP	☐
No.10		Presentation Set	Contains 122 Austin Seven, 145 Routemaster Bus, 157 Rover 3 litre, 158a/2 Bedford Tanker, 165 Vauxhall Cresta, 166 Renault Floride, 185 Fiat 500, 211 Austin Seven, 215 Daimler Dart and 262 Morris 1100	£400-500	☐
173		Terrapin Building Set	A constructional set	£20-30	☐
208/a		Road Construction Set	4 workmen, brazier, hut, poles, road sections and 18 other small items	£125-175	☐
259		Garage Set	A constructional set	£20-30	☐
701		'His, Her's, Junior's' Set	219 Austin-Healey Sprite, 267 MG 1100, 280 Vauxhall PB Cresta, in 'window' box	£200-250	☐
702		Gift Set 702	270 Zephyr Six, 274 Morris 1100 and canoe, 286 Austin 1800 and 135 Dinghy	£250-350	☐
702(a)		Gift Set 702	195 VW Rally, 217 Jaguar 'E' type, 261 Volvo P1800, 287 Hillman Minx	£300-350	☐
A		Presentation Set 'A'	102 Bentley (Lilac/Silver), 108 Triumph TR3 (Green body, Grey seats), 114 Jaguar 3.4 (Green), 118 BMW Isetta (Pale Green), 154 Austin A40 (Red/Black)	£350-400	☐
212	1963	Car, Dinghy & Trailer Set	Contains 165 Vauxhall PA Cresta and 135 GP Dinghy	£125-150	☐
269	1965	Ford Zephyr Six and Caravan	Contains 270 plus 264 Caravan. 262 mm.	£125-175	☐
308	1965	Land Rover and Trailer	Green bodywork, Fawn cover, 'LTR 145', 170 mm.	£65-85	☐
406	1966	Hillman Minx and Dinghy Set	Contains 287 Hillman Minx and 135 GP Dinghy and trailer. Various colours	£70-95	☐

'Tommy Spot' series Gift Sets (all include a building kit and Tommy Spot figure)

Ref. No.		Set Name	Contents	Market Price Range	
801		Home with Tommy Spot	287 Hillman Minx (with Mr Spot), 270 Ford Zephyr Six with driver	£200-275	☐
802		Cops 'n Robbers with Tommy Spot	309 BBC-TV 'Z-Car' with driver & criminal, 276 Jaguar & driver	£200-275	☐
803		Superville Garage with Tommy Spot	286 Austin 1800 with driver, 279 MG Midget, 2 garage workers	£200-275	☐
804		Sailing with Tommy Spot	280 Vauxhall PB Cresta and sailing dinghy with Tommy and Mr Spot	£150-225	☐
805		Fire with Tommy Spot	316 Fire Dept Land Rover and trailer, two firefighters	£195-260	☐
806		Royal Occasion with Tommy Spot	260 Royal Rolls-Royce with chauffeur and royal passengers, 6 guardsmen	£450-650	☐
807		Pit stop with Tommy Spot	Mercedes-Benz 230 SL and Jaguar 'S', 2 racing drivers	£300-400	☐
808		Motorway Rescue with Tommy Spot	402 'Crash Service' Land Rover and mechanic, A.A. van & man	£400-500	☐

Spot-On New Zealand Issues

When Tri-ang took over the production of Dinky Toys in 1967 they stopped production of Spot-On Models in the United Kingdom. Fourteen models were subsequently produced by the Tri-ang Pedigree company of New Zealand from the original dies sent out from the U.K. New Zealand production lasted just 2 years and ceased in 1969/70. The New Zealand model reference numbers were different to their U.K. counterparts as listed in the Spot-On 7th Edition catalogue. Extras such as roof racks and luggage were not included with N.Z. issues. The following listing first appeared in 'Mini Cars' ('The News Sheet for Caledonian Autominologists'), dated September 1972 and was prepared by Eric Brockie in New Zealand. Thanks are due to James McLachlan (Club Secretary) for his kind permission to reproduce the listing.

UK Ref. No.	NZ Ref No.	Model	Difference from UK version	NZ Colour
289	101	Morris Minor 1000	Not manufactured in New Zealand	?
219	102	Austin-Healey Sprite	Same as UK issue	White
281	103	MG Midget	No Policeman included	Dark Green
404	104	Morris Mini Van	No 'Shell' logo ladder or mechanism	Yellow
267	105	MG 1100	Single colour only	Green
262	106	Morris 1100	Same as UK issue	Blue
287/406	107	Hillman Minx	No roof rack or dinghy	Green
280	108	Vauxhall Cresta	Single colour only	Blue
276	109	Jaguar 'S' type	Same as UK issue	Blue
286	110	Austin 1800	No lady driver or schoolboy	Light Brown
270	111	Ford Zephyr 6	Same as UK issue	White
308	112	Land Rover	No trailer included	Green
407	114	Mercedes-Benz 230 SL	Not manufactured in New Zealand	-
401	115	Volkswagen Variant	No roof rack or skis	Blue

279	116	MG PB Midget	Same as UK issue	Blue & Black
265	117	'TONIBELL' Ice Cream Van	Same as UK issue	Turquoise
402	118	Crash Service Land Rover	Same as UK issue	Orange & Blue
316	119	Fire Dept Land Rover	No Firemen	Red
415	120	R.A.F. Land Rover	Not manufactured in New Zealand	

PRICES OF NEW ZEALAND ISSUES— All scarce — All NGPP
N.B. Wallis & Wallis sold 401 VW Variant for £500 in 1993.

Spot-On Catalogues, Leaflets and Pictures

Ref. No.	Year(s)	Publication	Cover Features & Details	Market Price Range	

Catalogues

	1959	'1st Edition'	Village scene with Spot-On buildings and models, 'Tri-ang' logo in bright red '6d', 'Dividers', 'SCALE 1/42'. Thick numbered pages with superb pictures	£30-40	☐
	1960	'2nd Edition'	Same cover as 1st Edition. 'Tri-ang' logo in maroon, '6d'. Pages not numbered but models displayed same as 1st Edition.	£30-40	☐
	1961	'3rd Edition'	Same as 2nd Edition	£25-35	☐
5a7383/DP	1963	'4th Edition'	Royal Rolls-Royce on cover, '3d', Page 19 lists the new type Presentation Sets 5-10, 14 plus boxes.	£20-30	☐
	1964	'5th Edition'	Blue Austin 1800 (286) on cover, '2d', concertina type leaflet featuring new type of Black/Red window boxes for Gift Sets and single models.	£20-£30	☐
	1965	'6th Edition'	Cover again features 286 Austin 1800 plus 289 Morris Minor, '2d', concertina type leaflet which includes 'Tommy Spot' and 'Magicar' listings and pictures	£20-30	☐
	1966	'7th Edition'	Booklet type featuring 407 Mercedes 230 SL and 287 Hillman Minx, '6d', 'Tommy Spot' featured with 'Royal Occasion' set and Car Spotters guide	£20-30	☐

Leaflets and Model Pictures

The early 'blue boxes' for cars and small commercial vehicles and the early card boxes for the large commercial vehicles, contained a model picture and a Yellow/Blue/White leaflet listing the models available. Prices of model picture cards can vary depending on the rarity of the model itself within a price range from £5 to £25. Spot-On 'Picture wallets' are to be found at £15-20.
It should be noted that no 'blue box' model or early large commercial boxed model is complete without the model picture.
Leaflets are not uncommon and may be obtained for £2-3.

Trade Display Material

Electric revolving Trade Display Unit .... **£300-400** ☐

Spot-On models sold at auction 1992 - 1993

All the items listed below were sold by Vectis Model Auctions and were in mint condition and boxed.

CARS

100	Zodiac, Bluish Grey/Brownish Pink	**£95**
100	Ford Zodiac, Light Grey/Blue	**£65**
100sl	Ford Zodiac, Grey/White	**£70**
100sl	Ford Zodiac, White/Yellow	**£75**
101	Armstrong Siddeley, Metallic Green	**£60**
101	Armstrong, Metallic Green/Black	**£65**
101	Armstrong Siddeley, Bluish Grey	**£90**
101	Armstrong Siddeley, Light Blue	**£120**
101	Armstrong, Cream/Metallic Charcoal	**£88**
101	Armstrong, Pale Green/Metallic Charcoal	**£100**
102	Bentley, Silver/Metallic Maroon	**£180**
102	Bentley, Silver/Light Blue	**£120**
104	M.G.A., Salmon Pink, Grey seats	**£170**
104	M.G.A., Deep Green, White seats	**£230**
104	M.G.A., Bluish Green, Lemon seats	**£150**
107	Jaguar, Lilac, Grey seats, Black tonneau	**£240**
114	Jaguar 3.4 Mk.I, Light Grey	**£150**
114	Jaguar 3.4 Mk.I, Blue	**£190**
115	Bristol 406, Metallic Dark Blue	**£190**
119	Meadows Frisky Sport, Green/Black	**£100**
157	Rover 3 litre, Dark Blue	**£140**
165/1	Vauxhall PA Cresta, Plum Red	**£130**
183	Humber, White/Turquoise, Grey roof rack	**£130**
191/1	Sunbeam (open), Deep Salmon Pink	**£130**
191/2	Sunbeam Hardtop, Yellow, Cream seats	**£130**
191/2	Sunbeam Hardtop, Mauve, Cream S	**£140**
195	Volkswagen Rally Car, Red, '11'	**£300**

211	Austin Baby Seven, Pink body	**£280**
213	Ford Anglia, Dark Blue	**£140**
215	Daimler Dart SP250, White, Red seats	**£160**
217	Jaguar 'E' type, Light Blue	**£240**
276	Jaguar 'S' type, Metallic Blue	**£130**
278	Mercedes 230SL, Metallic Blue	**£100**
281	MG Midget Mk.II, Red body	**£100**
289	Morris Minor 1000, Metallic Green	**£160**

COMMERCIALS, VANS, BUSES, etc.

106a/1c	Austin Prime Mover, Turquoise	**£250**
109/2	ERF, Turquoise, Silver chassis	**£190**
109/3	ERF Flat/Sides, Lemon/Silver	**£190**
109/3	ERF Flat/Sides, Red/Light Grey	**£340**
110/2pb	AEC Mammoth, 'London Brick'	**£280**
111a/0t	Ford Thames, 3 Logs, Light Yellow	**£330**
116	Caterpillar D9, Yellow/Black	**£710**
117	Jones Crane, White/Red, Light Grey chassis	**£130**
117	Jones Crane, Red/White, Light Grey chassis	**£380**
404	Morris Mini Van, plain Yellow	**£330**

PRESENTATION and GIFT SETS

702(a)	Gift Set 702: 195 VW Rally, 217 Jaguar 'E' type, 261 Volvo P1800, 287 Hillman Minx	**£380**
806	'Royal Occasion' (Tommy Spot): 260 Rolls, 6 Guards,	**£450**

Acknowledgements   Thanks are due to Phillip Grigglestone of Norwich and Gino Tartaglia of Aylesbury for their contributions to the Spot-On listings.

Lledo Promotional models

In 1985, in response to customer demand, Lledo began to provide models for promotional purposes using their standard range of castings. The models were originally produced in runs of as few as 500 and went direct to clients, making them unavailable through normal retail outlets.

Some of the earlier models were supplied with the 'Days Gone' logo on the baseplate although this was soon modified to read 'Lledo Promotional'. Production runs of up to 1000 units were finished with printed adhesive labels, but runs of 1000 or more warranted direct tampo printing (as on normal 'Days Gone' models).

The majority of Lledo Promotionals tend to be priced in the range **£5 - £10**. The examples that follow are those that have attained notable rarity or extra desirability for various reasons.

Ref. No.	Year(s)	Model Type	Model Features and Size	Market Price Range	
LP1 001a	1988	Horse-Drawn Tram	'MANX TELECOM', (tampo) Red/White, 'DG' base	£10-15	☐
LP2 001a	1989	Horse-Drawn Milk Float	'MILK INDUSTRY' on label, Red/White, 'DG' base	£25-35	☐
LP3 001a	1985	Horse-Drawn Delivery Van	'PHOENIX STEAM-DRY LAUNDRY', Blue/Black with tampo, USA model	£35-45	☐
LP4 001a	1985	Horse-Drawn Omnibus	'BRIDLINGTON' logo on label, Red, 'Lledo' base	£35-45	☐
LP5 004x	1986	Horse-Drawn Fire Engine	'METROPOLITAN Fire Brigade', tampo print, 'DG' baseplate	£20-30	☐
LP6 004a	1985	Ford Model 'T' Van	'OVERDRIVE MANPOWER', White/Green label, 'DG' baseplate	£150-200	☐
LP6 012a	1986	Ford Model 'T' Van	'SALVATION ARMY', Black, tampo, 'Promotional' base, (US issue)	£80-90	☐
LP6 022a	1986	Ford Model 'T' Van	'TERRY PRINTING GROUP' on label, Black, 'Promotional' base	£150-200	☐
LP6 023a	1986	Ford Model 'T' Van	'CHANNEL 4' on label, Royal Blue, 'Promotional' baseplate	£45-55	☐
LP6 030a	1985	Ford Model 'T' Van	'SERVICE OFFSET SUPPLIES' on label, Beige, 'Promotional'	£200-250	☐
LP6 038a	1987	Ford Model 'T' Van	'NATIONAL COAL BOARD', tampo print, Blue, 'Promotional' base	£100-150	☐
LP6 060a	1987	Ford Model 'T' Van	'KIT KAT', tampo print, Red/White, 'Promotional' base	£70-80	☐
LP6 192a	1989	Ford Model 'T' Van	'MAXWELL HOUSE', tampo print, White/Red body	£200-250	☐
LP6 248a	1990	Ford Model 'T' Van	'BILLON 1920-90', tampo print, Blue/White, French issue	£60-80	☐
LP7 001a	1986	Ford Woody Wagon	'FERGUSONS', White/Blue, 'DG' & 'Promotional' bases	£80-100	☐
LP8 006a	1986	Ford Model 'T' Tanker	'BONDY', Blue/Silver, 'Promotional' base, US issue	£55-75	☐
LP8 017a	1988	Ford Model 'T' Tanker	'BOEHMERS', Yellow/Green, 'Promotional' base, Canadian	£20-30	☐
LP8 020a	1990	Ford Model 'T' Tanker	'WYNNS', Blue/White, Dutch issue	£25-35	☐
LP9 001a	1986	Ford Model 'A' Car	'CAVE PHOTOGRAPHIC', Silver body with tampo print	£40-50	☐
LP10 001a	1985	Dennis Single Deck Bus	'THORPE HALL SCHOOL', Green/Yellow, 'Days Gone' baseplate	£20-30	☐
LP11 001c	1985	Horse-Drawn Removal Van	'LONDON POLICE' label, Mustard-Brown body, 'Promotional' base	£25-35	☐
LP13 060a	1986	Ford Model 'A' Van	'TIMEX CPGA' tampo print, White/Blue, Canadian issue	£80-100	☐
LP13 081a	1987	Ford Model 'A' Van	'KELLOGGS CORN FLAKES' tampo, White/Red, South African issue	£80-100	☐
LP13 092a	1987	Ford Model 'A' Van	'Le CRUNCH BUNCH' tampo print, Cream/Green body	£185-220	☐
LP15 007a	1985	AEC Double Deck Bus	'HASTINGS & Dist', ('HALLS WINE') tampo print, Maroon/Silver	£60-75	☐
LP15 008a	1985	AEC Double Deck Bus	'CITY Of COVENTRY' on label, Maroon/Cream	£135-155	☐
LP15 032a	1986	AEC Double Deck Bus	'CITY Of LINCOLN', ('LINCS ECHO') Green body	£70-80	☐
LP15 035a	1986	AEC Double Deck Bus	'FLEETWOOD 150' on label, 'DG' & 'Promotional' bases	£70-80	☐
LP15 079a	1987	AEC Double Deck Bus	'LONDON TRANSPORT', ('SRA') label, Red, 350 issued	£195-225	☐
LP15....	1990	AEC Double Deck Bus	'SUBBUTEO', 'ROME 1990', Green/White body	£20-25	☐
LP16 001a	1985	Dennis Parcels Van	'MODEL CARS 1985' tampo print, Yellow body, Japanese issue	£135-160	☐
LP16 020a	1986	Dennis Parcels Van	'RELIANCE ELECTRICAL' on label, Cream/Brown body	£85-100	☐
LP16 028a	1986	Dennis Parcels Van	'GRIMLEY & SON' on label, Red/White body	£90-100	☐
LP16 036a	1986	Dennis Parcels Van	'ALFRED QUAIFE', Black body with tampo print	£60-75	☐
LP17 001a	1985	AEC Single Deck Bus	'HEDINGHAM & Dist' on label, Blue/Cream, 'Days Gone' base	£85-100	☐
LP17 003a	1985	AEC Single Deck Bus	'MAIDSTONE & Dist' with 'RYE' destination, (label)	£75-85	☐
LP17 006b	1986	AEC Single Deck Bus	'SOUTHDOWN' with 'BRIGHTON destination, (label)	£55-65	☐
LP17 009a	1986	AEC Single Deck Bus	'STEVENSONS' tampo print on Yellow/Black body	£65-75	☐
LP17 015a	1986	AEC Single Deck Bus	'RIBBLE' with 'PRESTON' destination, (label)	£90-110	☐
LP18 003a	1986	1936 Packard Van	'MILK MARKETING BOARD' on label, Dark Green body	£80-100	☐
LP19 002a	1986	1931 Rolls-Royce	'ROYAL WEDDING', Blue/Red body	£20-25	☐
LP20 008a	1987	1934 Ford Stake Truck	'1905' livery, 1,000 issued	£30-40	☐
LP21 064a	1987	1934 Chevrolet Van	'BROOKE BOND PG TIPS', White/Red body	£50-60	☐
LP22 001a	1986	1933 Packard Town Van	'JUST CONTINENTAL 5th ANNIVERSARY', Blue body, 75 only	£70-80	☐
LP23 001a	1987	1954 Scenicruiser	'B & A TOP MARKS', Pink body, artwork on label	£15-20	☐
LP24 001a	1987	1934 Rolls-Royce	'FRANKLIN DIECAST', Black body, Red hubs, (Canadian)	£15-20	☐
LP25 001a	1987	1925 Rolls-Royce	'FRANKLIN DIECAST', Black body, Red hubs, (Canadian)	£15-20	☐
LP26 002a	1988	Chevrolet Crate Truck	'LOWCOCKS LEMONADE', Maroon body, 1,500 issued	£10-15	☐
LP27 002a	1988	Mack Breakdown Truck	'BOURNEMOUTH BUS MUSEUM', Yellow/Black, 500 issued	£10-15	☐
LP28 021a	1989	Mack Canvas-Back Truck	'LOCKHEED HYDRAULIC BRAKES', Brown/Black, 1,000 issued	£30-40	☐
LP29 002a	1990	1942 Dodge 4 x 4	'CROYDON LETTERS', Red body, 1,000 issued	£10-15	☐
LP30 003a	1989	1939 Chevrolet Van	'FAMILY REUNION', Red/Black body, artwork on label	£15-20	☐
LP31 002a	1988	Horsedrawn Brewers Dray	'EVERARDS', Green/Gold	£15-20	☐
LP33 006a	1991	Ford Model 'T' Car	'SUN CHEMICAL', Dark Green/Black	£10-15	☐
LP34 005a	1989	1932 Dennis Van	'3M FINESSE-IT', Red body	£10-15	☐
LP35 001a	1989	1932 Dennis Limousine	'ISLE of WIGHT FIRE BRIGADE', White/Red, 1,000	£10-15	☐
LP36 002a	1992	1939 Chevy Pick-up	'TYRE SERVICES', White/Blue	£15-20	☐
LP37 002a	1990	1932 Ford Panel Van	'HARTLEPOOL MAIL', Green/Black	£15-20	☐
LP38 004a	1991	1925 Rolls-Royce	'SHARON and PAUL', Green/Cream	£30-40	☐
LP39 002a	1990	1934 Mack Truck	'STAUFFER CHEMICALS', Black body	£15-20	☐
LP41 027a	1991	Karrier Trolley Bus	'ANADIN 1931-1991', Yellow/Green, 1,300	£35-40	☐
LP42 002a	1990	1934 Mack Tanker	'RED CROWN', Red body, (USA model)	£10-15	☐
LP43 014a	1991	1931 Morris Van	'PROJECT CONWAY', Cream/Dark Blue, 1,000	£25-30	☐
LP44 006a	1991	1937 Scammell	'LOVE ROMANIA', White, 1,000, (Romanian model)	£10-15	☐
LP46 001a	1991	1930 Bentley	'SARAH and MARK', British Racing Green	£20-25	☐
LP47 001a	1992	1933 Austin Taxi	'BLACKPOOL PLEASURE BEACH', White body, 1,000	£10-15	☐
LP49 025a	1992	1931 AEC Renown Bus	'LIVERPOOL FOOTBALL CLUB', Red/Silver, 1,100	£40-50	☐
LP50 010a	1992	1926 Morris Van	'CANNES 1992', White/Black, French	£100 +	☐
LP51 001a	1992	Chevrolet Box Van	'SWAN VESTAS', Yellow/Green, 1,000	£20-25	☐
LP52 001a	1992	1935 Morris Parcels Van	'WOLVERHAMPTON POLICE', Dark Green/White, 1,000	£8-10	☐
LP53 002a	1992	1926 Rolls-Royce	'QUEEN ELIZABETH 1952-1992', Green/Cream	£7-8	☐
LP54 001a	1992	1929 Rolls-Royce	'BADEN POWELL - JAM ROLL', Dark Green/Black	£5-7	☐
LP55 001a	1992	Horsedrawn Tanker	'POLARINE', Dark Green/Grey, (USA model)	£10-15	☐
LP56 001a	1992	Ford High Roof Van	'ATLAS TIRES', Blue/Black, (USA model)	£10-15	☐
LP59	1993	1950 Bedford 30 cwt Truck	'BRITISH DIECAST TOYS CATALOGUE' 5th EDITION See page 187	£7-9	☐

DON'T FORGET TO SEND FOR YOUR COPY OF THE FORTHCOMING 'LLEDO PROMOTIONALS PRICE GUIDE'.
FULL DETAILS WILL BE AVAILABLE EARLY IN 1994 IN THE 'MODEL PRICE REVIEW'.

THE TOYFAIR WORLD

Toyfair Organisers and the Fairs they arrange:

Julie and John Webb, (0526) 398198
Alexandra Palace, Alfreton, Bacup,
Beverley, Bishops Stortford, Borehamwood,
Bradford, Brentwood, Bury St.Edmunds,
Cambridge, Cleethorpes, Colchester, Colne,
Cradley Heath, Doncaster, Donington Park,
Droitwich, Gateshead (Exhibition Centre), Halifax,
Heanor, Heywood, Huddersfield, Ipswich, Keighley,
Kings Lynn, Leeds (City), Leeds (Guiseley),
Leeds (Morley), London (Dulwich), Lincoln
(Bailgate), Lincoln (Showground), Mansfield,
Mildenhall, N.E.C. (Birmingham), Newark,
Normanton, Norwich, Peterborough (East of
England Showground), Rotherham, Southend,
St.Neots, Telford, Wales (Royal Welsh
Showground, Bulith Wells), Walsall, Wisbech,
Wymondham (Norfolk), York (Racecourse).

Barry Potter, (0858) 462510/434902
Birmingham, Coventry, Dunstable, Harrogate,
Loughborough, Market Harborough, Sandown,
Solihull, Stoneleigh, Sutton Coldfield

Dennis Wright, (0335) 42093, Buxton Toyfair

Trevor Morgan, (0242) 524644,
Bath, Bristol, Cheltenham, Gloucester

Dave Jowett, (0602) 231639 Alexandra Palace,
Donington Park, N.E.C., Notts International

Mike Spencer and Geoff Martin, (0622) 35396
and (0732) 840787 Brighton, Crawley, Ditton,
Dorking, Lancing, Mitcham, Tunbridge Wells,
Woolwich, Worthing

Yesterday's Child Fairs, (0734) 313736/588666,
Ascot, Fareham, Newbury, Reading

John Moore Fairs, (0455) 636003, Atherstone,
Burton-on-Trent, Coalville, Coventry, Derby,
Grantham, Hinckley, Oakham, Stafford, Stone

Eric Creake, (0276) 681808, Farnham Maltings

Roger Mazillius, (0983) 292272,
South of England Fairs

Iain Hines, (081) 898 0681 (or Tricia (0753) 545383)
Heathrow International

Leslie Johnson, (04023) 48144, London Area Fairs

Keith Manning, (0372) 725063,
Eastleigh, Guildford, Havant

Stuart and Kevin, (0244) 346297,
Farnham Maltings, Telford (MICA Toyfair)

Richard or Joyce Atkins, (0869) 47489, Banbury,
Malvern, Oxford, Salisbury, Sevenoaks,
Swindon, Worcester, Leamington Spa

Bulldog Toyfairs, (0373) 452857 Bridgewater,
Exeter, Newbury, Shepton Mallet, Weymouth

Mike Rooum, (071) 499 0482, Bristol, Gloucester

Coventry Diecast Model Club, (0203) 418027,
Coventry Toy Fairs

John Bartrum, (081) 200 5020, Holt (Norfolk)

Ray Richardson's Southern Counties Toyfairs.
(0734) 313736 (eve, 24 hrs) or (0734) 588666 (day)
Ascot, Basingstoke, Cheddar, Chesham,
Cirencester, Devizes, Didcot, Dorchester,
Dursley, Frimley Green, Hartley Witney,
newbury, Petersfield, Reading,
Wokingham, Wootton Bassett

David Hinam, (0246) 232832, Barnsley, Bradford,
Dewsbury, Halifax, Harlow, Hull, Leicester, Scunthorpe,
Sheffield, Stockport, Wakefield, Wolverhampton

Maidenhead Static Model Club, (0256) 819141,
Windsor International Swapmeet

P. Hallam, (0270) 878519, Chester, Stoke

Dee Thomas, (0202) 521686, Bournemouth

Tim Mohon, (0429) 880253, Darlington,
Middlesborough, Newcastle, Tynemouth

Castle Models, (0453) 543432, Taunton

Sylvia and Nigel Thorogood, (0787) 61292,
Hedingham Swapmeets

Geoff Rudin, (0744) 885005, Manchester Toyfairs

Cliff Maddock, (0734) 833062, Big Southern Fair

Northern Toyfairs, (0246) 232832, Bradford

Pastimes, (041) 331 1008, Glasgow

Farquharsons Toyfairs, 03565 230,
Grampian and Tayside

Graham White, (0322) 349973, Eltham, S.E. London

Collectors Toy and Model Fairs, (04023) 48144,
Basildon, Glasgow, Harrogate, Hatfield, Kingston

P. Walters, (0923) 269884, Picketts Lock, N. London

Transtar Promotions, (021) 502 3713, Leicester,
Stourbridge, West Bromwich, Wolverhampton

Colin Penn, (081) 888 4485, Enfield, Wimbledon

Bob or Sue Fague, (0732) 867112,
Selsdon, South Norwood, etc

3 Counties Toyfairs, (0923) 263145,
Bucks, Herts, Middlesex

Bill Bourne, (0277) 624937, Essex, Southend

Toyman Fairs, (0992) 620376,
Chalfont St.Peter, Cuffley, Richmond

B. Mclaren, (0324) 31012, Falkirk

Devon Old Toy and Collectors Fairs,
(0392) 874662, Paignton

Dave Grounsell, (0442) 83278,
Harrow, Hemel Hempstead

Leeds International Swapmeet, (0535) 643825

Shropshire Toyfairs, (0952) 223939,
Bridgenorth, Llandudno, Telford

Corgi Collector Club Annual Toyfair,
(0533) 826666, Gaydon, Warwickshire

Herts and Essex Toyfairs, (0279) 417646,
Epping, Hertford, Wanstead, etc

Mid Kent Toy Fair, (0622) 753783, Maidstone

J. Lumly, (0532) 602251, Harrogate, Wetherby

John Curtis, (0926) 427724, Stratford upon Avon

Barry Stockton, (051) 334 3362, Altrincham,
Barton, Blackpool, Southport,
Warrington, Wigan Pier, Wirral

Mark and Dave's Swapmeets, (0322) 863983,
Bromley, Harrow, Hastings

Manchester Toyfairs, (0925) 818734, Manchester

South Wales & Valleys Swapmeets,
(0222) 754378, Cardiff, etc

Welsh Old Toy and Collectors Fairs,
(0792) 363200, Cardiff, Swansea

N. Thomas, (0272) 325780, Chippenham, Nailsea

Ray Strutt, (0825) 768776, Modelex Annual Show

B. Godfrey, (0865) 776778, Oxford, etc

Steele Promotions, (061) 796 9538,
Pontefract, Rochdale

Midland Toyfairs, (021) 502 3713, Wolverhampton

E. Lea, (0222) 761984, Chepstow

J.W. Promotions, (0923) 269884, Watford

Dennis Green, Denvor Promotions,
(0844) 343198, Aylesbury, Bucks

L. Kenwood, (0734) 733690, Cardiff, Newport,
Reading, Southampton, Winchester

Ian Shave, (0923) 263145, Biggleswade, Watford

Toymania, (010) 33 48 25 8833, Paris, France

J. Deroy, (010) 322 771 9223, Brussels, Belgium

MK Models, 0031 1134 1642, Belgium Toyfairs

Le Vesinet, (010) 33 139 764 515, France

Richelieu, (010) 33 47 58 1177, France

Copenhagen (010) 45 31 35 0146, Denmark

Stockholm (010) 46 87 31 0890, Sweden

Toronto Toy Show,
Doug Jarvis, 416-832-1481, Canada

Ontario Toy Show, 416-945-2775,
Mississauga, Canada

TRADE SOURCES OF INFORMATION

Bob Faye, Sevenoaks Models, Kent. Tri-ang Ships specialist. Tel (0703) 743437
Andrew Clark, 42 Pollard Lane, Bradford, West Yorkshire, BD22 4RN
Mail Order specialist and Toyfair trader.
Chris Brierley, 53 York Street, Heywood, Rochdale, Lancashire, OL10 4NR
Shopkeeper, Mail Order and Toyfair trader.
Roger Mazillius, Vectis Models, 96 High Street, Cowes, Isle of Wight, PO31 7AW
Shopkeeper, Auctioneer, Toyfair organiser and trader, Mail Order specialist.
George Hatt, Digby's, 16 Horse Road, Hilperton, Trowbridge, Wilts, BA14 7PE
Author, 'Corgi Classics Collectors Guide', Shopkeeper, Toyfair trader, Mail Order specialist.
John Clark, Oak Acres Farm, Park Hall Road, Somersham, Huntingdon, Cambs. Toyfair trader.
Kerri Stanley, Chelmsford. Specialist Dinky Toys trader. Tel (0245) 356918.
Kevin McGimpsey and Stewart Orr, Chester Toy Museum, 13a Lower Bridge Street Row, Chester
Museum owners, Editors 'Matchbox International Collectors Association', Toyfair organisers and traders.
Tim Walker, Waltham, Grimsby. Corgi specialist trader. Tel (0472) 822749
Mike and Sue Richardson, 15 Bell Lane, Elton Wick, Windsor, Berks, SL4 6LQ
Authors 'Dinky Toys and Modelled Miniatures', Toyfair traders and Mail Order specialists.
Tony Cooper, Specialist Hornby-Dublo Toyfair trader, Tel (0706) 213618
John Turner, 53a Models, 430 Hessle Road, Hull, HU3 3SE. Specialist Hornby-Dublo & railway models trader.
Martin Wright, Toyfair trader, specialist Mail Order dealer.
David Salisbury, Vintage Toy and Train Museum, Sidmouth.
John Marshall, 8573 La Baya, Fountain Valley, California 92708, USA. Collector and trader.
Norman Joplin, 29 Greenland Road, Southfield Green, Cranlington, Northumberland, Tel (0670) 714522
Author 'The Great Book of Hollow Cast Figures', specialist Mail Order trader.
Brian Secker, Trains and Olde Tyme Toys, Specialist Collectors Toyshop, Aylsham Road, Norwich, Tel (0603) 413588
Peter Crichton, Lacy Scott & Co, The Auction Centre, Bury St.Edmunds, Suffolk
Neil John Leonard, Phillips West Two, 10 Salem Road, Bayswater, W2 4BU
Hugo Marsh, Christie's South Kensington Ltd, 85 Old Brompton Road, London, SW7 3LD
Tony Butler, Wallis and Wallis, West Street Auction Galleries, Lewes, Sussex
John Hardy, Newmarket, Toyfair trader and Matchbox specialist
Paul Carr, specialist Matchbox trader, (081) 568 4084
Jim Whittaker, Bamford Toy Museum, Rochdale, Lancs
Tim Arthur, Toy Market, 5 Chapel Court, Tewkesbury, Glos. UK and USA Toyfair and Toy Market trader.
Steven Nagle, Stand B23, Grays Antiques Market, 1 - 7 Grays Mews, Oxford Street, London W1
UK and USA trader and Britains specialist.
Bill Soppitt, 'Westerley', Yeomanry Close, Daventry
Robert Taylor, Shackleton models specialist.

PERSONAL ACKNOWLEDGEMENTS

Susan Pownall, Editor of Corgi Collectors Club Magazine.
Ray Strutt, Deputy/Overseas Editor, Collectors Gazette.
Ken Benham, Editor of EFE Collectors Club Magazine.
Mr G. Tekerian, European Marketing Manager, Tyco-Matchbox for permission to quote his company's trade names.
Gerry Healey, Product Manager, Tyco-Matchbox, for his valuable assistance.
Frank Joyce, Managing Director, EFE, for supplying model listings and permission to quote his company's trade name.
Mark Sole of EFE for his valuable assistance.
Mr A.J.Russell, Managing Director of Lledo PLC for giving permission to quote his company's trade names.
Mr Chris Guest, Managing Director of Corgi Toys Ltd for permission to quote his company's trade names.
Richard Hopkins, Brand Manager of Britains Ltd for kind permission to quote his company's trade names.
Peter Lloyd, RDP Publications (publishers of 'Days Gone Collector' magazine) for extensive help with Lledo listings.
Don Fuller and Tracy (Photograph Dept) of Corgi for valuable assistance.
Robert Newson, author, for preparation of the revised Lone Star listing
Mr Richard Lines of Hornby Hobbies for permission to quote his company's trade names
Dick Fawcett, Kesgrave, Ipswich for technical assistance with the Hornby Dublo section and supplying models from his collection for photographic purposes.
John Kinchen, Hampshire, for supplying listings and models for photographic purposes
Patrick Talbot of London for supplying early Matchbox Toys information.
Gerry Savage of Bobingey, Cornwall, journalist and collector, for tremendous help with all sections.
Sally Ramsay for without her patience, encouragement and understanding the 5th Edition would never have happened.

OFFICIAL COMPANY ACKNOWLEDGEMENTS

Abbreviations

A
A.E.C.	Associated Equipment Company
AA	Anti-aircraft (or Automobile Association)
A.A.	Automobile Association
ABC	(ABC-TV) Associated British Cinemas (Television)
A.C.	Auto-Carriers
A.F.S.	Auxilliary Fire Service
AMC	American Motor Corporation
APC	Armoured Personnel Carrier
ATV	Associated Television

B
BA	British Airways
BAC	British Airways Corporation
BBC	British Broadcasting Corporation
BEA	British European Airways
BFPO	British Forces Post Office
bhp	Brake horsepower
BLMC	British Leyland Motor Corporation
BMC	British Motor Corporation
BMW	Bayrische Motoren-Werke
B.O.A.C.	British Overseas Airways
BP	British Petroleum
BR	British Railways
BRM	British Racing Motors
BRS	British Road Services
B.S.M.	British School of Motoring

C
CA	A type of Bedford van
CF	A type of Bedford van
CHEVVY	(or Chevy) Chevrolet
CLE	Certificated Limited Edition
cv	chevaux-vapeur (a measure of power)
C.W.S.	Co-operative Wholesale Society
cwt.	hundred-weight

D
DD	Double-decker
DG	(Lledo Models of) Days Gone
DH	De Havilland
Dk.	Dark (shade of colour)
DTB	'Dinky Toys' on base
DUKW	An amphibious vehicle developed by General Motors in wartime. The letters are not initials or an abbreviation but are simply part of an early drawing-office reference.

E
E	East
EEC	European Economic Community
E.F.E.	Exclusive First Editions
e.g.	exempli gratia (for example)
EMI	Electrical & Musical Industries Ltd
ER	Elizabetha Regina, (E II R, Queen Elizabeth II) or Eastern Region
ERA	English Racing Automobiles
ERF	Edwin Richard Foden
Est.	Established (or estimate/d)

F
Fiat	(or FIAT) Fabbrica Italiana Automobile Torino
fig(s)	figure(s)

G
GB	Green box
G.B.	Great Britain
GBT	Globe-Trotter
GER	Great Eastern Railway
GMC	General Motors Corporation
GP	Grand Prix
GPO	General Post Office
GR	Georgius Rex
GS	Gift Set
GSP	Gift Set price
GTO	Gran Turismo Omologato
GTV	Gran Turismo Veloce
GUS	Great Universal Stores
GWR	Great Western Railway

H
HM	His/Her Majesty
HMAC	His Majesty's Armoured Car
HMS	His/Her Majesty's Ship
H.M.V.	'His Masters Voice'
hp	horse-power
H.W.M.	Hersham & Walton Motors

I
IBM	International Business Machines
ICI	Imperial Chemical Industries
INTER	(or INTL) International
I.O.M.	Isle of Man

J
JB	James Bond
JCB	Joseph C. Bamford
J.M.T.	Jersey Motor Transport

K
K.D.F.	Kraft durch Freude
K.L.G.	Kenelm Lee Guinness
K.L.M.	Koninklijke Luchtvaart Maatschappij NV (Dutch airline)

L
L.A.P.D.	Los Angeles Police Department
LE	Limited Edition
LM	Le Mans
LMS	London Midland & Scottish Railway
LNER	London & North Eastern Railway
LNWR	London & North Western Railway
loco	locomotive
logo	lettering, trademark or advertising design
LP	Lledo Promotional
LT	London Transport
Lt.	Light (shade of colour)
Ltd.	Limited (Limited Liability Company)
LWB	Long wheel-base

M
MB	Matchbox
Met.	Metallic
MG	A make of car, derived from 'Morris Garages'
MGA, MGB	types of MG car
MGC	A type of MG car
M.I.C.A.	Matchbox International Collectors Association
mm.	millimetres
MOY	Models Of Yesteryear
MPR	Market Price Range
MR	Midland Region

N
N	North
NAAFI	Navy, Army & Air Force Institutes
N.A.S.A.	National Aeronautics & Space Administration
NB	nota bene (mark well)
NCL	National Carriers Limited
NCO	Non-Commissioned Officer
NCP	National Car Parks
NEC	National Exhibition Centre
NGPP	No guide price at present
nhp	(or n.h.p.) Nominal horsepower
No.	Number
NOR	Number of rails
NOV	Number of variations

NPE	No price estimate
NPP	No price possible
NRP	Normal retail price
NS	(or n/s) Nearside
NSPCC	National Society for the Prevention of Cruelty to Children

O
OPO	On-pack offer
OS	(or o/s) Offside

P
PB	Propeller blade(s)
PLC	Public Limited Company (see also Ltd.)
P.M.G	Post Master General (Australia)
PO	Post Office
PRM	Promotional model
PSV	Public service vehicle
P.T.T.	Postes-Telephones-Telegraphes

R
RAC	(or R.A.C.) Royal Automobile Club
RAF	(or R.A.F.) Royal Air Force
R.C.M.P.	Royal Canadian Mounted Police
RF	'Ring-field' motor
RHD	Right-hand drive
RM	Routemaster (bus)
RN(s)	Racing or Rally number(s)
RNLI	Royal National Life-boat Institution
RT	Route

S
S	South
SBRW	Solid black rubber wheels
SBX	Special box
SD	'Super Detail' (Hornby Dublo)
S.F.F.D.	San Francisco Fire Department
S.F.P.D.	San Francisco Police Department
SR	Southern Railway, Southern Region
St.	Saint or Street
STP	Scientifically-Treated Petroleum
SWB	Short wheel-base
SWRW	Solid white rubber wheels

T
TBA	'To be announced'
TC	Twin carburettors
TDF	Tour De France
TK	Type of Bedford truck
TS	'Touring Secours'
TT	Two-tone (or Tourist Trophy)
TV	Television
TWA	Trans-World Airlines

U
UB	Unboxed
UK	United Kingdom
UN	United Nations
US	United States (of America)
USA	United States of America
USAAF	United States Army Air Force
USAF	United States Air Force
USS	United Space Starship

V
VW	Volkswagen

W
W	West
WR	Western Region

Y
YB	Yellow box
YMCA	Young Mens Christian Association

Corgi Toys Numerical Index

Corgi Toys Numerical Index – continued

Ref No.	Model	page
230	Mercedes-Benz 220 SE	35
231	Triumph Herald	35
232	Fiat 2100	35
233	Heinkel Trojan	35
234	Ford Classic	35
235	Oldsmobile Super 88	35
236	Motor School Austin A60	35
237	Oldsmobile Sheriff's Car	46
238	Jaguar Mk.10	35
239	VW Karmann Ghia	35
240	Fiat 600 Jolly	35
241	Chrysler Ghia L64	35
242	Fiat 600 Jolly	35
245	Buick Riviera	35
246	Chrysler Imperial	35
247	Mercedes-Benz Pullman	35
248	Chevrolet Impala	35
249	Morris Mini-Cooper	35
251	Hillman Imp	35
252	Rover 2000	35
253	Mercedes-Benz 220 SE	35
255	Motor School Austin A60	35
256	VW Safari Rally	31
C257	Mercedes-Benz 500 SEC	35
258	'The Saint's Volvo	53
C258	Toyota Celica	35
259	Citroën 'Le Dandy'	35
C259	Penguinmobile	53
260	Renault R16 TS	35
260	Buick Police Car	46
C260	Superman Police Car	53
261	James Bond's Aston Martin	53
C261	Spiderbuggy	53
262	Lincoln Continental	35
C262	Captain Marvel's Porsche	53
263	Marlin Rambler	35
C263	Captain America's Jetmobile	53
264	Oldsmobile Toronado	35
C264	Incredible Hulk Van	53
C265	Supermobile	53
266	Chitty Chitty Bang Bang	53
C266	Spider Bike	53
C267	Batmobile	53
268	'Green Hornet'	53
C268	Batman's Bat Bike	53
269	James Bond's Lotus	53
270	James Bond's Aston Martin	53
271	Ghia De Tomaso Mangusta	31
C271	James Bond's Aston Martin	53
C272	James Bond's Citroën 2cv	53
273	Rolls-Royce Silver Shadow	35
273	Honda School Car	35
274	Bentley 'T' Series	35
275	Rover 2000 TC	35
C275	Mini Metro	35
C275	Royal Wedding Metro	35
276	Oldsmobile Toronado	35
C276	Triumph Acclaim	35
277	'Monkeemobile'	53
C277	Triumph School Car	35
C278	Dan Dare Car	53
C279	Rolls-Royce Corniche	35
C279/3	Rolls-Royce	35
C280	Rolls-Royce Silver Shadow	35
281	Rover 2000 TC	35
C281	Metro 'Datapost'	31
282	Mini-Cooper Rally	31
283	DAF 'City' Car	35
284	Mercedes 'Notruf'	46
C284	Citroën SM	35
C285	Mercedes-Benz 240 D	36
C286	Jaguar XJC V-12	36
C287	Citroën Dyane	36
C288	Minissima	36
289	VW Polo 'DBP'	56
C289	VW Polo	36
C290	Kojak's Buick	53
C290	Bell Helicopter	52
291	AMC Pacer	36
C291	Mercedes 240 Rally	31
C292	'Starsky & Hutch'	53
293	Renault 'Medicins'	36
C294	Renault Alpine	36
293	Renault 'Pompiers'	46
297	Ford Escort 'Police'	46
299	Ford Sierra 'Polis'	46
C299	Ford Sierra 2.3	36
C299	Ford Sierra Rally	31
C299/4	Ford Sierra	36
300	Austin-Healey 100-4	31
300	Corvette Stingray	36
C300	Ferrari Daytona	31

Ref No.	Model	page
301	Triumph TR2	36
301	Iso Grifo	36
C301	Lotus Elite	31
302	MG 'MGA'	36
302	Hillman Hunter Rally	31
C302	Volkswagen Polo	31
303	Mercedes-Benz 300 SL	36
303	Roger Clark's Capri	31
C303	Porsche 924 Racer	31
304	Mercedes-Benz 300 SL	36
304	Chevrolet Camaro	36
305	Triumph TR3	36
305	Mini Marcos GT	31
306	Morris Marina	36
C306	Fiat X1-9 S	31
307	Jaguar 'E'-type	36
307	Renault Turbo	31
C308	Mini-Cooper S	31
C308	BMW M1	31
309	Aston Martin DB4	31
C309	Volkswagen Turbo	31
310	Chevrolet Stingray	31
310	Porsche 924 Turbo	36
C310	Porsche 924 Turbo	31
311	Ford Capri V6	36
312	Marcos Mantis	36
312	Jaguar 'E'-type	31
C312	Ford Capri S	31
313	Ford Cortina GXL	36
314	Ferrari Berlinetta	31
C314	Fiat X1-9	36
C314	Supercat Jaguar	36
315	Simca 1000 Sports	31
C315	Lotus Elite	36
316	NSU Sport Prinz	36
316	Ford GT 70	31
317	Mini-Cooper 'Monte Carlo'	31
C317	Peugeot 'Politi'	46
318	Mini-Cooper 'Monte Carlo'	31
318	Jaguar XJS	36
318/8	Jaguar XJS	36
318	Lotus Elan	36
318	Lotus Elan S2	31
C318	Jaguar 'Motul'	31
319	Lotus Elan S2	31
319	Lotus Elan S2	36
319	Jaguar XJS	36
C319	Lamborghini Miura	32
320	Ford Mustang Fastback	36
C320	The Saint's Jaguar	53
321	Porsche 924 Saloon	31
321	Mini-Cooper 'Monte Carlo'	32
322	Rover 'Monte Carlo'	32
323	Citroën 'Monte Carlo'	32
C323	Ferrari Daytona	32
324	Marcos Volvo 1800	32
324	Ferrari Daytona LM	32
325	Chevrolet Caprice	36
325	Mustang Competition	32
C326	Chevrolet Police Car	46
327	MGB GT	36
C327	Chevrolet Cab	49
328	Hillman 'Monte Carlo'	32
329	Opel Senator	36
329	Ford Mustang	32
330	Porsche Carrera 6	32
C330/10	Mini 'AFTER EIGHT'	36
Q330/1	Mini 30th Anniversary	36
Q24/1	Mini 30th Anniversary & book	36
331	Ford Capri 'Texaco'	32
332	Lancia Fulvia Sports	36
C332	Opel Doctors Car	47
333	Mini-Cooper 'Sun/RAC'	32
334	Mini-Cooper 'Magnifique'	36
C334	Ford Escort 1.3 GL	36
335	Jaguar 'E'-type 4.2	36
336	James Bond's Toyota	53
337	Chevrolet Stock Car	32
338	Chevrolet Camaro	36
C338	Rover 3500	36
339	Mini-Cooper '67 Monte Carlo	32
C339	Rover Police Car	47
340	Sunbeam 'Monte Carlo'	32
C340	Rover 'Triplex'	32
341	Mini Marcos GT	36
C341	Chevrolet Caprice	32
342	Lamborghini P400	36
C342	'Professionals' Capri	53
343	Pontiac Firebird	36
343	Ford Capri 3 litre	37
344	Ferrari Dino Sports	32
345	MGC Competition Model	32
C345	Honda Prelude	37

Ref No.	Model	page
C346	Citroën 2cv Charleston	37
347	Chevrolet Astro	37
348	Mustang 'Pop-Art'	32
C348	Dan Tanner's Thunderbird	53
349	'Pop Art' Morris Mini	53
350	Thunderbird Guided Missile	52
C350	Toyota Celica	32
351	RAF Land Rover	52
C351	Ford Sierra Pace Car	32
352	RAF Staff Car	52
C352	BMW 325	37
353	BMW 325	37
353	BMW 'Notartz'	47
353	Decca Radar Scanner	52
C353	BMW 325i Rally	32
354	BMW 325	32
354	Military Ambulance	52
354	'Military Police'	52
356	Personnel Carrier	52
357	Ford 'Brandcheff'	47
357	Weapons Carrier	52
358	Sierra 'Police' Cars	47
358	Oldsmobile Staff Car	52
359	Field Kitchen	52
361	Volvo 'Polis'	47
370	Cobra Mustang	32
C370	Cobra Mustang	37
371	Porsche Carrera 6	32
372	Lancia Fulvia	37
373	Peugeot 505	37
373	Peugeot 'Politi'	47
C374	VW 1200 Police Car	47
C374	Jaguar 'E'-type 242	37
C374	Jaguar 'E'-type 5.3	37
375	Toyota 2000 GT	37
376	Chevrolet Stock Car	32
377	Marcos 3 litre	37
378	MGC GT	37
C378	Ferrari 308 GTS	37
380	Alfa-Romeo P33	37
C380	BMW 'BASF'	32
381	Beach Buggy	37
C381	Renault Turbo 'ELF'	32
382	Porsche Targa 911s	37
C382	Lotus Elite	37
383	Volkswagen 1200	37
383	VW 1200 Rally	32
383	VW 1200 'PTT'	56
383	VW 1200 'ADAC'	47
384	VW 1200 Rally Car	32
384	Adams Brothers 'Probe'	32
384	Renault 11 GTL	37
385	Porsche 917	32
385	Mercedes-Benz 190 E	37
386	Bertone Barchetta	37
386	Mercedes 'Polizei'	47
386	Mercedes 'SERVIS'	32
386/4	Mercedes 'Burlington'	32
386/8	Mercedes 2.3/16	32
387	Corvette Stingray	37
388	Mercedes-Benz C111	37
388	Mercedes-Benz Taxi	49
389	Reliant Bond 'Bug'	37
391	James Bond's Mustang	53
391	Fire Bug	53
392	Shake Buggy	37
C393	Mercedes-Benz 350 SL	37
394	Datsun 240 Z	32
394	Datsun Rally	32
396	Datsun Rally	32
397	Porsche-Audi 917	32
399	Peugeot 205	32
399/5	Peugeot 205 T16	32
C400	Volkswagen 1200	37
C401	Volkswagen 1200	37
402	BMW M1	32
402	Ford Cortina 'Police'	47
403	Bedford 'Daily Express'	40
403 M	Bedford Van 'KLG'	40
403	Ford Escort	32
403	Skip Dumper	55
404	Bedford Dormobile	40
404 M	Bedford Dormobile	40
404	Rover 'Daily Mirror'	32
404	Rover 'Texaco'	32
405	Fire Tender	47
405 M	Fire Tender	47
C405	Milk Float	40
C405	Chevrolet Ambulance	47
406	Mercedes Unimog	55
406	Land Rover Pick-Up	56
C406	Bonna Ambulance	47
407	Mobile Grocers	40
408	Bedford Van 'AA'	40

Corgi Toys Numerical Index – continued

Dinky Toys Numerical Index

Dinky Toys Numerical Index – continued

Dinky Toys Numerical Index – continued

Classified Advertising

BASINGSTOKE Squirrel Collectors Centre. We buy and sell diecast and tin toys, dolls, specialist interest books, silver and small antiques, militaria, jewellery, china, dolls house furniture, prints and many specialist interest collectibles. Established 1981. We are open Mon - Sat 10am - 5:30pm. Find us in **Squirrel Collectors Centre**, Joices Yard, off New Street, Basingstoke. Tel (0256) 464885

BOSCOMBE Model and Collectors Shop has Soldiers, Miniature Lead Toys, Railways, Cars, Planes, Ships, Dolls, Clockwork, Tin Toys. Sorry no lists but you'll be delighted by a visit to **Boscombe Model and Collectors Shop**, 802c Christchurch Road (on Somerset Road) Boscombe, Bournemouth. Tel (0202) 398884

BRIGHTON (near West Pier). A selection of old and new models, archive & modern Transport Videos, Display cabinets, Bus photos, Books. Toys, models & transport items taken in part exchange. Mail order service (Visa & Mastercard accepted). **Dinnages of Brighton**, 16 Little Preston Street, Brighton, BN1 2HQ. Tel (0273) 728028

CORNWALL Atlantic Models, Atlantic Forge, Lender Lane, Mullion, Nr Helston, Cornwall, TR12 7HW. Tel/Fax 0326 240294, Evenings 0326 240294. Specialist in Lledo Promotional and Days Gone Models. Shop or Mail Order — if you require help or advice please call or telephone the above. If you are thinking of calling, please telephone first as we may be away at a Toy Fair in your area. We always have a comprehensive stock and may be able to help you with a hard to get model. Why not call and see us in Cornwall.

GLASGOW Pastimes Vintage Toy Shop. Obsolete and new models bought and sold. Dinky, Corgi, Lesney, Britains, Trix, Tri-ang, Hornby, Hornby Dublo, Dolls house equipment, Scalextric, obsolete plastic kits, and much more! (Sorry, no lists). Open 6 days, 24hr Answerphone. **Pastimes Vintage Toy Shop**, 140 Maryhill Road, St Georges Cross, Glasgow, G20 7QS, Tel (041) 331-1008

GUILDFORD Sheric Mini Autos Worldwide Mailing Service for Emergency Services and other die-cast. All leading manufacturers products supplied. SAE for list, all competitively priced. For a really personal service contact: **Eric and Sheila** at 217 Worpleston Road, Guildford, GU2 6XJ. Tel (0483) 235127, callers by arrangement

HORNCHURCH Stockists of: Cars, Trucks and Kits from around the world. Dinky, Corgi, Brumm, Auto-USSR, Conrad, LBS, Tekno, Lion, AMT, MPC, Monogram, Revell, plus lots of obsolete items. We're three stops from the end of the District Line travelling east, or Junctions 28/29 of M25. See you at **Searles C.T.**, 187, Station Lane, Hornchurch, Essex, RM12 6LL. Tel (07084) 43430

HONITON Antique Toys - the best collectors' shop in the West Country. Excellent stocks of all old diecast, Dinky, Corgi, Lesney, etc. Also tinplate toys, trains ('0' and '00' gauge), lead soldiers, farm and zoo, teddys, dolls, games and jigsaws. Open Tues, Wed, Fri, Sat 10:30 to 5. **Honiton Antique Toys**, 38 High Street, Honiton, Devon, EX14 8PJ. Tel (0404) 41194

NORWICH Collectors Toyshop. Specialist dealers in old toys. Buying/selling Dinky, Corgi, Matchbox, Tin Toys, '0' gauge Trains, Hornby Dublo, Britains, Lead toys, Dolls & Teddies. **Norwich Collectors Toyshop**, St Marys Antique Centre, Duke Street, Norwich. Tel (0603) 57761 (or 612582). Open Mon-Sat 10-4:30

READING TV Related/Model Railway. Buy/sell/swop: G.Anderson - Who - Disney - Rupert - Beano - Eagle. Toys/books/games. Tinplate - Scalextric - Minic - Robots. Model railway/plastic kits/diecast. Also: Comics - Records - 50s/60s Pop Music items. **The Flying Scott**, Reading Emporium, 1a Merchants Place (off Friar St) Reading, RG1 1DT. Tel (0734) 588666/590290. (10-5 Mon-Sat)

SCOTLAND CALLING . . . Now & Then Old Toy Centre wishes to buy/sell/swap older tin trains (Hornby, Marklin, Bing, Plank, Lowke), boats, planes, mechanical banks, teddy bears and china dolls. As well as Dinky, Corgi, Matchbox, Spot-On, etc. **Now & Then**, 9 West Crosscauseway, Edinburgh, EH8 9JW. Tel (836) 552147. Shop hours 10:30 - 5:30, Tues - Sat

WALES Holidaying in North Wales? Then visit 'Collectables', Rhos point, Rhos-on Sea. Die-cast including Dinky, Corgi, Yesteryear and others. Some tinplate and advertising in stock. Will consider old postcards and cigarette cards in part exchange. Open 7 days a week (except Jan/Feb/March when open Fri, Sat, Sun) 10am to 5pm. Phone **'Collectables'** on (0492) 548889

WINDSOR Wide variety of old diecast. Mike and Sue Richardson buy and sell good quality old toys. Replacement tyres for old toy cars, plus books (including our own 'Dinky Toys and Modelled Miniatures') plus our own ranges of white-metal car kits. Access and Visa accepted. Send SAE for lists to **MIKANSUE**, 15 Bell Lane, Eton Wick, Windsor, Berkshire, SL4 6LQ. Tel (0753) 863899

WANTED! Dinky 505 1st cab Chain Lorry (maroon) by serious collector of rare Dinky Toys. Also: 501 (red/black chassis), 501 (duo blue), 2nd cabs 502 (blue/red), 503 (orange/yellow), 512/912 Guy (orange/green). Also Gift Sets: No.1 Farm, No.2 Commercial, No.3 Cars. Please phone **Kerri Stanley** on (0245) 356918

DANGER! Wealth Warning: Failure to notify Charles Barnett when disposing of your surplus model vehicles may seriously damage your wealth. Send him a copy of your price list now. He is especially interested in obsolete and special Brooklin models, handbuilt models, and mint or mint/boxed Dinky, Corgi, Spot-On and foreign 1:43 models. Also looking for 'Automobile Quarterly' periodical. Write **Charles Barnett**, 67 Coniston Avenue, Queensbury, Bradford, West Yorkshire, BD13 2JD. Tel (0274) 816437

MILITARY VEHICLES in Dinky 1/60th scale, plus 28mm. figures to match. Send SAE or 2 IRCs for list. Trade enquiries welcome on figures. Len Buller, **B & B Military**, 1 Kings Avenue, Ashford, Kent, TN23 1LU. Tel (0233) 632923

FOR '0' GAUGE TRAINS in pristine condition - Hornby, Bassett-Lowke, Marklin, Bing or Carette (mostly 1900 - 1940), just phone **Ron and Angela Budd** on (0435) 830340, or Fax (0424) 436986. Collecting since 1933, buying/selling worldwide since 1974

MARKS TOYS. Dinky, Corgi, Matchbox. Buy, Sell, Swap. **Mark Fenlon** Tel (0322) 863983

Index to Advertisers

'Model Price Review' Publication

The impact of the prices achieved at auction on price levels in general is very considerable. At the very least, collectors are made aware of the price a given model has achieved on a certain day. If similar models, in a similar condition, make similar prices at similar auctions, a 'Market Price Range' has surely become established.

Consequently to help underpin the 'Market Price Range' figures shown in the Catalogue, each main chapter includes a cross-section of recent auction results. In addition, to ensure that Catalogue users are kept fully up to date, the **'Model Price Review'** is published each Spring.
The 'Review' achieves its objective by comparing hundreds of key auction results, with both retail prices and the Catalogue's own 'Market Price Range' which has been developed over the past ten years. By following this procedure it is possible to clearly identify where the Catalogue's price guidance information is at variance with the market place.

As part of its overall updating role, the 'Review' also contains details of the important new colour and model variations which have emerged, together with details of the new models due to be released.

Remember to get your copy - see separate advertisement on next page for details.